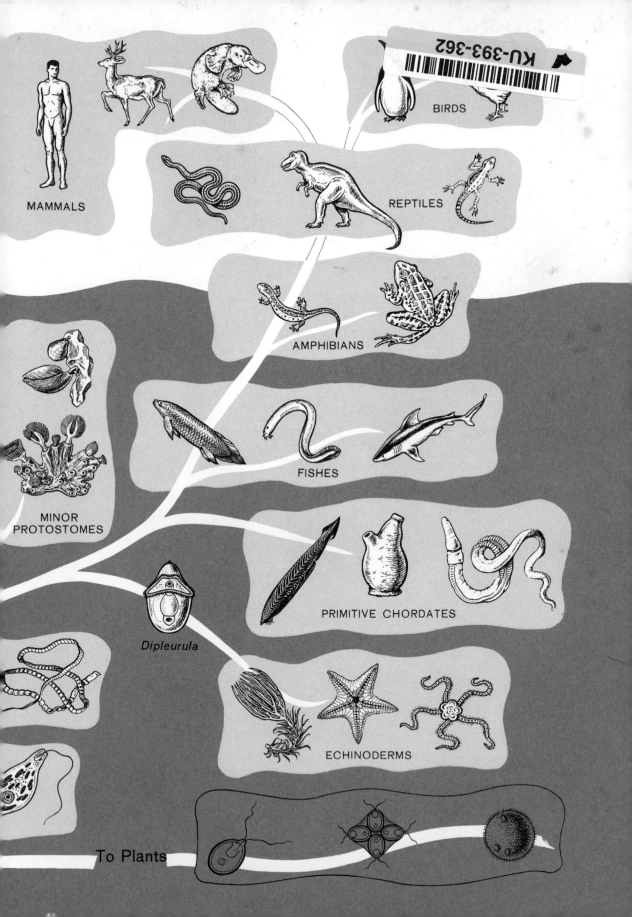

MAMMALS

BIRDS

REPTILES

AMPHIBIANS

MINOR
PROTOSTOMES

FISHES

PRIMITIVE CHORDATES

Dipleurula

ECHINODERMS

To Plants

General Zoology

UNDER THE EDITORSHIP OF **Bentley Glass**

STATE UNIVERSITY OF NEW YORK AT STONY BROOK

GAIRDNER B. MOMENT GOUCHER COLLEGE

General Zoology

SECOND EDITION

HOUGHTON MIFFLIN COMPANY • BOSTON

NEW YORK • ATLANTA • GENEVA, ILL. • DALLAS • PALO ALTO

DEDICATED IN GRATEFUL MEMORY TO

Edwin Grant Conklin

WHO DIRECTED MY EARLY INTERESTS INTO THE FIELD OF
DEVELOPMENT AND WHO SHOWED ME, IN THE WORDS OF
THOREAU, THAT

*"The frontiers are not east or west, north or
south, but wherever a man confronts a fact."*

Editor's Introduction

The science of zoology embraces a bewildering array of species — over a million of them, in all probability — as well as innumerable facts about them and the relationships between them. Nevertheless, zoology cannot stand apart from the other life sciences; it is part of a greater whole, the science of biology. As one penetrates the minuteness of an animal cell, analyzes its chemical composition and physical organization, and notes its beautiful relation of function to structure and its ways of reproducing itself and handing on its characteristics to new cells, the similarities of all living things become unmistakably evident. Again, as one gropes outward from the individual animal to a comprehension of its behavior in a community of living things and to a comprehension of its evolution as a species adapting itself in time and space, it becomes equally evident that no animal is an island, but each is a part of a continent, the slightest and remotest change in which affects it.

The teaching of zoology must above all else be oriented in these larger ways. It requires to be a part of biology, not a self-limited discipline. Encyclopedias and compendia have their useful places, but not as textbooks for the instruction of students in the nature of a science which is ever reaching out to encompass further relationships, big and little. The present textbook admirably fulfils this primary requirement of a good zoology text, perhaps because it has been written by a teacher whose outlook is primarily biological, in the broadest sense, but especially because the writer worked out his ideas first of all in a textbook of general biology, one long recognized as outstanding.

There is a second requirement of a good zoology textbook, and indeed of any science text. It must delineate its subject as a science, as a body of knowledge arrived at by careful observation and controlled experiment, through the correction of numberless errors, and often through the ultimate synthesis of apparently contradictory views into more perfect theory. If there is anything that perverts the true nature of science, it is a book that seems to say to its reader: "Take this as truth. Here are all the latest facts and the most up-to-date information, vouched for on the authority of the great scientist, Professor So-and-so." If seekers after scientific truth are in some measure to attain it, they must learn the nature of scientific methods and must absorb the dedicated spirit of a Darwin or a Huxley. They must come to see the importance of suspended judgment and of the open mind. They must perceive how our present concepts grew into being and the evidence upon which they rest.

This spirit pervades the present book and renders it unique among zoological texts. Fortunate the student who can thereby be helped to achieve an insight into what science truly is. Whether he becomes a zoologist or not, he will certainly be an informed citizen and a liberally educated man.

BENTLEY GLASS

State University of New York at Stony Brook

Preface

The objectives of this edition are essentially simple. The first and primary aim is to present a clear and detailed knowledge of the science of zoology in the light of modern biochemical and behavioral research. No age has seen more exciting or more far-reaching advances. On the biochemical level, a new world has opened up that will not only place enormous power in the hands of biologists but that already illuminates the classical fields of cell and organ physiology. These have by no means lost their importance—on the contrary! Endocrine glands, for example, have been known since the 19th century but only very recently was it discovered that hormones can produce their effects directly at the chromosomal level by activating (or derepressing) specific genes. The electron microscope is fast closing the gap, as old as Aristotle, between form and function. Physiologists have long investigated the properties of muscle contraction and fatigue, and anatomists and histologists the gross and microscopic structure of muscles. The electron microscope has now revealed how biochemical changes produce the structural change of contraction by the intersliding of protein fibers. The pituitary has heretofore been called the "master gland" but it now appears not to be the master but rather the executive officer carrying out the neurosecretory instructions of the hypothalamus and even of the pineal body whose function had so long defied detection.

It is the conviction of the author that unless a student is firmly grounded in the biochemical matrix of biology, his understanding will be both outdated and severely limited. It seems equally certain that unless he knows in considerable depth how a complex, multicellular animal functions, his comprehension will also be subject to drastic limitation. There is more to the study of reproduction or behavior than can be learned from microorganisms. As important as these organisms are, we would do our students a disservice to try to pretend otherwise. Current research is showing how the instructions in the genes are spelled out in the development of the cellular circuitry of the embryonic brain, and how this, in turn, determines the pattern by which a particular species of spider spins its web or how a salamander sees the external world. The roles of RNA and proteins in memory are becoming known. But all these discoveries on the macromolecular and cellular levels derive their importance precisely because of their relationship to the behavior of whole animals and their constituent organ systems.

Consequently, in a profound sense, the phenomena of organ physiology will always remain primary because it is on this level of organization that biochemical events make their impact on the lives of men and animals. For this reason a new section of seven chapters on organ physiology has been added to this edition.

A second aim, and an important one, is to convey a strong sense of zoology as a continuing human enterprise with a past and, let us hope, a future. This objective implies a sharp insistence on understanding the evidence supporting any set of facts and theories and a comprehension of their possible significance, because it is through such knowledge that a student comes to know how our science has been built up and to gain some real insight into the scientific process. It is certainly as easy to memorize in a purely mechanical way the four-carbon acids of the Krebs cycle as it once was to learn the appendages of the crayfish. Information without any time dimension may become a brilliant veneer but it is sure to be as brittle as it is shallow.

It is a satisfaction to acknowledge my debt to generations of students, both men and women, and to innumerable zoologists in all parts of this country and abroad with whom I have discussed the problems of teaching zoology. I owe special thanks to my colleagues, Dr. Helen B. Funk, Dr. Ann M. Lacy, Dr. Allen Rebuck, and Dr. H. M. Webb, who were kind enough to read appropriate chapters critically. I also wish to thank all who so generously provided illustrations; their contributions are individually acknowledged elsewhere in this volume. Best of all, the services of Mr. Elmer W. Smith of the Harvard University Museum staff were again available to provide superb and authoritative drawings. Special thanks are also due Edna Indritz of California for her fine art contributions to this edition. I also want to thank the staff of Houghton Mifflin Company for their skilled and indefatigable efforts to insure detailed accuracy and distinguished format. Finally, I wish to express my gratitude for the sharp insights and constant support of my wife, Ann Faben Moment, and for the cheerful interest of our children.

GAIRDNER B. MOMENT

Baltimore, Maryland

Contents

of genetics; probability and the product law; independent assortment: Mendel's second law. Chromosomes and heredity: *fertilization and meiosis: the cycle.* Genetic variation—role of meiosis and fertilization: *sex determination; sex linkage; autosomal linkage; crossing over; mapping chromosomes.* Genetic variation—role of mutation: *chromosomal and genic mutations; rate of mutation; artificially induced mutations.* Genes and chromosome structure: *what are genes? what are chromosomes? the code; how is the code duplicated? how is the code translated into proteins? is the code universal? cracking the code; directed mutations: a second look.* Gene action within the organism: *genes and enzymes; gene product interaction; how are genes turned on or off?* Heredity and environment: *the general problem; the human problem; heredity and environment in twins.* Control of heredity: *are the effects of environment and activity inherited? selection, outcrossing, and inbreeding; use of mutations.* Heredity and man: *some human genes; the blood groups; what of eugenics?* Review and references: *review topics; useful references.*

of life; the Proterozoic: the origin of phyla; the Paleozoic: era of invertebrates and fishes; the Mesozoic: the great age of reptiles; the problem of extinction; the Cenozoic: the age of mammals; the origins of man; Neanderthal and Cro-Magnon man. Review and references: *review topics; useful references.*

PART IV

Protostome Branch of the Animal Kingdom

Flatworms and the origin of metazoa. Turbellarians: Class Turbellaria: *evolutionary relationships; taxonomy; skeletal and locomotor systems; digestive system; excretory system; reproductive system; nervous system; natural history; regeneration; behavior.* Trematodes: Class Trematoda: *evolutionary relationships and taxonomy; functional systems; natural history; life cycles.* Tapeworms: Class Cestoidea: *evolutionary relationships and taxonomy; functional systems; life cycles.* Review and references: *review topics; useful references.*

Nematodes: Subphylum Nematoda: *evolutionary relationships and major groups; functional systems; reproduction and development; natural history and life cycles; hookworm; Trichina; other parasitic nematodes.* Horsehair worms: Nematomorpha. Rotifers: Subphylum Trochelminthes: *life cycles.* Minor Aschelminthes. Review and references: *review topics; useful references.*

The spiny-headed worms: Phylum Acanthocephala. Bryozoans: Phylum Bryozoa: *Kamptozoa.* Brachiopods: Phylum Brachiopoda. Phoronis: Phylum Phoronidea. Tardigrades: Phylum Tardigrada. Review and references: *review topics; useful references.*

Evolutionary relationships and major groups. Functional systems: earthworm: *setae; epidermis and muscle layers; digestive system; circulation;*

balance and nitrogen turnover. Respiration: *early research; classic laws of respiration; mechanics of breathing; regulation of breathing.* Review and references: *review topics; useful references.*

PART VII

Animals and Their World

of instincts to zoology; instinct vs. intelligence; some instincts among invertebrates; instincts among vertebrates. Mixed behavior. The way of learning: *five major types of learning; zoological preconditions of intelligence.* A synoptic view. Neural basis of behavior: *methods of investigation; some typical cases; biochemical basis of memory.* Hormones and behavior. Circadian rhythms and biological clocks. Animal societies: *social organization.* Review and references: *review topics; useful references.*

General Zoology

Part I

Basic Concepts

The most inclusive as well as the most useful orientating principle in present-day biology is the concept of levels of organization. The concept includes both the phenomena of life and its evolution, and also the nonliving world from which the living arose. It enables a biologist to find his way amid the vast mountains of data that surround him.

The idea itself is not new. It merely states that the world is composed of a series of levels of complexity so constructed that the units of any level are the building blocks of the units of the adjacent level. Thus, electrons and protons make up atoms, atoms are built into molecules, molecules can be organized into living cells, cells into higher plants and animals, and these in turn form societies.

The major current areas of advance in biology lie on two levels—the molecular one in biochemistry and the more complex one of animal behavior. It must not be imagined, however, that the level of cells or of the physiology of organisms have lost their importance or that knowledge in these areas is at a standstill. On the cellular level, the discoveries of the electron microscope are closing the ancient gap between form and function, notably in the case of muscle contraction. And new knowledge on the biochemical level illuminates all other levels. Even taxonomy, the oldest and in a sense the most basic of the zoological sciences, feels the impact. Similarly, discoveries about animal behavior throw new light on the meaning of structures like the pineal gland and the hypothalamus, which have puzzled anatomists and physiologists for generations.

Chapter 1

Zoology, the Science of Animal Life

Diverse motives have impelled men to study animal life. In different parts of the world and in different centuries, one or another motive has become predominant, but, in general, four main objectives can be distinguished.

Economic Objectives. One of the most universal objectives is the economic. Every modern nation—whether capitalistic, communistic, socialistic, democratic, or authoritarian—maintains research stations to discover and develop new types of animals or better ways of caring

Fig. 1–1. Two-year-old Santa Gertrudis bull, the result of crossing Asiatic heat-resistant cattle with European beef cattle. *(Kindness of Santa Gertrudis Breeders International)*

for them. "What is the best way to feed a pig?" is typical of the thousands of practical questions that arise. Zebu cattle from India are being crossed with Jersey and Holstein breeds from Europe in attempts to combine general hardiness against heat and poor food with superior milk and beef qualities. Russian zoologists have crossed the one-humped camel with the two-humped one and produced a larger, tougher draft animal than either parent. Most nations with seacoasts, even Italy and Israel on the Mediterranean, invest huge sums in marine research to help uncover the mysteries of the sea, and thereby enable their fishing fleets to improve their catch. It is even supposed by some enthusiasts that it will someday be possible to plant and harvest on the seas as on the land. Most agricultural research programs, however, have limited objectives, such as determining the optimum feed for cattle or the most effective poison for an insect pest.

Medical Objectives. A second universally understood motive is the medical one. So deep set is the unity of life that discoveries made on one animal can be applied to others far removed in the animal kingdom, including even man himself. Certain problems require experiment with a warm-blooded mammal, perhaps a dog or a monkey, before conclusions can be

4

applied to human beings, but the basic investigations can often best be carried out on cold-blooded animals like frogs or starfish.

The modern theory of the way the heartbeat is controlled was formulated in good part from work on the heart of *Limulus,* the horseshoe crab. The ideal place to study nerve conduction is not in the nerve of a man or a frog but in certain giant nerve fibers of *Loligo,* the squid, a close relative of the octopus. At first sight what animals could possibly be more different from man than the one-celled protozoans, *Amoeba, Paramecium, Tetrahymena,* and their like? Yet the requirements for vitamins and other dietary constituents of these organisms are almost identical with those of man. This is not to say that one-celled animals living in a test tube of water will soon replace white rats as the standard test animals for nutritional studies; yet important new facts are being uncovered in these microscopic animals that are of wide and perhaps universal importance among animals. In a thousand different ways zoological knowledge aids healthy and abundant living.

Psychological and Sociological Objectives. A third general objective of zoological studies is the attempt to gain greater insight into the problems of psychology and the social sciences. The behavior and personality of men and women cannot be adequately understood without a knowledge of their nervous systems, their endocrine glands, and even their general bodily conformations. It would be hard to name a topic about which there has been a greater spate of nonsense, both well-meaning and of evil intent, than the relationship between human heredity and human character. Animal behavior has always been a study of great fascination for its own sake. Recent discoveries about the animal nervous system and the rise in the past decade of a new school of thought about animal behavior seem likely to result in important revisions in the field of human psychology.

Lure of the Unknown. The economic and medical objectives are compelling, and the desire to create a basic foundation on which to build an understanding of psychology and sociology is widespread and enduring. Yet all

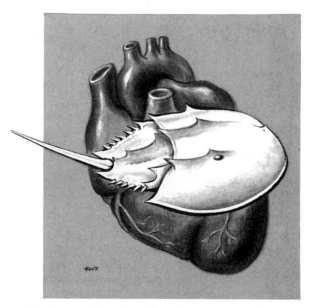

Fig. 1–2. *Limulus,* the horseshoe crab. New principles governing the action of the human heart were discovered by research on this animal.

together they do not explain the sustained drive that generation after generation has pushed forward the boundaries of zoological knowledge. A final factor must be reckoned with. As Aristotle, the ancient Greek philosopher and founder of the scientific study of animals, said, "All men by nature desire to know." This desire to know ranges all the way from a simple curiosity about the number of humps on the offspring of the cross between a one-humped and a two-humped camel (the answer is one hump) to a bold intention to plumb the depths of the universe and fathom the secrets of the life that is in it. This thirst to know and to understand is as natural to man as the desire for food or air. It is one of the characteristics that distinguish him from what our ancestors called "the beasts."

Bertrand Russell, probably the most eminent of modern mathematicians and philosophers, once said that if knowledge be true and deep it brings with it a sense almost of comradeship with other seekers after truth in other lands and distant times. The feeling of partnership in a long tradition of human enterprise plays an important role in the progress of zoology.

Truth and Motivation. It is essential to remember that the general objectives and the personal motivations of the investigator are no test whatever of the truth or falsity, the importance or triviality, of a discovery. The validity of Mendel's laws of heredity is completely independent of the nationality, religion, skin color, or table manners of Gregor Mendel. We do not know whether Mendel spent those long hours in his garden crossing peas primarily as refreshment from the routines of monastery life, because he was fascinated with the problem of inheritance, as some sublimation of an interest in sex, or through a determination to show that an Augustinian could make scientific discoveries of the first rank. Some, all, or none of these factors may have been involved. The only relevant questions are whether or not his experiments can be repeated and whether his conclusions hold true for other organisms besides peas.

The importance of objectives lies in their ability to lead an investigator toward certain discoveries and to blind him to others. There is an old saying in German laboratories that you can make a discovery without meaning to but not without knowing it. This is another way of saying that lucky accidental discoveries come to prepared minds. Many a bacteriologist had seen that troublesome mold, *Penicillium,* ruin his cultures of bacteria before Alexander Fleming had the insight to see that in this obstacle to routine bacteriological research lay a spectacular method of curing many bacterial diseases.

LEVELS OF ORGANIZATION

During the latter part of the 19th century and the earlier years of our own, the theory of organic evolution formed the theoretical basis for most, if not all, biological thought and investigation. The theory of evolution furnished the frame of reference within which a multitude of diverse facts could be meaningfully organized. It provided the biologist with points of orientation in his research and thinking.

In our own times a broad new concept has come into prominence as the most inclusive framework for biological thought. This new frame of reference does not negate the theory of organic evolution but goes beyond it to include also the nonliving world from which the living arose. The new concept is simple on the surface: it postulates that the known universe is composed of a series of levels of organization of such a nature that the units of one level of complexity form the building stones for the units of the adjacent level. Simple as it appears, the concept of a series of levels of organization, each creatively linked to adjacent levels, involves profound philosophical problems. Indeed, it is by no means a new concept to the philosopher—but it has recently come into greatly increased use by biologists. It is a creative framework that enables us to know where we are and to find our way among vast mountains of data. It suggests new areas of research and illuminates the whole landscape of biology.

The first, but not necessarily the simplest, level of organization is the realm of the hundred or so subatomic particles or wave-particles—electrons, protons, neutrons, mesons, and the rest. The next adjacent level comprises the atoms built up from the subatomic particles. The units of this level are the well-known chemical elements—hydrogen, oxygen, nitrogen, carbon, phosphorus, iron, etc.

The third or molecular level can be roughly equated with the biochemical level. The molecules of this level are composed of the atoms of the previous level organized in hundreds of thousands—in fact, in millions—of different patterns. Some are as simple as water, H_2O, and some as intricate as a molecule of hemoglobin or as large as DNA, the deoxyribose nucleic acid that carries the code of heredity in the chromosomes.

Above the molecules is the level of living cells, and above that the level of multicellular organisms, the familiar plants and animals which may contain millions of cells. It will be noted that organs—the liver, brain, kidney, etc.—do not constitute a primary level of organization. A primary level is composed of units that can have an independent existence. Electrons or photons, for example, can exist independently. So also can atoms of nitrogen or iron, and cells and whole multicellular animals. A liver or a leg can exist for any length of time only as part of an organism. Such structures plainly belong to a secondary level of organization not comparable to the primary levels we are discussing here.

Above the level of many-celled animals is the level of populations of many-celled animals. Why is a school of fishes or a swarm of bees or a flock of geese regarded as a new, sixth level? Each of these groups can do things which no single individual can do. One goose cannot fly in a V. The language of the bees presupposes a community of bees. Evolution itself takes place on the level of populations. No single organism evolves into a new species. Only populations existing through long periods of time evolve. All animals are members of populations. This applies equally to the lone albatross flying over the ocean and to the local field mouse.

Each level has its own characteristic properties and laws and its own independent validity. A fact established on one level remains true regardless of what is discovered about it on another level, but the meaning we give to the discovery may change. Thus the elementary laws of heredity discovered by Mendel working with groups of whole organisms continued to be valid even after T. H. Morgan and others showed the relationship of those laws to the chromosomes about which Mendel was ignorant. Likewise, the facts of gene linkage on the chromosomes remained valid after the contemporary discoveries of the biochemical basis of heredity in DNA. At the other end of the spectrum, knowledge of DNA will remain true whatever may be discovered in the future about population genetics in large numbers of animals.

In the shift from one level of organization to another, new properties emerge. The properties of water molecules are not the sum or the average of the properties of the gaseous hydrogen and oxygen atoms of which water is composed. The freezing point, the boiling point, the chemical attributes—all these are new. This is what biologists mean when they say that the whole is more than the mere sum of the parts. It is the *organization* that makes the difference even within a single level. The brain of a fish and the brain of a fisherman are alike on the atomic level and essentially the same on the cellular level. All nerve cells are basically the same. The design and the pattern make the difference.

New properties also emerge when you break up complex patterns and descend to "lower" levels. Any freshman in chemistry knows that the pure metallic element sodium has many exciting properties not found in the sodium chloride of table salt. An oak tree which has grown all its life as a single individual in the center of a field spreads out and becomes a far different thing from the tall, straight-trunked forest tree with only a small crown of branches at the top. One can say that, in a sense, the parts may be more than the whole.

WHAT IS LIFE?

Any science should define its basic concepts. Yet life is almost as difficult to define as the redness of red. The essential difference between the living and the nonliving has, however, become increasingly clearer. It is not a difference in the kind of matter, as was once supposed, for the same atoms which make up the one also compose the other. Nor has the difference anything to do with an escape from the laws of conservation of matter and energy. These laws hold firmly for respiration and all other activities of living things.

Modern physicists have sometimes said that life is something which feeds on negative entropy. Entropy is a measure of the unavailable energy in a thermodynamic system; in other words, entropy is a measure of the degree of utter randomness, which means an average uniformity. A simple illustration is to place a large crystal of salt in a jar of water. As long as there is a difference in concentration of salt in different parts of the water, osmotic work can be done. Once the random Brownian motion of the water and salt molecules has produced a random uniform distribution with no concentration differences, no further work is possible. In the same way, in a closed system, a heat engine can work only so long as there is a temperature difference between some of its parts. With the passage of time the random motion of the atoms will equalize the heat throughout.

Life, in contrast to the random disorder of entropy, represents a high degree of patterning, of organization, of matter and energy. Only when atoms are organized into the largest and most complex molecules, proteins and nucleic acids, does that constellation of properties emerge which we call life. This constellation of activities is familiar: respiration—the immemorial "breath of life"—plus assimilation, excretion, growth, reproduction, and sensitivity. Taken separately, each can be duplicated in the nonliving world. Even self-regulating feedback systems such as thermostats are now commonplace. Reproduction remains as the only possible exception. As one wit put it, you need have no fear that you will wake up some morning to find your desk crawling with little typewriters. As for defining either life or the redness of red, biologists would do well to remember Gödel's Proof, one of the milestones of modern mathematics: in any system there will always remain one unprovable postulate.

THE GREAT DICHOTOMY OF LIFE

On this planet, and probably on any planet where life has existed for any length of time, life diverges in two main directions. One line of evolution leads to organisms which have the ability to manufacture their own food from very simple inorganic molecules, ultimately carbon dioxide, water, and a few salts. In other words, green plants. The other line of evolution leads to organisms unable to manufacture their own food from simple inorganic substances; they are dependent on outside sources of complex organic molecules. This line obviously leads to the animals. Instead of evolving complex biochemical synthetic systems able to carry on photosynthesis and the making of amino acids, the animals evolved complex nervous and muscular systems enabling them to move to places where they could find and capture complex food prefabricated.

On the biochemical level plants and animals are basically the same except for the special synthetic abilities of plants and the neuro-muscular systems of animals. And even here the differences are not as great as one might suppose. Respiration is closely similar to photosynthesis, except that many of the reactions are run backwards. In cellular respiration both plants and animals burn sugar and do so with the same chemical machinery. With only minor variations the way genes replicate and the way they produce their effects are the same throughout the living world. Animals and plants are also basically the same on the cellular level of nucleus with chromosomes, and cytoplasm with mitochondria and other cell organelles. In fact, the reason that Mendel's laws of heredity hold true for both animals and plants is that the chromosomes of both behave in the same way.

However, when the level of multicellular organisms is reached, profound differences emerge between the two great divisions of the living world. A complex multicellular animal is a very different kind of phenomenon from a complex multicellular plant. Our concern here is to explore those complex multicellularities characterized by the possession of nerves and muscles.

MAJOR DIVISIONS OF THE ANIMAL KINGDOM

In the great sweep of evolution, animal life has deployed in two main directions and several lesser ones.

The two major divisions are the deuterostomes and the protostomes. The **deuterostomes** include only two large phyla, the **chordates,** to which all the animals with backbones belong, and the **echinoderms,** including the starfish and their relatives, making some 80,000 described species in all. The **protostomes** are an overwhelmingly larger group in number of species. They include the 750,000 species of **arthropods,** the 95,000 species of **mollusks,** and the 15,000 to 500,000 species of **nematodes** or roundworms, plus the **annelids** and several smaller phyla. The deuterostomes and protostomes are separated by a number of basic developmental and anatomical characters which will be discussed in connection with each of these groups.

The lesser phyla which are neither deuterostomes nor protostomes are simpler and clearly more primitive animals. In them it is possible to see many of the elementary forms and problems of life. The phylum **Protozoa,** with about 40,000 species, is the largest and most important of these medically and in most other ways. The Protozoa remain on the one-cell level of complexity, although some have certain tricks that enable them partially to escape the limitations of size that are imposed by the single-cell body plan.

Far smaller in number of species are the **Porifera,** or sponges. Only about 3,000 kinds of these extremely peculiar animals have been described. They appear to be in an evolutionary blind alley.

The **coelenterates,** with some 10,000 described species, include such well-known types as the jellyfish, corals, sea anemones, freshwater hydras, and other animals. Their relationship to other phyla is problematic although there is some recent evidence that they evolved from flatworms.

CLASSIFICATION: TAXONOMY

Essential to any useful science of zoology is some system of classification. The number of animal types presents a bewildering jungle of thousands, tens of thousands, and, in some groups, hundreds of thousands of different kinds. Over 14,000 species of bony fishes have been described, nearly 2,000 species of tapeworms, well over half a million species of insects. From whatever point of view zoology is approached, whether that of agriculture, medicine, economics, or pure research, classification is necessary to bring manageable order out of this confusion.

If an insect, for example, is destroying crops or transmitting a human disease, the first thing that must be done is to determine definitely what kind of insect it is. Only then can the accumulated knowledge of entomology—the science dealing with insects—be brought to bear on the case. Only by knowing with certainty the species of an animal under observation can any new discoveries about it be integrated into the great body of scientific knowledge. Thus **taxonomy,** as the science of classification is called, forms the indispensable framework of zoological science.

A further aspect of taxonomy must be recognized. The naming of animals appears to fill some deep and all but universal human desire. It will be recalled that in the Biblical story of creation, one of the first acts of Adam was to name the animals.

Since the latter part of the 18th century taxonomy has become increasingly concerned with animal relationships. At first the similarities between different kinds of animals were not thought of as due to descent from common ancestors. Under the leadership of the great Swedish naturalist Carl Linnaeus (1707–1778) and the anatomists Georges Cuvier (1769–1832) in France and Richard Owen (1804–1892) in England, the similarities between animals were regarded as the expression of a logical relationship, just as different kinds of triangles, quadrilaterals, or other geometrical figures are related. There is some truth here. How much? This is a hard question, perhaps a deep-reaching one, and a question that remains still unanswered.

With the publication in 1859 of the *Origin of Species* by Charles Darwin (1809–1882), the study of classification became part of the study of evolution. Ever since, taxonomic arrangements of animals have been intended to reflect evolutionary relationships. The closer two kinds of animals are thought to be to a common ancestral population, the closer they are placed on the taxonomic scale.

PRESENT SYSTEM OF CLASSIFICATION

The present-day system of classification is an indispensable tool for all branches of biological science. At its base is the **binomial** or **Linnaean system** which was established by Linnaeus in the 18th century. According to this scheme each distinct kind of animal receives two names which together constitute the scientific name of the species. Thus all human beings belong to the species *Homo sapiens,* all wood frogs to the species *Rana sylvatica.* The name written first is the name of the **genus,** which is defined as a group of related **species.** Most frogs belong to the genus *Rana.* Following the generic name is the specific name. The wood frog bears the specific name *sylvatica.* Note that the generic name is capitalized while the specific name is not. Both names are italicized unless part of a title. The word species is the same in both singular and plural. Specific names are commonly adjectives referring to some characteristic of the species; thus *sylvatica* (of the woods) is the specific name for the wood frog, and *pipiens* (chirping) for the common laboratory frog. However, the specific name may be taken from a person, as in the case of *Rana catesbeiana,* the bullfrog (whether male or female) named after Mark Catesby, one of the early American naturalists.

This system is an international one, the same in Baltimore and in Bombay. The rules governing the binomial system, as well as the way in which species and genera are organized into larger categories, are formulated and interpreted by the International Commission on Zoological Nomenclature. This commission is at present composed of 30 men from about 20 countries and is controlled by the International Congress of Zoology, a voluntary organization meeting from time to time in various parts of the world.

The form of both generic and specific names must be Latin. The scientific name of an animal should be followed without punctuation by the name of the zoologist who first described and named the species and by the date on which he published his work. Thus *Felis leo* Linnaeus (1758) indicates that the lion was so named by Linnaeus himself in 1758. *Felis oregonensis* Rafinesque indicates that the puma of the Rocky Mountains and Pacific Coast was named by Constantine Rafinesque—a Turkish-born American naturalist of French and German ancestry. In actual practice the name of the discoverer of the animal and the date are usually omitted, and often the genus name is merely indicated by its initial capital letter.

An important rule governing the binomial system is that of priority. According to this, the first person to describe an animal has the right to name it. As fair and in fact inevitable as this rule seems to be, it causes some inconvenience in practice when it is found that an organism long familiar under one name had been given a different name earlier by a man who published in some little-known journal. The tenth edition of Linnaeus' book, *Systema Naturae*, 1758, is the starting point for questions of priority in zoological nomenclature.

Similar genera are grouped into **families,** the families into **orders,** and these into **classes.** Above the classes stand the **phyla.** Each phylum constitutes a major division of the animal kingdom.

The 1949 report on nomenclature of the American Association for the Advancement of Science strongly advocates the use of uniform endings for taxonomic categories, i.e., **taxons,** above the genus. Many zoologists continue to use the old endings which can only be described as a deplorable hodgepodge. However, standard endings are coming into increasingly wider acceptance. The advantages of a logical system are so great that such endings will be used throughout this text for orders and families, although not for phyla and classes. There are only a couple of dozen phyla and rarely more than five classes in any phylum, so the number of these groups is very small in contrast to the many thousands of orders and families. It is important to remember that only the endings are involved in these changes. The basic names remain the same. The standard ending used in this text for an order is -iformes, and for a family, -idae. The classification of two familiar organisms is given below:

TAXON	AMOEBA	MAN
Phylum	Protozoa	Chordata
Subphylum	. . . . . .	Vertebrata
Class	Rhizopoda	Mammalia
Order	Amoebiformes	Primatiformes
Family	Amoebidae	Hominidae
Genus	*Amoeba*	*Homo*
Species	*proteus*	*sapiens*

THEORETICAL BASIS OF CLASSIFICATION

Homology. The basis on which animals are classified is homology. Homology is defined as fundamental anatomical similarity regardless of function. In the words of Richard Owen (1804–1892), a contemporary of Charles Darwin and the man who made homology the central concept in comparative anatomy, homologous organs are really "the same organ in different animals under every variety of form or function."

In a series of different vertebrates or different insects, such homologies are easy to see. Compare the skeleton in the arm of a man, the flipper of a seal, the foreleg of a horse, an elephant, or a dog, and it will be clear that they are all constructed of the same basic parts organized on the same basic plan. An upper arm, the humerus; a forearm composed of two bones, the ulna making a hingelike joint at the elbow, and the radius alongside it; a group of wrist bones, the carpals; five (or fewer) bones in the palm called the metacarpals; and lastly a series of five (or fewer) fingers (or toes), the digits. So

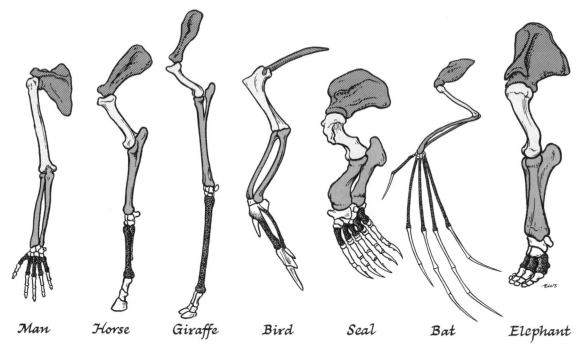

Man   Horse   Giraffe   Bird   Seal   Bat   Elephant

Fig. 1–3. Forelimbs of vertebrates shaded to show skeletal homologies. The uppermost bone in each is the scapula or shoulder blade; then the humerus; the radius and ulna, semi-fused side by side in the horse and giraffe; the carpals in the wrist; the metacarpals in the palm; and the digits, each with three phalanges, except the thumb which has two.

also for the bones of the hind legs or of the skull. So too for the mouthparts of different insects or for their wings. Other tests of homology have been proposed from time to time. Similarity of embryological development is one of the most useful of these tests. This is really anatomical similarity projected backward in time through the life of the animal.

The explanation of homology lies in common ancestry. The closer the evolutionary relationship, the closer the homology. A full discussion of this subject will be postponed until Chapter 10, but, briefly stated, the arm of a man is more like the front leg of a dog or any other mammal than it is like the wing of a bird because man and dog are much more closely related than man and bird.

Analogy. Similarity of function is known as analogy. The wing of a bird and the wing of an insect are analogous because they have a functional likeness, although their anatomy is basically very different. On the other hand, the wing of a chicken and the arm of a man are homologous, since they are built on the same

anatomical plan and develop in the same manner. Thus birds and men are related in a way birds and insects are not.

THE CHALLENGE OF TAXONOMY

Many zoologists regard the present state of taxonomy as a scientific scandal. This feeling arises in part because of the exasperating confusions that are inevitable whenever a species familiar under one name is given a new one. This may happen because it is found that the species had been named earlier but in an obscure journal, or because some taxonomist assigns the species to another genus. The common North American pond salamander, *viridescens*, has been assigned to at least three genera in recent years. The list of species that have had their names changed is a long one.

The underlying difficulty as well as the great challenge of taxonomy is that there are as yet no objective criteria by which to determine zoological relationships. The whole field appears like chemistry before Mendeleeff introduced the periodic table of the elements.

11

What Is a Species? The most commonly accepted definition of a species is a group of interbreeding, or potentially interbreeding, animals — that is, a group of animals sharing the same gene pool. It is the best definition we have but it presents thorny problems both practical and theoretical. In most cases it is impossible for the taxonomist either in the field or in the museum to know whether or not two somewhat different animals actually interbreed and share the same pool of genes. And then there are certain special problems. The lion, *Felis leo,* and the tiger, *Felis tigris,* are clearly distinct, noninterbreeding species in the field, but will interbreed successfully in the artificial conditions of a zoo. This also holds true in the case of wild ducks and other animals.

Polytypic species present an awkward paradox. In these cases a series of more or less distinct but interbreeding populations exist over a considerable geographical range. Each population can interbreed successfully with adjacent populations, but the groups at each end of the series are intersterile. For example, the common species of leopard frog, *Rana pipiens*, extends from Maine and Canada down into Florida and most of Mexico. The leopard frogs of Maine can interbreed successfully with those of southern New England, those of southern New England with those of New Jersey and even Georgia, while those of Georgia can interbreed with those of northern Mexico. However, the Maine frogs cannot interbreed with the Mexican. It almost seems like saying A equals B and B equals C, but A does not equal C. The common harbor gull, *Larus,* forms a similar series of races in the lands around the North Pole. Another such series is known for finches in China.

To be truly valid, a concept of classification must apply to animals during the long course of their evolution. But the ancestors of the modern horse, for instance, during their evolution have constituted a continuous interbreeding population, though a gradually changing one. If the ability to interbreed be made the only criterion of a species, then horses from the present all the way back to a small generalized doglike creature in the Eocene Period about 60,000,000 years ago are one species. In a sense, the horse, in its evolution, can be regarded as a polytypic species spread through time rather than space. The same argument can be applied to all other animals. Since all mammals have evolved, according to the fossil record, from the same population of small doglike lizards or lizardlike dogs, logic would seem to force the conclusion that all mammals form only one species! Yet this seems to reduce the whole concept of the species to an absurdity.

What is a Genus? A genus is defined as a group of related species. The trouble with this definition is that it relies on the subjective judgment of the taxonomist to decide how important or unimportant any particular resemblance or difference is. Should a certain group of similar species be placed in a single genus, or do they seem to divide themselves into two or even four or five smaller genera? This is the kind of tough question faced by anyone who attempts to classify animals or plants. Those who emphasize resemblances tend to make fewer but larger genera and are known as "lumpers." Those who tend to notice differences make more but smaller genera and are known as "splitters." The same problem plagues workers with the higher taxons. Should a group of genera be regarded as making one family, or several? Should several families be placed in a single order, or in several orders? Equally disturbing, with the higher taxons a new problem is added. There is no way of determining whether or not the families, orders, and classes of one phylum correspond to the families, orders, and classes of another phylum. In cold fact there are good reasons for believing that sometimes they do not. Even the best scientific dictionaries can define the taxonomic categories only in terms of each other. An order is a taxon composed of one or more families. A family is a taxon composed of one or more genera.

The ease with which a very few genes or even a single gene can override characters that set taxons apart from each other is strikingly illustrated in the case of "bithorax," a mutant form of the fruit fly, *Drosophila.* Like all the flies, gnats, and mosquitos, *Drosophila* is a member of the order Dipteriformes which, as its name implies, is composed of insects with two wings. The normal wild-type fly has a sin-

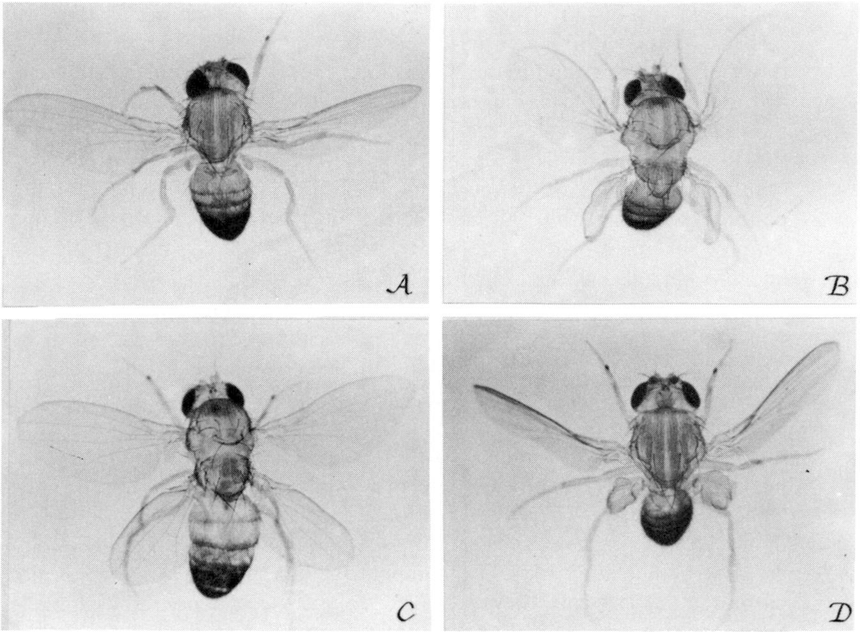

Fig. 1–4. *Drosophila. A.* normal wild-type with a pair of wings and a pair of halteres. *B, C,* and *D,* bithorax mutant forms, showing two pairs of wings. *(Kindness of E. B. Lewis)*

gle pair of wings extending from the middle region of the thorax, and behind them, where insects of other winged orders have a second pair of wings, the fly has a pair of drumsticklike appendages called halteres. In the mutant forms, as can be seen in Figure 1–4, the halteres are converted into recognizable wings!

Even the basic concept of homology presents difficulties as soon as you look beyond the mammals or the insects. For example, as William Bateson, one of the founders of Mendelian genetics, pointed out, virtually all mammals—man, giraffe, elephant, and mouse—have precisely seven neck or cervical vertebrae and hence it is easy to recognize a one-to-one correspondence. The second cervical vertebra of a horse corresponds to the second of a cat or a pig or a man. But how can the seven cervical vertebrae of a mammal be homologized with those of a pigeon which has 15, or those of a pigeon with those of a swan which has 26?

NEW APPROACHES IN TAXONOMY

Competitive Exclusion. Homology, uncertain as it may be, remains the basis on which comparisons between species are made. The fossil record is sometimes available to help decide relationships, especially between higher taxons. Newer work has been characterized by a lively realization of the importance of studying a population, rather than basing species and even genera on one or two individuals. This followed the knowledge gained from Mendelian genetics that there is much genetic variation within most groups of animals.

Ecological studies of natural populations in their environment have led to the **Principle of Competitive Exclusion,** sometimes called the Volterra-Gause Rule after the men who formulated it. According to this rule, no two species can occupy precisely the same ecological niche within the same territory. In other words, no two species will be found which compete in every aspect of their lives. At least one, and usually several, important ways will exist in which similar species living in the same territory do not compete. This principle furnishes an important insight which enables one to make sense out of what often appears to be a meaningless hodgepodge of species.

Examples of competitive exclusion are all around us. The turkey vulture and the black vulture both hunt carrion over the same territory but the turkey vulture hunts from a far greater height and ranges over greater distances than does the black. Both have enormous olfactory areas within their nasal passages but those of the turkey vulture are larger than those of the lower-flying black vulture. The five common species of frogs in North America east of the Rockies and north of central Mexico constitute a beautiful case of the principle of competitive exclusion; this will be described in the chapter on amphibians. The great horned owl and the barred owl, the "eight-hooter," are virtually the same in size and general appearance and live in the same regions. But the horned owl frequents dry woods and hills, nests on rocky ledges or on old crows' nests, and eats animals as large as skunks and chickens, while the barred inhabits swamps and moist forests, nests in hollow trees, and eats small prey — mice, frogs, and the like. There are 35 or more species of warblers living over eastern North America. At first glance they look like competitors but careful study reveals they are all specialists. Some nest in one kind of site, some in another or at a different time of the summer. Some feed close to the tops of trees, others only near the trunk, others close to the ground. As en-

lightening as this principle is, it provides little help in the routine determination of species, and none at all in connection with classification of higher taxons.

Behavioral Traits. With the rise of the ethological school of animal behaviorists and the new emphasis on instincts, several taxonomists have successfully used behavioral traits to help distinguish and relate species. The kind of web spun by a particular species of spider, the way a certain species of cricket chirps or a certain kind of frog croaks or a caterpillar spins its cocoon are as characteristic and constant traits as are any anatomical features. The instructions for this behavior are programmed in the gene code in the chromosomes just as truly as are the instructions for the development of any anatomical feature in the embryo. But useful as behavioral characters may be when they can be discovered and studied, they are not essentially different from other traits, all of which are expressions of gene action. Consequently, in themselves they do not offer an objective method for the determination of species and

Fig. 1–5. The principle of competitive exclusion keeps these two similar species apart in nature. Left: the great horned owl, *Bubo virginianus*, inhabits dry woods and uplands. Right: the barred owl, *Strix varia*, frequents swamps and riverbottom forests.

genera any more than do such gene-controlled traits as the number of legs or bristles.

Numerical Taxonomy. At the present time attempts are being made to develop objective methods for taxonomy along three different lines. These are actually old ideas with a modern twist.

The first approach is the revival of numerical or Adansonian taxonomy, after 200 years, now that computers are available. All traits are regarded as of equal taxonomic value. At least an approximation of a complete description of each species or candidate for a species or for a genus is fed into the computer. Whether or not an animal has a backbone, whether it has two wings or four, hair or feathers, are facts of no more and no less importance than whether the hair is straight or curly, the wings chitinous membranes or fur-covered skin, the eyes red or milk white. Perhaps this can be justified on the grounds that as many genes are required to produce one bristle as to produce a backbone. No one can be certain. But it is certain that grave difficulties beset numerical taxonomy in the selection of the facts to be fed into the computer. When the wing of a bat or butterfly or vulture is described for a computer, how many "bits" of information are required? Once the computer has received the facts the taxonomist has *selected,* then it can follow the instructions the taxonomist has *chosen* and produce an answer.

Protein Similarity. A second line of approach began with the work of Nuttall at the turn of the century. The degree of relationship between animals is determined by measuring the degree of similarity of their proteins, especially their blood proteins. Serological methods are used. As readers of detective stories know, this method can distinguish human from chicken or other animal blood. If a foreign protein is injected into a mammal, say a horse, after some days the horse's blood will contain special proteins, gamma globulins, called antibodies, which will precipitate the protein originally injected but not other proteins. Fortunately, from the zoologist's point of view, some cross reactions with other proteins do occur. Antibody against human blood will not precipitate chicken pro-

tein but will cause some precipitation of chimpanzee protein. Antibody against dog protein will cause marked precipitation of fox protein and some of seal protein. Seals, like dogs, are carnivores. By accurately determining the amount of precipitate, it is possible to get an objective measurement. There is much evidence that the closer the relationship, the more precipitate.

This immunological comparison of protein similarities has been most successful in answering rather general questions. For example, is the manatee, the Florida sea cow, related more closely to the porpoise, the ox, or the elephant? The answer is the ox. If no more than three species are considered at a time, their degree of relation can be represented as points on a triangle. When many animals are compared, impossible multidimensional models are required.

Proteins can also be compared by a new method known as **electrophoresis.** In this procedure proteins are driven by an electric current through a starch or acrylamide gel. Different proteins move through the gel at different rates due to differences in molecular size, electrical charge, and perhaps shape. Characteristic bands of protein are formed which can be stained. The proteins of one species can be compared in various ways with those of another. But, it can be argued, the number of bristles can be counted and their lengths measured. True. The advantage of comparing proteins is that the whole organism and all its anatomy can be reduced to a common denominator in its proteins. Wings, hair, bristles, and all the rest are either proteins themselves or the products of special proteins called enzymes.

Common Genes. The third and most exciting of the newer attempts is the effort to take a direct reading on the number of genes or, more accurately, nucleotide sequences that different organisms have in common. The present assumption, although it will not necessarily be followed in the future, is the postulate of numerical or Adansonian taxonomy that all similarities are equally significant. The immense advantage of this approach is that no selection or even verbal formulation of the "bits" of information to be used is necessary.

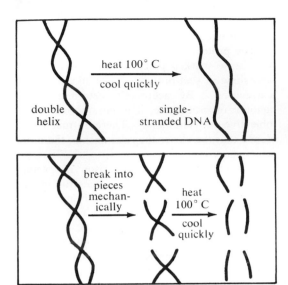

Fig. 1–6. Two stages in preparing DNA from two species for determination of the number of genes held in common. *(After Hoyer, McCarthy, and Bolton)*

The procedure is simple in principle but complicated in practice and much more will have to be learned about it. It is well established that the genetic code in the chromosomes is carried in a double strand of deoxyribose nucleic acid (DNA). The double strands of DNA from one species are heated to separate the strands and then quickly cooled to prevent the single strands from spontaneously pairing up again. Then separately prepared DNA double strands from another species are broken into small pieces mechanically and heated and cooled to produce many very short single strands. If these short pieces have been made radioactive, they can be followed. In the final steps of the procedure the long single strands from one species are mixed with the short radioactive single strands from the other. When a short piece meets a section of one of the long strands which is like itself, it pairs with it. Consequently, the more regions of the long strands which are like the short pieces, the more of the short pieces will adhere to them. Thus the more short pieces which pair with the long strands, the more genes the two species have in common.

One criticism of the early results of this method is that there is difficulty in distinguishing between a man and a chimpanzee, al-though the method does easily distinguish between man and the gibbon, an anthropoid ape closely related to both man and the chimp. It must be remembered that it is reasonable to suppose that all vertebrates have many genes in common, and all mammals would be expected to share an even greater number. Hemoglobin is synthesized by all vertebrates and many other animals, probably even *Paramecium*. The whole battery of enzymes of respiration appears to be virtually universal. The enzyme system producing melanin and other pigments is very closely similar in all organisms, and so it goes with a host of other biochemical processes. Great refinements may be necessary before much useful information comes from this method of comparing the DNA's of different species.

ZOOLOGICAL SCIENCES

For both theoretical and practical reasons zoology is divided into a great many subsidiary specialties. **Taxonomy** is the science of classification. It forms the frame of reference for all the zoological sciences. It indicates the evolutionary relationships of animals, and, for many persons from Adam onward, has been an absorbing interest in its own right. **Physiology** is the science of function. Physiologists investigate how a muscle contracts, the laws which describe the action of the heart, the processes of digestion, nature of a nervous impulse, the way the kidney works, and how the eye sees. **Anatomy** is the science of structure, whether macroscopic gross structure or microscopic cellular structure or, in recent times, the structures revealed by the electron microscope. Obviously, all the zoological sciences have their physiological and anatomical aspects.

Many of the zoological sciences deal with some particular side of animal life. **Genetics** is the science of heredity and variation. Because the theory of the gene has become one of the central concepts of modern biology, genetics is basic to an understanding of any of the other specialties. **Biochemistry,** sometimes called molecular biology, also underlies all fields of zoology because it concerns the chemistry of living processes. It underlies genetics as genetics underlies anatomy. Biochemistry is one of

16

the regions of most active present-day advance, where discoveries of great importance about the inner chemistry of cell activities are being made. The way enzymes control cellular activities and the mode of action of antibiotics are all part of biochemistry.

Embryology is the science of development and regeneration. It seeks to explain how a single cell, the fertilized egg, becomes transformed into the complex adult, and how some animals are able to regenerate new parts for those lost. Clearly this knowledge, if it can be obtained, holds the promise of a new and heroic age of surgery which may enable us to grow new organs for those injured. **Histology** is the science of cells as organized in tissues: muscle, liver, brain, etc.—a science of medical importance. **Cytology** is the study of cellular anatomy especially in relation to genetics and biochemistry. **Biophysics** is a newly emerging discipline concerned with many biological problems suggested by its name, such as the physical aspects of nervous impulses, cell membrane permeability, and vision.

Enzymology concerns the mode of action of enzymes, a field of vast theoretical and practical importance for medicine and industry. **Endocrinology** is the specialty dealing with the endocrine glands: thyroid, pituitary, adrenal, sex, and pancreatic. **Neurology** concerns the structure and action of the nervous system. **Parasitology** specializes in parasitic organisms. **Ethology** is the newly active science of animal behavior and its evolution. **Ecology** deals with the relationships of living things to their environment, both living and nonliving. It is basic to an understanding of animal populations.

For practical reasons many taxonomic groups have generated their own sciences: **protozoology, helminthology, entomology,** and **acarology** concern the Protozoa, the several groups of worms, the insects, and the ticks and mites, respectively. All are fields of medical, agricultural, and scientific importance. **Ichthyology** concerns fishes; **herpetology,** amphibians and reptiles; **ornithology,** birds; and **mammalogy,** the mammals. Zoology presents a broad spectrum of problems and subject matter.

Review and References

REVIEW TOPICS

1. What are the major motivations underlying zoological research? Cite some practical results of this research in three different areas. Is there such a thing as "pure research"?

2. What are the importance and limitations of personal motivations in research?

3. Define: taxonomy, taxon, phylum, genus, species, binomial system, homology, "lumper," DNA, polytypic species.

4. Why is taxonomy basic to the practice of any zoological science?

5. How great is the independent validity of the phenomena on any one level of organization? Can phenomena be understood on the basis of knowledge of only one level, or is this the only way they can be understood?

6. What difficulties are presented by the following concepts: homology, species, genus, living, numerical taxonomy?

7. What is the principle of competitive exclusion? Give two examples.

8. What have immunological methods contributed to taxonomy?

9. How can the number of genes two organisms share be measured?

10. Briefly, what is the agricultural, medical, and economic importance of: protozoology, physiology, biochemistry, acarology, neurology, cytology, endocrinology, ichthyology, parasitology, histology?

USEFUL REFERENCES

Alexander, R. D., "The Role of Behavioral Study in Cricket Classification," *Systematic Zoology,* vol. 11, 1962.

Boyden, A., "Fifty Years of Systematic Serology," *Systematic Zoology,* vol. 2, 1953.

Hagberg, K. H., *Carl Linnaeus,* New York, E. P. Dutton and Co., 1953.

Hanson, E. D., *Animal Diversity,* 2nd ed., Englewood Cliffs, N.J., Prentice-Hall, 1964.

Huxley, J., *The New Systematics,* Oxford, Clarendon Press, 1940.

Leone, C. A., ed., *Taxonomic Biochemistry and Serology,* New York, The Ronald Press Company, 1964.

Mayr, E., *Animal Species and Evolution,* Cambridge, Harvard University Press, 1963.

Mayr, E., E. G. Linsley, and R. L. Usinger, *Methods and Principles of Systematic Zoology,* New York, McGraw-Hill Book Co., 1953.

Moore, J. A., ed., *Ideas in Modern Biology,* New York, Natural History Press, 1965.

Pennak, R. W., *Collegiate Dictionary of Zoology,* New York, The Ronald Press Company, 1964.

Schrödinger, E., *What is Life?* New York, The Macmillan Company, 1945.

Simpson, G. G., *Principles of Animal Taxonomy,* New York, Columbia University Press, 1961.

Simpson, G. G., "Spoofs in Taxonomy," *Science,* vol. 140, 10 May 1963.

Stoll, R. N., ed., *International Code of Zoological Nomenclature,* London, International Trust for Zoological Nomenclature, 1964.

Chapter 2

The Cellular Level

The realization that all animals, including man, are built up of semi-independent units — cells — has come gradually, extending over four centuries and involving the work of investigators of many nations. Furthermore, the present decade is in the middle of an explosion of new knowledge about cell structure resulting from work with the electron microscope. This powerful instrument is closing the gap, as old as Aristotle and Hippocrates, between form and function. The anatomists of the past described, for example, the muscles and their arrangements. The physiologists learned about matter and energy requirements and waste products of muscular contraction, and about its characteristics, latent period, fatigue, etc. But in spite of the best that the ordinary light microscope could do, the muscle cell, like all other cells, remained very much what physicists call a "black box," impenetrable to human knowledge. The electron microscope can look inside that box and see the events that constitute contraction.

THE CELL THEORY

The idea that cells are the basic units of animal form and function is essentially simple, but difficult to assimilate fully into everyday thinking. No one feels subjectively that he is composed of thousands of semi-independent cells.

Nor is it easy to be convinced that the actual bridge between parents and children is a single cell, the fertilized egg. A feeling of surprise comes naturally when a frog killed by decapitation still jumps and makes accurately aimed motions with its legs. The answer, of course, is that the frog's nerves and muscles are made of cells which remain alive and able to function for a considerable time after other parts of the animal have been destroyed.

In short, a knowledge of cells is essential to an understanding of animals — how, for example, muscles contract, or the nervous system functions, or reproduction takes place, or recovery from injury or disease occurs, why the laws of heredity are as they are, or even how an animal digests its food.

Cells were first seen and so named by the versatile English mathematician and microscopist, Robert Hooke (1635–1703), in the 17th century. What Hooke saw was the honeycomb-like structure in the surface of leaves and in the substance of cork, which is the bark of a species of oak. This boxlike structure of cells is relatively easy to see in plant material (the skin of a red Italian onion, for instance), but the outlines of the cells which Hooke saw are the nonliving cellulose walls. Everyone who had one of the newly invented microscopes observed cells. In Holland, Anton van Leeuwenhoek (1632–1723), the gifted Dutch lens-

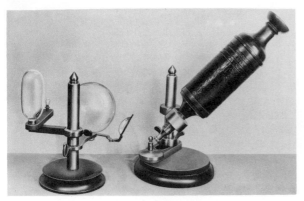

Fig. 2 – 1. Replica of the microscope through which Robert Hooke in 1665 saw cells in bark. *(Kindness of Bausch & Lomb)*

maker, described many kinds of cells from blood corpuscles to human sperms, though no one then suspected their basic similarity in structure. In the south of Europe Marcello Malpighi (1628 – 1694), a professor on the Faculty of Medicine in his native Bologna, turned his microscope on parts of large and small animals, and thus became the founder of microscopic anatomy, or histology. The innermost cellular layer of the skin is named, after its discoverer, the **Malpighian layer.**

The cell theory as we know it today is mainly the achievement of the 19th century. Microscopists all over Europe began to notice some kind of "mucus" within the boxlike "cells" of Hooke. Then in 1830 a young Scottish army surgeon and botanist, serving in tropical Australia, discovered a nucleus in the cells of orchids and subsequently in many other kinds of cells. In 1839 a Czech, Johannes Purkinje (1787 – 1869), usually known for his studies of vision, showed in a classic paper, "On the Structural Elements of Plants and Animals," that both plants and animals are constructed of cells. It was Purkinje who introduced the term **protoplasm** to denote the living material of the cell. At about the same time Schleiden and Schwann in Germany popularized similar ideas about the cellular structures of all living organisms, although their views about the origin of cells from a noncellular matrix turned out to be very wrong. Finally, in the 1860's, Max Schultze of Bonn drew together the diverse facts that adult animals are made of cells, that eggs and sperms are cells, and that microscopic animals like *Amoeba* and *Paramecium* are essentially single cells. At the same time he formulated the famous definition of protoplasm as "the physical basis of life."

It remained for a group of investigators in the latter part of the 19th century, mostly in Germany and Belgium, to show that all cells come from previous cells by a process of cell division known as **mitosis.** Due to their ingenious development of preservatives for protoplasm and to the then newly discovered aniline dyes, they were able to work out the essentials of chromosome behavior in cell division and fertilization.

It has now become clear that all the higher organisms, both plant and animal, are **eukaryotes** (*eu*, true, + *karyon*, kernel), that is, organisms in which the cells consist of **cytoplasm** composed of a **plasma membrane** enclosing various organelles, plus a discrete **nucleus** composed of a **nuclear membrane** enclosing **nuclear sap** and the **chromosomes.** Certain lower plants — the blue-green algae, the bacteria, and, according to some, the viruses — are known as **protokaryotes.** They lack discrete nuclei although they possess nucleic acid and some possess chromosomes.

Fig. 2 – 2. Cell types. Left to right: nerve cell, muscle cell, mammalian egg cell, human sperm cell, pigment cell, white blood cell, two red blood cells, and a free-living amoeba. Note the different shapes of the nuclei. (The various cells shown are not drawn to scale.)

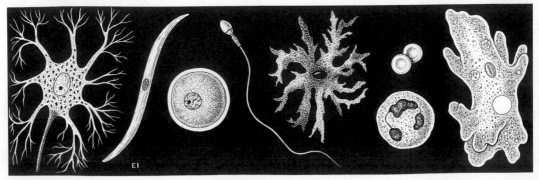

Within their limits of size and structure, cells show remarkable diversity of form and function. (See Fig. 2–2.) Muscle cells, nerve cells, liver cells, bone-secreting cells, skin cells, blood cells, egg cells—there are hundreds of different types. Red blood cells of mammals have even lost the nucleus and are virtually little more than cytoplasmic bags of a special protein, hemoglobin. Muscle cells still retain a nucleus, though it is often pushed to one side by the fibers of a contractile protein, actomyosin. Liver cells are cuboidal in shape and show abundant enzyme-bearing mitochondria, as is to be expected, for liver cells are among the most complex chemical factories in the body.

CELL SIZE

In addition to the basic nuclear-cytoplasmic organization, there is another important respect in which all cells are essentially alike, and that is size. The enormous difference in bulk between a mouse and an elephant is due to an enormous difference in number of cells, not in their size. The sperms and eggs, the cells of the liver, skin, brain, and other organs are the same size, within very small limits. In fact, the largest body cells of any animal are found in salamanders, not in horses or whales. Even the dramatic difference in size between the egg of a wren and an ostrich is more apparent than real, because the size of the nucleus and the amount of protoplasm are about the same in each. The great difference lies in the amount of nonliving yolk and albumen.

Some very potent factors must set both the upper and the lower limits of cell size. Apparently the upper limit is set by the volume of cytoplasm that can be serviced by a single nucleus. Part of the evidence for this is that those protozoans which exceed the normal size range for cells either have several nuclei of the usual size or have one small nucleus and one or more giant macronuclei. Another factor is the geometrical fact that as size increases, volume increases roughly as the cube of the radius of the cell, while surface increases as the square. This means that the amount of surface, through which all food and oxygen must enter the cell and through which all wastes must leave, becomes relatively less and less in proportion to the amount of cytoplasm.

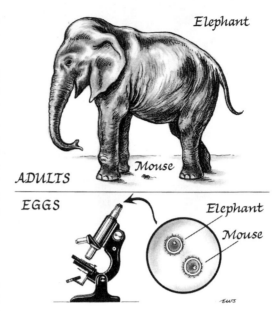

Fig. 2–3. Elephant and mouse drawn to show comparative sizes of adults and of their egg cells.

The lower limit of size is set by equally inescapable facts. Cells and protoplasm are built of proteins, lipids, water, and nucleic acids. These are the bricks. To construct a cell with at least one chromosome, a nuclear membrane, some surrounding cytoplasm, and a cell membrane, obviously some minimum number of protein molecules is required. You cannot make the cell any smaller unless you can find smaller protein molecules. You cannot find smaller molecules unless you can get smaller atoms to make them of. But atoms of hydrogen, oxygen, nitrogen, and the other necessary elements come only in the standard sizes. To find toy-sized atoms you would have to go, not just to another world, but to another universe. And so the old verse sometimes attributed to Jonathan Swift, the author of *Gulliver's Travels,*

> Great fleas have little fleas
> Upon their backs to bite 'em
> And little fleas have lesser fleas,
> And so *ad infinitum.*

is clearly false when it gets to the *ad infinitum* in the last line. There is a lower limit set by the structure of matter itself.

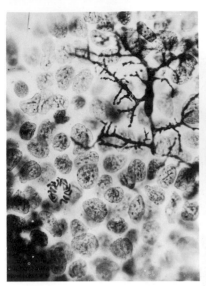 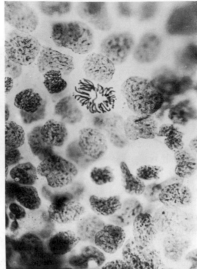 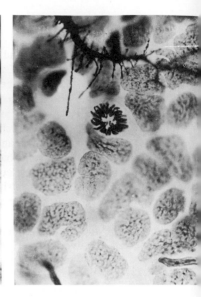

Fig. 2–4. Epidermal cells from tail fin of a larval salamander, *Triturus (Diemictylus) viridescens*. Left to right: with one, two, and three sets of chromosomes. Note many nuclei with membranes and dots of chromatin plus, in each, a single nucleus with thread-like chromosomes. The irregular, dark, rootlike structures are black pigment cells. Original magnification × 523. *(Kindness of G. Fankhauser)*

Much remains to be learned about what controls the size of cells within the basic limits just described. For example, if cells contain only one set of chromosomes instead of the two sets they normally have, both the nuclei of the cells and the cells themselves are smaller than usual. If cells possess three sets of chromosomes, the nuclei and the cells are larger than normal. Exactly how this regulation is accomplished, no one knows. Even more puzzling, the triploid animals, as those with three sets of chromosomes are called, although having much larger cells, have fewer cells so that their body size is about normal! The photographs in Figure 2–4 show a portion of the tail fin of each of three larval salamanders. This is the classic material on which Walther Flemming in the 1870's first described cell division clearly and in detail and coined the word mitosis (*mitos,* thread). Flemming's success was due in part to his choice of very favorable material and in part to his development of improved methods of preservation and staining. Each of these modern photos shows many nuclei in the so-called resting or interphase condition and one nucleus in which the nuclear membrane has disappeared and the threadlike chromosomes are arranged in a circle ready for cell division.

MODERN RESEARCH METHODS

One of the crucial differences between modern science and the science of the ancient Greeks, perhaps *the* crucial difference, is the modern realization of the importance of experiment, of laboratory experience, of technique. The techniques for studying cells have formed sciences in their own right. **Histology** is the study of cells as they form the various tissues: muscle, liver, skin, nerve, etc. **Cytology** is the study of individual cells. It embraces a series of techniques of great importance in understanding heredity and in diagnosing cancer.

The indispensable instruments are the light microscope and more recently the **electron microscope.** Most of the work in examining cells is preparing them for observation under the microscope. Progress has been continuous ever since Robert Hooke used a razor to cut slices of cork thin enough so that he could see the cells. Living cells can be studied best when they are grown *in vitro* (literally, in glass), outside the body in very thin sheets. Since World War II the **phase contrast method** has been perfected to investigate living cells. This method utilizes differences in the optical properties of different cell constituents like chromosomes and mitochondria. The most important result of this spectacular new method is that it has confirmed through observations on living cells what had hitherto been seen only in preserved material.

Most cell research is based on material that is preserved. Special fluids known as **fixatives** are used. Fixatives are mixtures of chemicals such as formaldehyde, alcohol, and acids in proportions in which the tendencies to shrink protein and other protoplasmic constituents are counterbalanced by the tendencies to cause swelling. The result is that the protoplasm is "fixed" approximately as it was in life. The next step is to infiltrate the tissue with paraffin and then slice it into paper-thin slices with a **microtome,** a device that works much like a bacon-slicing machine. The slices are then placed on a glass slide and stained with aniline or other dyes.

If there is a pressing need for speed, as when a piece of suspected cancer is to be examined while the patient lies on the operating table, or if the object is to be tested for substances that may be removed or changed by the procedures of fixation and infiltration with paraffin, another method is used. The tissue is quickly frozen by evaporating carbon dioxide. (See Fig. 2−5.) It can then be sliced immediately, stained, and examined. This method is important in the rapidly developing field of cell- or cyto-chemistry.

Both physical and chemical methods can be used to identify and accurately locate specific chemical entities within cells. Different chemical substances absorb **ultraviolet light** of different and characteristic wave lengths. For example, nucleoproteins absorb ultraviolet light of wave lengths between 2,600 and 2,700 Angstrom units. Other materials found within cells do not. Hence by determining the wave length absorbed, an identification can be made. Since ordinary glass does not transmit ultraviolet light, lenses of fused quartz are used, and since the human eye cannot see ultraviolet, the image formed must be photographed.

A commonly used **chemical method** is the Feulgen reaction which stains the deoxyribose sugar in the chromosomes—and hence the chromosomes as whole structures—a light bright red while leaving the rest of the cell unstained. Enzymes can often be identified in cells by using various substrates which are known to be split by specific enzymes into two new substances, one of which can be stained in some characteristic way. Because fixatives commonly destroy an enzyme's ability to act, the freezing microtome is especially useful in this work.

Specific proteins in cells can be identified by using **fluorescent antibodies.** If it is desired to identify, for example, lens fiber protein or muscle fiber protein, that kind of protein is injected into a rabbit which will then produce a specific antibody against the specific protein. The antibody is made fluorescent and applied to a section of the test cells. Wherever the corresponding protein is located, the antibody against it will adhere very firmly. Handsome pictures of great brilliance can be obtained by this method showing exactly where a specific type of protein appears.

A combined physical and chemical method is to feed cells amino acids, sugar, or other metabolites that have been radioactively labelled. **Radioactive isotopes** of various chemical elements are first prepared. The isotopes have the same chemical properties as non-radioactive

Fig. 2−5. A freezing microtome. The pipe at left conducts the CO_2. The knife blade is horizontal. (*Kindness of Frank White*)

Fig. 2−6. An electron microscope. (*Science Service*)

Use of the electron microscope requires very special methods. The material to be studied is usually fixed in a vacuum with osmium tetroxide at freezing temperatures. The material is then embedded in a special plastic and sectioned ultra thin with a special microtome using a glass- or diamond-edged knife. The section is placed on a supporting membrane and then put into the electron microscope.

The source of the electrons, which take the place of the light waves of an ordinary microscope, is a cathode filament, much as in a television tube. The electron beam is focused by magnets rather than by glass or quartz lenses. Since electrons travel only very short distances in air, the entire path of the beam is enclosed in a vacuum. The magnified image is projected either onto a fluorescent viewing screen or a photographic plate. Magnifications up to over 100,000 diameters are possible. The ordinary light microscope can magnify up to about 2,500 times.

The table indicates the size of some biologically important objects. One micron, μ, is equal to one-thousandth of a millimeter; i.e., $1 \mu = 0.001$ mm. One Ångstrom is equal to one ten-thousandth of a micron; i.e., $1 \text{ Å} = 0.001 \mu$.

Size of Some Biological Objects

OBJECT	DIAMETER	
	μ	Å
Human egg	100	1,000,000
Red blood cell	10	100,000
Bacterium	1	10,000
Virus	0.1	1,000
Protein molecule	0.01	100
Amino acid	0.001	10

atoms and therefore can be built into the molecules of amino acid or hormone or whatever substance is to be followed. The reactions the labelled molecules undergo are the same as those of "normal" molecules, except that from time to time a labelled atom will disintegrate, liberating a beta or other particle which will register on a photographic plate. Tritium, which is radioactive hydrogen, H^3, is frequently used. It has a half-life of 12 years. This means that of a group of tritium atoms, one-half will have "decayed" to ordinary hydrogen within 12 years. Phosphorus-32 and iodine-131, both frequently used as labels, have half-lives of 14.3 and 8.1 days, respectively.

A definite time after the radioactively labelled material has been made available to the cells to be studied, the tissue is fixed and sectioned, and the sections applied to a sensitive photographic plate. Radioactive disintegrations will occur wherever the labelled amino acid, hormone, or other material is located. This produces a black spot on the photographic film. The way chromosomes duplicate themselves has been determined by this method. (A chromosome organizes a duplicate of itself along its entire length rather than swelling in size and then dividing down the middle.)

A light microscope can resolve, i.e., distinguish as separate, two lines separated by 0.2 μ; an electron microscope can resolve lines separated by somewhat less than 3 Å. Resolving power depends both on the type of lenses and the wave length of light used. In general, an object cannot be resolved if its diameter is less than half the wave length. The enormous difference between the two types of microscopes is indicated by the difference between the wave

24

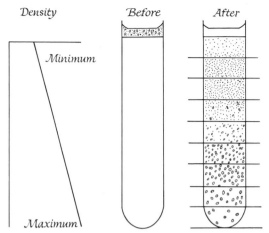

Density *Before* *After*

Minimum

Maximum

Fig. 2–7. Particles of different densities form layers when centrifuged down through a medium with a density gradient. *(After De Duve)*

length of white light—about 5,500 Å—and the wave length of the electrons that are used—about 0.05 Å.

The fortunate coincidence which has made so many of the discoveries with the electron microscope meaningful was the simultaneous development of ultrasensitive methods to separate cell constituents. If cells are homogenized and centrifuged in the cold, enzyme activity is not destroyed. With relatively light centrifugation the nuclei, being the largest and heaviest con-

stituents, move to the bottom of the tube first and can be separated from the cytoplasmic components. Somewhat higher speeds throw down the mitochondria, and still higher speeds throw down minute cytoplasmic particles called **ribosomes.** By filling the centrifuge tube with fluids of different densities, a **density gradient** can be produced and very accurate separations achieved. Particles come to rest when they reach a layer with a density closely approximating their own. Each cell component can then be investigated by biochemical methods to study its function and with the electron microscope to study its structure.

However, cells—even human cells—can be examined without elaborate equipment or scientifically sophisticated techniques. Thousands of epithelial cells can easily (and painlessly) be scraped from the inside of your cheek with a fingernail, mixed with a drop or two of methylene blue or other dye on a glass slide, flattened with a cover glass, and examined under an ordinary light microscope. The slightly elongate nuclei are easily visible. With practice it is possible to distinguish cheek cells from a genetic man from those of a genetic woman. Female tissue shows so-called satellite chromatin adhering to the edge of the nuclear membrane in a high proportion of the cells, male tissue very rarely. In the white blood cells, especially the polymorphonuclear leucocytes, of

Fig. 2–8. Nuclei, showing chromatin (arrows) characteristic of female tissue. Left: human cheek cells. Right: monkey nerve cells. *(Kindness of Murray L. Barr)*

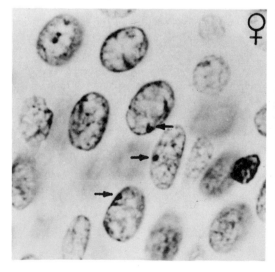

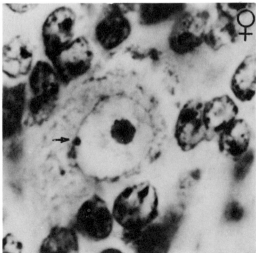

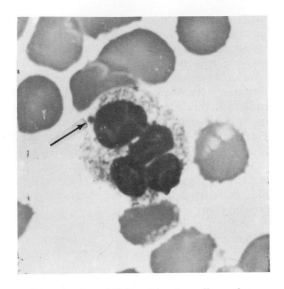

Fig. 2–9. White blood cell, polymorphonuclear leucocyte, showing (arrow) the characteristic "drumstick" chromatin present in the cells of female primates. This sample was from a female macaque. The leucocyte is more or less surrounded by red blood cells. *(Kindness of B. Chiarelli, University of Turin)*

man and other primates a characteristic "drumstick" of chromatin can be seen attached to the nucleus in cells from females but not in cells from males (Fig. 2–9).

ANATOMY OF THE CELL

All animals are eukaryotes, that is, the protoplasm of the cells is divided into a **nucleus,** with a nuclear membrane, and **cytoplasm,** which comprises all the protoplasm outside the nuclear membrane. The outer surface of the cytoplasm forms a very thin but very important cytoplasmic membrane, often called the **plasma membrane.** Everything that enters or leaves a cell must pass through that membrane. Many of the properties of living things are really properties of the plasma membrane. If it is broken by any method in the absence of calcium ions, it is not reconstituted and the cell contents stream out like sawdust out of a doll. This is only one of the many important roles calcium plays in living things.

Within the nucleus are the **chromosomes** and **nuclear sap.** In most cells there are two similar sets of rod-shaped or thread-shaped chromosomes. These condense and stain darkly during cell division but at other times are more diffuse and stain with great difficulty. Attached to a certain chromosome in each set is a rounded **nucleolus** which commonly retains its stainability. Thus many cells possess two nucleoli although the two often fuse into one between cell divisions.

The ultrastructure of cells has now become known through the achievements of an international group of electron microscopists. A glance at a diagram of a cell (Fig. 2–10) reveals that it is far from being merely a bag of loosely mixed chemicals plus a nucleus. A photograph made with the aid of an electron microscope (Fig. 2–11) shows six or seven different cellular structures or organelles.

The enclosing plasma membrane has a definite and measurable thickness. Calculations based on electron microscope measurements plus chemical properties indicate that this membrane is four molecules thick and that the outermost and innermost layers are protein molecules while the two middle layers are lipids, probably mostly phospholipids, the commonest kind of fatty material in cell structures. (See Fig. 2–12.) The environment of most cells is aqueous and most of the cell content is either water or water soluble. Thus a lipid membrane is an effective barrier between the cell and its exterior world. The protein layers give tensile strength. After all, the cell membrane must be stronger than a soap bubble.

A conspicuous feature of the cell membrane of certain types of cells (such as epithelial cells) as seen under an electron microscope are the **desmosomes.** These are darkly staining, thicker appearing portions of the cell membrane. The thickened patch of the membrane on one cell exactly coincides with that of another cell. Fibrils can be seen extending from the desmosomes into the cytoplasm but apparently the fibrils do not cross from one cell into another. The function of desmosomes is probably related to cell adhesion.

The most easily identified organelles in the cytoplasm are the **mitochondria.** These are found in virtually all cells of all animals and

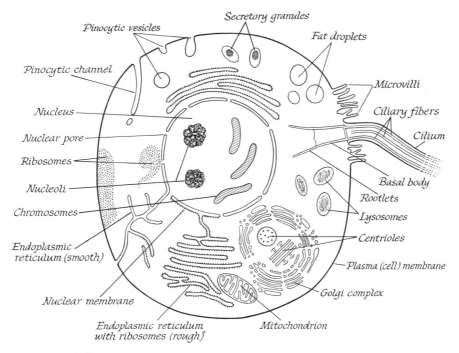

Fig. 2–10. Diagram of a cell.

Labels (clockwise from top): Pinocytic vesicles, Secretory granules, Fat droplets, Microvilli, Ciliary fibers, Cilium, Basal body, Rootlets, Lysosomes, Centrioles, Plasma (cell) membrane, Golgi complex, Mitochondrion, Endoplasmic reticulum with ribosomes (rough), Nuclear membrane, Endoplasmic reticulum (smooth), Chromosomes, Nucleoli, Ribosomes, Nuclear pore, Nucleus, Pinocytic channel

higher plants. Under a light microscope mitochondria appear as longer or shorter rods or threads which stain greenish-blue with Janus Green B in living cells. They can be observed unstained in living cells by the use of special techniques such as dark field and phase contrast microscopy. Long mitochondria wiggle about as though they were independent creatures—in fact, they bear a resemblance to bacilli.

Biochemical analysis shows that mitochondria are the "powerhouses" of cells. The enzymes of aerobic respiration are located on the walls of the mitochondria. The final energy-giving steps in respiration take place here, yielding so-called "packaged energy" in ATP (adenosine triphosphate) molecules. The ATP is then available for muscular contraction, secretion, or the synthesis of new complex molecules, such as proteins.

Fig. 2–11. Human lymphocyte (plasma cell), a white blood cell, as seen under an electron microscope. *N,* nucleus in lower left; *NM,* nuclear membrane; *P,* pore in nuclear membrane; *M,* mitochondrion; *GC,* Golgi complex; *L,* lysosomes; *ER,* endoplasmic reticulum; *CM,* cell or plasma membrane. The small dots on the endoplasmic reticulum are ribosomes. Original magnification 49,000 ×. (*Kindness of James A. Freeman*)

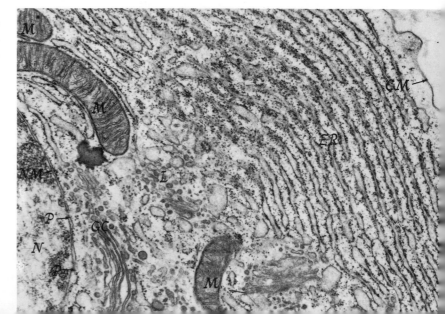

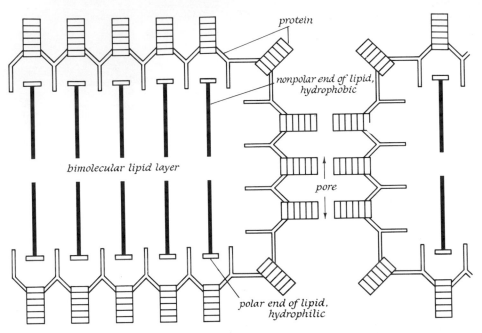

protein

nonpolar end of lipid,
hydrophobic

bimolecular lipid layer

pore

polar end of lipid,
hydrophilic

Fig. 2–12. Molecular
organization of a cell
membrane. Note the
pore lined by protein
molecules. (After N. S.
Cohn)

Under an electron microscope each mitochondrion is revealed as composed of a double membrane, the inner one forming folds that extend into the interior of the mitochondrion. These folds are called **cristae.** The mitochondria found in some cells are small and rounded. Those in sperm cells are very long. Those in muscles are very numerous (muscles are heavy users of energy) and are crowded between rows of contractile fibers (Fig. 2–15). How new mitochondria are produced is still uncertain. It appears that they merely divide in half, transversely.

A second conspicuous feature of the cytoplasm is the **endoplasmic reticulum.** This system of double membranes, often running parallel to each other, is found in virtually all types of cells but is especially abundant in cells that

synthesize protein. For example, lymphocytes, the white blood cells that make protein antibodies, are rich in endoplasmic reticulum. On the outer side of the endoplasmic reticulum are minute granules of very uniform size. These

Fig. 2–14. Mitochondria in *Paramecium*, as seen with an electron microscope. Note the complexity of the inner membrane due to coiling of the cristae. Original magnification 53,000 ×. (Kindness of Dorothy R. Pitelka)

Fig. 2–13. Diagram of a mitochondrion, showing the double membrane. The partitions formed by the inner membrane are the cristae.

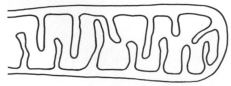

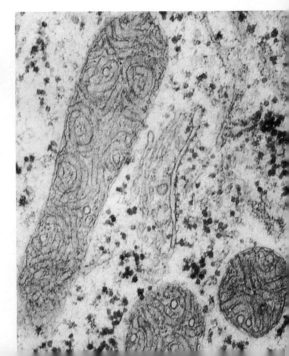

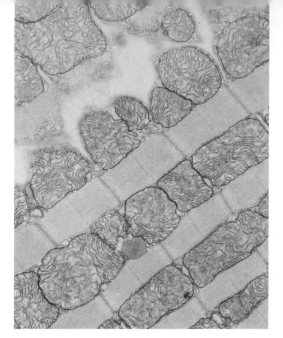

Fig. 2–15. Electron microscope photograph of muscle fibers, showing rows of mitochondria. Original magnification 6,800 ×. *(Kindness of Keith R. Porter)*

are the **ribosomes.** Evidence to be presented in a later chapter indicates that they are the actual sites of protein synthesis.

A third virtually universal organelle is the **Golgi complex.** This is a concentric series of three or four to many membranes much like the membranes of the endoplasmic reticulum but lacking ribosomes and hence smooth. Usually the Golgi complex lies near the nucleus. In both the electron photograph (Fig. 2–11) and the diagram (Fig. 2–16) it can be seen that the ends of membranes of the Golgi complex appear to be giving off droplets. The Golgi apparatus, as it is often called, apparently secretes material, and is in fact well developed in secretory cells.

A fourth cytoplasmic structure, one not so well understood as the others, is the **lysosome.** Lysosomes are small, rounded vesicles varying in diameter from much smaller than the width of a mitochondrion to about the width of a mitochondrion. The membranes surrounding lysosomes are single, in contrast to those of the endoplasmic reticulum, the mitochondria, and the Golgi complex. The interior of lysosomes varies. Sometimes it is very dense, perhaps solid, sometimes granular, sometimes with

vacuoles. Lysosomes apparently contain lytic (digestive) and other enzymes which become active when the lysosome membrane is ruptured. In some cases at least, lysosomes seem to be formed from the Golgi complex.

Many animal cells have one or more cytoplasmic structures called **centrioles** or **basal bodies.** These may lie close under the plasma membrane or close to the nuclear membrane. Under an electron microscope they appear to be composed of a circle of nine small rods like a circle of nine match sticks. **Cilia** and **flagella,** which are cytoplasmic contractile fibrils extending from some cells, appear to originate in basal bodies. Centrioles play a key role in cell division. They evidently reproduce since their number increases during the growth of a ciliated cell or during cell division but the manner of their increase is unknown.

The electron microscope has revealed the essential similarity of the flagella and cilia of all animal cells—the cilia of parameciums and other ciliated protozoans, the cilia of annelid worms, the ciliated cells lining the human trachea, and the large cilia called flagella that form the tails of mammalian sperms. They consist of a circle of nine fibers plus two more in the center, all enclosed in a membrane (Fig. 2–17).

The **nuclear membrane** is a double membrane. Like the plasma membrane of the entire

Fig. 2–16. A Golgi complex. Note the droplets that appear to be given off from the ends of the membranes.

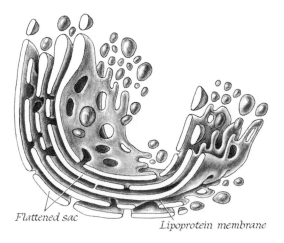

Flattened sac   *Lipoprotein membrane*

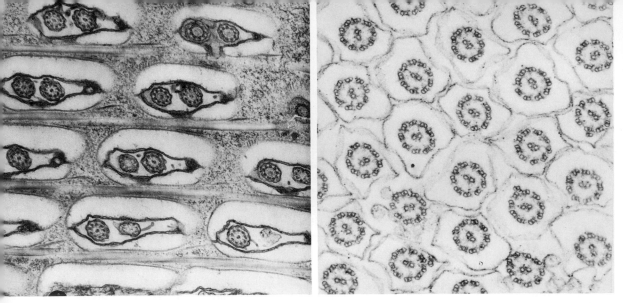

Fig. 2–17. Cross sections of cilia as seen under the electron microscope. Left: cilia from *Paramecium*. Right: cilia from an annelid. *(Kindness of Dorothy R. Pitelka, Bjorn Afzelius)*

cell and the membranes of the endoplasmic reticulum, the mitochondria, and the Golgi complex, it is composed of four layers of molecules, the outer and inner ones protein and the two middle layers lipid. Pores in the nuclear membrane allow fairly large molecules to pass between the nuclear contents and the cytoplasm.

MORE ON MEMBRANES

Why all these membranes? Is life at base a membrane phenomenon? The necessity for the cell membrane that separates a cell and its contents from the outside, nonliving world seems clear enough. In multicellular animals the cell membrane separates one kind of cell from another and partitions the cytoplasm into functionally manageable units. But what of the nuclear membrane? It is full of pores large enough to pass protein molecules. Furthermore, in cell division the nuclear membrane is lost and only later reformed from endoplasmic reticulum. Would it be disastrous to permit the chromosomes to be loose in the cytoplasm? No one really knows. But everywhere there are double membranes—the endoplasmic reticulum, the Golgi complex, the mitochondria. A nervous impulse travels as a change in the cytoplasmic membrane of the nerve fiber. The electron microscope has revealed that photoreceptors in both plants and animals are tightly packed groups of double membranes. This can be seen in the chloroplastids, where photosynthesis occurs, and in the rods and cones of the visual retina (see Fig. 31–25).

One function of intracellular membranes is **compartmentalization.** With different parts of the cytoplasm more or less separated, conflicting chemical reactions can occur simultaneously in different parts of the cell. This seems especially true of mitochondria which are known to be permeable to some substances and impermeable to others.

A second function appears to be the **ordering of enzymes** in sequential functional assemblies. Many metabolic reactions require a series of enzymes to act in a particular sequence. The interior of a cell is enormous compared to the size of a molecule. If sequential reactions are to take place with reasonable speed, the necessary enzymes need to be lined up in the proper order, or, at the very least, kept in the vicinity. Hence it is not surprising that many, though not all, enzymes are located on membranes. The best-understood case is the mitochondrion where the enzymes of aerobic respiration are lined up on the membrane.

Many cellular membranes have an active energy-requiring function in the **maintenance of concentration differences** between the two sides of the membrane. Membranes of nerve fibers have a so-called sodium pump which transports sodium ions across the membrane to the exterior of the cell. Kidney tubules have cells with membranes which actively secrete certain substances and cells with membranes which differentially absorb certain molecules such as sugar. Intestinal cells possess similar properties.

Such membranes contain special enzymes called **permeases** which are responsible for bringing specific materials into the cell. In cases where cells form secretory tubules, the permeases work in pairs and enable the cell to absorb a compound against a concentration gradient and then secrete it into the tubule. At the surface of the cell facing the exterior of the tubule an enzyme unites substance A from outside the cell with substance B within it. Compound AB then moves through the cell to the membrane that faces the lumen of the tubule. There the second of the paired enzymes breaks AB into A and B. B remains within the cell, and A passes out into the tubule.

One of the most striking characteristics of cellular membranes is selective or **semi-permeability.** Water and small molecules and ions, such as those of the common salts of sea water, sodium, calcium, and potassium chlorides, for example, pass through very readily while larger molecules, such as cane sugar or proteins, pass very slowly or not at all. The result is that living cells are very sensitive to the concentration of molecules dissolved in the medium surrounding them, specifically to what is called the osmotic pressure of that environment. **Osmosis** is defined as the passage of water through a semi-permeable membrane. **Osmotic pressure** is the pressure resulting in the fluid on one side of a semi-permeable membrane when the concentration of certain molecules is greater on one side than on the other.

For example, parchment and cellophane are both semi-permeable in that water molecules pass through them readily but cane sugar molecules do not. If a cellophane bag of concentrated sugar solution is tied tightly and placed in a beaker of water, water will pass in but sugar molecules cannot pass out. The result? The bag will swell until it ruptures. Contrariwise, if a cellophane bag of distilled water is placed in a beaker of concentrated sugar solution, water will pass out of the bag but sugar will not enter. Consequently the bag will shrink. Similar results can be obtained with many other materials, such as salt solutions and proteins.

Comparable phenomena can easily be seen in living cells. If the surrounding medium has a greater osmotic concentration than the cell interior, it is said to be **hypertonic** and will cause the cell to shrink. If the medium has a lower osmotic concentration, it is said to be **hypotonic** and will cause the cell to swell and burst. If the osmotic concentration of the medium is the same as that of the cell, it is said to be **isotonic, or isosmotic.**

Osmotic pressure can be measured by filling a thistle tube with sugar solution, covering it tightly with cellophane, and inverting it in pure water. As the sugar solution becomes diluted by water entering through the semi-permeable cellophane, the solution will be forced up the tube. The more concentrated the sugar, the greater the osmotic pressure and the higher the solution will climb. The pressure can be measured directly by determining the height of mercury necessary to prevent a rise. (See Fig. 2–18.) The pressure reached can be very great, up to over 24 times atmospheric pressure.

Osmotic pressure depends not on the actual weight of material dissolved in a given volume of solvent, but on the number of molecules or ions dissolved in a given volume. Therefore the osmotic concentration or the potential osmotic pressure of a solution is described in terms of **molarity.** Molar solutions of different substances have the same number of molecules regardless of the size and weight of the individual molecules. A 1.0 molar solution of sucrose or other solute is just about isotonic with a sea urchin egg. The cytoplasm of most plant cells shrinks markedly at this concentration.

pH, ACIDITY-ALKALINITY

Living cells are also extremely sensitive to the acidity or alkalinity of their environment. This factor is measured on a logarithmic pH scale which runs from 0 to 14. A pH of 1.0 represents an acidity equivalent to that of 1/10 normal hydrochloric acid. A pH of 7.0 is neutral, while a pH of 14 represents an alkalinity like that of 1/10 normal sodium hydroxide. Most enzymes function only at a very definite and restricted pH.

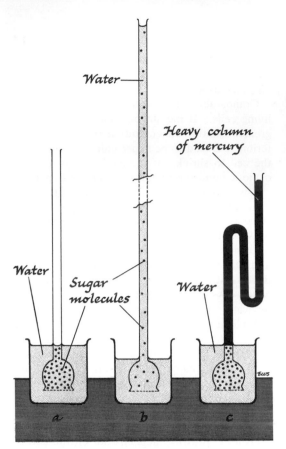

Fig. 2–18. Experiment to show osmotic pressure. *a*, initial condition of set-up. *b*, final condition. *c*, osmotic pressure of the sugar solution balanced against the weight of a column of mercury.

The pH of a solution is best measured by an electric pH meter. However, many dyes, including natural plant pigments, assume different colors at different pH's. Consequently they can be conveniently used as indicators. Litmus, a pigment obtained from certain lichens, and anthocyanin, the purple pigment in red cabbage, are such indicators.

CELL DIVISION

It is now just about a century since Rudolph Virchow (1821–1902) announced his famous aphorism, *Omnis cellula e cellula,* "Every cell from a cell." Since his time, a small army of investigators has sought to describe the facts and explain the mechanism of cell division. Such knowledge is important, first, because cell division is the method by which the continuity of life is maintained and therefore by which heredity is passed from cell to cell; and second, because of its relationship to cancer. Malignant tumors are essentially populations of cells which have escaped from the normal controls of cell division.

In both animals and plants, cells divide in two quite different though related ways. In embryos and in growing tissues new cells are formed by **mitosis.** This is an asexual process in which the chromosomes of the parent cell are duplicated and passed in identical sets to the two daughter cells. The other method is called **meiosis,** from a Greek word meaning to reduce, because the result of this kind of division is daughter cells having only one instead of the usual two sets of chromosomes. Meiosis occurs in gonads (sex glands) and results in the formation of sperms or eggs. Despite much work, often ingenious and penetrating, very little is known about the physiology and causation of cell division, and even less about what factors induce cells to divide by mitosis on one occasion and by meiosis on another.

In dividing, cells pass through five more or less arbitrary but universally recognized phases: interphase, prophase, metaphase, anaphase, and telophase.

MITOSIS

1. Interphase. Interphase is the period between divisions, and is the phase in which most cells spend most of their lives. The nucleus is surrounded by a membrane within which only a finely granular material plus a nucleolus is visible. In adult cells the cytoplasm may be full of some special product of the cell's synthetic activity, perhaps muscle fibers or animal starch, in which case cell division is difficult or impossible, and interphase is permanent.

It has now been firmly demonstrated that the duplication of chromosomes takes place during interphase and occurs by the building of a new chromatid alongside the parent one. This conclusion has been reached by feeding cells radioactive thymidine which is taken up and incorporated into the DNA of chromosomes. All the radioactivity appears on one and only one of each pair of chromatids. If chromosomes

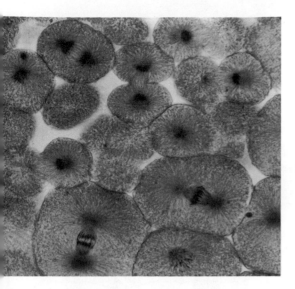

Fig. 2–19. Photomicrograph of dividing cells in whitefish eggs. Note absence of nuclear membranes. *(Courtesy, General Biological Supply House, Inc., Chicago)*

reproduced by enlarging and then splitting down the midline, the radioactivity would be found randomly placed in both members of the chromatid pairs. (See Fig. 2–20.)

2. Prophase. Prophase is the preliminary stage of division, during which the nuclear membrane disappears and the chromosomes become visible, first as long thin threads and finally as short thick threads or rods. It is because of the threadlike appearance of the chromosomes that cell division was named mitosis *(mitos,* thread). Chromosomes in late prophase and subsequent stages of mitosis can be clearly seen in living cells with a phase contrast microscope. In preserved cells they are easily stained with dyes like hematoxylin or various aniline stains. The fact that they can be stained gave them their name *(chroma,* color, + *soma,* body).

It was early learned that the number of chromosomes in every cell of any species of animal is the same, and it was soon realized that each cell normally contains two similar sets of chromosomes. This means that each chromosome has its own permanent individuality. If the chromosomes in a set from one cell be lined up

from the longest chromosome to the shortest and compared with the set from any other cell, provided that it is from the same species of animal, this one-to-one correspondence becomes very evident. In *Drosophila,* the little fruit fly widely used in genetic research, there is always one long chromosome in a set, two middle-sized chromosomes, and one short one.

The most conspicuous feature of a chromosome is its **kinetochore.** This is a small, rounded region that stains differently from the rest of the chromosome and appears to be the kinetic or controlling point in chromosomal movements in the cell. It may be in the middle of a chromosome, at one end, or at some intermediate point. But on a specific chromosome of the set, it is always located at the same point. During cell division the kinetochores become attached to the spindle fibers which appear in the protoplasm. It has been proved that the hereditary factors are lined up on the chromosomes in single file and in fixed order.

Fig. 2–20. Sister chromosomes (chromatids) of the Chinese hamster at the second division after feeding the cells radioactively labelled thymidine. Note that one chromatid in each pair is labelled and one is not. *(Kindness of T. C. Hsu)*

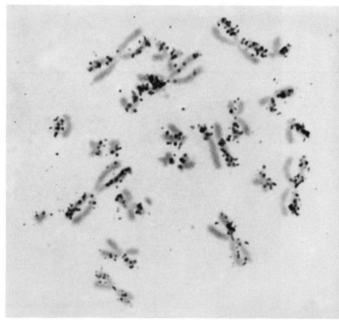

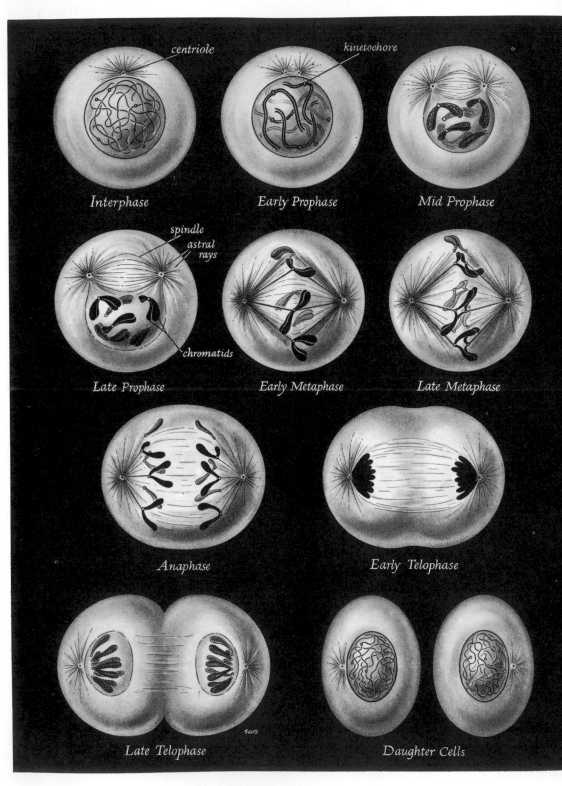

Fig. 2 – 21. Stages in mitosis. (Diagrammatic)

During early prophase the chromosomes appear as very thin threads which gradually shorten and thicken. In well-preserved material it is easy to see that each chromosome is really double along its entire length. Each member of such a pair is called a **sister chromatid** (although it would be more accurate to call them mother and daughter), and each pair is held together by a single kinetochore.

At the same time that the chromosomes are condensing, the nuclear membrane disappears and the centriole divides, forming astral rays and a spindle-shaped structure on which the chromosomes become attached at their kinetochores. The star-shaped astral rays are well developed only in large cells such as those of cleaving eggs. The spindle fibers are of a special kind of protein containing RNA and some lipid which forms a highly elastic gel.

3. Metaphase. Following prophase is metaphase, the brief period in mitosis when the chromosomes are arranged at the equator of the spindle. Actually it is only the kinetochore of each chromosome that is on the equator. The rest of the chromosome may dangle at any angle. Each chromosome is still double along its entire length.

4. Anaphase. Following metaphase comes anaphase when each of the double chromosomes separates, one duplicate going to each pole of the spindle. This action requires but a few minutes. As the chromosome moves toward a pole, its kinetochore leads the way. In most animals it looks as though the kinetochore were being pulled by a spindle fiber, but in several cases where there is no spindle, the kinetochores still lead the way. During anaphase the surface membrane of the cell begins to constrict in between the two poles of the spindle at the level of the equator.

5. Telophase. The final phase is known as telophase. The cell is divided into two daughter cells. The important point is that as a result of mitosis, each of the two daughter cells has two sets of chromosomes, just as the original cell had. During telophase the nuclear membrane reappears, and the chromosomes lose their stainability as they return to the interphase condition.

MEIOSIS

When the facts of mitosis and fertilization became known, particularly that each egg and each sperm carries chromosomes, and that fertilization is the fusion of two such cells, August Weismann (1834–1914) made an important prediction. He foresaw that a stage would be found in the life history of every animal when the number of chromosomes is reduced by half. Were this not true, he pointed out, the number of chromosomes would double with each fertilization, i.e., with every generation. There are various times and places where this process, known as **meiosis,** could conceivably take place. Weismann was nearly blind when he made this prediction and could not himself discover where meiosis does in fact occur. Others investigated this problem and found the following facts.

1. Meiosis takes place in testes or ovaries during **gametogenesis,** that is, during the formation of the gametes, or germ cells, whether sperms or eggs. This is true of all animals from jellyfish to honeybees, and from starfish to human beings.

2. The result of meiosis is that each sperm and each egg before fertilization carries but a single set of chromosomes. In other words, sperms and unfertilized eggs are haploid.

3. In all animals, and in plants as well, meiosis requires two cell divisions. This is just as true between the gills of a mushroom or in a one-celled protozoan as it is in the gonads of a mouse or a man. Neither of these two cell divisions is a normal mitosis, although the cell goes through a prophase, metaphase, anaphase, and telophase. Discussion of the details of meiosis will be postponed until the chapter on genetics, where a knowledge of meiosis is essential for an understanding of the laws of inheritance.

CHROMOSOME NUMBER

The number of chromosomes in a single set is known as the **haploid** number. In man there are 23, in the horse 30, in the dog 10, in the chicken 9, and in a certain species of butterfly 190, the highest number yet recorded. When there are two sets present, as is usual, a cell is said to be **diploid.**

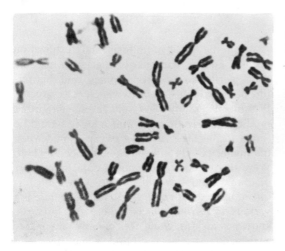

Fig. 2–22. Normal human karyotype (male). The full diploid complement is shown as it appears in a cell grown *in vitro* to make the chromosomes easy to distinguish. *(Kindness of V. A. McKusick)*

The number of chromosomes characteristic of any species can be counted, though with some difficulty (try in Fig. 2–4), in well-fixed and stained material either from a thin piece of epidermis or in sectioned tissue. The best stage for doing this is anaphase viewed from a pole of the spindle. The standard modern method, however, gives superb results far surpassing even the best attainable by the classic fixation plus sectioning. The new technique was originated by J. H. Tjio in Finland and consists of growing the cells in glass dishes so that they spread out as a flat single layer of thin cells. The culture is first treated with hypotonic solutions in such a way that the chromosomes tend to move apart; the cells are then fixed and stained. The whole set of chromosomes of any species—their number, sizes, and shapes—is known as the **karyotype** of that species. The normal human karyotype is shown in the photograph in Figure 2–22. (See also Fig. 8–5.)

SOCIAL RELATIONS OF CELLS

So far cells have been considered as isolated individuals, but for the higher animals one of the most important properties of cells, in fact *the* most important, is the ability of individual cells to unite firmly into tissues: muscle, liver, skin, and the rest. Were this not so, we would all be protozoans, one-celled animals like the *Amoeba* or at best a *Paramecium*. In some way cells are able to recognize each other so that they can distinguish not only between themselves and the cells of other species but between cells of different histological types. Thus muscle cells will adhere firmly with other muscle cells, liver cells with liver cells, so that coherent tissues, muscle or liver, are formed.

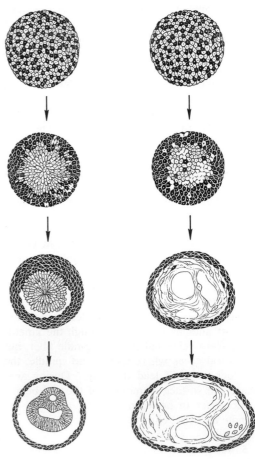

Fig. 2–23. Social properties of cells. Left: mixture of embryonic brain and epidermal cells. Right: mixture of embryonic gut and epidermal cells. Note that the darker epidermal cells come to lie outside either brain or gut cells. *(After Townes and Holtfreter)*

The instructions which enable cells to do all this are carried by each individual cell, presumably on the cell membrane. Little is known with any certainty about what mechanisms are involved though a beginning has been made. Many years ago, H. V. Wilson discovered that the scarlet encrusting sponge, *Microciona,* which commonly grows over rocks and oyster shells on the Atlantic coast, could be squeezed through very fine silk cloth and the individual cells would be separated but not killed. Such dispersed cells, if permitted to settle in a jar of sea water, will crawl together and reconstitute minute sponges!

More recently it has been found that the cells of vertebrate embryos can be separated by gentle treatment with digestive enzymes and calcium-free water. If dispersed cells destined to form brain are mixed with cells programmed to become epidermis, they will all coalesce into a well-mixed ball of cells. (See Fig. 2–23.) However, when two future brain cells happen to meet, as the cells move about slowly in the mass, they cohere more firmly together than they adhere to the epidermal cells or than the epidermal cells cohere with each other. The result is that as time goes on, larger and larger clumps of brain cells are formed as one clump coalesces with another. Finally the brain cells are all located in the center with the epidermal

cells around the outside which is, of course, their proper position in the organism. A similar result is obtained if epidermal cells are mixed with future gut cells. The gut cells end up inside the epidermis, the result not of any directed migration but of a greater cohesive force between gut cells than between them and the epidermal cells or the epidermal cells with each other. If three kinds of cells are mixed, the kind with the strongest cohesion will end up in the center, the next most cohesive around them, and the least cohesive on the surface.

For this behavior to occur, cells must have certain properties. They must be discrete, motile, and possess differential mutual adhesiveness. It is tempting to think that the reason calcium is important in holding cells together is that calcium is divalent, i.e., it has two chemical binding sites, and hence could conceivably act as a link between two cell membranes. But obviously there must be much more to the story to account for the great specificity of this behavior. Proteins are known to possess great specificity, being uniquely characteristic of different species and of different tissues within each species. This is clearly shown in the well-known antigen-antibody reaction of immunology. Thus it would seem reasonable to suppose that in some way the proteins of the cell membranes are involved.

Review and References

REVIEW TOPICS

1. What has been the role of the electron microscope in contemporary biology? What rays are used and how are they focused?

2. Identify: Hippocrates, Aristotle, Robert Hooke, van Leeuwenhoek, Malpighi, Schleiden and Schwann, Max Schultze, Virchow.

3. Define: chromosome, mitochondrion, eukaryote, mitosis, kinetochore, centriole, osmosis, metaphase, haploid, endoplasmic reticulum, lysosome, hypotonic, Golgi complex.

4. Why is it unlikely that living cells several orders of magnitude smaller than those we know on this planet will be found on some other planet?

5. What is a histological fixative? What is the advantage of a freezing microtome? How

are radioactive isotopes, ultraviolet light, and fluorescent antibodies used in cell biology?

6. What is known about the structure of biological membranes? Why do membranes play key roles in living processes? What are these roles?

7. By using solutions of different osmotic pressures, how could you determine the osmotic pressure within a certain type of cell?

8. What degree of acidity or alkalinity is represented by pH 7.0?

9. In general terms, what is the difference between the results of mitosis and meiosis? Where does each occur?

10. What is the evidence that a chromosome reproduces by organizing a duplicate alongside itself?

11. What are some of the methods that have been used to determine the number and the characteristics of the chromosomes in a given species?

12. Why suppose that proteins in the cell membrane are involved in a cell's ability to discriminate among a group of different kinds of cells?

USEFUL REFERENCES

Ackerknecht, E. H., *Rudolph Virchow,* Madison, University of Wisconsin Press, 1953.

Cohn, N. S., *Elements of Cytology,* New York, Harcourt, Brace & World, 1964.

De Robertis, E. D. P., W. W. Nowinski, and F. A. Saez, *General Cytology,* 4th ed., Philadelphia, W. B. Saunders Co., 1965.

Freeman, J. A., *Cellular Fine Structure: An Introductory Student Text and Atlas,* New York, McGraw-Hill Book Co., 1964.

Ham, A. W., *Histology,* Philadelphia, J. B. Lippincott Co., 1965.

Hooke, R., *Micrographia,* Chicago, University of Chicago Press, 1926.

Swanson, C. P., *The Cell,* Englewood Cliffs, N.J., Prentice-Hall, 1960.

White, P. R., *The Cultivation of Animal and Plant Cells,* New York, The Ronald Press Company, 1954.

Chapter 3

The Biochemical Level

Life has often been compared to a flame. This ancient analogy is useful because it points to the central fact that life is a dynamic equilibrium which maintains essential constancy of form amid a continually changing flow of matter and energy. But the flame of life is a very unusual flame, highly structured and complex. The previous chapter considered these complexities as they appear on the cellular level of organization. Now we will consider the key events on the biochemical level, where the matter and energy changes take place.

Animals utilize energy in countless ways, in the flight of butterflies and the tramping of elephants, in the formation of urine and of a contractile vacuole, in the secretion of spider's silk, and in the transmission of a nervous impulse. Yet all energy demands can be reduced to three basic categories. First, energy is required for the synthesis of large molecules from small ones. Most important in this category is the synthesis of proteins and nucleic acids, DNA and RNA. Second, energy is required to move molecules across membranes, often against concentration gradients. To live and grow, cells must actively transport many kinds of molecules and ions across semi-permeable membranes against concentration gradients, i.e., from regions of lower into regions of higher concentration, making the concentration still

higher. Such active transport across membranes is essential for cells living in fresh water. If they do not continually pump out excess water they will swell up and burst. It is also essential in most absorption and secretion in intestines, endocrine glands, kidneys, even in conducting nerve fibers. Third, energy is required for the mechanico-chemical work of contraction in muscles, cilia, cell division, and other types of motion.

THE STUFF OF LIFE: SUBATOMIC LEVEL

The outstanding fact about events on the subatomic level of electrons, protons, and other wave particles is that they do not seem to follow the rules that hold for the physics and chemistry of our familiar large or macroscopic world. This peculiar behavior of particles on the subatomic level led to the enunciation of the quantum theory by Max Planck in 1900. Prediction appears to be possible only statistically. This is the realm in which the famous indeterminacy principle holds sway, a principle which seems to demand a revision of classical ideas of causality. Physicists are almost unanimous in their belief that quantum mechanics is here to stay.

The pertinent question for the zoologist is: "Do quantum phenomena on the subatomic level play a significant role in animal life?" Some competent zoologists believe that quantum phenomena are of the profoundest importance in living processes. They argue that through quantum phenomena free will and purpose enter life, perhaps through some kind of trigger action in the nervous system. Others think that such speculations will turn out to be as absurd as the attempts of Descartes three centuries ago to locate the physical site of the soul in the pineal gland.

Up to the present there are only a few places where the quantum theory has been brought into direct relation to living processes. The number of photons necessary to liberate one atom of oxygen in photosynthesis has been at least approximately determined. Similar studies have been made on the action of light falling on the rods and cones in the retina. No doubt other studies will follow, but to date such facts constitute very slim evidence on which to draw far-reaching conclusions.

Electrons, of course, do play a vital role in biological processes, specifically in energy transfers during oxidations. The loss of electrons is termed **oxidation** and the gain of electrons, **reduction.** Thus if a substance is an electron donor, it is called a reducing agent. If a substance is an electron acceptor, it is an oxidizing agent.

THE ATOMIC LEVEL

On the atomic level, a number of questions—some old, some new—arise. Are living organisms composed of the same chemical elements that are found in the nonliving world of rocks and rivers, oceans and clouds, and even the sun and the other planets? If we are so made, which elements are involved? Most of the 100-odd or but a few?

The answer to the first question has been clear for many decades. If an animal is killed, dried, and the water that evaporates then measured, it will be found that a very large portion of living matter is water and that the hydrogen and oxygen in this water are the same as any other hydrogen and oxygen. The dried corpse can be burned. Carbon dioxide and water vapor will be given off; this reveals a third element, carbon. The remaining ash, on chem-

ical analysis, yields the following elements in decreasing order of amount: nitrogen, calcium, phosphorus, potassium, sodium, sulfur, chlorine, magnesium, and iron. Again these elements are indistinguishable from those found in the rocks and seas. The big four, as far as quantity goes, are oxygen, carbon, hydrogen, and nitrogen, the chief constituents of protein molecules.

The most interesting as well as most important problem in this field today concerns what are called trace elements, or better, **micronutrients.** These are elements essential for health but required in only minute amounts. Some have been known for many years. Iodine, the lack of which produces goiter, is one. That traces of cobalt are necessary was discovered as a result of an attack of bush disease in sheep on Australian ranges in 1895. Since then other micronutrients have been discovered: copper, zinc, and manganese. As seems reasonable for material essential only in minute amounts, these elements are either part of enzyme molecules or behave as catalysts for enzyme action. This subject is one of great practical importance on which much remains to be learned.

THE MOLECULAR LEVEL—ORGANIC COMPOUNDS

On the molecular level living organisms are characterized by what are called **organic compounds.** These are molecules containing the element carbon. At one time it was believed that all compounds containing carbon had been produced by living organisms and could be synthesized only by them; hence the names organic compounds and organic chemistry. This misconception was cleared up when a young German chemist, Friedrich Wöhler, slightly over a century ago became one of the first to synthesize an organic compound in a laboratory. It was urea, $CO(NH_2)_2$, the colorless, odorless, harmless compound which is a waste product of protein breakdown. Since then, of course, an enormous number of organic compounds have been made in the laboratory: dyes, drugs, explosives, nylon, photofilm—the list goes on indefinitely. It is now known that carbon compounds like methane, CH_4, and carbon dioxide, CO_2, are abundant on some planets such as Jupiter and Saturn, where it seems certain that conditions have never been such that life could exist.

The carbon atom has a number of properties that make it biologically important. Each carbon atom has four valence bonds, chemical "links" that enable it to unite with four other atoms. However, it may unite with fewer than four atoms by using two of its bonds to link to a single atom. This is a double bond. The valence bonds are determined by the number of electrons rotating around the nucleus of the carbon atom, and in written formulas are usually represented by short bars, as in the accompanying figures. Each atom in a molecule is represented by the letter symbol for its name: H is hydrogen, C is carbon, Cl is chlorine, and so on.

methane   carbon tetrachloride   chloroform

Methane is known as marsh gas because it is a waste product of bacteria living in the decaying debris on the bottom of quiet ponds and can often be seen bubbling to the surface. Carbon tetrachloride has a similar structure except that in place of four hydrogen atoms, four chlorine atoms are attached to the carbon. Carbon tetrachloride has been widely used in fire extinguishers and as a cleaning fluid. Substituting a hydrogen atom for one of the chlorines produces chloroform.

Carbon atoms also have the ability to unite with each other and in this way make extremely large molecules. The carbons may join in short or long single chains, in rings as in benzene, or in many other configurations. Glycerol (also called glycerine) is a sweetish lubricant that can be obtained from fats and oils. Ethylene is a sweetish, colorless, highly explosive component of coal gas. Benzene is obtained from coal tar and is used as a solvent and cleaning fluid and also as the chemical base for the synthesis of thousands of other substances, from dyes to explosives. (See formulas at top of next column.)

The existence of chemical radicals is of considerable biochemical importance. Radicals are small groups of atoms which behave as

benzene   glycerol (glycerine)   ethylene

units. One of the most familiar is the carboxyl radical, $-COOH$, which is also written

$$-C\overset{\displaystyle O}{\|}-O-H.$$ The formula of this radical may look like a base, but in water it is the hydrogen which is released so that it is in fact an acid. The carboxyl radical makes the amino acids and fatty acids acids. The amino radical, $-NH_2$, is a basic group found in amino acids and other important compounds. It behaves like ammonia and forms ammonium hydroxide with water, $NH_3 + H_2O \rightarrow NH_4OH$. Thus the amino radical is alkaline. Other important radicals are the methyl group, $-CH_3$, and the highly reactive keto radical, $-C\overset{\displaystyle O}{\diagdown}$, and aldehyde radical,

CARBOHYDRATES, THE FUEL OF LIFE

Carbohydrates are familiar in the form of sugars and starches. A simple sugar is composed solely of carbon, hydrogen, and oxygen, $C_6H_{12}O_6$. Chemically, a carbohydrate often is defined as a simple sugar or a substance which yields simple sugars on hydrolysis, that is, on splitting with the addition of water. Carbohydrates may also be defined as substances with the general formula $C_x(H_2O)_y$. The values of x and y may range from three to several thousand.

Simple sugars with three carbons ($C_3H_6O_3$) are called triose sugars or merely trioses. Those with four carbons are tetroses; with five, pentoses; and with six, hexoses. Glucose, a simple hexose, $C_6H_{12}O_6$, is regarded as the most important sugar. It is the primary sugar into which the various carbohydrates of food are broken down by digestion. Hence it is the sugar found in the circulating blood, the sugar utilized as fuel by muscles, and the sugar used in intravenous feeding. Glucose is also the carbohydrate formed by photosynthesis and from it many of the more complex sugars as well as the starches and cellulose are built.

Another extremely important sugar for the zoologist is a pentose called ribose and the related sugar deoxyribose, *deoxy* because it has less oxygen than is given by the general formula, $C_x(H_2O)_y$, which applies to ribose. Deoxyribose is the sugar that is combined with other compounds to make up the nucleic acids of the chromosomes.

Like other sugars, ribose can be represented in a variety of ways. All are symbolic models intended to indicate chemical properties and certainly not to suggest how the molecule might look. In the formulas below, (a) indicates the kinds of atoms in the ribose molecule and their proportions, (b) shows a great deal more about the chemical properties of ribose, and (c) shows still more. Diagram (d) is a more accurate way of representing the behavior indicated in (c), and (e) and (f) are merely abbreviated forms of other diagrams.

Sugar, specifically glucose, can be truly called the "fuel of life," but it would be incorrect to think that sugars are only fuels. As mentioned, the pentose called ribose forms an essential part of the nucleic acid molecule. Sugars in general have a marked ability to combine with other molecules, both nonsugars and other sugars. A combination of a sugar and a nonsugar is called a **glycoside,** irrespective of the kind of sugar. If the sugar is glucose, the term glucoside can be used. Many glycosides are biologically and medically important. The cardiac glycosides have a strong action on the heart. The nonsugar part of the molecule is usually a steroid similar to the sex and adrenal hormones, though this is not true of digitalis, the best-known such glycoside. Phlorizin, a glycoside from the roots of apple, cherry, and related trees, inhibits the intestinal absorption of glucose and interferes with the metabolism of carbohydrates. At the same time phlorizin produces a loss of blood glucose via the kidneys.

If the nonsugar part of a glycoside is an amino acid or simply an amino radical, a nitrogen-containing glycoside is formed called a glucose amine (if the sugar is glucose) or simply an **amino sugar.** Amino sugars are built up into chitin, the highly protective skeletal material of insects, lobsters, and related animals. Interestingly enough, chitin forms the cell wall of

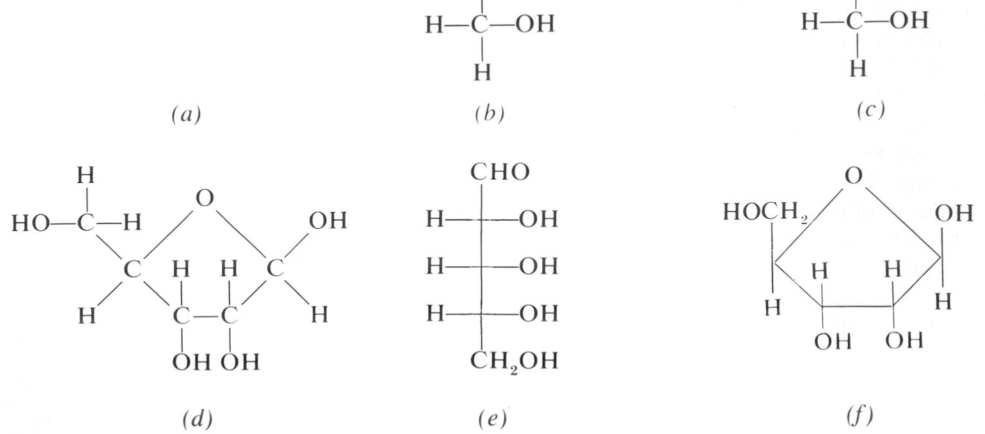

$$C_5H_{10}O_5$$

(a)

(b)

(c)

(d)

(e)

(f)

certain molds. Glucose amines are important in the connective tissues of vertebrates.

When two or more simple sugars link together, a **disaccharide** or **polysaccharide** is produced. This kind of process is termed **polymerization** and with sugars is accomplished by the elimination of a molecule of water where each two sugars join. Sucrose, the common sugar of commerce and the coffee cup, is a disaccharide, a molecule of the hexose glucose linked with a molecule of the hexose fructose. The connection between two sugars usually is close to the end of the molecule and is called a **glycoside linkage** which may be represented as:

$$H—C—O\boxed{H \quad HO}—C—H$$

The formula for sucrose is $C_{12}H_{22}O_{11}$. As polymerization continues and more and more sugars become linked in various ways, a whole array of important substances are produced — starches, glycogen, gums, cellulose, waxes. Glycogen, known as animal starch, is the chief form in which carbohydrate is stored in animals. Glycogen granules can be seen in the liver of a man and the cytoplasm of a protozoan. Cellulose is the chief component of wood; it is also the major constituent of the hide of a group of complex marine animals closely related to the vertebrates, the tunicates.

The molecules of sugars are asymmetric. Asymmetric structure results in a remarkable property of carbohydrates which is characteristic also of proteins. The chemical behavior of the molecule depends not only on the kind and number of atoms in it, but on their arrangement, their configuration. One of Pasteur's first discoveries, made when he was a very young man, was that there are asymmetric, that is, "right-handed" and "left-handed," sugars. A digestive enzyme that will act on a right-handed sugar by splitting it into smaller pieces will leave a left-handed sugar strictly alone. Such asymmetry becomes inevitable whenever a carbon atom is attached to four different atoms or groups of atoms. The levo and dextro forms of a simple triose sugar will illustrate this principle nicely. Note that the H and OH in the two structural formulas shown at the top of the next column are in opposite positions.

$$\begin{array}{cc}
CHO & CHO \\
| & | \\
H—C—OH & HO—C—H \\
| & | \\
CH_2OH & CH_2OH
\end{array}$$

Note also that the short formula for both structures is the same, $C_3H_6O_3$. They are, therefore, called **isomers**; in this case, **stereoisomers**. Because they rotate the plane of vibration of polarized light in either a clockwise (dextro) or counterclockwise (levo) direction, such pairs of substances are also termed **optical isomers.** They are extremely difficult for a chemist to separate, but a yeast cell and many animal cells do so readily by their enzymes.

LIPIDS

Lipids are the fats, oils, steroids, and related compounds. Lipids are such a heterogeneous group that a satisfactory definition is difficult to formulate. In general they are composed of the same three elements as carbohydrates — carbon, hydrogen, oxygen. Unlike carbohydrates, lipids are insoluble in water but are soluble in various organic solvents such as chloroform, ether, and alcohol. As will be described below, many lipids can be split into two components, glycerol and fatty acid.

The most obvious function of lipids is as a form in which energy can be stored. Migratory birds develop large deposits of fat before they begin their long flights. On arrival hundreds or even thousands of miles from their start, the fat is used up. Hibernating animals also begin the winter with large deposits of fat. This is used partly during the winter and partly when they first emerge and food is scarce. The almost universal role of lipids is doubtless as the middle layer of all cell membranes, both plant and animal. Many other functions are well established. The blubber of a whale is a heat-insulating layer nearly a foot thick which surrounds the entire animal just under the skin. Lipids serve as vehicles for certain vitamins which themselves are lipoidal in character. Some lipids play important roles in the internal chemistry of cells. The sex hormones are lipids, as are cortisone and other hormones.

Historically the chemical nature of fats was understood before that of either carbohydrates or proteins. In fact, a rule-of-thumb knowledge of fat chemistry has been used for centuries in soap-making. If a fat is heated by steam under pressure it adds molecules of water and breaks into glycerol (glycerine) and a weak organic or fatty acid. No matter what the fat or oil, the glycerol is always the same, though the fatty acids are different for each fat or oil. The acid end of a fatty acid is made up of the carboxyl radical, —COOH. Attached to this radical is anywhere from one to over a dozen carbon atoms. Formic acid secreted by ants is the simplest possible organic acid, H—COOH. Acetic acid of vinegar is CH_3—COOH. Stearic acid of beef fat is a veritable train, usually written $C_{17}H_{35}COOH$.

Glycerol is a three-carbon chain, as shown in the formula. If the three OH's are removed and NO_3 radicals substituted, the result is nitroglycerin, or dynamite.

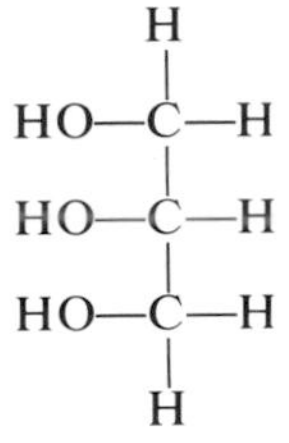

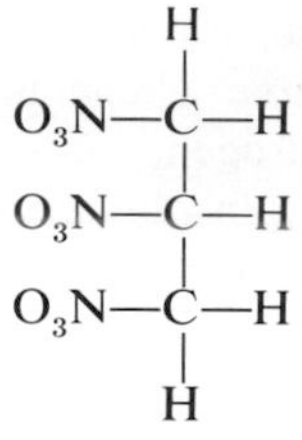

The basic reaction by which a lipid is split into glycerol and fatty acid by splitting and the insertion of a molecule of water is called **hydrolysis** (*hydro*, water, + lysis, to loosen) or hydrolytic splitting. It is virtually equivalent to digestion, for hydrolysis is what happens to carbohydrates and proteins as well as fats in the digestive tract. The reverse process by which two chemical substances are combined is much more complicated and involves a series of steps. Diagrammatically it can be represented by the reaction proceeding toward the left in the equation at the bottom of the page, where three fatty acid molecules are joined to each molecule of glycerol.

When every carbon in the fatty acid chain is holding two hydrogens, the fat or oil is said to be **saturated.** When two adjacent carbons are linked by a double bond, the lipid is **unsaturated.** Butyric and crotonic acids illustrate this contrast. The structural formulas of these two acids are:

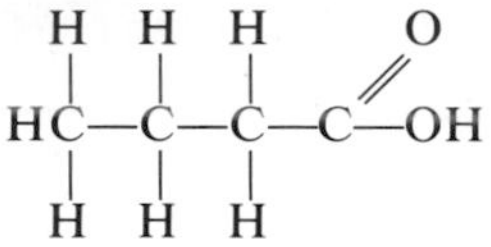

glycerol   dynamite

butyric acid (saturated)   crotonic acid (unsaturated)

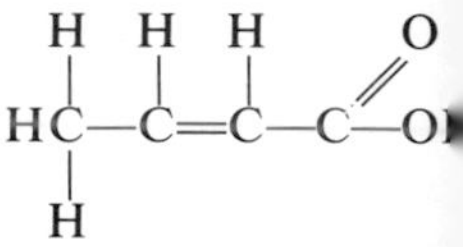

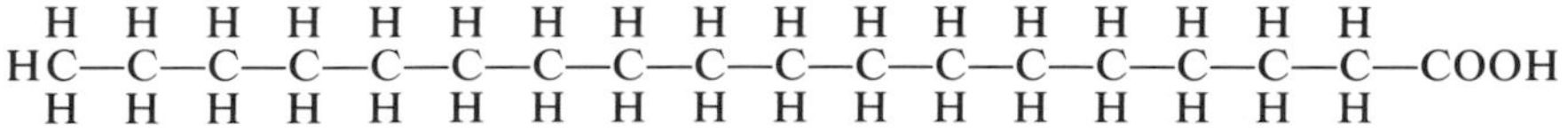

stearic acid

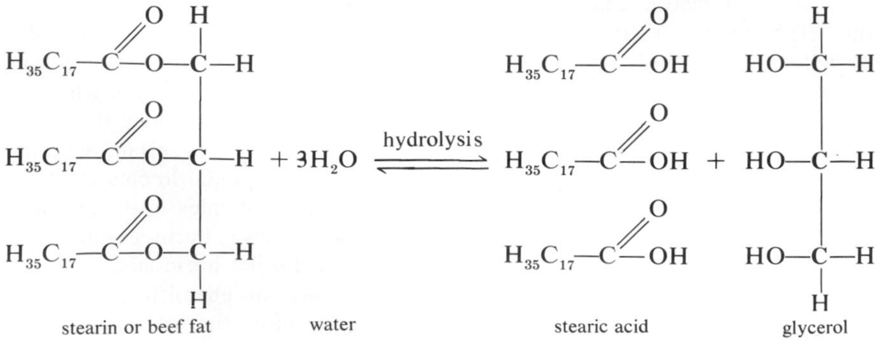

stearin or beef fat   water   stearic acid   glycerol

The melting point, which determines whether a lipid is an oil or a solid fat at any given temperature, depends on two factors. The shorter the chain of fatty acids and the more unsaturation, the lower the melting point.

When a lipid has three fatty acid chains, as does stearin or beef fat, it is known as a **triglyceride.** Most of the familiar oils and fats are triglycerides and in most of them not all of the three fatty acids are the same. In fact, each of the three may be different. When a lipid has only two fatty acid chains, it is called a **diglyceride.** These also are important to animals.

We can now take a second look at the lipids in cell membranes. This extremely important group of lipids are diglycerides with a phosphate group attached where the third fatty acid might have been on the glycerol. Attached to this phosphate group is usually an additional molecule. In the case of **lecithin,** the most abundant **phospho-diglyceride** in cell membranes, this last group is choline. The lecithin molecule looks like this:

g—fatty acid
l
y
c—fatty acid
e
r
o
l—phosphate + choline

Choline is a small molecule consisting of a nitrogen atom to which is attached three methyl groups, —CH_3, plus two carbons with hydrogens attached. Choline will be mentioned again in connection with the conduction of a nerve impulse, which is a membrane phenomenon. The phosphate group is an energy-related group similar to energy-carrying compounds of respiration. This suggests a role for lecithin in pumping molecules across cell membranes.

PROTEINS AND AMINO ACIDS

Of all the known molecules, proteins are the largest and most complex. Their only rivals are the nucleic acids which carry the genetic information necessary for each species. But the nucleic acids carry all the complex information for making an animal in a very simplified code composed of only four "letters" and only

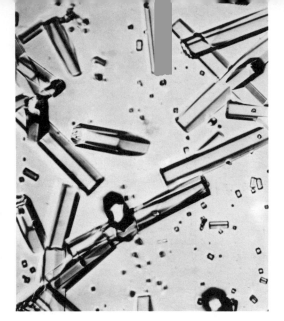

Fig. 3–1. Crystals of animal protein. *(Kindness of Harvard Medical School)*

three-letter "words." In the proteins the complexities are expressed in an all but endless variety of forms. Every species of animal has hundreds of different kinds of proteins and each of the hundreds of thousands of species possesses its own characteristic proteins. The total runs into the millions.

The most obvious places to find animal proteins are in muscles, blood, horns, finger nails and claws, hair and feathers, tendons and ligaments. Egg white is almost pure protein. But proteins are also essential components of every cell. The cell membranes, both surrounding the cell and within the cell, are proteinaceous. Most important, enzymes are proteins.

Proteins (Greek *proteios,* of the first rank) have been recognized for only a little more than a century as a distinct group of compounds containing nitrogen, in addition to the carbon, hydrogen, and oxygen of carbohydrates and lipids. They were so named by a Dutch chemist, Johannes Mulder, because he held that protein "is without a doubt the most important of the known components of living matter." Since then investigators have succeeded in obtaining over 150 proteins in pure form and have even crystalized them. Their molecular weights are enormous, ranging from several thousand up to several million. It will be recalled that the molecular weight of water is only 18, oxygen 16, and hydrogen 1.

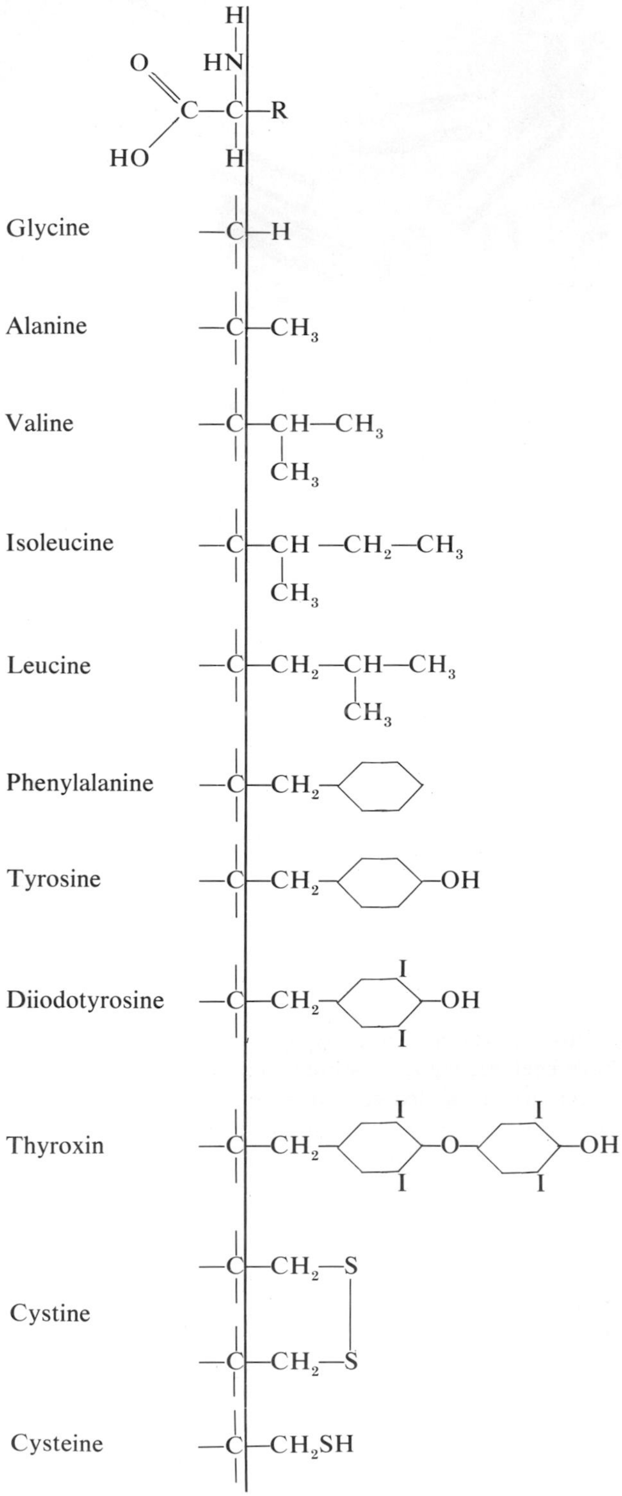

General structure:

$$O=C(HO)-C(H)(HN-H)-R$$

Glycine —C(H)—H

Alanine —C(H)—CH$_3$

Valine —C(H)—CH—CH$_3$, CH$_3$

Isoleucine —C(H)—CH—CH$_2$—CH$_3$, CH$_3$

Leucine —C(H)—CH$_2$—CH—CH$_3$, CH$_3$

Phenylalanine —C(H)—CH$_2$—⬡

Tyrosine —C(H)—CH$_2$—⬡—OH

Diiodotyrosine —C(H)—CH$_2$—⬡(I)(I)—OH

Thyroxin —C(H)—CH$_2$—⬡(I)(I)—O—⬡(I)(I)—OH

Cystine —C(H)—CH$_2$—S | | —C(H)—CH$_2$—S

Cysteine —C(H)—CH$_2$SH

Proteins may be defined as substances of high molecular weight composed of chains of linked amino acids. The amino acids will be discussed below.

No completely satisfactory way of classifying proteins is available, but they are conveniently divided into three major groups:

1. Simple proteins. These yield only amino acids on hydrolysis. Albumins and globulins belong here. (Remember the gamma globulins of the blood which are the antipolio and other antibodies.)

2. Conjugated proteins. In these the protein is combined with a nonprotein group called the **prosthetic group.** In nucleoproteins the prosthetic group is a nucleic acid. In glycoproteins, found, for example, in the mucus of jellyfish and men, the prosthetic group is a carbohydrate. In enzymes the prosthetic group is usually a vitamin. In porphyrino-proteins, like hemoglobin and chlorophyll, the prosthetic group is a porphyrin.

3. Derived proteins. This is more or less a "scrap basket" category and contains such substances as histones, which can be extracted from nuclei.

Simple proteins are usually separated on the basis of solubility. Albumins, for example, are soluble in distilled water, while globulins are almost insoluble in distilled water but readily dissolve in neutral salt solutions. Proteins are also separated by electrophoresis. Because different proteins have different electric charges, different sizes, and different shapes, they migrate at different rates in an electric field across moist paper or through certain gels. Proteins are also separated and their molecular weights determined by centrifugation. The actual structure of protein molecules, to be discussed later, is investigated by X-ray diffraction studies.

Every cell is what its proteins make it. This is basically because all cell activities—synthetic, locomotor, and the rest—are under the direct control of enzymes or enzyme products, and enzymes are proteins. Yet all the millions of kinds of proteins from both animals and plants can be broken down by boiling with acid or by digestive enzymes into only about two dozen amino acids!

All amino acids have an alpha carbon atom to which is attached four other atoms or groups of atoms. There is always a hydrogen, an acidic carboxyl group, —COOH, a basic amino group, —NH_2, plus an additional radical designated as R in the model amino acid shown at the top of the column.

In the simplest case possible, glycine, the fourth radical or R is merely a hydrogen atom. If R is a methyl group, —CH_3, the amino acid is alanine. If a phenol ring is substituted for one of the H's in the methyl group, phenylalanine is the result. Phenylalanine is an extremely important substance because it can be made into the amino acid tyrosine merely by the addition of an OH group to the phenol ring. Tyrosine, it can be seen, is a precursor of thyroxin, the hormone of the thyroid gland. Tyrosine is also the precursor of the hormone adrenalin, and of the brown, reddish, and black melanin pigments of skin, hair, and feathers. Tyrosine also forms part of many proteins.

The nutritional value of protein from meat, fish, peanuts, corn, or any other source depends on the amino acids it contains. If an animal cannot make a particular amino acid by modifying other amino acids, its diet must provide it. For men and rats, for example, tryptophan (or indol alanine) is essential in the diet, or growth does not take place.

Notice cystine and cysteine. Both possess a special sulfur atom. It may be linked to a hydrogen atom or another sulfur atom, —SH or —S—S—, but in a protein molecule, the sulfur of one cystine links with the sulfur of another in a different part of the protein and helps hold it in shape.

About 50 years ago a German chemist, Emil Fischer, discovered the way amino acids are joined together to form proteins. It is by what is called **peptide linkages.** The —OH is lost from the carboxyl group and an —H from the amino group; a molecule of water is produced, and the two amino acids are linked through the nitrogen of the amino group of one and the carbon of the carboxyl group of the other. This is the peptide bond. A peptide is a miniature protein or, more accurately, a short chain of amino acids,—but even the longest chains are linked by peptide bonds.

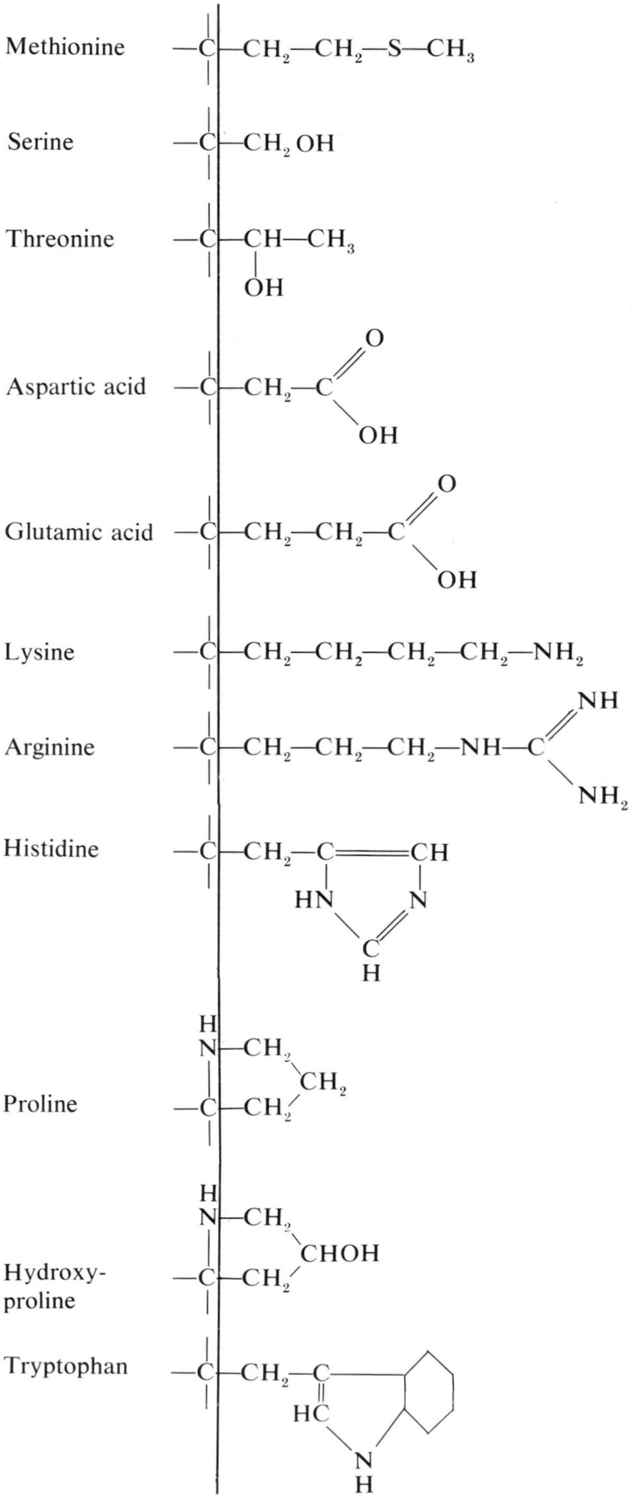

Methionine —C—CH_2—CH_2—S—CH_3

Serine —C—CH_2OH

Threonine —C—CH—CH_3 / OH

Aspartic acid —C—CH_2—C (=O) OH

Glutamic acid —C—CH_2—CH_2—C (=O) OH

Lysine —C—CH_2—CH_2—CH_2—CH_2—NH_2

Arginine —C—CH_2—CH_2—CH_2—NH—C (=NH) NH_2

Histidine —C—CH_2—C==CH / HN N / C / H

Proline HN—CH_2 / CH_2 —C—CH_2

Hydroxy-proline HN—CH_2 / CHOH —C—CH_2

Tryptophan —C—CH_2—C == ... HC N H

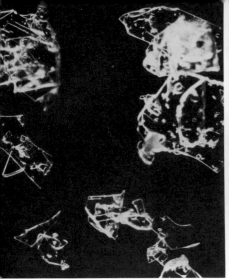

Fig. 3–2. Crystals of two amino acids. Left: glutamic acid, squarish crystals. Right: tryptophan, elongate crystals. (*Kindness of Lederle Laboratories*)

$$H_2N-\underset{\underset{H}{|}}{\overset{\overset{H}{|}}{C}}-\overset{\overset{O}{\|}}{C}-OH \;+\; H_2N-\underset{\underset{CH_2}{|}}{\overset{\overset{H}{|}}{C}}-\overset{\overset{O}{\|}}{C}-OH \;\longrightarrow\; H_2O \;+\; H_2N-\underset{\underset{H}{|}}{\overset{\overset{H}{|}}{C}}-\overset{\overset{O}{\|}}{C}-\underset{\underset{H}{|}}{N}-\underset{\underset{CH_2}{|}}{\overset{\overset{H}{|}}{C}}-\overset{\overset{O}{\|}}{C}-OH$$

glycine   tyrosine   water   a dipeptide

Notice that when two amino acids are united through a peptide bond into a dipeptide, the resulting molecule still possesses a carboxyl radical on one side and an amino radical on the other. Consequently, a dipeptide can unite with another amino acid and form a tripeptide, and this in turn with other amino acids until a long **polypeptide** and finally a protein is formed. The linkage is always the same, passing through the alpha carbon to the carboxyl carbon to the nitrogen to the adjacent alpha carbon.

The sequence of amino acids in the chain determines the character of a protein. This sequence is what is spelled out by the DNA code in the chromosomes, as will be further clarified in the chapter on genetics. The sequence is termed the **primary structure** of a protein. The asymmetrical shapes of the amino acids result in the twisting of the long chain into a corkscrew-like helix. The helix is called the **secondary structure** of a protein. But few proteins remain as long filaments. They become folded and bent on themselves in characteristic ways. This is called the **tertiary structure** of the protein. It is determined by several factors, such as the presence in the chain of amino acids containing sulfur atoms which unite with sulfur atoms in other amino acids at other parts of the chain. Since the position of the sulfur-containing amino acids is determined by the genetic code, the folding of any particular kind of protein is determined by heredity.

The primary structure—that is, the actual sequence of amino acids—in an actual protein was determined for the first time by Frederick Sanger in Cambridge, England. He used insulin. Why insulin? Partly because its molecules are relatively small for a protein and can be obtained commercially in virtually pure form, and partly because of its great medical importance. The method is both laborious and tricky. It consists of breaking up the molecule by several different methods into pieces of different lengths which overlap, determining the amino acids in each piece, usually at the ends of the piece, and finally fitting all the data together into a consistent picture. This is how the primary structure of insulin looks:

Notice the two disulfide bonds which tie the two polypeptide chains together. Notice also one intra-chain disulfide linkage which would surely produce a kink. There are also hydrogen bonds between chains but they are not shown.

The importance of the correct amino acids in the correct sequence has been dramatically shown in sickle cell anemia, a disease prevalent in some of the lands surrounding the Mediterranean. In this disease the hemoglobin is abnormal; the abnormality consists in a single error in each of the four chains which together

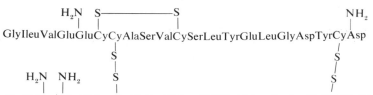

Fig. 3–3. The primary structure of one of the polypeptide chains of a human hemoglobin molecule showing the sequence of amino acids and also the porphyrin iron-containing prosthetic group.

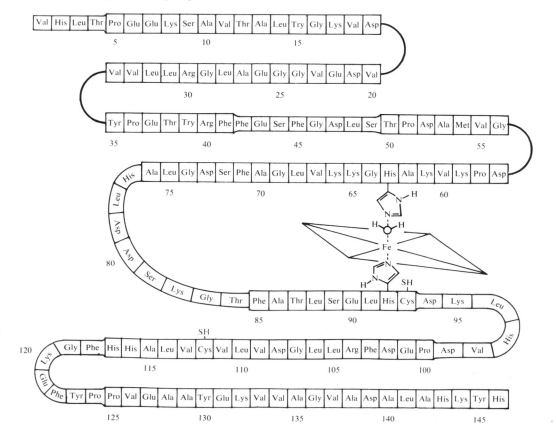

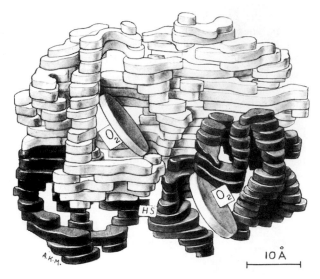

Fig. 3–4. Model showing the tertiary structure, i.e., folding of the polypeptide chains, of a protein molecule. This model was constructed by Perutz from X-ray diffraction studies of hemoglobin. The two alpha polypeptide chains are shown white, the two beta chains black, and the porphyrin heme groups that bind the oxygen are shown as disks. *(Kindness of M. F. Perutz)*

make up a hemoglobin molecule. In place of one of the valines is glutamic acid! This is one error out of about 300 amino acids. Figure 3–3 shows the sequence in one of the four polypeptide chains and also the porphyrin prosthetic group with its centrally placed iron atom, Fe.

The tertiary structure of hemoglobin from muscle is shown in the model pictured in Figure 3–4 above.

NUCLEIC ACIDS

The most famous case of an important biological discovery that was neglected for decades is probably Mendel's discovery of the laws of heredity, but the discovery of nucleic acids, which constitute the physical basis for those laws, is another. This emphasizes the urgent and tricky nature of the problem of recognizing which discoveries are truly important.

Discovery of the molecular structure of nucleic acids and proof that this structure carries the code in which genetic information is transmitted from cell to cell and from generation to generation is the achievement of the past few years. But it is nearly a century since a young Swiss investigator, Friedrich Miescher, began to explore the biochemistry of nuclei. He used the white blood cells of pus which have large nuclei (lymphocytes almost lack cytoplasm altogether) and also the heads of sperms, which were known to consist of little more than condensed nuclei. In those days before pollution became a problem, Atlantic salmon migrated up the Rhine as far as Basle so that Miescher was able to obtain enormous quantities of salmon sperms for the chemical analysis of virtually pure nuclei.

Miescher discovered that pure nuclei were composed almost entirely of an acid, later called nucleic acid. It was unusual in containing not only nitrogen but also phosphorus, a fact so peculiar that his major professor refused to allow him to publish his discovery until after it had been very carefully confirmed more than two years later.

From then until the 1920's little work was done on nucleic acids. In 1924 R. Feulgen and others found that the nucleic acid of the chromosomes, and only of the chromosomes, could be stained a brilliant red after proper treatment of the deoxyribose located there. This reaction not only afforded a very elegant method for staining chromosomes but it demonstrated the presence of deoxyribose along the entire length of every chromosome.

Analysis by a variety of chemical and physical methods has by now revealed the actual structure of nucleic acids and shown clearly that there are two kinds, deoxyribose nucleic acid, DNA, and ribose nucleic acid, RNA. DNA is found in close association with proteins and makes up the chromosomes. RNA is found in both the nucleus and the cytoplasm. The structure of both compounds is very similar and accords well with the familiar Watson–Crick model now to be described.

Nucleic acids resemble proteins in that both types of compounds are composed of a long sequence of smaller molecules—nucleotides and amino acids, respectively. Each nucleotide consists of a ribose (or deoxyribose) sugar, a phosphoric acid group, PO_4H, and a nitrogen-containing base.

The structures of the polynucleotides of DNA and RNA are shown below.

There are only four of these bases in DNA and only four in RNA, and three of them are the same in both. Two of the bases are purines, adenine and guanine. Two are pyrimidines, cytosine and thymine in DNA; in RNA, uracil substitutes for thymine. This fact offers a use-

ful research tool. Labelled thymine will appear in the DNA in the chromosomes. Labelled uracil will appear in RNA.

When the nucleotides are linked together they form two parallel rows with links between them, and resemble a ladder twisted like the stripes on a barber pole. The sides of the ladder are built of alternating phosphoric acid and ribose sugar molecules. The rungs of the ladder are made of the nitrogen bases, two bases in each rung, one purine and one pyrimidine. In

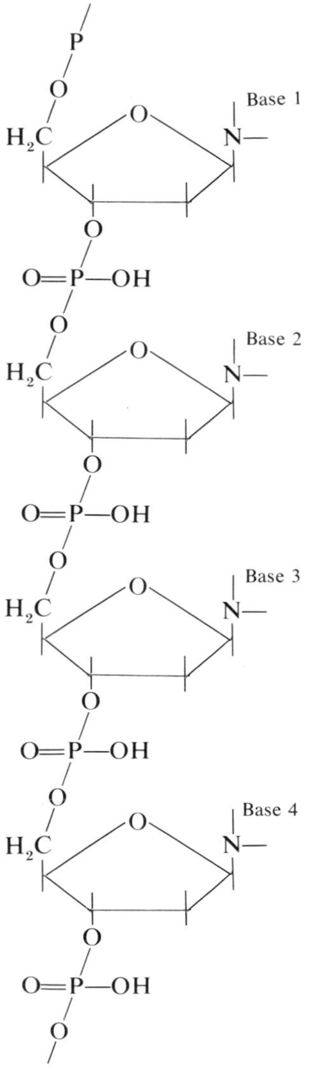

DNA polynucleotide

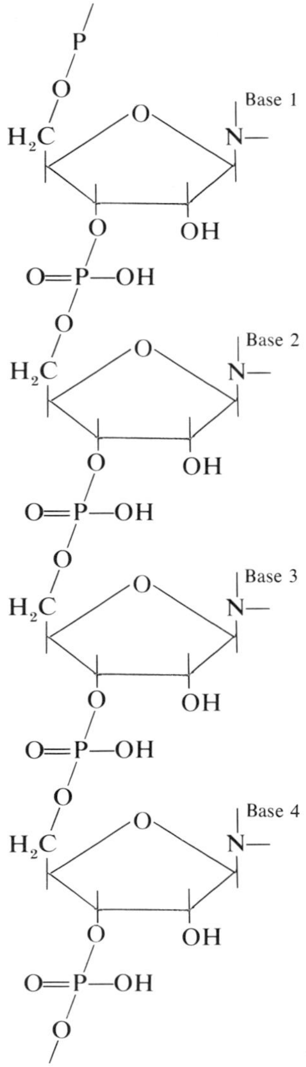

RNA polynucleotide

DNA, adenine is always paired with thymine, and guanine with cytosine. In RNA, adenine is paired with uracil. The rungs are attached to the uprights of the helical ladder at the sugars. How these four bases constitute a code for making proteins will be discussed in the chapter on genetics.

In living cells the DNA in the chromosomes makes more DNA like itself. It also makes RNA. The RNA moves out into the cytoplasm where it furnishes the instructions for making proteins, including the most important proteins, enzymes. Thus animal life is based on a tripod: DNA, RNA, protein. All the other materials—carbohydrates, lipids, pigments, and the rest—are secondary.

Fig. 3–5. Diagrammatic representation of the double-helix structure of nucleic acids. *(After Watson and Crick)*

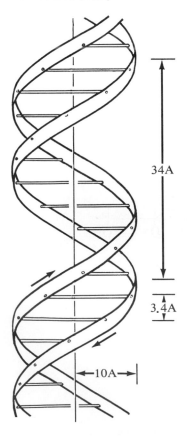

Nucleotides have an additional function of great importance. They are the chief carriers of all the energy made available to cells by respiration, whether aerobic or anaerobic. In both plants and animals, energy is "packaged" in molecules of the nucleotide ATP, adenosine triphosphate. How this is accomplished is discussed in the following section.

METABOLISM

Proteins, carbohydrates, lipids, and even nucleic acids in a living animal are continually undergoing change and renewal. The old comparisons of life to a flame or to a fountain turn out to be even truer than the ancients knew. How do we know so much better than they? By the use of radioactively labelled tracers. The nitrogen of amino acids, for example, can be labelled in this way. If a measured amount of labelled amino acids is fed to an adult, nongrowing animal and the amount of nitrogen, both labelled and unlabelled, that is excreted is measured, it can be demonstrated that the actual proteins of which the tissues are built are continually exchanging their amino acids with those in the bloodstream. The very structure of the animal is in flux, with a definite turnover rate!

However, the main stream of matter and energy which flows through an animal is utilized in one of the three ways indicated at the beginning of this chapter—to make big molecules from small ones, to transport material across membranes, or to produce motion, usually either muscular or ciliary.

The sum of all the chemical activities within a living organism is called **metabolism.** Synthetic metabolism—biosynthesis, for example—which constructs more complex molecules, is known as **anabolism.** Destructive metabolism—hydrolysis, for example—which breaks up large molecules, is called **katabolism.** The most important single aspect of metabolism which is externally obvious is respiration. In fact in medical literature the word metabolism is often used to denote the chemical side of respiration.

Although respiration, in the sense of the breath of life, has been a criterion of living from time out of mind, it is only within the last four centuries that anyone has known what breathing meant, what it is for. The growth of knowledge about respiration makes one of the most long-continued and important series of achievements in the history of science. In the 17th century a group of young investigators like Robert Boyle in London discovered what is still an amazing thing. A breathing mouse and a burning candle both do the same thing to air. By enclosing candles and mice together and separately under glass belljars, these men were able to show that a candle cannot burn in air in which a mouse has suffocated, nor can a mouse live long in a closed space in which a candle flame has burned out.

With the growth of chemistry in the 18th century, Antoine Lavoisier (1743 – 1794) and Joseph Priestley (1733 – 1804) proved that in respiration oxygen is taken from the air and carbon dioxide returned to it. By keeping small mammals in confined vessels and measuring accurately both the CO_2 and the heat (i.e., calories) given off, they went further and proved that animals obey what are now known as the **laws of conservation of matter and of energy.** A breathing guinea pig and burning charcoal give off the same number of calories of heat energy when the same amount of oxygen is burned or carbon dioxide given off.

The 19th century workers refined the discoveries of their predecessors and added some of their own. The simple sugar, glucose, is the material usually burned in the living organism. The over-all formula is:

$$C_6H_{12}O_6 + 6\,O_2 \longrightarrow 6\,CO_2 + 6\,H_2O + energy$$

One molecule of glucose combines with six molecules of oxygen to yield six molecules of carbon dioxide and six of water. The energy released is measured in calories. A small calorie, the unit usually used in cellular metabolism, is defined as the amount of heat necessary to raise 1 gram of water 1° Centigrade. (Note that the large calorie or kilocalorie is the usual dietetic unit.) At the same time studies were being made on the caloric value of different foodstuffs, extensive knowledge was gained of the methods used to absorb oxygen and transport it and carbon dioxide in the blood, and also about

the way respiration is controlled. These topics will be considered later. The facts and principles established in the 19th century are of great importance in aviation medicine, deep-sea diving, dietary programs, etc.

The achievement of the present century has exceeded the wildest dreams of the 19th. It is nothing less than the successful exploration of the inner workings of cells. The living cell is a complex chemical factory with many diverse and interconnected production lines. Knowledge of how oxygen and sugar power these activities, and how they are controlled by enzymes, has led directly to important practical results. This is especially true in understanding how to choose antibiotics and antimetabolites that will block living processes at specific points. It is a large topic to which we will return. At present it must suffice to cite some basic facts about enzymes.

ENZYMES

Enzymes are of the greatest industrial, medical, and theoretical importance because they control the inner workings of cells. Poisons are poisonous because they inhibit one or another enzyme. Antibiotics act on enzymes. Vitamins are essential because they form parts of enzyme molecules or cofactors for enzymes. Yet the 19th century understood as little about the inner workings of a cell as a child knows about the workings of a juke box. In one case you put in a coin and music comes out; in the other you put in oxygen and sugar, and carbon dioxide, water, and energy come out.

Enzymes as digestive agents have been known in a general way ever since René Réaumur (1683 – 1757) obtained gastric juice from his pet falcon by inducing it to swallow small sponges on strings. The juice softened and dissolved meat. Modern knowledge about enzymes really begins with the famous controversy between Louis Pasteur (1822 – 1895) in Paris and Justus Liebig (1803 – 1873) of the University of Heidelberg. Pasteur claimed that alcoholic fermentation was the result of the living activity of yeast cells. Without intact living yeast cells, no fermentation. Liebig, a brilliant chemist, claimed that fermentation was a purely chemical process analogous to the rusting of iron. Neither view is entirely wrong nor entirely true. It was Eduard Buchner (1860–1917) who found the answer. He was able to extract from yeast a cell-free juice that had the power of fermentation, that is, it could turn sugar into alcohol and carbon dioxide. He called that active ingredient in his yeast juice an enzyme which means, literally, in yeast. He called the alcohol-producing enzyme in yeast zymase.

The terminology of enzymes is simple. The material on which an enzyme acts is called its **substrate.** In the case just mentioned, sugar is the substrate. The name of the enzyme is formed by adding **-ase** to the substrate. Thus an enzyme that acts on protein is proteinase, one that acts on lipids is a lipase. Unfortunately the names of various common enzymes were given before this system arose. Pepsin in gastric juice and ptyalin in saliva are such cases.

The activities of enzymes are approximately coextensive with the chemical activities of cells. There are oxidizing and reducing enzymes, digestive (hydrolytic) enzymes that split carbohydrates, lipids, proteins, and nucleic acids, and synthesizing enzymes that build up these molecules. Enzymes are extremely specific in their activities and particular about the conditions under which they will work. A given enzyme will bring about one and only one reaction and only under the proper conditions of temperature and pH. Since the enzyme molecule is not destroyed in action, only very few molecules are necessary to convert large amounts of substrate. A single enzyme molecule can unite or split from 50,000 to 100,000 substrate molecules per second.

Chemically most enzyme molecules consist of two parts: a large protein portion, the **apoenzyme,** and a small nonprotein part, the **coenzyme** or **prosthetic group.** Many vitamins serve as coenzymes or prosthetic groups of particular enzymes.

The discovery that enzymes, the keys to life's activities, are proteins was the work of James B. Sumner of Cornell. After ten years of frustrating but single-minded labor he succeeded in crystallizing urease, an enzyme abundant in the jack bean. Crystallization proved that he had a pure substance. It gave all the standard tests for a protein and, when dissolved, showed urease activity. At first no one believed that it could be true, but today his achievement stands as a landmark in biological science.

The action of respiratory enzymes on their various substrates is commonly investigated by placing either slices of tissue or finely minced

Fig. 3–6. Crystalline enzymes. Left: pepsin. Right: trypsin. Original magnification (left) 90×, (right) 202×. *(Kindness of J. H. Northrop)*

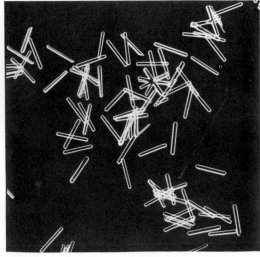

Fig. 3–7. James B. Sumner, who first proved that enzymes are proteins. *(Kindness of Cornell University)*

tissue into a Warburg flask and recording the rate at which respiration takes place. Such a Warburg vessel is shown in Figure 3–8.

Enzyme reactions can be controlled and the reaction stream guided into one metabolic pathway or another by several methods. Because most enzymes can function only within a very narrow pH range, their action can be blocked by relatively slight pH changes. Furthermore, many, if not all, enzymatic reactions can be made to slow down or even run backwards if the products of the reaction are allowed to accumulate or are added. Many enzymes are irreversibly blocked by combining with various poisons (inhibitors). Some poisons are highly specific but others inhibit many enzymes. For example, the heavy metals like lead, mercury, and arsenic block many enzymes. This is the basis of the toxicity of war gases like Lewisite, which contains arsenic. Such enzyme poisons can be counteracted by compounds like BAL (British anti-Lewisite) which have a greater affinity for the heavy metals than do the enzyme molecules themselves.

How do enzymes work? There is convincing evidence that enzymes produce their results at their surfaces and that there is a **lock-and-key relationship** between the shape of a particular substrate and the enzyme that acts on it. To be effective, the substrate must fit tightly against the enzyme. Once this molecular intimacy has been achieved, chemical forces cause a large substrate to split or two small ones to unite.

Fig. 3–8. A Warburg vessel, used to measure tissue respiration. The vessel is shaken within a constant temperature bath. Tissue or cells are placed in the fluid in the vessel. The dark central cup holds KOH to absorb CO_2 produced. The stopper at right is removed to introduce additional materials. From the top extends a tube to measure the volume of O_2 consumed. *(Reprinted with permission. Copyright by* Scientific American, *Inc. All rights reserved.)*

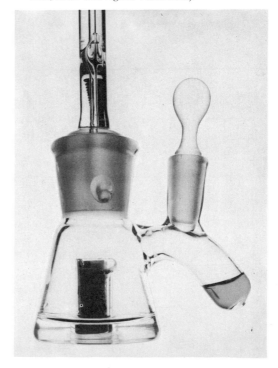

Part of the proof of this theory can be illustrated by succinic dehydrogenase, an enzyme important in the respiration of virtually all cells. A dehydrogenase is an enzyme that splits off hydrogen from its substrate. In this case, as shown in the diagram, succinic acid fits neatly into the reactive site of the enzyme. Two hydrogen atoms are split off and fumaric acid is formed. The fumaric acid falls away from the enzyme, leaving it ready to repeat the act. If, however, malonic acid, which is very similar to succinic, is substituted, the malonic acid is accepted by the non-discriminatory enzyme, but since it is not a perfect fit, no reaction occurs. The enzyme is more or less permanently blocked because its reactive site is occupied. This type of block is called **competitive inhibition.** Its discovery has led to an extensive hunt for such compounds, analogs of substrates which can be used to block unwanted enzymes.

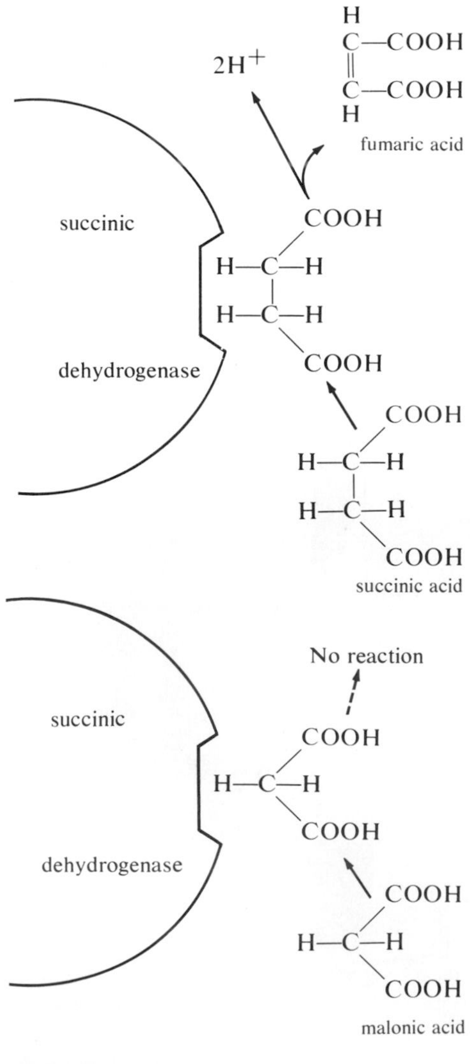

A second, though related, method of inhibiting enzymes is to give them a "phony" vitamin instead of a "phony" substrate. It will be recalled that enzymes are really double structures, a large more or less rounded protein and a nonprotein prosthetic group. If a given animal cannot synthesize the prosthetic group, it must have it in its diet. In such a case, the prosthetic group is known as a vitamin. If an animal or bacterium is fed a **vitamin analog,** which the protein part of the enzyme does not distinguish from the genuine vitamin, a nonfunctional pseudo-enzyme is produced. This is the way sulfa drugs work. Luckily, the enzymes of certain bacteria are far more seriously damaged than are any essential human enzymes.

CELLULAR METABOLISM

There have been two massive achievements in this century in the biological sciences. One is the discovery and then the breaking of the genetic code. The other is the discovery of the dynamics of life as it takes place within living cells. Not only have the general contours of energy flow been sharply delineated but even the fine details have been traced in an amazingly intricate and extensive system of change and interchange of matter and energy. This new knowledge confers a profound understanding of living processes and their relationship to the nonliving world. It also means a vastly increased possibility of control over living processes in many areas — anesthetics, therapeutic medicine, fermentation industries, agriculture, control of the nervous system and of animal and human behavior.

At the same time this new knowledge has resulted in a very real simplification. What once seemed a puzzling jumble of unrelated processes now is revealed as forming a single system. Aerobic and anaerobic respiration, fermentation and photosynthesis, all fit together smoothly. The chief energy-yielding processes are everywhere the same, in bacteria, plants, and animals, whether in fermenting yeast or breathing potatoes, in beef hearts, in the flight muscles of honeybees, or in the cilia of a clam. Consider the main contours of energy flow first.

The Main Energy Pathway. The main course of flow by which energy is made available for living organisms has two quite different parts. The first portion does not require free oxygen and is therefore called **anaerobic respiration.** Since sugar is broken down it is also called **glycolysis,** and because alcohol and related substances are the end products, it is also referred to as **fermentation,** although this term is sometimes restricted to the very final steps of glycolysis. Another name for this anaerobic process is the **Embden-Meyerhof glycolytic pathway.** The second portion of the main course of flow requires the presence of free oxygen. Hence it is **aerobic respiration.** It consists of the **citric acid or Krebs cycle,** which receives the products of glycolysis, and a final nucleotide and **cytochrome series,** which takes the waste hydrogens from the original glucose to unite them with molecular oxygen with the formation of water.

Glycolysis begins with glucose. The glucose is first united with phosphate, a process called **phosphorylation.** The glucose molecule is then further modified and torn apart by a series of enzymes until it is converted into pyruvic acid. During this process, CO_2 is given off as a waste product and two molecules (three, in the case of muscle cells) of ATP are produced. It will be recalled that ATP is the nucleotide, adenosine triphosphate, in which energy is "packaged" and then distributed within cells where it furnishes the energy for muscular contraction, synthesis of protein, secretion, bioluminescence, and various other energy-requiring processes.

The **pyruvic acid** which results from the Embden-Meyerhof glycolytic series is highly reactive. It consists of three active radicals:

the methyl, $-CH_3$, the keto, $-\overset{\displaystyle O}{\underset{\displaystyle \parallel}{C}}-$, and the carboxyl, $-COOH$; thus, $CH_3\overset{O}{\overset{\parallel}{C}}COOH$. Pyruvic acid stands at a metabolic crossroads. If

Fig. 3–9. Diagram of main energy-yielding pathway.

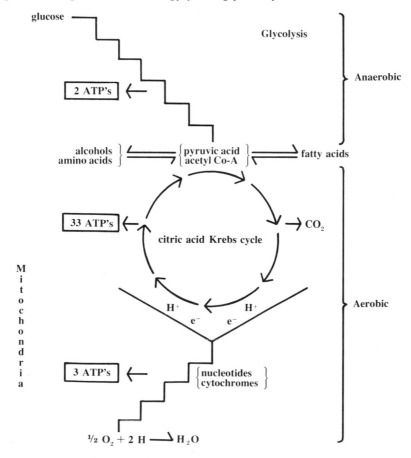

no oxygen is present but certain enzymes are, the pyruvic acid is converted into lactic acid (as happens in muscular exercise) or some other fatty acid, or into some kind of alcohol (as happens in certain yeasts and bacteria), or into various other products of the process of fermentation.

If oxygen is present and also the proper enzymes, then pyruvic acid unites with **coenzyme-A** and enters the citric acid or Krebs cycle. It is at the level of pyruvic acid and coenzyme-A that fat metabolites enter the main energy flow. Residues from amino acids also enter the citric acid cycle at this point although this is not the only place where they come into it and are used as energy sources. The cycle itself consists of nine different and relatively small organic acids. The pyruvic acid, slightly modified and riding on coenzyme-A, enters the cycle by uniting with the last of the nine acids in the cycle, thereby forming citric acid which is the first in the circle. As one acid in the circle is formed from its immediate predecessor by a series of splittings, coalescences, and modifications, CO_2 is released as waste, more ATP's are produced, and finally the last acid in the cycle is reached. It then unites with more modified pyruvic-coenzyme-A to form more citric acid and the cycle begins again. The hydrogens from the original glucose are passed along to nucleotides which pass them or their electrons on to the **cytochromes** which pass them along to molecular oxygen with which they form water. All this second or aerobic portion of the respiratory pathway takes place within mitochondria.

The amounts of energy packaged into ATP molecules by glycolysis and by the aerobic portion of the pathway are very different. For each molecule of glucose, glycolysis yields only two (or three) molecules of ATP. The aerobic portion yields a total of 36. Actually this varies a bit with the substrate and the organism. Yeast cells get 38 ATP's from the aerobic process. The efficiency of the total process is roughly 50 per cent. One mole of glucose, i.e., one gram molecular weight, which is 180 grams of glucose, represents about 680,000 small calories. One mole of ATP carries about 8,000 cal. Thus the two moles of ATP from glycolysis of one mole of glucose equal about 16,000 cal. The 36 moles from the aerobic

part equal about 288,000 cal. Hence the entire process from glucose to CO_2 and water yields approximately 304,000 cal packaged as ATP, out of a total of 680,000 cal in one mole of glucose. The remaining energy is used mostly in the processes of breaking down the glucose and producing the ATP's. Evidently there is a packaging charge of over 50 per cent.

Methods and Evidence. When you look beneath the bald dogmatic assertions about glucose uniting with phosphate as the first step in the utilization of sugar, or about a cycle of small organic acids going round and round grinding up pyruvic acid and producing energy in neat little ATP bundles, or beneath any of the dozens of other assertions about what is supposed to go on inside the cell, what do you find? How convincing is the whole complicated story, or even any of its parts? How could anyone ever get so much as a finger in a crack to gain access to such deeply hidden events?

A natural starting point is the achievement of **Eduard Buchner,** already cited. It was he who brought together the oversimplified vitalistic views of men like Pasteur and the equally oversimplified chemical views represented by Liebig. It is worth noting that Buchner began his work with the encouragement of his elder brother Hans, a bacteriologist, and the disapproval of his superiors at the University of Kiel. By killing yeast cells by grinding in sharp sand and then filtering and testing the cell-free extract on sugar, he expected to show that such nonliving material could not convert sugar to alcohol and CO_2,—but it did. This was the beginning. The active agent was not itself living but it was produced in living cells.

Buchner was killed in World War I but his discovery excited **Arthur Harden,** then teaching and writing textbooks in Manchester, England. Harden studied the cell-free extracts of yeast and found that they converted sugar into alcohol and CO_2 very rapidly at first and then more and more slowly until action finally stopped. He sought to discover why. Was the enzyme being gradually worn out or used up? Was there some way to protect it? After a long search, Harden found that the addition of blood serum or of boiled fresh yeast extract (which would not in itself ferment since it had been boiled) would restore activity. He finally found that the restorative agent was inorganic phosphate. Fermentation could be virtually at a standstill but then be fully restored by the addition of phosphate. Clearly the enzyme was not wearing out. The surprising thing about this discovery was that neither sugar nor the enzyme zymase nor alcohol contain any phosphate! Harden at last discovered that the phosphate combines with the sugar. This is now recognized as the first step in glycolysis.

The discoveries about fermentations in yeasts came to be seen, after some years, to be related to the metabolism of muscle contraction. It became known that muscles contain glycogen, the "animal starch" discovered long ago in livers by Claude Bernard at the Sorbonne. Further, F. G. Hopkins, one of the discoverers of vitamins, showed that a working muscle accumulates lactic acid, an organic acid also produced by various bacteria, notably those which cause milk to sour. It also became known that as a muscle works, it uses up its glycogen.

At this point **Otto Meyerhof,** at the University of Kiel where Buchner had worked a generation earlier, succeeded in showing, first, that there is an exact quantitative relation between the amount of glycogen that disappears and the amount of lactic acid produced, just as there is between the sugar used and the alcohol produced. Second, Meyerhof showed that in the absence of oxygen this relation between glycogen and accumulated lactic acid remained the same. In other words, the energy metabolism of muscle in the first stage is anaerobic, i.e., glycolysis. When oxygen was again admitted to muscle, the lactic acid disappeared and oxygen was utilized. Muscle metabolism then appeared to be of two kinds, a first, anaerobic part, i.e., glycolysis, and a second, aerobic portion. The first part is called the Embden-Meyerhof glycolytic pathway, from the men who established its existence. The working out of the actual steps and enzymes in the pathway, of which there are many, between glucose at one end and pyruvic and lactic acids at the other, was largely the work of a husband and wife team, Carl and Gerti Cori, who began work in Prague but later came to Washington University in St. Louis. Among other accomplishments they identified the actual structure of the phosphate-sugar compounds which Harden had described only in vague terms.

What about the aerobic part of respiration? The clues and much of the evidence here was obtained by a remarkable Hungarian, Albert Szent-Györgyi, who has become the patron saint (perhaps not surprising with his name) of Woods Hole, Massachusetts, and a remarkable German, Hans Krebs, who became a professor at Oxford. The final hydrogen runoff was worked out by Otto Warburg, David Keilin, and others. Most recently, the actual link between the glycolytic pathway and the citric acid cycle has been established by Fritz Lipmann.

Szent-Györgyi was interested in investigating the oxygen-requiring part of respiration in muscles. He minced muscle and placed it in a Warburg flask with oxygen. At first, oxygen was consumed rapidly, but gradually this slowed to a halt. Szent-Györgyi speculated that maybe something was being used up, and since it was by then well known that working muscles produce lactic acid, he guessed it might be some compound that was on the pathway between lactic acid and CO_2 and water. After many attempts he finally discovered four substances which restored oxygen uptake. They were all short-chain organic acids — succinic, fumaric, malic, and oxaloacetic. Because any one of the four would work, he concluded correctly not only that they are on the pathway from glycolysis to CO_2 and water, but that they were probably in some kind of a series and could be formed from each other.

At this point, **Hans Krebs,** who had been working on how amino acids are broken down and utilized as sources of energy, left that problem and took up the investigation of aerobic respiration. He found that in addition to the four four-carbon acids (succinic, fumaric, malic, and oxaloacetic) which Szent-Györgyi had discovered would restore oxygen uptake in muscle brei, there were several six-carbon acids, notably citric acid, which would do the same thing. Then, in a series of brilliant experiments, he showed how all these acids fit together in a circle, and that fresh fuel — i.e., material from pyruvic acid — enters the circle by uniting with oxaloacetic acid which is the last in the ring. When the new material unites with oxaloacetic acid it forms more citric acid which is thus the beginning of this circular series. From citric acid all the others are formed until finally oxaloacetic acid is reached and the cycle is ready to begin again. The evidence for this is obtained by several methods. Radioactive markers can be placed on certain acids and then the markers traced. By the use of appropriate inhibitors, such as described earlier in connection with enzymes, the cycle can be stopped at various points and the substances which accumulate discovered or the compounds identified which can be fed into the system and permit it to proceed, thus indicating that their location is after the roadblock in the circle.

What is the nature of the actual link between the glycolytic pathway and the citric acid cycle? Pyruvic acid at the lower end of the anaerobic series has three carbons but the material entering the citric acid cycle has only two. Fritz Lipmann, working in Germany, Denmark, and finally the United States, found the answer to this question. Pyruvic acid loses CO_2, making the acetyl radical CH_3C—. This acetyl group unites with coenzyme-A, forming a compound called acetyl Co-A. The four-carbon oxaloacetic acid unites with the two carbons of the acetyl group, forming the six-carbon citric acid. Acetyl Co-A stands at one of the chief metabolic crossroads because derivatives from lipids, amino acids, and other organic compounds enter the citric acid cycle here.

What about **terminal respiration,** that portion at the very end of the series with nucleotides and cytochromes? This is the part which permits the citric acid cycle to keep running by taking care of its waste hydrogens and their electrons, and incidentally produces three more ATP's. The discovery of this part of the process was largely the work of Warburg and Keilin.

After he had devised his famous respirometer, **Warburg** began to investigate the rate at which tissues and carbohydrates and amino acids use oxygen. He found that charcoal containing iron, which is true of charcoal made from dried blood, acted as a catalyst speeding up oxygen consumption in his respirometer. Charcoal which lacked iron—charcoal from sugar, for example—failed to do this. He concluded, therefore, that some iron-containing compound was an essential catalyst for respiration. He went on to show that his iron-containing charcoal plus carbohydrate made an amazingly useful "model" of cellular respiration. Cyanide in very low concentrations inhibits cellular respiration. Very low concentrations of cyanide also inhibited his models. Anesthetics which inhibit cellular respiration only in high concentrations behaved in the same way towards his models. Perhaps most important, he showed that iron was the metal involved rather than some other, say copper. Carbon monoxide will inhibit cellular respiration in the dark but not in the light. This was true also of the action of carbon monoxide on his model. Copper complexes, on the other hand, are indifferent to light or dark.

From such facts Warburg concluded that there is an enzyme containing iron which makes it possible for foodstuffs to be oxidized in the presence of free oxygen. He went on to isolate this enzyme which he called "the respiratory enzyme." It was the first enzyme known that was concerned in aerobic respiration. All the others were enzymes of fermentation.

Meanwhile, **David Keilin** in Cambridge rediscovered a faint reddish pigment in the wing muscles of honeybees and in yeast cells. It is always a safe bet that any substance found in two such widely separated organisms will turn out to be important. Keilin named the substance **cytochrome** (*cyto*, cell, + *chrome*, color). When in the oxidized condition, produced by bubbling oxygen through the solution containing the pigment, the cytochrome lost its color entirely. But if oxygen was excluded and the cytochrome kept in the reduced state, it appeared reddish and showed a characteristic absorption spectrum. If oxygen was readmitted, the bands of the spectrum faded away and the color disappeared. On analysis, cytochrome proved to be an iron-containing compound similar to hemoglobin. It is an iron-containing porphyrin attached to a protein.

The cytochrome story can be demonstrated with an elegant simplicity worthy of the ancient Greek philosopher-scientists. No apparatus more complicated than a test tube and a spectroscope are required. Merely hold a test tube with a rich suspension of yeast cells between a light source and the spectroscope and the characteristic bands will appear. Bubble oxygen through the suspension and they will disappear. Allow the yeast cells to use up the oxygen and the bands will reappear. Add a pinch of cyanide and the bands of the reduced cytochrome will remain, no matter how much oxygen you bubble through. Start with a fresh lot of yeast, add a drop or two of chloroform, and the cells will remain oxidized, as shown by the absence of any absorption bands, no matter how long you wait for the yeast to use up the oxygen.

But the really exciting facts came into view when cytochrome was compared with Warburg's respiratory enzyme. They both contained iron. They were both inhibited by cyanide and carbon monoxide. With these poisons cytochrome remained permanently reduced, i.e., reddish, no matter how much oxygen was bubbled through it. Ergo, Warburg's enzyme was an enzyme which oxidized cytochrome. Such an enzyme is called a **cytochrome oxidase** because it oxidizes cytochrome in the presence of free oxygen.

In addition, it was found that anesthetics which blocked "respiration"—at least, oxygen uptake—in Warburg's model, also blocked change in the cytochrome but held the cytochrome permanently oxidized. Anesthetics then block a different enzyme, one which reduces cytochrome. Reduction, it will be recalled, is the addition of hydrogen or electrons.

The enzyme blocked by anesthetics evidently grabs hydrogens or their electrons from something, presumably some breakdown product of a foodstuff, and hands them on to cytochrome. Such an enzyme which accepts hydrogens is commonly called a **dehydrogenase.** The series evidently runs from some substance by means of a dehydrogenase to cytochrome, and from cytochrome by means of an oxidase to oxygen. If hydrogens are somehow being moved along, what can the end product be in these circumstances but water? Subsequent work has shown that there are at least four slightly but significantly different cytochromes which act in series and that there are two nucleotides which stand between them and the Krebs cycle, in this terminal segment of the respiratory pathway.

Review of the Energy Pathway. The results of the work of many investigators in many parts of the world give the following picture of the main energy-yielding pathway.

Glycolysis, the Embden-Meyerhof anaerobic pathway. Glucose is the usual starting point. It is converted into glucose-6-phosphate (1) by the

The Glycolytic Pathway

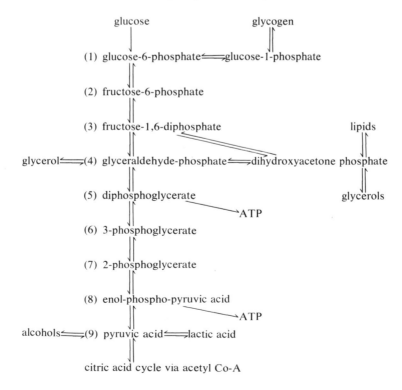

```
      H                    H                      H                      H
      H                    H   O                  H   O                  H   O
6   H—C—OH            H—C—O—P—OH            H—C—O—P—OH             H—C—O—P—OH   6
                               ‖                      ‖                      ‖
5   HO—C—H            HO—C—H   O            HO—C—H   O             HO—C—H   O   5

4   HO—C—H            HO—C—H                HO—C—H                 HO—C—H       4

3   H—C—OH            H—C—OH                H—C—OH                 H—C—OH       3

2   HO—C—H            HO—C—H                 C=O                    C=O   H     2
                                                                          O
1   H—C=O             H—C=O                HO—C—H                 H—C—O—P—OH    1
                                               H                     H   ‖
                                                                         O

    glucose        glucose-6-phosphate    fructose-6-phosphate    fructose-1,6-diphosphate
       (1)                                      (2)                      (3)
```

enzyme hexokinase in the presence of magnesium ions and ATP as a source of energy. Glucose-6-phosphate is so called because the phosphate is attached by the sixth carbon in the glucose molecule. (Glycogen, animal starch, is another common initial compound. It is converted into glucose-1-phosphate, which is then changed into glucose-6-phosphate.)

Glucose-6-phosphate is converted into fructose-6-phosphate (2) to which is added another phosphate, this time to the first carbon, making fructose-1,6-diphosphate (3). The first and third changes require the expenditure of energy.

These are the phosphorylating reactions discovered by Harden. Many authors use the term phosphorylation to mean any reaction in which a phosphate radical, —HPO$_4$, is added to another compound. Others restrict it to those cases where the phosphate radical is connected by an energy-rich bond. The context will usually tell which is intended.

To return to fructose-1,6-diphosphate. This compound splits into two compounds, each with a single phosphate, namely, glyceraldehyde phosphate (4) (also called phospho-glyceraldehyde or PGAL) and dihydroxyacetone phosphate. These two compounds easily change into each other so there is a triangle here. Moreover, glyceraldehyde-P stands at one of the two chief metabolic crossroads in the entire pathway. By way of dihydroxyacetone-P it leads off into fats and alcohols or back from them into the energy-yielding pathway. Glyc-

eraldehyde-P can be formed from glucose via the route just outlined, from glycerol, in plants from early products of photosynthesis, and, of course, from dihydroxyacetone.

Continuing down the main pathway, glyceraldehyde-P is converted into diphosphoglycerate (5) in the presence of co-enzyme NAD (nicotinamide adenine dinucleotide). It is then converted into 3-phosphoglycerate (6) with the production of a molecule of ATP. This is converted into 2-phosphoglycerate (7) by changing the position of the phosphate group. This compound is converted, by the loss of a molecule of water, into a simpler compound enol-phospho-pyruvic acid (8), which becomes pyruvic acid (9), plus a second ATP.

The molecular structure of these compounds is not very complicated. Glyceraldehyde-phosphate consists of the three carbons of glycerol in a row with an aldehyde group,

$$—C\overset{\displaystyle O}{\diagup}\!\!\!\!\diagdown H,$$ at one end and a phosphate group at the other. The enol form of phospho-pyruvic acid is also simple.

```
HC=O              COOH            COOH

HC—OH             C—O—P            C=O
                  ‖
HC—O—P            CH              HCH
   H               H                H

glyceraldehyde-P  enol-phospho-pyruvic acid   pyruvic acid
     (4)                (8)                       (9)
```

Aerobic respiration. Aerobic respiration includes the citric acid or Krebs cycle and terminal respiration. This portion of the metabolic pathway of energy production begins with the formation of **acetyl coenzyme-A** from pyruvic acid. The two-carbon acetyl group leaves the coenzyme and unites with the four-carbon oxaloacetic acid in the citric acid cycle to produce the six-carbon citric acid molecule, as already described (page 60). It will be recalled that acetyl Co-A is the second major metabolic crossroads in the pathway since not only the breakdown products of carbohydrates enter the system at this point but also products from amino acids and lipids.

The Citric Acid Krebs Cycle

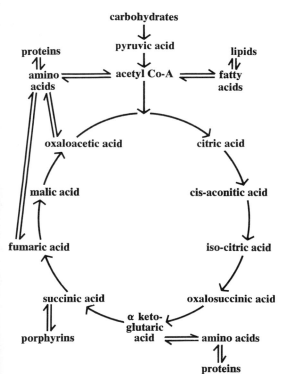

Coenzyme-A was discovered by **Fritz Lipmann,** who had studied under Meyerhof at Heidelberg. Lipmann was a refugee from the Nazis who migrated first to Denmark and then to the United States ending in the Rockefeller Institute in New York. He found that some phosphate bonds have only a low energy yield when broken while others have a high energy yield and thus elucidated the role of ATP, adenosine triphosphate. Coenzyme-A, which was found as something which controlled the entrance of pyruvic acid into the citric acid cycle, turned out to be similar to ATP. It is a very large molecule, consisting of adenine, ribose, three phosphates, the vitamin pantothenic acid, and thiol (sulfur-containing) ethylamine. The tiny two-carbon acetyl radical is linked on by the sulfur. Small wonder the complex is usually called merely acetyl Co-A!

The citric acid cycle is made up of four six-carbon acids (citric, cis-aconitic, iso-citric, and oxalo-succinic), one five-carbon acid (alpha keto-glutaric acid), and the four four-carbon acids discovered by Szent-Györgyi (succinic, fumaric, malic, and oxaloacetic). Once again the structure of the acids is rather simple.

$$H_3C-C- \qquad \begin{matrix} COOH \\ | \\ C=O \\ | \\ H-C-H \\ | \\ COOH \end{matrix} \qquad \begin{matrix} H \\ | \\ H-C-COOH \\ | \\ HO-C-COOH \\ | \\ H-C-COOH \\ | \\ H \end{matrix}$$

acetyl radical   oxaloacetic acid   citric acid

By a series of dehydrogenations, decarboxylations (removal of CO_2), condensations, splittings, etc., a total of 33 moles of ATP's are produced for every mole of sugar which enters the process as pyruvic acid. Carbon dioxide, water, hydrogen ions, and electrons are given off as wastes.

Both alpha keto-glutaric acid and succinic acid are notable. Alpha keto-glutaric acid is another point at which amino acid breakdown products may enter the system and is the starting point in the formation of amino acids by transamination, that is, the transfer of an amino group from one molecule to another. Succinic acid forms the backbone of porphyrin, an important prosthetic group for hemoglobin, cytochrome, and other compounds.

Let us now consider **terminal respiration.** This expression refers to the enzymatic pathway over which the electrons travel which have been separated from the hydrogen atoms split off from the various acids in the citric acid cycle. The hydrogen ions themselves enter the water and make it more acid until they and the electrons are united with oxygen in the formation of water. The first molecules in the electron transport system are nicotinamides, followed by flavins, followed by the cytochromes. It is of interest to note that the nicotinamide, NAD, nicotinamide adenine dinucleotide, is a nucleotide related to the stuff of which chromosomes are made. The nicotinamide derives from the vitamin nicotinic acid which is one of the substances produced from the amino acid tryptophan. The next molecule is FAD, flavin adenine dinucleotide. The flavin is derived from riboflavin, once called vitamin B_2. In both cases the adenine is one of the purines which make up part of the genetic code in nucleic acid, and the nucleotides are similar to the breakdown products of nucleic acids — namely, adenine plus ribose, plus a phosphate group.

The four cytochromes are protein-porphyrin complexes. The atom in the center of the porphyrin is iron so these are iron porphyrins like hemoglobin. (See formula for hemoglobin shown on page 49.)

As a result of terminal respiration, the citric acid cycle is kept functioning and three additional moles of ATP are produced.

Thus a grand total of 38 moles of ATP, representing 38 × 8,000 (small) calories, is produced for each mole of glucose, which represents about 680,000 calories. Hence the overall efficiency is 304,000/680,000, or about 45 per cent.

ATP, adenosine triphosphate, is the key product of both anaerobic and aerobic respiration and is the way energy is packaged and transported within cells regardless of whether the energy will be used in the synthesis of more complex molecules, the contraction of a muscle, the doing of osmotic work, or the lighting of a firefly. Its structure is shown below. The energy-rich bonds are indicated by waved lines.

All of the enzymes of the aerobic portion of the pathway are located within mitochondria. As explained previously, this can be demonstrated by separating the mitochondria from other cell components by differential centrifugation. The enzymes are either on or in the membranes of the mitochondria. Perhaps they form part of the membrane. They may also be lined up in a way that facilitates the sequential reactions which these enzymes bring about. If mitochondria are broken up into small pieces, the activity of their enzymes is drastically reduced. This indicates that their structure is very important to their functioning. Thus we return to the union of structure and function but now on the submicroscopic, molecular level.

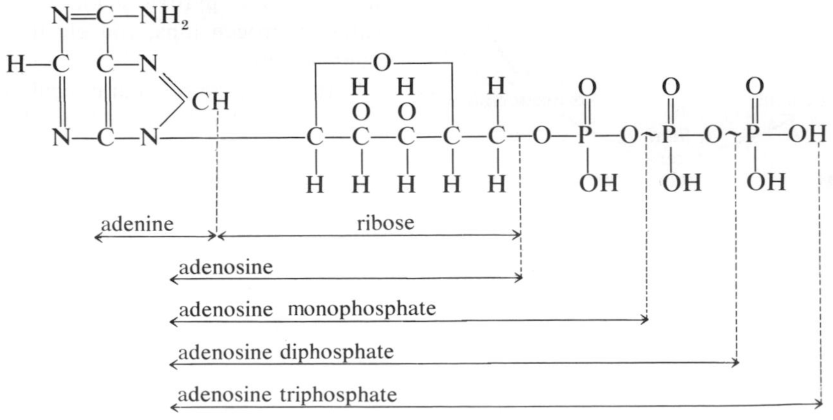

Review and References

REVIEW TOPICS

1. In what ways is the analogy of life to a flame useful? Misleading?

2. What are the three primary activities living things need energy for?

3. Write the formula for pentose in four ways. What is a glycoside? A glycoside bond?

4. Write the formula for a short-chain, unsaturated fatty acid. What are some important functions of lipids in addition to food storage?

5. What is a "simple" protein? What is the role of proteins in membranes? Distinguish between primary, secondary, and tertiary protein structure.

6. Write the formulas of five amino acids, indicating the alpha carbons. What is a peptide bond? Why is tryptophan important?

7. What was the chief contribution of: Emil Fischer, Pasteur, Eduard Buchner, Albert Szent-Györgyi, Fred Sanger, Friedrich Miescher, James Sumner?

8. How do enzymes work? What is the evidence? What two kinds of enzyme inhibition are known? Give examples.

9. Distinguish fully between glycolysis and the citric acid cycle. What is a mole of ATP? What is the link between aerobic and anaerobic respiration?

10. What is fermentation and how is it related to the main energy pathway?

11. What did David Keilin discover in the wing muscles of honeybees and how could you show something about its role in respiration?

12. What are the first three phosphated sugar compounds in the glycolytic series? From where do they obtain their precursors in addition to glucose?

13. Where may breakdown products of proteins enter the energy-yielding pathways?

14. What is the structure of coenzyme-A and what is its function?

15. What is the formula of ATP and what is its function?

USEFUL REFERENCES

Benfey, O. T., *From Vital Force to Structural Formulas,* Boston, Houghton Mifflin Company, 1964.

Lehninger, A. L., *The Mitochondrion,* New York, W. A. Benjamin, 1964.

Loewy, A. G., and P. Siekevitz, *Cell Structure and Function,* New York, Holt, Rinehart & Winston, 1963.

McElroy, W. D., *Cell Physiology and Biochemistry,* 2nd ed., Englewood Cliffs, N.J., Prentice-Hall, 1964.

Schrödinger, E., *What is Life?* New York, The Macmillan Company, 1945.

Stern, H., and D. L. Nanney, *The Biology of Cells,* New York, John Wiley & Sons, 1965.

Part II

Primitive Phyla

The protozoa, sponges, coelenterates, and ctenophores are commonly regarded as primitive, and indeed they are. Yet a human egg placed in a glass dish with the proper salt solution will become amoeboid and show the same four cytoplasmic layers that *Amoeba proteus* possesses. A ciliate, *Tetrahymena,* not very different from *Paramecium,* has almost exactly the same nutritional requirements as a man. The Krebs cycle of respiration takes place in the mitochondria of a protozoan just as it does anywhere else. Among coelenterates, many jellyfish reproduce by one of several types of asexual processes, but all jellyfish are either male or female and reproduce by eggs and sperms at some point in their life cycle. Coelenterates possess most of the basic differentiations common to higher animals — muscular and nervous systems, including sense organs, and digestive and reproductive systems. In fact, some of the oceanic jellyfish are equipped with eyes having refractile lenses and cup-shaped retinas.

There is a story, relevant here, about E. B. Wilson, the first great American investigator of cell structure, who taught invertebrate zoology at Columbia University for many years. He began his course in the fall with the protozoa but when May came and the course was drawing to a close, the class would only be finishing their study of the coelenterates. Professor Wilson felt that if a student had thoroughly studied the protozoa and the coelenterates, he had met all the important problems in zoology and could then, if he were any good at all, work out a knowledge of any of the other groups on his own. This is not quite the outlook of the author of this book — but Professor Wilson had a real point. As you read the next chapters, judge for yourself to what extent Wilson was right.

Chapter 4

Protozoa

Ever since the work of Max Schultze of Bonn in the 1860's, it has been evident that protozoans are essentially one-celled animals. During the course of evolution some species have developed certain devices which enable them partially to overcome the limitations set for single cells. For this reason some authors prefer to define the Protozoa as noncellular animals. But this is largely a verbal question.

It is only necessary to compare an amoeba with one of the cells of a metazoan—for example, a cell taken from an early frog or human embryo—to see how close and detailed the similarity is. If the cell of an early embryo be placed in dilute salt solution, it will become amoeboid and wander about. This is not to say that it becomes identical with *Amoeba proteus* or any other species of *Amoeba;* far from it. But examination will reveal a basic identity of organization.

1. In both, the outermost layer of cytoplasm constitutes a thin cytoplasmic membrane or **plasmalemma.**

2. Immediately within this membrane in both cases is a clear or hyaline layer of cytoplasm.

3. Within this, in both cases, is a granular layer of relatively stiff jellied cytoplasm called **plasmagel.**

4. The central region, again in both cases, is a granular cytoplasm which is fluid and called the **plasmasol.**

5. Lastly, within this central fluid cytoplasm is the nucleus.

In an amoeba the surface membrane (plasmalemma) and the clear hyaline layer are sometimes called ectoplasm, and the granular layers of plasmagel and plasmasol, endoplasm. Unfortunately other competent authors refer to the plasmagel as ectoplasm and the plasmasol as endoplasm. Consequently, the terms ecto- and endoplasm are to be avoided.

In the course of hundreds of millions of years, different populations of protozoans have evolved in many different directions. There is at least as much diversity among the Protozoa as there is among all the different kinds of birds or mammals. Yet all this extraordinary diversity is achieved within the limitations of size imposed by a single cell. The largest Protozoa, like some of the big ciliated ones and some of the amoebas, escape to a slight degree from the limitation imposed by the volume of cytoplasm which one nucleus can serve by having several nuclei or a special giant macronucleus. But even these large protozoans are still semi-microscopic.

The main difference between the metazoans and the protozoans is this: in metazoans, like jellyfish or men, size and complexity are attained by grouping together many cells, with individual cells narrowly specialized. Each metazoan nucleus governs a discrete mass of

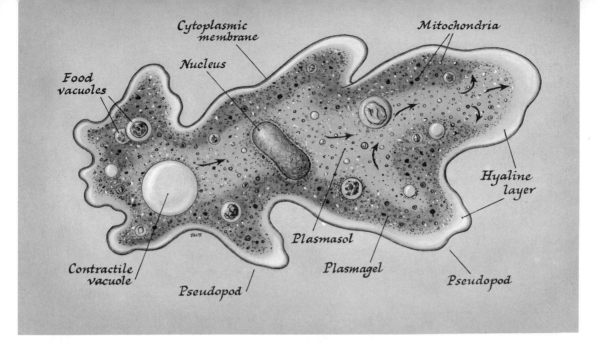

Fig. 4–1. *Amoeba proteus.* Observe that only the plasmasol flows.

specialized cytoplasm containing muscle fibers, or bearing cilia, or producing pigment, but not doing all three. In the protozoan, one nucleus governs a mass of cytoplasm with many different specializations. Contractile fibers, cilia, and pigment granules may all be present in the same cell.

Importance. Protozoa are important in at least four ways. Many are pathogens producing serious diseases of man and domestic animals. The list of protozoan diseases is a long one. Malaria, which afflicts more people than any other single disease, African sleeping sickness, and amoebic dysentery are three familiar ones. Second, the protozoans are extremely useful as tool animals in basic research. They have been employed extensively in investigating problems of sex and reproduction and the biochemical side of nutrition. Occasionally protozoans are of economic importance, though this is usually indirect. For example, the fossil shells of a group of protozoans known as Foraminifera are widely used as guides in drilling for oil. Lastly, the world of the protozoans has a fascination of its own, like the study and collection of pheasants or gems.

Classification. Between 30,000 and 50,000 species of Protozoa have been described. They fall into five major groups based primarily on their method of locomotion. The **Sarcodina** move by means of pseudopodia, flowing cytoplasmic fingers. The familiar *Amoeba* belongs in this group. The **Flagellata** like *Euglena* are characterized by the possession of one or more flagella, long protoplasmic whiplike structures by which they move. The **Ciliata**, like *Paramecium,* move by cilia, tiny hairlike threads of protoplasm covering the cell surface. The **Sporozoa,** like *Plasmodium,* the malarial parasite, generally lack specialized organs of locomotion and are usually intracellular parasites during some period of their life history. Last is a small group, the **Suctoria.** In them a motile ciliated young stage is followed by an adult attached to a stalk and bearing "tentacles."

SARCODINA

The Sarcodina (*sarkos,* flesh) or Rhizopoda is the class of Protozoa to which *Amoeba* belongs. It is a very large and diverse group. Its simpler members may closely resemble the form in which life first appeared on this planet, although many zoologists believe this distinction belongs to the flagellates or perhaps to viruslike units. Despite their enormous diversity encompassing many thousands of species, all the Sarcodina are characterized in two ways.

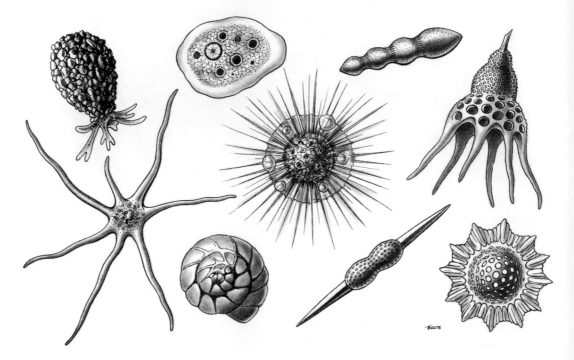

Fig. 4–2. Diverse protozoans of the Class Sarcodina, to which the amoebas belong. These specimens give some idea of the immense variety of the group.

1. They are either **irregular** blobs of protoplasm with no permanent symmetry or they have a **radial symmetry,** like a ball or a tree. They lack the permanently defined anterior-posterior axis that the flagellates and the ciliates possess.

2. Their means of locomotion consists of flowing protoplasmic extensions, falsefeet or **pseudopods.** These pseudopods vary all the way from one or two broad, tonguelike structures to fine spun threads of protoplasm which may radiate like conventionalized sun rays. The Sarcodina never possess cilia, although many species at some time in their life history have one or two flagella. In actuality there are so many amoebalike species which are permanently flagellated and so many flagellates which regularly lose their flagella during part of their life cycle that the distinction between sarcodinans and flagellates is regarded by some protozoologists as an arbitrary one based largely on convenience.

Like other groups of Protozoa, the Sarcodina are abundant in both fresh-water and marine environments. A very few species are parasitic. The most familiar of these protozoans are the various species of *Amoeba* which are commonly found among the debris on the bottom of quiet ponds. The largest species is big enough to see with the unaided eye—so big it can ingest 20 parameciums in a single food vacuole. This giant amoeba illustrates the fact that when a protozoan exceeds a certain size it is either multinucleate or possesses a large macronucleus. This "giant" has anywhere from several to over 100 nuclei. It also illustrates the present unsatisfactory state of zoological nomenclature. Because of various uncertainties, it is known by four different names: *Amoeba carolinensis, Chaos carolinensis, Chaos chaos,* and *Pelomyxa carolinensis,* to list them alphabetically.

Some fresh-water amoebas secrete little shells or "tests" in which they live, and still others cement minute stones together to make houses.

One of the few pathogenic species is *Endamoeba histolytica,* the cause of amoebic dysentery. The most complex sarcodinans anatomically are the marine Radiolaria, many of which form radial skeletons of incredible intricacy. A similar but simpler group, called Heliozoa, lives in fresh water.

Locomotion. The amoeboid movement by which the amoebas and their relatives move from place to place has fascinated zoologists for generations. Not only is it a remarkable thing to watch, but it involves basic problems including the mechanism of cell division. White blood cells, leucocytes, also move by amoeboid movement.

This type of movement is still far from completely understood, but important progress has been made. Many of the older German investigators believed that surface tension played an important part. It is possible to make a drop of oil or mercury send out "pseudopods" and move from place to place by touching one spot on the surface with any agent which lowers the surface tension. The "pseudopod" flows out where the surface has been weakened. Such procedures make a drop of mercury look very lively indeed. However, meticulous observation showed that with the oil or mercury, any particle of dirt that happened to be stuck to the surface was pulled by the contracting surface away from the advancing edge of the pseudopod, but this is not true of the cytoplasmic pseudopods of a living animal. Particles stuck to the surface of a living pseudopod either remain stationary with respect to the foundation on which the amoeba is moving or they move forward. Consequently localized differences in surface tension can be ruled out as the cause of amoeboid movement.

At present there are two different though closely related theories about amoeboid movement. The oldest theory, dating back to Dujardin (circa 1835) and Schultze (circa 1875), is that protoplasmic contractility is the major factor in amoeboid motion. The other theory, developed by American students of Protozoa like Jennings, Hyman, and Mast in the first half of this century, places emphasis on the reversibility of the gel and the sol phases of the colloidal cytoplasm.

Let us first consider the old theory of protoplasmic contractility. If you observe an amoeba like *Arcella,* which lives in a little shell, you will notice that when it moves, a pencillike pseudopod first flows out to a length of somewhat more than the diameter of the shell. (See Fig. 4–3.) The end adheres to the bottom, the pseudopod contracts, and pulls the body of the amoeba and its shell toward the point of attachment. A similar thing can be seen in Sarcodina like the heliozoans and foraminiferans, which send out thin threads of cytoplasm like sunrays.

Added to these old observations are newer lines of evidence. If the long end of a pseudopod be cut off with a thin glass thread, the cut surface will heal together, leaving the severed end as a miniature amoeba composed of merely the cytoplasmic membrane, i.e., the plasmalemma, enclosing some of the clear hyaline layer of the amoeba. It includes no gel and no granular cytoplasm whatever, and of course no nucleus. Yet such a fragment will crawl around by amoeboid movement for many hours! On the biochemical level, it is said that contractile proteins like those found in muscles have been extracted from some of the giant amoeboid organisms known as Mycetozoa which have thousands of nuclei and spread out over damp and decaying wood as thin plasmodium sometimes the size of a half dollar.

The reversible sol-gel theory of amoeboid movement is based on equally valid observations. If an advancing pseudopod of an amoeba like *Amoeba proteus* be watched, it will be seen that in the center of the pseudopod is a stream of flowing granular protoplasm. Tiny crystals, mitochondria, food vacuoles, and the nucleus are carried forward pell-mell by this stream.

Fig. 4–3. *Arcella,* showing the helmetlike shell and extruded pseudopod.

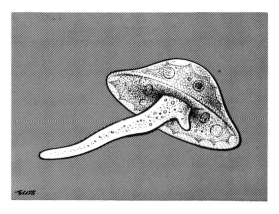

Around the edges of the stream and completely enclosing it as a tube or sleeve (remember the pseudopod is more or less cylindrical) is a continuous layer of protoplasm in the gel phase and in which the granules remain stationary. At the advancing end, the central core of flowing protoplasm spreads out sideways and solidifies, thus elongating the gel sleeve. Some German biologists have likened this to a magic fountain in which the water freezes as it falls and so instead of splashing builds up a collar of ice. At the posterior end of the amoeba the inner surface of the gel can be seen becoming fluid and adding itself to the forward flowing stream.

What makes the fountain flow? The answer is not completely known, but part of the answer seems to be the contraction of the plasma membrane. The newly formed end of the pseudopod adheres to some substrate, say a glass slide or a leaf. Then a wave of constriction passes backward over the surface, in some way squeezing the contents forward. It may be that in an intact amoeba the gel contracts as well as the plasma membrane. Calcium is essential for amoeboid movement. This can be easily demonstrated in marine amoebas by placing them in sea water from which the calcium ions have been removed. It is worth noting that calcium is also essential for muscular contraction.

Where the contraction waves end at the "tail" of the amoeba they often leave irregular little masses of cytoplasm. Such an aggregation is called a **uroid** (*oura,* tail). They are more prominent in some species of *Amoeba* than in others. They can also be seen well in some of the very actively amoeboid white blood cells. From time to time the uroid is completely pinched off and a new one begins to form.

Behavior. The variety of responses to stimuli possible for an animal that moves by pseudopods is limited and hence the behavior of amoebas and other sarcodinans is simple. A floating amoeba extends long thin pseudopods in many directions. If one comes in contact with a solid object it adheres and the animal proceeds to crawl along it. If an amoeba comes in contact with another animal smaller than itself, or with various algae, it will flow around and over the prey and enclose it within a food vacuole.

To most stimuli an amoeba responds negatively by moving away. The characteristics of response are closely similar to those in the higher animals and man.

1. There must be an adequate stimulus. In the case of light, the adequate stimulus is a more or less sudden change in intensity. If an amoeba moves into a region of brighter light, or if a beam of light is suddenly focused on the advancing lip of a pseudopod, the movement ceases and the animal will move off in another direction.

2. There is a latent period between the application of the stimulus and the first visible response. The stronger the stimulus, the shorter is this period.

3. Finally comes the response itself. In the case of a sudden enough increase in light intensity this is a gelation of the protoplasm, which stops the advance of the pseudopod.

When subjected to direct electric current, an amoeba will withdraw the pseudopods on the side toward the anode (positive) and move toward the cathode (negative). The amoeboid end of an outgrowing nerve fiber behaves in a similar way.

The most remarkable and in many ways instructive case of social behavior in amoebas is seen in the *Mycetozoa* or slime molds. This is a group of amoeboid organisms usually regarded as animals by zoologists and as plants by botanists, for during one part of their life they have the form of amoebas while at another stage they produce spores in structures with cellulose walls like those of plant cells. However, this proves little inasmuch as cellulose is characteristic of a large group of animals, the tunicates, which are very closely related to the vertebrates. And on the other hand, some molds, admitted universally to be plants, instead of cellulose secrete chitin, which is the material used by ants and other arthropods as the basis of their skeletons.

The amoebas of the mycetozoa are rather small but otherwise ordinary looking amoebas. They reproduce by mitosis and pay no attention to each other until the population reaches a certain density and the food supply falls. At such a time, here and there, certain individuals act as centers of attraction. Other amoebas crawl toward them, forming branching streams

Fig. 4 – 4. Mycetozoan amoebas crawling together to form a reproductive structure.

joining each other and all flowing in toward the center. At this center the amoebas pile up. Finally a long stalk arises, bearing on its tip a clump of spores or reproductive bodies. The whole process looks something like a miniature volcano working in reverse, with the branching streams of lava running uphill and building the volcanic cone.

What attracts these originally solitary amoebas? It has recently been discovered that they secrete a chemical which has been called acrasin from Acrasina, the suborder to which *Dictyostelium,* the slime mold used, belongs. Here and there an individual amoeba, a shade more crowded or starved than the rest, begins to secrete acrasin. Others then move toward it and begin secreting acrasin too. Thus the process snowballs as more and more amoebas move toward the center.

Skeleton. Exoskeletons secreted on the outside of the animal, and also endoskeletons secreted within its body, are found among the sarcodinans. Many common fresh-water amoebas like *Arcella* secrete an exoskeleton in the form of a hemispherical chitinous shell or test, with a single opening through which one or more pseudopods protrude. Set in the chitinous matrix of the shell are siliceous prisms like minute tiles. Other common genera like *Difflugia* secrete a chitinous shell to which tiny sand grains or other material adhere.

The foraminiferans are well known not only as indicators in identifying oil-bearing rocks, but for the remarkable variety of exoskeletons they produce on a single simple pattern, that of a small chamber to which others, each a little larger, are added. Some species of "forams" secrete a chitinous base to which they stick

Fig. 4 – 5. Shells of representative foraminiferans.

minute grains of sand. Others secrete tiny shells, pierced by numerous minute openings or foramina through which the filamentous pseudopods are extruded. These foramina give the order its name.

Complex and beautiful endoskeletons, more intricate than the wildest imagining, are produced by an oceanic group of the Sarcodina called radiolarians. This old taxonomic group, it is now realized, really consists of two, one related to the fresh-water Heliozoa and the other to some protozoans to be discussed later, the dinoflagellates; but both produce remarkable skeletons. Figure 4–6 is taken from the monumental study that Ernst Haeckel (1834–1919), the noted German evolutionary theorist and popularizer, made of the specimens collected on the famous voyage of *H.M.S. Challenger*. Only in the sponges can anything comparable to these endoskeletons be found in the whole sweep of the animal kingdom. The problems such structures present will be discussed in connection with sponges.

Nutrition. The nutrition of amoeba and its numerous relatives is **heterotrophic** (*heteros,* other, + *tropho,* food), that is, they are dependent on other organisms for their food. Other organisms, even animals as large as a paramecium, become entangled in their pseudopods and enclosed in a fluid-filled cavity, a **food vacuole,** within their cytoplasm. Sometimes the pseudopod flows around the prey without the victim appearing to be aware of what is happening. At other times the victim appears to be temporarily immobilized the instant it comes in contact with the plasma membrane.

The progress of digestion can be watched while hydrolytic enzymes cause the animal in the food vacuole to dissolve. The changing pH of the food vacuole may be traced by feeding the amoeba food stained with an indicator that changes color with changing pH. As in the human digestive tract, the pH is first acid and then alkaline. The amino acids and other nutrients obtained from the food are absorbed through the membrane of the vacuole into the cytoplasm. A discussion of nutrient requirements and what happens to the absorbed foodstuffs will be postponed to the sections on flagellates and ciliates, groups in which many discoveries

of nutritional and physiological importance have been made.

The indigestible residue of the prey remains in the shrunken vacuole and is finally left behind, usually by the pinching off of a uroid at the posterior end of the amoeba. The process of eliminating undigested material is called egestion.

Excretion. In common with fresh-water protozoans in general, an amoeba has a conspicuous organelle, its **contractile vacuole.** The function of this remarkable structure, as it rhythmically swells and bursts to the exterior and then swells again, is the excretion of excess water which is continually being drawn into the cell by osmotic forces. If a protozoan is placed in solutions of increasing osmotic pressures, less and less water will pass into the cell and the rate of pulsation of the vacuole decreases until, when the osmotic concentration of the environment equals that within the cell, the contractile vacuole ceases to function altogether. The fact that marine protozoans generally lack contractile vacuoles supports this view, because of the relatively high osmotic concentration of sea water. Metabolic wastes, such as CO_2, diffuse out through the plasma membrane around the entire cell.

What is the mechanism that works a contractile vacuole? No complete answer can be given. If a protozoan is subjected to a little cyanide, the action of the contractile vacuole ceases. Of course, the animal itself continues to have a higher osmotic concentration of substances inside its cell membrane than there is in the surrounding medium, and as a result, when poisoned with cyanide, it continues to absorb water until it swells and bursts. Cyanide is known to inhibit definite respiratory enzymes, i.e., it cuts off most of the energy supply. This evidently means that energy is needed to push the water out of the cytoplasm against osmotic pressure into the vacuole. According to this theory, the problem of how a contractile vacuole functions is part of the general problem of secretion.

Reproduction. The common amoebas like *Amoeba proteus* reproduce, so far as is known, solely by asexual cell division, specifically by

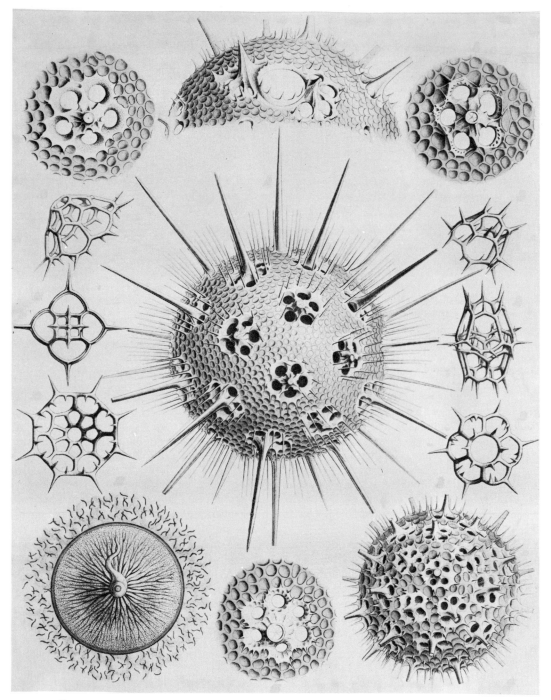

Fig. 4–6. Radiolarians taken from the high seas by the famous *H.M.S. Challenger* expedition (1872–1876). This set of drawings appeared in the original *Challenger Report*.

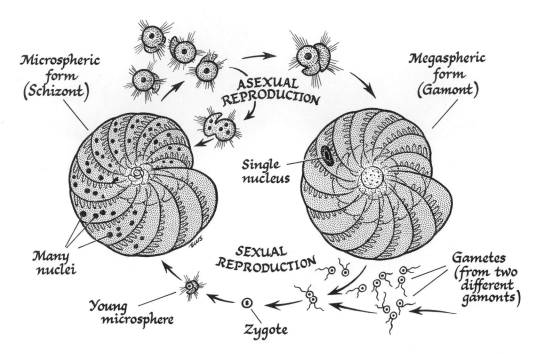

Fig. 4–7. Life cycle of a "foram." An asexual (schizont) individual is on the left and a sexual (gamont) individual on the right.

mitosis. Amoebas like *Arcella* have a special problem because of their shells. In *Arcella* the nucleus divides mitotically and half of the protoplasm and one nucleus flows out of the shell, rounds up, and secretes another shell like the first. One daughter cell thus forms a new shell and one keeps the old one. Many amoebas produce rounded cysts with protective walls when conditions become unfavorable. This is true of *Endamoeba histolytica*.

Many sarcodinans, however, reproduce both asexually by mitosis and sexually by the fusion of gametes or germ cells. The sexual forms are often flagellated. This is the case in foraminiferans and radiolarians. Such cells, whether flagellated or merely amoeboid, act as gametes and they fuse to produce a zygote and a new generation.

In the "forams" a beautiful reproductive cycle has been evolved. There are two slightly different body forms. In one, the original chamber of the shell is larger than in the other. Consequently the two forms are known as **mega-** and **microspheric.** The microspheric individuals are also known as **schizonts** (a

term to be met later in connection with the malarial parasite). The schizonts are multinucleate. When they attain maximum size they break up asexually into hundreds of tiny amoebas which develop into more schizonts.

A time comes, however, when for unknown reasons some of the offspring of the schizonts do not develop into more schizonts but into megaspheric **gamonts.** These remain uninucleate until they attain maximum size, when the nucleus and cytoplasm divide repeatedly and ultimately form thousands of biflagellate gametes. The gametes from two different gamonts fuse in pairs, forming zygotes, or fertilized eggs, which in turn grow into schizonts.

FLAGELLATA

All the flagellates or Mastigophora possess one or more flagella during most or all of their life history. This is not a rigorous criterion (there is none), because many flagellates have amoeboid stages and many Sarcodina at some time bear flagella. However, for practical purposes it is a very useful distinction.

Flagellates are extremely abundant in fresh water and in the ocean; some cause serious diseases. They are also of interest because they may be the original form in which life arose on this planet; and in such colonial species as *Volvox* they show in simple form some basic problems of metazoan life. Their vitamin requirements and metabolism have been intensively investigated in connection with problems of evolution and in seeking ways to control pathogenic, i.e., disease-producing, species.

Among the easiest free-living flagellates to find and study are the numerous species of *Euglena.* Euglenas often form velvety green films over soft mud on the edges of ponds, especially small barnyard ponds. One species, *Euglena rubra,* forms red pigment granules in its cytoplasm and may cover a pond as a bright red scum. The significance of the red pigment is unknown. Some flagellates possess the green pigment chlorophyll. Many lack chlorophyll and are colorless, like *Peranema,* a form often studied in the laboratory. Some become colonial, like *Volvox,* which is a sphere with as many as 10,000 cells.

Among the commonest microorganisms of the ocean are the **dinoflagellates.** Many are lu-minous and most of the tiny sparks of light seen in sea water originate from them. *Noctiluca* is the best known of the luminous genera. It is a large spheroid form with vacuolated cytoplasm and a long protoplasmic tentacle in addition to a flagellum. It is responsible for the "tapioca soup" occasionally seen in parts of the ocean.

In appearance, dinoflagellates resemble medieval armored helmets. They have two flagella. One extends out from the animal, the other encircles its "equator" in a groove called the girdle or **cingulus.** The famous "red tides" that cause the death of thousands of tons of fishes are due to vast swarms of dinoflagellates. Along the Florida coast the organism responsible is *Gymnodinium;* on the California coast, *Gonyaulax.* The latter is known to produce a toxic alkaloid. About 1 microgram of this substance, enough to kill a mouse, can be extracted from 3,000 of these dinoflagellates.

The numerous pathogenic and commensal species of flagellates will be discussed later.

Locomotion and Behavior. Most flagellates possess two flagella, one which extends anteriorly as the animal moves forward, and one which trails behind, although there are nu-

Fig. 4–8. Diverse protozoans of the Class Flagellata. Left to right: three species of *Euglena,* a rotund *Noctiluca,* an elongate dinoflagellate, a roundish *Gonyaulax,* and a trypanosome.

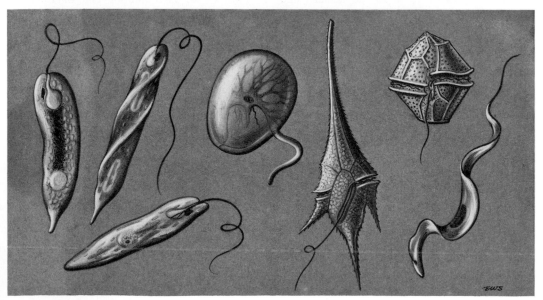

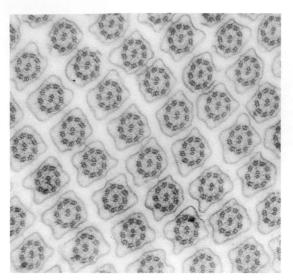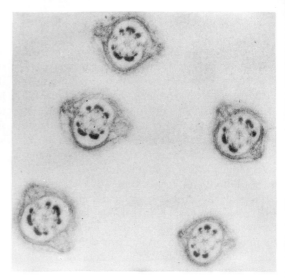

Fig. 4–9. Protozoan cilia and mammalian sperm tails reveal the same basic structure under the electron microscope. Left: cross section of a group of cilia of *Diplodinium*. Right: cross section of rat sperm tails. Note two central fibers surrounded by a circle of nine. Original magnification (left) 80,000×, (right) 42,500×. *(Kindness of L. E. Roth, H. Swift)*

merous species with but one and many others with a large number. Under the light microscope it is evident that the flagella of different species and even of the same animal vary greatly in length and thickness. They always appear to arise from a basal granule in the cytoplasm. There are many variations in different species. Often the basal granule is connected to the centrosome, a granule close to the nucleus and around which the mitotic aster forms.

Under an electron microscope all flagella appear to be virtually identical, and the distinction between a flagellum and a cilium is lost. The central core consists of two strands surrounded by a tubelike sheath; outside that is a circle of nine strands, which in turn is enclosed in a sheath. Somewhere, probably in the sheath, is a spiral structure.

The action of flagella is complicated and difficult to observe. In *Paranema*, which has an easily observed flagellum, the structure is held extended forward as a stiff rod of which only the extreme tip wiggles like a snake's tongue as the animal progresses. In *Euglena* the flagellum extends backwards at an angle of about 45° to the long axis of the body. Its beating pushes the animal forward and sideways, and causes it to rotate on its long axis. The result is that the animal gyrates forward as though following the path of an invisible corkscrew.

One of the most striking facts about *Euglena* and *Volvox* is the way they congregate on the illuminated side of a dish. How can these simple organisms do this? In *Euglena* there is, near the anterior end, a shallow cup-shaped red pigment spot (eyespot); and in each individual making up a volvox there is a similar pigmented

Fig. 4–10. The anterior end of *Euglena*. (Diagrammatic)

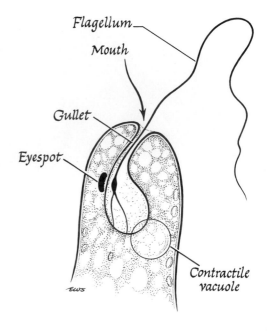

spot, only much more definitely cup-shaped. These pigment cups shield the light-sensitive material from light coming in the direction of the back or outside of the cup. Without such a shield, a euglena would have no means of detecting the direction from which light was coming, because the light-sensitive material would be stimulated by light rays from all directions.

In *Euglena,* the shallow cup is so oriented that the light-sensitive material is continually illuminated as long as the euglena is moving toward the light. If the direction of the light rays is changed so that the shadow of the cup falls on the photosensitive material, then the animal turns until the sensitive area is again illuminated. In *Euglena* the light receptor seems to be a swelling on one of the flagella just at the point where its basal part passes close by the pigment cup. For an organism that can carry on photosynthesis, the adaptive advantage of staying in the light is clear.

Nutrition and Excretion. Because flagellates may have been the original form of life, their nutrition, including their vitamin requirements, is of considerable interest. The amazing thing is that the nutrition of these one-celled animals is closely similar to man's. This is equally true of the ciliates. Research into the metabolism of flagellates has also been stimulated because it furnishes useful information about possible antimetabolites (poisons) that can be used against pathogenic species like the trypanosomes.

Some flagellates are **autotrophic** — that is, they synthesize their own food, others are **heterotrophic,** and still others can be either as their environment demands. The autotrophic species possess the green pigment chlorophyll which is able to use sunlight in order to split water and make its hydrogen available to unite with carbon dioxide. As a result, sugar is formed with oxygen as a waste product. The over-all formula for this process (known as **photosynthesis**) runs as follows:

$$6\ H_2O + 6\ CO_2 \xrightarrow[\text{sunlight}]{\text{chlorophyll}} C_6H_{12}O_6 + 6\ O_2$$

Such organisms thus derive their food directly from simple inorganic compounds without the intervention of other living things.

The heterotrophic flagellates like *Paranema* depend for their nutrition on other organisms which they ingest bodily. Under high powers of a compound microscope flagellates can be observed grazing on the bottom and pushing particles of food into their mouths. Sometimes the flagellum seems to help, sometimes the "lip" which is strengthened by a hairpinlike trichite. Flagellates also have the power of absorbing dissolved nutrients, a heterotrophic ability, often referred to as **saprozoic** (*sapros,* rotten) because such species live on dead plants and animals.

The best-known dietary requirement of flagellates is for thiamine (vitamin B_1). In man and other animals thiamine is essential for carbohydrate metabolism and without it, pyruvic acid ($CH_3COCOOH$), an important intermediary compound in carbohydrate metabolism, accumulates in the bloodstream, heart, and nerves until toxic concentrations are reached and death results.

When various saprozoic flagellates were tested — *Euglena pisciformis, Polytoma,* and *Chilomonas* — a curious situation was uncovered. Some species had to be supplied with thiamine and so are like a man in this respect. Other species could grow and multiply without thiamine, but only if they were supplied with pyrimidine and thiazole, the two halves of the thiamine molecule. Evidently they possess enzymes able to put the two halves together. The majority of colorless flagellates tested are more versatile. They can synthesize thiamine all the way from very simple inorganic beginnings. It is interesting to remember that pyrimidine is one of the constituents of the nucleotides that are built into the nucleic acids of the chromosomes.

The question then arises as to which are the more primitive, those species which have the least synthetic ability and are like mammals, or those which have the most and are in this respect like plants? Evidence is accumulating that the animals with the least synthetic ability are more primitive as far as their nutrition is concerned. We will meet this problem again with several different groups of animals.

Food is stored in *Euglena* and other flagellates in the form of round, oblong, or even link-shaped masses of paramylum or glycogen, the animal substitute for starch. Close to the gullet is a contractile vacuole which eliminates excess water.

Flagellate Reproduction. In asexual reproduction, the nucleus of a flagellate divides by mitosis, followed by a longitudinal division of the cytoplasm beginning at the anterior end. The flagella may be absorbed and then re-formed anew in each of the daughter cells, or one of the new cells may get the old flagella and the other form new ones. The possible fates of the eyespot are similar.

In sexual reproduction, two cells meet and fuse, a process called **syngamy,** since it is a coming together of two gametes. If the two gametes are alike in size, they are known as **isogametes;** if one is larger than the other, they are called **heterogametes,** the larger or macrogametes being regarded as eggs or ova. The small cells are microgametes or sperms. The product of syngamy, the fertilized egg, is the **zygote.** In flagellates the zygote often becomes covered with a protective cyst, able to withstand drying and other unfavorable conditions.

Reproduction in Volvox. Over 300 years ago, the immortal lens-grinder of Delft in Holland, Anton van Leeuwenhoek (1632–1700), discovered the creature, half plant, half animal, that is now called *Volvox.* It makes a handsome sight under a dissecting microscope where it is seen to be a revolving ball of glistening cells set on a hollow sphere of clear jelly. Volvox has fascinated generation after generation of biologists because it presents in simple form some of the fundamental problems of multicellular life that have to do with reproduction and development.

The body of the mature volvox consists of anywhere from a few hundred to over 50,000 cells, depending on the species. Each cell is biflagellate and resembles a euglena complete with eyespot and chloroplastid. Adjacent cells are connected by strands of cytoplasm. The cells at one pole of the spherical colony are appreciably smaller than elsewhere and their eyespots a bit larger. This pole normally is in front as the creature moves. Here are the beginnings of a cellular division of labor expressed as cellular differentiation.

In reproduction, either asexual or sexual, only certain cells near the equator take part. Thus in *Volvox* there can be seen for the first time the distinction between **germ cells** or Keimbahn and the nonreproductive cells, called collectively the **soma,** which do not participate directly in the continuity of life from one generation to the next. This distinction between somatic cells and germ cells was made pivotal in biological thinking by August Weismann (1834–1914) and has continued to play an important part in genetical and evolutionary theory ever since.

When a volvox reproduces asexually several cells at approximately equal distances around

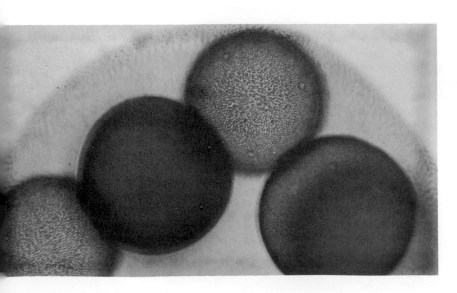

Fig. 4–11. *Volvox* with four living daughter colonies within the parent. *(Kindness of William H. Amos)*

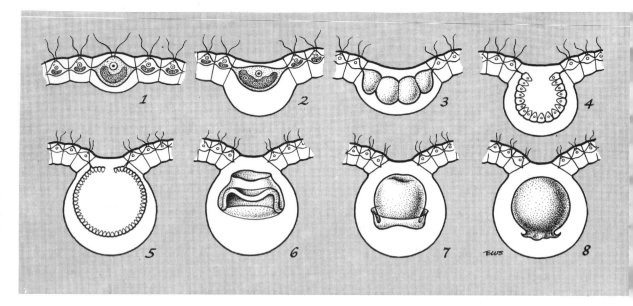

Fig. 4–12. *Volvox.* Eight stages in the development of a daughter colony from a single parental cell. By stage 3 the original large single cell has divided into several large cells. By stage 6 the process of turning inside out has been about half accomplished.

the equator enlarge. Then each undergoes a series of mitotic cell divisions and produces a little cup of cells depressed towards the interior of the colony. The polarity of the cells remains unchanged during this process. Consequently, as Figure 4–12 shows, the flagellar ends of the new cells face inward toward the center of the daughter colony. This, of course, is all wrong as far as moving the colony is concerned. As one student of *Volvox* put it, it is "like having the propeller of an airplane madly churning the air inside the cabin."

Volvox solves this awkward problem very simply. It merely turns inside out. This it does by invaginating one side of the daughter colony much as one might push in one side of a hollow rubber ball. Soon thereafter the daughter colonies break completely loose from the wall of the parent and can often be seen swimming around within her. Ultimately the parent disintegrates and releases the daughter colonies.

The zoologists' excitement about this inversion derives from the fact that it closely resembles a process called gastrulation in the early embryos of all vertebrates and echinoderms. Does this mean that *Volvox,* or an organism like it, led to the Metazoa? Those who think not and believe it more probable that the many-celled animals arose from multinucleate

ciliates, hold that *Volvox* is more plant than animal. After all, it produces chlorophyll. They also note that a very similar invagination occurs in the development of many sponges, which all agree represent an evolutionary blind alley. On the other hand, a very pretty series of colonial flagellates exists from very simple associations of a dozen cells through species with 50 cells, up to *Volvox* with thousands. No conclusive answer to these questions can be given.

In sexual reproduction a few cells scattered near the equator enlarge, much as in asexual reproduction. If the colony is a male, each of these large cells undergoes many divisions to form a mass of tiny biflagellate sperms. If the colony is female, the germ cells do not divide but continue to enlarge into ova. The zygote or fertilized egg falls into the interior of the colony and develops a hard protective coat. Some species of *Volvox* are **hermaphroditic,** that is, bisexual; but in them sperms are produced before eggs, and self-fertilization is avoided.

One important question remains and will be discussed in the chapter on development. How is it that certain cells become germ cells and form eggs or sperms while others become somatic cells? This is part of the problem of differentiation, one of the major problems of 20th century biological science.

Parasitic and Commensal Flagellates. Six species of flagellates, all members of the Trypanosomidae, attack man. The best known is *Trypanosoma gambiense,* the causative agent of nagana, African sleeping sickness. This is not to be confused with encephalitis lethargica, a form of sleeping sickness due to a virus. The trypanosome responsible for nagana lives in the bloodstream, then in the lymph nodes, and finally in the central nervous system. In advanced stages the patient sleeps continually, becomes incredibly emaciated, is shaken by convulsions, and finally dies in profound coma. The parasite is transmitted from man to man and from man to the larger mammals, such as cattle, pigs, goats, and antelope, and back to man again by the bite of *Glossina,* the tse-tse fly. Within the vertebrate host, man or beast, the trypanosome presents an elongated form, with an undulating membrane extending the entire length of the animal. Within the tse-tse fly the trypanosome assumes a crithidial form, shorter and with an undulating membrane extending only half the length of the body. Nagana is an

Fig. 4–13. The four body forms of trypanosomes. *a,* "typical." *b,* crithidial. *c,* leptomonal. *d,* leishmanial.

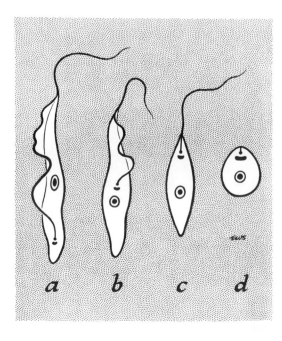

ancient disease and was known to slave traders. Mortality is high, and large areas of Africa are rendered unfit for human habitation because of it's toll.

Probably the next most important trypanosomal disease is kala azar, which extends in a broad belt around the world from China through the Mediterranean countries and into South America. It is caused by *Leishmania donovani* which is transmitted by the bite of the sand fly *Phlebotomus.* Dogs are the common "reservoirs" of this flagellate, for in them the symptoms are mild. In man, especially in children, it produces an enormous swelling of the spleen and other viscera. In the vertebrate, the leishmania lives within the host cells and assumes a nonflagellated form. In the sand fly the leishmania develops an elongated and flagellated form.

Chagas' disease, which is widespread in Latin America, is interesting zoologically because the responsible organism, *Trypanosoma cruzi,* has a typical elongate trypanosome form in the human bloodstream during attacks of fever, the shorter crithidial form in the midgut of *Rhodnius* and other bugs that transmit it, and the nonflagellated leishmanial form within the cells of the human liver, spleen, brain, and other organs.

Many species of trypanosomes parasitize fishes, frogs, salamanders, birds, and, of course, mammals. Blood-sucking flies are the usual vectors, although one species is known to be transmitted by a leech and another, *Trypanosoma equiperdum,* the cause of a disease in horses and mules, is transmitted from one horse to another during mating.

Most trypanosome diseases can be controlled by injecting compounds of the heavy metals, mercury, antimony, or arsenic. Paul Ehrlich, who discovered that heavy metal compounds are effective against the organism of syphilis, also found as long ago as 1907 that heavy metals and some dyes are more poisonous to trypanosomes than to men. Yet much remains to be learned about how these agents work. Because heavy metal compounds will combine with the —SH (sulfhydryl) group of glutathione, a substance found in most cells, it is believed by some that this is the mode of action of the mercurials and other metal trypanocides. Others hold that they attack the —SH groups on enzymes. The actual effectiveness of any anti-trypanosomal agent is really controlled by the difference in its toxicity to trypanosomes and to man. Unfortunately trypanosomes are frequently able to develop an immunity to these poisons.

The best known **commensal** flagellates (living in mutual dependence) are those found in the guts of termites and wood-roaches. They are peculiar-looking creatures adorned with hundreds of flagella. Some species are uninucleate; others possess over a dozen nuclei. Termites are completely dependent on these protozoans for the digestion of the wood which they eat, and the flagellates in turn are found only in termites and their relatives. Thus the termite-flagellate relationship is one of true commensalism.

If termites are placed in an oxygen tent for 24 hours, subjected to high temperatures (96°F), or starved for ten days, their intestinal flagellates are killed while the termites themselves appear to be unharmed. After treatment the termites eat wood as usual but because they are unable to digest cellulose, it passes unchanged through their digestive tracts. Recently elaborate studies have been made of the chromosome cycle of mitosis and meiosis in these flagellates. When the termite molts, its intestinal flagellates undergo meiosis, apparently under the influence of the insect's molting hormones.

Fig. 4 – 14. Flagellates from the intestine of a termite.

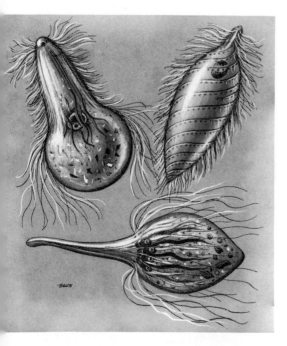

CILIATA

Ciliates are easily identified by their cilia, which usually cover most if not all of the body surface. They are notable also for their large size, which is attained by cheating, as it were, and either having many nuclei or, more often, developing a giant macronucleus which services the over-sized cell but does not take part in sexual reproduction. This function is left to a micronucleus of about the same size as the nucleus of cells in other organisms.

Ciliates are great favorites for study by students and research workers alike — not so much because they are of medical or economic importance, for they are not — but because they are easy to culture abundantly in the laboratory and are large and beautiful things to watch under a microscope.

Ciliates abound in both fresh-water and marine habitats. A few are commensal, or probably somewhat parasitic, in the intestine of frogs, tadpoles, and most herbivorous animals. Pond debris will almost always yield one or more species of *Paramecium* and representatives of other genera as well. *Stentor coeruleus* is an especially striking species, large, active, and bluish green, with a long, beaded macronucleus. *Stentor* is second only to *Paramecium* and perhaps *Tetrahymena* as a research animal. *Tetrahymena* has one immense advantage for nutritional research because, unlike *Paramecium*, it will thrive in a liquid medium without solid food particles and can therefore be raised in media of known composition free of bacteria.

Other notable ciliates are *Blepharisma*, a very large pink creature; *Lacrymaria*, with a long swanlike neck; *Didinium*, which attacks and eats *Paramecium*; *Vorticella*, which looks

Fig. 4-15. *Paramecium* stained with silver to show the arrangement of cilia over the body surface. Left: aboral surface showing exits of contractile vacuoles as black spots. Right: oral surface showing the oral opening, the preoral suture as a white line where the right and left ciliary fields fail to meet, and, near the posterior end, the cytopyge as a dark line where residues from food vacuoles are egested. *(Kindness of T. M. Sonneborn)*

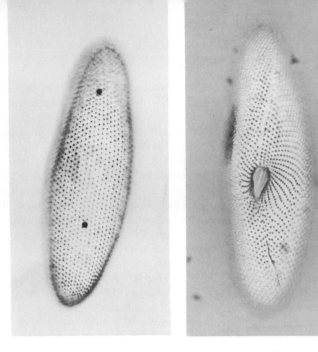

like a bell on a long stalk and is often colonial; *Opalina,* a pancake-shaped multinucleate ciliate that lives in the gut of frogs: *Diplodinium,* which swarms in the intestines of cattle. The structure of *Diplodinium* is shown in Figure 4-16.

Ciliates like *Diplodinium* are universally present in the stomach and large intestine of cows and related animals. Such ciliates resemble the metazoans remarkably. They not only possess a permanent mouth and anus, they have a complex locomotor system, a series of retractile myonemes corresponding to muscles, a skeletal axis, and even a "nerve" center. The number of these ciliates in a cow is truly prodigious, 100,000 to 400,000 per ml of intestinal contents. Are they harmful, useful, or even indispensable to the cow, in the way intestinal flagellates are to the termite? Cattle can be freed of ciliates by feeding them copper sulfate and maintained this way for at least a year without noticeable harm although some of the more recent experiments tend to contradict this finding.

Locomotion and Behavior. The behavior of *Paramecium* has been studied for well over a century by many investigators, but it is still far from completely understood. Some have even believed that the behavior of all animals, including that of man himself, can be understood in terms of *Paramecium.* This is a large claim, yet it contains some truth.

Fig. 4-16. *Diplodinium,* a ciliate from the stomach of a cow. *(From Wolcott,* Animal Biology, *McGraw-Hill Book Company. Copyright 1946. Used by permission)*

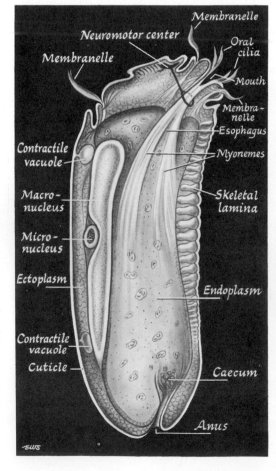

The cilia by which a paramecium moves are arranged in accurately spaced rows and coordinated in the direction and timing of their beats. This coordination is controlled by an elaborate system of subsurface fibers which are now being investigated with the aid of the electron microscope.

Except when feeding heavily, the natural state of a healthy paramecium is swimming forward. The rows of cilia are so arranged and the animal so shaped that a paramecium rotates on its long axis at the same time it moves forward in a corkscrewlike spiral. When it runs into an obstacle—a piece of dirt, the surface of the water, a place where the water is too warm or too cold—a paramecium shows an **avoidance reaction.** It stops, reverses the ciliary beat, backs off, pivots through a moderate angle, and starts off in a new direction. The animal continues in this direction until it runs into something that elicits the avoidance reaction again. This type of behavior was described by Jennings, a life-long student of these animals, as **trial and error.**

Parameciums sometimes appear to seek out favorable spots. For example, if one end of a trough of water be heated and the other iced, they will collect in the middle. On close inspection such behavior can be seen to be due to trial and error. The parameciums swim in all directions, and whenever one runs into an area that is too cold or too hot, it turns away. Trial and error methods are also employed by human beings in the face of completely new and strange problems, like trying to open a Chinese puzzle box for the first time. It should be noted that parameciums do not always react to noxious substances by an avoidance reaction. They will readily enter corrosive sublimate or copper sulfate and quickly die.

The avoidance reaction is an innate unlearned response. It plays a major role in the behavior of the lower animals and an important one in the behavior of many of the higher ones. Another type of innate response shown by parameciums is the **tropism** or **taxis** which is an orientation of the organism in a field of force. Parameciums are negatively geotropic and, other things being equal, will swim away from the pull of gravity. Jarring will induce a positive geotropic response.

The response of parameciums to a direct electric current has been much studied ever since the original experiments of Max Verworn in the closing years of the last century. With the current from two 1.5-volt dry cell batteries,

Fig. 4–17. Cilia, their basal bodies (kinetosomes), and their interconnecting fibrils. Note that the fibrils run between kinetosomes and also deep within the cell. Observe the three mitochondria on the left, and the cilia shown in cross section on the extreme right revealing the characteristic circle of nine fibrils. (*Kindness of H. E. Finley*)

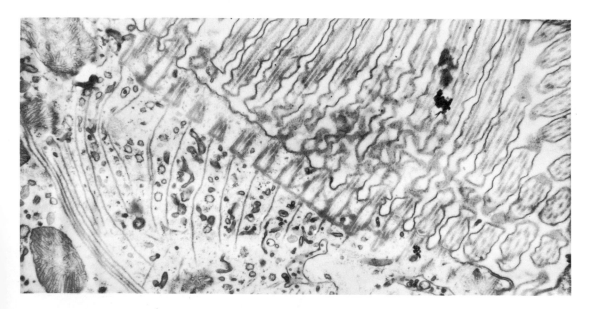

it is easy to show that parameciums swim toward the cathode. This behavior is referred to as **galvanotropism.** The mechanism is puzzling. The beating of the cilia on the side toward the cathode is reversed. This causes the animal to swing around until it heads toward the cathode. In this position only those cilia located at the extreme anterior end beat backwards. The animal consequently moves toward the cathode. However, if the current is made progressively stronger, more and more cilia reverse their effective stroke, and the paramecium swims slowly backwards away from the cathode, i.e., toward the anode. The complexity of this reaction will be realized when it is observed that if potassium or certain other salts are added to the medium, parameciums swim head-first toward the anode.

A characteristic reaction of many ciliates, including the parameciums, is to shoot out trichocysts in the face of noxious circumstances. Before discharge, a trichocyst appears as a minute, elongate vesicle a short distance under the surface membrane. When discharged by the paramecium and later examined with an electron microscope, the trichocyst is seen to consist of a pointed tip and a long striated shaft (Fig. 4–18). How effective these supposed weapons are is uncertain. They have little effect against a paramecium's arch enemy, *Didin-*

Fig. 4–19. *Stentor,* showing waves of ciliary beats around edge of oral surface. *(Kindness of P. S. Tice)*

ium. In fact, the trichocysts have even been observed to backfire into the paramecium itself.

A paramecium appears totally unable to learn anything (despite recent efforts to prove the contrary), but the behavior of some of the big stentors, such as *Stentor coeruleus,* can be modified by experience. If an extended stentor with its "foot" fixed to some object be squirted with a gentle current of water, it will jerk down into a rounded position. If, after the stentor has extended again, it is squirted a second time, it will not contract. Perhaps the mechanism is some increase in the threshold of stimulation, for a stronger stimulus will produce a vigorous contraction. If the stimulus is repeated several times, the stentor will loosen its "foot" and swim away.

Nutrition and Excretion. Ciliates feed by sweeping particles, usually bacteria, into their mouths by the action of cilia. Very commonly there are specialized cilia semi-fused into a membranelle along the edge of the mouth which assists in this action. The food particles collect at the bottom of the gullet until they are pinched off in a food vacuole which drops into

Fig. 4–18. Discharged trichocysts of *Paramecium,* as seen under the electron microscope. *(Kindness of Marie A. Jakus)*

the cytoplasm, breaking off like a conventionalized tear drop. The food vacuole is now carried by the streaming of the cytoplasm, i.e., by cyclosis, on a tour completely around the animal. If the paramecium has been fed yeast cells stained with a colored indicator, it will be seen that the vacuole first becomes very acid, pH 1.4, and later definitely alkaline, pH 7.5 to 7.8. These changes are probably connected with the fact that different digestive enzymes require a different pH. The spherical vacuole gradually but greatly decreases in size and then increases again. Undigested particles are egested near the posterior end of the animal.

Ciliates are heterotrophic, that is, dependent on other organisms for nutrition. As noted earlier, *Tetrahymena* has been the ciliate of choice in nutritional studies, because it lives well on bacteria-free liquid media. This makes it possible to test the animal on chemically defined diets and investigate basic problems in cellular metabolism. Surprising as it may at first seem, vitamin and other dietary requirements of this ciliate resemble those of a rat or a man. Like some species of flagellates, *Tetrahymena* also requires an outside source of purines and pyrimidines, the nitrogenous bases

Fig. 4–20. *Tetrahymena,* a ciliate widely used in nutritional studies.

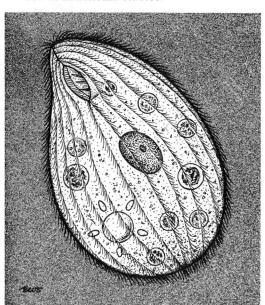

forming the nucleotides that constitute nucleic acids. Interestingly enough, rats and pigeons can synthesize their own purines and pyrimidines and make them up into nucleic acids.

Ciliates eliminate excess water via one or more contractile vacuoles. The structure of these vacuoles is more complex than those of the amoebas, but their function appears to be the same.

Reproduction. The time, thought, and effort that has been expended on the problems of ciliate reproduction is truly stupendous. This great interest derives from questions about the nature and biological meaning of sex. The early work of Hertwig in Germany, Maupas in France, and Calkins in the United States confirmed the fact that *Paramecium* and other ciliates reproduce both asexually by fission and sexually by conjugation. In addition, these workers found that if parameciums were kept on a regime of purely asexual reproduction generation after generation, there seemed to be irregular rhythms in reproductive rate and a progressive decline in general vitality until finally the race died out. But if, shortly before racial death, sexual reproduction was permitted, the outcome was very different. The strain seemed to become reinvigorated and would last another six or eight weeks before sexual reproduction again appeared to be necessary. Did this mean that the function of sex was to rejuvenate the race?

Before this question could be answered, it was necessary to know the facts of reproduction. In **binary fission,** i.e., asexual reproduction, the macronucleus merely pulls apart without undergoing mitosis. The micronucleus, however, at the same time divides by mitosis. It contains numerous chromosomes. In some strains of *Paramecium caudatum* the haploid number is 18; in others it is 40 or even more. The cytoplasm divides at right angles to the long axis of the body, approximately midway between the two ends. This process requires about half an hour.

Sexual reproduction, i.e., **conjugation,** is more complicated. Two animals come together by their oral groove surfaces. The pairs swim around together for 24 to 48 hours, depending on the species. In different ciliates the details differ, and even different species of *Paramecium* do not behave exactly alike. The following account applies to *Paramecium caudatum,* often regarded as typical. While the animals are paired, the following events occur. (The numbered stages are shown in Fig. 4–21.)

(1) In each animal the micronucleus divides twice, making four haploid micronuclei. This is of course meiosis, as in the formation of the eggs or sperms of the metazoa. (2) Three of the four micronuclei degenerate—how or why is not known. (3) The remaining micronucleus divides by mitosis to give two haploid nuclei which come to lie near the oral region. (4) Each **conjugant,** as the conjugating individuals are called, now extends a cone-shaped protrusion toward the other. These protrusions in the oral region establish a cytoplasmic bridge be-

tween the two animals. (5) One of the two haploid nuclei from each conjugant migrates across the cytoplasmic bridge into the other animal and fuses with the stationary micronucleus. The migratory nucleus is comparable to a sperm, the stationary nucleus to an egg. The fused nucleus that results is, of course, diploid. It is comparable to the zygote of a metazoan. (6) The conjugants then separate. Each animal is now called an **exconjugant.** (7) In each exconjugant the macronucleus becomes irregular in shape and, during the subsequent divisions of the micronucleus, stretches into twisted skeins and is finally completely absorbed (digested) by the cytoplasm. (8) The diploid micronucleus divides by mitosis three times, giving eight micronuclei. (9) Four of the eight micronuclei in each exconjugant enlarge and grow into new

Fig. 4–21. Conjugation in *Paramecium caudatum.* The events that occur in each of the numbered stages are described in the text.

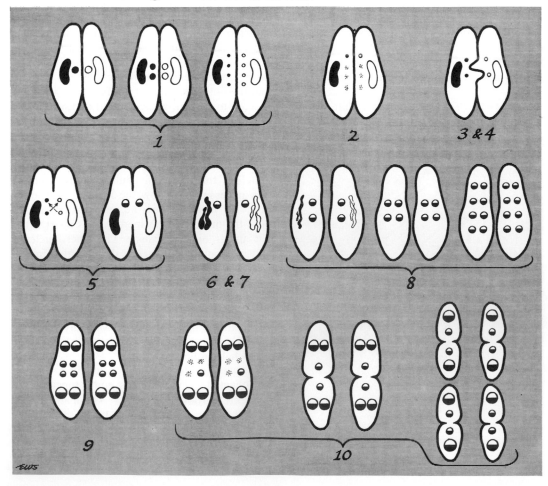

macronuclei. (10) The behavior of the other four micronuclei appears to be related to cell division. Three degenerate and the remaining one divides twice by mitosis. Each time this micronucleus divides, the whole animal divides in half, as in asexual reproduction, at right angles to the long axis of the cell. The first division gives two daughters from each exconjugant, each with two immature macronuclei and one diploid micronucleus. The second division yields four granddaughter parameciums from each exconjugant, each with one diploid micronucleus plus one diploid macronucleus. All the individuals produced asexually by mitosis from such an animal constitute a **clone.** Genetically, they are identical.

These facts make it clear that sexual reproduction in ciliates is basically the same as in the higher animals. There is a cycle of meiosis producing haploid nuclei which fuse to form a diploid zygotic nucleus, and this, after a period of multiplication by mitosis, again undergoes meiosis. The most important genetic difference between a ciliate or other protozoan and a metazoan is that a protozoan lacks the distinction between germ cells and somatic cells. This means that characters acquired by the cytoplasm of a protozoan can be transmitted to subsequent generations because the cytoplasm of the parents is passed on directly to the offspring. Furthermore, during conjugation there is for a brief time a cytoplasmic bridge between the two ciliates so that an interchange of cytoplasmic particles may take place.

Ciliate Mating Types. In investigating the effects of sexual reproduction and hence its meaning in the Protozoa, there was one all but insuperable obstacle. Neither parameciums nor other ciliates could be brought together and mated the way most animals can. Groups of parameciums could be mixed together easily enough, but except on rare occasions no conjugation took place. Occasionally, however, and for no known reason, there would be what protozoologists used to call an "epidemic of conjugation." At such times researchers would work around the clock preserving animals in various stages of conjugation.

A new era in the study of sex in ciliates was made possible by the discovery of mating types. The way in which this discovery took place illustrates the accidents that Pasteur claimed happened to "prepared" minds. One winter weekend, Sonneborn, an American protozoologist, happened to pour two cultures of parameciums together and was astonished to find that they immediately began to clump together, the first stage of conjugation. Mixing other samples of the same two cultures produced the same result. Here at long last appeared to be two sexually differentiated strains, male and female, plus and minus, or whatever one chose to call them. But on Monday morning the experiment failed to work. Subsequent trials at intervals during the week also failed to produce conjugation. Then on the next weekend conjugation again occurred when the two strains were mixed. The answer was now evident. The university was saving fuel over the weekend. The laboratory cooled off, and for conjugation to occur, this species requires a fairly low temperature.

It turns out that every species of *Paramecium,* and of other ciliates so far tested, can be divided into two or more mating types. Strangely enough, there may be more than two inter-reacting mating types within a species, as well as mutually exclusive groups of mating types. Conjugation will take place only if the conditions of temperature, light, etc., are right. *Paramecium bursaria,* for example, conjugates most readily in the middle of the day, and never before sunlight or after 6 P.M. If an animal belongs to a mating type called A, it can conjugate with any member of type B or type C, but not with another member of A. Likewise a member of type B can conjugate with a member of type A or C but not with one of type B.

Paramecium bursaria, the species which is green due to symbiotic algae, has six mutually exclusive mating type groups. In group 1 there are four mating types that have been called A, B, C, and D. In group 2 there are eight mating types. A member of any one of these can conjugate with a member of any of the other seven in group 2, but not with another member of its own mating type or any of the four mating types in group 1 or with any of the types in the remaining four groups. Of the six mutually exclusive groups of mating types, groups 1, 2, and 3 are from the United States, 4 and 5 are from Russia, and 6 is from England, Ireland, and Czechoslovakia.

In *Paramecium aurelia,* in which Sonneborn first discovered mating types, there are eight mutually exclusive groups, each with only one pair of mating types. In group (or variety) 1 there are mating types I and II; in group 2, types III and IV. Thus far 16 mating types have been found in collections from many parts of the United States and Canada. Clones of *Paramecium aurelia* collected in Puerto Rico, Chile, Scotland, France, Japan, and India all belong to one or another of the types found in North America.

Paramecium caudatum is like *Paramecium aurelia* in mating type pattern. Collections made in China, Japan, and the United States have uncovered 13 mutually exclusive groups with only two mating types in any one. *Paramecium multimicronucleatum* is like *Paramecium bursaria* in having a system of multiple mating types. So far only one group has been found. It has four mating types, each of which will conjugate with any of the other three.

Two lines of work converged to provide at least a partial answer to the old question as to whether the function of sex was rejuvenescence. Soon after Hertwig, Maupas, and Calkins proposed revitalization as the function of sex, the American protozoologist Woodruff began work with his "Yale strain" of *Paramecium aurelia.* He isolated his animals after each binary fission, that is, about once a day, so that conjugation was impossible. Despite some ups and downs he was able to maintain his animals generation after generation and month after month. At first the advocates of rejuvenescence said that Woodruff's animals merely hadn't died yet, but as the strain continued year after year it became clear that parameciums can live by binary fission indefinitely.

However, there was a catch. It was discovered that this strain of parameciums which was not allowed to conjugate nevertheless did undergo periodic nuclear reorganization every so many generations. From both cytological evidence (i.e., microscopic study of stained animals) and genetic evidence, this nuclear reorganization within a nonconjugating strain is a process called **autogamy.** The events are closely similar—in fact, for the most part identical—to those of conjugation. The micronucleus divides by meiosis to give the haploid nuclei, all of which degenerate save one. The macronucleus disintegrates and is absorbed. The difference is merely that the haploid migratory and stationary nuclei of a single individual fuse together instead of exchanging partners with nuclei of another individual. The results are thus the same as in fertilization except that the animal being self-fertilized by sister nuclei is genetically pure bred, that is, it is homozygous.

Where does this leave the problem? There is no doubt that ciliates can live for an indefinite number of generations without conjugation. It is also true, as both the older and present-day workers found, that after conjugation and to a lesser extent after autogamy, there are both vigorous and weak strains. The offspring of some exconjugants are, to be sure, "revitalized." The offspring of other exconjugants are actually devitalized, a fact which the older workers overlooked. This means that meiosis and fertilization—in short, sex—produce variability. If, in the course of time, conditions begin to become unfavorable for a given strain of parameciums, perhaps because the bacterial flora they are eating changes for the worse, or the pH or the temperature becomes less favorable for a given strain, sexual reproduction yields animals with new assortments of chromosomes and hence somewhat different traits. Some individuals will be even less well adapted to the changed conditions; these are the so-called senescent strains. Others may be better adapted to the changed conditions; these are the so-called "revitalized" strains.

Development and Regeneration. In the ciliates binary fission, whereby one individual becomes two, raises a new and different kind of question of basic importance. Regeneration raises similar questions. Where do the new cytoplasmic structures come from? The nature of cytoplasmic organelles like the mouth and oral groove, the contractile vacuoles, or the cilia, is controlled by the hereditary nature of the species. How does this heredity make itself felt? In other words, how do genes act?

In binary fission the various organelles may be absorbed and then remade, or one of the daughter cells may get the old structures and the other form new ones. Different species differ in this respect. In parameciums the first sign that division is imminent is a duplication of the cilia in the ventral rows near the mouth. The area of duplication spreads in a band around the middle and subsequently out to the ends of the animal. Then a new contractile vacuole is formed immediately anterior to each of the old ones. Thus each new animal will have a new anterior contractile vacuole and a second-hand posterior one. The anterior one of the new animals gets the old mouth, the posterior one a new mouth that seems to be budded off from the old gullet. The cilia certainly seem to be self-duplicating, and the other structures may be, although the contractile vacuoles seem to form *de novo*.

The **hypotrichs** are ciliates in which the cilia on the under surface are fused into several locomotor **cirri** (see Fig. 4–22). In these animals, after injury, most or all of the organelles are either shed or absorbed, and new ones arise to take their place. The new ventral cirri arise in a small "regeneration field" near the center of the animal and migrate to their definitive positions near the ends of the animal. Perhaps it is significant that this field is near the macronucleus. The silver-staining network that covers

Fig. **4–22.** *Stylonychia*, a common hypotrich. Note the locomotor cirri.

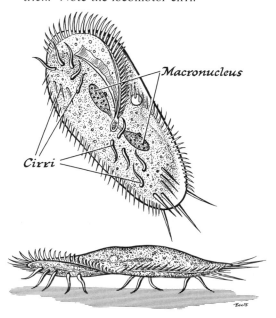

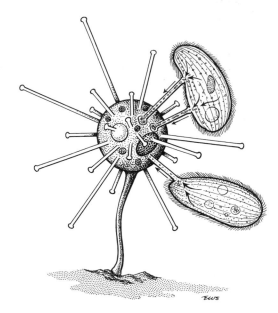

Fig. **4–23.** *Podophrya*, a suctorian, feeding on two parameciums.

the animal like chicken wire forms first as a very fine mesh, and then enlarges as the cell grows without adding new parts.

In *Stentor* the first sign of division is the formation of a new mouth apparatus about halfway between the old mouth and the "foot."

SUCTORIA

The Suctoria constitute a small class of protozoans which begin life as rounded ciliated forms and then become sessile or fixed, usually on a stalk, lose their cilia, and develop semirigid tentacles. They are common in both fresh and salt water. Like ciliates, they possess both macro- and micronuclei.

Their favorite food is a ciliate the size of a paramecium or smaller. When a paramecium bumps into one or more of the suctorian's tentacles, it appears to become quickly paralyzed. The cytoplasm of the paramecium then begins to flow through the tentacles into the suctorian. It looks as though the suctorian had stuck a soda straw into the unfortunate paramecium. Food vacuoles form at the bases of the tentacles in the suctorian.

The Suctoria reproduce asexually in a unique way. Part of the surface invaginates, making a blind tube connected with the exterior of the animal. Cilia are formed which project into this tube. Significantly, these cilia develop from the basal granules left when the cilia of the parent degenerated at metamorphosis into the adult form with tentacles. The macronuclei and micronuclei divide, and new contractile vacuoles are formed. The interior of the tube now evaginates or turns outward, and into the ciliated bud thus formed flows cytoplasm with one macronucleus, one or two micronuclei, and contractile and food vacuoles. It is like filling up a rag doll by pouring in the organs along with cytoplasmic sawdust.

If a suctorian is injured, its protoplasm streams out, rounds up, and forms a ciliated "embryo" which swims off to become a sessile form in some new place.

SPOROZOA

The Sporozoa are parasitic protozoans which lack locomotor organs. They have no cilia, no flagella, no pseudopods. At some stage in their life histories, they are usually intracellular parasites. They usually pass from host to host in protective capsules called **spores** which enclose zygotes or juvenile stages. However, species transmitted by blood-sucking vectors like mosquitoes lack true spores.

The Sporozoa is a very large and diverse class with at least four subclasses and many thousands of species. They cause disease in a wide variety of animals from earthworms and rats to silkworms (the disease called pebrine) and fishes. Malaria is easily the most important sporozoan disease. Coccidiosis, which afflicts poultry and cattle, is second. Some sporozoans, like the malarial organism, live primarily in the blood cells; others, like Coccidia, live in the epithelial cells lining the intestine. Still others live in muscles, kidneys, and other organs.

Malaria. Mankind entered a new medical era when the cause of malaria and its mode of transmission were discovered. Descriptions of the disease are found in ancient Chinese and Indian medical writings. There is good evidence that malaria played an important part in the decline of classical Greece. During the Middle Ages the rise and fall of human populations in and around Rome appear to have been correlated with the absence or prevalence of malaria. Even today more people suffer from malaria than from any other single disease. Yet within the lifetime of many men now living malaria was supposed to be due, as its name implies, to bad air, especially some vague noxious miasma that arose from swamps.

The story of how the cause of malaria was discovered well illustrates the way science advances by the cumulative efforts of many individuals. It should be part of the cultural inheritance of every modern man. A good point of departure is the arrival in London of Ronald Ross, a young army surgeon from India. He went to famous old St. Bartholomew's Hospital determined to find out all he could about malaria. There he learned the varied facts that had been uncovered; later he drew them together with new ones of his own into a convincing explanation of the true cause of this great scourge. These are some of the things he learned:

1. Ross learned that some 14 years earlier a French Army doctor, Alphonse Laveran, while stationed in North Africa, had found microscopic parasites in the blood of malarial patients, and that despite a few skeptics Laveran's discovery had been confirmed in the most convincing manner. Golgi in Italy had accurately described how the parasites break out of the red blood cells and are found free in the blood plasma every time the patient has one of the periodic fever-chills characteristic of malaria. Laveran's discovery in turn has a history and goes back to the pathologist Virchow and through him to the zoologist Meckel. Meckel had discovered that the internal organs of malaria victims are dark; Virchow then found pigment granules in their cells.

2. Ross learned also of the speculations and observations of Patrick Manson and entered into correspondence with him. Manson practiced medicine up and down the China coast. He was credited with the discovery that elephantiasis, a disease characterized by great swelling of the legs and caused by a minute worm, was transmitted by the bite of a mosquito. He thought that malaria probably was also. The work of Manson had its antecedents too, in the work of Fedschenko and through him to Leuckhardt and Chamisso, who discovered alternation of generations.

3. Several other lines of work contributed to Ross's synthesis. One was the development by Romanowsky of ways to stain blood cells and the malarial parasites in them. The various blood stains now in common use in every medical laboratory, Wright's stain, Giemsa's stain, and the rest, are lineal descendants of Romanowsky's stain. Another ingredient that contributed to the final result was the discovery by Danilewsky that many animals such as lizards and birds are subject to malaria.

Ross returned to India and, fortified with all this knowledge, was able to make new discoveries which showed conclusively how malaria is transmitted from one person to the next. Ross found that the infection was not carried by bad air but by the bite of a particular kind of mosquito, the *Anopheles,* or, as Ross said, the dappled-winged mosquito. He discovered the life cycle of the malarial parasite within this species of mosquito. In a way this discovery was the real turning-point, and Ross in his autobiography tells of how late one night, after many fruitless searches, he finally saw the parasites in the gut wall of an *Anopheles.* Then in 1897 Ross succeeded in transmitting bird malaria from one bird to another by allowing mosquitos to bite infected birds and subsequently bite healthy ones.

Various workers soon demonstrated the transmission of human malaria by mosquitos. An unpleasant controversy arose as to who really first discovered the cause of malaria. The report of an international commission resulted in a Nobel prize for Ross; but the controversy illustrates the fact that often when a scientific problem is ready for solution, i.e., when the factual and theoretical background has been built up, several people reach a solution at about the same time. The formulation of the theory of natural selection by Darwin and Wallace, and the rediscovery of Mendel's laws, also illustrate this principle.

At least four species of malarial sporozoans are now known which parasitize man. *Plasmodium vivax* is the cause of tertian malaria, i.e., malaria in which the attack comes every "third" day (every 48 hours). Each attack consists of a shaking chill accompanied by high fever with severe malaise, vomiting, and muscular and abdominal pains followed by a drenching sweat that leaves the patient exhausted until the next paroxysm. *Plasmodium vivax* malaria is the most widespread form of the disease, being common in both tropical and temperate climates. *Plasmodium falciparum* causes malignant tropical malaria, which is also tertian. Fortunately it is rare outside the tropics, for much more frequently than with other types, the paroxysm from falciparum includes, in addition to the symptoms listed above, convulsions, coma, and heart failure. Extensive breakdown of red blood cells causes the urine to become black; hence falciparum malaria is often called blackwater fever. *Plasmodium malariae,* the species Laveran first studied, causes quartan malaria, in which the paroxysm occurs every 72 hours. *Plasmodium ovale* has been known only in recent times. It produces a tertian malaria.

Plasmodium goes through several stages in its life cycle, some stages while it is in the mosquito and some in man. (See Fig. 4–24.) Infection in man begins when elongate forms called **sporozoites** enter the bloodstream with mosquito saliva. Within a few hours the sporozoites have all entered fixed cells in the blood passages of the liver, the spleen, and other organs. Within a fixed cell each sprozoite grows into a nutritive stage called a **trophozoite** (*trophos,* feeder). The trophozoite feeds at the expense of the host cell and then becomes a **schizont** in which the nucleus divides four or five times to yield somewhere between 16 and 32 nuclei. It is in this stage in a red blood cell that what is left of the hemoglobin forms the black granules Meckel discovered. The schizont divides into 16 to 32 little parasites called **merozoites.** The merozoites break out of the cell and enter the bloodstream. Presumably because they all started to develop at the same time after the bite of an infected mosquito, all the merozoites in different cells break out at the same time. The merozoites enter red blood cells, become nutritive trophozoites, which develop into schizonts that produce merozoites again, which enter fresh red blood cells — and so the asexual cycle in the red blood cells continues. At the time when the merozoites break out of the erythrocytes the patient suffers a paroxysm, as Golgi first observed and reported some years earlier.

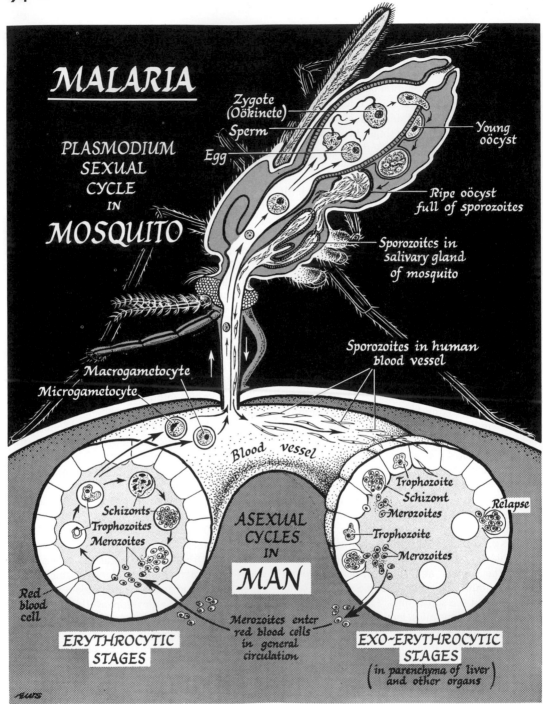

Fig. 4–24. Life cycle of malarial *Plasmodium* in man and mosquito.

The sexual cycle begins when, for unknown reasons, trophozoites develop not into schizonts but into either **microgametocytes** or **macrogametocytes.** These develop no further unless they get sucked into a mosquito's stomach. But there they form **sperms** (microgametes) or **eggs** (macrogametes). Fertilization yields a zygote (also called an **oökinete** by malariologists). The zygote is mobile and crawls through the mosquito's stomach wall, on the outside of which it forms a round cyst. Within the cyst the zygote undergoes repeated nuclear and then cytoplasmic divisions producing thousands of the elongate **sporozoites.** The sporozoites break out of the cysts, collect in the mosquito's salivary glands, and are ready for inoculation into the vertebrate host.

The first known therapeutic agent effective against malaria was quinine, an alkaloid derived from the bark of the cinchona tree. Its use was discovered by Peruvian Indians and was introduced into Europe by Jesuit missionaries. It is very effective against the asexual stages in the blood but ineffective against the exoerythrocytic stages in the fixed cells of liver and spleen. Consequently patients treated with quinine are usually subject to relapses, sometimes every nine months or so.

The first successful attempt to produce a substitute for quinine was achieved by a team composed of students of the great German pioneer in bacteriology, Robert Koch, and chemists of the I. G. Farben Trust. Other workers in England, the United States, and elsewhere have continued to synthesize possible antimalarial compounds. During World War II over 14,000 compounds were tested in the United States alone. There are now a dozen or more anti-malarials available, plasmochin, atabrine, chloroquine, daraprim, and others. The last named is an antagonist of the vitamin folic acid. Since folic acid contains *p*-aminobenzoic acid, it is not surprising that the sulfa drugs (which stop bacterial growth by antagonizing *p*-aminobenzoic acid) have some effect against malarial parasites. Many investigations have been carried out on the nutritional requirements and metabolism of *Plasmodium*. One interesting find is that at least for monkey malaria, caused by *Plasmodium knowlesi*, the amino acid methionine is essential. If this is

omitted from the monkey's diet, the parasites stop multiplication. If it is given to the monkey, the animal dies of malaria. The great problem is that by the mid-1960's, strains of malaria have arisen which are immune to the action of these chemicals!

One important aspect of malaria remains to be considered, the social or public health aspect. Ross himself made a major contribution with his malaria statistics. While the actual figures he used hold only in the special conditions under which he worked, they illustrate in simple fashion the nature of epidemiology, the science of distribution of diseases.

Ross found that under his conditions the chance that a mosquito would bite a person was $1/4$, which means that only one out of four mosquitos succeeds in biting anyone. The chance that a mosquito will live the 21 days required for the sexual phase to take place within her and make her infective with sporozoites in her saliva is $1/3$, which is another way of saying that within 21 days two out of every three mosquitos are either killed by dragon flies, hit by raindrops, or meet their fate in some other manner. This means that the chance of a given mosquito biting someone and then living three weeks is $1/4 \times 1/3$, or $1/12$. This is an application of the **product law** that the probability of two independent events happening coincidentally is the mathematical product of the separate probabilities. Thus, in tossing pennies, the chance of tossing a head is $1/2$. If two pennies are tossed simultaneously, or the same penny twice, the chance of getting two heads is $1/2 \times 1/2$, or $1/4$. This means that two heads will appear in 25 per cent of the cases. This product law will be met again in Mendel's laws of heredity. With a disease like malaria or polio, when it is possible to gain some idea of the relationships between the number of carriers in a given area and the percentage of the population with the disease, the likelihood that the disease will increase or decrease can be predicted. For example, if there is one case of malaria on an island with 1,000 people and one mosquito, the chance that that one mosquito will bite the one malarial patient is $1/4 \times 1/1,000$, or 1 in 4,000. The further chance that this extremely lucky mosquito will live 21 days and then bite someone is $1/4,000 \times 1/3 \times 1/4$, or 1 in 48,000.

Coccidia and Other Sporozoa. Except for the malarial parasites, the subclass Coccidia is the most important group of sporozoans because its members cause widespread, highly contagious, extremely fatal diarrhea in many vertebrates, including chickens, turkeys, other poultry, cattle, sheep, pigs, goats, dogs, cats, and other domestic animals. Fortunately, although the species is occasionally found in man, its effects are usually not serious and seldom fatal.

Coccidia have both sexual and asexual life cycles but require only one host. Their life cycle resembles that of the malarial *Plasmodium*. *Eimeria stiedae,* a species commonly infecting rabbits, lives in the intestine and liver where it causes white nodules. It is easily obtained from rabbit feces and is a convenient species to study. Its life cycle is almost identical with that of *Isospora hominis* of man, *I. felis* of the cat,

Eimeria tenella of birds, and *E. schubergi* of centipedes and other species.

The zygote or fertilized egg forms a cyst, but instead of remaining on the wall of the gut like the zygote cysts of the *Plasmodium* of malaria, the cysts pass to the exterior with the feces. It is by ingesting these cysts that the infection is transmitted from one animal to the next. This is the reason for keeping poultry off the ground on wire meshes.

As in malaria, the zygote forms elongate sporozoites. These break out of the egg cyst, after they get into the intestine of some animal, and enter the epithelial cells lining the gut. Here each becomes a nutritive trophozoite which grows at the expense of the host cell until it becomes a schizont. The schizont ultimately breaks up into a dozen or so merozoites which escape from the cell and infect new cells.

Fig. 4–25. Life cycle of *Eimeria,* a coccidian parasitic in the intestine of chickens.

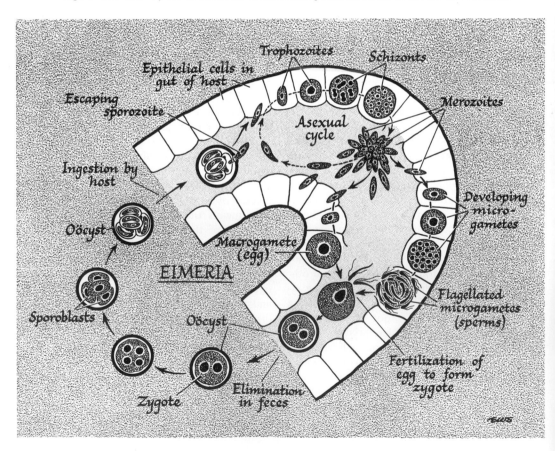

The sexual cycle is also like that of *Plasmodium* except that it takes place in the same host as does the asexual cycle. Some of the merozoites enter gut cells and become macrogametes or eggs, others enter cells and there grow and divide many times to produce microgametes or sperms. The fertilized egg or zygote secretes a cyst around itself and passes outside the body with the feces.

The Gregarinidia is a class of sporozoans that commonly parasitize earthworms and other annelids, and insects and other arthropods. Gregarines are transmitted from one host to another by the ingestion of egg cysts. The life cycles, both asexual and sexual, are in part different from those of the malarial parasite and the coccidians. (See Fig. 4–26.) The elongate sporozoites enter certain cells. *Monocystis* enters the sperm mother cells in the sex organs of earthworms; *Gregarina,* the epithelial cells lining the gut of a grasshopper. Here the sporozoite becomes a trophozoite, but one that grows so large it hangs out into the lumen of the gut or other cavity. The large free-hanging part drops off from its host cell and pairs with another similar gregarine. The pair forms a cyst within which one partner divides into many macrogametes or eggs and the other into even more

Fig. 4–26. Life cycle of a gregarine, a common sporozoan parasite of invertebrates.

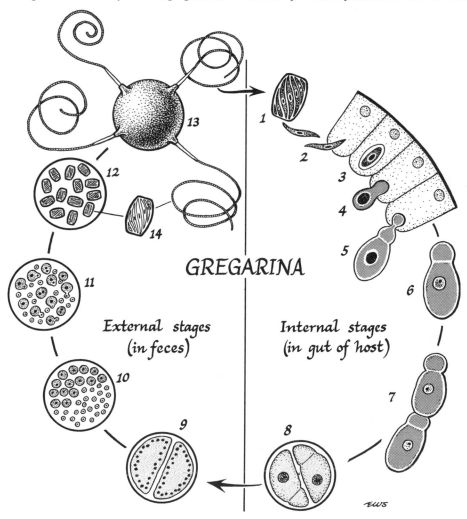

GREGARINA

*External stages
(in feces)*

*Internal stages
(in gut of host)*

microgametes or sperms. After fertilization each zygote secretes a barrel-shaped cyst around itself within which it divides into eight sporozoites. The large original cyst now contains thousands of minute zygotic cysts each containing eight sporozoites. The big cyst may simply break open; or, as in the case of the grasshopper gregarine, it may develop several protruding spigots from which the little zygotic cysts are extruded like strings of beads.

Review and References

REVIEW TOPICS

1. What is the essential difference between a protozoan and a metazoan?

2. What are the four main areas of human importance of the Protozoa? Into what four classes are protozoans divided?

3. What is the evidence for the protoplasmic contractility theory of amoeboid motion? The reversible sol-gel- theory? Are the theories mutually exclusive? Why?

4. Compare and contrast heterotrophic and autotrophic protozoans in regard to nutritive raw materials, requirements, wastes, and associated structures.

5. What is the evidence that the green bodies in the cells of *Paramecium bursaria* are algae cells, not merely chloroplastids?

6. What types of behavior are found among the Sarcodina? Among ciliates?

7. Compare and contrast asexual and sexual reproduction in *Paramecium*. What is the advantage of each?

8. What basic problems of metazoan life does *Volvox* illustrate in simplified form?

9. What is the life cycle of the malarial organism? What were the scientific precursors of Ross's discovery of the mode of transmission of malaria?

10. Describe the life history of a pathogenic amoeba, a pathogenic flagellate, and a sporozoan other than the malarial organism.

11. Define: flagellum, macronucleus, contractile vacuole, schizont, "red tide," dinoflagellate, commensalism, autogamy, sporozoite, photosynthesis.

USEFUL REFERENCES

Faust, E. C., *Animal Agents and Vectors of Human Disease,* Philadelphia, Lea & Febiger, 1955.

Gojdics, Mary, *The Genus Euglena,* Madison University of Wisconsin Press, 1953.

Hall, R. P., *Protozoology,* New York, Prentice-Hall, 1953.

Jahn, T. L., and F. F. Jahn, *How to Know the Protozoa,* Dubuque, Iowa, William C. Brown Company, 1949.

Kudo, R. R., *Handbook of Protozoology,* 3rd ed., Springfield, Ill., Charles C Thomas, 1946.

Leidy, J., "Freshwater Rhizopods of North America," *Rept. U.S. Geol. Survey,* vol. 12, 1879.

Ross, R., *Memoirs,* New York, E. P. Dutton & Co., 1923.

Tartar, V., *The Biology of Stentor,* New York, Pergamon Press, 1961.

Wichterman, R., *The Biology of Paramecium,* Philadelphia, P. Blakiston's Son & Company, 1951.

Wolken, J. J., *Euglena: An Experimental Animal for Biochemical and Biophysical Studies,* New Brunswick, N. J., Rutgers University Press, 1961.

Chapter 5

Sponges

Sponges are universally regarded as an evolutionary blind alley. Their bodily organization is so utterly different from that of any other group of animals that most zoologists feel they could scarcely be more different were they from another planet. For this reason, among others, sponges will repay some study. They can be defined as metazoans without organs, mouth, or nervous tissue, and with a body permeated by pores and cavities some of which are lined with flagellated collar cells. They constitute the Phylum Porifera.

Sponges have been articles of commerce from very ancient times. Sponge diving is one of the oldest occupations and, despite competition from plastics, is still an active business. Sponges also have their harmful aspects. In the seafood industry, for example, certain sponges are a serious problem because they smother oysters by boring into their shells and then overgrowing them.

Although Aristotle over 2,000 years ago held sponges to be animals, many competent zoologists right down to a time within the lives of men now living believed them to be plants. This is surprising, because one of the most obviously animal-like traits of sponges was discovered in George Washington's day: currents of water continually stream into and out of a living sponge. The final blow to the plant theory of sponges was delivered by a student of "the father of American zoology," Louis Agassiz.

This student, James Clark, discovered in the 1860's that sponges have flagellated collar cells closely resembling a well-known group of protozoans. Professor Agassiz found this hard to believe and tried to dissuade the student from putting his discovery into print. The professor turned out to be wrong.

Habitats and Variety. Most sponges are marine, and flourish especially in warm seas. There are, however, several fresh-water species, some brown and others a handsome vivid green from symbiotic algae. In North America, they can be found growing over stones and submerged sticks and logs in ponds and streams from southern Canada southward. Anyone who has looked around in the clear waters of a coral reef has been struck by the weird shapes and variety of marine sponges. There are enormous round "loggerheads" like short fat barrels well able to stop a good-sized motor boat. There are brilliant red and orange species, some extremely poisonous to the skin if handled. There are chrome yellow, deep purple, and sky-blue species, along with others velvety black, like the commercial sponges. In temperate waters the two most notable species are the scarlet *Microciona* and a yellow oyster-boring sponge with a sulfurous odor, *Cliona*.

The habitat of fresh-water sponges is restricted, but in the oceans sponges live both near shore and at great depths of over a mile.

TYPICAL STRUCTURE

What makes sponges so peculiar? First, the degree of integration and coordination of their cells is extremely low. They possess no organs and no nervous system. They are simply epithelia, thin sheets of cells covering surfaces, plus an irregular aggregation of cells called **mesenchyme.** Secondly, they lack a mouth but have instead countless minute pores for the intake of water. Third, their body plan is built around chambers lined with flagellated collar cells, a unique feature known in no other group of animals. Lastly, their embryology, so far as is known (the development of very few sponges has ever been followed), seems to be the reverse of that found elsewhere in the animal kingdom. In any case, the small flagellated cells that cover the upper pole of the cleaved egg and become ectoderm (the outer layer of tissue) on other animals, in sponges fold in and become the flagellated chambers. The larger nonflagellated cells at the lower pole of the cleaved egg, which in other animals become the endodermal lining of the gut, in sponges become the **epithelium** covering the body.

The anatomy of sponges is built around the chambers lined with the flagellated cells. Water enters these cavities through minute pores called **prosopyles.** In most sponges these pores are not actually on the surface of the sponge but are reached only through incurrent canals. Water enters these canals through much larger openings which are called the dermal pores or **ostia.**

Within the body of the sponge are the flagellated chambers lined with the flagellated collar cells or **choanocytes.** It is the beating of their flagella that produces the currents which bring in food particles and oxygen. The flagellated cells also ingest food, or carmine particles — should you feed some to a sponge.

Water leaves the flagellated chambers by pores known as **apopyles,** which lead into excurrent canals that empty into one or more large canals, which in turn empty into one or more large central cavities called **spongocoels.** Water leaves the spongocoel by a conspicuous opening, sometimes fringed with large spicules, and called the **osculum.**

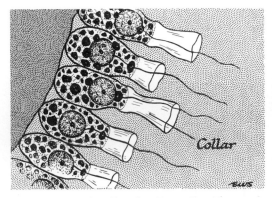

Fig. 5 – 1. Flagellated collar cells of sponges.

Within this simple pattern, sponges have achieved three degrees of complexity (see Fig. 5 – 2). The simplest is the **ascon** type (*askos,* bladder). In this sponge the central cavity, the spongocoel, is itself the flagellated chamber, and the prosopyles or incurrent pores are actually on the surface of the sponge. There are very few sponges that show so simple a structure as this.

The second degree of complexity is the **sycon** type (*sykon,* fig). The flagellated chambers are fingerlike cavities radiating out from the central spongocoel, which is itself no longer flagellated. Water first enters ostia or dermal pores and passes through incurrent canals before reaching the minute prosopyles at the entrances of the flagellated chambers. Most of the sponges that are available for use in laboratory study are sycons.

The third type is the **leucon** (*leukos,* white). All the larger sponges, and in fact most sponges, are organized according to this scheme. The flagellated chambers, instead of radiating like fingers, are rounded and arranged somewhat like bunches of grapes deep in a mesenchyme or connective tissue layer.

On the cellular or histological level, sponges are not as peculiar as they are on the anatomical level. Perhaps this is because the basic structure of all cells must consist of nucleus and cytoplasm, and the number of effective variations in cell type is not as great as the number of patterns that can be constructed out of these units.

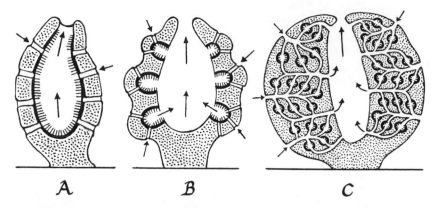

Fig. 5–2. The three types of sponge organization. *A*, ascon. *B*, sycon. *C*, leucon. *(After Woodruff,* Foundations of Biology, *6th ed., 1941, The Macmillan Company)*

Covering the surface of a sponge and lining the canals is a layer of flattened epithelial cells. Around the ostia in some sponges there are contractile cells. No one has found evidence of nerve cells of any sort. Interspersed between the pavement of polygonal epithelial or lining cells are the pore cells or **porocytes.** These are large cells shaped somewhat like an old-fashioned tubular napkin ring. The nucleus lies in one side, and a hole through the center of the cytoplasm is the pore. It is these porocytes which make the prosopyles through which water enters the flagellated chambers. Within the mesenchyme making up the main mass of the animal are many amoeboid cells. They are undifferentiated, embryonic cells capable of replacing others after wear and of playing a leading role in growth and regeneration. There are spongin fiber-secreting cells, and spicule-forming cells or scleroblasts. There are gland cells secreting slime to the surface. There are food storage cells. There are ova and sperms, and lastly the flagellated collar cells.

SPICULES AND EVOLUTION

Fully as distinctive of sponges as their flagellated collar cells are their spicules. In the words of the eminent English zoologist Adam Sedgwick:

The spicules of sponges in their diversity, symmetry, and intricacy of their form, in the perfection and finish of their architecture, constitute some of the most astonishing objects in natural history. In view of them it is impossible to regard the sponges as low in the scale of evolution. Such finish and such perfection of structure can only have been reached as a result of a long process of evolutionary changes.

And then he puts the real problem:

While it is pretty clear that the main function of the skeletal structures is to give support and protection to the sponge body, it is by no means easy to give explanations of the diversity and complexity of form they present.

No sane person, except a specialist in sponges, would think of memorizing all the different kinds of spicules that exist in sponges, but a close look will reveal the magnitude of the problem they present for the student of evolution. The spicules fall into two groups, **megascleres,** which make up the main skeletal frame of the sponge, and the little **microscleres,** which are scattered through the mesenchyme. Some spicules are monaxons with one axis, other triaxons, tetraxons, even polyaxons. Within this scheme there exists such a vast array of forms that it has so far defied analysis. The types have merely been named. There are curved sigmas (Σ), S-shaped sigmaspires, bow-shaped toxas, and hooked chelas. There are more or less star-shaped sterasters, chiasters, pycnasters, oxyasters, spherasters, spirasters, metasters, plesiasters, saniasters, and amphiasters. Some spicules are monolophous (single-crested), others dilophous, trilophous, tetralophous. There are microcalthrops, each of which occurs in three forms. There are at least ten kinds of trienes,

Fig. 5 – 3. Types of sponge spicules.

some resembling anchors, some tridents. There are dragmas, rhaphides, discohexacts, scipulas, and other forms difficult to describe. A variety of sponge spicules is shown in Figure 5 – 3.

The formation of these complex and varied structures must involve profound problems of cell behavior, physiology, and biochemistry. At least in the simpler cases, spicule formation begins by the deposition of a rod-shaped crystal within the cytoplasm of a binucleate cell. Before the completion of a large complex spicule many scleroblasts, i.e., spicule-forming cells, have taken part. Likewise in the formation of spongin fibers, many cells cooperate.

Because sponges are merely loosely organized aggregations of cells and because they are the only multicellular animals to possess choanocytes, many zoologists believe that they probably arose from some of the colonial choanocyte protozoa. However, the embryology of sponges resembles the development of *Volvox* and other colonial flagellated green algae. Whatever their origin, the sponges are so different from all other animals that some people

wish to divide the animal kingdom into three branches, the Protozoa or one-celled animals, the Parazoa or sponges, and the Metazoa—all the remaining multicellular animals.

THE THREE MAJOR SPONGE GROUPS

Sponges fall into three classes distinguished from each other by the character of their spicules and other traits.

1. The Calcaria or calcareous sponges constitute a small group of marine species living in shallow water and constructing their spicules from lime. Although these sponges never grow very big, their cells are much larger than those of sponges in the other two classes. All the ascon and sycon sponges are calcareous, although a few leucon sponges also belong to this class. Most of the species studied in laboratories are in this group.

2. The glass sponges or Hexactinellida are typically inhabitants of the great depths of the sea where, in eternal darkness, the only current is the slow "arctic creep" of the heavy cold

polar water moving along the bottom toward the equator. Their spicules are of silica, mostly hydrated silica, $H_2Si_3O_7$, with traces of other elements. These spicules are unique in possessing six rays.

The body of a glass sponge is of an openwork construction and appears to be loosely made of spun glass. The flagellated chambers are ar-

Fig. 5–4. *Euplectella*, Venus' flower basket, a glass sponge from the deep sea. *(Kindness of Mildred Adams Fenton)*

ranged in a simple leucon manner. Venus' flower basket, *Euplectella*, from deep water off the coast of Japan, and Neptune's cup, *Hyalonema*, from the coast of New England, are commonly seen in museums. In *Hyalonema*, the stalk of spicules which holds the sponge upright in the soft bottom ooze is composed of a hundred or more individual spicules, each over a foot long.

3. Most sponges belong to the third class, the Demospongiae, or spongin sponges. Although their spicules are also of silica, they do not have six rays. However, the body of these sponges is firmly bound together by a proteinous fiber, spongin. One group of demosponges lacks spicules altogether. These are the sponges of commerce. Most demosponges are constructed on the leucon plan, with many tiny flagellated chambers deep in the mesenchyme, but a few are ascons or sycons. Most of the large familiar sponges, including the fresh-water species, belong to this class. Some of the common subtropical marine sponges that are poisonous to the human skin are of this class.

REPRODUCTION AND REGENERATION

Reproduction. Sponges reproduce both asexually and sexually. In sexual reproduction both sperms and eggs are usually produced in the same individual. Gametes develop from amoeboid cells in the mesenchyme and from the flagellated collar cells. The spermatozoa are typical metazoan sperms with a head, midpiece, and long tail. The ova are also typical eggs, with nucleus and a large amount of cytoplasm containing yolk granules. Sexual reproduction appears to reach its height in fresh-water sponges during the summer.

Sperms pass out of the oscula into the surrounding water and then are drawn into the same or other sponges. Fertilization and cleavage of the eggs occur within the body of the parent sponge. The events of fertilization are strange. The sperm does not enter the egg cell directly but enters a choanocyte. The collar cell then carries the engulfed sperm to the egg, fuses with its cytoplasm, and thus introduces the sperm nucleus into the egg cytoplasm! The peculiar type of early development has already been described. In the known cases a very small roundish ciliated larva is formed. It swims freely for some hours before settling down to grow directly into a new sponge.

The commonest method of asexual reproduction in fresh-water sponges is by gemmule formation. The **gemmules** are rounded bodies, very small but visible to the naked eye, each consisting of a solid central mass of amoeboid mesenchyme cells surrounded by a triple capsule. This protective coating consists of an outside layer of dead cells, a middle layer of spicules shaped like empty photo-film spools, and a tough inner skin. The gemmules are produced all summer but are released when the rest of the sponge dies and disintegrates as the water dries up or winter comes. Gemmules are carried by wind and water currents, and in the way many pond animals get carried for long distances — in mud between the toes of water birds.

Regeneration. Sponges have great powers of regeneration, but regeneration and normal growth are essentially the same in organisms of such a low degree of specialization. Commercial bath sponges can be propagated by being cut into small cubes, each of which will grow into a full-sized sponge.

The most remarkable discovery ever made about sponges was that of H. V. Wilson in 1907. He found that the common scarlet *Microciona* can be squeezed alive through fine silk bolting cloth of the kind used in mills to sift flour. Many of the cells are killed by this treatment, but those that survive will creep together and organize themselves into little sponges if allowed to settle in a dish of sea water. Almost nothing is known about what properties of cells enable them to do this. (It has been found, however, that the cells of various other animals in addition to sponges have this ability.) Nor is it known for certain whether the collar cells, epithelial cells, gland cells, and other specialized cells of the new sponge are derived in each case from corresponding specialized cells in the original sponge or whether the specialized cells of the old sponge, once they are squeezed through the silk cloth and have become amoeboid, truly dedifferentiate and hence are able to form any of the cell types necessary to build the new sponge. This is a question of great importance for the theory of development and gene action.

Recent experimenters have discovered that it is possible to induce cells from two different species of sponge to unite into a single individual. This happens only under special circumstances. How does a cell "know" the species to which it belongs? And what makes a cell "forget"?

Review and References

REVIEW TOPICS

1. In what ways are sponges very different from other animals?

2. What is the organization of ascon, sycon, and leucon sponges? How are these types of organization related to the three taxonomic groups of sponges, the calcareous, glass, and spongin sponges?

3. What is remarkable about the regenerative power of sponges? What basic scientific problems does it present?

4. How did a discovery of a student of Louis Agassiz support the view of Aristotle about the nature of sponges?

5. Define: collar cell, epithelium, mesenchyme, prosopyle cell, leucon, megasclere, microsclere, symbiotic, osculum, binucleate.

USEFUL REFERENCES

de Laubenfels, M. W., *Sponge Fauna of the Dry Tortugas in Particular and of the West Indies in General,* Washington, D.C., Carnegie Institution, 1936.

de Laubenfels, M. W., *Sponges of Woods Hole and Adjacent Waters,* Cambridge, Mass., Museum of Comparative Zoology, Bull. 103 (1), 1949.

Hyman, L. H., *The Invertebrates: Protozoa through Ctenophora,* New York, McGraw-Hill Book Company, 1940.

Pennak, R. W., *Fresh-Water Invertebrates of the United States,* New York, The Ronald Press Company, 1953.

Wilson, H. V., and J. T. Penny, "The Regeneration of Sponges from Dissociated Cells," *Journal of Experimental Zoology,* vol. 56, 1930.

Chapter 6

Coelenterates

For many people jellyfish and sea anemones, corals and sea fans typify the invertebrates. The coelenterates as a group carry an aura of mystery and adventure in the distant places of the seven seas. Superficially, the coelenterates appear very unlike each other. Contrast a jellyfish with a coral, or a simple hydra with a sea fan. Yet all the diverse members of this phylum can be rather easily defined as radially symmetrical animals that produce nematocysts. Radial symmetry is the symmetry of a wheel; nematocysts are cysts containing a poisonous thread that is thrust out when the animal is stimulated. Nematocysts are so characteristic and so distinctive of coelenterates that Cnidaria (*cnida,* nettle) is another name for the phylum. Except in some of the ciliates among the Protozoa, nowhere else in the animal kingdom are nematocysts produced. They not only serve for defense, but are used to paralyze and kill the animals on which coelenterates feed.

Coelenterates have impinged directly on human affairs in a number of ways. Precious corals have been sought from time out of mind. Coral reefs continue to be important as sites for human habitation, as breakwaters for harbors, and as dangerous impediments to navigation. Coelenterates have also played an important part in the development of zoological science.

In the 18th century no animal experiments caused such widespread interest as those of Trembley on the newly discovered fresh-water hydra. In the 19th century Weismann's theory of the germplasm, which he based on studies of coelenterates, provided the hinge on which much of biological thought has turned ever since. And in our own century coelenterates are often the animals of choice in studies on mechanisms of growth and regeneration.

It was not until 1812 that the great French zoologist Cuvier (1769–1832) established that jellyfish and sea anemones belong to a single group. He did this on the basis of their adult anatomy, specifically their radial symmetry, circle of tentacles, and central digestive cavity. It was later still when a Norwegian investigator, Michael Sars, made the amazing discovery that the eggs of jellyfish do not develop into jellyfish, or medusae, to use the scientific name, but into a sea anemone-like form scientifically called a hydroid or polyp. The hydroid, he found, produces the jellyfish or medusa by asexual methods. As a result of the work of these pioneers, including Darwin's famous champion, Thomas Henry Huxley (1825–1895), the coelenterates have come to be recognized as members of a single phylum.

Classification and Structure. There are three classes of coelenterates. The Hydrozoa include most of the very small jellyfish and the familiar hydroids seen growing on wharf pilings and other submerged objects. The Scyphozoa include the large jellyfish—all those which attract public notice except the Portuguese man-of-war, which is a very special type of hydrozoan. The third class, the Anthozoa, include the sea anemones, the corals, and the sea fans.

No matter how diverse in outward appearance, all coelenterates have certain anatomical features in common:

1. They possess a radial symmetry.

2. At the hub is a central blind sac or gut cavity called the **coelenteron** (*coel,* cavity, + *enteron,* gut) or gastrovascular cavity (*gastro,* stomach, + *vascular,* pertaining to vessels which transport body fluids). There is but one opening into the coelenteron, the mouth. The coelenteron and its extensions in radiating canals are as much of a circulatory system as coelenterates possess. There is no body cavity or coelom such as is found in many of the higher animals.

3. **Nematocysts,** stinging capsules (*nema,* thread, + *cyst,* vesicle), are universally present in coelenterates.

4. Coelenterates exhibit two different body forms, the **medusoid** or jellyfish and the **hydroid** or **polyp** form. In many but by no means all coelenterates, the two forms alternate, one giving rise to the other in succession. This is called **alternation of generations** or metagenesis. The basic structure of the hydroid or polyp form and that of the medusoid or jellyfish form is alike (see Fig. 6–1). A major difference between the two is the extent of development of the mesogleal jelly.

5. The tissues of coelenterates are commonly said to consist of but two primary germ layers, an **ectoderm** covering the outer surface and containing the nematocysts, and an **endoderm** lining the coelenteron. Separating the ectoderm and endoderm is a thinner or thicker layer called the **mesoglea.** In the first of the three classes of coelenterates, the mesoglea is a jelly layer containing very few cells. For them the orthodox description of a coelenterate as a diploblastic (two-layer) group of animals with ectoderm and endoderm but no middle layer of cells (**mesoderm**) holds true. However, in the other two classes of coelenterates, which include the big jellyfish and all the sea anemones and corals, there is a well-developed, highly cellular middle layer.

What is a student to do in the face of a situation like this among the coelenterates? Certainly to memorize a simplification so very far from the truth would not only be puerile, it would clearly be unscientific. No one can ask too often, what are the facts? The facts in this case are that in the class of coelenterates to which the small jellyfish and hydroids belong (the Hydrozoa), the coelenterates are diploblastic. In the other great groups, the Scyphozoa and the Anthozoa, the coelenterates are triploblastic with ectoderm, mesoderm, and endoderm.

6. Lastly, the organs of coelenterates are very simple. The most complex coelenterate organs are the marginal sense organs of some of the larger jellyfish which are provided with a lens and a retina. A tentacle is also an organ, though of a simple sort. There is hardly anything that can be called an organ system in the sense in which a fish or an insect has a nervous or reproductive system.

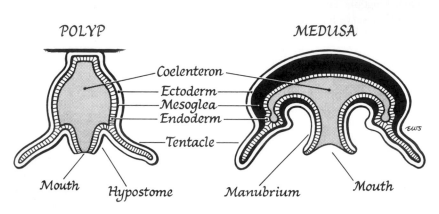

POLYP   MEDUSA

Coelenteron
Ectoderm
Mesoglea
Endoderm

Tentacle

Mouth   Hypostome   Manubrium   Mouth

Fig. 6–1. The relationship between the polyp or hydroid and the medusoid or jellyfish forms in coelenterates.

HYDROZOA

The class Hydrozoa (*hydra,* a many-headed monster, + *zoa,* animals) is a very large class containing many thousands of species of hydroids and smaller jellyfish. To it belong the familiar fresh-water hydras and the less familiar but fairly common fresh-water jellyfish. It contains most of the coelenterates used in class study and in research. Among these are the hydroids *Obelia* and *Tubularia* which appear like clusters of pink and white flowers growing on marine pilings or submerged rocks. Other extremely interesting species like *Hydractinia* grow over the snail shells inhabited by hermit crabs. Here too is the common little jellyfish, *Gonionemus,* found in coves and bays along the shores of both the Atlantic and Pacific Oceans, and the beautiful but rapacious *Liriope,* which is seldom found within sight of land but which roams the high seas sometimes in incredible millions. The most spectacular hydrozoan is the Portuguese man-of-war, *Physalia.*

Hydrozoan Characteristics. No matter how outwardly diverse in appearance, all Hydrozoa are united by four anatomical traits which distinguish them from both the Scyphozoa and Anthozoa:

1. The hydrozoan jellyfish or medusa always possesses a **velum.** This is a thin circular band of muscle around the margin of the bell. It extends horizontally inward towards the proboscis or **manubrium,** and by its contraction helps force water out from the bell through a narrow orifice. Thus the medusa achieves jet propulsion. Scyphozoan jellyfish lack a velum.

2. Another difference is in the marginal sense organs that all medusae possess around the edge of the bell. The marginal sense organs of the hydrozoans are small and simple, usually tiny vesicles containing a small concretion.

3. The hydroids or polyps of the Hydrozoa are usually much better developed than those of the Scyphozoa.

4. The coelenteron (gastrovascular cavity) is a simple cylindrical space undivided by partitions, the so-called **mesenteries** or **septa.** Lack of mesenteries is an important Hydrozoa trait.

Modern knowledge of the coelenterates is still inadequate for the task of logical classification. When Alfred Goldsborough Mayer, America's greatest student of coelenterates, wrote his magnificent three-volume monograph, *Medusae of the World,* in 1910, he expressed the hope that some day a really logical classification would become possible and said that the Linnaean system seemed inadequate to express the interrelationships of hydrozoans.

Now, over half a century later, when an eminent English student of coelenterates, F. S. Russell, has published a weighty monograph on the *Medusae of the British Isles,* the same inadequacy of our knowledge is evident. *Liriope* swims the seas in great abundance; but no one can answer the seemingly simple question—is there one highly variable species of *Liriope,* or are there 20 separate ones? And to Russell's great regret he is forced to continue in many cases calling the medusa by one name, the hydroid that produced it by another. It seems the only thing to do when there are still so many medusae for which the corresponding hydroid is unknown, and vice versa, and it is not surprising that each should be discovered and named separately before their relationship becomes known. A familiar case is the fresh-water jellyfish, *Craspedacusta sowerbyi,* and the hydroid which produces it but bears the name *Microhydra ryderi.*

Hydra and Some Basic Problems. The fresh-water hydra is the most important coelenterate for study and research. A variety of species is available. *Chlorohydra viridissima* is a bright green species found in quiet ponds in most parts of the world. The green is due to tiny symbiotic algae, probably *Chlorella,* living within the cytoplasm of the endoderm cells. Since the ectoderm cells do not harbor the algae, the ectoderm appears as a translucent, colorless epithelium covering the green endodermal lining of the coelenteron and its extensions out into the tentacles. The green algal cells are so minute that to a casual observer they appear like the chloroplastids of some plant, and one might be tempted to think that *Chlorohydra viridissima* was an exceptional animal which produces chloroplastids. Why not? The evidence is clear. With proper staining, a nucleus can be distinguished in each of the very small algal cells and some can be seen

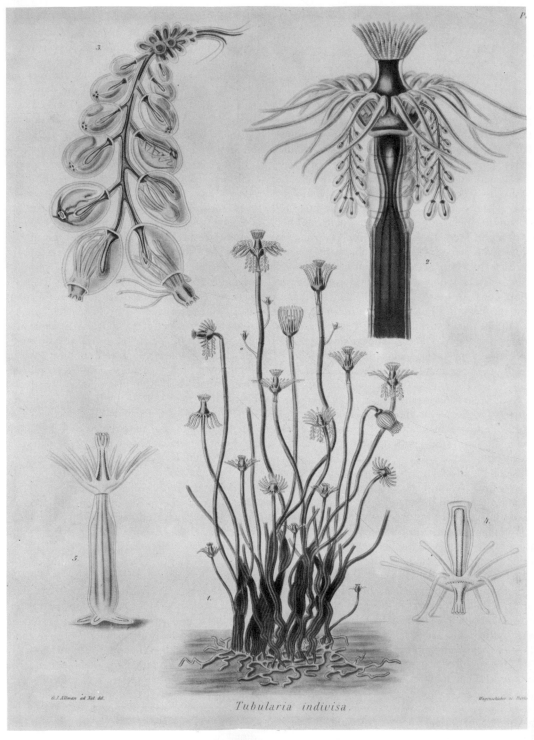

Fig. 6-2. *Tubularia*, a hydroid widely used in research. *1*, adult colony, approximately life size. *2*, mature hydranth with three hanging clusters of gonophores. *3*, single gonophore from which larvae (actinulae) are beginning to emerge. *4*, free motile larva. *5*, fixed larva developing into a hydroid. From G. J. Allman's famous monograph on tubularian hydroids, published by the Ray Society of London in 1872.

in division. An intimate symbiosis of this kind inevitably raises many questions. To begin with, why should the symbiotic algae be confined so rigidly to the endoderm and never live in the ectoderm?

In many parts of the northern hemisphere the commonest species of brown hydra is *Hydra oligactis,* so named in 1766 by Peter Pallas (a German zoologist living in Russia) from Trembley's description. This species can usually be identified because when fully extended the basal half or third of the body is very much thinner than the distal portion adjacent to the tentacles and makes merely a stalk. It is the largest of the brown hydras and under favorable conditions, i.e., in a pond-water aquarium in a cool room and abundantly fed with daphnias, it

Fig. 6–3. Above: *Hydra (Pelmatohydra) oligactis,* the common brown hydra, shown expanded to its full 4 inches, and also contracted. Below: *Hydra littoralis,* showing characteristic testes and asexual budding. *(After Hyman)*

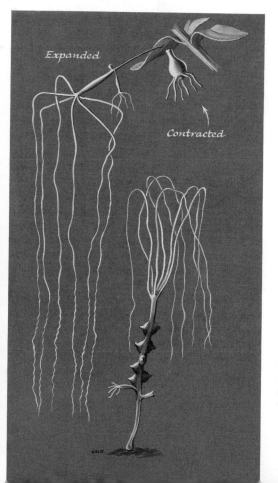

will grow to an over-all length of at least 4 inches. It is the only species able to paralyze and eat fish fry. Other names for this species are *Pelmatohydra oligactis* and *Hydra fusca.* Another widespread American hydra is *H. littoralis,* which lives in moving water. The description which follows applies primarily to *H. oligactis.*

The general body form of hydras is evident from the accompanying illustrations. The conical region below the mouth and above the tentacles is known as the **hypostome.** The opposite end of the animal is the **basal disk.** Regions nearer the mouth are called **distal** or **apical,** those nearer the base **basal** or **proximal.**

Types of Ectodermal Cells. In higher animals the ectoderm covers the exterior of the body and also forms the nervous system. In coelenterates its functions are more inclusive and there are six major types of ectodermal cells.

1. Cuboidal or **columnar epithelial cells** form a covering for the body. These may also be glandular and secrete mucus or gas.

2. **Epithelio-muscular cells** are similar to simple columnar epithelial cells, but each is extended, at the inner end where it abuts against the mesoglea, into a long narrow process, so as to make the whole cell T-shaped. This extension contains one or more smooth muscle fibers. All the ectoderm muscle fibers run parallel to the long axis (apical-basal axis) of the body. Their contraction makes the hydra shorten. These longitudinal fibers are the **antagonists** of similar but circular muscle fibers in the endoderm that by their contraction cause the hydra to become thin and elongated. The arrangement of muscles into antagonistic pairs and sets is a universal principle within the animal kingdom, from hydra, worms, insects, and mollusks, to men. The necessity for this arrangement is obvious once it is realized that muscles can contract and pull but cannot push. This is the meaning of all the sets of flexors and extensors in the human arm or leg, the protractors and retractors of the mollusks, and the sphincters and dilators of innumerable eyes. A tricky and important problem that has been much investigated in dogs and other vertebrates is the nature of the neural mechanisms that enable a set of extensors to relax in exact correlation with the contraction of the corresponding

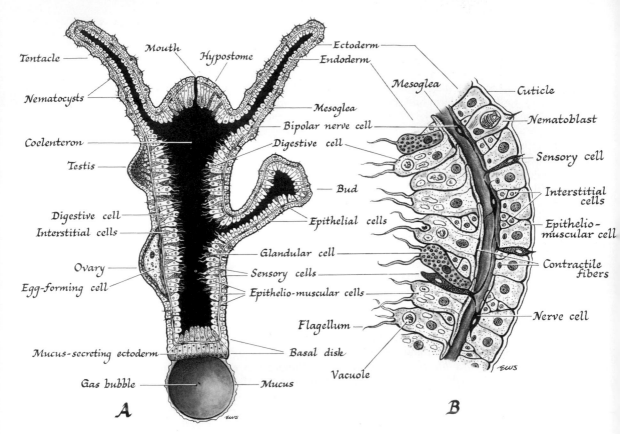

Fig. 6–4. *A*, longitudinal section of an hermaphroditic hydra. *B*, cross section of wall.

flexors. This problem will be discussed in connection with the vertebrates, but the phenomenon is first encountered here among the coelenterates.

3. **Nematoblasts** (*nema*, a thread, + *blastos*, a bud) are the cells which form and enclose the stinging capsules or nematocysts. Each nematoblast bears a pointed threadlike process of cytoplasm called the **cnidocil**. The cnidocil projects out from the cell surface and is believed to act as a trigger which sets off the discharge of the nematocyst with its thread, barbs, and poison. The nucleus of the nematoblast is pushed to one corner of the cell by the capsule or cyst, which can be seen under the high power of a microscope to contain a coiled thread and, in some cases, barbs.

In the largest and most easily observed type of nematocyst in hydra (a penetrant), discharge results in a small lid opening from one end of the egg-shaped cyst. Out shoots a long thread from a short base which bears several barbs.

Disregarding the thread, such a discharged nematocyst resembles an electric light bulb. In discharging, the thread turns itself inside out.

Four types of nematocysts are found in hydras. Those known as **volvents** coil around hairs of the victim. **Bristly** and **smooth glutinants** entangle the victim, while the large **penetrants** inject the poison.

No one knows what induces a particular cell in a hydra to produce a nematocyst, much less why some nematoblasts produce the big penetrants while others form volvents or glutinants. Here again we are faced with a basic problem of zoology, differentiation. What causes one cell of an animal to become a gland cell, another a muscle or nerve cell? It is known that the nematoblasts of hydra arise from small interstitial cells and only in the more distal portions of the body cylinder, never in the basal parts of the body or the tentacles or hypostome. They migrate from their sites of origin by passing through the mesoglea and endoderm into

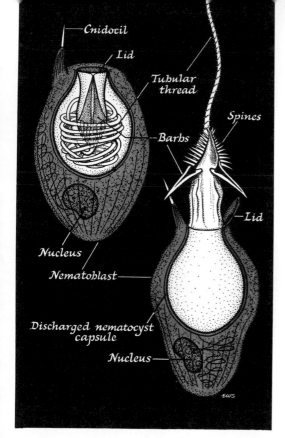

Labels on figure:
Cnidocil
Lid
Tubular thread
Spines
Barbs
Lid
Nucleus
Nematoblast
Discharged nematocyst capsule
Nucleus

Fig. 6-5. Hydra nematocysts (penetrants) before and after discharge, as seen under the high power of the compound microscope.

the coelenteron, where they are carried to the tentacles or hypostome by the coelenteric circulation.

About 15 different types of nematocysts are found among coelenterates as a group, including the big scyphozoan jellyfish and anthozoans like corals and sea anemones. They are essential to the lives of their bearers both for protection and for obtaining food. They must have undergone a long and complex evolution, and are an important taxonomic tool.

The nature of the stimulus necessary for discharge of the nematocysts is uncertain. Mechanical stimulation seems to be involved, yet the commensal or ectoparasitic ciliates, *Kerona* and *Trichodina,* can be seen to run over the cnidocils and bend them down without inducing a discharge. Chemical stimuli are also believed involved, yet the juice of *Daphnia,* a favorite food of hydra, is without appreciable effect. The fact that it is extremely difficult to elicit a discharge of nematocysts in an animal satiated

with food has led some workers to think that the discharge was under nervous control. But only in *Physalia,* the Portuguese man-of-war, where the contraction of fibers in the nematoblast is involved in the discharge, do anesthetics have any effect. In other species, cancelling out the action of the nerve fibers by anesthetics fails to interfere with nematocyst action. Perhaps with more basic knowledge about the physiology of stimulation, it will be possible to answer some of these puzzles. Likewise, knowing more about stimulation in coelenterates would help clarify the problems of stimulation elsewhere in the animal world.

The mechanism that produces the discharge itself is somewhat better understood. The actual explosion that throws out the thread and causes it to turn inside out appears to be an increase in osmotic pressure within the cyst. This old theory has been confirmed by recent investigators who have demonstrated by observing the intake of dyes that a change takes place in the permeability of the cyst. Changes in permeability are often connected with stimulation and response.

What are the potent toxins which produce redness of the skin, swelling, pain, and paralysis in a man and death in many small animals? Paper chromotography and other modern methods of analysis have shown that nematocysts either contain or are closely associated with a number of active substances. Serotonin (5-hydroxytryptamine), a powerful pain-producer and histamine releaser, is abundant in a variety of coelenterates, especially in the tentacles and acontia where the nematocysts are concentrated. The theory that serotonin is an agent in producing the effect of the nematocyst is strengthened by the fact that wasp venom is rich in serotonin. An ammonium compound called tetramine (tetramethyl ammonium hydroxide) which blocks neural junctions is also found in nematocysts. There is also evidence that various poisonous proteins are present which block cholinergic nerves.

The coordinated feeding reaction of hydras is elicited by glutathione, a tripeptide in the body fluids of worms, crustaceans, and all higher animals. These facts suggest that hydra did not evolve until after worms and therefore is not a very primitive animal.

4. A fourth type of cell in the ectoderm is the **nerve cell.** There are sensory cells in the ectodermal epithelium and bipolar or multipolar nerve cells, i.e., nerve cells with two or more protoplasmic nerve fibers, at the base of the epithelium against the mesoglea.

Because the coelenterates are the most primitive animals with a nervous system, there has been a great deal of interest in what their nervous system is like and how it works. A generation ago it was believed that the coelenterate nervous system was a "nerve net." So it is, but not quite in the sense of the older workers. For them the nerve net was a reticulum of continuous, unbroken protoplasmic fibers. Beginning with careful investigations of the German embryologists, the Hertwig brothers, it has become clear that the nerve net is a plexus made up of discrete nerve cells with nerve fibers connected by **synapses.** A synapse is the name given to the place where the tip of one nerve fiber comes close to or in virtual contact with the tip of a nerve fiber from another nerve cell, or with the body of another nerve cell. All or at least most synapses act as valves and will transmit a stimulus in one direction only. Many of the remarkable properties of nervous systems, learning and possibly memory, are thought to involve changes in the properties of synapses. Thus the basic structure of the coelenterate nervous system is the same as that in a frog or a man.

The nervous system of hydras is indeed simple, but it is responsible for many coordinated activities. Green hydras have no known eyes or photoreceptors, yet by a process of trial and error they will collect on the lighted side of an aquarium. The tentacles of a brown hydra will cooperate in capturing prey and drawing it toward the mouth. The mouth itself often begins to open *before* it is touched by the prey. In moving from place to place a hydra may glide along on its pedal disk. It may also move in a series of somersaults, bending over its body until the hypostome and tentacles touch the bottom, releasing the basal disk, pulling the body up over the hypostome so the animal is upside down, and then bending over the body until the pedal disk comes in contact with the bottom in a new spot after completing a somersault.

5. The **interstitial cells** are small, undifferentiated cells found singly or in clusters between the other ectodermal cells, usually close to the mesoglea. They are the reserve cells that are the continuing source of nematoblasts. They also seem to give rise to the germ cells that become eggs or sperms. They play an important and probably essential role in regeneration and growth.

6. The **gametes** appear in the ectoderm. The eggs become relatively very large and amoeboid. The sperms are formed in rounded testes. The green hydra is hermaphroditic, with testes on the distal portion of the body and ovaries on the basal portion. *Hydra oligactis* is dioecious, that is, there are separate males and females, but this is not true of all species of brown hydras. Here again we are faced with basic issues, far-reaching in their implications. Why are some species hermaphroditic and others dioecious? Why does a certain cell develop into an ovum or a sperm? The environmental conditions inducing the appearance of sexuality will be discussed below.

Types of Endodermal Cells. In higher animals the endoderm forms the epithelial lining of the digestive canal and the structures derived from it, such as the liver. In the Hydrozoa many of the several types of endodermal cells lining the gastrovascular cavity or coelenteron are flagellated. The flagella maintain a lively current which can be seen, under a dissecting microscope, flowing first in one direction and then in another in the coelenteron. Under the electron microscope it can be seen that these flagella have the same structure (a circle of nine strands with a core of two) that is found in the cilia of protozoans or the tails of the sperms of mammals.

1. Among the most conspicuous endodermal cells are large cells with **amoeboid** inner ends. These engulf food particles and digest them within the cytoplasm.

2. Large **glandular cells** secrete digestive enzymes into the coelenteron. Thus there is both intra- and extracellular digestion. These cells can be recognized by their content of large granules of enzyme precursors.

3. Large **epithelio-muscular cells** bear long contractile fibrils in basal extensions against the

mesoglea. These smooth muscle fibrils run around the body of a hydra. Thus their contraction causes the body to become elongated. They are the antagonists of the muscle fibers in the ectoderm, which run lengthwise on the body.

4. Small **sensory cells** occur in the endoderm. Their filaments connect via synapses with the nerve net already described.

5. Scattered throughout are undifferentiated **interstitial cells.** These cells replace the loss of specialized cells from injury and wear and tear.

Trembley's Experiments. The work of Abraham Trembley (1710–1784) of Geneva, a scientist and philosopher, began a new epoch in zoology, one not yet ended. Trembley raised the question of the genesis of animal form and of regeneration in a new and startling manner. His work astonished his contemporaries. The great Voltaire, a bit of a scientist himself, was so dumbfounded that he questioned Trembley's accuracy. Fielding, Smollett, Goldsmith, and other writers parodied and ridiculed him. Karl Ernst von Baer, often called the father of embryology, said some years after Trembley's death that his work had led to a revolution in physiology. The work of Trembley is of first importance in its own right, but is also important because of the light it focuses on the nature of scientific discovery itself.

Trembley discovered the green hydra, now called *Chlorohydra viridissima,* in 1740. It seemed like a little "water herb," yet it had the power of motion. Was it an animal or was it a plant, perhaps resembling the then recently discovered sensitive plant? In November of that year he cut the first hydra in a regeneration experiment. If the basal half, which was just a stalk, grew new tentacles, Trembley thought it would show that the thing was a plant. For who ever heard of cutting an animal in half and seeing it grow a new head? Trembley was pretty sure, however, that his creature was an animal. Consequently he was amazed at the results. In his own words, "Who would have thought a head would have returned to it!" If Trembley had followed his own original logic, he would have concluded that the green hydra was indeed a plant. But he didn't. He concluded that the green hydra was an animal, and

that animals therefore can regenerate missing parts of their bodies. There can hardly be a better case to demonstrate the necessity for utmost care in setting up an experiment to make certain that the results can in fact tell you what you want them to tell you.

Trembley's second experiment is even more instructive, because its story extends over three centuries and involves many persons. It began with a very simple question. Can the ectodermal cells covering the exterior of the animal assume the form and digestive functions of the endodermal cells lining the coelenteron? To answer this Trembley turned a brown hydra inside out. He did this by first allowing the hydra to become engorged with food. This makes the animal short and rotund. He then took the blunt end of a "wild boar's bristle" and simply pushed the basal disk up and out through the mouth, just as you might turn a sock inside out by pushing the toe up through the inside and out the top.

To hold the hydra in this condition, Trembley then transfixed it by pushing a bristle through it at right angles to the long axis of the body. The bristle and the transfixed hydra were immersed in a beaker of water with a knot tied in the bristle so that·the hydra could not slip off the end of the bristle and so become able to turn itself right side out again. Under these stringent conditions Trembley found that within four or five days the new outer layer of such a hydra became as clear and smooth as the original one, while the new inner layer assumed the normal digestive characteristics. He could even make the digestive cells lining the cavity of such a transfixed hydra fill up with red or black granules, depending on the color of the food he gave his hydras. He demonstrated his experiments showing that when a hydra is reversed, the outer layer assumes the character of the inner layer, and vice versa.

At the time it all seemed completely convincing, but over a century later new ideas and new facts made it necessary to reinvestigate this question. Trembley's conclusions were shown to be all wrong—surely a case to remember as an antidote to dogmatism in zoology.

What caused the reinvestigation? In the century that had elapsed since Trembley performed his "reversal" experiments the germ layer theory had become dominant in anatomy. In the rigid form in which this theory was then held, it was theoretically impossible for ectoderm and endoderm to turn into each other. Realizing that either the theory was seriously wrong or Trembley was mistaken, Engelmann, a professor at Utrecht, attempted in 1873 and in several subsequent years to repeat Trembley's "inside-out" experiments, but never succeeded. He thereupon rashly concluded that Trembley had been wrong. In fact, he plainly suggested that in regard to this experiment Trembley was something less than honest! At this point Nussbaum, a German zoologist and co-originator with Weismann of the germtrack theory, took up the problem. He confirmed Trembley's results but showed that the ectoderm cells of an inside-out hydra do not transform themselves into endoderm. Instead they migrate to their proper position on the outside of the hydra, mostly by passing out through the mouth and through the holes made by the silver wire on which the animal has been transfixed.

Further light was shed on the problem by a Japanese investigator, Ishikawa, who came to Freiburg to work with Weismann. Ishikawa showed that a transversely transfixed hydra could turn itself right side out without individual cell migration or tearing itself or getting off the wire. This seemingly impossible feat is accomplished by pushing the basal disk up and out through the space around the transfixing wire. This observation led to an attack on Ishikawa's work by Nussbaum and a defense by Weismann.

Anyone can easily confirm the geometrical possibility of Ishikawa's explanation. Cut a pair of holes opposite each other in the leg of an old sock and push a long stick through them. The sock can nevertheless be turned inside out simply by grasping the toe, pushing it up inside the sock and out the space between the stick and the sock. The upper end can be inverted by a similar maneuver.

In recent years an investigator in Iowa, Roudabush, has repeated this experiment with a modern twist, statistical analysis. Of 60 hydras turned inside out on a single day, 21 decomposed, 18 turned themselves right side out in the way Ishikawa had reported, and 21 underwent reorganization by the migration of ectoderm cells as first seen by Nussbaum.

Structure and Alternation of Generations. It is over a century since two Scandinavian zoologists, Michael Sars and Johann Steenstrup, showed that the eggs of jellyfish do not develop into jellyfish but into hydroids; and that hydroids, by asexual budding, produce jellyfish or, more properly, medusae.

An excellent example is *Obelia*, a genus of hydrozoan found commonly growing on rocks and wharfs in both the Atlantic and Pacific. The hydroid generation is a beautiful little pink colonial organism. The stalk consists of a nonliving chitinous (proteinous) protective sheath, the **perisarc,** and a living content, the coenosarc which secretes the perisarc. The living **coenosarc** consists of an ectoderm, a mesoglea, and an endoderm surrounding the central cavity —

Fig. 6–6. Trembley's famous hydra-inside-out experiment illustrated with a sock. Nussbaum and Ishikawa found the explanation a century after Trembley's death.

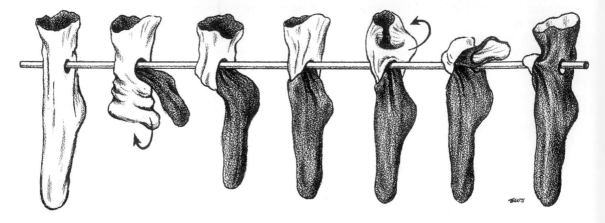

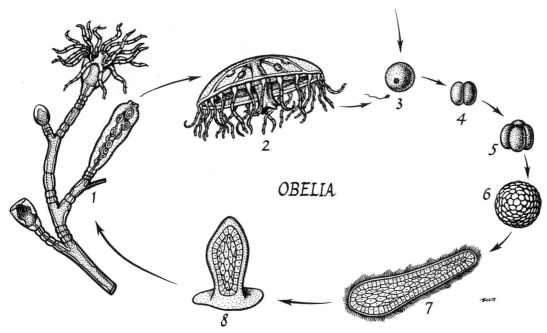

Fig. 6–7. Life cycle of the colonial hydrozoan, *Obelia*. A part of the colony *(1)* is shown, with feeding polyps and vaselike reproductive polyp, which releases free-swimming medusae *(2)* of separate sexes. These produce eggs or sperms *(3)* which unite, and by cleavage *(4, 5)* form a blastula *(6)*. The swimming larva or planula *(7)* attaches itself *(8)* and develops into a new colony. *(From Pauli,* The World of Life, *Houghton Mifflin)*

the coelenteron or gastrovascular cavity. The endoderm is flagellated and in a healthy specimen keeps a brisk current of fluid with digested and partially digested food flowing first one way and then the other in the coelenteron. The whole colony can thus be compared to a type of biological communism in which all the individual polyps share a single common digestive tract.

The individual polyps, or **hydranths,** are of two types. The nutritive hydranths resemble the familiar fresh-water hydra. The body of the hydranth is a stomachlike cavity continuous with the coelenteron that runs through the stalk. At the opposite end of the stomach is the hypostome, at the tip of which is the mouth. Around the base of the hypostome is a circle of tentacles. From the end of the stalk the nonliving perisarc flares out like a little wine glass around the base of the hydranth. It is called the **hydrotheca.** When attacked, the hydranth jerks itself down into the protective hydrotheca. In identifying hydroids, it is important to note whether or not there is a protective hydrotheca around the hydranths. The two largest groups

of hydroids are the **calyptoblastic** ones (*kalyptra,* a covering) like *Obelia,* which have such a protective cup, and the **gymnoblastic** (*gymnos,* naked) ones, like *Tubularia* in which the nonliving perisarc ends at the base of the hydranth. Colony formation in calyptoblastic hydroids is sympodial (i.e., the oldest hydranth is at the base of the colony); in gymnoblastic hydroids, monopodial (i.e., the oldest hydranth is at the tip of the colony). See Figure 6–16.

In *Obelia* the reproductive polyps grow out in the angles where the stalks of the nutritive polyps join the main stalk of the colony. The nonliving perisarc is continued out over the reproductive polyp as a protective **gonotheca.** Within the protecting gonotheca the living coenosarc forms a central core, along the sides of which are medusa buds. They are produced asexually as outgrowths from the core of the coenosarc. These buds develop into miniature medusae, which emerge from the upper end of the gonotheca.

The medusoid or jellyfish generation of a typical species like *Obelia* is the sexual generation. Each medusa is either a male or a female, and all the medusae produced by a single colony of hydranths have the same sex. Moreover, both generations, the hydroid and the medusoid, are diploid, having two sets of chromosomes in every cell. Thus the alternation of generations in coelenterates is different from the similar phenomenon in plants, where one generation is haploid (with one set of chromosomes) and the other diploid. Of course, the sperms and unfertilized eggs of both coelenterates and plants are haploid. The number of chromosomes varies from one species of coelenterate to another. *Gonionemus*, to be described below, has 12 chromosomes in a set.

The medusae produced by *Obelia* are extremely small. Consequently the jellyfish of some other genus such as *Gonionemus* is commonly used for study. The margin of the bell has a **velum,** the muscular band that distinguishes the hydrozoan jellyfish and is its chief swimming organ. Around the margin of the bell is the circle of tentacles. At the base of each of these is a swelling suspected to be some kind of sense organ, although it is difficult to prove this. In any case there is a depot of nematocysts at the base of each tentacle, where they are formed and stored before being supplied to the tentacles. Between the bases of the tentacles are tiny vesicles containing **statoliths,** which are clearly organs of equilibration.

Hanging down on the under (sub-umbrellar) surface of the bell is a proboscis, or **manubrium,** at one end of which is the mouth. At the other end of the manubrium from the mouth is the **stomach.** From the stomach four radial canals extend to the margin of the bell, where each connects with a marginal gastrovascular canal encircling the margin of the bell. The gonads (ovaries or testes, depending on the sex of the medusa) form a wrinkled cross immediately underlying the four radial canals of the coelenteron. In reproduction, the gametes— eggs or sperms—are shed into the sea water. The zygote or fertilized egg develops into a solid, multicellular, completely ciliated larva called a **planula** about the size and shape of an overgrown paramecium. The planula swims about and may be carried long distances by ocean currents, thus disseminating the species. It finally settles on an object and develops into a hydroid. The life cycle is now ready to begin again with asexual reproduction of the hydroid.

The balanced system of hydroid and medusoid generations just described is common enough to be called typical. However, there are many variations. At one extreme are organisms like the fresh-water hydra or the marine *Hydractinia,* to be described below, in which there is no medusoid generation whatsoever. At the other extreme are genera like

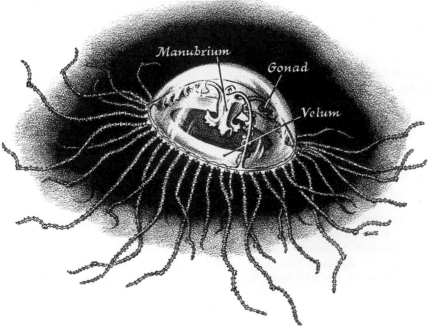

Fig. 6–8. *Gonionemus,* a familiar hydrozoan medusa.

Liriope, which lives in the open ocean in countless millions as an actively swimming jellyfish but has no hydroid stage. The egg of the medusa *Liriope,* as carefully described by Metschnikoff (1845-1916) in France and by Brooks (1848-1908) in the United States, develops into a ciliated larva that grows directly into a medusa. All this is strange enough, but there are things stranger still. On August 21, 1846, the pioneer English naturalist, Edward Forbes, discovered in that famous lair of pirates, Penzance Bay in Cornwall, a jellyfish that was producing other jellyfish by asexual budding. In his words, "What strange and wondrous changes! Fancy an elephant with a number of little elephants sprouting from his shoulders and thighs!" The medusa which produced other medusae by budding was a member of the genus *Sarsia.* Some species, like *S. prolifera,* bud new jellyfish from the base of the tentacles at the margin of the bell. Another species, *S. gemmifera,* has a very long proboscis or manubrium hanging far below the margin

Fig. 6−9. *Liriope,* a common medusa of the Gulf Stream, lacks a hydroid stage.

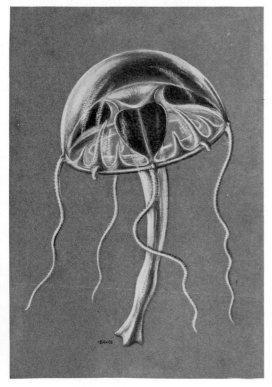

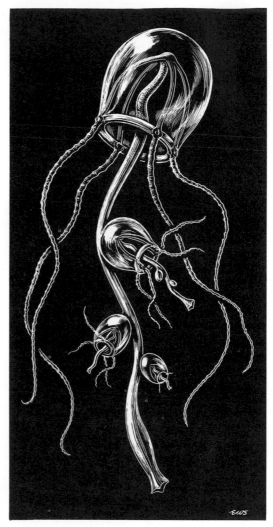

Fig. 6−10. *Sarsia gemmifera,* a medusa of the high seas which buds young jellyfish from its manubrium.

of the bell. From the sides of this manubrium baby jellyfish are budded asexually. *Sarsia* medusae also reproduce sexually, in addition to budding.

Polymorphism: Facts. What does this diversity of life histories mean? Before attempting even a partial answer, consider first a related phenomenon, **polymorphism.** Polymorphism is the possession of several different body forms within a single species. In coelenterates the term is commonly employed to mean more than one body form in the same generation, usually the hydroid generation. A familiar example of polymorphism in coelenterates is seen in *Hydractinia*. This animal is most often found growing on a snail shell inhabited by a hermit crab. The first few "individuals" to develop are nutritive polyps not too different from a freshwater hydra. Over the surface of the shell or stone on which they are growing these nutritive hydras send out **stolons**. These are perisarc tubes containing the living coenosarc of ectoderm, mesoglea, and endoderm surrounding the gastrovascular cavity essentially as in the tubing that connects the polyps of *Obelia*. At first only more nutritive polyps grow up from the stolons, but later other types of "individuals" arise: reproductive polyps that have no mouth and only short knobs in place of tentacles. A little distance below the rudimentary tentacles, oval **gonophores** develop that fill with either eggs or sperms. Still other forms of polyps arise, some defensive against predators and taking the form of long flexible stalks terminating in a big knob of nematocysts, others cone-shaped and becoming covered with a thick, protective perisarc. These protect the whole colony when the snail shell on which it grows is rolled against the rocks.

Normally all the reproductive individuals from the same stolon are of the same sex, though under certain conditions a few hermaphroditic or female individuals arise from male colonies.

Fig. 6–11. Snail shell inhabited by a hermit crab and overgrown by a colony of *Hydractinia*.

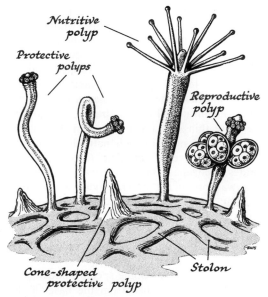

Fig. 6–12. Enlarged view of a *Hydractinia* colony showing polymorphism with four types of individuals.

Polymorphism: Problems. In thinking about polymorphism and the special form of it called alternation of generations, two major problems arise. The first is one of developmental mechanics. How does a stolon "know," so to speak, just when it should send up a nutritive polyp and when a reproductive or protective one? All the polyps from the same stolon obviously bear the same heredity. How can they be so different? A similar question can be asked about alternation of generations. With the same heredity, how can two organisms as different as a hydroid and a medusa be produced? We can restate this question in terms of the cell theory. How can the cells derived from a single egg differentiate into so many different cell types, such as muscle, nerve, and gland cells, when all the cells carry the same two sets of hereditary determinants, the chromosomes? This problem of differentiation remains, after nearly a century of investigation, one of the central unsolved problems of biological science.

The second is an evolutionary problem. Of what advantage is polymorphism and alternation of generations? It is easy to see that a swimming or even a free-floating stage serves to disseminate the species. A species that could get to a new site only by the growth of a stolon would clearly be greatly handicapped in the competition for living space. A medusoid stage overcomes this. Or suppose that by some sudden hereditary change, i.e., mutation, the eggs of a given jellyfish were to produce nonciliated planulas which merely dropped to the bottom. Their chance of survival, let alone of dispersion, would be greatly diminished. On the other side, a sessile form is able to remain in a favorable location, grow there, and reproduce. All the varieties of form are variations on these two themes, the dissemination of the species and the feeding and growth of its individuals. Even such a genus as *Liriope,* which lacks a hydroid completely, is well fitted for the life it lives far at sea, where no resting place for a hydroid exists.

Many zoologists have asked, "Which came first in evolutionary history, the sexual medusoid or the asexual hydroid?" Perhaps the hydroid, since many hydroids exist without any medusoid stage and many produce their sex cells in rudimentary medusa buds, the gonophores. But these seem to be degenerate medusae rather than primitive structures, so it can be argued that a more probable ancestral population was a group of jellyfish in which the planula larvae took to a sessile existence and asexual reproduction. Some lifelong students of this problem, like W. K. Brooks of the Johns Hopkins University, came to the conclusion that neither the swimming medusoid nor the sessile hydroid was the original coelenterate, but a crawling form somewhat like the actinula larva found in *Tubularia* and other hydrozoans and like the adult *Haliclystus,* both to be described below. It may be that this question can never be answered, but it is a question of fact, a scientific question.

Reproduction and Its Control. The usual course of reproduction and some of its variants among the Hydrozoa have been described. To summarize briefly: except for species of jellyfish that live far at sea and reproduce by direct budding off from the parent, medusae are either males or females and reproduce sexually. The zygote or fertilized egg develops into a ciliated larva, the planula, which after a brief period of free life becomes fixed to some object. The planula grows into a hydroid which produces new medusae by asexual budding.

Hydroids are always produced from planulas or from stolons growing out from existing hydroids. The fresh-water hydras are partial exceptions in that, like many other fresh-water animals, the larval form (planula, in this case) is lacking. Hydras develop either directly from eggs or by asexual budding from pre-existing hydras.

Medusae are formed in at least four ways. They may bud asexually from hydroids, as in *Obelia* and some of the relatives of *Hydractinia.* Or medusae may bud asexually from the manubrium or the tentacle bases of other medusae, as in *Sarsia.* Or they may be produced almost directly from the egg, as in ocean jellyfish like *Liriope.* Or, fourthly, they may be produced from actinula larvae, even though actinulae commonly develop into hydroids. This is the case with the actinula of *Tubularia.* Actinulae crawl actively and some are said to be able to swim.

Fig. 6–13. The ambulatory larva or actinula, characteristic of certain hydrozoans, and a recently attached individual. Compare with Figure 6–2.

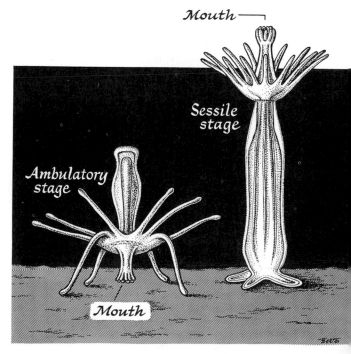

Modern interest in coelenterate reproduction has centered on its physiology, especially its control mechanisms. Three important problems common to animals in general are noteworthy.

The induction of sexuality is one such problem. What are the environmental factors that induce sexual reproduction in an organism that has been merely growing, or perhaps reproducing by asexual budding? Once this question is answered, a second arises. What does the environmental change do to an animal to bring about sexual reproduction? What is the physiological chain of events within the organism?

This problem has been much studied in fresh-water hydras, which reproduce solely by asexual budding for long periods of time but finally produce eggs and sperms. In the hands of different experimenters (which, of course, means non-identical conditions and usually different strains of animals) different factors have seemed responsible. Some recent experiments show that when temperature, food, crowding, and other factors are held constant, sexuality can be induced by an increase in the concentration of dissolved carbon dioxide. Other careful experiments have not confirmed these results; further work is necessary.

A related problem is that of sex determination. Since maleness or femaleness is determined by the chromosomes at the time of fertilization in so many different animals from insects to men, there is a very high probability, almost a certainty, that this is true also of coelenterates. But this leaves unanswered the basic question of what it is that the chromosome complex does to the organism that makes it either a male or a female. Recently German and Canadian investigators have been looking into this problem in *Hydractinia.* Normally all the polyps growing on a single snail shell are from one original polyp and consequently all the reproductive "individuals" are of the same sex. However, in male "colonies" there occasionally occur a few polyps that form **ovotestes,** that is, gonads which produce both eggs and sperms. On the edge of such a zone of hermaphroditic polyps there may even occur a few purely female individuals. These can be shown to be genetic males. Presumably some environmental factor must have overcome the

genetic bent toward maleness. If it can be discovered what this factor is and how it works, then an important new insight will have been gained into how genes produce males, and something of how genes act in general.

A third reproductive problem common to many animals but especially urgent with sessile marine organisms is the establishment of mechanisms to synchronize spawning. The ocean is a big place. If sperms and eggs are to stand a biologically useful chance of meeting, a mechanism must exist that results in males and females shedding their gametes simultaneously.

Within recent years it has been discovered that many hydroids achieve synchrony of spawning by means of a reaction to light and darkness. *Hydractinia* in a state of nature always spawns shortly after sunrise. *Pennaria,* a hydroid much like *Tubularia,* spawns several hours after sunset. In the laboratory, by controlling the light, such animals can be made to shed gametes at any desired time. Continuous light or continuous darkness results in no spawning whatever. To achieve maximum shedding in *Hydractinia* a preparatory period of at least one hour in the dark is necessary. Only a very brief period of illumination, as little as ten seconds, will provide sufficient stimulus to result in widespread shedding, which may take place in the dark after the illumination is ended. The mechanism of shedding of the gametes is the contraction of the gonophore musculoepithelium. If these muscles are paralyzed chemically, shedding is blocked. On the biochemical level it seems reasonable to suppose that darkness permits the accumulation of a light-sensitive material, perhaps a substance found in hemoglobin and chlorophyll called porphyrin. The porphyrin (or some other light-sensitive material) is then changed by light into a form which initiates muscular contraction.

Light also initiates meiosis, the process by which eggs or sperms become haploid, that is, change from having two sets of chromosomes to having one set. In *Hydractinia* the first minute cell, called a **polar body,** which contains the discarded set of chromosomes, is given off by the egg about 45 minutes after exposure to light. The importance of light as a controlling factor in reproductive activity is widespread in the animal kingdom, especially among birds.

The Germtrack. The great classic interest in coelenterate reproduction arose out of Weismann's pivotal theory of the *Keimbahn,* or **germtrack,** which he based, in his own mind at least, on investigations on hydroids. The importance of this theory lay, according to "the father of American cytology," E. B. Wilson, in showing that the problems of heredity and of cell and chromosome structure are basically related. Weismann thus united the study of cells and heredity with the problems of animal development and evolution.

According to Weismann's theory, the animal arises out of the potentialities of the germ or reproductive cells which produce the body, or soma, of the animal plus more germ cells. Thus there need never be any doubt which came first, the hen or the egg; it was, of course, the egg. A hen is an egg's way of protecting and nourishing itself and making more eggs.

But the distinction between somatic or body cells and germ or reproductive cells turned out to be not quite as rigid as Weismann had supposed. Even in coelenterates gametes arise from rather generalized embryonic cells and not from a special line of segregated germ cells. This can be clearly seen in painstaking studies made on coelenterates like *Sarsia,* which bud off new jellyfish. The germ cells that produce the eggs or sperms in the gonads of the budded-off jellyfish are not derived directly from germ cells in the gonads of the parent jellyfish. In simple fact, a germtrack or *Keimbahn* in the literal sense is largely a myth. But the idea behind the theory remains true and is still central in present-day zoology. The raw material of evolution and the structure of the individual animal develop out of the potentialities of germ cells and from them alone.

Development and Regeneration. The zygotes, i.e. fertilized eggs, of jellyfish and hydroids develop much like those of other animals. With two sets of chromosomes, one from each parent, the zygote divides by mitosis into two cells or blastomeres, then into four, eight, sixteen, and so on, each cell with two complete sets of chromosomes, until a ball of cells is produced. This series of mitotic cell divisions is referred to as **cleavage,** and the ball of cells finally produced as a **blastula.** There is no precise

pattern of cleavage in coelenterates. The blastula normally develops into the ciliated planula and this into a motile actinula or, more often, directly into a sessile hydroid.

The experimental analysis of development and regeneration in hydroids has yielded results of far-reaching significance. In fact, modern knowledge of the principles of developmental mechanics is in part an outgrowth of research on hydroids. Chief among these principles are the organizer phenomenon and axial gradients.

A developmental **organizer** is a tissue which, when grafted into a competent but relatively unspecialized region of another animal, will induce the formation of a new secondary individual. Ethel Browne Harvey discovered this phenomenon while experimenting with the green hydra, *Chlorohydra viridissima.* The hypostome above the base of the tentacles, when grafted into the side of another hydra, will induce the formation of a new individual. Mrs. Harvey ingeniously bleached the hydra which served as donor but left the host hydra bright green. In this way she was able to prove that a piece of donor tissue actually induced

Fig. 6–14. Induction of a secondary hydra on the side of the host after the implantation of foreign hypostome and tentacles. (*After Ethel B. Harvey*)

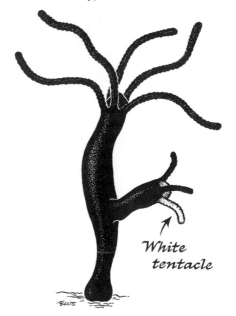

White tentacle

the host tissue to take part in the formation of the new individual. Some of the new tentacles were indeed white, showing they had formed from graft tissue, although others were the bright green color of the host. Tissue taken from other parts of a hydra will produce no such results when grafted on to the side of another animal. In fact, many parts of a hydra when so grafted are completely reorganized into conformity with their new location.

Axial and **physiological gradients** have been more intensely investigated in hydroids than in any other group of animals. There can be little doubt that axial gradients exist. Respiration and other physiological activities are more intense at one end of an animal and decrease in a regular graded manner along the long axis of the body. Such gradients have been held by C. M. Child of the University of Chicago and his followers to control body form in development and regeneration. But how this is done has remained obscure. The most definite statement that can be made is that the behavior of a regenerating part is dependent on its position in relation to the organism as a whole.

To illustrate, if a narrow band near the middle of a hydra is vitally stained and the animal is cut in two just below the stained band, the stained region will form a new basal disk. The unstained cut surface of the basal piece which was just adjacent to the cut will form a new hypostome and set of tentacles. If, however, the hydra is cut in two immediately above the stained zone, then the very same region that in the first experiment formed a basal disk, now becomes the site of hypostome and tentacle formation!

Growth Patterns. In gymnoblastic hydroids like *Tubularia* or *Pennaria*, which lack a protective theca around each hydranth, colony growth is **monopodial.** In this type of growth the main stem and all the branches are tipped by a permanent hydranth. The stems continue to elongate by a growth zone just below each hydranth. The oldest hydranth is thus at the extreme tip of the colony. In the calyptoblastic hydroids like *Obelia* or *Campanularia*, which are thecate, the growth of the colony is **sympodial.** The oldest hydranth is the one closest

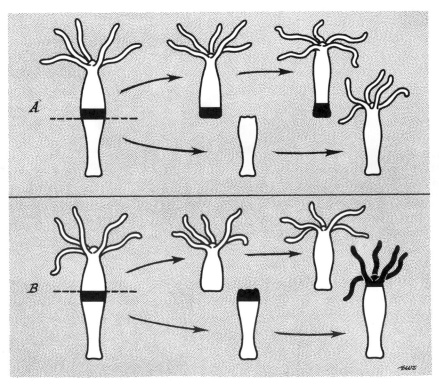

Fig. 6–15. Regeneration of different parts from the same region depending on level of cut in a hydra. *A*, the stained region regenerated a basal disk. *B*, the stained region regenerated tentacles and hypostome.

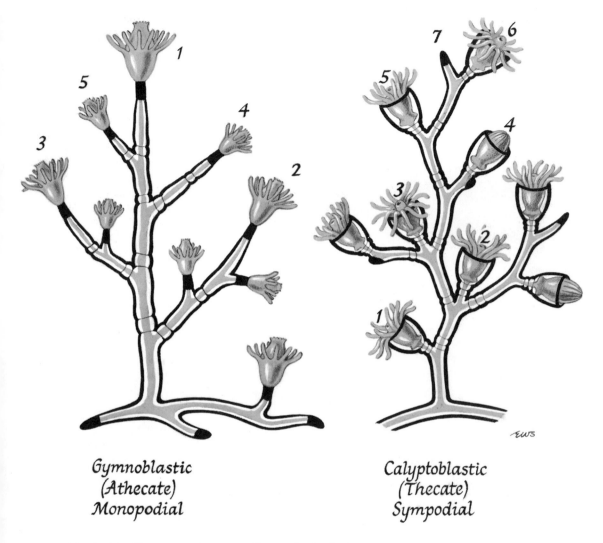

**Gymnoblastic
(Athecate)
Monopodial**

**Calyptoblastic
(Thecate)
Sympodial**

Fig. 6-16. The two major types of growth of colonial hydroids. Left: monopodial growth typical of gymnoblastic (athecate) hydroids like *Tubularia*. Right: sympodial growth typical of calyptoblastic (thecate) hydroids like *Obelia*. The black regions represent zones of growth. The black outer edge indicates the perisarc. The numbers indicate the relative age of hydranths: number 1 is the oldest. *(After Kuhn)*

to the base of the colony. In growth a bud forms at the base of a hydranth and over-tops it. Variations occur in different groups. In the higher calyptoblasts, for example, growth occurs by a terminal growing zone after the manner of the terminal meristem of a plant or the tip of a horizontal stolon of a hydrozoan colony. Monopodial and sympodial colony growth is illustrated in Figure 6-16.

SIPHONOPHORES AND UNSCIENTIFIC QUESTIONS

Siphonophores are known to the general public, and to most professional biologists as well, because of *Physalia*, the Portuguese man-of-war. This is a truly spectacular crea-ture, with an incredible pink and blue gas-filled float and a long trail of graceful if highly

Fig. 6–17. *Physalia,* the Portuguese man-of-war, swallowing a fish. *(New York Zoological Society)*

From the stolon grow many diverse structures. There are **siphons** which are essentially like the manubriums of jellyfish. These siphons ingest food. There are swimming structures like the bells of jellyfish, each complete with velum. But these muscular swimming bells or **nectophores** have no manubriums, no tentacles, no gonads. From the stolon there also grow long **tentacles** with nematocysts. There are various types of closed, fingerlike structures, sometimes bearing one or more long tentacles which may or may not be branched. There are **gonophores,** mere sacs containing ovaries or testes. In many species there are **bracts,** which seem to be leaflike sectors of medusa bells and serve as shields for the rest of the animal.

What is a siphonophore? The fact that the swimming bells are provided with velums around their margins marks siphonophores as hydrozoans, in so far as taxonomic relationships are concerned. In the closing years of the

Fig. 6–18. Organization of a siphonophore.

venomous tentacles stretching out as much as 60 feet when fully extended. Portuguese men-of-war frequent the Gulf Stream but are occasionally blown to land anywhere from Florida to Nova Scotia. They have been seen cast up on the beaches of the Bahama Islands by the tens of thousands.

Different kinds of siphonophores appear outwardly very different, and all are obviously very complicated anatomically. However, all are constructed on the same basic plan, illustrated in Figure 6–18. There is first what appears like a modified medusa bell containing a gas gland on one edge of a gas chamber lined with very thin chitin. This modified medusa bell forms a gas-filled float, or **pneumatophore.** The gas on analysis appears to be similar to but not identical with air. From the pneumatophore grows a longer or shorter **stolon.**

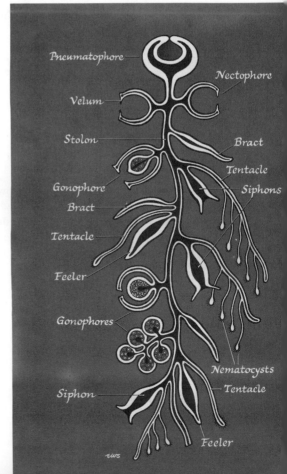

Pneumatophore

Nectophore

Velum

Stolon

Bract

Tentacle

Gonophore

Siphons

Bract

Tentacle

Feeler

Gonophores

Nematocysts

Tentacle

Siphon

Feeler

last century a fantastic but instructive controversy arose over the nature of siphonophores. It involves principles and distinctions of the widest possible application in physics and philosophy as well as zoology. Many of the most illustrious zoologists of Europe were drawn into the controversy. On one side were T. H. Huxley, Metschnikoff, and others. These men held what was called the "poly-organ" theory of siphonophore organization. According to this view a siphonophore like *Physalia* is "really" a single medusoid individual or "person" in which many of the organs, such as the manubrium, tentacles, gonads, etc., have multiplied separately. A similar situation is familiar in Hindu mythology, where a goddess may have four pairs of legs, six pairs of arms, and three tongues.

The opposing view, known as the "poly-person" theory, was supported by the great comparative anatomist Gegenbaur, by Haeckel, the man who introduced Darwinism on the continent of Europe, by Balfour, and by Leuckart, Sedgwick, Chun, and many others. Disregarding certain minor variants, according to this view a siphonophore is "really" a colony of many individuals or "persons," each so specialized as to be reduced to a single organ. Thus one "person" was specialized into nothing but a manubrium, another into a gonad, yet another a tentacle. In structure some siphonophores support one view, some the other.

The controversy itself well illustrates how easy it is to slip from a scientific question that can be answered into a meaningless question that has no answer, at least no scientific answer, or is purely a matter of definition. (What is the color of red blood corpuscles in absolute darkness?) If you ask, "What were the ancestral siphonophores like?" you have asked a question that is, in theory at least, capable of answer. The original siphonophores might have been medusae that budded extra parts, several manubriums, extra tentacles, and the like. They might have been loosely organized colonies of medusae, conceivably related to *Sarsia*, or they might even have been floating hydroid colonies. But when you ask whether an animal is essentially a single "person" in which many of the organs have become reduplicated, or a colony of many "persons" each of which is so specialized that it is reduced to a single organ, you have asked a meaningless question, scientifically speaking.

SCYPHOZOA

All the really big jellyfish belong to the class Scyphozoa (*scyphos,* cup, + *zoa,* animals). Some grow to immense size, like *Cyanea,* the common red and purple medusa, which has been recorded at over seven feet in diameter. Some scyphozoans, however, remain medium or even small in size. Most of these medusae are very beautiful, graceful in form and motion, exquisite in delicacy of coloring. Unfortunately, most are extremely vicious animals for a swimmer to meet. The infamous "sea nettle," *Chrysaora,* of the Atlantic and its bays from Cape Cod south into the tropics is a scyphozoan. So also are the even more venomous "fire medusae" of the Sea of Japan and the "sea wasps" of the tropics. These handsome and fragile-looking creatures are rightly feared. They are, in fact, voracious feeders, living mostly on fishes.

The members of the class Scyphozoa are characterized in the medusoid stage by the lack of a velum, the muscular shelflike ribbon around the edge of the bell of hydrozoan jellyfish, and by the possession of complex sense organs called **rhopalia** on the margin of the bell.

The hydroid stage is characterized by these features:

1. Septa, or **mesenteries,** that extend from the sides of the hydroid in toward the center of the gastrovascular cavity. In this respect they are like sea anemones and corals, which also have septa, or mesenteries.

2. As in the case of the sea anemones, the septa bear filaments and gonads projecting into the gastrovascular cavity.

3. Finally, they have a peculiar method of asexual reproduction in which the planula larva grows into a small hydroid called a **scyphistoma.** The scyphistoma reproduces by a process, to be described below, called strobilization.

Altogether there are only about 300 species in this class of coelenterates. They are divided into five orders. The members of one order are notable for remaining in an anatomical state that is roughly half-way between a medusa and a hydroid. Such an animal is reminiscent of an actinula. Here belongs *Haliclystus,* the common North American genus which, in its somersaulting mode of progression and its curious structure, resembles a clown wearing baggy pants with frills around the ankles. It is frequently found climbing about among seaweed, catching and eating small crustaceans. *Haliclystus* can be likened to a rather thin medusa with a long stalk growing up out of the top of the bell. The margin of the bell is extended into eight leglike processes, each ending in a cluster of tentacles. The end of the stalk and the ends of the tentacles are adhesive. Some zoologists suppose that *Haliclystus* resembles the original ancestral coelenterates.

Structure and Life Histories. A common coastal jellyfish, *Aurelia,* is usually taken as an example of this class of coelenterates, presumably because of its availability and relatively simple structure. Actually, *Aurelia* has a rather distinguished scientific history. This was the form used by Michael Sars in establishing the existence of alternation of generations; and the development of *Aurelia* was investigated by no less a person than Ernst Haeckel, with interesting results to be described below.

Fig. 6–19. The scyphozoan, *Haliclystus,* the "clown."

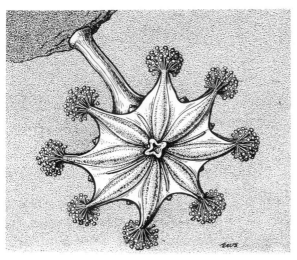

The medusa of *Aurelia* is a flattish, translucent, slightly bluish disk. From the edge of the short manubrium trail four long oral tentacles, and around the margin of the bell are numerous small marginal tentacles. The margin itself is punctuated by eight slight indentations, each the site of a sense organ or rhopalium. Four conspicuous horseshoe-shaped gonads are placed symmetrically about the mouth. They lie on the floor of gastric pouches which are extensions of the central gastrovascular cavity. Eggs or sperms, when mature, are shed into the coelenteron and pass out through the mouth. Beneath each gonad, but on the under or sub-umbrellar side of the jellyfish, the surface is indented upwards into a subgenital pit. This pit is supposed to allow fresh sea water to come into close contact with the gonad and thus facilitate respiration.

Extending from the central portion of the gastrovascular cavity is a symmetrical system of **radiating coelenteric canals** which connect with a marginal canal around the edge of the bell. Eight of the radial canals run without branching directly from the central region to the marginal canal. These unbranched canals are termed **adradial.** They carry a current, produced by flagella, outward toward the periphery. Other canals, which are branched, extend from either the gastric pouches toward the sense organs, in which case they are termed **interradial,** or directly from the stomach toward the sense organs, when they are termed **perradial.** The coelenteric current in these branching systems flows toward the center, carrying food and oxygen.

The muscular system consists of well-developed fibers, both radial and circular, in the subumbrellar surface. There is of course no velum in these animals.

The percentage of water in a jellyfish has been a matter of repeated and sharp controversy. Various jellyfish have been weighed, dried, and reweighed. Specimens of *Aurelia* from the Gulf of Maine and from the Baltic gave values ranging from 95 to 97 per cent water. In brackish water, the water content of this jellyfish may increase to 98 per cent. It should be remembered that sea water itself is only about 97 per cent water because of its salt content.

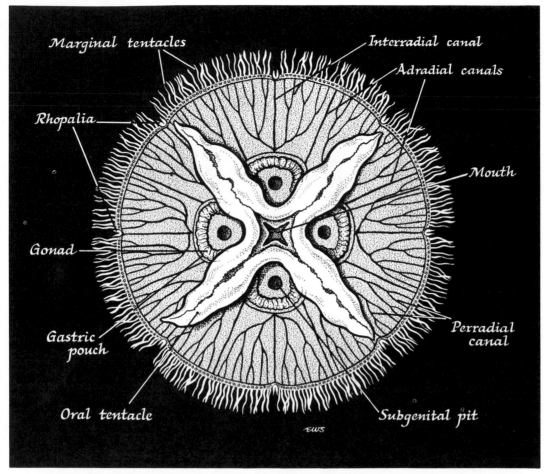

Marginal tentacles

Interradial canal

Adradial canals

Rhopalia

Mouth

Gonad

Gastric pouch

Perradial canal

Oral tentacle

Subgenital pit

EWS

Fig. 6–20. The scyphozoan, *Aurelia,* a common inshore medusa. Oral view.

The development of *Aurelia* was investigated by Haeckel with thought-provoking consequences. The eggs vary considerably in size. The smallest eggs develop into planulas, which become sessile hydroids in what is thought of as the "normal" way. The largest eggs develop directly into medusae without passing through any hydroid stage. In this they behave like the eggs of several purely oceanic jellyfish, *Liriope* and *Pelagia,* for example, in which there is direct development and no hydroid stage. Eggs of intermediate size, Haeckel discovered, form elongated planulas which develop tentacles and a mouth while still motile, or in other words, become actinulas. These facts make it appear possible that very slight genetic changes could produce profound differences in life histories.

The fertilized egg of the "typical" scyphozoan jellyfish, like *Chrysaora* the sea nettle, develops into a ciliated planula which becomes a sessile hydroid, the **scyphistoma.** These are small hydroids usually less than half an inch in length. Within about a year each undergoes a series of transverse constrictions, a process known as **strobilization.** As a result the old scyphistoma is converted into a series of little medusae upside down one on top of another like a pile of soup dishes. They break apart and swim off as immature medusae or **ephyras,** like little eight-rayed stars. In some species strobilization produces 15 or more ephyras from each scyphistoma. *Chrysaora,* at least in Chesapeake Bay, seems to produce six, once a year. Little definite appears to be known about

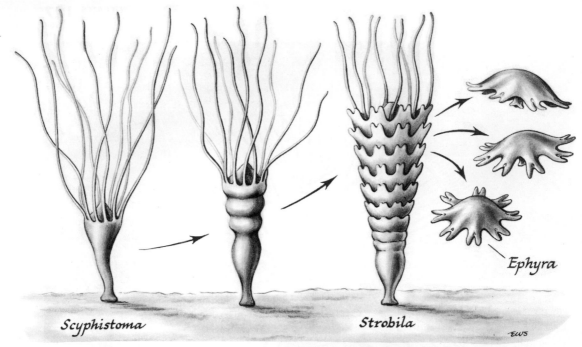

Scyphistoma *Strobila* *Ephyra*

Fig. 6–21. Hydroid stages of a scyphozoan, as seen with a hand lens.

the rate of growth from newly formed ephyras to full-sized adult medusae. No doubt it depends on species, temperature, and food supply.

Regeneration occurs at least in some species of jellyfish.

Behavior and Nervous System. In a state of nature, jellyfish are usually doing one of two things, depending on the species. Those that live near shore, like *Aurelia* and *Chrysaora*, spend their time fishing by first swimming up to, or almost to, the surface of the water, then turning over so the sub-umbrellar surface is uppermost, and slowly drifting to the bottom. When they hit bottom, muscular contractions begin which send the medusa upward again in a series of rhythmical contractions. This cycle is repeated hour after hour. Any small animals that become caught in the tentacles are dragged into the mouth and digested.

Pelagic jellyfish, like the rapidly swimming *Liriope* or the luminescent *Pelagia*, could not behave in this way where the sea is perhaps a mile or more deep. They swim singly or in great shoals, keeping near the surface and meanwhile being carried along by the vast ocean currents. Of course, there are many deviants. *Cassiopeia*, a tropical jellyfish found off southern Florida, habitually lies on its "back" on the bottom in quiet shallow water. With languid pulsations of the bell it keeps water currents flowing over its mouth and bringing in food and oxygen.

The anatomy and physiology of the jellyfish neuromuscular system have been extensively studied in the laboratory. As in coelenterates generally, the nerve fibers form a subepithelial network, apparently with synapses making connections in many directions. There is usually some concentration of fibers near the sense organs. An interesting type of "nerve-muscle preparation" was devised by A. G. Mayer, who showed that impulses could be transmitted around doughnut-shaped pieces cut out of a medusa. In fact, impulses will be transmitted through any zigzag kind of piece and over regions denuded of muscle. Transmission in such a system must be very diffuse.

The rhythmic pulsations depend almost entirely on the presence of the sense organs, the rhopalia. A single rhopalium is usually sufficient to maintain the rhythm. If long radial cuts are made from the margin of the bell in toward the center, so as to separate the rhopalia, each sector will beat with its own rhythm. How the sense organs originate and control this rhythm is a problem of great interest to those concerned with heart action.

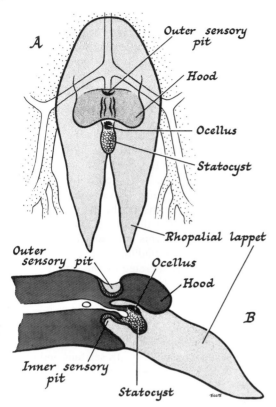

A

Outer sensory pit

Hood

Ocellus

Statocyst

Rhopalial lappet

Outer sensory pit

Ocellus

Hood

B

Inner sensory pit

Statocyst

Fig. 6-22. The marginal sense organs of *Aurelia*. *A*, dorsal view. *B*, radial section.

A righting reflex is elicited when the bell is tipped out of the horizontal. This response is due to greater muscular contraction on one side of the bell than on the other. It is abolished by removing the rhopalia. Most medusae are sensitive to light and will retreat into deeper water on very bright days, though other species act in the reverse manner. The **ocelli**, or simple eyes, of *Aurelia* are extremely simple, but they have been proved to be photosensitive. The rhopalium of a "sea wasp" like *Carybdea* has a refractile lens and a cup-shaped retina.

ANTHOZOA

The class Anthozoa (*anthos*, flower, + *zoa*, animals) includes the corals, sea anemones, sea fans, and gorgonians, a truly gorgeous array. From remote antiquity men, and naturally women also, have prized red coral, *Corallium rubrum*, as an ornament. Pliny, writing in the 1st century A.D., reported that the trade in

precious coral from the Mediterranean had become so brisk with Persia and India that it was difficult for the Gauls to obtain what they wanted to decorate their weapons.

Corals and their relatives were generally regarded as plants until the beginning of the 18th century. Then two citizens of Marseilles made the remarkable discovery that corals are animals. The first was Count Marsilli (or Marsigli), who built a marine laboratory outside Marseilles. This was in 1706, more than a century and a half before Louis Agassiz founded the first American marine laboratory on Cape Cod, or Anton Dohrn the one at Naples. One day the Count accompanied some local fishermen on a coral-hunting trip. On his return he placed some of the red coral in a glass of sea water. The next morning he was astonished to find it "all covered with white flowers, each with eight rays of equal length and equally spaced. . . . Even the fishermen had never seen anything of the kind." It is hard to believe that that December day in 1706 was the first time that anyone had seen the coral animals, but such appears to be the case. Count Marsigli believed coral to be a plant. It was not until two decades later that the studies of a Marseilles physician named Peysonnel showed that corals are animals which move and eat. In this he was supported by the then recent discoveries of Trembley on hydra.

Two and a half centuries of study have shown that all the Anthozoa from the simplest sea anemone to the most complex coral or gorgonian are united by certain common traits:

1. There is never any indication of a medusoid stage. The eggs develop into planulas that grow directly into hydroids.

2. The anthozoan polyp differs from the hydrozoan, like the fresh-water hydra or *Tubularia*, in being relatively short and stout and in having a flat oral disk instead of a dome-shaped hypostome. On the other hand the anthozoan polyp resembles its scyphozoan counterpart except that it never undergoes strobilization. Both possess septa, gastric filaments or acontia, and gonads. **Acontia** are filaments, sometimes longer than the animal itself, heavily armed with nematocysts. Where the sea anemones and corals are different from the scyphozoans is in their possession of a **pharynx**. This is an infolding of the ectoderm around the mouth to

form a tube extending some distance into the gastrovascular cavity.

3. Most anthozoans have one or two **siphonoglyphs,** ciliated grooves running down opposite sides of the pharynx.

4. The mesoglea is a true cellular layer—so much so that many zoologists have come to believe that the only sensible, and in fact accurate, thing to do is to recognize this as a mesoderm and the anthozoans as triploblastic animals with ectoderm, endoderm, and mesoderm.

Structure and Life Histories. A sea anemone is usually cited as an example of the structure of the members of this class, and rightly, for the anatomy of the complicated corals, sea fans, and sea pens can be understood once the anatomy of a solitary sea anemone is clear. A sea anemone resembles a gigantic (they may grow to be over a foot long), muscular hydra with a flat oral disk surrounded by a circle of hollow tentacles. The mouth is not round but elongate. At its two corners are the beginnings of the ciliated grooves or siphonoglyphs that conduct a continuous current of water into and out of the coelenteron.

The coelenteron is partially subdivided by septa or mesenteries arranged in symmetrically placed pairs. Those that extend to the position of the siphonoglyphs are called **primaries.** On the free inner edges of the mesenteries are the gonads. Both eggs and sperms are produced by the same individual, but **protandry** is the rule, i.e., the animals are males when they are young and small, females when fully adult.

Many of the anthozoans become very complicated, especially those with only eight tentacles and eight septa, like precious coral and the sea fans and sea pens. The structure of sea pens and similar forms can be understood most clearly by regarding them as a bundle of individual polyps. Forms like sea fans are produced by extensive budding.

The skeleton is secreted by the ectoderm. In the stony corals the pedal disk is thrown into folds which secrete the correspondingly folded and fluted calcareous coral. In other corals tiny spicules are secreted in a complex tissue composed of ectodermal tubes ramifying through the mesogleal mesoderm. In sea fans and other gorgonians a horny skeletal core is secreted in a similar manner.

Fig. 6–23. *Metridium,* a common sea anemone of rocks and wharf pilings. *A,* general anatomy. *B,* section through pharynx region. (Diagrammatic)

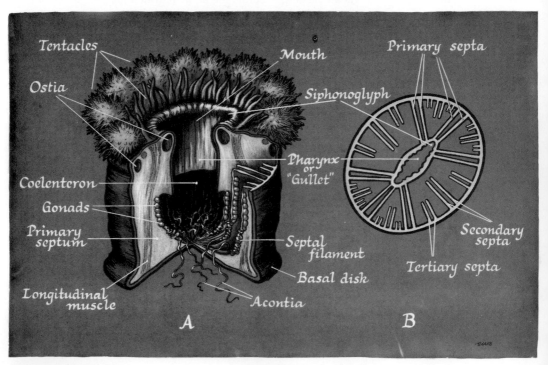

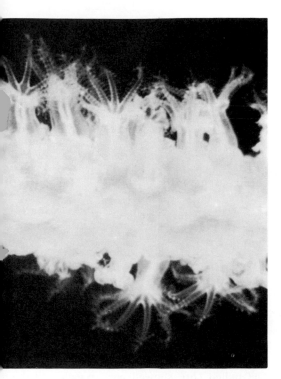

Fig. 6–24. *Leptogorgia,* a relative of the precious coral, showing the eight-tentacled hydroids. *(Kindness of William H. Amos)*

Coral Reefs. There are three main types of coral reefs: fringing reefs, atolls, and barrier reefs. **Fringing reefs** are sometimes within a stone's throw of shore but are often separated from it by a lagoon. Such reefs are common in the Caribbean Sea including southern Florida, and may also be seen in Bermuda and around most of the islands of the South Pacific and Indian Oceans.

Atolls are circular or oval reefs enclosing a lagoon but no island. There are usually several breaks in the ring of coral where the tide goes in and out. Within the lagoon the water is relatively shallow, 10 to 20 feet deep, and numerous masses of coral are commonly exposed at very low tides. Atolls vary from half a mile to over 50 miles in diameter and look like fringing reefs that have lost their central island. Some fringing reefs enclose such very small islands that a couple of centuries of erosion by tropical rain storms may obliterate these tiny islands completely.

The third type of reef is the **barrier reef.** Such a reef is 50 to 100 miles from shore and separated from it by deep and usually navigable water. The Great Barrier Reef of Australia extends for over 1,000 miles along the northeast coast of that continent where the water never falls below 20°C.

Algae play an important and probably essential double role in reef formation. The entire reef is solidified by the encrusting skeletons of calcareous algae. In addition, the reef-building corals possess in their tissues symbiotic algae, zooxanthellae. It has recently been demonstrated that radioactively labelled calcium is deposited by corals about ten times as rapidly in the light as in the dark. On a cloudy day the rate is cut in half. The precise reason for this is uncertain but a good guess is that the removal of carbon dioxide from the tissues by the photosynthesis of the algae throws the equilibrium between soluble calcium bicarbonate and insoluble calcium carbonate toward the latter. This is still a guess. In any case, corals which do not have symbiotic algae do not build reefs.

The existence of coral reefs presents a curious problem. Reef-forming coral is able to grow only in shallow water. At 100 feet their growth begins to be slowed, and at 150 feet they cease to grow altogether. How then can the existence of hundreds of atolls in the open ocean thousands of miles from land be explained? The bottom drops sharply around many of these atolls to very great depths, a mile or so in some cases.

In parts of the Pacific Ocean thousands of square miles are sprinkled with coral atolls. What are these atolls resting on? Are there submerged mountain tops, each reaching to about 100 feet of the surface? This seems highly unlikely. Charles Darwin, who visited and studied these reefs immediately after his college years, proposed the subsidence theory. According to this theory these atolls began as fringing reefs around mountain tops that showed normal variability in height above sea level. In the long course of time the floor of the ocean slowly sank and with it the marine mountains. As the mountain tops sank, the coral continued to grow upward until ultimately there was only coral remaining anywhere near the surface.

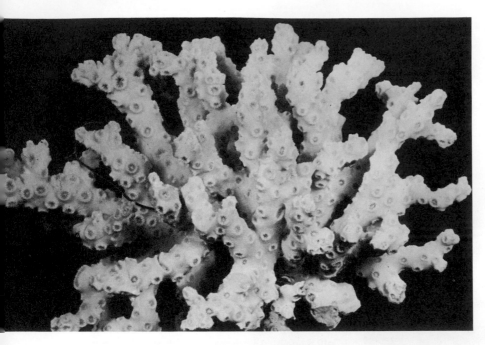

Fig. 6–25. *Oculina,* an Atlantic reef coral. *(From F. G. Walton Smith,* Atlantic Reef Corals; *photo by Frederick M. Bayer)*

Some years later Sir John Murray, leader of the famous *Challenger* expedition which explored the life of the oceans, proposed a different theory. According to this view most atolls are resting on marine sediments which accumulated on submerged mountain tops and built them up until they were within about 150 feet of the surface, at which depth corals could begin to grow. Sediments on the ocean floor are known to have built up rock hundreds of feet in thickness.

With increasing knowledge of geology, particularly of past glacial ages, a third possibility became evident. The glacial control theory proposed by the geologist Daly holds that during glacial ages such enormous volumes of water become locked up as ice on the continents that the level of the ocean is drastically lowered. When the glaciers melt as warmer ages follow, the water runs back into the ocean and the sea level slowly rises. This in a sense is the reverse of Darwin's theory that the ocean floor was sinking.

Seeking facts by which to settle this question, various expeditions have made deep borings in Pacific atolls. The first was a party sent out by the Royal Society of London in 1904. They drove a boring to a depth of 1,114 feet in the reef of Funafuti Atoll, north of the Fiji Islands. The pulled core showed coral remains all the way down. That result apparently disposed of the Murray sedimentation theory, for according to it coral rock should end at a depth of some 150 feet and be followed by sedimentary material. In the years since 1904 other deep borings have been made, most recently by the United States Armed Services at Bikini in connection with atomic explosion tests. All the subsequent borings confirm the original result at Funafuti. Coral rock extends down well over 1,000 feet, far below the depth at which coral can live.

While these results throw out the sedimentation theory, they do not distinguish between the theories of submergence and glacial control, and there is some evidence in favor of each. In various parts of the world there is clear and unmistakable evidence that the ocean level was once at least 300 feet lower than it is today. The Hudson River is clearly a "drowned" river. Its steep-sided valley can be followed many miles out into the Atlantic, to the edge of the continental shelf. Other evidence that sea level was hundreds of feet below its present height can be found in Bermuda, Europe, and other parts of the world.

POSITION OF THE COELENTERATES IN THE ANIMAL KINGDOM

What is the relation of the Coelenterata to the other phyla? The orthodox view, dating from Haeckel and earlier, holds that the coelenterates stand at the base of all the Metazoa, immediately above the unicellular animals. This view accounts for the location of the chapter on the coelenterates in this book and is still generally accepted. Nevertheless, it has recently been challenged by a very different view, first proposed by the English zoologist Adam Sedgwick some 60 years ago and now revived in strengthened form by a Yugoslavian student of coelenterates, Jovan Hadzi.

According to the Haeckelian view, the first metazoans were derived from a spherical colonial flagellate which became a two-layered sack by the invagination of the cells of one hemisphere. It will be recalled that *Volvox* and sponges both do something very like this. The original hollow sphere of cells is comparable to the blastula stage of a vertebrate or other embryo, and the invagination of one side of the sphere can be compared to gastrulation, by which the blastula of the higher animals becomes a two-layered sack or gastrula. Thus a coelenterate is regarded (T. H. Huxley is largely responsible for this) as a group of animals which are essentially permanent gastrulas, diploblastic, with only two germ layers, ectoderm and endoderm. There were various other theories, including a proposal by Metschnikoff that the original metazoan was essentially a solid planula, but at the time Haeckel won the argument and, in the words of Hyman, "overwhelmed his opponents by a flood of expository literature."

The challenging theory, which is supported by much new evidence and which is causing many zoologists to rethink this problem, holds that the metazoans arose not from flagellates but from multinuclear ciliates. If this is true, the basic metazoans are not the coelenterates but the acoelous flatworms. This notion will be discussed later in connection with flatworms (Chapter 11). Suffice it to say here that some flatworms do bear many fundamental resemblances to the multinucleate ciliates. For example, most of their nuclei are not separated from others by cell membranes. They also possess a real similarity to the planula larva of coelenterates.

This theory holds that coelenterates are descended from bilaterally symmetrical ancestors, since flatworms have a head and are bilateral. That in turn would mean that simple Anthozoa, which in their mesenteries and siphonoglyphs show some bilaterality, are the most primitive of coelenterates. Forms like the fresh-water hydra, instead of being the most primitive of coelenterates, would be the farthest from the original ancestors.

The evidence? Surprisingly cogent.

1. The acoelous flatworms clearly have far more in common with multinucleate ciliates than any colonial flagellate like *Volvox* has with the Metazoa. For one thing, *Volvox* and its relatives are haploid while ciliates, flatworms, and coelenterates are diploid.

2. The Anthozoa are essentially triploblastic animals like flatworms, with ectoderm, mesoderm, and endoderm. In the words of the contemporary zoological encyclopedist, L. H. Hyman, "If one frees oneself from outworn theories dating from Haeckel, one sees at once that there is no essential difference between a cross section of a sea anemone commonly called 'diploblastic,' and a cross section of a flatworm commonly called 'triploblastic.'"

3. The Anthozoa show a tendency to bilateral symmetry not only in the adult, but also in early development. Some sea anemones are biradial, that is, they have a symmetry like that of a ferry boat with similar ends and similar sides. But the early stages of these biradial sea anemones are bilateral. To quote Hyman again, "This fact suggests that the Anthozoa may have been a bilateral group originally."

4. The bilaterality of anthozoans is internal. Hadzi emphasizes that this is precisely what would be expected. The possession of a head with mouth, sense organs, and brain at the anterior end is an adaptation for locomotion. Sessile organisms, like trees, tend to become radial. The barnacles are a notable example, for as crustaceans they clearly had bilateral ancestors. Outwardly they have assumed a superficial appearance of radial symmetry while inwardly they are obviously as bilateral as a lobster.

5. The embryos of many, perhaps most, sea anemones form their endoderm by invagination. The consequent opening into the coelenteron is known as the **blastopore.** In sea anemones the blastopore develops into the mouth. This fact is important, because it places the coelenterates among the Protostome division of the animal kingdom, just where they should be if they have in fact evolved from flatworms. On the other hand, cleavage of these animals is not of the flatworm type.

6. Some marine polyclad flatworms (see Fig. 11–4) have a central mouth, a many-branched gut, and a row of marginal tentacles which are hollow, as are the tentacles of the sea anemone. If such a flatworm assumed a sedentary life, it would bear a striking resemblance to an anthozoan coelenterate.

In view of a controversial situation like this, what should a student do? First, know the issues. Second, weigh the evidence on all sides. And third, keep an open mind.

Review and References

REVIEW TOPICS

1. What six traits characterize all coelenterates?

2. Compare and contrast the Hydrozoa with the Scyphozoa in regard to both the medusoid and hydroid generations.

3. Define: coelenteron, nematoblast, nematocyst, cnidocil, hypostome, manubrium, velum, planula, actinula, Keimbahn.

4. Describe Trembley's experiments with hydra. What conclusions did he draw, and how have his conclusions been modified subsequently?

5. Describe alternation of generations and polymorphism. What advantage are they to the coelenterates, and what problems do these phenomena present in the mechanics of development?

6. What is known of the factors which induce sexuality in coelenterates? Synchronous spawning?

7. What is the Keimbahn theory? Evaluate its place in present-day biology.

8. What is the possible role of organizers and axial and physiological gradients in coelenterate development?

9. What is a siphonophore?

10. What are the nervous system and sense organs of jellyfish like? What kind of behavior do jellyfish show, and how is this adapted to the environments in which they live?

11. What are the three principal types of coral reefs, and how have they been formed?

12. What are the probable relationships of the coelenterates to other phyla, and what evidence supports each view?

USEFUL REFERENCES

Baker, J. R., *Abraham Trembley of Geneva,* London, Arnold and Company, 1952.

Berrill, N. J., and C. K. Liu, "Germplasm, Weismann, and Hydrozoa," *Quarterly Review of Biology,* vol. 23, 1948.

Lenhoff, H. M., and W. F. Loomis, *The Biology of Hydra and of Some Other Coelenterates,* Coral Gables, Fla., University of Miami Press, 1961.

Mayer, A. G. *Medusae of the World,* Washington, D. C., Carnegie Institution, 1910.

Pennak, R. W., *Fresh-Water Invertebrates of the United States,* New York, The Ronald Press Company, 1953.

Russell, F. S., *The Medusae of the British Isles,* Cambridge, England, The University Press, 1953.

Chapter 7

Ctenophores

Ctenophores (the C is silent) are among the commonest of marine animals but also among the least familiar. They do not sting like jellyfish, which they resemble, and their economic value is indirect. They are among the most beautiful creatures known. A ctenophore, as the poet Thomas Gray wrote in an only slightly different connotation, is a "gem of purest ray serene." These are living gems, found not in "the dark unfathomed caves of ocean" but in the dazzling brilliance of the sunlight on the high seas. Examined alive in a glass of sea water, their bodies possess the incredible glistening transparency of the finest glass. They are iridescent by day and luminescent by night. The complexities of their glasslike anatomy are adjusted with exquisite delicacy. Remarkable animals, ctenophores!

The first question most people ask about ctenophores is why they are not coelenterates. Zoologists themselves did not generally recognize the distinctions until about 1900. There are, however, several clear-cut and basic differences.

1. Ctenophores never produce nematocysts, which are characteristic of all coelenterates.

2. The chief locomotor system of ctenophores consists of eight vertical rows of comblike plates of cilia, hence the name of the phylum (*ctenos,* comb, + *phoros,* to bear).

3. The type of cleavage of the egg and the early development of the embryo are both very different from that found in the coelenterates. The cleavage follows a complex and precisely determinate pattern, as it does in flatworms, annelids, and mollusks, but not in coelenterates. The embryo does not form a planula, but develops directly into a small edition of the adult.

4. There is never anything corresponding to a hydroid stage, and the swimming adult is very different in its bodily organization from a medusa. There is no circular band of muscle fibers around the margin of a bell. The body is not umbrella-shaped, and there is no manubrium. Instead, the body is generally egg shaped.

5. The reproductive system of a ctenophore is very different from that of jellyfish. They are hermaphroditic, while in coelenterates the sexes are usually separate. In fact, the more one knows about a ctenophore, the less it seems like a coelenterate. Ctenophores may be briefly defined as biradial animals without nematocysts and having eight meridional rows of ciliated comb-plates.

Importance. The possible economic importance of ctenophores arises from the character of their food. They are carnivorous. Their food consists of any small animals that get swept into their mouths or get caught in their two long tentacles: oyster larvae in the swimming stage, crab larvae, floating fish eggs and recently hatched fishes, copepods, and other minute animals that make up the plankton. While it is possible that the great swarms of ctenophores living in bays and sounds may seriously affect the abundance of oysters and crabs, no one really knows. It is also possible that since animals like oysters do produce eggs in the countless trillions, the depredations of ctenophores never become a limiting factor for these populations.

Habitats and Examples. The distribution of ctenophores is world-wide. They occur, often in great swarms, in all oceans from the polar seas to the tropics. Most are **pelagic,** i.e., living far at sea near the surface, but some species are found down to a depth of well over a mile. Other species are frequenters of bays and harbors. Such a one is *Mnemiopsis* (the M is silent), a very handsome and very luminous form, abundant along the middle Atlantic coast and often in very dirty harbor water. It grows to be about 4 inches (100 mm) in length. Another frequently seen ctenophore is *Beroë*, found in both the Atlantic and Pacific as well as the Mediterranean. It is about the same size as *Mnemiopsis,* but instead of being glass-clear is pink or whitish. The "cold water jelly," *Pleurobrachia,* is the ctenophore commonly preserved for laboratory study. It is found in the north Pacific and in the north Atlantic south to Long Island and Europe.

Most ctenophores are rounded or oval; but *Cestus veneris,* or Venus' girdle, is a thin ribbon growing to over 3 feet long and about 3 or 4 inches wide. It is transparent, shimmering with violets, blues, and greens. This spectacular species is an inhabitant of the tropic seas but is occasionally carried northward by the Gulf Stream.

It seems strange that a group of animals like the ctenophores, which are so common in the oceans in all parts of the world, should be represented by so few species. This is a real problem for the student of evolution. However, the fact is that ctenophores do constitute a phylum small in the number of species; scarcely 100 have been described.

TYPICAL STRUCTURE

With a few notable exceptions, like Venus' girdle, ctenophores are spherical or football-shaped. At the lower or oral pole is the mouth. At the upper or aboral pole is a sense organ. The bulk of the body is mesogleal jelly.

The locomotor system consists of eight rows of **comb-plates.** These rows begin up near the aboral sense organ and run down toward the mouth, following eight meridians over the surface of the animal. Each comb-plate consists of a brush of king-sized cilia. The cilia are more or less fused in a way that makes them look like the teeth of a comb. Waves of ciliary beating of the combs begin at the aboral end and pass down toward the mouth. The effective beat is towards the sense organ, and the ctenophore thus moves with a steady glide, mouth first.

Ctenophores have muscle fibers in the mesoglea. Unlike the coelenterate condition, the muscle fibers are not part of epithelial cells. Species like *Mnemiopsis* which have large lobes are able to move them vigorously by means of these muscles.

The food-catching and digestive system of a ctenophore consists of ciliary currents, tentacles, and a gastrovascular cavity with a system of canals. Species without tentacles or with very short ones appear to catch their prey like baleen whales, merely swimming through the plankton with their mouths open. Most ctenophores possess tentacles, but they are very different from the tentacles of coelenterates. There are only two, on opposite sides of the body. The plane cutting through each of them and the sense organ and mouth is known as the tentacular plane. It divides the animal into two similar halves. Each tentacle is retractile into a tentacle sheath deeply set in the mesoglea. The tentacle itself consists of a long single filament from which there grows a single fringe of short lateral tentacles. The lateral tentacles bear clumps of peculiar adhesive cells known as **lasso cells,** or **colloblasts,** and found only in ctenophores. Each colloblast consists of a hemispherical head covered with adhesive granules. This head is connected to two long filaments, one straight and one coiled. The

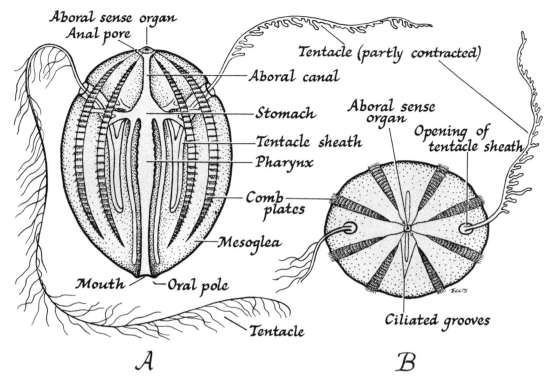

Fig. 7–1. A ctenophore, approximately life size. *A*, lateral view. *B*, aboral view. Note that the transparency of the animal permits the digestive cavities to be seen.

coiled filament is supposed to hold when a victim tries to jerk free. Small animals are brushed off the tentacles as they are pulled past the mouth.

The mouth leads into a **pharynx,** or **stomodaeum,** extending directly upward toward the sense organ. It is a narrow cavity flattened at right angles to the tentacular plane. The flattened pharynx thus marks a second plane on which the animal can be cut to give two mirror-image halves. This type of symmetry is called **biradial.**

Somewhat above the equator, the pharynx opens into the "**stomach,**" which is flattened in the plane at right angles to the pharynx, i.e., in the tentacular plane. From the stomach seven canals run out. One goes directly upward to end under the aboral sense organ in four little branches or prongs. Two, diagonally opposite each other, open to the exterior by small anal pores. From the floor of the stomach two

Fig. 7–2. Digestive system of a ctenophore. Note the system of canals.

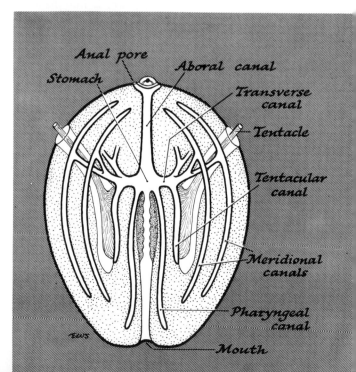

pharyngeal canals extend down through the mesoglea toward the mouth on either side of the pharynx. Finally, from each side of the stomach runs a short transverse canal, one extending toward each tentacle. Each transverse canal divides three ways. The center branch extends down along the tentacle sheath. The two side-branches each branch again to make four branches that extend out to meridional canals which underlie the meridional bands of comb-plates.

Reproduction. Ctenophores are hermaphroditic. Eight elongate gonads lie beneath the eight rows of comb-plates. Each gonad is half testis, half ovary, divided lengthwise down its entire extent. In two adjacent gonads, ovary faces ovary or testis faces testis. This whole situation poses difficult problems in the mechanism of sex determination and development. Each of the eight gonads lies along the wall of one of the eight meridional canals. Hence the gametes are shed by way of the canals into the gastrovascular cavity and pass to the exterior via the mouth. The eggs undergo a very precisely determinate cleavage. If the first two cells (blastomeres) are separated, each will develop into half an embryo with four rows of comb-plates. If the first four cells are separated from each other, each develops into a quarter embryo with two rows of comb-plates.

The embryo develops directly into the adult. The so-called **cydippid larva** is merely a round generalized little ctenophore with eight short rows of comb-plates. It is converted into the adult form by differential growth. There is never any asexual reproduction.

Nervous System. The nervous system consists of a subepithelial plexus of nerve cells. Their fibers stimulate the fibers of other neurons or are themselves stimulated across synaptic junctions, as in coelenterates and the higher animals. Concentrations of nerve fibers underlie the eight rows of comb-plates.

The aboral sense organ controls the posture of the animal by controlling the beating of the comb-plates. The accounts of the anatomy of this sense organ would strain belief did not so many competent observers agree. The most obvious structure in it is a roundish calcareous

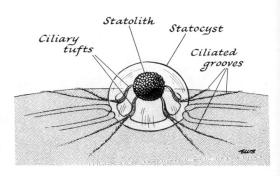

Fig. 7–3. Aboral sense organ of a ctenophore.

statolith supported on the ends of four symmetrically placed tufts of long cilia resembling the prongs which support a mounted diamond. Beneath the elevated statolith is a bowl-shaped floor, covered with a carpet of short cilia. The entire structure is covered by a transparent dome reminiscent of a plastic observation bubble in an airplane. This dome is composed of extremely long cilia fused together. The cavity thus formed is a **statocyst**. Four equispaced fine **ciliated grooves** leave the statocyst at the bases of the four long tufts holding up the statolith. Each ciliated groove divides into two immediately after leaving the dome, thus

Fig. 7–4. Comb-plates of a ctenophore in action, photographed under a dissecting microscope. (*Kindness of William H. Amos*)

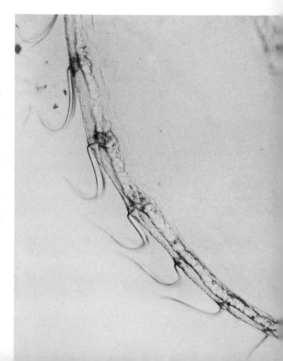

making a total of eight grooves, one to each row of comb-plates. Presumably, impulses from the sense organ are transmitted to the rows of comb-plates via these grooves.

Nervous control of the comb beats has been proved in many ways. The orderly sequence of beating is destroyed if the nerve fibers underneath the comb-plates are cut but not if even several comb-plates are removed or paralyzed by various means. Cutting the ciliated groove from the sense organ interferes with coordination of the comb-plates. Extirpation of the statocyst interferes with coordination and with postural reactions.

LUMINESCENCE

Of all the animal phyla, ctenophores are easily preëminent in luminescence. To anyone familiar only with the light of fireflies and glow-worms, the lighting arrangements of ctenophores are truly a revelation.

Aristotle described the glowing of dead fish and flesh, something now known to be due to light-producing bacteria. Nothing much was learned about bioluminescence, however, until the second half of the 17th century when Robert Boyle, in the course of his famous experiments with the air pump, showed that air is essential for the luminescence of dead fish and of glowworms. Since then a long line of scientists from diverse fields have contributed to our present knowledge. Following Boyle were such men as Newton, Franklin, Priestley, Spallanzani, Réaumur, Humboldt, Becquerel, and even Sir Humphrey Davy and Michael Faraday.

It has become evident that there is a vast array of light-producing animals: protozoans like *Noctiluca,* jellyfish, hydroids, sea pens, deep sea squids, various shrimp, brittle stars, marine worms, many fishes, even some earthworms. E. Newton Harvey, a lifelong student of bioluminescence, finds in an extensive recent survey that 11 out of 17 major phyla contain luminous species. Luminescence has been intensively investigated, however, in only three organisms — luminescent bacteria, a tiny but very brilliant Japanese crustacean called *Cypridina,* and the common North American fireflies *Photinus* and *Photuris.*

Of what use is the light to each or all of these diverse organisms? In the fireflies and some marine worms it is known to be a mating signal. In some of the weird deep-sea fish, the light-producing organs may serve as lures to attract prey or as mating signs, but in many luminous animals like ctenophores it is difficult to imagine a function for the light.

The anatomy of light production in ctenophores is simple. The light is produced most intensely in the walls of the gastrovascular canals that underlie the eight vertical rows of comb-plates. The luminous tissue is either that of the gonads themselves or cells immediately

Fig. 7–5. *Mnemiopsis,* a common coastal ctenophore, luminescing. *(Kindness of George G. Lower)*

covering the gonads. Since the segmenting eggs of ctenophores are luminous, it seems possible that the gonads are directly involved.

The physiology of light production by ctenophores presents some puzzles. Ctenophores do not emit their light continuously but in brilliant flashes upon stimulation. The emission of light is under nervous control and in some way inhibited by external light. A ctenophore acclimated to daylight will not luminesce until it has been in a dark room for five to forty minutes, depending on the intensity of the light to which it has been subjected. Injured but still living ctenophores picked up on the beach in bright sunlight will luminesce brilliantly when touched with a pencil if they are placed in a glass of seawater and allowed to remain in a lightproof closet for a half hour.

Modern knowledge of the biochemistry of light production in animals began with the work of René Dubois in 1885 on luminous clams. He found that if the luminous organs are immersed in hot water, the light is extinguished permanently. He also discovered that ground-up luminous organs will glow for a considerable time but that finally such a brei ceases to luminesce. In brief, neither a hot-water nor a cold-water extract will glow indefinitely, but if they are mixed, even long afterwards, light will reappear. An extract made in hot water evidently contains some heat-stable substance capable of emitting light under the proper conditions. This substance was named **luciferin** by Dubois. The cold-water extract evidently contains an enzyme capable of oxidizing luciferin with the production of light. Dubois named it **luciferase.** (Remember that enzymes are inactivated permanently by heat.) A formula can be imagined as follows:

$$\text{luciferin} + O_2 \xrightarrow{\text{luciferase}} \text{oxyluciferin} + \text{light}$$

By suitable procedures the oxyluciferin can be reduced to luciferin again. Modern research has shown that this scheme will fit all known cases. In fireflies the color of the light is controlled by the species contributing the luciferase. *Photinus* emits an orange light and *Photuris* a yellow one. In reciprocal mixtures of luciferin and luciferase between fireflies of these two genera, the color of the light corresponds to the enzyme used.

Luciferase has all the usual chemical and physical properties of an enzyme and is thus presumably a protein. Luciferin is a relatively small molecule with a molecular weight between 250 and 500. Recent work shows it to be an aldehyde associated with a flavin nucleotide, a type of substance concerned with cell respiration. Interestingly enough, ATP (adenosine triphosphate), the phosphorus-containing compound essential for the transfer of energy in muscle contraction and in secretion, is also essential for the production of animal light — so deepset is the unity of living processes on the biochemical level! In fact, the study of bioluminescence has become an important research tool for the investigation of general problems in the dynamics of enzyme action and in the way drugs, temperature, pressure, anesthetics, and the like produce their effects on living systems.

RELATIONSHIP TO OTHER PHYLA

Two conflicting proposals have been made about the origin of ctenophores. One is that ctenophores are derived from medusae. Since there are a few jellyfish with an aboral sense organ, and since species of jellyfish occur with almost any desired number of radial canals, including eight, and also with only two tentacles, this theory has a certain likelihood. The competing theory, advocated by Hadzi, derives the ctenophores from flatworms. The evidence for this is that many marine flatworms have a stage known as Müller's larva. This creature has eight ciliated "arms," or lobes, and aboral sensory spots. Neotenous — that is, sexually mature — Müller's larvae have been found in Monterey Bay on the Pacific Coast. Consequently this theory also carries a degree of plausibility.

Review and References

REVIEW TOPICS

1. How do ctenophores differ from coelenterates?

2. Describe the food-catching and digestive apparatus of ctenophores. Of what possible economic importance are these animals?

3. How do ctenophores move? How do they reproduce?

4. Write a brief article, suitable for a desk encyclopedia, on the phenomenon of bioluminescence.

5. What are two possible relationships of ctenophores to other phyla? On what facts are these theories based?

USEFUL REFERENCES

Agassiz, L., *Ctenophorae, Contributions to the Natural History of the United States,* vol. III, Boston, American Academy of Arts and Sciences, 1860.

Coonfield, B. R., "Apical Dominance and Polarity in *Mnemiopsis,*" *Biological Bulletin,* vol. 70, 1936.

Harvey, E. N., *Bioluminescence,* New York, Academic Press, 1952.

Harvey, E. N., *Living Light,* Princeton, N.J., Princeton University Press, 1940.

Mayer, A. G., *Ctenophores of the Atlantic Coast of North America,* Washington, D.C., Carnegie Institution, 1912.

Part III

The Stream of Life

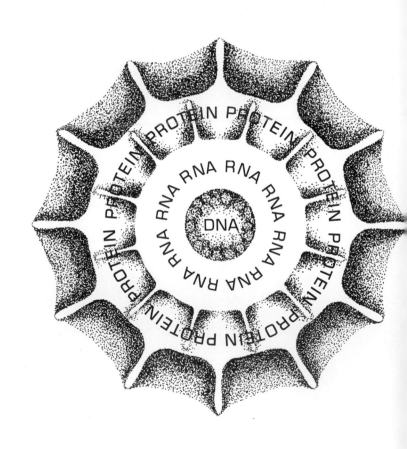

Biology can be defined as the study of the properties of deoxyribose nucleic acid. This is the modern version of August Weismann's late 19th century dictum that an animal is an expression of the potentialities of the germplasm. In the words of a writer of the time, Samuel Butler, "A hen is only an egg's way of producing another egg." This is still the hinge on which our science turns.

The laws of heredity are reflections of the way DNA is duplicated, correctly or incorrectly, shuffled, exchanged, and transmitted from one generation to another. Embryology is the study of the way the information in the DNA code is translated and expressed in enzymatic proteins and thence in the macroscopic world of organisms. The study of evolution concerns itself with the principles that determine which DNA shall survive on our particular planet.

This modern insight does not mean that biological science has been reduced to very simple terms. Although DNA is central, there is something wrong with Samuel Butler's use of the word "only." Wonderful indeed are the ways of an egg and the DNA within it. To remember the complexity and dazzling brilliance of a ctenophore on the high seas or the fantastic anatomy of fishes inhabiting the depths of the ocean, the pattern of a spider's web or the thoughts of a man, is to know that DNA, with its two dozen three-letter words, is deceptively simple. It speaks a rich and varied language calling forth a world of creatures far beyond our utmost imaginings.

Chapter 8

Genetics

From remote antiquity mankind has wondered how it comes to be that children resemble their parents. What is it that carries resemblances from parents to sons and daughters? How is it possible, asked the ancient Greeks, for a daughter to resemble her father? How can a child resemble both parents? Or resemble a grandparent rather than a parent? In modern times transmission of characteristics has been of great interest also regarding the possibilities of standardizing or even improving domesticated breeds of plants and animals.

After thousands of years of largely fruitless speculation by many men in many parts of the world, it was the achievement of Gregor Mendel in the second half of the last century to uncover the basic, universal laws of heredity. Mendel is clearly the Newton of biology. The theory of the gene has become the central theory in all biological science. The first half of our own century will be known for the work of T. H. Morgan and a host of others who identified the chromosomes as the physical basis of Mendel's laws and, as a consequence, the additional phenomena of linkage and crossing-over. Together, these discoveries constitute what is commonly termed "classical genetics."

In the 1960's the genetic code which carries the instructions for making a man or any other organism, and an organism of a very particular sort, has been discovered to lie in the nucleic acids in the chromosomes; furthermore, the code itself has been broken. Exciting advances have also been achieved in discovering the actual biochemistry of how the information in the code is translated into the finished organism, be it paramecium, drosophila, or octopus.

Before the newer discoveries are discussed, it is important first to gain a clear understanding of classical genetics because it is the framework within which biochemical genetics operates.

Ancient Beliefs That Die Hard. The ancient Greeks believed that the embryo was formed of a mixture of male and female reproductive fluids. Hippocrates (460?–377 B.C.), "the father of medicine," taught that heredity is due to a swarm of "seeds" or particles which come from all parts of the bodies of the two parents and are carried in the reproductive fluids. Aristotle, a younger contemporary of Hippocrates, attacked the theory that heredity is due to particles from all over the body. He argued instead that the reproductive fluids are produced only in the reproductive organs and that the embryo is formed, not out of the particles, but by the action of a vital formative force or "entelechy."

Aristotle's views prevailed. They came down into the beginning of modern times in the teaching that the new individual is coagulated out of a blend of seminal fluid and menstrual blood. William Harvey's famous experiment with the king's deer, to be described in the chapter on development, discredited this view, but the use of the word "blood" for genetic relationship still remains, as in the phrases "blood relatives" or "Indian blood," meaning Indian ancestry.

Another blow to the theory of coagulation resulted from the studies of human albinos and a family in which about half the individuals had six fingers. To explain such cases, a French genius named Pierre-Louis Moreau de Maupertuis (1698–1759) revived the idea of discrete hereditary particles in a way suggestive of the modern concept of genes, but his ideas were ridiculed out of court by no less a person than Voltaire.

The nature of heredity remained almost as obscure as before. Most people still thought in terms of the mixing of fluids. Many followed the theory (to be discussed later in this chapter) of Charles Darwin's grandfather, Erasmus Darwin (1731–1802), and of the great French zoologist, Jean Baptiste Pierre Antoine de Monet, Chevalier de Lamarck (1744–1829). These men believed that the characteristics acquired by the body of an adult animal would be transmitted to the offspring. It was supposed that effects due to use and disuse, or even to more generalized responses to environmental stimuli such as diet or sunlight, were transmissible. If a man persisted in running, the proponents of this theory held, his sons would be better runners.

To account for this imagined kind of heredity, Charles Darwin proposed the theory of **pangenesis.** With a real echo of Hippocrates, Darwin suggested that each part of the body might be continually producing particles, "pangenes," that were carried by the bloodstream to the gonads where they nourished the corresponding particles in the germ cells. A view not very different from this was until recently official doctrine in Soviet Russia. To test the theory of pangenesis Galton (1822–1911), a cousin of Darwin and a renowned student of heredity in his day, attempted to produce hybrids by injecting the blood of one kind of rabbit into another; but to no effect.

A turning point came with the theories of August Weismann (1834–1914) which he backed up with his work on coelenterates and mice. He showed that for multicellular animals, heredity is a matter of the germ cells alone, not of the somatic or body cells. By amputating the tails of both male and female mice for 57 generations and then permitting the 58th to grow tails, he demonstrated that lack of an organ for many generations in both parents fails to influence inheritance. The 58th generation of mice had tails of normal length. In the words of E. B. Wilson, America's first great investigator of chromosomes, Weismann "placed the keystone between the study of cytology [cells] and that of heredity, thus bringing the cell-theory and the evolution-theory into organic connection."

The ancient belief that heredity is a matter of blending fluids drawn from all parts of the body was dead. At least it was scientifically dead, although it lingers on in common speech and even in the thoughts of otherwise well-informed people.

Doors to Modern Knowledge. The puzzle of heredity was first solved by Gregor Mendel (1822–1884), an Augustinian monk who lived and worked in Brno, Czechoslovakia, and published his results for a local natural history society there in 1865. How he came to make his discoveries and why the scientific world was not prepared to appreciate their importance are much too complex problems to be fully dealt with here. Nevertheless, it is important to remember that Mendel's discoveries, like all scientific advances, had antecedents. Mendel himself was widely and actively interested in many branches of science. One of the keys to his success was that he used in his basic experiments a plant, the garden pea, that had been used by many others in studies of heredity. In fact, as early as 1823 Thomas Knight had confirmed still earlier reports of dominance and recessiveness and the appearance of ancestral types. Although neither Knight nor any of the others who crossbred peas noticed regular laws, the necessary basic information about the breeding of pea plants had been obtained.

In addition, several workers, including Charles Darwin (1809–1882), who had studied hybrid pigeons, had stated the problem of heredity very clearly. In his epoch-making book *Origin of Species,* Darwin wrote:

> The offspring from the first cross between two pure breeds is tolerably and sometimes (as I have found with pigeons) quite uniform in character, and everything seems simple enough: but when these mongrels are crossed one with another for several generations hardly two of them are alike, and then the difficulty of the task becomes manifest. . . . The slight variability of hybrids in the first generation, in contrast with that in succeeding generations, is a curious fact and deserves attention.

The final factor which may have given Mendel the clue to his discovery was his interest in beekeeping and bee-crossing. Mendel was a contemporary and almost a neighbor of Johann Dzierzon, the most famous beekeeper of all time. Dzierzon crossed German with Italian bees and found that in the following generation half the drones were German, half Italian. Mendel was thus alerted to the possibility of finding definite ratios, and chose to work with a plant about which a considerable amount was already known.

Why the importance of Mendel's analysis was not appreciated at once is also a complex story. One factor was the time required for Weismann's ideas to gain general acceptance. Chromosomes were not taken very seriously by most biologists who were primarily interested in evolution, and the facts of meiosis had not been worked out even though Weismann had predicted that meiosis must take place. Another factor was that Galton and his school had not yet shown the importance of applying statistics to the study of variation.

In 1900 three experimenters eventually rediscovered Mendel's basic laws. They were de Vries in Holland, Correns in Germany, and von Tschermak in Austria. Mendel's paper was found almost immediately afterwards. (It had been mentioned in a book by the renowned American botanist, Liberty Hyde Bailey.)

At about the same time, de Vries (1848–1935) discovered **mutations,** that is, sudden changes in heredity. Once alerted to mutations, zoologists began to find them in many animals. One of the first, discovered by a sharp-witted student, was a mutation that converted the red eyes of the wild (normal) fruit fly, *Drosophila,* into white (colorless) eyes. It was soon found that most, if not all, of these mutations followed Mendel's laws, and the modern science of genetics began.

MENDEL'S FUNDAMENTAL DISCOVERIES

Segregation: Mendel's First Law. Mendel's experiments lasted eight years and included the cross-fertilization and raising of many hundreds of plants and the counting of some 8,000 peas. He succeeded where others had failed, first, because he simplified his problem and considered single pairs of characters, tall vs. short plant, or wrinkled vs. smooth seeds, instead of thinking about the whole complex organism. He also succeeded because he had the patience to apply statistics to the problem.

To explain and illustrate the principles discovered by Mendel and to demonstrate that the laws are valid for animals, consider a cross between two special kinds of chickens, a so-called "splashed white" and a black. If two such chickens are crossed, 100 per cent of the first generation, the F_1 or **first filial generation,** will be neither splashed white nor black but a slaty blue, the "blue Andalusian" (Fig. 8–1). If one of these hybrid blue chickens, either a rooster or a hen, is mated with a black chicken, 50 per cent of the offspring will be black and the other 50 per cent blue. None will be splashed white. These are the facts.

What do these facts mean? Mendel's explanation turned out to be simplicity itself. It has since come to be called the **law of segregation.** Each individual produced by sexual reproduction possesses within itself a double set of hereditary factors, one set from each parent. The hereditary make-up of a pure-bred black chicken can be represented as ••, and the hereditary constitution of a pure-bred white chicken oo. The hereditary constitution of the first generation cross between the two is then •o. This produces the intermediate "blue" feathers.

What happens when a black rooster, ••, is crossed with a blue hen, •o? Obviously the black rooster can contribute only a factor for black, represented here by •, to its offspring.

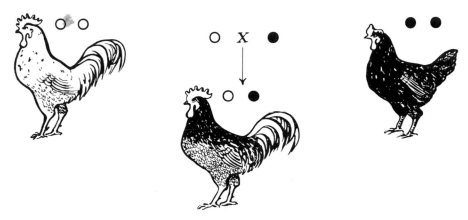

Fig. 8–1. A pure-bred "splashed white" rooster crossed with a pure-bred black hen produces only "blue Andalusian" offspring. Each offspring carries a factor for white from one parent and a factor for black from the other.

The blue hen, however, can contribute either a factor for white, o, or a factor for black, ●. In other words, all the sperms will carry a factor for black, and one half of the eggs will carry a factor for black and one half a factor for white. An egg carrying a factor for black fertilized by a sperm carrying a similar factor forms a pure black individual, ●●. Consequently 50 per cent of the offspring will be black. The 50 per cent of the eggs which carry a factor for white will also be fertilized by "black" sperms. This 50 per cent of the eggs will thus form the intermediate blue chicks, ●o.

This situation can be diagrammed by the construction of a Roman square in which the different kinds of eggs are represented along one side, and the different kinds of sperms (in this case only one kind) along the other side. Within the squares the possible crosses are then written. These represent the zygotes or fertilized eggs. (See Fig. 8–2.)

Suppose you attempt to breed a race of blue Andalusians by crossing two blue chickens. What will be the result? Now there will be two kinds of sperms as well as two kinds of eggs. Again the possible combinations can easily be seen by placing the two kinds of eggs along one side of the squares and the two kinds of sperms along the other. (This is really just a graphic form of multiplication, to find all the kinds of products.) Each kind of egg can then be united with each kind of sperm. It is at once evident that there are four possibilities. The egg and sperm may both carry a factor for black, or both may carry a factor for white. In the third and fourth possibilities, the sperm may carry a factor for black and the egg a factor for white, or vice versa. You can then predict from the Roman square that the result of crossing two blue fowl would be 25 per cent black, 50 per cent blue, and 25 per cent white. You could predict further that if the black offspring are

Fig. 8–2. Diagram to show the genetic situation when a pure-bred black rooster, which produces only sperms carrying a factor for black, is mated with a "blue Andalusian" hen, which produces two kinds of eggs in equal numbers.

mated to other black chickens all their offspring will be black, that the white segregated out of the cross of two blues will also breed true, but that the blues if mated together will again give offspring in a 1:2:1 ratio. This cross has been made repeatedly and the results always agree with prediction.

To generalize in the words of a man second only to Mendel in the study of heredity, T. H. Morgan (1866–1945):

> Mendel's fundamental law of segregation was announced in 1865. It is very simple. The units contributed by each parent separate in the germ cells of the offspring without having had any influence on each other. This is Mendel's first law. It has been found to have the widest application, both to animals and plants, both high and low in the scale.

There are a number of other points to bear in mind. Fertilization takes place at random. In this case a sperm bearing a factor for black is just as apt to fertilize an egg bearing a factor for white as it is to fertilize an egg with a factor for black.

Terminology of Genetics. At this point let us introduce some modern terminology to facilitate discussion. The hereditary factors are now called **genes.** If an animal has received similar genes for a given trait, say white feathers, from each parent, it is said to be **homozygous** for that trait. If an animal has received differing genes for a given trait, it is said to be **heterozygous** for that trait. All blue Andalusians are heterozygous for feather color. All black sheep must be homozygous for wool color because black is

Fig. 8–3. Diagram to show the genetic basis of the 1:2:1 ratio in the offspring of two individuals hybrid for a factor which does not show dominance.

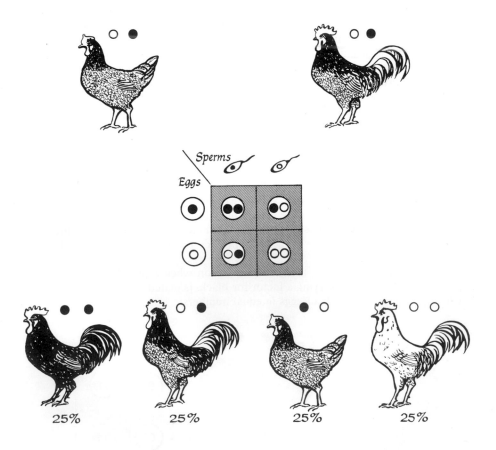

recessive to white in sheep. If a sheep bore a gene for white, the sheep would be white even though it also carried a gene for black. A gene for white is said to be **dominant.** Thus white sheep may be either homozygous or heterozygous for color. A heterozygous individual is called a **carrier,** because it carries a gene for the recessive trait although it does not show it.

The different forms of a gene are called **alleles.** Thus the genes for black and for white wool in sheep are alleles. In many known cases there is a series of alleles, as in some of the genes for eye color in *Drosophila.* Because alleles must be at the same position or locus on a specific chromosome (otherwise they would not be called alleles), any diploid animal can carry a maximum of only two alleles.

In symbolizing genes it is customary to capitalize the gene symbol for a dominant trait and put its recessive partner or allele in small letters. For example, *a* symbolizes a recessive gene for albinism and *A,* the corresponding dominant allele, the gene for normal pigment. Thus an albino man has the genetical constitution *aa* and is homozygous for albinism. A normal individual may be either homozygous *AA,* or heterozygous *Aa;* in the latter case he is a carrier.

Crosses of the kind just described, in which the two individuals differ in respect to a single pair of genes, are said to be **monohybrid** crosses.

Individuals which look alike are said to belong to the same **phenotype** (Gr. *phainein,* to show), whether they are genetically the same or not. If they are genetically the same, they are said to belong to the same **genotype** (Gr. *genos,* race). Thus all albinos belong to the same genotype *aa.* All individuals with normal pigmentation belong to the same phenotype but may be of either the homozygous genotype *AA* or the heterozygous genotype *Aa.* The complete haploid (single) set of chromosomes characteristic of the cells of any individual constitutes that individual's **genome.**

Probability and the Product Law. A moment's thought will show that in any cross in which Mendel's law of segregation is involved, the results depend on chance, that is, on **probability.** If 50 per cent of the sperms carry a gene for albinism and 50 per cent carry a gene for normal pigmentation, then there is a 50:50 chance that any particular egg will be fertilized by a sperm carrying the gene for albinism. It will soon be seen that probability also applies to Mendel's second law, as well as to sex determination, and to the genetics of populations in general.

Although it is not possible to control the kind of sperm which will fertilize a given egg, it is possible to make some useful predictions about the sex of unborn children, the likelihood of a given marriage producing an albino child, and many other matters. These predictions are based on very simple laws of probability and have an extremely wide application not only in genetics but also in games, war, business, public health, and elsewhere.

Fractions are used to express probabilities. Thus if the chance of an event happening is 1 in 2, its probability is said to be $1/2$. For example, the probability of heads when a coin is tossed is $1/2$. Likewise the chance of getting tails is $1/2$. A dice cube has six sides, consequently the chance that a "four" will land uppermost is $1/6$, and so for each of the other sides.

The law of probability most important for an understanding of the workings of heredity is the **Product Law,** or the rule of the multiplication of probabilities for independent events. It is very simple and can be simply stated. The probability that two independent events will coincide is the product of their individual probabilities. If two coins are tossed simultaneously, the chance that two heads will land uppermost is $1/2 \times 1/2$, or $1/4$. This means that in a sufficiently large series of such double throws, two heads will appear in 25 per cent of the cases. Any skeptic need only get two coins and try for himself. It's a fact, but you must do it often enough to eliminate the vagaries of chance in small numbers.

The various ratios obtained in monohybrid crosses can be readily understood on the basis of the Product Law. For example, if a heterozygous (blue) Andalusian rooster, **o●**, is crossed with a heterozygous, **o●**, blue hen, the chance that any given sperm will carry gene o is $1/2$ and the chance that it will carry gene ● is $1/2$. The same holds for the eggs. Since it is a matter of chance which egg will be fertilized by which sperm, the chance of a **o** sperm fertilizing a **o** egg is $\frac{1}{2} \times \frac{1}{2}$, or $\frac{1}{4}$. Thus 25 per cent of the zygotes will be oo. Similarly the chance that a ●-bearing sperm will fertilize a o-bearing egg is $\frac{1}{2} \times \frac{1}{2}$, or $\frac{1}{4}$, which means that 25 per cent of the zygotes will be ●o. The reciprocal combination is of course equally likely, a o sperm and a ● egg, $\frac{1}{2} \times \frac{1}{2}$, or $\frac{1}{4}$, which makes 25 per cent of the zygotes heterozygous o●. The sum of these last two possibilities, which both yield heterozygous zygotes, is 50 per cent. And, of course, the chance that two gametes unite that each carry a gene for black is $\frac{1}{2} \times \frac{1}{2}$, or $\frac{1}{4}$. Thus 25 per cent of the zygotes will be ●●. This yields the familiar 25:50:25 or 1:2:1 ratio.

Apply this now to a specific problem. A man and his wife are both normal but each is known to carry a gene for albinism because each had one albino parent. One half of the man's sperms carry a gene for albinism and so do one half of the woman's eggs. Thus the chance that any particular child will be an albino is $\frac{1}{2} \times \frac{1}{2}$, or $\frac{1}{4}$, or one in four. Every time they have a child there is one chance in four that it will be an albino. What is the chance that it will be homozygous for normal pigmentation? Again $\frac{1}{2} \times \frac{1}{2}$, or a one in four chance.

Suppose they have two children. What is the chance that *both* will be albinos? The chance that the first child will be an albino is $\frac{1}{4}$. The chance that the second child will be an albino is also $\frac{1}{4}$. The second egg and sperm have no way of "knowing" what the first egg and sperm were like. Therefore the second child is an independent event. But by applying the product law it becomes evident that there is only one chance in sixteen that both children will be albinos: $\frac{1}{4} \times \frac{1}{4} = \frac{1}{16}$.

As Mendel himself pointed out, the results of crossing a group of monohybrids can be predicted by the use of a formula as simple as the binomial theorem, $(a + b)^2$ or, as more often used, $(p + q)^2 = p^2 + 2 pq + q^2$, where p represents the frequency of one gene and q the frequency of its allele. Thus if 0.5 of the gametes in a given cross carry gene p and 0.5 carry its allele, gene q, then there will result 0.25 individuals with pp, 0.50 individuals with both p and q, and 0.25 with qq. The use of this formula in population genetics will be discussed further in the chapter on evolution.

Independent Assortment: Mendel's Second Law. Mendel's second law is the **law of independent assortment.** This comes into play when the two individuals in a cross differ in respect to two, three, or more pairs of genes. Such crosses are called **dihybrid, trihybrid,** etc. For example, in rabbits black is due to a dominant gene, *B,* and white to its recessive allele or partner gene, *b.* It is also known that short hair is due to a dominant gene, *S,* and long hair to its allele, *s.* What happens when a homozygous (i.e., pure-bred) black, short-haired rabbit, is crossed with a homozygous white, long-haired one? All the offspring in the first generation will look alike or be of the same phenotype, black and short-haired. Their genetical constitution or genotype will be heterozygous for both traits, *BbSs.*

When two of these heterozygous rabbits are crossed, the genes inherited from each parent separate in the germ cells of the offspring without any influence on each other. This is the normal segregation of Mendel's first law. Independent assortment means that the way one pair of genes segregates into the germ cells is independent of the way another pair does. In the present illustration one half the gametes, either eggs or sperms, will receive a gene for black. *B,* and one half its allele, the gene for white, *b.* But whether a given gamete gets gene *B* or *b* has nothing to do with whether or not it gets the gene for short or for long hair. This is determined simply by chance, so that one half the gametes that get the gene for black will get the gene for short hair and the other half will get the gene for long. This results in four kinds of gametes in equal numbers symbolized as follows: *BS, Bs, bS, bs.* To predict the results of a dihybrid cross, the four possible types of sperms are written along one side of a Roman square, and the four possible types of eggs along the other. Within the squares appear the possible genotypes resulting from the cross.

It can be seen from the grid in Figure 8–4 that there are only four phenotypes present: black, short-haired; black, long-haired; white, short-haired; and white, long-haired; and that they occur in a ratio of 9:3:3:1. The ratio of the genotypes is very different. For instance, although $\frac{9}{16}$ of this generation are of the black,

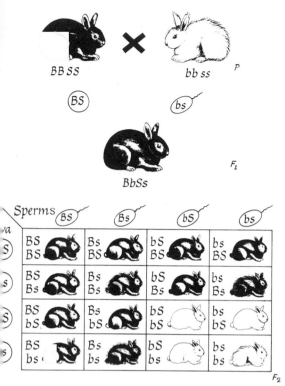

Mendel knew nothing of chromosomes, but after the rediscovery of his laws in 1900 several lines of evidence converged to prove that the unit factors Mendel had talked about, the genes, as we say today, are located on the chromosomes. This evidence is the precise and extensive parallelism between the behavior of the units of heredity and the behavior of the chromosomes. It is a parallelism so detailed and so extensive that there is no room for doubt that the chromosomes are the very stuff of heredity and hence provide the physical basis of evolution itself. The parallelism runs all through the cycle of fertilization and meiosis, as well as in particular aspects of it like sex determination and linkage. Furthermore, abnormalities of chromosome behavior are followed by abnormalities of inheritance.

Unravelling the story of chromosome behavior was not the achievement of a single individual but of a group of men in various European countries and in North America in the closing years of the last century and the opening years of the present one.

Fertilization and Meiosis: The Cycle. The facts of fertilization in themselves provide some of the most cogent and obvious evidence for the chromosomal theory of heredity. The male contributes equally with the female to the heredity of the offspring, yet the only physical contribution of the male is the head of a sperm. What is the head of a sperm? Microscopic examination of sperm formation in the testis of any animal will reveal that the head of a sperm is virtually nothing but a condensed packet of chromosomes. Consequently it follows that chromosomes are the physical bearers of inheritance. Once inside the egg cytoplasm, the sperm head gradually swells up into a nucleus which ultimately fuses with the egg nucleus.

It was discovered that the number of chromosomes in every cell of a given animal is always the same, 46 in man, 8 in drosophila, the fruit fly, 36 in chickens. It was also found that each chromosome has its own permanent individuality as indicated by its size, shape, and the position of its **kinetochore,** the place where it is

Fig. 8–4. A pure-bred short-haired, black rabbit and a pure-bred long-haired, white rabbit were crossed to produce the F$_1$ offspring. Two F$_1$ animals were crossed to produce F$_2$. This is an illustration of Mendel's second law, the law of random assortment of genes.

short-haired phenotype, only $\frac{1}{16}$ are of the genotype *BBSS* which is homozygous for both traits. Notice also that only 1 out of 16 is the double recessive phenotype—long-haired and white, and that in this case there is only one genotype, *bbss,* that can give this particular phenotype.

It is important to remember in genetic prediction that fertilization is at random. When it is said that one-half or one-sixteenth of the offspring will be of a particular sort, what is really meant is that there is one chance in two or one chance in every sixteen that the offspring will be so. The genetic ratios predicted are thus actually realized only in sufficiently large samples.

attached to a spindle during mitosis. The visible complex of chromosomes, their number, sizes, and shapes, which is characteristic of any species or individual, is called the **karyotype,** which means, literally, the nuclear-type. (See Figs. 2 – 22 and 8 – 5.)

It was early discovered that every cell has two sets of chromosomes, one set derived from the sperm and one set from the egg. Yet the number of chromosomes characteristic of any species remains the same, generation after generation. How can this be? It was this question which led Weismann to predict that there must be some time when the number of chromosomes is reduced by half, for otherwise they would double in number with every generation. The place where meiosis (*meiosis,* to diminish) occurs is in the formation of gametes. Specifically, meiosis takes place during the two final cell divisions in the formation of a sperm or an egg.

When finally unravelled, the over-all facts of fertilization and meiosis turned out to be rather simple. In meiosis the double set of chromosomes found in all the somatic or body cells is reduced to a single set in each sperm or egg. In fertilization the double set is restored by the meeting, in the nucleus of the fertilized egg, of a single set of chromosomes from the sperm with a single set in the egg. It will be recalled from the simplified account of mitosis and meiosis in Chapter 2 that the number of chromosomes in a set is called the **haploid** number, and that a cell like a sperm containing only one set is said to be haploid. A body cell with two sets is said to be **diploid.**

To understand heredity, it is a great advantage to understand in more detail than in the previous account exactly what happens during the process of meiosis. These details are very much the same in all animals and plants, which is of course the reason why the laws of heredity are the same throughout the living world. In all forms of life meiosis requires two successive divisions. It always begins with a single diploid cell and ends with four haploid cells. Two divisions are required to segregate all the pairs of genes because of the occurrence of crossing over (see below), which is about as universal as meiosis itself and which permits different pairs of genes in the same chromosome pair to undergo recombination.

Meiosis begins like ordinary mitosis with a prophase, during which the chromosomes gradually stain more darkly and become shorter and thicker. As in mitosis, a good microscope will show that each chromosome is really double along its entire length, and hence must have duplicated sometime before prophase began, or very early in prophase.

The first important difference between mitosis and meiosis occurs in late prophase. In mitosis the two sets of doubled chromosomes, one from the male and one from the female parent, pay no attention to each other. But in meiosis the corresponding chromosomes of paternal and maternal origin seem to seek each other out and come to lie side by side, closely aligned at every point from one end to the other. Thus the largest chromosome in the paternal set lies alongside of the largest in the maternal set, and so on down to the two smallest chromosomes. This pairing of corresponding or homologous chromosomes is called **synapsis.** Synapsis does not occur in mitosis.

Since in meiosis the chromosomes have doubled themselves during the previous interphase, there are really two maternal and two

Fig. 8 – 5. Normal human male karyotype. The 22 pairs of homologous autosomes plus the single X and single Y are shown from a cell grown *in vitro* to make the chromosomes easy to distinguish. Note that each chromosome has duplicated itself, but that the duplicates, or chromatids, are still held together by the kinetochore. *(Kindness of V. A. McKusick)*

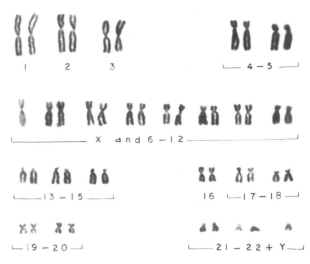

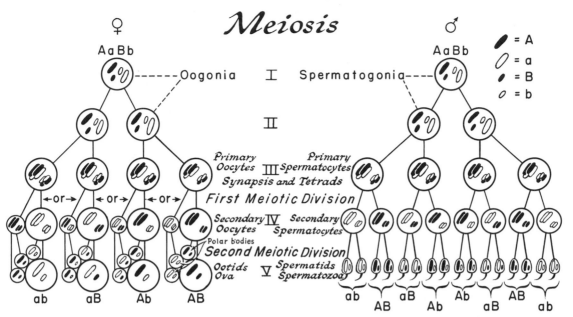

Fig. 8–6. Meiosis leading to oogenesis and spermatogenesis. There are two chromosomes in a haploid set, one large and one small, in the animal represented here. *(From Pauli, The World of Life, Houghton Mifflin)*

corresponding paternal chromosomes that come to lie side by side in synapsis. The two maternal chromosomes are still held together by their kinetochore or spindle fiber attachment point, and the same is true of the paternal pair. Such a synaptic group is called a **tetrad**. The four chromosomes still held together by their two kinetochores are usually called **chromatids** until they separate. In a species which has 3 chromosomes in a set, there will, of course, be three tetrads. In the human organism, which has 23 chromosomes in a set, there are 23 tetrads in the prophase and metaphase of the first meiotic division. In other words, there are four complete sets of chromosomes at the first metaphase of meiosis. This is precisely enough to provide four sperms (or four eggs) each with one set of chromosomes. To do this two cell divisions are required.

The cells in which synapsis takes place with the formation of tetrads and which undergo the first meiotic division are called **primary spermatocytes** or **primary oocytes**. The cells formed as a result of the first meiotic division are called **secondary spermatocytes** or **secondary oocytes**.

At the first meiotic division each pair of two **kinetochores,** one pair for every tetrad, separates; and the members of each pair pass to opposite poles of the spindle, each pulling after

it its two chromosomes (more accurately, chromatids). Thus, in each tetrad the chromosomes of paternal and maternal origin are segregated into separate cells, and hence into separate gametes. This obviously affords a physical basis for Mendel's law of the segregation of hereditary factors in the formation of sperms or eggs. If, for example, a paternal chromosome carried a factor for red hair, and the homologous maternal chromosome carried the allele for black hair, one half of the gametes would receive the chromosome carrying the gene for red, the other half the chromosome carrying the gene for black. Said in another way, Mendel's unit factors are present in pairs in the adult animal. So are chromosomes. Mendel's unit factors separate from each other during reproduction. So do the chromosome pairs.

The way one pair of maternal and paternal chromosomes separates after synapsis is independent of the way any other pair separates. This means that almost no two eggs or no two sperms will have exactly the same assortment of maternal and paternal chromosomes.

Although each pair of kinetochores of maternal and paternal origin is separated by the first meiotic division, the chromosomes are still double and held together by the kinetochores. The kinetochores now duplicate themselves,

153

and the secondary spermatocytes and secondary oocytes undergo the second meiotic division. This second division separates the doubled chromosomes so that each of the resulting cells, which are called **spermatids** or **ootids,** has one chromosome from each of the original tetrads. There is now a total of four sperms or four potential eggs, each with one complete set of chromosomes, resulting from each primary spermatocyte or oocyte.

GENETIC VARIATION — ROLE OF MEIOSIS AND FERTILIZATION

The primary origin of genetic variation is **mutation,** that is, permanent changes in genes. In addition, all animals which reproduce sexually possess a built-in mechanism to guarantee continual variation by the formation of ever new combinations of the genes. This mechanism is meiosis and fertilization. The way any particular pair of synapsing chromosomes segregates is entirely independent of the way any other pair does. This means that, on the average, every egg and every sperm receives a thoroughly mixed set of chromosomes partly of paternal and partly of maternal origin. What is the chance that a sperm (or an egg), in an animal with only three chromosomes in a set, might receive only paternal chromosomes? Using the Product Law for the coincidence of two or more independent events you can easily calculate this chance. For each pair of synapsing chromosomes there is a probability of $\frac{1}{2}$ that the paternal member of the pair will enter a particular sperm. Consequently the chance that all three paternal chromosomes will enter the same sperm is $\frac{1}{2} \times \frac{1}{2} \times \frac{1}{2} = (\frac{1}{2})^3 = \frac{1}{8}$. In other words, one in every 8 sperms of such a species will contain only paternal chromosomes. By the same reasoning it follows that one in every 8 sperms will receive only maternal chromosomes. And of course 6 of every 8 sperms (or eggs) will contain a mixed set. The total number of possible kinds of sperms is thus 2^3, or 8.

The probability that a given human sperm will carry only paternal chromosomes is $(\frac{1}{2})^{23}$ or one chance in 8,388,608. This is another way of saying that every man and every woman can produce over 8,000,000 kinds of sperms or

eggs! In fact, crossing over, to be discussed below, increases even this staggering number.

Fertilization then enters the picture to compound the amount of variation already vouchsafed by meiosis. In a given mating, if there were 8,000,000 kinds of sperms and only two kinds of eggs, there would obviously be 16,000,000 possible kinds of zygotes. However, since any woman can theoretically produce over 8,000,000 kinds of eggs, the total possible kinds of zygotes any human couple can produce is over 8,000,000 times 8,000,000, without counting crossing over! Such is the biological basis of human individuality.

Sex Determination. In the early years of the present century American cytologists (specialists in the study of cells) made a peculiar discovery about chromosomes in certain insects where chromosomes are favorable for study. In females all the chromosome pairs match perfectly. In males, however, there is one pair in which the two chromosomes do not match even though they pair together in synapsis, but end to end rather than lengthwise as other chromosomes do. These two chromosomes are called *X* and *Y* **chromosomes.** During meiosis it can be observed that females always possess two *X* chromosomes, the males an *X* and a *Y*. After meiosis every egg will carry an *X* chromosome but half of the sperms will carry an *X* and half a *Y*. The two kinds of sperms will be produced in equal numbers because at synapsis for every *X* chromosome there is a *Y*.

This means that 50 per cent of the eggs will be fertilized by a *Y*- and 50 per cent by an *X*-bearing sperm. The result is equal numbers of *XX* female-producing zygotes and *XY* male-producing zygotes. In most animals males and females are produced in approximately equal numbers. In some species, perhaps in most, a differential mortality begins before birth and continues long afterward, so that in different age groups the sex ratio varies somewhat to one or the other side of the 50:50 ratio. Since sex is determined by the nature of the sperm, the sex of an individual is determined at the instant of fertilization.

In some groups of animals, including amphibians and butterflies, it is the female which is heterogametic for sex determination. Two kinds of eggs are produced, and only one kind of sperm. In such species the sex chromosomes are commonly designated W and Z, rather than X and Y. All sperms carry a W chromosome; therefore any egg carrying a Z chromosome will produce a zygote carrying WZ, which will develop into a female.

The control of sex determination has long been sought, but no method has been found that gives positive results. If some way could be found to separate X-bearing from Y-bearing sperms, it would have immediate practical applications in animal husbandry where artificial insemination is widely practiced. Some have expressed fears lest such knowledge would upset the sex ratio in human populations, but there is good evidence that most people desire both boys and girls among their children.

Even though sex determination cannot as yet be controlled, it is possible to make some useful predictions about the sex of the unborn. This is done by the use of the Product Law already discussed. Since all human eggs carry an X chromosome while 50 per cent of sperms carry an X and 50 per cent carry a Y chromosome, the chance of any particular child being a boy is $1/2$, and likewise the chance of its being a girl is $1/2$. In a family of three children, what is the probability that all three will be boys? Applying the product law, $1/2 \times 1/2 \times 1/2 = (1/2)^3 = 1/8$. This means that if a survey were made of families with only three children, it should be found that in $1/8$ of the families all three children are boys. It also means that in $1/8$ of the families all three of the children should be girls and in $6/8$ of the cases there should be a mixture of boys and girls. In how many families of nine children should all nine be boys? The answer is again easy to calculate, $(1/2)^9 = 512$. This means that on a basis of pure chance, one family out of every 512 in which there are nine children should have nine boys. Likewise one family in 512 of all the families with nine children should consist of nine girls. The remaining 510 nine-child families should include both boys and girls.

Do the facts fit this statistical theory? They do if you toss coins. With human sex determination the facts fit the theory at least approximately. In some surveys there have been a few more families with only boys or only girls

than chance alone would account for. If this really turns out to be true, a plausible explanation might be that the uterine environment in some women is more favorable to zygotes of one sex than those of the other. It is also conceivable that in some men there might be a difference in viability or activity between the X-bearing and the Y-bearing sperms.

In an insect such as drosophila, where all XY zygotes develop into males, XO zygotes, which have no Y chromosome due to its loss during early development of the egg, also develop into normal though sterile males. Any XXY zygote develops into a normal-appearing and fertile female. The situation in humans seems to be somewhat different. Human XO zygotes do not develop into males but into females. Such girls develop normally until the age when puberty should occur. But menstruation does not take place and there is no development of breasts nor of axillary and pubic hair. Such a condition is called **Turner's syndrome.** At first it was thought that the trouble might be a failure of the pituitary gland to secrete its normal gonad-stimulating hormone but it was soon shown that there is ample gonadotropin from the pituitary in the blood of afflicted individuals. Biopsy, however, revealed that the gonads, i.e., the ovaries, were virtually absent.

An egg which contains two X chromosomes plus a Y chromosome develops into a man with **Klinefelter's syndrome.** Such men appear more or less normal but are sterile because of lack of spermatogenesis.

The facts of Turner's and Klinefelter's syndromes make it evident that sex determination in human beings (and probably all other mammals), while basically determined by an X and Y chromosomal mechanism as in insects, nevertheless has some important differences. The Y chromosome, which appears to be without any function in insects except to exclude the presence of a second X, in man carries genes which have a positive male-producing action.

Eggs with abnormal numbers of chromosomes can be produced by various agents — radiations, extremes of temperature, certain chemicals. Any derangement of meiosis by which an X or Y chromosome was lost, or the X chromosomes failed to separate properly, could lead to the sexual abnormalities just discussed.

Sex Linkage. When a gene is located on an *X* chromosome it is said to be **sex-linked** because its inheritance follows the transmission of the sex chromosomes.

The best known sex-linked genes in man are those for red-green color-blindness and for hemophilia (a faulty clotting mechanism of the blood that results in excessive bleeding, even from a scratch). The gene for white eyes in drosophila, the fruit fly, is similarly a sex-linked one.

A male has only one *X* chromosome. Therefore he can carry only one gene for such traits. The one *X* chromosome may carry a gene for red-green color-blindness or a gene for normal vision. But his *Y* chromosome has no corresponding part. Consequently even though the genes for white eyes and for color-blindness are recessive, they will produce their characteristic effects in a male. For example, if a man has a gene for hemophilia on his *X* chromosome he is bound to be hemophilic because there is no possibility of the recessive gene being counteracted by a dominant gene for normal blood-clotting on a second *X* chromosome. This type of inheritance is illustrated in the case of white eyes in drosophila (Fig. 8–7).

Of course a female with her two *X* chromosomes will carry two genes for each sex-linked trait, one gene on each of the *X* chromosomes. She may be either homozygous or heterozygous. If she is homozygous she may carry two genes for normal or two genes for white eyes (if she is a fruit fly), or two genes for color-blindness (if she is a woman). Of course, if she is heterozygous she will carry one gene for normal eyes and one gene for the abnormal eye trait involved.

A female who is heterozygous for a recessive sex-linked trait is known as a **carrier.** She will be normal, but will transmit a gene for the recessive trait in 50 per cent of her eggs. Whether or not the trait appears in her children will depend on whether they are boys or girls and, in the case of the girls, whether or not the father has a recessive or dominant gene in his *X* chromosome. If a given child is a boy, he will show the results of whichever gene was on the *X* he received from his mother, since he could not have received an *X* from his father, or he would have been a girl.

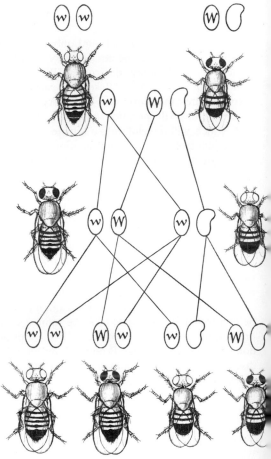

Fig. 8–7. Sex-linked inheritance of white eyes in drosophila. Males can be distinguished by their shorter, more rounded abdomens. The ovals represent *X* chromosomes; the bean-shaped symbols represent *Y* chromosomes. *(From Pauli,* The World of Life, *Houghton Mifflin)*

It is important to distinguish the sex-linked genes, like those just described, from genes whose action is influenced by sex hormones. For example, there are genes in certain breeds of sheep which will produce horns in a normal male. In a castrated male or in a female where male sex hormones are lacking, these genes do not produce horns. Such genes are not necessarily on the sex chromosomes — in fact, usually they are not.

Autosomal Linkage. Just as Weismann predicted meiosis, so a young graduate student named Sutton at Columbia University in 1903 predicted **linkage.** He did it on the eminently reasonable grounds that there are many more hereditary factors than chromosomes and that hence each chromosome must carry a group of genes. The group of genes on a single chromosome cannot assort independently at meiosis but has to pass as a unit into the same gamete. In other words, the genes tied together in the same chromosome cannot follow Mendel's second law, the law of independent assortment. To assort quite independently, genes must be on different chromosomes of the set.

There are, consequently, as many linkage groups in any animal as there are chromosomes in its set. So Sutton predicted, and so it has turned out. In drosophila there are four chromosomes in a haploid set, one large, two middle-sized, and one small. Likewise there are four linkage groups of comparable sizes. After linkage was first established in drosophila by T. H. Morgan and his students, it was found to exist in all animals and plants investigated. In man there are 23 chromosomes in a set and hence 23 possible linkage groups. Twenty-two of the chromosomes are called **autosomes,** and one the sex chromosome, either X or Y. So far, only five autosomal linkage groups plus the sex-linked group have been identified; only about two dozen genes are involved. In mice the situation is somewhat better known, for at least 13 linkage groups have been identified involving about 50 different genes.

Crossing Over. It was learned early in the original work on linkage in drosophila that a phenomenon called **crossing over** occurs. This takes place between the two members of a pair of homologous chromosomes. In the words of T. H. Morgan, "Linkage and crossing over are correlative phenomena, and can be expressed by numerical laws that are as definite as those discovered by Mendel."

For example, on the long second chromosome of drosophila are located the mutant genes for star eyes, black body, purple eye color, dachs (very short) legs, vestigial wings, plexus veins, and speck (black dot at base of wings). Suppose a fly had received a number two chromosome carrying all these genes from one parent and a number two chromosome with the normal alleles from the other parent.

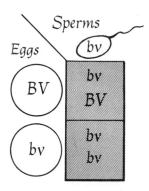

Fig. 8–8. Genetic grid illustrating cross for linked genes between homozygous male and heterozygous female, assuming that no crossing over occurs.

Then according to the usual events of linkage, the offspring of this fly will either get all these mutant genes and none of their normal alleles, or else all the normal alleles and none of the mutant genes. (See Fig. 8–8.)

But in a predictable percentage of cases some offspring will get the genes for speck, plexus, and vestigial, and normal alleles for the other mutants, while other offspring will get the normal alleles for the genes first mentioned and the mutant genes for dachs, purple, black, and star. (See Fig. 8–9.) The new combinations now remain as firmly linked as had the old.

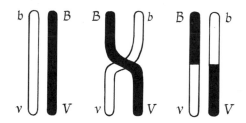

Fig. 8–9. Diagram showing crossing over.

Examine now a specific instance more closely. Let b symbolize a recessive gene for black body and B its normal allele, and let v symbolize a recessive gene for vestigial wings and V its normal allele. Then, if a fly homozygous for the recessive genes, $bvbv$, is crossed with one homozygous for the normal alleles, $BVBV$, all the F_1 generation flies will be heterozygous $BVbv$ and appear normal. When these heterozygous individuals are mated, crossing over

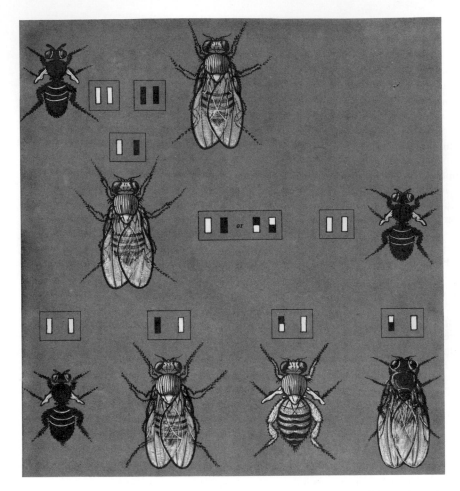

shows itself. This can most easily be seen if one of the phenotypically normal heterozygotes, a female, is bred to a homozygous recessive, vestigial-winged, black male. In the heterozygous female parent, one number two chromosome carries both recessive genes *b* and *v* while the other number two chromosome carries their normal alleles *B* and *V*. Thus, with complete linkage, 50 per cent of her eggs will be *bv* and 50 per cent *BV*. When mated with a homozygous recessive male all of whose sperms must carry *b* and *v*, as a grid will show, 50 per cent of her offspring would be expected to have normal wings and pigmentation, and 50 per cent black and vestigial. Breeding experiments, however, show that only 83 per cent of the offspring of such a cross belong to either of these two types. The other 17 per cent are recombinations in which either vestigial is combined with normal body pigmentation, or normal wings with black pigmentation. It is

significant that these two new combinations appear in equal numbers. Crossing over in drosophila is illustrated in Figure 8–10.

This result can be explained on the assumption that in the formation of 17 per cent of the gametes the homologous chromosomes in the heterozygous female have exchanged parts, so that gene *V* is now on the same chromosome as gene *b*, and gene *v* on the chromosome with *B*. Direct visible evidence of such crossing over can be seen in meiosis. During synapsis the tightly paired chromosomes become twisted, and when separation occurs the chromosomes have exchanged parts. Healing appears to be perfect, for once the new combination is formed the chromosomes are as stable as before.

Crossing over produces new combinations of traits in animals and in all other sexually reproducing organisms. This is important both in natural evolution and in producing desirable new types of domestic animals.

Mapping Chromosomes. Crossing over makes it possible to construct chromosome maps. It is reasonable to assume that the farther apart along a chromosome two genes lie, the greater is the likelihood of a break (with crossing over) between them. Assume also, and this appears to be true, that crossing over is equally probable at any point along the chromosome. Conversely, the closer together two genes are, the less likely it is that crossing over will occur between them.

Suppose that the percentage of recombinations, i.e., crossovers, between one pair of alleles, say Aa, and another pair, say Bb, is 5 per cent. It can be said that the two alleles are located 5 arbitrary units apart. Suppose now that crossing over is determined between the A alleles and a third pair of alleles, Cc, and this is found to occur in 15 per cent of the cases. Evidently locus A and locus C are 15 units apart. (See I and II in Fig. 8–11.) There is no way of telling from these data whether locus B and locus C are on the same side of locus A or on different sides. This question can be answered by determining the percentage of crossing over between B and C. If they are on the same side of A, then the percentage of crossing over would be only 10 per cent between them (IV in Fig. 8–11). If, however, B and C are on opposite sides of A, then the crossing over should be the sum of their individual values with respect to A (III in Fig. 8–11).

Very detailed chromosome maps have been constructed by this method, using a large number of genes, not only in the fruit fly and maize plant, but in the chicken, the mouse, the fungus *Neurospora,* and other organisms.

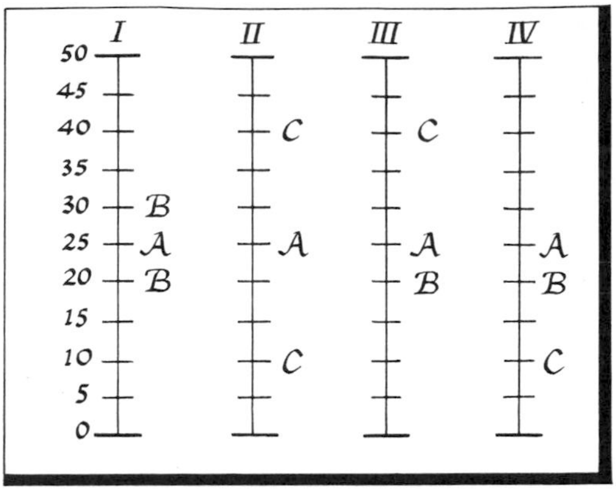

Fig. 8–11. Method of mapping the position of a gene on a chromosome. See text for procedure. In tentative map I, gene B is shown 5 units from gene A and in both possible positions, either above or below A. In tentative map II, gene C is shown in both possible positions in relation to gene A. In tentative maps III and IV, possible positions are indicated considering all three genes simultaneously.

In addition, there is both logical and direct visual evidence of the linear order of genes on chromosomes. The fact that in cell division chromosomes duplicate themselves and pull apart longitudinally rather than breaking in half transversely argues that their important constituents are arranged in a linear series.

Chromosomes, as seen in most cells including the sex cells, are tiny irregular rods. However, about 75 years ago an Italian investigator, Balbiani, discovered that the chromosomes in the salivary glands of flies, gnats, and mosquitos are gigantic in comparison with chromosomes in most cells. He also noticed

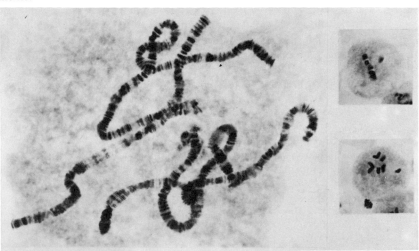

Fig. 8–12. Banded salivary gland chromosomes from a fly, *Sciara,* magnified only 600×. The normal-sized chromosomes of this fly, shown on the right, are magnified 1,600×. *(Kindness of H. V. Crouse)*

that these **giant chromosomes** are banded. Beginning in 1930, various workers in this country and in Germany reinvestigated the bands which Balbiani had described so long before the rediscovery of Mendel's laws. It soon became obvious that the bands were not haphazard but were constant in number, thickness, and position on any particular chromosome. From this fact it was possible to show that specific bands correspond to the position, or locus to use a more technical term, of particular genes. An abnormality in any particular band is invariably correlated with a particular abnormality in the animal. Thus the chromosome maps constructed from crossover data have been validated by visual evidence.

GENETIC VARIATION—ROLE OF MUTATION

Chromosomal and Genic Mutations. Mutations are sudden and relatively permanent changes in the hereditary material. These changes can sometimes be seen under the microscope as changes in the chromosomes. Other mutations are actual changes in the genes themselves.

At the chromosome level of structure, mutations are of four general types. All are caused by the breakage and incorrect rejoining of chromosome fragments. **Deletions** are losses of larger or smaller pieces of chromosomes. If too much of a chromosome is lost so that some essential enzyme is not formed, then the mutation will kill the animal or perhaps not permit development even to start. Such a mutation is called a **lethal.** A well-known deletion is "notch" in drosophila; this causes a small abnormality in the wings and is lethal when homozygous. This abnormality can be identified cytologically as a small section missing from the third chromosome. **Duplications** are repetitions of a portion of a chromosome. These also can be seen in the salivary gland chromosomes. A well-known example is "bar" eye in drosophila. **Inversions** are cases where part of a chromosome has been rotated 180° so that the genes, instead of running *ABCDEF,* run *ABEDCF.* Such events produce a wide variety of complications, such as loops, when homologous chromosomes attempt to pair during meiosis. Some inversions are lethal. **Translocation** is the term given to mutations in which

part of one chromosome becomes permanently attached to the end of a nonhomologous chromosome. Translocation is sometimes called "illegitimate crossing over."

The most interesting and important mutations are those which occur at the gene level and represent mistakes in gene duplication. As will be seen shortly, this means an error in the duplication of the sequence of purine and pyrimidine bases in the DNA.

The word mutation was coined by Hugo de Vries in 1901 to describe the sudden, drastic, and spontaneous changes in heredity he had just discovered in *Oenothera,* the evening primrose. Actually several mutations had been known for a long time. The ancon mutation in sheep, for example, which produces very short "dachshund" legs occurred in 1791 on the farm of a Mr. Wright in Massachusetts. Although de Vries started the modern study of mutations, it was not until the following decade that T. H. Morgan finally found a suitable animal, *Drosophila melanogaster,* in which a large number of mutations could be investigated.

Mutations were found to affect virtually every part of organisms. In drosophila they change the size, shape, and color of the body; they alter the size, shape, color, and bristles of the eyes. There is even a mutant gene which abolishes eyes! Other genes produce truly revolutionary changes converting mouthparts into legs, legs into wings, wings into halteres, and halteres into wings or abolishing wings completely. Some mutations do not produce anatomical results but change physiological or biochemical abilities such as resistance to ether or various nutritive capabilities. Such nonmorphological mutations are commonly called biochemical mutations but of course all mutations are really biochemical ones because all the anatomical effects are the result of some change in the enzymatic activity of the cells during development.

Rate of Mutation. The spontaneous rate of mutation is very low and varies from one gene to another. In drosophila, millions of which have been scrutinized in laboratories all over the world, the mutation rate at any one locus on a chromosome may be as high as 1 in every 1,000 gametes or as low as 1 in over 1,000,000

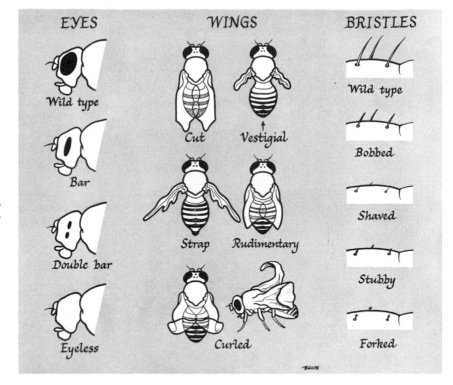

EYES

Wild type

Bar

Double bar

Eyeless

WINGS

Cut   Vestigial

Strap   Rudimentary

Curled

BRISTLES

Wild type

Bobbed

Shaved

Stubby

Forked

Fig. 8–13. Series of eye, wing, and bristle mutations in drosophila.

gametes, depending on the gene. The gene mutation that causes ancon sheep was reported a second time, in 1925 in Norway, i.e., twice in almost 200 years. Examination of 11,600 flies turned up a mutation which causes yellow body only three times, while a gene for "echinoid" eyes appeared 18 times.

Records of 94,075 babies born in Copenhagen hospitals showed 10 chondrodystrophic dwarfs. This is the kind of dwarf in which the head and body are normal in size but the arms and legs are abnormally short. The trait is inherited as a dominant. Two of these children had a dwarf parent but the other eight did not; that is, they represent new mutations. These facts show that the gene involved mutates to produce chondrodystrophy once in 11,759 births. Since each child is the result of the fusion of two gametes, an egg and a sperm, and since this trait is a dominant, this means that one out of every 23,518 human gametes in Copenhagen carried this mutated gene. Other studies indicate that one in about 33,000 human gametes carries a mutated gene for hemophilia, the sex-linked "bleeder" disease.

Fig. 8–14. Chondrodystrophic dwarfs, father and son. Note the very short arms and legs. (*Kindness of Ernst T. Morch*)

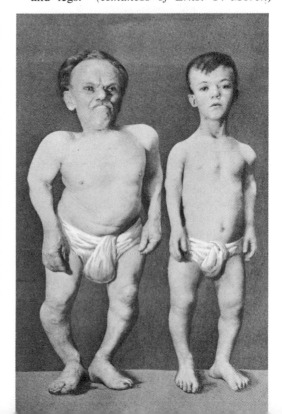

Artificially Induced Mutations. Random mutations can be produced artificially. This epoch-making discovery was achieved in 1927 by H. J. Muller, then of the University of Texas, and independently by L. J. Stadler of the University of Missouri. Muller, a former student of T. H. Morgan, worked out an extremely ingenious method of drosophila crosses that enabled him to detect even lethal mutations. Barley was used by Stadler because the seeds and the manner of development make it especially favorable material.

Both experimenters used X-rays, and both found an extraordinary increase in the rate at which mutations appear. Many were mutations which had been seen before, some were new, but the important fact was that there might be 100 times as many in the radiated as in the control organisms, depending on the dosage used. With too little radiation, the increase in mutations is hard to detect; with too much, the organism is rendered sterile. Between these limits there is a range, varying greatly with the species, where viable mutations are produced. The effect of radiation is cumulative. If 500 roentgen units will produce a certain average number of mutations, five doses of 100 r's administered at intervals will do the same.

Fortunately only about 2 to 5 roentgen units are required for a single medical X-ray picture so that the danger of producing genetic effects in the patient from a single exposure is negligible. However, this is enough radiation to have a cumulative effect, which means that X-rays should be used with discretion.

Unfortunately it is not only conventional X-rays that cause mutations. So also do any α, β, and γ radiations and high-energy protons and neutrons from all sorts of radioactive material. These facts, in no way surprising, are unhappily of deep concern to all mankind. From the strictly biological point of view, clouds of radioactive dust drifting around the world might be more disastrous than a series of atomic explosions in centers of population.

X-rays have a strong tendency to produce mutations on the chromosomal level. After treatment with X-rays, broken and visibly abnormal chromosomes can often be seen. Less penetrating and non-ionizing radiations such as ultraviolet light will also produce mutations.

The higher the dosage, the more mutations will appear. A considerable number of chemicals have been found which are mutagenic. These discoveries open up very exciting possibilities for the artificial control of mutation but further discussion of this topic will be postponed until after a discussion of the chemical nature of genes and the nature of the genetic code.

Mutations are **random** in two different senses. They are random in the sense that they cannot be predicted except in a statistical way. Mutations are also random in the sense that they are not related to the needs of the animal. At least 99 per cent of mutations are harmful; this is not surprising when it is remembered that living species of animals are well adapted for their modes of life. Consequently any random change in the developmental blueprint is all but certain not to be an improvement. Whether or not a mutation is advantageous or disadvantageous depends on the environment. For example, mutations reducing the wings so that an insect cannot fly will be a very serious, perhaps fatal, disadvantage in most environments but on a tiny windswept oceanic island it will be a life saver. Many such islands support many kinds of flightless insects. Similar mutations have occurred in laboratory cages where they are indifferent as regards survival value.

There is a sense in which mutations are not random. The kinds of mutations which are possible depend upon the chemical properties of the hereditary material.

GENES AND CHROMOSOME STRUCTURE

What Are Genes? The word gene was first defined as a unit factor of heredity which followed Mendel's laws. It was coined without reference to chromosomes frankly as a verbal tool to make it easier to talk and think about heredity. It is in this sense that we have been using the term. However, after T. H. Morgan and his students had mapped the position of many genes on specific chromosomes by the use of crossing over rates, it became fashionable to define a gene as the smallest unit of heredity not divisible by crossing over. Others preferred to define a gene as the smallest unit of mutation. Because each gene controls the formation of an enzyme, or at least a polypeptide chain, others define a gene as the smallest functional biochemical unit of a chromosome.

Obviously all these definitions are very similar although none is precisely like any other. Each is useful under slightly different circumstances so that none can be called wrong. This situation will doubtless continue until the biochemical details of gene structure and action become known. It is to this topic that we now turn our attention.

What Are Chromosomes? It will be recalled from Chapter 3 that the essential and characteristic component of chromosomes is nucleic acid. Combined with the nucleic acids are simple proteins, histones, as well as larger proteins. The function of these proteins is little understood. Some may cover certain genes, preventing them from acting; some may be enzymes since many reactions are involved in the duplication and functioning of chromosomes; some may be purely structural.

The DNA, deoxyribose nucleic acid, is formed something like a ladder twisted around a broomstick. The sides of the ladder are composed of linked and alternating molecules of phosphoric acid and deoxyribose, a five-carbon sugar. The rungs are connected to the sugars as shown on pages 51, 52, and 165. The rungs carry the genetic information. They must if the code really is written in the DNA because only the rungs vary as you climb the twisted ladder.

Only four kinds of molecules make these rungs. Two of the molecules, adenine and guanine, are **purines,** which are two-ringed compounds containing nitrogen; the other two, cytosine and thymine, are **pyrimidines,** which are similar to the purines but have only one ring. The RNA, found both in the nucleus and in the cytoplasm, is the same as DNA except that the sugar is ribose instead of deoxyribose and uracil takes the place of thymine. This latter fact makes it possible to put a label on DNA by feeding the organism radioactive thymine, so it can be distinguished from RNA.

The structural formulas of the nitrogenous bases of nucleic acids, i.e., the alphabet of the genetic code, are shown here.

Purines

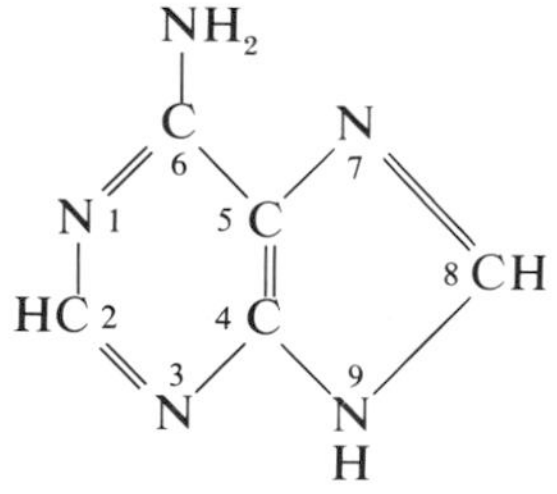

adenine

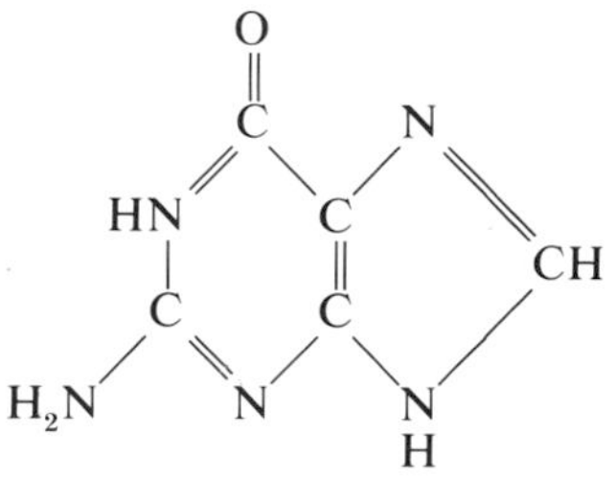

guanine

Pyrimidines

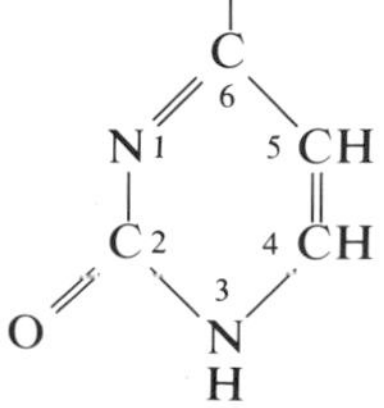

cytosine

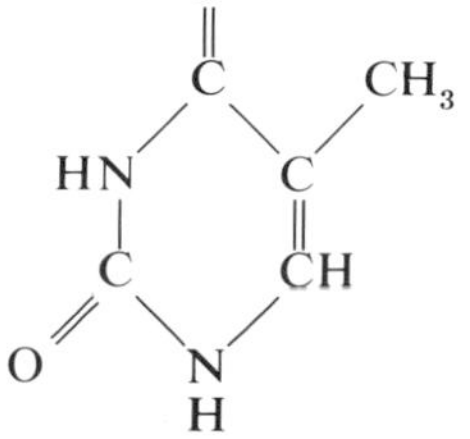

thymine

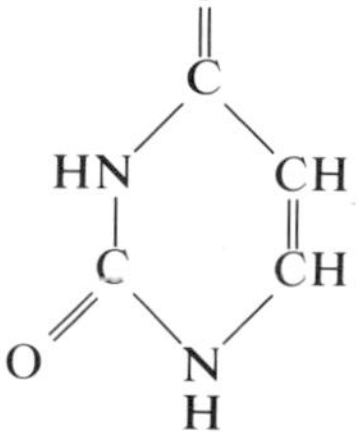

uracil

Two molecules, one purine and one pyrimidine, make a rung. Since the length of the rungs does not vary, the pattern of a purine matched with a pyrimidine remains constant. Two pyrimidines would make a short rung that would not fit. Two purines would make a rung that was too long. So it comes about that, due to the shape of the molecules, adenine is always matched with thymine by hydrogen bonds, and guanine with cytosine, also by hydrogen bonds. From this it follows that if the nitrogen bases on one side of the ladder are, in order, adenine, guanine, guanine, thymine, thymine, thymine . . . , then the corresponding bases on the other side will be thymine, cytosine, cytosine, adenine, adenine, adenine. . . .

An adenine-thymine rung in a nucleic acid helix can be pictured:

adenine   thymine

There is a slightly different but also useful way of looking at DNA structure. A single phosphoric acid group plus the sugar plus the purine or pyrimidine constitute a **nucleotide.** Thus when the double helix, or twisted ladder, separates lengthwise into two separate single strands of nucleic acid, each strand will consist of a series of nucleotides just as a protein consists of a series of amino acids.

The Code. There is much evidence, some presented in an earlier chapter and some to come later, that genes preside over the synthesis of enzymes, i.e., proteins. Not very surprising, since cells are what their enzymes make them, and genes control cells. Both nucleic acids and proteins are long chains of smaller units, nucleotides in one case, amino acids in the other. Consequently, it would

seem probable that the sequence of the four bases in the DNA represents the sequence of amino acids in the proteins.

Since there are four bases, there is a four-letter alphabet. There are about 20 amino acids to specify. Consequently, one-letter words will not suffice because with four letters, let us say A, T, G, and C, there could be only four one-letter words. How many two-letter words can be made from four letters? The first letter of each word might be A, T, G, or C. That makes four possibilities. The second letter might be any one of the four in each case, AA, AT, AG, AC, TA, TT, TG, etc. This makes 4 × 4, or 16, words. Still not enough. With three-letter words the possibilities are 4 × 4 × 4, or 64. Enough and perhaps too many, unless some words are merely nonsense or some are synonyms.

One of the first questions about a three-letter word system is whether the words can overlap. For example, if ABC spells a certain amino acid, and BCD spells another amino acid, would ABCD spell them both or would you have to write ABCBCD? How can this question be put to a test? One way is to note that if the code is an overlapping one, a change (i.e., a mutation) in one letter (one nucleotide) would affect two adjacent amino acids in the protein. The fact is that many cases are now known where a mutation changes a single amino acid but, so far, none have been found where two adjacent ones are changed—something which would happen with most mutations if the code were an overlapping one. Furthermore, if the code were overlapping, it would mean that a given amino acid in a protein would always have one of only four amino acids following it, which is not true. For example, if ABC was the code word for glycine, then glycine could only be followed by whatever four amino acids were coded by BCA, BCB, BCC, and BCD.

To summarize, the code consists of three-letter words made from a four-letter alphabet. It spells out the sequence of the amino acids in the proteins. These three-letter "words" are commonly referred to as **triplets** or **"codons."** Whether the code is universal, the same for bacteria, plants, and animals, and how the code can be "broken" will be discussed in a later section of this chapter.

How Is the Code Duplicated? In the life cycle of dividing cells, the chromosomes become duplicated and then in mitosis the duplicates separate, one passing to each pole of the spindle. The conditions and specific stimulus, if indeed there is one, which result in chromosome duplication and mitosis are virtually unknown. However, Watson and Crick have been able to propose a theory, supported by considerable evidence, as to the way in which the actual DNA duplicates. The weak hydrogen bonds which hold the two helices together break and the helices separate. Each helix then acts as a model or template for the formation of a new helix complementary to itself along its entire length. The result is two double helices each similar to the original. In each, one strand will be from the old original double helix and one will be new. (See Fig. 8–15.) In the words of Watson and Crick:

Now our model for deoxyribonucleic acid is, in effect, a *pair* of templates, each of which is complementary to the other. We imagine that prior to duplication the hydrogen bonds are broken, and the two chains unwind and separate. Each chain then acts as a template for the formation on to itself of a new companion chain, so that eventually we shall have *two* pairs of chains, where we only had one before. Moreover, the sequence of the pairs of bases will have been duplicated exactly.

Much still remains to be learned. It is clear that this is an energy-using process and also that an enzyme, DNA polymerase, is essential. One of the ways of proving that chromosomes duplicate in this manner, i.e., by serving as models which induce a new structure to form alongside of themselves, is to feed cells before division with radioactive thymine. After the formation and separation of the new chromosomes, one of each homologous pair has all the radioactivity and the other member of the pair has none. Q.E.D. (See Fig. 2–20.) Because there are two strands of duplicating DNA in a chromosome, it actually requires two cell divisions before all the radioactivity is located in one chromosome and none of the radioactivity in its replicate.

How Is the Code Translated into Proteins? It will be recalled that DNA not only makes more DNA but also, with the help of the proper enzymes, produces RNA which then moves out of the nucleus into the cytoplasm. The formation of RNA from its template DNA is referred to as **transcription.** The formation of proteins from the code in the cytoplasmic RNA is called **translation.**

Three types of RNA can be identified in the cytoplasm by differential centrifugation and other methods. The first type is **messenger RNA,** usually written mRNA. The messenger RNA occurs in long strands or chains, as Watson and Crick would say. It is the equivalent of long tapes carrying the code. A second type is **ribosomal RNA,** rRNA. This makes up about 60 per cent of the structure of ribosomes; the rest is protein. A third type is soluble or **transfer RNA,** sRNA or tRNA. Transfer RNA consists of relatively short pieces of RNA in solution in the cytoplasm.

Fig. 8–15. Duplication of DNA, according to the theory of Watson and Crick.

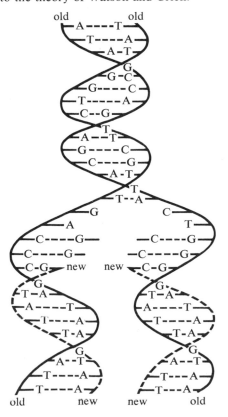

Translation of the RNA code is merely a somewhat more informative way of saying **protein synthesis.** It occurs as follows. Ribosomes become attached to the starter ends of the long strands of mRNA and move along these strands reading the code and producing proteins by adding one amino acid after another. Series of ribosomes lined up along mRNA can sometimes be seen under an electron microscope. Such a series of ribosomes is commonly referred to as a **polysome** or polyribosome.

At the same time as the ribosomes are moving along the mRNA strand, specific enzymes in the cytoplasm activate amino acids. ATP (adenosine triphosphate) reacts with an amino acid, forming ADP (adenosine diphosphate) plus an amino acid adenylate. This compound, specifically the amino acid, then becomes attached to one end of the tRNA molecule.

Transfer RNA is found in the form of an elongated twisted U or hairpin. At the closed curved end of the molecule a triplet of the code is left exposed; in Figure 8 – 16 this is uracil, guanine, adenine, the "word" for the amino acid methionine. At the opposite open end of the molecule of tRNA the appropriate amino acid, in this case methionine, will become attached by its carboxyl group.

The tRNA molecules, each carrying an amino acid which corresponds to the code it bears, move through the cytoplasm, presumably by Brownian movement, and thus come into contact with ribosomes on the mRNA.

Each ribosome, as it passes along the series of triplets in the mRNA, accepts at each position only the appropriately coded tRNA. The tRNA molecule in Figure 8 – 16 could not get functionally tied up with a ribosome until the ribosome reached a place along the mRNA which read for methionine. When this happens the methionine-carrying tRNA moves into place on (or perhaps in) the ribosome and the tRNA previously there falls free minus its amino acid. Its amino acid, whatever it was, becomes attached to the methionine carried by the newly arrived tRNA. In this way a chain of amino acids, linked by peptide bonds is built up, forming a polypeptide chain. Thus the code is translated into the primary structure of any protein, i.e., the characteristic sequence of amino acids.

It seems reasonable to suppose that the secondary structure—the twisted helical form of the protein molecule—would show itself as soon as the polypeptide chain formed. Likewise, there is no reason to suppose that the forces which produce the tertiary structure—the various foldings of the protein molecule—would wait to act until after the full length of the primary structure was complete. Consequently, when the finished protein finally drops free as its ribosome comes to the end of the mRNA ribbon, it would be held in its characteristic folds and bends by its sulfhydryl (—S—S—) and other bonds.

Is the Code Universal? Is the genetic code the same for microorganisms, plants, and animals? Since it has been firmly established that the proteins of all living things are composed of the same 20 amino acids, and that the nucleic acids of all living things contain the same four (five, counting uracil) purines and pyrimidines, it would be hard to believe that the code would be different. However, plausibility does not constitute proof. The best evidence supporting the idea that the code is, in fact, the same in virtually all, if not all, organisms has been obtained by mixing amino acid-charged tRNA from bacteria with mRNA and ribosomes from hemoglobin-producing cells from rabbits. The result was always rabbit hemoglobin!

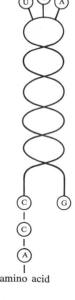

Fig. 8 – 16. Diagram of tRNA bearing a code word UGA for the amino acid methionine.

amino acid

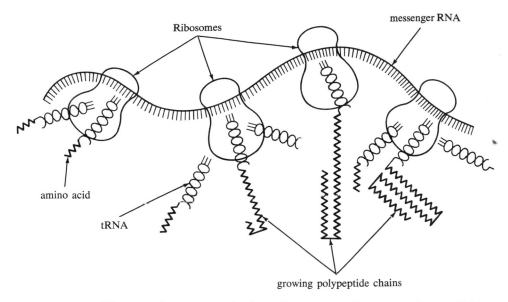

Fig. 8–17. Diagram of protein synthesis at ribosomes as they move along mRNA.

Fig. 8–18. How transfer RNA locks onto messenger RNA and adds an amino acid to the growing polypeptide chain. I, II, and III are three molecules of tRNA, each coded for a different amino acid. I represents empty tRNA falling away from the mRNA. III represents tRNA carrying an amino acid and moving into position to add it to the polypeptide chain. *(After R. C. King)*

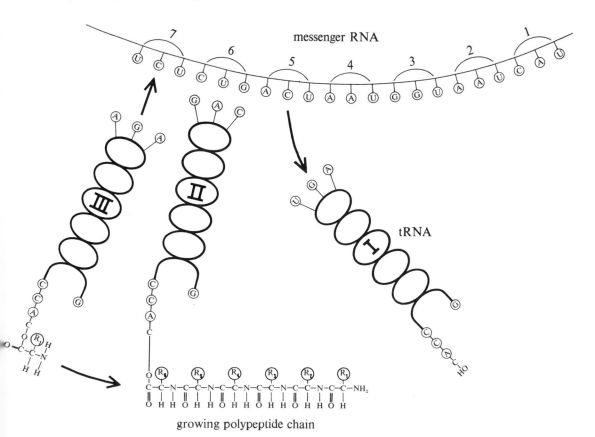

growing polypeptide chain

Cracking the Code. One way of discovering what the code actually is, i.e., how to spell the word for any specific amino acid in the three-letter purine-pyrimidine words, is to make your own messenger RNA. This quite spectacular achievement was first accomplished by Marshall and Nirenberg. If the mRNA has no nucleotides except those carrying uracil, it will cause the synthesis of a polypeptide chain of repeating units of the amino acid phenylalanine. Thus, UUU codes for phenylalanine. Similarly mRNA carrying only adenine will produce, in a test tube when mixed with activated tRNA charged with all 20 naturally occurring amino acids, the necessary activating enzymes, and ribosomes, a polypeptide chain consisting of repeating units of only one amino acid, lysine. Thus AAA codes for lysine. Three cytosines code for the amino acid proline. By changing the percentages of the different purines and pyrimides in the mRNA it has been possible to deduce the code words for all 20 of the naturally occurring amino acids. With different percentages of different mixtures of the four bases built into the mRNA, different amino acids are incorporated into the protein synthesized. For example, if there is no guanine in the mRNA, the amino acid glycine is not incorporated into the polypeptide formed. Therefore the triplet for glycine must contain at least one G (guanine). Messenger RNA with nothing but guanine will not produce glycine, hence there must be some code "letter" in addition to G. In fact, there has to be twice as much guanine as there is of some other base. Therefore the triplet for glycine has two G's plus one of the other bases. By this kind of analysis it has been found not only that all the 20 amino acids can be spelled in triplet form but that the code is redundant, i.e., that there is more than one way to spell most of the amino acids. Thus UUU and CUU both correspond to phenylalanine.

Directed Mutations: A Second Look. The mutations produced by radiations are highly unpredictable except in a statistical sense. There seems little possibility that their use would ever lead to the ability to produce specific types of mutations at the will of the experimenter. Chemical mutagens are a very different thing. Conspicuous among these are the sulfur and nitrogen mustards, urethanes, phenols, formaldehyde, nitrous acid, and several derivatives of phenanthrene, i.e., steroidal compounds. It is of interest to note that these last substances are related to the steroid hormones of the adrenal and reproductive glands and to certain very potent carcinogens.

Most exciting of all, analogs of the purines and pyrimidines and various of their derivatives produce mutations. Some of these exist in nature, such as caffeine and theophylline (found in tea); others can be produced in the laboratory, such as 5-fluorouracil and 2-aminopurine.

The way in which these compounds produce mutations is only beginning to be understood. Nitrogen mustards undergo esterification reactions with the phosphoric acid groups in the nucleic acids. Nitrous acid deaminates the bases. Both events lead to errors in DNA duplication, i.e., mutations. Acridine orange dye opens up the nucleic acid helix in such a way that a "letter" is skipped or added. The purine and pyrimidine analogs seem to be incorporated into nucleic acid as nucleotides where they apparently attract the wrong bases when nucleic acid is duplicated.

None of these methods makes it possible to obtain specific mutations on demand. It is known that certain loci, "hot spots," are very susceptible to mutagens and that certain mutagens have a strong tendency to affect certain loci on given chromosomes. But this is still a long way from man-directed mutation. That is an achievement awaiting us in the future.

GENE ACTION WITHIN THE ORGANISM

Genes and Enzymes. "One gene, one enzyme," or at least, "one gene, one polypeptide chain" (for there are cases known where it requires two genes to produce the complete enzyme), is a central concept of modern biochemical genetics. The idea, however, that genes produce their effects by producing, or failing to produce, specific enzymes was proposed by a physician and biochemist at Oxford, Sir Archibald E. Garrod, during the first decade after the rediscovery of Mendel's laws of heredity. As happened with Mendel's discovery of the elementary laws of inheritance and MacMunn's discovery of the respiratory pigment cytochrome, no one paid much attention to Garrod's book, *Inborn Errors of Metabolism,* even though he was Regius Professor of Medicine at Oxford. The reasons for this complete neglect are complex but the basic one is surely that biologists were not intellectually ready to incorporate any of these ideas into the general body of their thinking. After the battle, it is always much easier to see what the general should have done.

Garrod studied a hereditary disease called **alkaptonuria** which still serves as a model of how genes work and how the point at which they act can be discovered. The chief symptom of this rather benign disease is a blackening of the urine after exposure to air. This happens because the urine contains an abnormal constituent, alkapton or homogentisic acid. In normal individuals, the amino acid phenylalanine from food is incorporated into body proteins and also converted into a number of other products, including homogentisic acid. This is then converted into CO_2 and water.

In the families of people with alkaptonuria, Garrod showed that the disease behaves like one of Mendel's recessive factors (genes). He went on to argue that the accumulation of homogentisic acid which results in its being excreted by the kidneys is due to the absence of a specific enzyme. The missing enzyme is called homogentisic acid oxidase because it can oxidize homogentisic acid, not into a black pigment but into simpler products which in turn are converted into CO_2 and water.

The reasoning is simple. Within the body one compound, say some amino acid or amino acid precursor, is converted into some other compound via a series of steps. If a mutation changes a gene so that it no longer forms the enzyme responsible for some specific conversion of A to B, then A will accumulate in the body and bloodstream and may be excreted in the urine. This scheme can be diagrammed as follows:

$$A \xrightarrow{E_a} B \xrightarrow{E_b} C \xrightarrow{E_c} D$$

If compound A is converted into B, and B into C, and C into D, then three enzymes are required. Enzyme E_a converts A into B, enzyme E_b has B as its substrate and converts B into C,

and so forth. Suppose now that after a certain mutation the organism no longer produces D but that B is excreted in the urine. Then it is reasonable to suppose that enzyme E_b is no longer produced. This is the point at which the gene's action becomes effective. If this is true, then if the animal is fed C, compound D should be produced. If fed A, then B should accumulate but not either C or D.

This mode of thinking about how genes express themselves did not appear again until about 1935 when Boris Ephrussi and George Beadle undertook to investigate the biochemistry of the formation of various eye pigments in drosophila which were known to be under the control of specific genes. The difficulties of this work led Beadle and E. L. Tatum to turn to *Neurospora,* the pink bread mold. Actually it is more orange than pink and is found growing wild on sugar cane. B. O. Dodge of the New York Botanical Garden had long urged T. H. Morgan to work with *Neurospora* as "even better than drosophila." Morgan took some strains of *Neurospora* with him when he left Columbia University for the California Institute of Technology. It was there that Beadle and Tatum obtained this organism and then the study of biochemical genetics really "got off the ground."

The advantages of *Neurospora* are several. It can be grown readily in pure culture in test tubes and on media of known and very simple minimal chemical composition. This means that the mold can synthesize for itself a large number of compounds from very few simple raw materials. The asexual spores, conidia, can be irradiated or otherwise treated to produce mutations. When germinated, the growth from these conidia can be crossed with wild-type strains. After crossing, fruiting bodies are produced which contain cigar-shaped capsules, each holding eight haploid spores. There are two adjacent spores for each of the usual four products of meiosis. Hundreds of these haploid cells can be planted singly in tubes with a complete medium containing a rich variety of vitamins, amino acids, and other substances so that they can grow up and produce conidia even if they should carry mutations which deprived them of one of the enzymes necessary for some essential step in the synthesis of a necessary

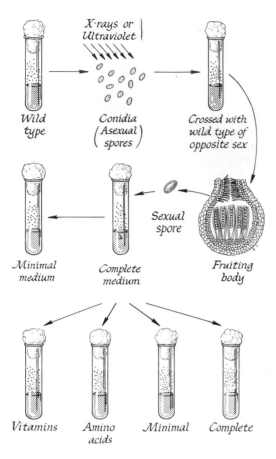

Wild
type

X-rays or
Ultraviolet

Conidia
(Asexual)
spores

Crossed with
wild type of
opposite sex

Minimal
medium

Complete
medium

Sexual
spore

Fruiting
body

Vitamins

Amino
acids

Minimal

Complete

Fig. 8-19. *Neurospora.* Experimental design to produce and detect mutations affecting synthetic enzymes in nutritional pathways. (*After Beadle, from G. B. Moment,* General Biology, *2nd Ed. Copyright 1950 by Appleton—Century—Crofts, Inc. Reprinted by permission*)

metabolite. After a good growth has been obtained, each strain can be tested in minimal medium. If it can no longer grow on it the way its ancestor did, then a mutation has occurred depriving it of some particular enzyme. The next step is to test its ability to grow in media containing one after another of the various vitamins, amino acids, and other growth substances to discover exactly where the biochemical lesion is located.

In man, one of the best-studied systems of biochemical synthetic pathways begins with phenylalanine (Fig. 8-20). The case of alkaptonuria has been discussed with the pioneer

work of Garrod. It is now possible to take a second look at this disease in the light of recent knowledge. If the conversion of a given compound into a second compound is blocked, the substance should accumulate in the blood and be excreted if added to the diet. And so it is with alkaptonuria. If homogentisic acid (alkapton) is fed to an alkaptonuric, he will excrete an equivalent extra amount in his urine. If homogentisic acid in amounts not greater than 5 grams are fed to a normal man, no homogentisic acid is excreted, showing that an enzyme is present in normal people which will metabolize this compound. If very large amounts are fed, then even a normal man will begin to excrete alkapton, showing that the system for oxidizing this substance can be overloaded. There are actually four steps in the conversion of homogentisic acid to CO_2 and water.

Phenylketonuria (PKU) is a disease due to a recessive autosomal gene which blocks the conversion of phenylalanine into tyrosine. This is a very simple reaction, merely the addition of an —OH group (hydroxylation) to the phenol ring. Since tyrosine (*p*-hydroxyphenylalanine) is a normal precursor for adrenalin, melanin, and thyroxin, it might be thought that PKU sufferers would lack adrenalin, and be albinos with goiters. This is not the case because tyrosine is an amino acid found in a normal diet just as is phenylalanine. Some of the ingested phenylalanine in the human diet is used, and indeed is essential, for protein formation but not all of it can be used in this way. If it is not hydroxylated into tyrosine, phenylalanine and its derivatives, phenylpyruvic acid, etc., accumulate in the blood and cerebrospinal fluid and in the urine. It will be noted that phenylpyruvic acid differs from phenylalanine merely in having had its amine group, —NH$_2$, removed and replaced by a keto group, —C$\stackrel{O}{\diagdown}$, hence the common term, phenyl-keton-uric. Most phenylketonurics are feebleminded or worse. A very tiny percentage are only slightly retarded. The brain damage is thought to be due to excess phenylalanine or one of its derivatives. The diagnosis of this disease is simple because the phenylpyruvic acid will turn green with the addition of FeCl$_3$. This is the basis of the so-called "diaper test." The majority of medical opinion holds that brain damage can be avoided

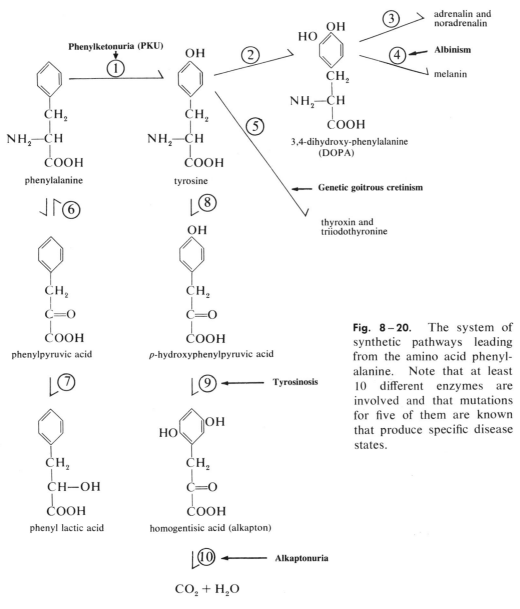

Fig. 8–20. The system of synthetic pathways leading from the amino acid phenylalanine. Note that at least 10 different enzymes are involved and that mutations for five of them are known that produce specific disease states.

by feeding only enough phenylalanine to provide for essential protein building. Results are extremely hard to assess because of the great variability of untreated cases. About 1 to 2 per cent of all individuals in mental hospitals suffer from this disease.

Thus it can be seen that the "one gene, one enzyme" hypothesis fits the facts and can elucidate the biochemical basis of mutational effects in organisms as widely separated as man and a mold.

Gene Product Interaction. Genes themselves probably rarely if ever interact with each other directly but their products can interact in a variety of ways. A number of instances are known of what is called **epistasis**. In these cases a gene in one locus overrules the effect of a gene in a different locus, perhaps even on a different chromosome. Since this reaction is not between alleles, i.e., alternative forms of the same gene at a given locus on the same chromosome, it differs from ordinary dominance.

A well-known case of epistasis occurs in dogs where the dominant gene B gives a solid black coat; the recessive allele b gives a brown coat when in the homozygous bb condition. However, there is another gene I (for inhibitor) on a different chromosome which prevents pigment formation except in the eyes. To have fur of any color whatever, a dog must be homozygous ii for this inhibitor gene. Thus a dog may be homozygous for dominant black and yet be white because of the inhibitor gene I which masks the effect of the genes at the other locus. This I gene is different from the gene for albinism which prevents the formation of melanin even in the eyes.

Another type of gene product interaction occurs in all cases where many genes influence a single trait. Body size, intelligence, skin color, eye color, and many other general characteristics fall into this class.

Human skin color is a good example of a trait due to a combination of multiple factors both environmental and genetic. In all races of mankind the basic pigment is melanin. This is formed from the amino acid tyrosine in a series of at least seven steps through intermediate compounds. Consequently there are at least seven points at which the process can be controlled. In "white"-skinned people the final amount of melanin depends not only on the genes, but also on the amount of sunlight to which the individual has been exposed. In Negroes, on the other hand, the environment has a lesser role and the genes a greater one in determining the amount of melanin deposited.

In skin color the genes have a primary control. Unless a gene for normal pigmentation is present at a certain locus, an albino is the result, regardless of sun. Given this gene which makes possible any pigment at all, then the amount of melanin is controlled by genes that act later in the series of biochemical steps. In Europeans there appear to be several genes that exert a modifying influence. There are probably four to seven pairs of genes involved in the differences in skin color between people of European and of African descent.

The hybrid of a cross between homozygous Europeans and Africans will all be intermediate in skin color, because they will be heterozygous at every locus involved, and there is no clear-cut dominance. However the offspring of two such multiple heterozygous individuals will sometimes be darker than either parent, sometimes the same shade as their parents, and sometimes lighter than either parent. The fact that descendants sometimes resemble not their immediate parents but their grandparents or more remote ancestors puzzled the old naturalists greatly. It was called **"atavism"** and given various ill-defined and even mystical explanations. With a knowledge of modern genetics it is possible to calculate the percentage of any generation that is likely to resemble either the darkest or the lightest ancestors.

The differences in skin pigmentation between Europeans and Chinese appear to be due to even fewer genes. This is shown by the fact that in the F_2 generation after a European-Cantonese cross some of the children have brown hair with a golden glint and also have a "pink-and-white" complexion. From all these crosses it is evident that the physical character of hair, the mongolian eye fold, thickness of lips, position of cheek bones, and many other traits are due to separate genes inherited independently and do not seem to interact.

The classic case of so-called gene interaction is found in two pairs of genes for comb shape in chickens. When a breed with a pea comb is crossed with a breed bearing a rose comb, all the offspring have walnut combs, which are quite different from those of either parent. If two walnut-combed birds are bred together, the offspring appear in the following ratio: 9 walnut, 3 rose, 3 pea, and 1 single. This single comb is the ancestral form found on the jungle fowls of southeast Asia and in most domestic breeds. Its appearance here is a beautiful case of "atavism." These results are easily explained on the basis of two pairs of alleles on different chromosomes. Rose comb is due to a dominant gene R. When a rose-combed bird is crossed with a normal wild-type single-combed individual ($RR \times rr$), the first generation will all have rose combs Rr, while the F_2 generation will be rose to single in a 3:1 ratio. The same is true for the gene P and its allele p for pea comb and normal. When individuals with rose combs, $RRpp$, are crossed with pea-combed $rrPP$, the first generation will all be $RrPp$, which is the walnut.

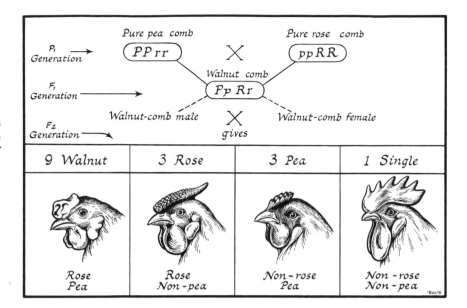

Fig. 8–21. Four types of chicken combs due to the interaction of two pairs of alleles. (*From Pauli,* The World of Life, *Houghton Mifflin*)

How Are Genes Turned On or Off? One of the great paradoxes of modern biological science is the undoubtable fact that all the cells of a multicellular animal or plant have the same diploid set of chromosomes and therefore the same genes, and yet these cells become differentiated in many very different directions. Some are muscle cells, some nerve, liver, skin, or red blood cells, each rich in its own specific kind of protein. Clearly there must be some way in which certain genes are turned on in certain cells while other genes are activated in other cells. Or perhaps it should be said the other way around, most of the genes are kept permanently inactive in most cells but the genes that are inactivated are different in different kinds of cells.

The control of the action of one gene by other genes has been known for many years. Epistasis is this kind of thing. The cases of repressor genes in drosophila and position effects in corn (maize) also show that somehow genes can affect the action of each other. But it was not until the work of F. Jacob and J. Monod in 1960 that a plausible model backed up with convincing evidence was proposed to explain how the activity of genes is regulated. Jacob and Monod worked with bacteria but it appears highly probable that their theory applies throughout the living world.

It should be noted first that enzymes are of two general types. There are **constitutive enzymes** which are formed by cells whether or not their substrate is present, at least in detectable amounts, and there are **inducible enzymes,** formed when and only when their substrate is present. It was found in the bacterium *Escherichia coli,* by the equivalent of crossing over experiments, that the genes for certain enzymes, specifically β-galactosidase and β-galactoside permease, can be turned on or off by another gene which is present as a pair of alleles that we can call R and R_1. When R is present, the β-galactoside genes remain turned on permanently and thus the two enzymes, β-galactosidase and β-galactoside permease, are constitutive enzymes — part of the standing equipment of the cells. When R_1 is present the enzymes are not produced unless the substrate for them, which is lactose, is present. Thus they have become inducible enzymes! Further analysis showed that the gene R or R_1 produces a **repressor substance,** presumably a protein. This repressor substance inhibits a fourth gene called the **operator gene.** It is located adjacent to the two β-galactoside genes and turns them off or on together. In some way the substrate acts as an inducer for those enzymes, apparently by inactivating the repressor substance. Perhaps it combines with it. The general scheme by which inducers may regulate gene action can be diagrammed as in Figure 8–22.

In a number of cases in bacteria it has been found that the genes responsible for the enzymes necessary for the series of steps in a particular biochemical pathway are arranged side by side in sequential order along the DNA! The best understood case is the synthesis of the amino acid histidine. Nine steps in this pathway are controlled by nine different enzymes and each is produced by a different gene located in sequential order in the chromosome. Such a series or cluster of genes responsible for a given product, plus its adjacent operator gene, is called an **operon.** An operon has been defined by Jacob and Monod as "a unit of coordinated expression, comprising an operator and the group of genes for structure which it coordinates."

Inspection of the diagram below will suggest ways in which gene action could be modified. A mutation, for example, which changed the repressor gene so that its repressor had somewhat different affinities might make an inducer no longer effective.

End product feedback inhibition has been shown to occur in a number of cases, notably in the histidine pathway already discussed. So many cases, in both bacteria and mammals, have been found that end product feedback inhibition is probably a very widespread and important mechanism of gene regulation. In most cases it is the very first enzymatic step which is inhibited. This means that the production of all the intermediate compounds is also brought to a standstill.

HEREDITY AND ENVIRONMENT

The General Problem. Which is more important, heredity or environment? The answer depends on cases, even on your point of view. This is because the development of any organism is like the flight of an arrow. At every point the trajectory of the arrow is the resultant of two forces. One is the initial impulsion imparted by the spring of the bow. This may be compared to heredity, specifically the set of genes in the fertilized egg. The other force is the environmental force of gravity, modified by wind; and this may be compared to the action of regular and random environmental forces on the course of development.

In one sense the genes reign supreme. We are men, and not starfish or even anthropoid apes, precisely because of the kind of fertilized eggs we developed from and for no other reason. In the teeming waters of the ocean the eggs of thousands of kinds of animals develop: fishes, worms, sea urchins, medusae, clams, and the rest. The environment may be the same over hundreds of cubic miles of sea, but the animals that come from these different kinds of eggs are all drastically different.

In some minor aspects as well, the genes are supreme. If a man is born without a gene for normal pigmentation he will be an albino regardless of environment. The blood groups to which a person belongs are determined by his genes and by them alone.

But in another sense environmental forces are equally important. Genes do not function in a vacuum. Only within a narrow range of

Fig. 8–22. Diagram of mechanism for regulation of gene action.

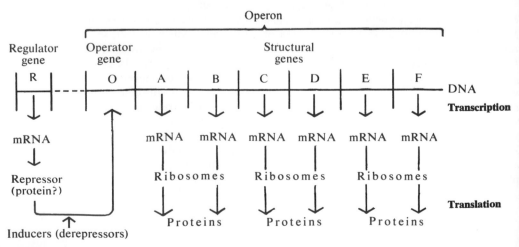

temperature found only on a planet within a certain distance from a sun is it at all possible for genes to form and function. In innumerable lesser ways the environment controls the actual as contrasted with the potential behavior and form of animals. *Daphnia,* the common "water flea," is so sensitive to environment that individuals raised from the same homogeneous strain but under different conditions appear like different species. In oysters it requires no gourmet to distinguish the flavor of those raised in water of ocean salinity from oysters taken from a very brackish estuary.

Within any animal, all the genes together form the internal genetic environment conditioning the action of each particular gene. Without the genes that permit the development of eyes, genes for eye color cannot produce their characteristic effect. A walnut comb is not produced in chickens unless both the gene for rose comb and the gene for pea comb are present. There is no actual gene for walnut but only two genes which must act together to produce this trait. And they cannot cooperate to produce this kind of comb unlesss multitudes of other genes have worked together to produce a chicken.

One of the most clear-cut cases of environmental influence over gene action is seen in the Himalayan rabbit. When this breed of rabbit is raised at "room temperature," about 25°C, the head and body are white, while the ears, nose, tail, and feet are black; but when they are raised at 10°C, the hair over the entire body is black. If the fur is shaved off the back of a rabbit kept at 25°C and a saddle-shaped ice bag is kept over it while the hair is growing, a saddle of black fur will be produced. In other words, the phenotype can be environmentally controlled to a certain extent. With a Himalayan genotype to begin with, two different phenotypes can be produced. According to temperature, the rabbits will be either white with black extremities, or entirely black. Presumably by warming the animal's extremities sufficiently a third phenotype, all white, could be produced.

In drosophila, by manipulation of the environment, it has been possible to produce copies of most of the well-known mutants. The embryo is treated with heat or various chemicals at a certain stage of its development. Such

Himalayan rabbit

Fur plucked from back and ice pack applied

Black fur grown out in plucked region

Fig. 8–23. Himalayan rabbit. *(From Winchester,* Genetics, *Houghton Mifflin)*

copies of the phenotype characteristic of one genotype in animals of another genotype are called **phenocopies.** For example: in wild-type flies, up to 75 per cent of the individuals can be converted into phenocopies of the "curly" mutant by heat; or in man, by persistent use of sunshine an individual with a genotype producing a very light skin can convert himself into a phenocopy of an individual of a genotype which in a relatively sunless environment produces an equally dark hue.

One of the most instructive cases of the interrelationships of heredity and environment was uncovered by a statistician, Raymond

Pearl. He found that wild-type drosophila raised in the standard laboratory milk bottles have an average life span about twice as long as that of flies with the mutant genes for vestigial wings. However, if the normal wild-type flies are sufficiently crowded, their life span becomes the same as that of the vestigials. With complete starvation the average life span of both wild-type flies and vestigials also becomes the same, though shorter than in either of the situations given above.

In summary, what is inherited by fruit fly, man, or other creature is a capacity to respond in certain ways or a lack of ability to respond. As far as the external environment is concerned, there is a whole spectrum of cases, from genotypes that produce their characteristic effects in all known environments to genotypes that are very sensitive to environmental factors. Albinism is in the first class, melanin production or sun tanning in the second.

The Human Problem. Nowhere is disentanglement of the twin forces of heredity and environment of greater interest or of greater difficulty than in our own species. In the light of present knowledge some of our predecessors seem to have been extremely uncritical—in fact, downright gullible. Charles Darwin's famous cousin, Francis Galton, who was regarded as the world's leading investigator of heredity before the rediscovery of Mendel's laws, succeeded in proving statistically that achievement in many lines of work such as law, medicine, the army, politics, music, and so on tends to run in families. He thought that this proved ability in these vocations was inherited biologically rather than to any appreciable extent through cultural, psychological, and other environmental forces. The amazing thing is that he wrote extensively about the difference between "nature" (heredity) and "nurture" (environment), and yet never realized that environment plays such an enormous role in the kind of achievement he studied that it renders much of his work worthless.

From earliest childhood everyone is surrounded by a host of influences molding interests, outlook, ambition, and character generally. If a boy knows that his grandfather or even his uncle was a successful surgeon, or musician, or cattle breeder, it cannot help but strengthen the feeling that such a career is within the circle of the possible for him. Even the possession of a well-known name can help a young man or woman over some of the difficulties that beset infant careers. And from start to finish such boys or girls stand an above-average chance of having a first-hand and realistic knowledge of a wide variety of factors that go into the making of a successful career.

At the same time there is no doubt that members of the human race differ very widely in thousands of ways due to our built-in mechanism guaranteeing genetic diversity to the point where everyone is unique. Remember that with 23 pairs of chromosomes it is possible for every man and woman to produce 2^{23} or over 8 million different kinds of sperms or eggs. Genetic differences are responsible for differences in height, color of hair, skin, and eyes, blood groups, shape of ear lobes, the substances excreted by the kidneys, ability to taste certain chemicals, and dozens of other ways. There can be no doubt that both the functioning and the gross and microscopic structure of the nervous system and endocrine glands are included in this genetic variability.

What does our built-in hereditary variability do to the belief that all men are created equal? When the authors of the Declaration of Independence wrote in 1776 that they held it to be self-evident that all men are created equal, they could not have meant equal in height, or physical strength, or even in native wit. What our forefathers were protesting was the belief, which is still prevalent in India, certain parts of Japan, and keeps lingering on here and there in the United States, that some people are "better" than others not by virtue of greater physical strength, intelligence, talent, or moral integrity, but by having been born into a certain caste or clan, or even section of town.

Heredity and Environment in Twins. The best place to investigate the relative roles of heredity and environment in human beings is in monozygotic or one-egg twins. These are the twins frequently called "identical." They are produced when two centers of development form in one blastocyst. Because they arise from the union of a single sperm and a single egg, the twins will have the same genetical constitution; they are an exception to the rule of human hereditary uniqueness.

Most twins are fraternal twins. Fraternal twins result when two separate eggs are fertilized, each by its own sperm. Such twins are no more closely related than brothers or sisters that result from separate pregnancies. Fraternal twins may be of the same sex, or one may be a boy and one a girl.

Monozygotic twins are, of course, of the same sex. Usually they can be diagnosed as monozygotic because they resemble each other so closely that even their parents have difficulty distinguishing them. Very often they can be diagnosed at birth because they are both enclosed within the same chorion, the fetal membrane that separates the embryo from the lining of the uterus; but this is not a sure indication. More commonly identity in a sufficient number of blood groups and other physical traits known to be inherited in a simple way is used to diagnose twins as monozygotic.

The physical, mental, and personality traits of monozygotic twins raised together and raised under widely different environmental circumstances have been extensively studied.

The findings in regard to tuberculosis are especially instructive because they demonstrate how inextricably intertwined are the twin forces of heredity and environment. In one series of twins with tuberculosis, it was found that 25 per cent of the fraternals had a twin who also had tuberculosis, but that about 70 per cent of the monozygotics had an afflicted twin. Among those actually hospitalized for tuberculosis it was found that about 30 per cent of the fraternal twins had a twin who also had the disease but that 87 per cent of the monozygotic twins did so. These facts appear to make one thing very certain, namely, that heredity plays an extremely important part in whether or not a given person becomes a victim of tuberculosis. But it is no less certain that this disease is due to the growth of a specific kind of bacterium, *Mycobacterium tuberculosis,* in the lungs. Only a greater or lesser degree of susceptibility or resistance is inherited. To produce tuberculosis many factors work together. Malnutrition will lower whatever resistance is present. Crowding people together helps to spread the infecting bacteria. Finally, the bacteria must have a susceptible host. The statistics show that probably everyone becomes infected with the tuberculosis organism at some time. It is what happens thereafter that makes the difference. The nature of inherited resistance or susceptibility is a difficult question, though medically a very important one. It may have to do with the shape of the lungs, or with the ability of certain cells to manufacture antibodies. The study of monozygotic twins tells us that one of the important factors influencing resistance is inherited, but the study of all the facts makes it clear that heredity is only one of several factors determining the course of events.

This conclusion is confirmed by other studies of identical or monozygotic twins. Some pairs are so constituted genetically that they develop through their lives in closely similar ways even though their environments differ widely. Other pairs have a more plastic nature and do become rather different when subjected to divergent environments. As is to be expected, physical traits are least affected, behavioral and psychological traits most affected. It should never be forgotten that the sheer fact of the coexistence of two human beings so alike that they can be distinguished only with difficulty can represent a profound psychic force in the lives of both.

And now for some specific examples. Clara and Abby Beach were a typical pair of identical

Fig. 8 – 24. Identical or monozygotic twins before and after long separation. *(From Kallman,* Heredity in Health and Mental Disorder, *W. W. Norton)*

twins, almost indistinguishable at the age of 18 when one married a farmer and became Mrs. Mills, and the other entered a school for missionaries and then went to the Orient, where she lived for nearly half a century. When the unmarried missionary returned to the United States after 47 years of separation to live with her now widowed sister who had spent her life on a farm, the two sisters of course looked very, very different from the way they had at age 18, but they were still almost indistinguishable in physique and personality.

Ralph and Norman X were monozygotic twins. Ralph received a severe birth injury that made him a spastic paralytic, so that his speech, gait, posture, and manual dexterity were all severely affected. His brother was normal in these respects. Clearly, there have been many environmental differences for these two young men. Yet they shared similar I.Q. scores, college grades, and friendly, good-humored personalities. Cases of this sort are of obvious interest in connection with theories that birth trauma and very early childhoood experiences play a predominant role in character formation.

In contrast is the case of Gladys and Helen Q., studied by Professor H. H. Newman, who devoted the greater part of a lifetime to such investigations. These girls were separated at the age of a year and a half. Gladys went to school only through the second grade and was then employed in a knitting mill and in other routine employments. Helen went through college and became a teacher in the Detroit public schools. When they were examined at the University of Chicago as young adults they were very much alike in appearance, but widely different both in personality and in scores on intelligence tests. Where Helen was "an interesting and animated conversationalist" and met people easily and with mutual pleasure, her sister lacked these qualities and scored markedly lower on standard intelligence tests. The difference amounted to 24 points, or a difference between "normal" and "superior" intelligence. Cases like this emphasize the importance of the role played by environment. So once again we return to the analogy of the flight of the arrow, where the initial direction and impulse of the bow represent heredity, and gravity and wind represent environment.

CONTROL OF HEREDITY

Are the Effects of Environment and Activity Inherited? As was pointed out at the beginning of this chapter, the belief that the effects of use and disuse and of the environment upon the bodies of animals and man are inherited, is both extremely ancient and still with us. It is taken for granted in the story of Jacob as told in the book of Genesis. It appears in the writings of the father of medicine, Hippocrates, and was formulated in the 18th century by Erasmus Darwin and by Lamarck. Charles Darwin's theory of "pangenesis," whereby particles from all over the body were supposedly carried by the bloodstream to the gonads and there nourished corresponding parts in the germ cells, was an attempt to suggest a possible mechanism for this imaginary type of heredity.

The theory of the inheritance of acquired characteristics has important implications for agriculture, for the theory of evolution, and indeed for human life. It is amazingly persistent and widespread. (It isn't just the older generation of Russian communists and the authors of children's books who cling to this theory.) For all these reasons investigators have sought evidence for or against it decade after decade despite the experiments of Weismann on the tails of mice.

Shortly after the turn of the century an American zoologist, Castle, and his colleagues tried a new way to get at this problem. They removed the ovaries from a pure-bred white guinea pig and ingrafted ovaries from a black animal. Later this white female with ovaries from a black animal was mated to a white male. The offspring were all black. In no case was it possible to detect any modification of the black inheritance even though the ovaries from the black female were actually within the white female and were necessarily nourished by her bloodstream.

After the drosophila work was well advanced, T. H. Morgan pointed out that some of the observations of his school really gave the old theory of the inheritance of acquired characteristics the *coup de grace*. If a fly with very small vestigial wings, which of course cannot be used in flight, from a long line of flies all with vestigial wings, is crossed with a normal fly, all the first generation will have normal wings, just as large and functional as ever even though half of their ancestors had never used their wings for many generations.

In Russia, the great physiologist and student of conditioned responses in dogs, Ivan Pavlov (1849–1936), studied the speed with which white rats learn a maze. At first he found that each generation learned in fewer trials than the previous generation. This certainly looked like a good case of the inheritance of the effects of training. Later it was both reported and denied that Pavlov subsequently discovered that the rats hadn't been getting any smarter. He had been becoming a better teacher of rats! His experiments were repeated by William Mc-Dougall in the United States, who confirmed Pavlov's first conclusion. This isolated work stood for many years as almost the sole Lamarckian experiment with apparently positive results.

This anomalous situation has been cleared up, perhaps forever, by a long-term study by W. W. Agar in Australia. He had two lines of rats. One, which served as controls, were tested at intervals to find how long they would take to learn a maze. The rats of the other group were given continuous and systematic education in maze running. Agar found that there were indeed periods of progressive improvement extending over several generations in the educated strain. But there were also periods of progressive decline in rapidity of learning. These periods of improvement and decline seemed to be correlated with periods of improvement and decline in the general health of the colony. The records clearly showed that they were correlated with fluctuations in fertility. Similar periods of fluctuation in learning speed and fertility took place in the controls.

With all this evidence from so many sources the conclusion seems inescapable: the germ cells are not influenced by what happens to the somatic or body cells.

Selection, Outcrossing, and Inbreeding. A method of heredity control that does produce improved breeds of animals is the application of selection alone or, better, in conjunction with outcrossing and inbreeding. This is the method that gave such spectacular results with corn.

With a relatively unimproved group of cows, chickens, or other animals to begin with, rigorous **selection** of the best individuals results in hereditary improvement. This is the way most of the current breeds of farm animals have been produced. By this method improvement is usually rapid at first, but a plateau is reached after a variable number of generations.

To achieve further results a method originated over a century ago by the great French plant breeder, Louis de Vilmorin, has been applied with success. This is the **progeny test.** It has been especially successful in dairy herds and in chickens. A bull obviously cannot be judged on his milk production. It is the milking records of his daughters that reveal whether or not he carries genes that make for high milk productivity. No one familiar with modern genetics will be surprised to learn that bulls which are superior in various anatomical traits that make them prize winners at cattle shows are not necessarily those whose daughters have superior abilities as milk producers. Nor is it surprising to learn of two pedigreed bulls, full brothers, whose daughters possessed markedly different milking qualities. Without the progeny test there would be no way to distinguish between the bull which transmitted genes for high milk production and his full brother who lacked this gene or genes.

Excellent results from using the progeny test on chickens have been achieved in agricultural experiment stations in several states. The older method of selecting hens for breeders on the basis of their own egg-laying records was followed until no further improvement for several years was obtained. Then the selection of the hens and roosters to be used as breeders was based on the egg production records of their offspring. This new method of selection gave marked additional improvement.

Outcrossing (or **crossbreeding**) is an extremely valuable method. Outcrossing is used for two purposes. First, it may combine in one animal desirable traits from various breeds. A notable case is the Santa Gertrudis cattle of Texas, which have been produced by crossing Herefords and Shorthorns with Brahman cattle from India. The resulting breed has some of the superior beef qualities of the European breeds combined with the resistance to heat, drought, and insects of the Indian cattle. The second generation after any such cross shows a considerable variability, as would be expected from the segregation and recombination of genes. Consequently in the second and later generations selection must play an important part in the elimination of undesirable genes. Some of the later generations might equally well combine the poor beef qualities of the Indian cattle with the susceptibility to drought and heat of the European breeds. For several years geneticists in the U. S. Department of Agriculture and in similar institutions in England have been crossing Jersey with Indian Zebu cattle in an attempt to combine the good milking qualities of the Jersey with the heat and drought resistance of the Zebu.

Crossbreeding has another effect in addition to producing new combinations of traits from which the desirable ones can be selected. It also produces hybrid vigor or **heterosis.** Heterosis was defined by Gowen as "the evident superiority of the hybrid over the better parent in any measurable character such as size, general vegetative vigor, or yield."

The effect is very marked in corn (maize), where it was first studied. Two inbred lines of corn can be maintained year after year at the same level of production, provided of course the soil, moisture, etc., are approximately constant. If two such standardized inbred strains are crossed, the first generation is markedly superior in size, production of corn, and general vigor. The explanation of hybrid vigor is still obscure. Part of it may be due to heterozygosity for harmful recessive genes that were inadvertently made homozygous in the inbreeding that produced the original breeds. Some think that for unknown reasons heterozygosity is in itself beneficial. Others believe that in certain strains there just happen to be genes for "vigor" which have a complementary reinforcing action when brought together.

Less is known about hybrid vigor in animals, although in drosophila heterosis, as defined above, has been shown to exist to a very marked degree in lifetime egg production and to lesser degrees in various other traits. Marked heterosis, as measured in rate of growth of the animals, has been achieved by crossing inbred lines of pigs.

Several well-known hybrids seem to show the effect. The mule is a much hardier animal and able to thrive on poorer food than either the donkey or the mare, its parents. The deplorable lack of fertility in mules is not due to any fault in reproductive anatomy or physiology but to a failure in chromosome behavior during meiosis. In synapsis, the horse chromosomes do not pair properly with the donkey chromosomes. The eggs or sperms produced do not have complete sets of chromosomes and hence do not give rise to viable offspring.

The cross between the one-humped and the two-humped camel gives an animal a bit taller and a bit heavier than either parent and is said to have more endurance. It has one hump.

The value of **inbreeding** is based on the fact that inbreeding produces homozygosity. This is a point made by Mendel in his original paper. For he established what perhaps should be called Mendel's third law, namely, that under conditions of self-fertilization or close inbreeding the proportion of homozygous individuals becomes greater and greater and the proportion of heterozygotes becomes less and less. It is easy to understand why this should be so, because with close inbreeding the homozygous individuals will produce only homozygous offspring, whereas only half the offspring of the heterozygotes will be heterozygous. In the tenth generation of self-fertilized peas, Mendel calculated the ratio in a monohybrid cross would be 1,023 homozygous dominants: 2 heterozygotes: 1,023 homozygous recessives. In other words, homozygotes to heterozygotes would be in a ratio of 1,023:1! Of course the effect could not be so extreme with inbreeding in animals, but with brother-sister and father-daughter crossing similar results follow.

The first great practical result of inbreeding is that the resulting homozygosity "stabilizes" the desirable traits so that animals breed true. This is the method that has been used in the production of most present-day breeds of domestic animals. The first step may or may not be a series of crosses, but there is always selection of the animals having the desirable genes, and this is usually followed by inbreeding to make the strain homozygous.

A second practical use of inbreeding is that homozygosity reveals desirable and undesirable recessives. Such genes can then be either bred into the strain or eliminated. In corn breeding, which sets the pattern, inbreeding produces a number of strains, some very poor. Only the best inbred strains are subsequently used in the crossing that gives the spectacular hybrid vigor.

Use of Mutations. Methods for producing new and improved breeds of animals which depend on hybridization, outcrossing, selection, inbreeding, and more selection depend on genes already present in the population. A very different and more basic method depends on mutation followed by a screening program, i.e., selection. Because spontaneous mutations are so very rare, the usual procedure is to irradiate the animals or plants (actually this method has been used chiefly with plants), raise many thousands of the offspring of the irradiated individuals, and then hunt for desired mutations. It is a long and costly business. Real progress with this method awaits knowledge which will make it possible to produce specific kinds of mutations at will, a problem we have already discussed (page 168).

HEREDITY AND MAN

Some Human Genes. A logical way to survey human heredity is to begin with the linkage groups. Since there are 23 chromosomes in a haploid human set, there are of course 23 linkage groups. Very few of these have been identified in addition to the X and Y sex chromosome linkage group. And unfortunately some of the groups have as yet only two or three identified genes. An examination of the accompanying figure from L. H. Snyder will show how meager our information really is. The explanation for this lack of knowledge is that the study of human heredity is beset with great difficulties. Compared with drosophila or mice, man is a slow-breeding animal. Moreover, a single female does not produce 75 to 100 offspring, nor can specific crosses be made to order for genetic purposes. Added to these basic difficulties are several minor ones. Occasional individuals are not completely honest in reporting the facts. Furthermore a number of human genes either vary in the degree to which they are expressed in different individuals

Fig. 8–25. Six probable linkage groups in man. *(After L. H. Snyder)*

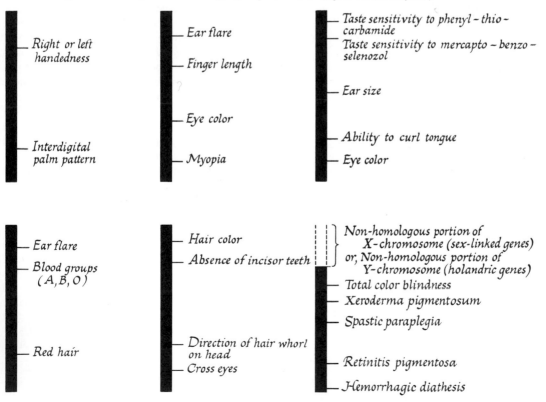

or lack 100 per cent **penetrance**. In other words, the same gene may manifest itself more strongly in one person than in another, or in some cases it may not produce any detectable effect. The genes for hyperextension of the thumb and for lack of a complete set of permanent teeth fall into this category.

Various aspects of human heredity have already been discussed: the interaction of heredity and environment in human life, the kinds of sex-linked inheritance, skin color in Caucasian-Negro crosses, the excretion of phenylpyruvic acid.

The Blood Groups. It is now over half a century since Karl Landsteiner, in reinvestigating the old problem of blood reactions, discovered that the blood serum of some people would cause an agglutination, i.e., clumping, of the red cells of certain individuals but not of others. Following up this discovery it became evident that all people fall into one of four blood groups, now called **O, A, B,** and **AB.** A man who belongs to group O has blood serum (the fluid part of his blood minus the clotting fibrin) which carries proteins known as **antibodies** that will clump the red cells from any person belonging to group A, B, or AB. If a man belongs to group A, his serum carries antibodies that will agglutinate cells from a member of group B

Fig. 8–26. Agglutination test for blood groups A, B, and O.

or AB. If he belongs to group B, his blood will clump cells from members of groups A and AB. Finally, if a man is of group AB, his serum will not clump other blood cells. A necessary corollary of the presence in group O serum of antibodies against both A and B cells is that the anti-B antibody in A serum and the anti-A antibody in B serum will not clump group O red blood cells.

In transfusions it is important to use blood of a type matching that of the recipient. In extreme emergencies group O blood can be transfused into persons belonging to the other three groups because the O cells cannot be agglutinated by the anti-A or anti-B antibodies present in the blood of the recipient, and at the same time the antibodies in the O serum are so diluted that they do not clump the recipient's own cells.

The inheritance of the A, B, O factors is simple. Three alleles, all located at the same or nearly the same position on the chromosome, produce the four blood groups. Gene I^A (abbreviated from isoagglutin A) yields A cells and anti-B antibody in the serum. Its allele I^B produces B cells and anti-A antibody in the serum. When a person receives gene I^A from one parent and gene I^B from the other, he is of the genotype $I^A I^B$ and belongs to group AB. Gene I^O, if homozygous, puts a man in group O.

Subsequent studies have uncovered a dozen or more other blood groups by which people can be distinguished. The best known of these are the **MN** system and the **Rh** or **rhesus factor** blood group system. In these systems there are normally no corresponding antibodies in the serum, but only antigens on the red cells. All are inherited according to Mendelian rules. The rhesus factor was discovered first in the blood of the macaque or rhesus monkey, *Macaca*, which is the short-tailed, brown monkey of Southern Asia used in medical research. The medical importance of the rhesus factor lies in the fact that if a rhesus-negative (Rh−) person receives a transfusion of rhesus-positive (Rh+) blood, the Rh− person forms antibodies against the Rh+ erythrocytes or red cells. On a subsequent transfusion with Rh+ cells, the foreign Rh+ cells will be clumped, and that can lead to serious blocks in the vascular system. Furthermore, if an Rh− woman becomes

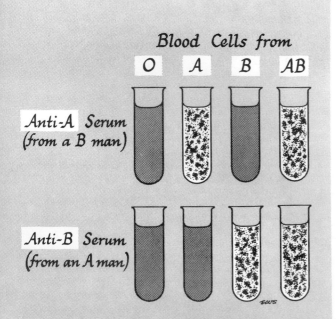

Blood Cells from

O A B AB

Anti-A Serum
(from a B man)

Anti-B Serum
(from an A man)

pregnant with an Rh+ child, some rhesus-positive factors may pass through the placenta into the blood of the mother. She will then produce antibodies against the Rh+ cells. These antibodies from the mother will pass through the placenta into the fetal bloodstream. Consequently, in a subsequent pregnancy with an Rh+ child, this child may develop a hemolytic disease called **erythroblastosis fetalis** because its red blood cells are destroyed.

Although about 15 per cent of people of European ancestry have Rh− blood, which means that about 12 per cent of all marriages are between Rh− women and Rh+ men, fortunately not all of the 12 per cent of marriages result in erythroblastic babies. This is partly because some women do not make Rh+ antibodies at all or fast enough or strong enough to be very harmful, and partly because many of their husbands are heterozygous for the Rh factor. Rh+ is a simple dominant. One half of the sperms of such men carry a gene for Rh−. A child resulting from such a sperm would be homozygous for the rhesus negative factor and would be unharmed by the mother's Rh+ antibodies, even if abundant. Consequently instead of 12 per cent of marriages yielding one or more erythroblastic children, only about ½ of 1 per cent do so. Erythroblastic babies, if not too badly affected, can be tided over the crisis by transfusion with about 500 ml of Rh-negative red cells which are immune to the antibodies the baby has received from its mother and cannot get rid of immediately.

Blood group genes are especially useful to anthropologists interested in the historical interrelationships of the various races of mankind. This is because, unlike skull shape or tooth wear or skin color and many other traits, blood groups are (1) not changed by differences in food, climate, or other environmental influences, (2) they are inherited according to very simple Mendelian laws, and (3) they are sharply defined, "all-or-none" characters in marked contrast to the blending nature of traits like skull shape or hair structure. (4) The blood group substances can even be determined for prehistoric mummies and from bones of other ancient human remains.

All three of the A,B,O blood group genes have been found in all racial groups, but their

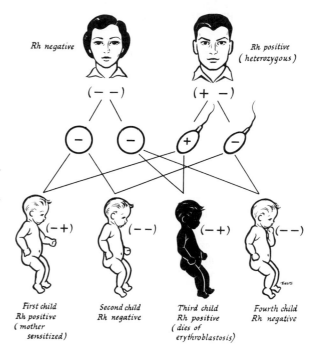

Fig. 8–27. Possible results of the marriage of an Rh-positive man and an Rh-negative woman. (*From Winchester,* Genetics, *Houghton Mifflin*)

frequencies vary widely. Gene I^A, for example, is almost completely absent among the Indians of Central and South America but very common among the Blackfeet and other tribes centering in Montana and among the natives of northern Norway.

The table on page 184 shows the distribution of I^A, I^B, and I^O gene frequencies among a variety of people. Gene frequencies are calculated from the number of people who belong to each blood group. Each person in group O contributes two I^O genes. Everyone in group AB contributes one I^A and I^B gene to the total number of A,B,O alleles. Likewise the A and the B individuals, being of genotypes $I^A I^O$ and $I^B I^O$ as well as $I^A I^A$ and $I^B I^B$, may contribute I^O genes in addition to the I^A's and I^B's.

As far as blood transfusions are concerned, the only thing that matters is that the two individuals concerned belong to the same blood group. Thus a native of Sweden and of China or Africa can safely exchange bloods if they are of the same blood group, while two brothers cannot if they do not belong to the same blood group.

Frequency of A,B,O Blood Group Genes in Various Populations
(Data taken from Boyd)

POPULATION	PLACE	FREQUENCY (PER CENT)		
		I^A	I^B	I^O
Sioux Indians	South Dakota	3.5	1.0	95.5
Blackfeet	Montana	51.6	0.0	48.5
Australian Aboriginals	West Australia	30.6	0.0	69.4
Polynesians	Hawaii	38.2	1.8	60.4
Eskimos	Cape Farewell	33.3	2.7	64.2
Asiatic Indians	Bengal	15.4	27.8	57.1
English	London	25.0	5.0	69.2
Germans	Berlin	28.5	11.0	60.4
Russians	Moscow	25.0	18.9	56.5
Kirghiz	USSR	20.6	23.6	56.3
Chinese	Peking	19.3	25.0	55.4
Pigmies	Congo	22.7	21.9	55.4
Basques	San Sebastian	23.9	0.8	75.6
Spanish	Spain	29.4	6.8	64.5

The distribution of the Rh-negative gene is very peculiar. It is unknown or rare among the native populations of Australia, Asia, and the Americas. But about 15 per cent of the people of Europe from Scandinavia to Spain and from Ireland to the Near East have Rh-negative blood. At the same time among the Basques, a very ancient people speaking a non-Indo-European language and living in northern Spain, Rh-negative individuals make up almost a third of the population. Some students interpret this as meaning that the Basques are the remnant of a prehistoric population with which the present Europeans mingled and so picked up their Rh-negative genes. Another view is that the high frequency of this gene results from a process, to be discussed in Chapter 10 on evolution, called random genetic drift, which occurs in small isolated populations like the Basques.

What of Eugenics? Many people, including zoologists, have been interested in eugenics, "the science of being well born." In fact, this concern extends far back into history. Plato and other Greeks of his age discussed it. The citizens of Sparta, that stern and bleak prototype of the dictator state, practiced a crude form of race improvement by exposing all weak or deformed infants to die.

A number of issues are involved in eugenics, and all are of the greatest human importance. These questions fall into two basically different, although closely interrelated, groups. The first questions concern what is biologically possible and what is impossible or extremely difficult to do. These are questions of fact and are a normal part of science. It is the duty of the zoologist to present the facts, for only then can anyone make sound decisions and guard against dangers. The second group of questions concern value judgments. What traits are desirable in human beings? These questions begin in biology but extend far beyond the province of ordinary science.

What is biologically possible and what could be done without great social change depends to a large extent on whether or not a particular gene is dominant or recessive, and on how great are the changes desired. Consider some specific cases. There are genes which produce results so horrible that few sane men would wish to see them perpetuated. It was pointed out 700 years ago by St. Thomas Aquinas that some frightful types of idiocy are hereditary. There are hideously deforming and fatal atrophies. There are severe convulsive diseases, and conditions in which there are no hands or feet. The only real question here is one of method. The Spartans would have exposed such infants on a hillside. The Nazis would have sent them to a gas chamber. Most present-day eugenists would insist on minor surgery that ties off the sperm ducts or oviducts and so makes conception of offspring impossible for them.

How effective such measures would be depends on whether the genes concerned are dominant or recessive. A dominant gene could be completely eliminated in a single generation. Unfortunately most of the known deleterious genes are recessive. Albinism is a good example, and one which is well understood. There are about 5 albinos for every 100,000 people. On the basis of random marriages this requires approximately 1,420 heterozygous carriers in every 100,000. In such a case, what would be accomplished by sterilization, or by exposure of every albino infant on a mountain top? The 5 albinos who are homozygous, *aa*, carry a total of only 10 genes for albinism. The heterozygous *Aa* carriers represent 1,420 *a* genes which are hidden in the gene pool of the population. Consequently the elimination of the five albino individuals would reduce the total number of albino genes only from 1,430 to 1,420, a negligible amount. At this rate 5,000 years would be required to reduce the number of albinos in the population by even one-half.

The best that can be said in behalf of this kind of negative gene-by-gene eugenics program is:

1. Deleterious genes can be eliminated in a single generation if they are dominant.

2. If the gene concerned is completely recessive, preventing the afflicted individuals from reproducing will have only a meager result. In specific cases, of course, this little may be worth while. What is the purpose of preventing two hopeless idiots from producing more idiots? It avoids tragedy for all the individuals concerned.

3. When more is known about linkage groups in human chromosomes, some useful predictions will be possible. For example, Huntington's chorea is a nervous disease which begins with involuntary twitching of the face and limbs, becomes more and more severe, and finally ends in cellular degeneration of the brain, a complete amentia. This nightmarish disease

is inherited as a simple dominant, but unfortunately from the eugenic standpoint it does not generally make its appearance until the carrier of the gene is in his thirties or forties, after children may have been produced. If enough were known about the linkage relations of the gene for Huntington's chorea, it would be possible to say that any child of a particular marriage would stand about a 50:50 chance of developing the disease while any child of another marriage would have almost no chance of developing it even though the disease was in the family.

4. In some diseases it may be possible to detect the heterozygous carrier of a deleterious gene by chemical tests.

What are the possibilities for more positive results? The desire that children should come into the world sound in body and mind is universal. It is when increased numbers of superior children are demanded that eugenics runs into a difficulty far transcending the proper bounds of zoology. Who is to judge what are the really desirable traits and in what proportions they are desirable? A world without Shakespeares, Pavlovas, Beethovens, Gandhis, Edisons, Einsteins, and opera singers would surely be a poor place. Yet who would care to face a world composed solely of such people? Or who would advocate producing a standard model human being so all men would be as much alike as twins? Clearly a golden mean of rich human diversity, perhaps not very different from what we now have, must be our aim. There is even some evidence that certain afflictions can serve as gadflies to achievements of great benefit to the human race. Homer was blind, Edison deaf, Steinmetz crippled, Byron club-footed.

There are further and truly alarming possibilities that must be included if the whole truth is to be told. Under a ruthless dictatorship, either of a single man or of a group of so-called philosopher kings, it would be possible to produce as diverse and fantastic breeds of men as has already been done with dogs and pigeons. What are the methods? The same methods that have produced the various breeds of domestic animals, methods already discussed—induction of mutations, crossbreeding, selection, inbreeding, and more selection.

Review and References

REVIEW TOPICS

1. What were the common pre-Mendelian ideas about heredity? What discoveries and ideas led up to Mendel's laws?

2. State and give an example of Mendel's first law: of his second: of his "third."

3. A normal man, whose mother was an albino, marries an albino woman. What is the chance that their first child will be an albino? If they have 10 children, how many of them will probably be normal? Why?

4. Define: gene, homozygous, phenotype, karotype, Product Law, dihybrid, allele, synapsis, kinetochore, sex linkage, autosome, diploid.

5. Make a diagram of meiosis in an animal with a haploid set of three chromosomes, one long, one short, one middle-sized. Represent the paternal chromosomes as solid, the maternal as hollow. How do meiosis and fertilization produce variation?

6. What is linkage and crossing over, and how can they be used to map the location of genes on chromosomes?

7. What are mutations and how can they be induced?

8. Distinguish between: purines and pyrimidines: DNA and RNA; mRNA and tRNA; nucleotides and amino acids; phenylalanine and tyrosine.

9. What genetical ideas are associated with: Mendel, Garrod, de Vries, Morgan, Weismann, Jacob and Monod, Beadle, Lamarck?

10. What are Turner's and Klinefelter's syndromes and how can they be accounted for?

11. What is the evidence that the genetic code uses three-letter words rather than two- or four-letter words?

12. Why is it believed that the genetic code is the same in plants and animals?

13. How is the genetic code translated into proteins?

14. Into what major compounds is phenylalanine converted? What diseases may result from blockages at what points in the biochemical pathways of phenylalanine derivatives?

15. Define: structural gene, operon, phenylketonuria, alkaptonuria, constitutive enzyme, inducible enzyme, ribosome, monozygotic, heterosis, mutagen.

16. Discuss the methods of selection, outbreeding, and inbreeding in producing improved breeds of animals. What is the purpose of inbreeding? Where does heterosis fit in? Mutations?

17. Is it possible to have a useful or even meaningful discussion of the relative importance of heredity and environment in the lives of animals and man? Why?

USEFUL REFERENCES

Barish, N., *The Gene Concept,* New York, Reinhold Publishing Corp., 1965.

Dunn, L. C., *A Short History of Genetics,* New York, McGraw-Hill Book Co., 1965.

Dunn, L. C., and T. Dobzhansky, *Heredity, Race, and Society*, Baltimore, Penguin Books, 1946.

Gowen, J. W., ed., *Heterosis*, Ames, Iowa State College Press, 1952.

Hartman, P. E., and S. R. Suskind, *Gene Action,* Englewood Cliffs, N.J., Prentice-Hall, 1965 (paperback).

Herskowitz, I. H., *Genetics*, 2nd ed., Little, Brown & Co., Boston, 1965.

Hutt, F. B., *Animal Genetics*, New York, The Ronald Press Company, 1964.

Iltis, H., *Life of Mendel*, New York, W. W. Norton & Company, 1932.

King, R. C., *Genetics*, 2nd ed., New York, Oxford University Press, 1965.

Scheinfeld, A., *Your Heredity and Environment*, Philadelphia, J. B. Lippincott Co., 1965.

Wallace, B., *Chromosomes, Giant Molecules, and Evolution*, New York, W. W. Norton & Company, 1966.

Winters, L. M., *Animal Breeding,* 5th ed., New York, John Wiley & Sons, 1954.

Chapter 9

Development

Speculation about the origin of new life, especially new human life, is at least as old as history and as universal as the inquiring mind of man. Some ancient ideas merit study because they point to basic problems, and some because they still influence our thinking.

Basic Problems and Classical Answers. One of the oldest beliefs holds that the embryo, and the human embryo in particular, is coagulated out of fluids in the uterus or womb. This idea is expressed in the Book of Job in the Bible. It was found among the Greeks of classical antiquity. The idea took various, sometimes contradictory forms. The father of medicine, Hippocrates, in the 4th century B.C. taught that the "seed" which is in the supposed reproductive fluids came from all parts of the body, probably at the very time of copulation. This doctrine that hereditary seeds or factors of some kind come from all parts of the body of the parent is known as **pangenesis.** It implies the inheritance of acquired characteristics, for if a parent's arm were injured or amputated, how could it any longer contribute its proper share of hereditary "seeds" to the reproductive fluids?

Aristotle and other Greek biologists asked some very sharp questions about this idea. They also made some very bad guesses, which have echoed down into the present. If the seeds of the new individual come from the entire body of the parent, as Hippocrates taught, do they represent tissues like muscle, bone, etc., or do they represent complex parts like hands and faces that are organized from several different kinds of tissues? In modern terms, do embryos begin with genes, hereditary factors, for things like hands and ears, or only for general things like muscles, or for something more general still, merely the ability to make certain enzymes? Aristotle wanted to know how a girl could resemble her father more than her mother. Challenging Hippocrates, he also asked if the seminal particles or factors really did come from the entire body instead of from special reproductive organs. It took Gregor Mendel to answer the first question and August Weismann to answer the second. Aristotle supposed that the male parent contributed primarily the form and spirit, the female the material and nutrition. It is obvious that here lie many questions in developmental genetics that we are only beginning to answer after some 2,000 years.

By the time printing was invented (about 1500), it was commonly believed, more or less as Aristotle had taught, that the embryo is a coagulated mixture of seminal fluid from the male and menstrual blood from the female. Such a view has a certain plausibility and is partly the basis for the legal phrase "blood relatives." Some authors even went so far as to suppose that the white parts of the embryo, like the bones and the nervous system, are inherited from the father, while the red parts, like the muscles, liver, and blood, come from the mother. Drawings of the supposed seven stages in the supposed coagulation of the embryo were published.

The work of Fabricius at Padua and of his famous student, William Harvey, discoverer of the circulation of the blood, are often taken as the starting points of modern embryology. Harvey's work, published in the middle of the 17th century, illustrates the bewildering confusion then current. Like many others, the learned Harvey believed that mares could become pregnant not only by mating with stallions but also, according to ancient tradition, from breathing in the air on hilltops at certain seasons. He seriously discussed the comparison between the conception of an idea by the brain and the conception of an embryo by the uterus, and argued for a basic similarity.

Amid all this confusion two important truths stand out. First, in a truly royal experiment on the king's deer, doubtless what we would today call "government-sponsored research," Harvey showed that the popular and age-old idea of coagulation could not be true. Harvey took some does very shortly after mating and divided them into two groups. One he left as controls. These gave birth to fawns at the end of the normal time, eight months. The does in the other group Harvey sacrificed at intervals and examined their uteri. At no time, least of all soon after mating, was there any coagulating mass in the uterus. He also examined hens before and after mating. In Harvey's words, "After coition there is nothing at all to be found in the uterus, more than there was before." These experiments disposed of the blood and seminal fluid coagulation theory.

Secondly, Harvey promulgated a doctrine of **epigenesis** which he modified from Aristotle and by which he meant that the embryo is formed step by step, some structures before others, through the action of a vaguely defined formative force or principle. The location of this vital action was the egg, though it must be admitted that Harvey had very confused ideas about

eggs and for some unexplained reason appears to have made no use of the magnifying lenses then available. Both Fabricius and Harvey followed the advice of Aristotle in using hens' eggs for their investigations.

In the 18th century, after Harvey's time, a doctrine very different from epigenesis became dominant. This was the theory of **preformation,** according to which there is no true development but only an unfolding and enlargement of parts already present. This view leads to startling conclusions. Within the egg is a miniature individual and within the ovary of this miniature individual are other eggs each containing a miniature individual of a second order of smallness, and so on to infinity. This doctrine is also extremely ancient and extends back through St. Augustine to Lucretius and through him to Democritus and the Greek anatomists. But in the 18th century the improved and more generally available microscopes led otherwise competent workers like Malpighi to draw pictures of what they thought they must be seeing, well-developed individuals in unincubated hens' eggs. Some even thought they saw a little man, a "homunculus," in the heads of human sperms. A foolish controversy then arose between the ovists, who held the embryo to be preformed in the egg, and the spermists, who held it to be preformed in the sperm.

Further observation killed the theory of preformation in this absurd form, but recent knowledge still leaves us with the twin problems of epigenesis and preformation in a new guise. The structures of the animal are certainly not present in the fertilized egg. But they are each and every one represented in the chromosomes, in a coded message, as it were, written out in the nucleic acids of the genes.

Basic Problems as They Seem Today. The science of **embryology** is the study of how the genetic code in the chromosomes becomes expressed as the complex and fully developed adult organism—of how the word, if you will, becomes flesh. This long story begins with the transcription of messenger RNA from the DNA of the genes. From that primary event a series of processes lead out in concentric circles of ever-increasing structural and physiological complexity.

The second key event is the synthesis of specific enzymatic and other proteins as the ribosomes read and translate the code in the mRNA. Any cell is what its proteins and especially its enzymes make it and differs from other kinds of cells because the enzymes are different. Muscle cells contain mRNA and enzymes which form myoglobin and contractile proteins, pigment cells contain mRNA and enzymes which manufacture melanin, and so on for all other types of cells.

A third category of events lies in the complex interactions between individual cells and groups of cells. Cells respond to each other in many ways. One of the first things that happens in the earliest development of an egg is extensive cell migrations as one group of cells slides over another. One group may call forth latent properties of other cells which would not otherwise be expressed. Without an optic vesicle to grow out of the embryonic brain and press against the ectoderm of the face, that ectoderm would form no lens for the eye. The most intricate of all developmental processes, the patterned growth of nerve fibers within the brain and spinal cord, depends on intercellular responses. Once a cell has become differentiated as a particular kind of cell, it appears to be permanently set in its specialization and does not need the continued influence of whatever factors led to its initial differentiation. Once a muscle cell, always a muscle cell. However, it may merely seem this way. Cases are known where it is undeniable that it is a dynamic equilibrium which maintains cells as they are. If the retina is removed from the eye of a salamander (which can be done relatively easily), the pigmented cells which form a continuous black layer immediately behind the retina lose their pigment, become embryonic in appearance, undergo mitosis, and form a thick double layer of cells. Those which are innermost redifferentiate into a new retina, those on the outer side redifferentiate into melatin-containing cells. Clearly some kind of influence from the retinal cells is continuously necessary to maintain the differentiated state of the pigmented cells.

The central problem of modern embryology has been inherited from the past century. This is the problem of differentiation, specifically, what determines which genes will become active in which cells. Something must turn DNA on or off so that only certain kinds of messenger RNA are transcribed in one kind of cell and certain others in other types of cells. Were this not so, all cells would possess the same enzymes, all cells would be alike, and differentiation of a complex multicellular animal impossible.

Around the central problem of differentiation many other problems await solution. Cell division is obviously essential for the development and growth of an animal, but no one knows very much about the actual mechanism or the initiating stimulus of mitosis. Certain cells in the gonads undergo meiosis rather than mitosis. Why? A simple question but without an answer. Our knowledge of fertilization has advanced since the turn of the century when Jacques Loeb at the Marine Biological Laboratory at Woods Hole asked, "How does the sperm save the life of the egg?"—but it has not advanced very far. Entire clusters of problems surround the role of hormones in development, the development of sexual differences, or of the heart, or antibodies, or the limbs, or the nervous system. No one knows how it is possible for certain organs such as the heart and intestine to become asymmetrical. If a salamander loses a leg, it grows a new one. No mammal can do this. Why not? The answers to these and other questions like them seemed just around the corner to our predecessors in 1910. They still seem just around the corner.

GAMETOGENESIS AND GAMETES

The process by which gametes, whether sperms or eggs, are produced is called **gametogenesis.** It has two aspects. One is the formation of gametes, either motile sperms or yolk-laden eggs. The other concerns the reduction of the chromosomes from two sets to a single set in the sperm or egg. This process, meiosis, has been discussed in the previous chapter.

The mechanisms underlying gametogenesis are very obscure. Both vitamin E (tocopherol) and vitamin A (a carotene derivative) are essential for gametogenesis, especially in males. A sufficiently high level of pituitary hormone is also essential. If the pituitary gland is removed, spermatogenesis stops in males, and in females all ova above a certain size degenerate.

Spermatogenesis and Sperms. Spermatogenesis, the formation of sperms, takes place in **testes.** The testes vary in number, position, and shape according to the kind of animal, and will be described with each phylum. In many invertebrates and in fishes and salamanders among vertebrates, the testis is composed of boxlike compartments often called **lobules.** All the sperm cells in a given lobule develop more or less simultaneously, so they will all be approximately in the same stage of development. Such a testis is relatively easy to study, and much of the pioneer research on spermatogenesis was done on the testes of insects for this reason.

In the higher vertebrates, from frogs to men, sperms are produced in **seminiferous tubules.** Around the periphery of such a tubule are diploid cells called **spermatogonia.** The spermatogonia divide by mitosis more or less continually and thereby push new cells in toward the central cavity or lumen of the tubule. These cells are called **spermatocytes** and are in the actual process of meiosis. In the primary spermatocytes the chromosomes undergo synapsis with the formation of tetrads. Primary spermatocytes can be distinguished from the spermatogonia from which they arose by their somewhat larger size and by the presence of tetrads. Secondary spermatocytes are clearly smaller than the primary from which they originate in the first maturation division. Each secondary spermatocyte divides once, forming two haploid **spermatids** each a bit smaller than the cell which produced it. Each spermatid comes to lie with its head within the cytoplasm of a special nurse or **Sertoli cell** while it completes its development into a mature **spermatozoan.** Usually a dozen or more spermatids enter each Sertoli cell.

Fig. 9–1. Longisection through a lobe of the testis of a grasshopper (locust). Note that all the cells in any one compartment are in the same stage. *1,* spermatogonium. *2,* early primary spermatocyte. *3,* primary spermatocyte in diakinesis, i.e., prophase with tetrads of first meiotic division. *4,* metaphase of first meiotic division. *5,* metaphase of second meiotic division. *6,* spermatid with nebenkern, a mass of mitochondria. *7* and *8,* stages in transformation of spermatid into sperm.

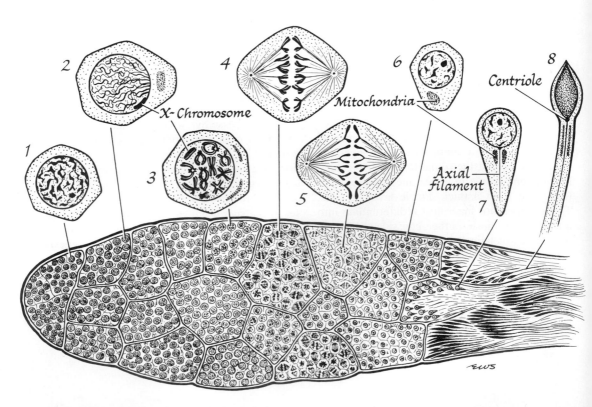

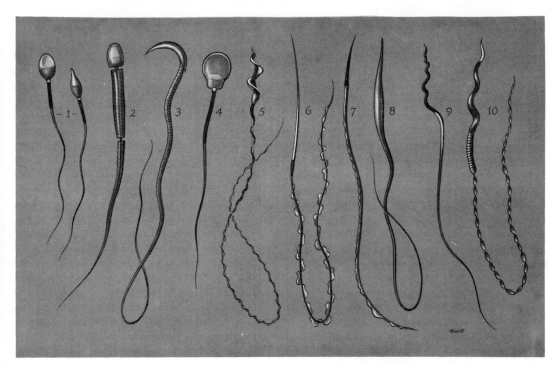

Fig. 9–2. Some types of sperms. *1*, man (two views). *2*, bat. *3*, rat. *4*, deer. *5*, bird. *6*, salamander. *7*, beetle. *8*, cricket. *9*, snail. *10*, skate.

The structure of a mature sperm of either a vertebrate or an invertebrate varies little from species to species. These "little travelling libraries of genetic information" invariably consist of a head, a midpiece, and a tail. The **head** of a sperm is the condensed nucleus of the spermatid and is covered over its tip by a cap-like membrane called the **acrosome**. This plays an important part in penetration of the egg. The **midpiece** is notable chiefly because it contains mitochondria, sometimes several spirally wound around a central axial filament. The midpiece may be a mere dot or as long or longer than the head, depending on the species. Where the head and midpiece join, there is a pair of **centrioles** similar to those found at the base of any flagellum or cilium. Evidently the function of the midpiece is to furnish the power for the action of the flagellum. In many species of animals the midpiece enters the egg cytoplasm along with the head and contributes one or both of its centrioles which form the division centers of the first cell division of the egg. The **tail** has the same basic flagellar structure in all animals, from sponges to mammals. There is a pair of central **fibrils** surrounded by a circle

Fig. 9–3. Head, midpiece, and tail (in part) of typical mammalian sperm as seen with electron microscope. *A*, side view. *B*, cross sections. *C*, edge view. *(After D. W. Fawcett)*

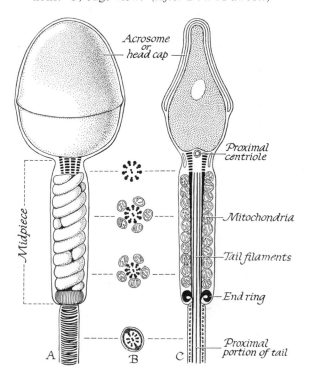

Acrosome
or
head cap

Midpiece

Proximal centriole

Mitochondria

Tail filaments

End ring

Proximal portion of tail

A   B   C

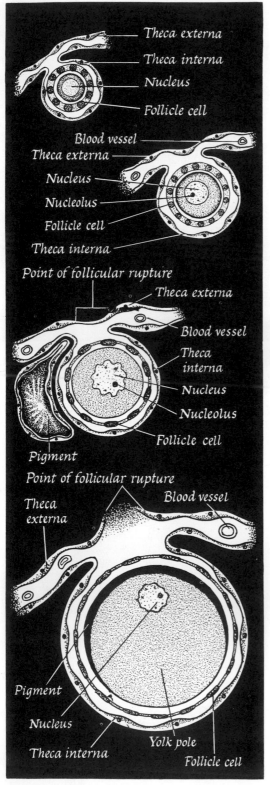

Theca externa
Theca interna
Nucleus
Follicle cell

Blood vessel
Theca externa
Nucleus
Nucleolus
Follicle cell
Theca interna

Point of follicular rupture
Theca externa
Blood vessel
Theca interna
Nucleus
Nucleolus
Follicle cell
Pigment

Point of follicular rupture
Theca externa
Blood vessel
Pigment
Nucleus
Theca interna
Yolk pole
Follicle cell

of nine fibrils, the whole surrounded by a membrane. In some kinds of sperms a beautiful undulating membrane extends the length of the tail. This can readily be seen with a compound microscope in the living sperms of salamanders. To see the two plus nine fibrils a cross section must be viewed with an electron microscope.

Oogenesis and Eggs. Oogenesis, the development of ova, takes place in **ovaries** which, like testes, vary in number, shape, and position according to the kind of animal. In frogs, the two ovaries are hollow sacs each made of a thin double membrane composed of an **external** and an **internal theca.** Between the two thecae are blood vessels, nerves, and developing eggs in different stages. Each egg is surrounded by **follicle cells,** which are important in supplying the egg cytoplasm with yolk. Surrounding the egg cell, between it and the follicle cells, is a yolk or **vitelline membrane.** In mammalian eggs this is a thick conspicuous structure. As a developing frog's egg increases in size, the follicle cells stretch out flat and thin. They remain behind at ovulation, that is, when the egg breaks out of the ovary. In the mammalian egg, on the other hand, a fuzzy coat of follicle cells surrounds the egg even after ovulation. They are not dispersed until fertilization. The smallest, least-developed egg cells are known as **oogonia.** The larger ova undergoing meiosis are called **oocytes.**

During their gradual growth in the ovary, eggs acquire a polarity. The yolk accumulates more densely around one pole of the egg, which is known as the lower or **vegetal pole,** because the old naturalists believed it was primarily vegetative and plantlike in function. The opposite pole of the egg contains the nucleus and much more cytoplasm. This pole floats uppermost and is called the **animal pole.** The follicle cells not only provide yolk but also nucleoproteins, which are absorbed by the ovum and are ready to be built into new chromosomes during the rapid series of mitoses of the cleavage stages.

As the ovum develops in the ovary, the nucleus becomes very large and is commonly

Fig. 9–4. Four stages in the development of a frog's egg. The ova are shown hanging down into the central cavity of the ovary.

192

called a **germinal vesicle.** This is characteristic of egg cells in general and can easily be seen in a starfish egg. The germinal vesicle of a frog's egg that has been removed from the ovary before the first maturation division can be dissected out with finely pointed watchmaker's forceps and is large enough to be clearly visible to the naked eye. The most conspicuous object within the germinal vesicle is one or more nucleoli. Chemical tests reveal that the **nucleolus** is a storage body for RNA and histones, which are small protein molecules otherwise found associated with chromosomal DNA.

The most notable fact about a germinal vesicle is that the chromosomes within it can be observed in the actual process of functioning, that is, producing RNA and protein! These chromosomes have long been called **"lampbrush" chromosomes,** though today "test tube brush" chromosomes would seem a better name. From their sides extends a series of loops which give the chromosome its brushlike appearance. DNAase, which digests DNA, breaks the loops. Hence the central axis of the loops must be DNA.

If radioactively labelled uridine, which is incorporated into RNA but not DNA, is injected into a newt, it will be observed that the tritiated uridine is incorporated into one end, apparently the growing end, of each loop. With time the entire length of the loop will become labelled. Thus it is clear that RNA is being transcribed along the loops. If some tritiated amino acid such as phenylalanine is injected into the salamander, labelling takes place at once along the entire length of the loops, indicating that protein synthesis is occurring. Whether each loop corresponds to a single gene is uncertain. The fact that each pair of loops shows its own pattern of activity strongly suggests that they do represent genetic units. Some loops become large and active only in very small young germinal vesicles. Others become active in very large mature germinal vesicles. The only other place where gene activity can actually be observed is in the giant chromosomes of the salivary glands and certain other tissues of the larvae of flies and other dipteriform insects, to be discussed later. (See page 209.)

Fig. 9–5. Portion of a pair of living lampbrush chromosomes from a frog's egg photographed under a phase contrast microscope. Original magnification 700×. *(Kindness of J. G. Gall)*

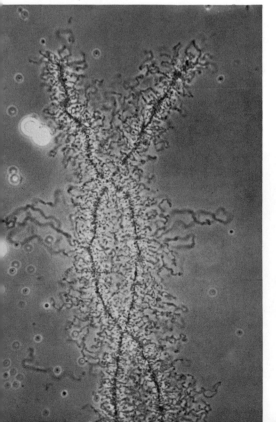

Fig. 9–6. Autoradiograph showing labelling along the entire length of a pair of loops of a lampbrush chromosome from a salamander oocyte after injection with tritiated uridine. Original magnification about 1,000 ×. *(Kindness of J. G. Gall)*

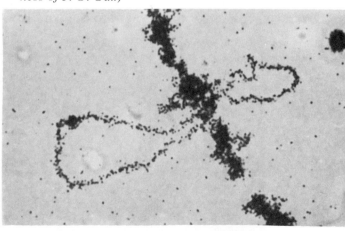

One additional fact about egg structure must be noted. In the cortical or surface layer of cytoplasm, immediately under the vitelline membrane, is a layer of small granules easily visible under a microscope in living and in preserved, sectioned eggs. These **cortical granules** disappear right after fertilization and evidently play an important role in that event.

When the primary oocyte with its giant nucleus, i.e., the germinal vesicle, undergoes the first meiotic division, the division of the cytoplasm is so unequal that the egg seems to be extruding a tiny sphere. This small—often minute—cell is called the **first polar body.** It is, of course, a secondary oocyte, the egg itself being the other secondary oocyte. The first polar body seldom, if ever, divides. The egg undergoes a second meiotic division extruding a **second polar body** containing a single set of chromosomes. The egg, now an **ootid,** also contains a single set of chromosomes.

Eggs of different species differ in the time at which the polar bodies are extruded. In the sea urchin and starfish, both polar bodies are extruded before the egg is ready to be fertilized. In mammals, the first polar body is given off before fertilization. It is not until the sperm touches the egg's surface that the second polar body is given off. In some animals, like snails, neither polar body is given off until after the moment of fertilization.

Eggs differ in two other important respects. The most far-reaching distinction is between the **spirally cleaving, mosaic eggs** of the protostome branch of the animal kingdom, including flatworms, annelids, mollusks, and many others, and the **radially cleaving, regulative eggs** of the deuterostome branch, chiefly echinoderms and vertebrates. This distinction will be discussed more completely in the section on cleavage of eggs. (See Fig. 9–11.)

Eggs also differ in the amount and disposition of yolk. Those in which the yolk is fairly uniformly distributed throughout the cytoplasm, as in the human or starfish egg, are known as **isolecithal** (*isos,* equal, + *lecithos,* yolk). These eggs are all small. Egg cells in which the yolk is concentrated toward one pole (or end), as in frogs and birds, are called **telolecithal** (*telos,* end, + *lecithos,* yolk). Frogs and salamanders have moderately telolecithal eggs; reptiles, birds, and some very primitive egg-laying mammals of Australia, such as the platypus, have extremely telolecithal eggs. In these cases the actual ovum or egg cell is commonly called the yolk of the egg. Only this yolk is formed in the ovary of the bird or reptile. It is a single cell and is the true ovum. The white of the egg and the shell are secreted by the oviduct around the true ovum as it passes to the exterior. This enormous ovum is inert except for a small disk of living cytoplasm containing the nucleus and

Fig. 9–7. Some types of eggs differing in amount and distribution of yolk. The mammal and sea urchin eggs are isolecithal, the frog and bird eggs are telolecithal, and the insect egg is centrolecithal.

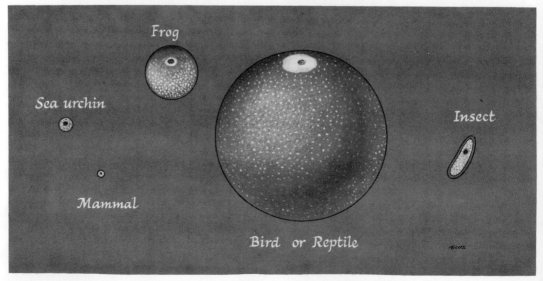

lying on the top of the yolk. The third type of egg is the **centrolecithal** type found in insects and other arthropods. It may be round, oval, or even sausage-shaped, but the living cytoplasm always forms a thin layer over a centrally placed yolk. As will be seen later, the amount of yolk has a profound effect on development.

Ovulation. Ovulation, the process of extrusion of the egg from the ovary, is, in vertebrates at least, under the control of the pituitary gland on the under side of the brain. Frogs and salamanders can be induced to ovulate by implanting pituitary glands or extracts at any time of the year, except, of course, so soon after they have laid their eggs that the ovary has not had time to grow more.

In many animals, especially birds but also various mammals such as deer, ovulation is also controlled by the number of hours of light per day to which the animal has been exposed. In most rodents and in the primates, including man, ovulation follows an internal rhythm, with a four- or five-day cycle in the mouse, a 28-day cycle in the human, and a 32-day cycle in the baboon. In a very few mammals, cats and rabbits, for example, ovulation occurs a short and definite time after the stimulus of mating. In all these cases, the pituitary is believed to be involved, stimulated in some way by light, mating, or internal rhythms. In human beings, when two eggs are ovulated simultaneously, each egg must be fertilized by a different sperm. The resulting twins are called fraternal twins because they are no more closely related than any brothers or sisters born as the results of separate pregnancies. Monozygotic or one-egg twins result when two centers of development appear in the ball of cells derived from a single fertilized egg.

FERTILIZATION

General Facts. Fertilization, the union of egg and sperm to form a single cell known as the **zygote,** is customarily taken as the starting point in the life of the new individual. The location of the egg when fertilized depends largely on the environment in which the adults live. Most, though by no means all, aquatic animals have external fertilization in which both eggs and sperms are simply poured out into the water to meet there. Many species of sharks and other live-bearing fishes are, of course, exceptions. Terrestrial animals such as insects and mammals are forced to have internal fertilization from the simple fact that neither their sperms nor their eggs can live or move on dry land. In reptiles and birds fertilization takes place at or near the upper end of the **oviduct,** before the albumen and shell are secreted around the yolk, the actual ovum. In mammals likewise, the sperms are carried to the upper ends of the oviducts, or **Fallopian tubes** as they are known in human beings, by muscular contractions of the ducts.

There are two major results of fertilization. First, it stimulates the egg to begin its development. It is also true that the egg enables the head of the sperm to undergo development into a nucleus. The second major result of fertilization is the restoration of diploidy, inasmuch as the sperm brings its set of chromosomes into the egg. Diploidy in itself seems to be a source of vigor, but the main advantage of introducing a second set of chromosomes is an evolutionary one, the production of variation, of new kinds of individuals which result from new combinations of the genes. This is one of the main driving forces of evolution, and what sex is really all about.

In addition to the two primary results of fertilization there are a number of lesser ones having to do with the activation of the egg. The most obvious is the almost immediate appearance of a **fertilization membrane** within which the egg is free to rotate. This membrane prevents other sperms from entering the egg. The fertilization membrane also serves to hold together and protect the **blastomeres,** as the first cells into which the egg cleaves are called. In the case of the human egg, where the first polar body is given off before and the second after fertilization, the first polar body lies outside and the second inside the fertilization membrane. The fertilization membrane appears to be formed directly from the vitelline membrane, which tightly surrounded the egg during its ovarian development, by the absorption of water and its collection immediately under the membrane. This lifts the membrane away from the cytoplasm.

Artificial Fertilization. This term refers to the introduction of sperms into the female reproductive tract by mechanical means. It has been used successfully in cases of human sterility. It is a common practice in certain branches of animal husbandry. Pedigreed lambs have been produced in Idaho from sires living on the U.S. Department of Agriculture farms in Beltsville, Maryland. Cows are frequently bred by this method because it saves the expense, trouble, and danger of keeping a bull, and allows wide use of sires that are known to transmit desirable milking qualities to their daughters.

The longevity of functional sperms has been much studied, especially in connection with artificial insemination. If chilled and kept in thermos jars, mammalian sperms can be kept about a week. If kept anaerobic at approximately −70°C in "deep deep-freeze," sperms seem capable of indefinite existence.

Microanatomy of Fertilization. Many of the details of fertilization were first clearly seen in the summer of 1875, which Oscar and Richard Hertwig spent on the shores of the Mediterranean Sea. There they discovered that the eggs of starfish and sea urchins are so transparent that the major events can be seen in the living egg. In these animals the head and midpiece of the sperm enter the cytoplasm of the ovum. The midpiece gives rise to a star-shaped aster, or division center, which soon becomes double. The head of the sperm moves toward the egg nucleus and gradually becomes transformed into a nucleus itself, lying pressed against the egg nucleus.

There is virtually no compelling evidence that animal sperms are attracted toward eggs. Swimming appears to be random. The first visible event in the actual fertilization process is the extrusion of the acrosome into a longer or shorter tubular thread or vesicle which penetrates the jelly around the egg and makes contact with the cytoplasm surface of the ovum. The **acrosome reaction** is almost certainly in response to a glyco-protein, fertilizin, which diffuses from the egg. The response of the egg is the formation of a cytoplasmic fertilization cone which engulfs the head and midpiece of the sperm.

As soon as a sperm has made effective contact with an egg, the cortical granules, which are present in the eggs of most species, disappear. Sometimes they are discharged outside the plasma membrane of the egg cytoplasm so that they lie under the vitelline membrane. This **cortical granule reaction** spreads out very rapidly from the point of sperm contact to

Fig. 9–8. Events within the sea urchin egg immediately following fertilization. After the sperm enters the egg and fuses with its nucleus, mitosis begins.

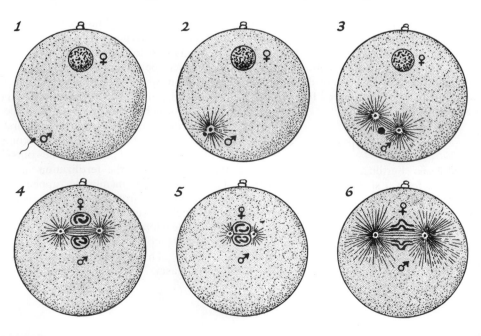

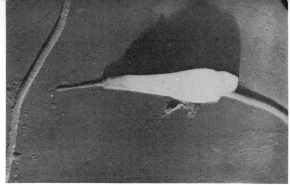

Fig. 9–9. Left: electron micrograph of sperms of Japanese sea urchin, *Hemicentrotus pulcherrimus*. Note the tail, the very short rounded midpiece, and the long cone-shaped head. Right: similar sperm after addition of egg water containing fertilizin. Note the extruded acrosomal filament. Original magnification (left) 18,000 ×, (right) 21,000 ×. *(Kindness of J. C. Dan)*

cover the entire egg. At the same time the vitelline membrane, from this time on commonly called the fertilization membrane, becomes elevated away from the egg (or perhaps the egg shrinks a bit) so that the egg is now free to turn within it. Elevation of the fertilization membrane and freedom of rotation of the egg are the signs that a frog's egg has been fertilized. In the eggs of many species, frogs, ascidians, etc., there are extensive movements of the cytoplasm and its pigments after fertilization.

Physiology and Biochemistry of Fertilization.
Despite nearly a century of hard work in many marine laboratories since that summer when the Hertwigs discovered what favorable material for research echinoderm eggs are, we still cannot answer Jacques Loeb's question—what does fertilization do to an egg which breaks the block to cleavage and subsequent development? We do not know the nature of the block. Nor do we know the similarity or dissimilarity be-

tween the stimulus of fertilization and the normal stimulus for ordinary cell division. There are at least two main possibilities. Entrance of the sperm might somehow inactivate or remove an inhibitor. Or it might trigger the activity of some enzyme or co-factor or even add a factor essential in minute amounts.

In addition to the elevation of the fertilization membrane and the disintegration of the cortical granules, three other events are known to occur very soon after fertilization. The **permeability** of the eggs changes. The egg becomes impermeable to other sperms but much more permeable to certain ions. Potassium and calcium exchange between the egg cytoplasm and the surrounding water increases about 15-fold. Radioactive phosphorus, P^{32}, is taken up by the egg over 100 times faster.

In some species the rate of **respiration** of the egg greatly increases immediately after fertilization. This is true of sea urchin eggs and was at first supposed to be the key aspect of the

Fig. 9–10. Electron micrographs of successive stages in the actual entrance of a holothurian sperm into the egg. Total time, 5 minutes. Note the small round head of the sperm and the dot-shaped midpiece still visible within the fertilization cone in *d*. *(Kindness of A. L. and L. H. Colwin)*

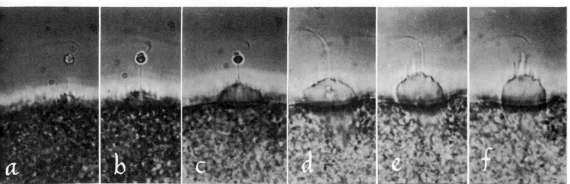

activation of fertilization. Then it was discovered that in some species, such as *Chaetopterus,* a marine annelid, and in various mollusks, the rate of respiration falls after fertilization. Worse still, if sea urchin eggs are fertilized immediately after they are shed and while they are still healthy, they show no appreciable change in respiration. It was once thought that unfertilized eggs respired through a non-cytochrome system. But this too has been shown to be untrue as a generalization.

Thirdly, there is a marked rise in **protein synthesis** following fertilization. This can be demonstrated by various methods such as measuring the rapid increase in uptake of labelled amino acids. It would be logical to suppose that immediately after fertilization the zygote nucleus begins to pour out messenger RNA into the cytoplasm. However, enucleated egg fragments can be stimulated to develop parthenogenetically without any nucleus whatever. They never develop beyond a ball of cells, but they form lots of new protein! Moreover, mRNA can be extracted by the usual methods from unfertilized eggs. Transfer RNA and ribosomes are also present in unfertilized eggs, along with amino acids.

Since all the protein-forming machinery is already present before fertilization, the possibility exists that one or more of the parts of this apparatus are present in inactive form. This hypothesis has been tested by several people in different laboratories and notably by Alberto Monroy at the University of Palermo. He measured the incorporation of radioactively labelled amino acids into proteins, *in vitro,* with a mixture of ribosomes from unfertilized eggs and mRNA from adult liver. The result was invariably negative. No protein formation took place. However, with ribosomes from liver and mRNA from unfertilized eggs, protein synthesis did occur. This clearly indicates that the ribosomes of unfertilized eggs are, somehow, inactivated or masked. There is some evidence from treating ribosomes from unfertilized eggs with proteinases that they can be rendered active. This would indicate that before fertilization the ribosomes are covered with an insulating coat of protein. This theory is supported by the fact that activity of proteolytic enzymes increases after fertilization. If the theory is

correct, a question to be answered is: how does the sperm release the activity of the ribosomes?

Many investigators have thought that **parthenogenesis,** the development of an egg without fertilization, would furnish the clue to the mechanism of activation, i.e., would reveal how fertilization removes the block to development. Parthenogenesis was first extensively studied by Jacques Loeb and others years ago at the laboratory at Woods Hole on Cape Cod. They and their successors have found that a large variety of procedures will stimulate unfertilized eggs to develop—weak organic acids such as butyric acid, temperature shock by exposure to either heat or cold, treatment with various fat solvents such as ether, alcohol, or benzene, various osmotic changes which can be produced by sugar or urea, ultraviolet light, the prick of a needle (especially if previously dipped in blood plasma), and many other agents. Among the most interesting and recent experiments are those of John Shaver who showed that injection of the unfertilized egg with small amounts of the granular, presumably mitochondrial and ribosomal, fraction obtained by centrifuging homogenated adult tissue will produce parthenogenesis, while the clear supernatant fluid will not. The possible relation of these experiments to those of Monroy is evident. The trick in all these experiments is to have the concentrations or dosage and the timing precisely right.

Artificial parthenogenesis has been successfully performed on many animals, including sea urchins, marine annelids, frogs, and rabbits. The new animals become normal-looking adults. Natural parthenogenesis has long been known in rotifers, certain small crustaceans, aphids (where it was discovered in the 18th century), and in honeybees where it gives rise to males. But here again the actual mechanism is unknown.

So many different procedures will result in artificial parthenogenesis that one can only conclude that an egg is set up to begin cleavage and embryo formation much as a muscle cell is set up to contract. A stimulus can elicit only the response of which the cell is capable. So far, the study of various possible stimuli has not furnished the clue to the old problem of how the sperm breaks the block to development.

CLEAVAGE OF THE ZYGOTE

Cleavage is the name given to the series of cell divisions which divide the fertilized ovum, or zygote, into successively smaller and smaller cells until a hollow ball called the **blastula** is formed. The chromosomes separate by ordinary mitosis, so that each new cell is diploid. The cell divisions follow each other rapidly; hence cleavage must be a period of rapid synthesis of nucleic acids and proteins into new chromosomes and new protoplasm generally.

Anatomically, depending on the amount of yolk, cleavage differs markedly in different kinds of animals. In eggs with little yolk, cleavage is total, or **holoblastic,** and completely divides the egg successively into two, four, eight, sixteen, etc., separate cells. Isolecithal eggs, such as those of echinoderms and mammals, have this type of cleavage. So also do the moderately telolecithal eggs of frogs. In the extremely telolecithal eggs found in reptiles and birds, where there is only a tiny disk of protoplasm on top of an enormous yolk, cleavage does not divide the entire ovum into separate cells. Cleavage here involves only a thin disk on top of the egg. This type of cleavage is termed partial or **meroblastic** cleavage (*meros,* part).

In mammals, cleavage takes place as the egg passes down the oviduct. This requires about 4½ or 5 days in all mammals regardless of size. On the fifth day, whether in mice or women, the egg is a hollow blastula, called the blastocyst in mammals, which enters the uterus and becomes more or less deeply implanted on the uterine lining.

Cleavage differs in the two main branches of the animal kingdom. In the deuterostomes, to which echinoderms and vertebrates belong, cleavage is **radial** and **indeterminate.** It is called indeterminate because there is only a very general relation between the position of any particular cell formed during cleavage and the specific tissues it will form in the embryo.

In contrast, in the protostomes, well illustrated by marine annelids and mollusks, the first two cleavages result in four equal cells, but the third time the cells divide they each give off a small cell in a clockwise direction, as seen from above. The large cells later give off a second quartet of cells, this time in

Fig. 9 – 11. Cleavage of the sea urchin egg at 23°C. Note the appearance of the fertilization membrane. *(Kindness of E. B. Harvey)*

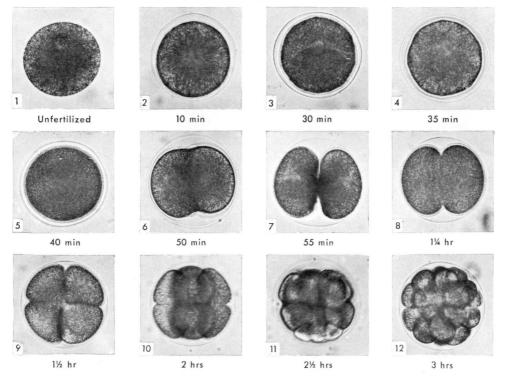

1 Unfertilized	2 10 min
3 30 min	4 35 min
5 40 min	6 50 min
7 55 min	8 1¼ hr
9 1½ hr	10 2 hrs
11 2½ hrs	12 3 hrs

a counterclockwise direction. At about the same time the first quartet of small cells divides in a spiral direction. In this way an elaborate and extremely precise design of cells is produced which is exactly the same in every egg, and in which the ultimate destiny of every cell can be precisely foretold. Consequently, protosome cleavage is termed **spiral** and **determinate**. Both types of cleavage are illustrated in the drawing.

Fig. 9–12. Cleavage of the zygote. *1* and *2*, the first two cell divisions, similar in both spiral and radial cleavage eggs. *3* and *4*, subsequent divisions in spiral cleavage. Note the precisely patterned cap of small cells formed, beginning with the third cell division, on top of four large vegetal pole cells. *5* and *6*, subsequent divisions in radial and irregular cleavage. Views looking down on the animal pole.

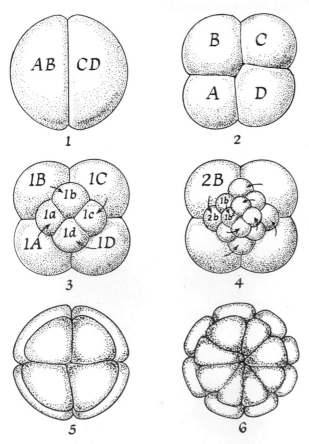

THE PROBLEM OF DIFFERENTIATION

Possible Role of the Nucleus. The first theory about embryonic differentiation led to a startling paradox from which we have not yet entirely escaped. It is the theory of differential segregation of genes according to the structures they will cause to develop. This was proposed by August Weismann, one of the originators of the germplasm theory. He proposed that during cleavage the ovum was not only subdivided into many small cells but that the hereditary factors—we would say genes—for the different parts of the body were sorted out into different cells. In the end, certain cells would contain only genes for the various parts of the right arm or only genes for skin and this was the reason certain cells developed into arms or skin.

Theodor Boveri, a very gifted experimenter, discovered that in the cleavage of the egg of the nematode *Ascaris*, differential segregation of chromosomes actually does take place as far as the germ cells are concerned. At the first cleavage one cell retains a full complement of chromosomes, the other discards some. This happens again at the second cleavage and continues through the fourth so that in the 16-cell stage only one cell has all its chromosomes. The other 15 have lost something. The one gives rise to all the germ cells, eggs or sperms, in the future adult; the 15 differentiate into the rest of the body. This is segregation of a very limited sort but it is nonetheless differential chromosomal segregation during cleavage.

Other investigators found that if you separate the first two **blastomeres** (as the cells in a cleaving egg are called) of the egg of a protostome which has spiral, determinate cleavage, two half-embryos develop. Each of the first four cells, if separated, form quarter-embryos. This result holds also for ctenophore and ascidian eggs. This type of development is commonly called **mosaic** cleavage. It seemed to support Weismann's differential chromosomal segregation theory.

But at about this point in the argument a speculative zoologist, Hans Driesch, showed that if you separate the first two cells of a starfish egg, as by shaking them in calcium-free sea water, each cell will form a whole embryo. In his flamboyant phrase, each cell is an "harmonic equipotential system." His experiment certainly argues against the idea that nuclei become different from each other in genetic content during cleavage so that all the genes for the left half of the body get into the left of the first two blastomeres, and the genes for the right half into the right blastomere. Hans Driesch himself became so excited by his experiment and its results that he left his laboratory forever and became a philosopher. He proposed that the development of an embryo is due to an "entelechy," which is something like Henri Bergson's vital force and which "carries its purpose within itself." No mechanical or truly scientific explanation of embryonic development is possible, he claimed. After all, one cannot cut a typewriter or other machine in half and expect each half to behave as an harmonic equipotential system and regulate into two perfect, though small, typewriters.

Other investigators continued to explore developmental phenomena. Hans Spemann found that you could produce two embryos from a single salamander's egg by carefully constricting one in the blastula stage with a baby's hair. This, of course, confirms Driesch's experiment on another deuterostome. Both results make it impossible to believe that all the genes for one side of an animal, and only for that side, get into one of the first two cells.

Careful studies of mitotic figures in the cells of many different tissues in many species of adult animals made it abundantly clear that all cells of an animal have a full complement of chromosomes. In addition the work of E. Pflüger demonstrated that the nuclei of at least the early cleavage stages are interchangeable. He squeezed cleaving frog's eggs between glass plates until the eggs were much flattened. In this way nuclei which would normally come to lie in the upper or animal hemisphere and produce nervous tissue are forced to lie in the lower vegetal hemisphere, and vice versa. With release of pressure the eggs resume their usual shape and normal embryos result, even though nuclei that would otherwise have been in nervous tissue are now in gut, and the other way around.

Thus echinoderm and vertebrate eggs are called **regulative** in contrast to the determinate or mosaic eggs of animals like the mollusks and ascidians. All these experiments seem to show beyond doubt that in regulative eggs differentiation cannot be due to the nuclei since all nuclei have the same sets of chromosomes and all of them have the capability of servicing cells of any type.

Possible Role of Cytoplasm. The causes of differentiation would thus seem certain to be in the cytoplasm. The cytoplasm of uncleaved eggs commonly shows its heterogenous character by differences in pigmentation and cytoplasmic constituents in different regions of the ovum. Perhaps these cytoplasmic substances are organ-forming, either directly or in some

Fig. 9–13. Method of producing identical twins by constricting a single salamander egg in the blastula stage.

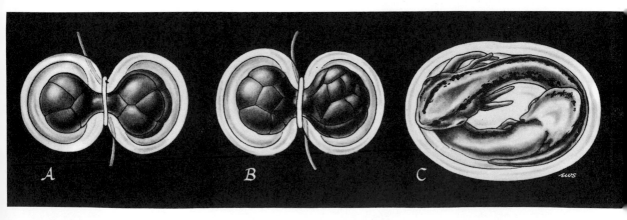

White half

White half
Recentrifuged

Clear quarter

Mitochondrial
quarter

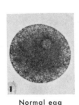

Oil

Clear layer (Nucleus)

Mitochondria

Yolk

Pigment

Normal egg   Partly stratified   Fully stratified

Fig. 9–14. Separation of the sea urchin egg into four quarters by centrifugation. Note that the cytoplasm is very different in each quarter. *(Kindness of E. B. Harvey)*

Red half

Red half
Recentrifuged

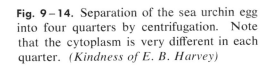

Yolk quarter

Pigment quarter

roundabout way by influencing the nuclei. To test such an hypothesis eggs can be centrifuged. If this is done in a solution of approximately the same density as the eggs, the eggs will be gradually pulled apart. At the same time the lighter components of the cytoplasm will move to the upper (centripetal) pole of the egg and the heavier to the lower (centrifugal) pole. By repeating this process with each of the separated halves of the egg, sea urchin eggs can be neatly separated into four quarters. Each quarter can be fertilized and thus tested for developmental potentialities.

The lightest, uppermost quarter contains mostly a clear fluid plus a few oil droplets, together with the egg nucleus. The second is a mitochondrial quarter which contains all, or at least all the detectable, mitochondria. The third and fourth are respectively a yolk-filled quarter and a pigment quarter. All four quarters upon fertilization will develop into ciliated swimming larvae, although, of course, all but those derived from the clear quarters are haploid. More remarkable, the clear quarters, which lack mitochondria, yolk, pigment, and whatever other substances are localized in the other three quarters, develop into approximately normal larvae with skeleton, gut, and pigment spots. The yolk quarters also form larvae with skeleton, gut, and pigment, but with a less normal

body shape. Other centrifugation experiments on the eggs of this and other species of echinoderms make it quite certain that the visible substances in the egg of sea urchins are not directly causal in differentiation.

Thus we are left with the paradoxical conclusion that neither the nuclei nor the cytoplasm is responsible for initiating differentiation! Yet differentiation obviously does occur and chromosomes can be shown to control the development of the specific traits of an animal.

Modern Answers. Several avenues of escape from this developmental dilemma are open. Perhaps sea urchin eggs are atypical and their behavior can be explained only after more is learned about the problem from the eggs of other animals. As long ago as 1909 Theodor Boveri showed that in *Ascaris* whether or not chromosome material is lost during any particular cleavage depends on the cytoplasm in which the nuclei come to lie. In 1914 Robert Hegner was able to demonstrate, in the elongated eggs of beetles, that removal of the tiny area of cytoplasm in which the germ cells normally develop, if done before any nuclei had reached that region, results in complete lack of germ cells. Then in a long series of largely neglected investigations, extending from 1917 to 1931, E. G. Conklin showed in the ascidian egg that abnormalities can be produced by centrifuging the cytoplasm to abnormal positions in the eggs, provided the centrifugal force is strong enough and applied at the right time. Conklin's line of work is said to be now carried forward by T. C. Tung in mainland China. It may turn out after all that there are substances in the cytoplasm which derepress or activate specific genes.

Recent attacks on two of these old problems have yielded important results. Markert and others have reinvestigated the puzzle of mosaic or determinate as contrasted with regulative development using new biochemical techniques. Actinomycin-D will block the transcription of RNA from DNA, puromycin will block protein synthesis, analogs of amino acids prevent the synthesis of proper proteins. If development is dependent on new RNA, then actinomycin will block that development and similarly for proteins with puromycin. Actinomycin blocks the development of sea urchin eggs in the blastula stage but ascidian eggs develop into normal tadpoles. However, they do not metamorphose. Hence it is clear that a difference, perhaps *the* difference, between them is that the regulative sea urchin egg begins making new RNA very early while the determinate ascidian egg does not make new RNA until it gets to metamorphosis. It begins as a zygote competely programmed for tadpole development and if the egg is divided into two separate cells, there is no ability to synthesize new instructions. Puromycin blocks the eggs of both types in the first two or three cleavages. Thus both are dependent on new proteins almost from the start.

The difference between determinate and regulative eggs thus appears to be that regulative eggs can make new RNA almost from the beginning of their development while determinate eggs cannot, or at least do not, until the end of larval life. This theory is substantiated by the difference in the time of first appearance of nucleoli in the two types of eggs. Nucleoli are associated with the formation of both ribosomal and transfer RNA. Hence it is not surprising to find that nucleoli appear during the blastula stage in echinoderms but are not present in the ascidian tadpoles until metamorphosis. Why all this should be, we do not know.

Very recently Briggs and King and others here and abroad have been reinvestigating the problem of whether or not the nuclei become different during cleavage or are interchangeable, which Pflüger had investigated in 1884 by squeezing frog eggs between glass plates. The new method, a very difficult one, is to transplant nuclei from various parts of frog embryos and even tadpoles in different stages of development into activated but enucleated uncleaved eggs. With proper care the host eggs with foreign nuclei will develop in as many as 80 per cent of the cases. The advantage of the new method is that it allows the testing of nuclei from much more differentiated stages than did the old Pflüger technique. The first results of the new method quickly confirmed Pflüger's conclusion that all the early cleavage nuclei are interchangeable and hence totipotent. However, when older and older donors are used, the resulting embryos show more and more abnormalities. Nuclei taken from such maldeveloping embryos and retransplanted into second and third generations of enucleated eggs have given clones of embryos showing similar abnormal development. The actual meaning of this is very puzzling because quite a few cases have been found where nuclei from older embryos gave entirely normal development. Furthermore, work by Gurdon at Oxford with the African toad *Xenopus* has given large numbers of normal tadpoles from nuclei from differentiated epithelial cells of the tadpole intestine.

There are really two related but different questions here. One is the theory proposed by Weismann that nuclei become different during the process of cleavage itself and that these differences then result in cellular differentiation. The other is the theory that cytoplasmic influences impose differences on the nuclei, perhaps by masking some of the genes, and that once a group of genes has been turned off, so to speak, the nuclei concerned are permanently changed. In both theories the nuclei lose their totipotency during cleavage and come to be able to produce only one kind of cell—muscle, intestinal, or other. Obviously the final word has not been said but present evidence strongly suggests that the conclusion of T. H. Morgan written in 1897 for early cleavage can be extended to all cell divisions as well: "The simplest and most obvious conclusion . . . is that the sequence of nuclear division during the early cleavage-period has no relation to the subsequent formation of the embryo, and that at this time the nuclei are all equivalent."

GASTRULATION AND THE GERM LAYERS

Gastrulation is the process that converts a ball of cells, the blastula, into an embryo. After fertilization, it is the most crucial stage in development. A gastrula stage occurs in most metazoans, but the following account will deal only with echinoderms and vertebrates. The details of gastrulation are very different in different kinds of animals, although the basic process is similar in all, as are the results.

After gastrulation three germ layers can be distinguished. The **ectoderm** covers the embryo externally and will form the external layers of the skin and skin derivatives like hair, hoofs, and nails, plus the entire nervous system. The **endoderm** forms the gut and will become the epithelial lining of the entire alimentary canal and also of all the structures derived from the gut in the course of development, such as the lungs, liver, and pancreas. The **mesoderm** lies between ectoderm and endoderm and is itself split into two layers. The **parietal** or **somatic layer** presses against the ectoderm. The **visceral** or **splanchnic layer** of mesoderm presses against the endoderm of the gut. The cavity between parietal and visceral mesoderm is the **coelom**. From the mesoderm are formed muscle, skele-

Fig. 9–15. Three stages in gastrulation in echinoderm, frog, bird, and mammal.

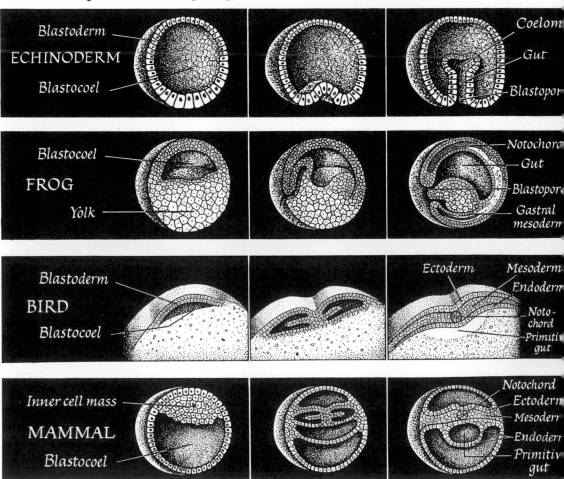

ton, vascular system, and the connective tissues which hold the body together.

In the eggs of starfish and sea urchins, where there is very little yolk, gastrulation begins with the inpocketing of the cells around the lower or vegetal pole. It looks as though a thumb had pushed in one side of an old hollow rubber ball. The cavity of the blastula, i.e., the **blastocoel,** is slowly obliterated. The new cavity formed (after the hypothetical thumb is removed) is the primitive gut or enteron and is therefore called the **archenteron** (*archaios,* ancient, + *enteron,* gut). The opening into the archenteron is called the **blastopore.** The archenteron is the origin of the endoderm. The mesoderm is formed as a pair of hollow buds from the inner end of the archenteron.

In a frog's egg there is so much yolk that the cavity of the blastula is very small, and consequently gastrulation of the type just described is impossible. The egg "cheats," as it were. The archenteron pushes into the blastula cavity from one side. Cells move down from the animal hemisphere and roll in over the dorsal lip or edge of the blastopore to add themselves to the wall of the archenteron.

In the telolecithal eggs of reptiles and birds, where the yolk is enormous, gastrulation takes place by the inpushing of cells along a line called the **primitive streak.** At the end of gastrulation the embryo consists of three layers of cells, a layer of endoderm against the yolk, a layer of mesoderm on top of it, and a layer of ectoderm over the mesoderm. The three are commonly adherent along the **notochord,** which lies in the mesoderm and is the forerunner of the backbone.

In mammals gastrulation occurs in the same way as in birds and reptiles, clearly an inheritance from our reptilian ancestors. The blastula of placental mammals, such as man, is a hollow sphere called the blastocyst, with a solid mass of cells at one pole. Two cavities form in this mass, and in the plate of cells separating the two cavities the primitive streak is formed and gastrulation takes place. The upper cavity becomes the **amnion.** A third cavity, the **primitive gut,** pushes into the lower cavity which is obliterated.

Gastrulation in echinoderms and in three vertebrates is illustrated in Figure 9 – 15.

NEURULATION

Neurulation is the process by which the primitive nervous system is formed. Immediately after gastrulation a broad strip of ectoderm overlying the notochord and the mesoderm adjacent to it begins to thicken. This strip of ectoderm, the **neural plate,** forms the brain and spinal cord, and in a most remarkable way. The edges roll up to form a groove, and by the meeting and fusion of the edges of the groove a tube is formed. The anterior part of this tube enlarges into the brain, and the posterior part becomes the spinal cord.

The motor (efferent) nerves grow out from the brain and the spinal cord and make connections with their appropriate muscles and glands. This remarkable fact was deduced from the study of sectioned embryos by two rather isolated investigators, Santiago Ramon y Cajal in Spain and Wilhelm His in Switzerland. However, the scientific world continued to hold to the prevailing theory that nerves are formed by the coalescence of long chains of cells until Ross G. Harrison discovered that cells can be grown outside the animal's body and was able to demonstrate the outgrowth of nerve fibers from isolated pieces of embryonic spinal cord. Harrison's famous experiment at Johns Hopkins was the beginning of tissue culture *in vitro* as a usable technique.

Along the edges of the neural folds is a narrow strip of tissue called **neural crest.** The cells of the neural crest separate from both the surface ectoderm and the neural folds as they are closing, and migrate down over each side of the body between the ectoderm and the underlying mesoderm. The neural crest cells develop into at least four different important tissues; although this has been hard for anatomists and embryologists to believe, it has been abundantly proved by microsurgical studies in which parts of the neural crest have been removed and transplanted to other sites in the embryo. The neural crest cells form the dorsal sensory ganglia and hence the sensory (afferent) nerves to both brain and spinal cord. They become the pigment cells, both the melanocytes of a fish or a frog and the pigment-forming cells in the feathers of birds and the hair of mammals.

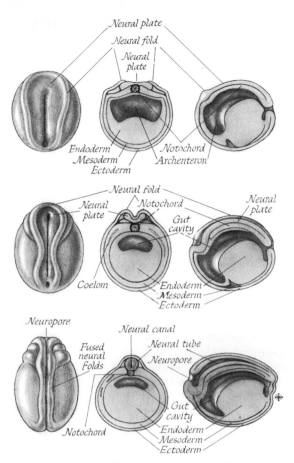

Neural plate

Neural fold

Neural plate

Endoderm
Mesoderm
Ectoderm

Notochord
Archenteron

Neural fold

Neural plate

Notochord

Gut cavity

Neural plate

Coelom

Endoderm
Mesoderm
Ectoderm

Neuropore

Neural canal

Fused neural folds

Neural tube

Neuropore

Gut cavity

Notochord

Endoderm
Mesoderm
Ectoderm

Fig. 9–16. Three stages of neurulation in a frog embryo. Top strip: very early neurula. Middle strip: middle neurula. Bottom strip: late neurula with neural tube almost completely closed. In each strip, the left drawing shows the whole embryo in dorsal view; center, the anterior half of the embryo cut transversely; right, the right half of the embryo cut in the median plane. Note that the blastopore is shown closed in the right drawing of the late neurula; the point at which the anal opening will break through is marked by an asterisk. *(After Balinsky)*

They form the cartilage and bone of the so-called visceral skeleton which comprises the jaws and gill arch skeleton of fishes and the jaws and hyoid bones of higher vertebrates. They form the medulla of the suprarenal (adrenal) gland and related endocrine structures. In connection with the nerves, some of the neural crest cells become Schwann cells which line up along the nerve fibers and, by winding around them, myelinate them, i.e., cover them with a special kind of protective sheath. This behavior may account for the old belief that nerves were formed from chains of cells.

EMBRYONIC INDUCTION

Investigators seeking the forces that produce gastrulation have made little progress, but important facts have been learned about the causes of differentiation, which begins during gastrulation. The pioneer work was carried out on amphibian embryos by Warren Lewis in Baltimore and Hans Spemann in Freiburg. Briefly, they found that the dorsal lip of the blastopore is in some unknown way the "**organizer**," or better, the **evocator**, which calls forth the development of an embryo. If an early blastula is constricted with a fine hair into two separate halves, two embryos, identical twins, form, as already noted, but only if the constriction cuts through the part of the blastula that will form the dorsal lip of the blastopore. If the blastula is so constricted that one half gets all the dorsal lip material, that half, and that half only, will form an embryo. The other half remains a mere ball of cells.

Even more dramatic, if the dorsal lip is cut out and implanted in another embryo, as by injecting it into the cavity of the blastula with a fine pipette, the transplanted dorsal lip will be pushed down against the ventral belly wall during gastrulation and will there induce or evocate a secondary embryo. (See Fig. 9–17.) Specifically, the cells which lie over the notochord and its adjacent mesoderm become induced to form neural plate. These inducing tissues, often termed **chordamesoderm,** are found as the dorsal lip of the blastopore in the early stages of gastrulation. In birds and mammals, where gastrulation occurs along the primitive streak which thus corresponds to the blastopore, the anterior end of the streak corresponds to the dorsal lip. It is a thickened knot of cells called **Hensen's node.** No one was surprised when it was discovered that Hensen's node is the essential evocator or organizer of the bird and mammalian embryo.

The dorsal lip is the primary evocator without which no embryo whatsoever forms. There are also **secondary evocators.** For example, the

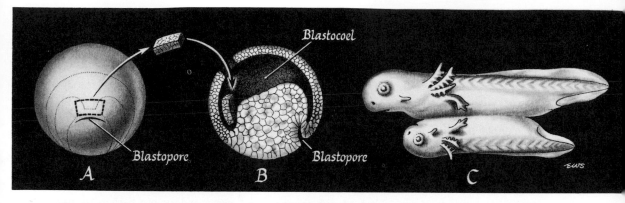

Fig. 9–17. Evocator action of the dorsal lip of the blastopore. Implantation of the dorsal lip of one embryo into another embryo results in the formation of a secondary embryo.

eye is formed as an outgrowth from the brain. Where this outgrowing **optic vesicle,** as it is called, comes into contact with the skin of the embryonic face, it evokes a lens to form in the embryonic facial ectoderm. If the optic vesicle is removed before it touches the skin, in most species of animals, no lens forms. The optic vesicle is therefore a secondary evocator.

How does the evocator evocate? Does the evocator have to be living? The answer to the second question is no. Subsequent work has shown that a wide variety of things can be soaked up with agar jelly, imbedded into a blastula, and there evocate a secondary embryo. These include extracts of adult brain and other tissues and various pure chemicals, especially phenanthrenes closely related to both the sex hormones and adrenal cortical hormones as well as to a number of cancer-inducing agents. But hypotonic salt solution will also cause ectoderm explanted into a glass dish to form neural tissue. The situation is comparable to that in fertilization and artificial parthenogenesis. So many agents will produce the effect that all one can say is that, as with muscular contraction, many agents can trigger the reaction.

Recent experiments suggest that diffusible chemical substances of some kind normally play the role of evocators. This approach has been pioneered by Clifford Grobstein who separated the inducing tissue from the inducible tissue by cellulose ester membranes of different thickness and porosity. For example, kidney tubules are induced in mesoderm by a certain region of adjacent neural tube. If the pores are small enough, about 0.1 μ in diameter, induction takes place though cytoplasmic contact between inducing and responding tissue is excluded. Twitty and Niu have shown that tissues grown *in vitro* exude inducing molecules into the medium. The work of Yamada in Japan strongly suggests that these inducer substances are proteins rather than RNA which other experiments seem to suggest.

Possible Biochemical Mechanisms. It will be recalled (Fig. 8–22) that the functional genetic unit consists of an operator gene and one or more structural genes which the operator controls. The structural genes are the templates for the formation of messenger RNA. Also, the operator gene itself is under the control of a regulator gene which keeps the operator gene repressed by a repressor substance, probably a protein. According to this Jacob and Monod model of gene action and its control, genes become activated, i.e., derepressed, by specific derepressor or, in other words, inducer substances. These may be proteins or other things that combine with or otherwise counteract the repressor substance. If embryonic inducers act in this way, they are acting almost at the gene level.

It is also possible that embryonic inducers act at the level of proteins by what is called **end product feedback inhibition.** There are a number of well-worked-out cases in microorganisms where the entire biosynthetic pathway is known from substance A to B to C to D to E, each step controlled by its own enzyme.

In such cases it has been found that if the end product E is supplied to the medium in which the organisms are growing, the cells no longer form E. Further investigation has revealed that it is not the final step from D to E that is blocked by the presence of excess E but that the enzyme governing the first step, A to B, is blocked. Here clearly is another mechanism that could function in induction of embryonic differentiation. Does it?

Meryl Rose, an investigator with wide experience with animals from different phyla, has proposed that as each tissue is differentiated it forms and exudes some kind of substance which inhibits the differentiation of additional cells of the same kind—a "don't-make-any-more-of-me" substance. Such a substance would explain the limitation of a given tissue though it does not explain how the genes controlling the next tissue to differentiate become derepressed (activated).

Many cases are well known of inhibition of differentiation and cases where it is clear that the condition which exists not only in the embryo but in the adult requires the continual action of some inhibitory factor or factors. The case of the pigmented layer of the salamander eye which will dedifferentiate unless the retina is present has already been cited (page 189). In many species of tubiculous polychaetes a circle of gills extends out from the top of the tube in which the worm lives. (See Fig. 14–14.) The last gill on one side of the animal is in the form of a club-shaped operculum which plugs the open end of the tube when the worm retreats into it. If this operculum is cut off, the corresponding gill on the opposite side of the body becomes changed in a profound metamorphosis involving cell death, mitosis, and differentiation in entirely new directions, until it is transformed into a new operculum. Meanwhile the severed end of the former operculum stalk slowly regenerates into a gill.

A similar kind of relationship is seen in the fiddler crab where there is a fantastic difference in size between the two big claws. If the larger of the two chelipeds is removed, then in the following molts the smaller remaining limb develops to a huge size while the position of the original large claw is occupied by a very small one. In all such cases it is easy to believe that the original structure gave off some kind of inhibitory material which prevented the development of a similar structure on the opposite side of the body. However, there is no proof. It is also supposed by some investigators that such cases of apparent inhibition are due to the exhaustion of an essential nutrient by the dominant region.

It is known that the nervous system is essential for regeneration in earthworms and salamanders and so in some unsuspected way the nervous system may be involved.

Active induction by an evocator, either primary or secondary, can perhaps be explained in terms of derepression at gene level. This does not exclude the possibility of inhibitory end product feedback. Both processes may play a part in the total phenomenon of differentiation.

Visible Gene Activation. It has been known for some time that the chromosomes in the nuclei of the cells of the salivary glands and various other tissues of the larvae of flies, gnats, and other dipteriform insects are giant-sized and banded. Moreover, the bands correspond to specific gene loci. (See Fig. 8–12.) Several years ago W. Beerman discovered that various bands showed puffs or swellings, that the bands that puffed were always the same ones, and that they always did so in a definite sequence during the development of the larva. More than that, he was able to cross two species of gnats (Chironomus). One species forms special granules in certain cells of the gland near its duct; the other does not. Conventional cross-breeding experiments showed that the ability to secrete these granules in the cells is inherited as a simple Mendelian dominant and that the gene responsible is located adjacent to the kinetochore. Cytological studies showed that in the cells which had these granules—and only in those cells—there is a conspicuous puff adjacent to the kinetochore. Most beautiful of all, Beerman then showed that in heterozygous individuals only the chromosome carrying the dominant allele shows a puff in that locus. What more convincing evidence could there be that puffing represents gene activity?

More convincing evidence has been presented by U. Clever. Also using Chironomus, Clever showed that injections of the insect

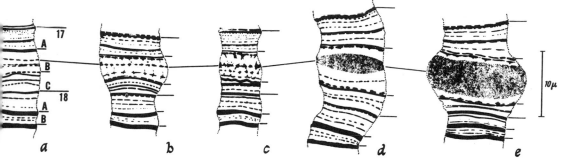

Fig. 9 – 18. Various degrees of puffing of a particular band in a chromosome of a salivary gland cell in the gnat, *Chironomus.* *a, b,* and *c,* from untreated larvae. *d* and *e,* from hormone-injected larvae. *(From Clever in Locke, ed.,* Cytodifferentiation and Macromolecular Synthesis, *Academic Press)*

steroid hormone ecdysone into the larva will result in pupation much sooner than would otherwise occur. Normal pupation in this gnat is preceded by some very characteristic puffs in specific chromosomes. The same puffs appear within two hours after ecdysone injection, and a long time before any other signs of impending metamorphosis can be detected. Histochemical

Fig. 9 – 19. A gene in action. Photo of salivary gland chromosomes of *Chironomus,* a gnat, to show what a puffed ring actually looks like. The puffed, i.e., active, band appears as a balloonlike structure on each side of the lower chromosome. Stained with toluidine blue. *(Kindness of H. Laufer)*

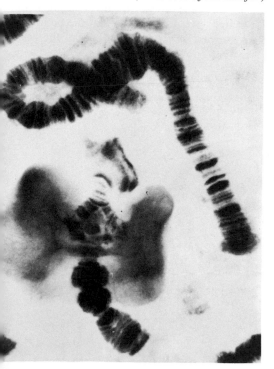

stains and radioactive labelling reveal that the puffs are, sites of RNA and protein synthesis. Hence the puffs apparently correspond to the loops of the lampbrush chromosomes found in the germinal vesicles of oocytes. Precisely what this newly formed material does has not been established, but that steroid hormones act directly at the gene level has been confirmed by experiments on mammals and will be discussed in the chapter on endocrine systems.

Histones and Differentiation. Histones are basic proteins of relatively small molecular weight found only in the nuclei of higher organisms in close association with the chromosomes. Indeed about 30 per cent of the dry weight of such a nucleus is histone. Over 20 years ago Edgar Stedman of the University of Edinburgh proposed that histones are gene inhibitors on the grounds (1) that since all cells contained the same chromosomes yet differ from each other, there must be something which masks the inappropriate genes in each kind of cell, and (2) that histones were found in nuclei and differed somewhat from one cell type to another. Recent work by James Bonner in California and others there and elsewhere have shown that DNA closely complexed with histones does not yield RNA. If the histone and DNA are separated, then RNA synthesis occurs, only to cease when the two are put back together again. The nucleus also contains characteristic acid proteins as well as the basic histones. One suggestion is that the acid nucleoproteins somehow reverse the inhibitory action of the histones. Obviously much remains to be learned about histones and how they themselves are controlled.

BUILDING THE EMBRYO

Evocation of neural tissue is the beginning, but only part of the beginning, of embryogenesis. Cells not only become nerve cells but become organized into a specific structure. When pure evocation takes place in a glass dish it results merely in disorganized masses of nerve cells. The process by which these tissues are organized into an embryo is known as **individuation**. The neural folds close to form the neural tube. The mesoderm on either side of the notochord becomes divided into a series of blocks called **somites**. These form the units of the backbone and the ribs as well as the muscles. The lateral mesoderm on either side of the somites splits, forming a cavity, the coelom, as mentioned earlier.

In the most anterior part of the gut in all chordates, **gill slits** develop. These are paired openings on the side of the throat from the exterior into the pharnyx or throat itself. At the most anterior and ventral part of the gut, the mouth breaks through, the trait which gives the deuterostomes their name. This stage in which pharyngeal gill slits appear is called the **pharyngula**. As a pharyngula, vertebrates of widely separate groups—birds, mammals, fishes—resemble each other more closely than in any other stage, for the eggs differ as markedly as do the adults. In this stage a simple diagram will do for them all. The heart is located forward, not far behind the mouth. Blood is pumped forward and then up to the dorsal side of the gut, through six pairs of aortic arches, the differing fates of which will be discussed with each. group of vertebrates. In larval frogs and salamanders the aortic arches send blood vessels out into feathery gills where the blood vessels become thin-walled capillaries through the walls of which oxygen and carbon dioxide are exchanged with the surrounding water. The capillary circulation in the gills makes a handsome sight when brilliantly illuminated under a binocular dissecting microscope. In mammals all the gill slits grow closed except the first pair, which forms the Eustachian tubes of the mammalian ears.

In reptiles and their descendants, the birds and mammals, the embryo develops flattened out on top of a large mass of yolk. In the mammals the yolk is no longer present except in very primitive species native to Australia. However, the higher mammals develop as though the yolk were present. The relationship between this condition and the frog embryo can be visualized by cutting a chick embryo off from the underlying yolk and pulling the edges together ventrally. (See Fig. 9–21.)

The general features of vertebrate development can be excellently seen in a 36- to 40-hour chick embryo because it can be stained and made translucent enough so that the optic vesicles growing out from either side of the brain

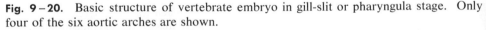

Fig. 9–20. Basic structure of vertebrate embryo in gill-slit or pharyngula stage. Only four of the six aortic arches are shown.

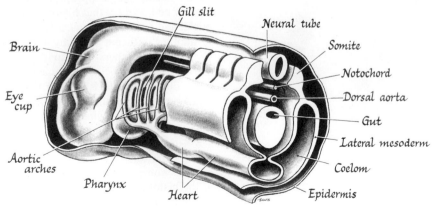

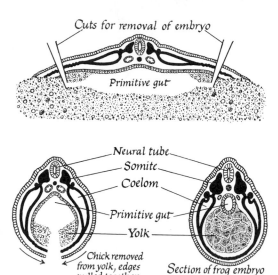

Fig. 9–21. Anatomical relationship of bird embryo to frog embryo.

are clearly visible, together with the mesodermal somites on either side of the neural tube, the curved but still tubular heart, and many other structures. A 72-hour chick embryo corresponds to a human embryo at about the end of the first month of intrauterine life. The first three or four gill slits are conspicuous, the extremely large brain, the heart, somites, limb buds, and eyes now equipped with lenses are all apparent.

The early formation of a mammalian embryo is closely similar to that of a chick and, of course, basically like that of a frog. An initial difference concerns the necessity of **implantation** onto or, in the higher mammals, into the epithelial lining of the uterus. Implantation occurs on the fifth or sixth day when the embryo is in a late blastula stage commonly called a **blastocyst**. Peristaltic-like contractions of the uterus or of the two divisions, right and left, of the uterus in mammals such as mice and cats which have two long uterine "horns," distribute the blastocysts evenly along the length of the uterus. Thus, approximately an equal number of embryos will develop, evenly spaced, in each side of a two-pronged uterus.

Gastrulation in mammals results in a primitive streak, at the anterior end of which is a knot of cells, Hensen's node, corresponding to the dorsal lip of the blastopore, as already described. Extending anteriorly from Hensen's node is a notochord and extending laterally

from it on both sides is a sheet of mesoderm. A neural plate then forms in the ectodermal layer lying immediately above the notochord and mesoderm. As in amphibians, the sides of the neural plate rise up, producing a neural groove which rapidly closes over, forming a neural tube. In a human embryo mesodermal somites, destined to become vertebrae and muscles, can be clearly seen about three weeks after conception. Covering the embryo is a membrane, the amnion, which is translucent enough to permit the embryo to be seen through it. By four weeks a balloonlike yolk sac is visible attached to the under side of the embryo. Gill arches and gill slits, tail, and bulging heart under the throat are all conspicuous. By four weeks the head is relatively enormous, the gill slits more or less grown closed, the limb buds, tail, heart, and adjacent liver all prominent.

Fig. 9–22. Chick embryo after 72 hours incubation. Parts of the brain: *1*, the telencephalon; *2*, diencephalon (with pineal rudiment); *3*, mesencephalon; *4*, metencephalon; *5*, myelencephalon. Note four visceral clefts or gill slits. Omphalomesenteric blood vessels run out over the yolk sac. (*After Huettner, Fundamentals of Comparative Embryology of Vertebrates, 1941, The Macmillan Company*)

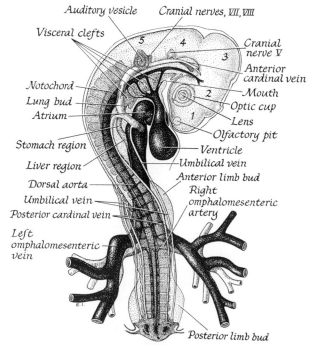

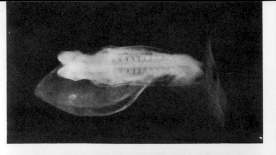
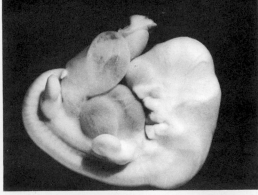
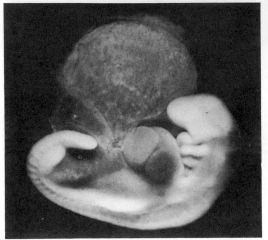
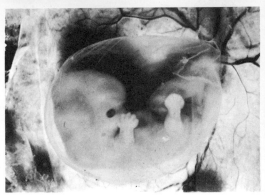

Fig. 9–23. Human embryos at approximately three, four, five, and six weeks. In the youngest, note the somites on either side of the neural tube. In the four- and five-week embryos, note the gill slits. The amnion surrounds the six-week embryo. *(Kindness of Carnegie Institution of Washington)*

In summary, then, beginning with the zygote, all vertebrate embryos pass through the same six stages:

1. The **zygote** or fertilized egg.

2. The **morula** (*morum,* mulberry) or cleavage stage.

3. The **blastula,** when the cells form a hollow sphere or at least a cap of cells, usually called the blastodisc, on top of the large mass of yolk.

4. The **gastrula,** during which stage the dorsal lip of the blastopore acts as the primary organizer or evocator of the embryo and the three primary germ layers—ectoderm, mesoderm, and endoderm—are formed in the process of gastrulation.

5. The **neurula,** the stage extending from the formation of the neural plate until the neural tube is fully formed.

6. The **pharyngula,** the stage characterized by the development of gill slits in the throat or pharynx. In this stage—and really only in this stage—the embryos of all groups of vertebrates from fishes to mammals are closely similar. All have a virtually complete set of organs similarly arranged, representing the common anatomical heritage of vertebrates in simplest visible form.

SEX DIFFERENTIATION

Both male and female vertebrate embryos begin development with the same set of reproductive primordia. In mammals a pair of gonads is located on either side of the midline near the kidneys, and two pairs of ducts, the mesonephric or Wolffian ducts and the Mullerian ducts, extend from near the kidneys posteriorly to connect with the exterior via the common urogenital opening. In addition there are the external genitalia. These consist of a median genital tubercle immediately anterior to the urogenital opening, on either side of which is a genital fold. If the zygote from which an embryo develops contains one X and one Y chromosome, i.e., is a male, the gonads will develop into testes and descend from the abdomen into a scrotum, the genital tubercle will grow into a penis, each Wolffian duct develops into a vas deferens which will conduct sperms to the penis, the Mullerian ducts will degenerate and virtually disappear, and the genital folds will form the scrotum.

If the egg carries two X chromosomes and develops into a female, the gonads become

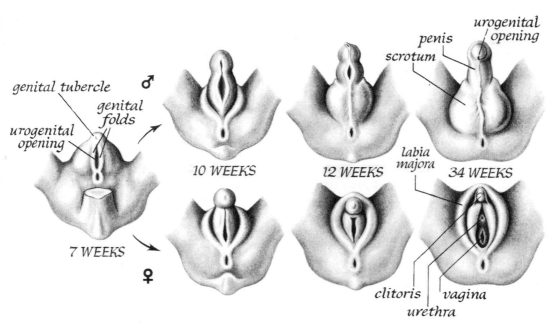

Fig. 9–24. The human male and female sex organs develop from common embryonic undifferentiated sex organs, shown at left. *(From Winchester,* Genetics, *Houghton Mifflin)*

ovaries and remain abdominal although they move much farther down toward the pelvis than they were originally placed, the Wolffian ducts degenerate and virtually disappear, the Mullerian ducts develop into the oviducts (Fallopian tubes of human anatomy), the uterus, and vagina. The genital tubercle becomes the clitoris and the genital folds become the labia majora.

The differentiation of sex is a very complex affair with considerable medical importance and much variation in mechanisms from one kind of animal to another.

In some vertebrates and invertebrates, notably insects and crustaceans, many sexual differences are controlled by local gene action within the tissues rather than by a circulating hormone. The classical and best-studied case is gynandromorphism in drosophila where one half of the body is male and the other half female. Cytological study of the chromosomes of such animals shows that the female side has the normal *XX* composition but the male side has lost one of the *X*'s and is *XO*, which gives a male in this fly. In the gynandromorph drosophila shown in Figure 9 – 25, the remaining *X* on the male side carried recessive genes for white

Fig. 9 – 25. A *Drosophila* gynandromorph. Note the typical more darkly pigmented and shorter abdomen on the male (left) side and the tiny sex comb on the inner edge of the left front leg. The single *X* chromosome in the male tissue carried the genes for white eye and miniature wing, while one of the two *X*'s in the female tissue carried the dominant alleles for these traits.

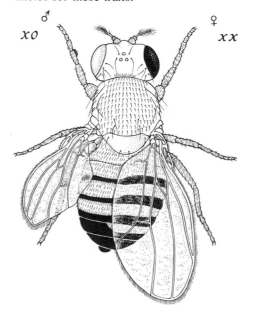

eye and for miniature wings. The normal female side must have had an *X* carrying normal dominant alleles for these characteristics.

In birds the secondary sexual characteristics, such as the differences between males and females in feathers, are sometimes due to local gene action as in insects, sometimes to hormonal factors, and sometimes to a combination of the two. In the common house sparrow, *Passer domesticus,* the difference in feathers between the sexes is due to local gene action. If baby sparrows are castrated while still wearing their juvenile plumage, which is the same in the two sexes, each will develop typical male or female plumage after the next molt just as though they had not been castrated. However, the pigmentation of the bill in the same species is a very sensitive indicator of the level of hormone in the blood. Many curious and even paradoxical results follow castration and hormone treatment in different breeds of chickens, ducks, and other birds.

In placental mammals present evidence indicates that Wiesner's theory first proposed in 1934 is correct. According to this theory female structures develop autonomously, male structures under the influence of some male sex hormone. If male genital primordia from a mouse or rat fetus are cultured *in vitro* with embryonic testes or with testosterone (male sex hormone), the Wolffian ducts continue to grow while the Mullerian ducts degenerate. If the testes or testosterone is omitted, the Wolffian ducts degenerate. If female genital primordia are explanted *in vitro,* the female ducts continue to develop with or without ovaries. In other experiments normal and castrated female fetuses and castrated males all developed essentially alike, furnishing further support for Wiesner's nonhormonal theory of female sexual differentiation.

Additional support comes from a study involving freemartins. A **freemartin** is a female calf which had a male calf as a twin and which has undeveloped or maldeveloped reproductive organs although the male calf is normal. F. R. Lillie showed long ago that in such cases the placentas of the twins are so closely joined that there is a vascular interconnection permitting blood — and consequently hormones — from the male twin to reach the female.

Finally, the fact that female sex hormone passes through the placenta and reaches the developing fetus from its mother virtually necessitates a system whereby the male develops under the influence of its own hormones while the female develops without hormones. If female sex hormone were necessary to insure

Fig. 9–26. Twin calves, male (left) and freemartin (right), removed from the elongated chorion. Note the chorionic fusion and interconnection of major blood vessels. *(After F. R. Lillie)*

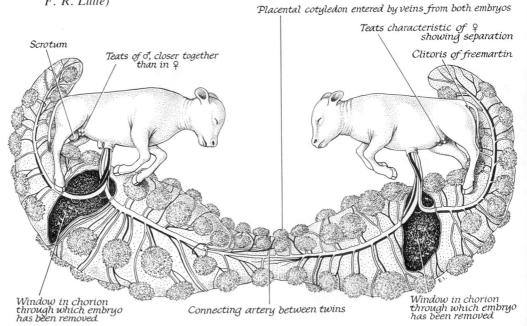

Placental cotyledon entered by veins from both embryos

Teats characteristic of ♀ showing separation

Clitoris of freemartin

Scrotum

Teats of ♂, closer together than in ♀

Window in chorion through which embryo has been removed

Connecting artery between twins

Window in chorion through which embryo has been removed

that a genetic female developed in that direction, then, since female sex hormone is always present by placental transmission from the mother, only females would be possible.

The development of the secondary sexual characters which appear at sexual maturity, such as differences in hair, voice, etc., are clearly under hormonal control in both sexes of mammals. Whether various other sex differences such as general bodily conformation are or not, is an open question. The well-confirmed existence of true gynandromorphs in certain strains of mice where the sex ducts and other structures are male on one side of the body and female on the other presents some interesting problems. It is perhaps possible that mammalian gynandromorphs can be explained by the loss of a chromosome as in insects, plus the operation of Wiesner's theory.

One recently discovered and important fact is that the hypothalamus (the portion of the brainstem immediately above the pituitary gland) behaves differently in males and females and that this difference is imprinted into the hypothalamus of the newborn mammal by male sex hormone very soon after birth. A single injection of as little as 1.25 mg of testosterone into a female rat 2 or 3 days old produces permanent sterility, apparently by producing a continuum of hormone production instead of the cyclical one characteristic of the female. Since it is the hypothalamus which signals the pituitary to release gonad-stimulating hormones at the appropriate intervals, the investigators, Barraclough and Gorski at U.C.L.A., tested the idea that the lack of rhythms of activity in the hypothalamus was responsible for lack of ovulation by stimulating the hypothalamus electrically. Such stimulation produced ovulation.

MEMBRANES

The membranes which surround an egg, it will be recalled, are of two different origins. The vitelline membrane is secreted by the follicle cells and probably also by the cytoplasm of the egg. It is formed while the egg is still in the ovary and becomes transformed into the fertilization membrane immediately after fertilization. Various other membranes are secreted around the egg by the oviduct during its passage to the exterior of the body. In a frog these are proteinous coats which swell to form a jelly as soon as the eggs reach the water. In the chick the first membranes secreted by the oviduct are several layers of protein, commonly called the white of the egg. The layer next to the yolk itself is drawn out into two whitish strings called **chalazas** which help keep the yolk properly oriented within the shell. Around the albumenous layers, the lower portion of the oviduct secretes two very thin but somewhat leathery shell membranes and finally a calcareous shell.

With reptiles, birds, and mammals, the embryo itself grows four membranes of living tissue which surround and protect the embryo as well as mediate its nutrition, respiration, and excretion. It is these four embryonic membranes that make it possible for reptiles and birds to lay their eggs on dry land, and for mammals to be effectively **viviparous,** that is, to bear living young.

The membrane closest to the embryo is the **amnion,** which completely encloses the embryo within a fluid-filled space—its own private pond in which it passes through the gill slit stage, although the gill slits are never used for respiration. Occasionally a baby is born with a bit of the amnion on its head. Termed a "caul," it is counted good luck in folklore. It will be noted later that it is the amnion which gives the name **"amniotes"** to the three groups of vertebrates possessing it.

The second membrane, the **yolk sac,** grows out from the belly side of the embryo and encloses the yolk from which it absorbs food. In the higher mammals also a yolk sac membrane forms, even though there is no yolk to enclose.

The third membrane is called the **allantois** (*allas,* sausage), because in many animals it becomes an elongate cylindrical structure. The allantois grows out from the hind gut, so that the cavity of the hind gut is continuous with the cavity of the allantois. In reptiles and birds it is highly vascular and lies under the shell, serving as a lung. The allantois stores fetal urine in mammals with poorly developed placentas, and plays a major part in the formation of the placenta in other mammals. The placenta is formed by the joint action of the allantois and the fourth membrane, the chorion, plus the

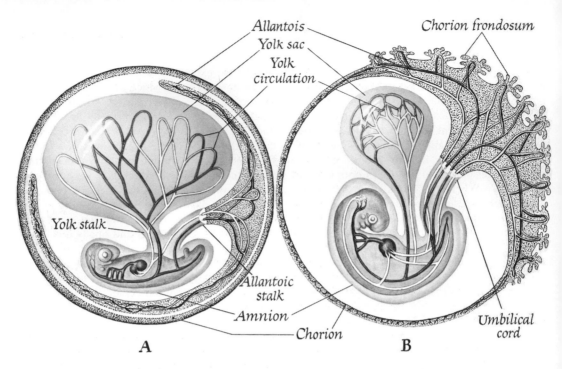

Fig. 9–27. Embryonic membranes of *A*, a bird, and *B*, a mammal.

uterine wall in higher mammals. It is the organ of physiological interchanges between mother and **fetus,** as the older embryo is usually called.

The **chorion** is the most external of the four membranes. In reptiles and birds it presses against the shell membrane. In mammals it develops directly from the blastocyst wall and presses against the lining of the uterus, and where the allantois fuses with the overlying chorion, the blood vessels sprout out into root-like extensions which fit tightly into the lining of the uterus. The region where these chorionic extensions grow out forms the **placenta,** which is the only place where actual exchanges of materials between mother and fetus occur.

In carnivores, like cats and dogs, the chorion is an elongate sac. The chorionic villi develop a placenta that encircles the sausage-shaped chorion like a cigar band. In deer and cows, many small rounded placentas are scattered over the chorion. In primates there is a single disk-shaped placenta; the lining of the uterus proliferates, forming part of the structure.

It is important to note that even in cases, as in man, where the maternal tissue lining the uterus is extensively digested away, forming

Fig. 9–28. Some types of placentas in mammals. *A*, diffuse distribution of villi in the pig. *(Patten) B*, detail from *A*. *C*, villous rosettes (cotyledons) in the lamb. *(Schultze) D*, encircling girdle of villi in the dog. *(Corning) (After Arey,* Developmental Anatomy, *5th ed., W. B. Saunders)*

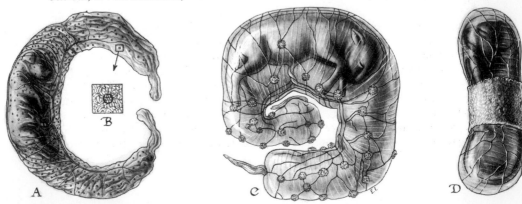

crypts into which maternal blood empties, there is no direct exchange of blood between fetus and mother. The fetal blood is enclosed within capillaries which are themselves enclosed within the various tissues of the villi. Only by some breakage, which may occur rarely, is there direct mixing of bloods. Nevertheless, a host of materials are continually exchanged via the placenta in both directions between fetal and maternal bloodstreams. Indeed, that is the whole point of the placenta! Carbon dioxide, oxygen, digested food, and metabolic wastes all pass through, as do antibodies. The odor of garlic, though not of onions, passes through, so that if a woman chews garlic shortly before her baby is born, it will come into the world with garlic on its breath, i.e., excreting it from its bloodstream via the lungs.

Fetal Membranes and Twins. Monozygotic, or genetically identical, twins bear a special relationship to the fetal membranes. One-egg twins develop from a single ovum in which there are two centers of development in the blastocyst. Then, since the chorion develops directly from the blastocyst, one-egg twins are always enclosed within a single chorion and have more or less fused placentas. Each twin is provided—or rather provides itself—with its own amnion and usually with its own yolk sac.

Fraternal twins, whether boys, girls, or a boy and a girl, result from simultaneous fertilization of two separate eggs. Each is enclosed in its own chorion and provided with a separate placenta. Unfortunately from the diagnostic point of view, now and again a pair of fraternal twins become implanted so close together on the wall of the uterus that their placentas and even their chorions tend to fuse. The embryonic membranes of fraternal and monozygotic twins are shown below.

The cause of fraternal twins, fraternal triplets, or any higher number of fraternal sibs is multiple ovulation. To produce a pair of fraternal twins two eggs must have been ovulated at approximately the same time. There is evidence that fraternal twinning tends to be inherited. A woman can inherit this tendency to ovulate two or even more eggs at a time from either her mother or her father, but obviously not from her husband. On the other hand, one-egg twins are produced by certain factors within the fertilized egg. Consequently, the male as well as the female parent might contribute the factor which makes for the appearance of two centers of development in a single egg. What factors actually cause this are unknown, but it has been found in many organisms from coelenterates up that if the original growth center is inhibited, then one or more secondary growth centers will arise. If the inhibition is removed or overcome, multiple buds will result. The study of the physical, mental, and emotional traits of twins has been discussed in Chapter 8 on Genetics.

Fig. 9–29. Embryonic membranes of (left) fraternal twins and (right) one-egg twins.

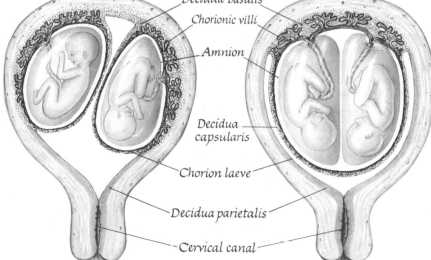

Decidua basalis

Chorionic villi

Amnion

Decidua capsularis

Chorion laeve

Decidua parietalis

Cervical canal

DEVELOPMENT OF THE NERVOUS SYSTEM

Brain and Neural Circuitry. The development of the vertebrate nervous system can be conveniently divided into three phases. First is the induction of the neural plate by the underlying chordamesoderm. The chordamesoderm is derived directly from the primary evocator or organizer of the vertebrate embryo, the dorsal lip of the blastopore. Immediately following this induction comes formation of the neural groove and neural tube.

The second phase is the conversion of the neural tube into the five basic subdivisions of the brain, plus the spinal cord. The five brain subdivisions are the same in all vertebrates from fish to man and form comparable structures in the adults. Virtually as soon as it is formed, the anterior end of the neural tube consists of three hollow swellings—forebrain, midbrain, and hindbrain.

The **forebrain** almost immediately shows two swellings. The anteriormost is called the **telencephalon** (*teles,* far off, or end). On either side, the telencephelon develops a hollow outpocketing. These outpocketings become the **cerebral hemispheres.** Each remains connected with the central cavity of the nervous system, i.e., brain and spinal cord, by an opening, the **foramen of Monro,** and the cavities within the cerebral hemispheres are the lateral ventricles of the brain.

The region of the forebrain immediately posterior to the telencephalon becomes the **diencephalon.** On either side of the diencephalon a vesicle also grows out. These are the **optic vesicles** and become the pigmented and retinal layers of the eyes. Dorsally from the diencephalon the **epiphysis,** or **pineal body,** grows upwards, and ventrally the **hypophysis,** or posterior portion of the pituitary gland, grows down. The anterior lobe of the **pituitary** is formed by an upgrowth from the roof of the embryonic mouth, where it is in contact with the downgrowth from the brain. The sides of the diencephalon become the **thalamus** and **hypothalamus,** part of the brain with centers for thirst, hunger, satiety, sleep, pleasure, etc., and for control of the pituitary gland by the secretion of neurohormones.

The **midbrain** does not subdivide but directly becomes the **mesencephalon.** Its roof is commonly called the **optic tectum** (*tectum,* roof) because nerves from the eyes penetrate the brain and have their endings there. In the frog, the roof of the mesencephalon develops two olive-shaped **optic lobes.** In mammals, the optic tectum forms two pairs of lobes and is consequently called the **corpora quadrigemina.** Running through the mesencephalon is a narrow canal, the **aqueduct of Sylvius.** It is the old neural tube and connects the cavity of the diencephalon, or third ventricle, immediately anterior to the mesencephalon, with the cavity of the hindbrain, the fourth ventricle, just posterior.

Like the forebrain, the **hindbrain** develops into two structures. Immediately posterior to the midbrain the hindbrain forms the **metencephalon** which grows up into the **cerebellum** dorsally and the **pons** ventrally, and, posterior to it, the **myelencephalon** which narrows as the **medulla oblongata** down into the spinal cord which extends along the back within the bony arches of the backbone.

The third phase in the development of the nervous system is the growth of **nerve fibers.** These are longer or shorter extensions of single nerve cells. When a group of nerve fibers run close together and parallel within the brain or spinal cord, they constitute a **fiber tract.** When a group of nerve fibers run together outside the central nervous system, they form a **nerve.** Ever since the descriptive investigations of Ramon y Cajal and His and the experiments of Harrison it has been clear that nerve fibers grow out from their cell bodies and make connections with their end organs—muscle, gland, sense organ, or, within the nervous system, other nerve cells.

During this third phase in the development of the nervous system a neural circuitry of enormous complexity is spun out between the hundreds of millions of cells in the system. The patterns of neural pathways thus formed are the physical basis for the behavior of the animal. The characteristic way a given species of jellyfish swims or the highly stereotyped and complex way each species of spider spins its own particular kind of web without ever having seen it before is an expression of the properties of the neural circuits in these so utterly different animals. And so with the vertebrates, the wink reflex, the ability to walk, and to think, are all reflections of the neural circuits laid down ultimately under the direction of the genes.

Relation to Behavior Development. The relationship between the development of the nervous system and the development of behavior has been the subject of much research and even more discussion during the past 50 years. We shall limit ourselves here merely to suggesting some of the issues and presenting some of the facts, because, although this is one of the most important areas in the biological sciences, knowledge is still in a rudimentary stage.

One issue has been the relative importance of maturation of the nervous system compared to learning in any specific type of behavior. G. E. Coghill early showed that the various swimming movements in a developing salamander larva appear in a fixed sequence, the same in every individual, and that these motions were correlated with the development of the appropriate connections within the nervous system.

The larva first bends only into a C, then later into an S. Swimming becomes more and more perfect as the neural connections become more and more completely formed. The growth of the nerve fibers concerned was traced in histological sections stained with silver, which blackens nerve fibers. Coghill was also able to show that if an embryo salamander was kept under an anesthetic until control animals had developed into swimming larvae, the anesthetized animal would swim immediately on being removed from the anesthetic and do so without passing through the usual awkward stages which look like learning!

Flying in many species of birds—pigeons, swallows, and cliff-nesting sea birds, among others—is not learned, but appears fully developed the first time the bird attempts it. For example, if a pigeon is raised by hand during

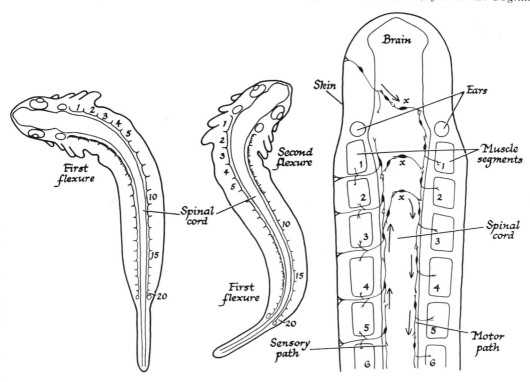

Fig. 9–30. The first swimming movements in a salamander larva are shown in the first two drawings, and their neuro-motor basis is shown at the right. The muscle segments are numbered. Notice how any stimulus to the left side of the body arising in either the skin or the muscles will pass over the connecting neurons, marked *X*, to the right side. This results in bending the body away from a stimulus. Since the crossover nerves are only at the head, the flexure has to begin at the head and pass toward the tail. Since the muscles on the right possess sensory nerves, their contraction results in impulses passing over to the muscles on the left side and there initiating a second flexure. *(After G. E. Coghill)*

the latter portion of its squabhood in a tiny cage, out of sight or sound of other pigeons and with no opportunity to attempt to fly, it will nonetheless fly up and join a strange flock of pigeons when released where it can see them flying overhead. There is no period of fluttering or awkwardness in the air. As soon as the pigeon joins the flock, it flies with them so well it can be distinguished from the others only if it is a different color! There is nothing remotely comparable to a boy learning to swim. One wonders about the difficulties of young robins which so commonly flutter to the ground able to fly only a few feet and then very imperfectly. It may be that in some species flying does require a great deal of learning. It may also be that robins tend to be crowded out of their nests before the flight reflex pathways are fully mature. In robins the selective advantages of a fully matured neuromuscular system on leaving the nest is apparently balanced by the advantages of a larger number of young.

A second question concerns whether individual reflexes or whole integrated patterns of behavior appear first in development. In salamanders, large integrated patterns arise first. The entire side of a larva will flex — neck, body, tail, plus both legs on that side, all simultaneously. Only later do the legs bend independently of the rest of the body and later still do parts of a leg move separately from the entire leg. In the chick embryo, however, the situation seems to be quite different. Individual parts move in an apparently haphazard order before groups of movements occur in a coordinated fashion.

A closely related and still baffling problem is whether or not the early activity of the nervous system is due to stimulation from peripheral sensory nerve endings, internal changes in the body fluids, or "truly" endogenous activity in the nerve cells. All three possibilities may occur in different species or in the same species under different circumstances. Isolated heart muscle cells *in vitro* contract rhythmically, so there is no theoretical reason why nerve cells may not have some internal mechanism that produces rhythmic activity out of a constant environment. There is, in fact, good evidence that endogenous neural activity occurs in both vertebrate and invertebrate embryos along with, of course, activity that is a response to external stimulation.

A central problem remains with still many unanswered questions. Does the developing nervous system grow as a diffuse, equipotential nervous network on which function, in the form of conditioned reflexes or some other type of learning, imposes reaction patterns? Or does the growth of nerve fibers within the central nervous system establish genetically programmed neural circuits which, in turn, result in' preordained behavior patterns such as the precise kind of web a spider will spin or the elaborate coordination of muscular action essential to produce skillful flight? It should be noted that the second alternative does not preclude the possibility that the same nervous system could also grow circuits which provide the physical basis for learning. How do the outgrowing nerve fibers know where to grow and what connections to make? How does the brain know which muscle or gland a certain nerve fiber innervates or from what spot on the retina, for example, a certain nerve fiber comes?

These are some of the facts. They give only partial answers but they are a beginning. In embryonic and even larval salamanders and frogs, muscles can be transplanted to unnatural sites on the body. A whole leg can be grafted into the socket from which the eye has been removed. In such cases nerves which would normally never see a leg will make functional connections with the strange muscles. Very commonly such transplanted muscles will contract synchronously with the corresponding muscles in the normally placed leg. Facts such as these have led to the conclusion that nerves merely innervate the first muscle they meet and are guided in their outgrowth purely by physical topography. The explanation of the synchronous contraction with the corresponding muscles in the normally placed limb is very obscure. In the higher vertebrates, especially in mammals, scrambling nerves and muscles leads to serious malfunction. The meaning of all these facts remains to be clarified.

Highly specific behavior based on the growth of nerve fibers from specific parts of the retina to specific parts of the brain (in the optic tectum, of course) has been shown by R. W. Sperry in fishes and by Leon Stone in salamanders. In the common pond salamander, *Triturus (Diemictylus) viridescens,* it is possible to transplant the eyes with return of vision because the low oxygen requirements of a coldblooded animal permit revascularization before the death of the eye. The new nerve fibers grow into the brain from their cell bodies located in the retina. It is necessary only to make sure that the cut ends of the optic nerve are held together; otherwise the regenerating fibers grow out of the cut end and form merely an irregular mass.

If a salamander is anesthetized and one eye cut out, rotated 180°, and replaced, when vision returns, that eye will see everything upside down and backwards. If both eyes are thus rotated the animal will live for many months but must be hand-fed because it never learns not to reach up for food placed below it or reach down in trying to grab food which is, in fact, dangled above it. If the left eye is grafted into the place of the right eye but not rotated, the salamander will see backwards but not upside down with that eye. If you rotate that left eye 180°, then the salamander will see upside down but not backwards with that eye. In other words, it will jump up to get food presented under its nose but lurch forward to get a piece of meat held a short distance in front of it. These facts indicate that nerve fibers coming from each particular spot on the retina carry some kind of label as to their place of origin in the retina, or else that in regeneration each nerve fiber somehow grows back to the proper location on the optic tectum.

The most beautiful experiments showing that each nerve fiber finds its way back to its proper ending on the optic tectum have been carried out by R. W. Sperry. Fiber tract studies show that the nerve fibers from every part of the retina of a fish end in specific regions of the optic tectum. For example, those from the ventral half of the retina end in the dorsal half of the tectum. If you remove the dorsal half of the retina from one eye (so it cannot be the source of any nerve fibers growing into the brain along the optic nerve from that eye) and then cut the optic nerve from that eye and rejoin it again in such a way that regenerating nerve fibers become scrambled when they grow across that joint, the behavior of the regenerating retinal nerve fibers should give the answer to the question of whether or not nerve cells really do grow back to their proper places in the optic tectum. If they don't, they would be expected

Fig. 9–31. Behavior of a salamander in which the eyes have been cut out, rotated 180°, and then replaced.

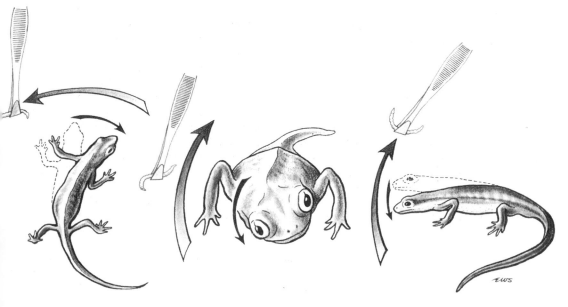

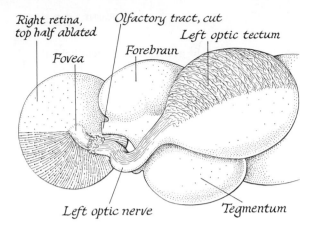

Right retina, top half ablated
Olfactory tract, cut
Left optic tectum
Fovea
Forebrain
Left optic nerve
Tegmentum

Fig. 9–32. Fish brain showing how the nerve fibers from the ventral half of the retina of the right eye grow back to their proper places in the dorsal surface of the left optic tectum. *(After R. W. Sperry)*

merely to fan out over the whole tectum. What happens is shown in Figure 9–32. When these fibers reach the brain they all make the correct turn and grow up and then fan out over the dorsal surface of the tectum. Similar experiments with other regions of the retina — anterior half, central region, etc. — all have given the same results.

Specific responses of the frog's leg after transplantation of the motor and sensory nerves from the right to the left side of the body also appear to confirm the theory that certain kinds of behavior, even in vertebrates, are due to genetically determined neural circuits. These experiments will be described in the chapter on the nervous system.

One of the many remaining questions is how the nerve fibers are guided in their outgrowth. To some extent this mechanism is certainly physical. Nerve fibers cannot grow unless they have something to grow along. The advancing end is amoeboid and, like an amoeba, needs an object on which to move. Again like an amoeba, growing nerve ends can be guided by electric currents. They move toward the cathode, as do amoebas. But selective chemical specificities of nerve fibers and guiding chemical gradients in the brain appear required to explain satisfactorily the highly precise manner in which the nerve fibers grow to their destinations.

AGING

The fact of aging is obvious to all, yet nothing certain is known about its causes. It may very well be that it is controlled in different kinds of animals by entirely different mechanisms. What sets the limits of growth, or the time when teeth will erupt, or the thymus gland undergo atrophy, or sexual maturity occur, or menopause take place? Why should a rat have a potential life span of 3 years, being the equivalent of a man in his 90's at 36 months, while a flying squirrel basically the same in size, anatomy, and physiology, will easily live to be 6 or 7 years? The life span of drosophila can be lengthened by a factor of three or more by low temperature, or cut in half or even less by raising the temperature. But despite some intensive studies, no one knows what age-control mechanisms temperature affects.

There are many theories about senescence, most of them easily disposed of. Metschnikoff held that aging was due to poisons absorbed from intestinal and other bacteria. But animals raised in a sterile environment grow and age like others — or even die sooner. Steinach proposed that aging is caused by changes in the reproductive glands. But castrated animals grow and age on almost exactly the same time curve as do normal ones. Bogomolets suggested that the connective tissue system is mainly responsible, but this theory is so vague it can scarcely be proved or disproved. Others have suggested dietary factors and changes in the calcium or water content of the cells.

Recently there have been several attempts to apply to reptiles a metabolic theory of longevity proposed many years ago by Rübner, an investigator of respiratory rates in man and other mammals. Briefly, this theory holds that every kind of animal, if allowed to live out its inherent life span, will burn a fixed number of calories per unit of weight. The value for all mammals is said to be roughly the same. For mammals some very interesting facts have been brought out. A mouse is very old at 3½ years, and an elephant at 70. So-called **physiological time** runs much faster in a mouse than in the elephant, and this shows itself in various ways. The heart beat of a mouse varies from 600 to over 700 contractions per minute, that of an elephant from 25 to 28. Yet at the end of its long life, an elephant's heart will have beat almost exactly the same number ot times as the heart of a mouse!

Investigators attempting to apply Rübner's hypothesis to reptiles have studied lizards living at different altitudes where the annual average temperature is very different. They have found that in nature the life expectancy of these poikilotherms is at least roughly proportional to temperature—the colder it is, the longer they live. This is hardly surprising and reveals little.

In many vertebrate tissues—heart, liver, and others—a curious yellowish pigment, lipofuscin, a complex of lipoids and proteins, accumulates with age. But whether it is merely a concommitant of aging, or is a cause of aging, or what its significance is, remains unknown.

Various investigators have attempted to discover a relationship between the normal life span due to senescence, the period of gestation, and the size of the adult in different species of animals. The table of such data shown on page 593 in Chapter 30 reveals that such relationships are common but not very precise.

Review and References

REVIEW TOPICS

1. What were William Harvey's two contributions to our basic knowledge of development?

2. Contrast epigenesis and preformation. What relation do these theories have to modern problems?

3. How do eggs differ in cleavage, in yolk, and in polar body formation? What is the relationship of yolk to cleavage?

4. What are the major prerequisites, results, and physiological mechanisms of fertilization?

5. What light may Monroy's work on ribosomes throw on Shaver's experiments on artificial parthenogenesis?

6. What seeming paradox arises from studies of nucleus and cytoplasm in early development? What light is thrown on these problems by separating blastomeres; by centrifuging eggs?

7. How do regulative eggs differ from determinative eggs in the biochemistry of development?

8. Compare gastrulation in iso- and telolecithal eggs. What is the relationship of gastrulation to the germ layers, and to differentiation?

9. How does the vertebrate nervous system, including the eyes, develop? What does the mesoderm form?

10. What are the functions of each of the four fetal membranes? What is the relationship of these membranes to fraternal and identical twins? Why?

11. What possible biochemical mechanisms have been proposed to account for differentiation?

12. What light may chromosome puffing throw on differentiation? What is the possible role of histones?

13. What is the Wiesner theory of sexual differentiation in mammalian development? What is the evidence for it?

14. Why are gynandromorphs difficult to explain in mammals? What about birds?

15. What is the evidence for and against the theory that neural circuits develop first and behavior follows?

16. Define: blastula, telolecithal, parthenogenesis, epigenesis, evocator, amnion, notochord, acrosome, diencephalon, Wolffian duct.

17. Can a gynandromorph mouse be explained in terms of the X and Y theory of sex determination and the nonhormonal theory of female sex differentiation? Defend your opinion.

USEFUL REFERENCES

Arey, L. *Developmental Anatomy,* 7th ed., Philadelphia, W. B. Saunders Co., 1965.

Balinsky, B. I., *An Introduction to Embryology,* 2nd ed., Philadelphia, W. B. Saunders Co., 1965.

Bonner, J. T., *Morphogenesis*, Princeton, N.J., Princeton University Press, 1952.

Corner, G. W., *Ourselves Unborn,* New Haven, Yale University Press, 1944.

DeHaan, R. L., and H. Ursprung, eds., *Organogenesis*, New York, Holt, Rinehart & Winston, 1965.

Ebert, J. D., *Interacting Systems in Development*, New York, Holt, Rinehart & Winston, 1965 (paperback).

Gottlieb, F. J. *Developmental Genetics*, New York, Reinhold Publishing Corp., 1966.

Hamilton, H. L., *Lillie's Development of the Chick*, New York, Henry Holt, 1952.

Patten, B. M., *Early Embryology of the Chick*, 4th ed., Philadelphia, Blakiston, 1951.

Rothschild, Lord, *Fertilization*, London and New York, Methuen and John Wiley & Sons, 1956.

Rugh, R., *Experimental Embryology, Manual of Methods*, Minneapolis, Burgess Publishing Co., 1948.

Rugh, R., *The Frog, Its Reproduction and Development*, Philadelphia, P. Blakiston's Son & Co., 1951.

Strehler, B. L., *Time, Cells, and Aging*, New York, Academic Press, 1962.

Chapter 10

Evolution

The great Greek dramatist Sophocles declared over 2,000 years ago that of all the wonders known to man, none is more wonderful than man himself. The present-day biologist would broaden this statement to say that of all the wonders known to man, none is more wonderful than the emergence of life out of the inconceivable vastness of time, space, and matter. The theory of the evolution of life from simple molecular beginnings and up to the phenomenon of man himself has made a greater impact on the intellectual life of mankind than has any other aspect of biological knowledge. It has profoundly influenced the thinking of many groups of people. Some of the conclusions that have been drawn about the meaning of evolution for human life and destiny seem doubtful or even fantastic to biologists. The chief task of this chapter will be to present evolution and its implications from a biological viewpoint, leaving the philosophy to the philosophers.

It is now a little over a century since 1859, when Charles Darwin published his epoch-making book, *The Origin of Species by Means of Natural Selection.* Since that event, new and certain knowledge has been won in many areas. One of the ideas Darwin accepted, the inheritance of the effects of use and disuse, has been shown to be untrue, except, perhaps, for unicellular organisms. However, Darwin's basic concept of evolution by variation and natural selection has been powerfully supported—and, in fact, greatly broadened and deepened—by modern genetic analysis. At the same time, much of the actual history of life on this planet has been spelled out in detail by new discoveries of fossils and new methods of dating them, especially by the use of radioactive carbon and other such techniques. Even the old question of the origin of life from the non-living material of a planet seems close to solution. Statistical and other new methods in ecology and biochemistry have also thrown new light on old problems of evolutionary theory.

THE CLASSIC DARWINIAN THEORY

We shall begin with Darwin and his achievement. Charles Darwin was born in England on February 12, 1809, on the very day and in the same year as Abraham Lincoln. His grandfather was Erasmus Darwin, a well-known 18th century physician, poet, and exponent of a theory of evolution later advocated by Lamarck and often called Lamarckism. When about 15, Charles Darwin was sent to Edinburgh with an elder brother to become a medical student. But he found the lectures, except those in chemistry, "intolerably dull" and wrote home that he thought there "are no advantages and many

225

disadvantages in lectures compared with reading." Furthermore, in that day before anesthetics, he found surgery an unendurable nightmare. Luckily, he became the friend of several other young men who had a keen interest in geology, marine animals, and plants. One of these friends was an enthusiastic supporter of Lamarck's theory of evolution, and probably helped fix the problem of the origin of species in Darwin's mind.

At the end of his second year, Darwin transferred to Christ's College, Cambridge, with the intention of studying for the ministry. Looking back on his undergraduate days at Cambridge he later felt that much of his time had been wasted. His father was worried about the amount of time Charles spent hunting, card-playing, and eating with friends. He belonged to a musical set but seems not to have played an instrument himself. Most important, he fell in with several undergraduates (all of whom later made their way in the world) who were avid beetle collectors. Through them Darwin came to know a Professor Henslow, a man of wide scientific interests and a plant hybridizer. Henslow held weekly open house for both undergraduates and congenial members of the faculty, and Darwin came to see a great deal of him. It was through him that Darwin was appointed as naturalist on the naval ship *Beagle* during its five-year voyage around the world (1831–1836). Perhaps because he had too many friends, Darwin was a mediocre student, but he did have to master thoroughly two classics of logical and extended argumentation, Euclid's *Elements of Geometry* and Paley's *Evidences of Christianity*. There is also evidence that the memory of a former student of Christ's College, John Milton, helped to focus Darwin's mind on the problem of origins.

Darwin's great achievement, like that of Newton, lay in drawing together into a new synthesis several different lines of scientific advance. Darwin's presentation in his *Origin of Species* made it impossible for anyone who could read to miss the point. At the beginning of each chapter he tells you what he is going to say, in the body of the chapter he says it clearly and with an overwhelming wealth of factual detail, and at the end of the chapter he tells you again exactly what he has said. Unlike the evolutionary theories of his many predecessors, Charles Darwin's could not be killed by ridicule or merely ignored. The breadth and force of his argument and the weight of his evidence were too compelling. Darwin formulated his theory that evolution occurs by means of variation and natural selection at the age of 29, soon after his return from the voyage on the *Beagle*. Yet he did not publish the theory until 1859, after 22 years had been devoted to amassing factual evidence and an intensive study of all aspects of the problem.

Four "Principles." Four primary groups of facts—principles, if you will—form the basis of Darwin's theory of evolution.

1. The first is the geological principle of **"gradualism,"** or "uniformitarianism," as it is also called. This is the theory that the world, with all its mountains, plains, and valleys, was not suddenly created in 4004 B.C. or on any other particular date, but is the result of gradual changes over millions of years. Streams and rivers are constantly wearing down the mountains; upthrusts of land continue to produce mountains and earthquakes; sediment still settles on the ocean floor to be pressed into stone. Without this geological background of the long past, a theory of evolution is almost impossible. The irrefutable evidence that the present surface of the earth is the result of a long process of change which is still taking place was summed up by Charles Lyell, one of the founders of modern geology and an older friend of Darwin.

2. The second principle on which Darwin based his theory was one made familiar by Lamarck, Cuvier, and a long line of naturalists. It was the realization that many different kinds of animals form **a graded series** from simpler to more complex, from generalized to specialized. From the time of Aristotle, these so-called ladders of being had been thought of as static, a part of the unchanging order of things. The important point, however, is not that the old naturalists like Linnaeus and Baron Cuvier thought of animal relationships as unchanging, but rather that they saw animals to be very clearly related to each other by their anatomy, and that these relationships permit us to arrange animals in logical sequences. The arm of a man, the foreleg of a horse, the foreleg of a

cat, the wing of a bat, or the flipper of a seal all show the same basic skeleton. Bone for bone these limbs are homologous. Among the insects, the crustaceans, or the coelenterates, everywhere similar basic patterns of structure had become evident. And as explorers and collectors brought in new kinds of animals and plants from the four corners of the world, it became increasingly clear that there are many graded series of animal types. Wild species of sheep were discovered which resemble goats, and in other parts of the world wild goats were found which possess sheeplike traits, until it became literally impossible to make anything but an arbitrary distinction between the two. The number of known species of mice and mouselike, and of rat and ratlike, animals seemed to increase endlessly. Similar groups of related species had been found among the insects, crustaceans, birds, and many other groups. Darwin provided a dynamic explanation for these ladders of living forms.

3. The third body of knowledge which Darwin utilized was from the practice of **plant and animal breeding.** In the two generations which had immediately preceded him, plant and animal breeders had produced markedly improved races of wheat, oats, poultry, cattle, and the like by the method of selective breeding, that is, by artificial selection. Domestic plants or animals which showed the desired traits were selected by the breeder to be the parents of his new crop. This method was in common use among many amateurs such as pigeon and chicken fanciers. It was well known to Darwin as a youth. Natural selection is the obvious counterpart among wildlife of artificial selection among domesticated plants and animals.

4. The fourth and perhaps crucial principle that entered into the Darwinian synthesis was the theory of T. R. Malthus on **population growth.** Malthus published his famous *Essay on the Principle of Population* in 1798. The thesis of Malthus is really very simple. He pointed out the rather obvious fact that no population can increase to any significant extent without an increase in its means of subsistence, especially food. He then argued that history shows that whenever there has been an increase in food and living space, the human population has always also increased. His conclusion from all this was excessively gloomy, for he held that only "moral restraint, vice, and misery" such as unwholesome occupations, or extreme poverty, bad nursing, diseases and epidemics, wars, plague, and famine could hold down the immense power of populations to grow if they are left unchecked.

Malthus' ideas have been attacked by many, Karl Marx among the first. It is perfectly true

Fig. 10–1. Varieties of domestic pigeon all derived from the wild rock pigeon by selection. (*After Darwin; from Pauli,* The World of Life, *Houghton Mifflin*)

that, primarily because of the Industrial Revolution and its agricultural counterpart, many human populations have increased in size and at the same time raised their living standards. Mankind is certainly not doomed to poverty and misery due to his reproductive potential.

However, it is also true that in any finite environment, whether a test tube or a continent, there must be limits to the size of a population. Each member of a pair of hermaphroditic sea slugs lays up to 478 million eggs in 17 weeks. One medium-sized female crab will carry over 4 million eggs. If 2 million of her eggs hatch into females, and if each were again to produce 4 million eggs, there would be 2 million times 4 million or 8×10^{12} offspring in the third generation. Assuming again the usual sex ratio of half males to half females, the 4×10^{12} females, each with 4×10^6 eggs, means 4×10^6 times 4 $\times 10^{12}$ potential individuals, a truly inconceivable number of crabs, 16×10^{18}, i.e., 16,000,-000,000,000,000,000.

This prodigious number is the result of the reproductive potential of but four generations from one fertilized crab, yet four generations are as nothing in the life of a species that continues decade after decade, century after century. To illustrate this point Darwin characteristically used the slowest breeding animal known, the elephant, which does not become sexually mature until between the ages of 17 and 20, has a gestation period of 22 months, brings forth but one calf at a birth, and usually stops breeding when about 50 years old. Yet in time, if no forces checked their growth, Africa would be solid elephants.

The significant fact is that any living population—of bacteria or elephants or men—tends to increase geometrically, like compound interest, until checked. Unless checked, the population of parameciums would soon come to equal the entire earth in volume.

This insight of Malthus gave Darwin his clue. In his own words:

I happened to read for amusement Malthus on population, and being well prepared to appreciate the struggle for existence which everywhere goes on from long continued observation of the habits of animals and plants, it at once struck me that under these circumstances favorable variations would tend to be preserved, and unfavorable ones destroyed. The result of this would be the formation of new species. Here then I had at last got a theory by which to work.

The theory of evolution by natural selection was proposed independently by Alfred Russel Wallace, a naturalist and explorer. Happily a dual publication led to mutual appreciation rather than bitterness. It is worth recording that Wallace also found his inspiration from reading Malthus.

In formulating Darwin's theory, two facts are basic. The first is the geometric or "compound interest" character of population growth just discussed. The second is the fact that animals vary in many ways and that many of the variations are inherited. These two factors lead to a struggle for existence which results in the survival of the fittest and the ultimate extinction of the less fit. Thus populations tend to change their character.

No one in Darwin's time understood variation, although Darwin himself saw its crucial importance for his theory and discussed it in the first chapter of his *Origin of Species*. "Variability," he wrote, "is governed by many unknown laws, of which correlated growth is probably the most important. . . . Over all these problematical causes of changes, the accumulative action of selection, whether applied methodically and quickly, or unconsciously and slowly . . . seems to have been the predominant power."

Wallace went even further with the surprising claim that "when a sufficient number of individuals are examined, variations of any required kind can always be met with." The important distinction between true hereditary variations due to changes in the chromosomes, and nonhereditary variations due to amount of food, exercise, sunlight, or other environmental factors, was not made clear until the work of a Danish geneticist, Johanssen, after the rediscovery of Mendel's laws. But for Darwin's argument, this distinction was not crucial. It was enough to know that animals do, in fact, vary widely and that many, if not all, of these variations are inherited. With no true understanding of the physical basis of heredity and mutation, it is little wonder that most of Darwin's immediate successors came to regard natural selection as the virtually self-sufficient cause of evolutionary change.

NON-DARWINIAN THEORIES: A NEW LOOK

Before beginning a modern critique of Darwin's classic theory, there are three additional views about evolution which have come down to us from Darwin's day or earlier, and which are still important enough to require some brief discussion.

Saint-Hilaire. Perhaps the oldest of these views was best formulated by Geoffroy Saint-Hilaire, Napoleon's official zoologist. According to his view, animals change in response to the direct action of the environment. If the change is favorable they survive and flourish; if it is unfavorable, they perish. It is now known that such environmental agents as high-energy radiations of all kinds and various chemicals can induce mutations, i.e., hereditary changes. Of course, these agents were unknown to Saint-Hilaire, who thought in terms of climatic and nutritional factors. There is no evidence that general changes in nutrition or in the environment can cause hereditary changes by any sort of direct action on the hereditary material in the chromosomes. Environmental changes, however, are important in producing evolutionary changes by means of selection. If a race of flies inhabits a windswept oceanic island, wings and an urge to use them are a disadvantage. Such individuals get blown out to sea. Natural selection in such a situation favors individuals with small or defective wings, because they are more likely to remain on the island and reproduce their kind. But this does not mean that the wind produces small wings directly. Flies with defective wings are hatched every now and then in populations of flies raised in laboratory bottles.

Lamarck. A second theory, one which Darwin accepted and which is even today a hardy perennial among uninformed people in many parts of the world, is Lamarckianism. This is the belief that the effects of use and disuse somehow produce corresponding changes in the genes and are thus transmitted to future generations. This theory was discussed and found lacking in Chapter 8 on genetics.

Richard Owen. A third view, which was rather ineffectively presented by Darwin's contemporary, anatomist Richard Owen, and somewhat later by the great German embryologist and humanitarian Oscar Hertwig, stands in marked contrast to either of the two theories just mentioned. Instead of looking to the environment or to the effects of use and disuse, this view emphasizes the inherent properties of living matter. It is a viewpoint that has been increasingly supported by modern biochemical knowledge about the genes. The forms and characters of living things are expressions of the properties of the nucleic acids of which their chromosomes are composed.

Evolutionary possibilities ultimately rest on the potentialities for change of nucleic acids and proteins, especially enzymatic proteins. In a similar way, the form and characteristics, such as the melting point, of a crystal depend on the properties of the molecules of which it is composed. Under certain conditions water forms six-pointed crystals. If the conditions are not right these crystals will not exist, any more than protoplasm can exist at extreme temperatures. But the fact that there are six points to an ice crystal and not five or eight or some other number is not determined by the direct action of the environment or any function useful to the crystal, but purely by the inherent nature of the atomic structure of water molecules. In like manner, crystals of a vast array of substances—sodium chloride, benzene, carbolic acid, or amino acids—all differ in form and properties in a way determined primarily by their molecular nature.

The original advocates of the view that we must look to the inherent properties of protoplasm for an explanation of animal forms pointed out that natural selection was not the primary creative force in evolution but rather a screen, a pruning device. Natural selection can select only from choices presented to it. It is, of course, mutation that presents the choices.

NEO-DARWINISM: MODERN SYNTHESIS

The modern, or neo-Darwinian, view of evolution sees four major causes which work together in producing evolutionary change. They are: (1) mutation and the subsequent and continual reshuffling of genetic factors through sexual reproduction; (2) natural selection; (3) the effects of chance, often called random genetic drift; and (4) isolation, especially geographical isolation, and its converse, gene flow between groups.

1. Mutation and Sexual Reproduction. Mutation is so basic to the subject of evolution that certain relevant aspects merit restatement here. Mutations are random in two senses. They are random in that they are unpredictable in kind. This is true of both naturally occurring mutations and mutations produced by radiations and by chemical means. The rate at which mutations occur is greatly speeded up by radiations, but there is no way of predicting specifically what mutation will occur next, much less of producing a specific gene change on demand. The ability to produce specific mutations artificially remains to the future, when much more is known about the chemistry of nucleic acids.

Mutations are also random in that they bear no necessary relation to the needs of the organism. In fact, some 99 per cent of all mutations are harmful. This is not at all surprising, since existing animals are the result of millions of years of adaptation. No wonder that the overwhelming probability is that no random change would be for the better. As with a ship or an airplane, making random changes in the blueprint is likely to be disastrous.

It should also be remembered that whether or not a mutation is advantageous is relative, relative to the environment. A mutation producing defective wings may be a serious disadvantage to an insect in most environments, but quite the reverse on the windswept oceanic island. A gene for defective eyes may be an advantage to an animal living in a cave, where eyes are both useless and highly vulnerable to physical injury.

Different genes possess different mutation rates, in accordance with variations in their stability. Many cases of back mutations are known. Thus a gene for normal pigmentation may mutate to a form resulting in albinism, and a gene for albinism may mutate into one for normal pigmentation. The net result of the difference between the mutation rate of a given gene in one direction and its mutation rate in the reverse direction is known as its **mutation pressure.**

Since mutations of any particular gene are rare events, to study enough cases to determine the frequency of any particular mutation is extremely laborious. Such rates are known for only a few organisms — drosophila, man, corn, and then only for a relatively few genes in each.

Evolution on the simplest level is change with time in a population of genes. Consequently evolution can be regarded as a problem in population genetics. The basic law of population genetics is a rule formulated in 1908 by an English mathematician, Hardy, and a German physician, Weinberg, and hence known as the **Hardy-Weinberg law.** It is a very simple, common-sense generalization, and also a useful tool in studying the frequencies with which certain genes, like the gene for the Rh blood factor, occur in a population. The Hardy-Weinberg law states that in the absence of mutation, selection, or some other factor causing change, the proportion of genes in any very large population will reach an equilibrium in one generation and thereafter will remain the same, generation after generation, regardless of what that proportion may be. Whether the genes are dominant or recessive makes no difference.

The Hardy-Weinberg equilibrium forms the basis for the calculations of population genetics. The effects of mutation, selection, and gene flow between populations are all superimposed on this basic equilibrium. If the population is very small, then the Hardy-Weinberg equilibrium cannot be maintained; this will be discussed later with the topic of genetic drift. If a particular dominant gene is disadvantageous, then the relative number of those genes will decrease through the action of selection. Of course, if a gene confers some advantage, then its numbers will increase in the population, regardless of whether it is dominant or recessive.

Consider a hypothetical case. Suppose a population is made up of 60 per cent homozygous normal individuals, Rh positive, *RhRh,* half males and half females, and 40 per cent homozygous Rh negative individuals, *rhrh,* half males and half females. It is simple to construct the familiar genetic grid (Fig. 10 – 2) to show what the results will be. This is in fact multiplying the terms of the gene frequencies within one sex by those of the other. Since 60 per cent of the males are *RhRh* and 40 per cent are *rhrh,* the ratio of the two kinds of sperms can be represented as 0.6*Rh*:0.4*rh.* In a similar way, 0.6 of the eggs will carry an *Rh* gene, and 0.4 an *rh* gene. Crossing takes place as follows:

sperms	.6*Rh* + .4*rh*
eggs	.6*Rh* + .4*rh*
zygotes	.36*RhRh* + 2(.24*Rhrh*) + .16*rhrh*

As far as individuals are concerned, only 16 per cent are Rh negative, instead of 40 per cent as in the parent population. However, if the ratio of genes in the filial population be noted, it will be found to be the same as before. 72*Rh* + (48*Rh* + 48*rh*) + 32*rh* = 120*Rh* + 80*rh,* or 60*Rh*:40*rh.*

In more general terms, if *p* = the frequency of one gene and *q* = the frequency of its allele, and there are only the two alleles at the locus in question, then $p + q = 1$. In the case just given, $p = .6$ and $q = .4$, and $.6 + .4 = 1$. In a freely interbreeding population, $(p + q)$ sperms $\times (p + q)$ eggs $= (p^2 + 2pq + q^2)$ zygotes. In the case just described, $(.6p + .4q)(.6p + .4q) = .36pp + .48pq + .6qq$.

Fig. 10 – 2. Genetic grid to show why, when 60 per cent of the genes at the Rh locus in a given population are Rh positive and 40 per cent are Rh negative, 16 per cent of the population will be Rh negative and 84 per cent will be Rh positive, with 36 per cent homozygous.

Sperms → Eggs ↓	.6*Rh*	.4*rh*
.6*Rh*	.36 *RhRh*	.24 *Rhrh*
.4*rh*	.24 *rhRh*	.16 *rhrh*

From a formula like this it is possible to calculate the actual frequency of any gene in a population if the percentage of homozygous recessives is known. For example, if 16 per cent, i.e., 0.16, of a given population are albinos or show any other recessive trait, it is evident from the formula that .40 of the alleles at this locus in the population must be recessive. It will be noted that Mendel's laws represent the special case of the Hardy-Weinberg law where *p* and *q* are equal. Thus $(p + q)^2 = 1pp + 2pq + 1qq$. If *p* represents a dominant gene, the phenotypic ratio here is the familiar 3:1. Indeed, Mendel himself expressed his results in terms of the binomial theorem: $(a + b)^2 = a^2 + 2ab + b^2$.

The Hardy-Weinberg generalization of Mendel's law expresses a stable state and thus represents the absence of evolution. But with such knowledge as a foundation, it is possible to make calculations about how great mutation pressure or selection pressure would have to be to produce a particular amount of evolutionary change. For example, it is possible to determine the number of generations that would be necessary to eliminate an undesirable gene, or to make a desirable gene universal in a population at various selection pressures. If 100*AA* or *Aa* individuals survive for every 99*aa,* the dominant gene is said to be favored by a selection pressure of .01. These calculations show that mild selection pressure is not very effective in very large populations, even for dominant genes. For a recessive gene, even 100 per cent elimination whenever it appears in the homozygous state will result in only a very slow decline in their proportion.

There are about 5*aa* albinos per 100,000 persons. Assuming that marriages are at random with respect to this trait, $q^2 = .00005aa$. Arithmetic will show that there must be 1,420 *Aa* individuals or carriers per 100,000. It is obvious that if either natural or artificial selection were to remove all the 5*aa* per 100,000 individuals, the total of 1,430 *a* genes would be reduced to 1,420, a trifling result. At this rate, e.g., by sterilizing all albinos in every generation, it would take 5,000 years to reduce the number of albinos by one half. On the other hand, it must not be forgotten that selection can be effective much more quickly than this result suggests when selection is really drastic. The application of DDT to a population of flies, or the introduction of a new variety of wheat that is resistant to smut-fungus, may produce a DDT-resistant strain of flies or a strain of smut-fungi of new virulence simply by the complete elimination of all individuals except the rare resistant or virulent types, respectively.

2. Natural Selection. Natural selection, and artificial selection as well, is of three different types.

1. **Stabilizing** selection tends to eliminate both extremes. A gull or tern whose wings are too long is at a disadvantage and so also is a gull whose wings are too short. For a bird of a given size with a given mode of life in a given environment, there is an optimum wing length. Natural selection will shorten the lives of individuals which deviate very far in either direction from this optimum. Most selection seems to be of this stabilizing type. This is an aspect of the known fact that most mutations are harmful. Stabilizing selection is an anti-evolutionary type of selection pressure, since it tends to prevent change.

2. The second type of selection is **directional.** It favors individuals which vary in one direction and works against those which vary in the opposite direction. This kind of selection can produce evolutionary change. Speed and maneuverability are advantages for a hawk; their opposites are serious handicaps. Increased ability to survive heat and drought are advantageous to desert animals, their opposites disastrous. A good example of the result of unidirectional selection is the horse's high-crowned, continuously growing molars when grass became the diet.

3. The third type of selection is **disruptive** selection. This is probably the rarest type, but it can also be important in producing evolutionary change. In such selection, the extreme variants at each end of the distribution curve are favored, while those in the intermediate range are at some disadvantage. Such a situation will tend to split a population into two parts, each of which may finally become a separate species. For example, in a population of tree-dwelling monkeys, the largest and heaviest individuals are able to defend themselves from attack by the others. The smallest and lightest, and therefore the most agile, can escape through the treetops. But alas for the middleweights, neither fast enough to escape nor heavy enough to win against the somewhat larger members of the species.

3. Genetic Drift. In addition to mutation and selection, an important limitation on the Hardy-Weinberg law — and almost certainly a very important factor in evolution — is the effect of chance in very small populations. This effect is commonly called genetic drift. When this term is used it must be remembered that no definite "current" is implied, only the purely random sampling that occurs for many genes whenever the population is drastically reduced in size. For this reason, this aspect of evolutionary dynamics is sometimes called sampling error, or even the bottleneck phenomenon.

As an extreme case, suppose 10 finches happen to get caught in the hold of a grain ship in Argentina and do not escape until they arrive at the coast of China. There they may or may not form a new population, but whether they do or not, such a tiny flock can certainly not be expected to carry a completely representative sample of the genes common to the whole South American population from which they came. Suppose that 20 per cent of the great South American population carries a dominant gene for an unusually wide white band on the wing feathers. If the flock of 10 were to be representative, two of the finches would have to carry this gene. If only one of the 10 happened to have it, then its frequency would have decreased by one-half. Actually such a gene could easily be missing altogether in the little flock. Or a gene that was uncommon in the parent population might just have happened to be common among the 10, and so become common in the resulting new population.

When all the thousands of genes present in a species are considered, it becomes evident that no very small group can be truly representative. A small group of survivors, escapees, or lost migrants might carry exactly the same percentage of gene X as the large parent population, and this might be true for several other genes. But of gene Y and many others, they will very likely have somewhat more, and perhaps very many more, in terms of percentage than the parent population, while of gene *Z* and many others, the small population will probably carry a smaller percentage, slightly smaller for some, drastically smaller for others. It is practically impossible for a very small population to transmit a representative sample, in its original proportions, of all the genes characteristic of the large population. This is true, first, because a few individuals will not in themselves be a representative sample. But besides the bottleneck phenomenon there are two additional points where pure chance can change the character of a small population. The first of these is in meiosis and fertilization. Many sperms with their genes are lost, many eggs and three times as many polar bodies never form new individuals. In a large population these losses average out, but not so readily in a small population. Here, say, most of the genes for red hair might get lost in polar bodies. The second point where chance enters is in purely accidental death or survival among the members of a very small population. In large populations the effects of chance, good or bad, tend to cancel.

How small does a population have to be for genetic drift to occur? That depends on the force of natural selection and on mutation pressure and so may be different for different genes. In putting an infinitely large population of equal numbers of black and white marbles through a bottleneck by drawing a random sample, the overwhelming probability is that a sample of a very few thousand would be representative. But in the living world ideal mathematical situations are seldom, if ever, found. Hence it is virtually impossible to determine how large any particular population of genes has to be in order to avoid the effects of random sampling, i.e., genetic drift.

How important has genetic drift been in the course of evolution? This also is extremely hard to measure. It is thought that in the remote human past, when the primates from which man arose, and the early men too, were wandering about in small bands, genetic drift must have been important. Recent careful studies have compared the gene frequencies in a very small population which emigrated from a known part of Germany and settled in Pennsylvania about 200 years ago. Because of their religious beliefs, this group has not intermarried appreciably with other people (although over the years some have left the little community and joined the mainstream of American life). If genetic drift is a fact, some of the gene frequencies among this group not only should be different from those of the general population of Pennsylvania and those of the large parent population in Germany, but should not even be intermediate between them. This turned out to be true for the A,B,O and M,N blood group genes, as well as some other minor hereditary characteristics.

It is also worth noting that natural selection, by drastically reducing a population, may put a species through a bottleneck where genetic drift becomes operative. For example, when an epidemic disease hits a population of wild ducks, there is a rigorous selection for any genes which make for resistance to this disease. All other genes, no matter how important in other situations — genes affecting speed in flight, correct migrating instinct, breeding ability, success in escaping foxes, snapping turtles, and hunters — for the time become irrelevant. Such genes that just happen to be in ducks which also carry the genes for disease resistance will escape through the population bottleneck. But the smaller the bottleneck the more certain that no representative sample of all these other genes will get through. Consequently, when the ducks increase again after the epidemic subsides, the new population will be genetically different in regard to the frequencies of many of its genes.

4. Isolation. Isolation was regarded by Darwin and his immediate followers as so important that it was virtually a prerequisite without which no evolution was possible. With their pre-Mendelian view that heredity involved a blending of vaguely understood hereditary material ("blood") from the parents, it seemed inevitable that any deviation would be averaged out as the result of crossbreeding in subsequent generations. The discovery of the Mendelian factors of heredity, the genes, which enter crosses and emerge from them unchanged, produced a modification of this view. If a gene or a certain combination of genes confers a selective advantage, it is not necessarily averaged out. On the contrary, it may be preserved and will tend to increase. In the case of a parthenogenetic or very closely inbreeding population, the proportion of homozygous individuals, whether homozygous for the dominant or the recessive gene, continually increases. This is because the homozygous individuals mated together can produce only more homozygotes, while the heterozygous individuals will give rise to only 50 per cent of heterozygous individuals like themselves; the other half of their offspring will be homozygous.

Nevertheless, it has come to be realized in recent years that isolation does play an extremely important role in the origin of new species. In the first place, different but related species are always separated in some way in nature so that they do not interbreed, even though they may be induced to do so under laboratory conditions. Secondly, wherever there is a barrier between two or more populations, these populations almost invariably show differences.

A classic case of the effect of geographic isolation on species formation is that of the snails of the genus *Partula,* which live on the small volcanic islands scattered over the Pacific Ocean. Each island has its own characteristic species, and in addition, every valley on each island has its own peculiar form of the snail, whether they be regarded as true species, subspecies, or merely varieties. The mountain ridges separating these little tropical valleys are very high and steep, and conditions on them are such as to form a barrier to the snails. Species, subspecies, or races of this kind which occupy different territories are called **allopatric** (*allos,* other, + *patria,* native land). Many such cases are known. Two which have been carefully studied are the species and subspecies of *Peromyscus,* variously called the deer mouse, wood mouse, and white-footed mouse, and the species and subspecies of *Melospiza melodia,* the song sparrow. Both genera have a range extending over most of North America. *Drosophila* has also been intensively studied on a world-wide basis. The *Drosophila* found in the Hawaiian Islands are different from those either in North America or in China and Japan. The most famous illustration of the effects of isolation is the case of Darwin's finches on the Galápagos Islands, which are off the west coast of South America.

How isolated do two populations have to be for speciation to occur? This is a hard question to answer because degree of actual isolation is difficult to measure. One of the few cases ever measured is that of the small rodents which live on prehistoric black lava flows in arid parts of the American southwest. Some of these lava flows are completely surrounded by sandy desert. Others have more or less contact with rocky areas. Those flows which are completely isolated by desert sand, or which make contact with rocky regions on less than 10 per cent of their periphery, have endemic races of very dark small rodents. **Endemic races** are races that are native to a particular region. However, when somewhat more than 10 per cent of the periphery of these lava flows is in contact with rocky zones, endemic rodents are not found. Evidently genetic flow between the rodents living on the lava and the general brownish population in rocky areas is too great and natural selection too weak to produce a special endemic race.

The effects of geographic isolation in the formation of new species is perhaps most clearly seen in a **"rassenkreis"** or "ring of races," A dozen or more such **polytypic species** — that is, species in which several "typical" forms occur in series — have been investigated. The common harbor gull, *Larus argentatus,* forms such a series in the lands encircling the north pole. Ornithologists believe that the original home of this gull was the eastern edge of Siberia just west of Alaska. This race or subspecies may be called A. In North America are races B, C, and D. Extending westward across northern Siberia into Europe and Scandinavia are races E and F. In the British Isles and coastal Europe, the North American races and the western European races both occur but do not interbreed. Paradoxically, the European subspecies or races interbreed with the western Siberian ones, these with the eastern Siberian forms, and these in turn with the North American races. If a species is defined, as is customary, as an interbreeding population, then the western European and North American races would appear to be separate species, but the Siberian race would be of the same species as each of the others!

A similar situation has recently been discovered in the common frog, *Rana pipiens*, a species with a range extending from Canada to Panama. Individuals from the northern part of this range can be crossed with individuals from New Jersey and give normal embryos. Likewise, New Jersey frogs can be successfully crossed with frogs from Louisiana. But a cross between individuals from the far northern and far southern parts of the range yield abnormal and nonviable embryos. From the point of view of a pre-Darwinian taxonomist cataloguing species like a logician, cases of this kind are paradoxical. But in the light of the theory of evolution, they are examples of species in the making. The frogs in the north are adapted for development at low temperatures, those in the south for development at high temperatures. The genes of the two races are just different enough to prevent successful cooperation. Should something happen to remove the central Siberian population of gulls, or the middle states group of frogs, the remaining populations at the geographical extremes of the ranges would then quite properly be regarded as distinct species.

Species which inhabit the same geographical range are called **sympatric** (*sym* or *syn*, together, + *patria*, native land). Sympatric species are isolated by various mechanisms which prevent interbreeding. Many birds will not mate except after a prolonged courtship of perhaps 10 days or more. This involves a special type of behavior and special responses to this courting behavior. If the genetic basis for this behavior is lacking in one individual, mating fails to occur. Many closely related species are effectively separated in nature by differences in breeding season. This is true of the various species of frogs. The wood frog, *Rana sylvatica,* breeds within a few days after the ice is off the ponds. The bull frog, *Rana catesbeiana,* breeds very late in the spring, in May or June. Other species breed at intermediate times. Some related species of animals, especially marine animals where the eggs and sperms are cast out into the sea water, are intersterile. Even though mixed together in a small bowl of sea water, the eggs of one species cannot be fertilized by the sperms of the other, or if fertilized, do not develop into viable embryos.

In the long sweep of evolution, **temporal isolation** is probably of paramount importance. The simple fact that no group of animals can interbreed and exchange genes with their ancestors means that evolution can be progressive under the pressure of natural selection and in the absence of any kind of geographical isolation. The obvious fact that all living populations are continuous back through time with ancestral populations presents a seemingly insoluble logical problem to those who try to apply the species concept to the historical evolution of animals. It is the problem of the ring of races in a polytypic species, extending in time instead of in space. In practice, however, there are plenty of gaps in the fossil record so that it is possible to use the same system of nomenclature for fossil as for living forms.

The modern conclusion is that the four factors discussed above, namely, hereditary variation produced by mutation and sexuality, natural selection, genetic drift, and isolation, are adequate to account for evolution. Within this general framework lie endless devices and stratagems and a number of groups of facts sometimes dignified by the name of laws.

There are, however, a few zoologists who harbor a lingering doubt. To suppose that all the myriad and intricately adjusted forms of life can be due to random mutation is to make a very large supposition indeed. Some of the doubters talk of orthogenesis, others of a supposed distinction between micro- and macroevolution. To these topics we now turn.

Orthogenesis. The tendency of certain organisms to evolve consistently along restricted evolutionary paths over long periods of geologic time is called **orthogenesis** or straight-line evolution. The evolution of the horse from a dog-sized, four-toed herbivore in the Eocene 60 or 70 million years ago to the familiar one-toed animal of today is the classic example, but the history of life abounds in examples—the elephant, the camel, certain cephalopod mollusks, and many others. In this sense, orthogenesis is clearly a fact. Once a race begins specialization which adapts it to a particular mode of life in a particular environment, in many cases further modification in the same direction has continued for long periods, often until extinction.

The differences of opinion concern an explanation. The paleontologists of a generation ago, men like Henry Fairfield Osborn in North America and Teilhard de Chardin in France, studying the fossil record, have seen in these series of fossils something more than they believed mutation and natural selection could explain. There must be, such people feel, some special directional driving force, in the famous phrase of Henri Bergson, an *élan vital*.

Their evidence for inner-directed straight-line evolution is in the broad outlines of the evolutionary history of a particular kind of animal. But as more and more of the fossil record has been uncovered, it has become more and more obvious that the evolution of the horse, to use the classic case, is not a single straight line but a series of branching lines with many diversifications and blind alleys. (See Fig. 10–13.) Moreover, the study of a fossil record does not show the mutations. These occur between one parent and its offspring, while successive fossils are commonly thousands or tens of thousands of years apart. Even more important, mutations are now known to occur in a vast number of directions affecting a vast range of characters so that the facts about mutations directly contradict the idea of a directional driving force. The direction comes from the environment, specifically from the relationship between the environment and the adaptations possessed by the species at any particular point in time. An animal already adapted for running and living on the plains or steppes will not be benefited by many mutations that would benefit an animal already fairly well adapted for climbing trees. To repeat, the set of adaptations already possessed by a species determines whether or not a specific mutation is advantageous and will probably be incorporated into the gene pool of the species, or is disadvantageous, as most are, and will be eliminated.

Micro- and Macro-Evolution. Zoologists are in fairly complete agreement that the formation of new species, as in the separation of one widely distributed species into two new and slightly different ones, can be adequately explained in terms of mutation, natural selection, isolation, and perhaps, now and then, genetic drift. Some zoologists call this micro-evolution, in contrast to what they, term macro- or even mega-evolution, by which they mean the emergence of radically new forms, the appearance of new orders, classes, or even phyla.

The emergence of new phyla is something we know almost nothing about because all the major phyla except the chordates are already present in the earliest fossil-bearing strata, and the chordates seem to have left no record of their origin.

No evidence, however, has ever been presented to show why the accumulated results of mutation over tens of thousands of years could not produce new orders, classes, or even phyla. Given the known facts of mutation and natural selection, it is hard to imagine a mechanism which would prevent micro-evolution from merging into and becoming macro-evolution. Certainly no such mechanism is known. Furthermore, mutations are known which profoundly change important structural characters of animals, and characters which set one order apart from others! Remember the mutant bithorax in *Drosophila* (Fig. 1–4) in which the second pair of wings, which is reduced to mere knobs called halteres in all the insects belonging to the Order Dipteriformes, is converted into fully developed wings! Everywhere that mutations have been studied in both plants and animals they have been seen to change in radical ways all manner of things basic as well as trivial.

Within the known phenomena of mutation and selection are two rather special kinds of events which do produce radical change rather suddenly. One of these is pre-adaptation and the other is neoteny.

Pre-Adaptation. When a set of adaptations acquired by a group of animals in one environment fits them to live in a new and different environment, the animals are said to have been pre-adapted. The most striking case is the way the three major adaptations making life on land possible for vertebrates were developed by fishes and were useful to them. The fishes were the muscle-finned fishes or Sarcopterygii, which include the lungfish. Of course their descendants, the primitive amphibians, were the beneficiaries of the pre-adaptation. Several localities have yielded masses of fossilized remains of these early amphibians (Stegocephalians) crowded in what had clearly been a mudhole in some drying lake or river. There is independent geological evidence that the Devonian Period, approximately 300 million years ago, when these tragedies occurred, was a period of violent climatic changes, of droughts and floods.

It is easy to see that lungs would have permitted fishes to survive in damp mud during a drought, and this is the chief function of the lungs in lungfishes today.

Legs, complete with muscles and skeleton in contradistinction to delicate fins, are obviously important in enabling an animal to clamber over the mud in a drying lake or river and to find water. The evidence is that the muscled appendages of the ancestral fishes were used not to "invade" the land but to get back into the water after the supply where the fish was had dried up. Ability to walk over dry land developed slowly later.

What about eggs that can be laid on land? Before the land was populated with vertebrate predators of various sorts, an aquatic animal that could lay its eggs far enough up on shore to put them out of the way of egg-eaters, which inhabited the water, would obviously be at an advantage. The eggs of these original amphibians were large-yolked things much like the eggs of reptiles and much larger than the eggs of familiar temperate zone frogs and salamanders. However, there are tropical amphibians living today which retain the very large eggs, protected with a proteinaceous coat, and laid on the land.

The ability of mankind to develop complex civilizations can be regarded as due to pre-adaptation. Man's average brain size is certainly no larger now than among the pre-historic Cro-Magnons, nor is there any reason to believe that his intellectual abilities have increased. It may well be that extremely primitive life in very small communities requires greater general competence on the part of all members of the group than does life in a great city.

Neoteny. An evolutionary stratagem known for many years but only recently viewed as of major importance in the history of life is **neoteny.** This curious phenomenon takes slightly different forms in different animals and is given different names, but the essential feature is always the appearance of sexual maturity in a larval or juvenile stage or condition. It now appears to have been a key event in the evolution of man, insects, the first vertebrates, and other animals.

Most radically new departures in evolution have arisen from small generalized species. The first mammals were all small animals about midway between a lizard and a mongrel dog in size and appearance. The ancestral lines of specialized mammals, such as bats, giraffes, seals, and horses, all lead back to this generalized form. So also with the dinosaurs and many other groups. Basically new departures arise not from the highly evolved and therefore specialized forms but from the primitive, generalized ones.

Neoteny makes it possible for a line to escape from the trap of specialization and give rise to a truly new departure. It may well be that here is the principle so many zoologists have sought that will account for some of the really big steps in evolution—for "macro-evolution," if you will—that seem hard to account for on the basis of small mutations in an already specialized animal.

The best-known case of neoteny occurs in the Mexican axolotl, *Ambystoma mexicanum*, a salamander native to certain Mexican lakes. It never loses its gills and tail-fin, nor does its skin metamorphose into the adult type of other salamanders. It becomes sexually mature and breeds in the larval condition.

Another case where neoteny seems to have been the starting point for a spectacular new evolutionary departure is in the origin of insects. Insects have only three pairs of legs and a moderate number of segments, but in common with other segmented animals, such as lobsters, they must have evolved originally from segmented worms. What group of animals stood between worms with many segments and the insects? The evidence points to the millipedes (myriopods). The adult is a long, many-segmented, wormlike arthropod with about 50 to 100 pairs of legs. The larval millipede, however, has three pairs of legs and a small number of segments like an insect. It would take only very slight changes to convert

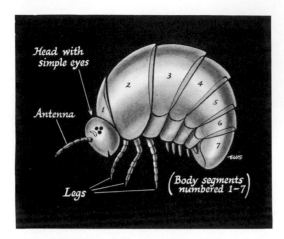

Head with simple eyes

Antenna

Legs

Body segments numbered 1-7

2 3 4 5 6 7 1

Fig. 10−3. Larval myriopod. Note antenna and three pairs of legs.

this larval millipede into one of the several groups of primitive wingless insects. The internal anatomy characteristic of insects, including respiratory tracheae and excretory Malpighian tubules, is already present in the millipede. The subsequent deployment of the hundreds of thousands of kinds of insects then took place by mutation, natural selection, and other factors acting on this "larval" form.

The argument that man arose from apelike ancestors by neoteny followed by further modification is an interesting speculation and may even be true. In any case it is supported by a number of facts.

1. In any mammalian fetus — dog, man, or rodent — the long axis of the brain makes a right angle with the spinal cord. In other words, the brain and head of the fetus are bent forward and even down against the chest. With growth, in the dog or any of the lower mammals, the head straightens out until the long axis of the brain is in line with the spinal cord. Were this to happen to us, or to other primates, our nostrils and eyes would be on the top of our heads. The retention of the fetal right angle of brain axis to spinal cord is of obvious importance in a creature which walks upright. It is a trait man shares with other primates, especially the apes, but which man has carried even further in the fetal direction.

2. A second and perhaps even more important fact is the relatively enormous size of the human brain. In the embryos of all mammals the brain is much larger in proportion to the size of the body than it is in the adult. A large brain is consequently an embryonic trait.

3. A third fetal trait characteristic of man, which is found although to a much lesser degree in the apes, is a flat face with a greatly reduced muzzle.

4. The lack of hair completely covering the body is a fetal trait in the apes, an adult trait in man. Some anatomists have even suggested that our lack of a proper covering of fur is not an adaptive trait but an unfortunate concomitant of our neotenous origin!

5. The age at which the bony sutures fuse in a man is much later than comparable fusions in the apes and monkeys.

6. The gross structure of the brain of a newly born chimpanzee more closely resembles the structure of a human brain than does the brain of an adult chimpanzee.

7. In tooth development man is greatly retarded compared with the apes. This holds both for the milk and for the permanent teeth.

8. The lack of pigmentation in Mongolian and Caucasian peoples is also a fetal trait.

From this point of view, man is a modified ape that becomes sexually mature without becoming fully adult anatomically.

Another case of the origin of radically new forms by building on a neotenous larva may have been the origin of the first vertebrates from a neotenous tunicate tadpole (see Chapter 19). A highly plausible case has recently been made for the origin of ctenophores from flatworms by way of Müller's larva, the common larva of marine turbellarians.

An aspect of evolution that is likely to be misinterpreted is a tendency in certain cases for natural selection of gene mutations to follow the effects of environment and fix these effects in the heredity of the species. For example, on small islands where food is not abundant, horses and other animals will be somewhat stunted compared with similar but well-fed animals on the mainland. However, an animal on such an island who happens to have a mutation which reduces its size, will have certain advantages. It will not so likely be half-starved, because it needs less food. In this way dwarf breeds like the Shetland pony are produced by mutation followed by natural selection.

"Laws" of Evolution. There are a number of so-called "laws" or rules which state certain generalizations about the usual results of the four major causal factors in evolution: mutation, selection, isolation, and genetic drift. **Dollo's "law"** states that evolution is irreversible. This is undoubtedly true in the large, although many reverse mutations for single steps are known. Drosophila that have mutated to eyelessness will mutate back to the eyed condition. But this is very different from having a horse change back into a small five-toed animal the size of a dog. Clearly the web of circumstances in the actual historical progress of events is too complex ever to recur in exactly the same form. The mutations will be different or at least appear in a different sequence, the environment will certainly have changed, and hence natural selection will be different and the effects of chance will be different.

There is a common tendency for animals to increase in size during the long course of evolution. This is known as **Cope's "law"** and is well illustrated in the great prehistoric reptiles, which increased in size until they became extinct. This was true in many different evolutionary lines among the dinosaurs. There has also been a very general tendency in many, but by no means all, lines of mammalian evolution for size to increase. Male lions are now so large and clumsy they have to leave the crucial part of hunting to the females while they merely help flush the prey. Meanwhile competition between males for females seems to be favoring a still greater increase in male size. Perhaps this is an evolutionary trap leading to extinction. Increasing size has also occurred in echinoderms, crustaceans, cephalopods, pelecypods, annelids, and other groups.

Many homoiothermal (warm-blooded) mammals and birds become larger in the more northern and colder parts of their range. This is **Bergmann's rule,** which often holds both for individuals of the same species and for related species. The biggest bears are in Alaska, the biggest tigers in Siberia. The largest Virginia deer are not in Virginia but in Canada. The explanation appears to be that a large animal has less surface area in proportion to its weight and so is better able to conserve heat.

A related phenomenon is expressed in **Allen's rule.** As animals live in colder and colder climates their extremities—ears, tails, etc.—become progressively smaller. This is an obvious adaptation against freezing. Both Bergmann's and Allen's rules—and others of a similar kind, for example, that animals living in damp forests tend to be darker than those in dry regions **(Golger's rule)**—find a ready explanation on the basis of mutation and natural selection.

Fig. 10–4. Allen's rule illustrated in rabbits' ears. *A,* Arizona jack rabbit, *Lepus alleni.* *B,* Oregon jack rabbit, *L. californicus.* *C,* Varying hare from northern Minnesota, *L. americanus.* *D,* Arctic hare, *L. arcticus.*

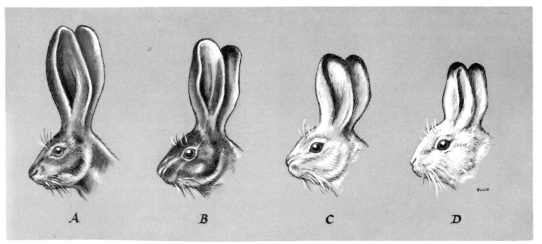

Functions of Color and Pattern. The color and pattern of animals have been molded by mutation and natural selection to serve three functions. The commonest is protective camouflage, which blends the animal into its surroundings. Examples of this can be found everywhere. A second function is to provide a means of species or sex recognition. This too is widespread and is especially common among mammals, birds, reptiles, fishes, and probably some insects. The cinnamon-red of a male bluebird's breast feathers serves as a challenge to other males. A third but less common function is to serve as a warning. Skunks, hornets, and bumblebees are not brilliantly colored and marked for nothing. Skunks present a rather special case because they seem to have the best of two worlds. Close up and in daylight they are extremely conspicuous and characteristic. At night and from a distance their bold black and white pattern breaks up the outline of the skunk's body and makes it appear like so much light and shadow.

In connection with warning coloration, **mimicry** has grown up. There are quite harmless flies that have come, in the course of evolution, to resemble bees. There are famous cases of an edible butterfly (edible for birds, that is) coming to resemble an unrelated but unpleasant-tasting one called the model. Such mimicry, in which one species is noxious and the mimic innocuous, is called **Batesian.** A dramatic verification of the effectiveness of mimicry has recently been obtained by Lincoln and Jane Brower in work with toads. A toad needs to be stung by a bumblebee only once to learn to avoid not only the bumblebees but also the harmless flies which mimic them.

In the more common **Mullerian** mimicry, both species are noxious. This probably more than doubles the value of the warning coloration for each species because the predator will find it easier to learn what to avoid. In other cases a rare species finds protection merely by resembling a common species.

THE EVIDENCE FOR EVOLUTION

For any science, the question of evidence must always be of central and overriding importance. The evidence that evolution has been a fact of history is of several kinds. (1) The fossil record furnishes an extensive and in some cases a detailed picture of the life of the past. This evidence is irrefutable, and will be discussed in the final sections of this chapter. (2) The facts of inheritance and mutation furnish a theoretical basis for an evolutionary theory, and make it more difficult to conceive how a species can remain unchanged than how it may evolve. It remains still to discuss the evidence from (3) geographical distribution, (4) comparative anatomy, (5) animal development, and finally (6) vestigial organs.

Fig. 10–5. Copperhead amid dead leaves. *(Kindness of Isabelle Hunt Conant)*

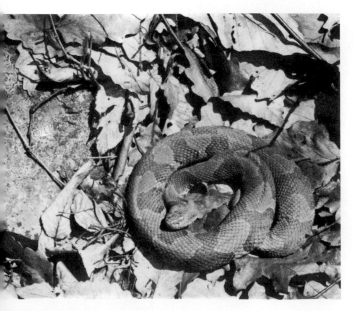

Geographical Distribution. Of the evidence for evolution based on geographical distribution none is more striking than the relationship between the animals on oceanic islands and those on adjacent continents. It was this kind of evidence that forcibly impressed both of the originators of the theory of evolution by natural selection. Charles Darwin, in his voyage around the world as a young naturalist on the *Beagle,* visited the Cape Verde Islands off the west coast of equatorial Africa and the Galápagos Islands off the west coast of equatorial South America, and was profoundly struck by their different fauna under similar conditions. Alfred Russel Wallace studied the life of the long series of islands making up the East Indies.

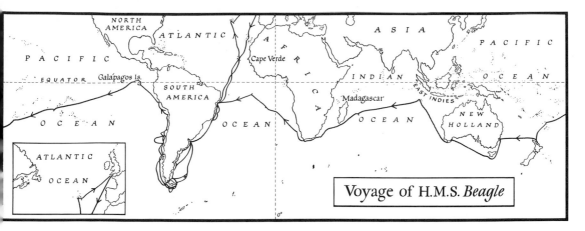

Fig. 10–6. Course of *H.M.S. Beagle* during its voyage of circumnavigation (1831-1836).

Each oceanic island has its own unique native animals and plants. But, and this is the point, in every case they resemble the animals and plants on the nearest continent. The Galápagos Islands are inhabited by turtles, lizards, birds, and other animals that are endemic, that is, native and unique, but are similar to lizards and birds on the adjacent shores of Central and South America. Likewise, the animals of the Cape Verde Islands resemble not those of South America or tropical Asia but those of the adjacent parts of equatorial Africa. These facts indicate that the animals have been derived from the nearest continent and then, under the influence of mutation, selection, genetic drift, and isolation, become different from the parent populations. There is some geological evidence that the Galápagos Islands were once connected to the mainland so that their populations and those on the continent were perhaps continuous in remote ages. Of course it is also possible for islands to be populated by the descendants of a few land birds blown off course by unusual storm winds, and for lizards and other animals to survive long sea voyages by clinging to floating logs.

The island of Madagascar off the east coast of Africa affords another informative example of the relationship between an island and its neighboring continent. Madagascar is a big island, over 1,000 miles long and separated from Africa by the Mozambique Channel. This stretch of the sea is in most places about 500 miles wide and at no point less than 250. Obviously the only animals that could cross that barrier, except birds and flying insects, would be small reptiles and mammals, small enough to ride on floating debris. It's a one-in-a-million proposition, and for that reason this kind of passage has been called a "sweepstakes route." Animals such as elephants, which are too big to ride a log, are not even in the lottery. Neither are animals which live inland and never approach the coast. Consequently, it is to be expected that of the mammals, a group which originated since Madagascar was isolated, only the small ones would appear on the island and that these would represent a more or less random sampling of the small mammals of the African shore. This is exactly the case. The mice got across. The small insectivorous shrews did not — perhaps because of their exceedingly high metabolism they would starve before they reached land.

Once established in isolation on an island, the natural processes of evolutionary change would modify the original species into new ones. In the Galápagos, Darwin found that at least 21 of the 26 land birds were unique to the islands, whereas only two of the 11 species of marine birds were endemic. A similar situation but in a body of water is seen in Lake Baikal. This is the deepest lake in the world, is over 500 miles long, and has been isolated from other bodies of water since the Age of Reptiles, the Mesozoic. Of 384 species of arthropods, 98 per cent are found nowhere else and of the 36 species of fishes, 81 per cent are likewise endemic.

Comparative Anatomy. The facts of comparative anatomy have always been regarded as basic supporting evidence for the fact of evolution. Basic to this interpretation itself are the twin concepts of **homology** and **analogy.**

241

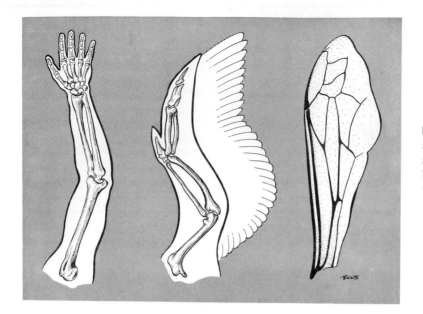

Fig. 10–7. The human arm and the bird wing are homologous; the bird wing and the insect wing are analogous.

Homology is basic anatomical similarity, regardless of function. The arm of a man, the front leg of a horse, and the wing of a bird are homologous. The wing of an insect, although used for the same function as the wing of a bird, has a radically different basic structure; hence these two are merely analogous to each other.

The classical criteria of homology are similarity of anatomy in the adult and similarity of development in the embryo. The human arm, the foreleg of a horse, and the wing of a bird all pass the second test also, for all begin as paddle-shaped buds, as though they were going to become five-toed (pentadactyl) limbs. Only in man does this generalized reptilian pattern of the pentadactyl limb complete itself. In the horse and bird the humerus of the upper arm and the radius and ulna of the forearm are well developed, but the bones of the wrist and hand are highly modified.

The homologies just given are examples of what is called **special homology,** that is, the homology between special structures like the forelimb, in two or more different kinds of animals. **Serial homology** is the homology between structures in an anterior-posterior series on the body of a single animal. The arm and leg of a man illustrate serial homology. The humerus of the upper arm corresponds to the thigh bone or femur, the radius and ulna of the forearm to the tibia and fibula of the leg, the wrist bones to the ankle bones, and so on. Both kinds of homology were made famous in the appendages of the lobster and the crayfish by T. H. Huxley. It can be shown that the big claw of a lobster corresponds part for part with the big claw of a

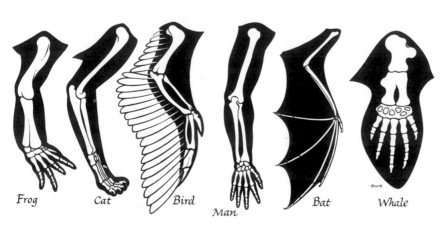

Frog   Cat   Bird   Man   Bat   Whale

Fig. 10–8. Skeletal homology in vertebrate limbs. *(From Pauli, The World of Life, Houghton Mifflin)*

crayfish or a crab. This is special homology. It can also be seen that there is a basic anatomical correspondence between the big claw and all the other appendages along the lobster's body. This is serial homology. The generalized ancestor was an animal like a fossil trilobite, with many segments each bearing a pair of similar appendages, and with all appendages having a basic similarity to the walking legs of the lobster. The anatomical correspondence between the scales of a shark and the teeth of a shark is known as **general homology,** i.e., basic similarity of structure and development without specific correspondence in the location or in the serial arrangement.

The facts of homology do not in themselves prove that evolution has occurred. However, the theory of descent with modification from a common ancestor provides the only scientific explanation. As Charles Darwin asked in his *Origin of Species:*

Why should similar bones have been created to form the wing and the leg of a bat, used as they are for such totally different purposes, namely flying and walking? Why should one crustacean, with an extremely complex mouth formed of many parts, consequently have fewer legs; or conversely, those with many legs have simpler mouths?

Comparative Embryology. The study of the comparative anatomy of embryos reveals many facts which can only be explained at all easily on the basis of evolution. How else explain the presence of gill slits in the embryos of reptiles, birds, and mammals, except by postulating ancestors in which gill slits were functional? The development of the heart and the main arteries from it, and the development of the kidneys also show fishlike stages in the embryos of higher vertebrates.

Martin Rathké, who discovered gill slits in the embryos of higher vertebrates, interpreted them according to the **theory of recapitulation.** This theory has enough truth back of it and was presented so persuasively in the 1880's by that great popularizer of evolution, Ernst Haeckel, that it still lingers on. According to it, **ontogeny,** the development of the individual, recapitulates **phylogeny,** the development of the race. In the minds of Haeckel and his followers, the adult stages of the ancestors are passed through quickly and in their proper historical sequence in the embryo, and the new stages of evolutionary development are added at the end of the series. In this form the theory runs into so many difficulties it clearly cannot be true. An immediate problem is presented by the fetal membranes, the umbilical cord, and other fetal structures that cannot represent adult features of any period. Furthermore, mutations have been shown to modify all stages of development, not just the final ones. The recapitulation theory is of course in hopeless conflict with the evidence demonstrating the importance of neoteny in evolution.

The modern interpretation of such embryonic structures as gill slits in mammals is that they correspond to the gill slits of an embryo fish rather than of an adult fish. Thus in a sense they are vestigial structures. Why do they remain at all? There are several reasons which taken together seem adequate to explain their persistence. Changes in genes which affect the earliest stages of development will be very likely to produce much more drastic and even lethal results than mutations which affect the later stages when the major organs have been laid down. This in itself will tend to make the early stages of development very conservative. Equally or even more important, natural selection has only a very indirect action on the developmental stages within an egg or a uterus. Its action is largely restricted to such matters as rates of growth and means of obtaining food and eliminating wastes. It is highly significant that it is in this respect that vast changes have taken place; witness the evolution of the placenta and the other fetal membranes. A third factor is often cited as making for embryonic conservatism. Some, at least, of the structures in which the embryo of a man resembles the embryo of a fish have a function in the machinery of embryonic development. For example, the primitive kidney or pronephros is present but virtually nonfunctional as a kidney in the embryos of higher vertebrates. However, it initiates the development of the pronephric duct, which becomes the vas deferens through which sperms pass to the exterior of the body. Likewise, the embryonic gill slits give rise to some of the endocrine glands.

Vestigial Organs. Vestigial organs, in the narrow sense of traces of hind legs in certain kinds of snakes, small pelvic bones in whales and porpoises, ear and tail muscles in human beings, and vestiges of toes in horses, can be explained only on the basis of evolution. In fact, combined with the fossil record, vestigial organs like these furnish convincing proof of the fact of evolution.

In the case of the horses which walk on one elongated and thickened toe on each foot — the hoof is the toenail — there are vestigial "hand" bones on either side of the main "finger," the bones horsemen call splint bones. In the recent fossil ancestors of horses the splint bones are much larger and each is tipped with a small hoof, while in the remote ancestral fossils, there are four functional toes on each front foot and three on each hind foot. In a similar manner all the primitive and generalized mammals are equipped with movable tails. Hence it seems reasonable to suppose that the vestigial tail muscles and tail bones in the human body are due to genes inherited from a tailed ancestor. If the snakes are in fact descended from primitive reptiles, they are descended from animals with hind legs. Likewise, the geological record clearly shows that all the early primitive mammals were four-legged; therefore whales and porpoises must be descended from ancestors equipped with hind legs. Small wonder then that cetaceans and some snakes bear signs of hind legs and pelvic bones.

Fig. 10–9. Vestigial hind legs of a python. *A,* external. *B,* internal. *(From Pauli,* The World of Life, *Houghton Mifflin)*

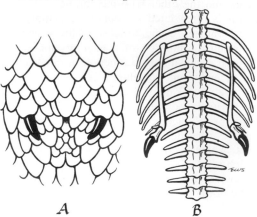

A   *B*

THE ORIGIN OF LIFE

"All Life from Life." The twin questions of the origin of life and the place of life in the universe are among the great themes of biological science. At one time or another, almost every conceivable theory has been proposed. Until very recently it was commonly believed by ignorant and learned persons alike that life continuously and spontaneously arises from dead matter. Maggots, people thought, were mysteriously generated in decaying meat, worms and even frogs were generated from the mud and muck on the bottoms of ponds, clothing moths originated from a mixture of wool and grease. Only a little over a century ago zoologists believed that tapeworms arose spontaneously in the intestines of their hosts.

The first great blow to the theory of **spontaneous generation** came from the experiments of a 17th century Florentine physician, Francesco Redi (1626–1698). This clear-headed man showed conclusively that the age-old belief that maggots arise spontaneously in decaying meat was false. Instead, he proved, they develop from eggs laid by flies. His method is a classic example of scientific procedure, for it was clearly conceived to yield a definite answer and made good use of controls. Redi used a wide variety of meats, singly and in combinations, for (who knew?) perhaps some meat was unsuitable. Apparently he had access to a good butcher shop and a generous zoo because he records using beef, lamb, venison, chicken, goose, duck, dog, lion, and even swordfish and eel from the river Arno. He placed the meat in two series of jars. One he covered with very fine cloth mesh, the other he left uncovered. The meat in both covered and uncovered jars became stinking masses, reeking with putrefaction. Yet only in the uncovered jars where flies gained access and laid their eggs did maggots develop. Neither the kind of meat nor its degree of decay made any difference. Increasing knowledge of the life histories and embryological development of insects, frogs, and other macroscopic animals made it clear that animals always develop from previously existing animals, not from nonliving material.

But, as often happens in the history of science, the old question was reopened on a new level by discoveries in later centuries. In fact, the question of spontaneous generation has been reopened three times and is now once again the subject of intense scientific interest. In the 18th century it was the widespread knowledge of bacteria that raised the question again. Bacteria certainly seem "just to appear" almost everywhere. However, Spallanzani (1729–1799) finally succeeded in showing that if meat or other broth was thoroughly boiled and the container sealed while still hot, bacteria never appear and the contents will remain unspoiled indefinitely. From a practical standpoint, this was a discovery of the first rank, because the canning of food, the control of contagious diseases, and the conduct of surgery are all heavily involved.

Again in the 19th century the question was raised, and given what seemed a final answer by Pasteur (1822–1895). The increasing knowledge of respiration made it seem possible, or even likely, that Spallanzani's heating had driven off the oxygen necessary for life. Moreover, the new chemical theories of fermentation seemed to support the idea of the spontaneous generation of life. Once again the results of Redi were confirmed for bacteria, this time in a long series of investigations ending in a brilliant demonstration by Pasteur given at the Sorbonne in 1864.

In brief, Pasteur showed that if beef broth or other foodstuffs were thoroughly boiled in open vessels no bacteria would appear in them so long as the opening to the exterior was a long curved tubular neck bent horizontally so that no dust or dirt particles carrying bacteria could pass up it. After the broth has remained sterile for weeks or months, all that is necessary to start a growth of bacteria is to tip the broth so that it flows out to the end of the neck and back again, carrying some dust with it. The subsequent putrefaction shows that there was nothing to prevent bacterial growth either in the composition of the broth or its access to the

Fig. 10–10. Apparatus used by Pasteur to prove that living organisms are essential for fermentation. *(Library of Congress)*

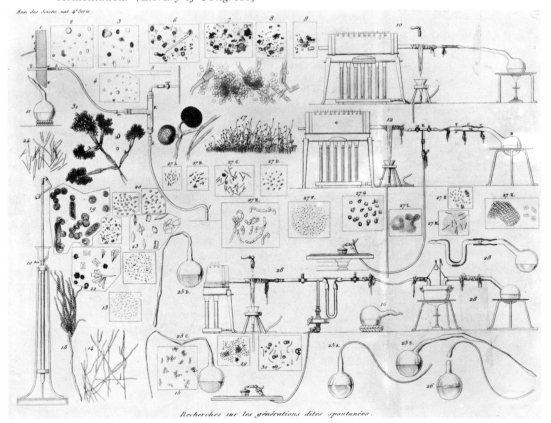

Ann. des Scienc. nat. 4.ᵉ Serie.

Recherches sur les générations dites spontanées.

atmosphere through the bent neck of the flask. Pasteur's work was beautifully substantiated by the investigations of the physicist Tyndall on optically empty, 100 per cent dust-free air. From this time on the phrase, *Omne vivum ex vivo,* all life from life, has been a basic tenet of all branches of biology.

To explain the presence of life on our planet, several eminent physicists in the closing years of the 19th century consequently felt compelled to accept fully the idea that life never arises from nonliving matter. Instead, they proposed that life had reached the earth from outer space as minute germs of some kind, wafted thither by the pressure of light. There was never any positive evidence for this so-called **cosmozoa theory,** and there are indeed serious objections to it. As soon as such spores approached a solar system they would be subjected to intense and destructive ultraviolet radiation, to say nothing of cosmic radiation throughout space.

The Heterotroph Theory. In very recent years the advancing knowledge of biochemistry and genetics, of historical geology, and of the possibilities of natural selection have combined to substantiate the heterotroph theory of life's origin. A **heterotroph** (*hetero,* other, + *trophos,* feeder) is an organism, such as an animal or a fungus, that is dependent on outside sources for complex nutritive materials, especially on a carbon source more complex than CO_2. An **autotroph** (*auto,* self, + *trophos,* feeder) is not thus dependent but can manufacture its own food from very simple inorganic materials, such as water and air. A heterotroph theory of the origin of life has been discussed off and on for a good many years, and in fact was proposed in 1871 by Darwin himself in the following words:

> It is often said that all the conditions for the first production of a living organism are now present, which could ever have been present. But if (and oh! what a big if) we could conceive in some warm little pond, with all sorts of ammonia and phosphoric salts, light, heat, electricity, etc., present, that a protein compound was chemically formed ready to undergo still more complex changes, at the present day, such matter would be instantly devoured or absorbed, which would not be the case before living creatures were formed.

The heterotroph theory holds that before the existence of any life on a planet, complex organic molecules could not only arise, but once formed would remain in existence because there would be no bacteria, molds, or protozoa to devour them for their own metabolism. The first living things would be composed of these complex molecules built up into still more complex arrangements. Darwin almost says nucleic acids when he mentions both proteins and phosphoric salts. A fundamental characteristic of the proteins and nucleic acids of protoplasm is their ability to duplicate themselves, exactly how we do not know. Because these primordial living units were dependent on their environment for the complex molecules of which they constructed themselves, they were heterotrophs. Whether these first forms of life were "free genes" something like footloose virus particles or were colloid globules, the so-called **coacervates,** is not certainly known. Coacervation, that is, the formation of discrete colloidal globules separated from their environment by a distinct boundary membrane, is something which occurs readily with nonliving material in the laboratory. Such a coacervate composed of self-duplicating nucleic acids and proteins would not be very different from an amoeba.

Much more recently the heterotroph theory has been set forth by J. B. S. Haldane in England and in great detail by A. I. Oparin in Russia. The evidence for the heterotroph theory does not constitute proof, but it is nonetheless very convincing.

The Nonliving Basis. The evidence from both astronomy and geology indicates that in the remote past before the appearance of life, the earth's atmosphere lacked appreciable amounts of oxygen but was rich in just those carbon and nitrogen compounds, plus water vapor, that are required to form amino acids, proteins, and nucleic acids. Today the other planets, where it is certainly too cold or too hot for life, have atmospheres of this type. Spectroscopic analysis shows that the "air" of Jupiter and Saturn is rich in methane (CH_4), ammonia (NH_3), and probably hydrogen (H_2). The atmosphere of Venus contains enormous amounts of carbon dioxide (CO_2), the atmosphere of Mars has both water (H_2O) and carbon dioxide. Our sea, after the first dozen million years—and it is important to remember that evolution is a matter of some billions of years—would contain salts of many kinds, including phosphates which seem essential for the energy transfers of living material, and for building nucleic acids.

The raw materials were certainly present. What were the chances that they would have combined into complex molecules like porphyrins, amino acids, and self-duplicating units like the combinations of nucleic acid and protein? There is first of all the enormous stretch of time during which the simpler compounds would have had opportunities to come together in all possible ways and combinations. Of course, if carbon, oxygen, nitrogen, and hydrogen could not form amino acids, no amount of time would avail; but these *are* the elements out of which amino acids are made. It is undoubtedly a possible reaction.

Not only were the raw materials present; at least three conditions, in addition to enormous stretches of time, were present that would have greatly facilitated such synthetic reactions. One factor, perhaps the most important, was the intense ultraviolet radiation reaching the earth's surface before there was any appreciable free oxygen in the atmosphere. Free oxygen under the influence of solar radiation forms ozone, which today constitutes a protective blanket around the earth in the upper atmosphere and shuts out most of the ultraviolet radiation. A second factor is lightning, which today is still producing in the atmosphere nitrogen compounds, brought to the earth's surface in rain. Thirdly, in the long course of geologic history, the earth's crust has undergone many upheavals. Mountains have appeared, continents have been submerged, and what is now dry land was once under the sea. In this process arms and bays of the sea are cut off from the ocean and may dry up completely, leaving salt beds, or may later be connected with the sea again. The Caspian Sea represents such a cut-off bay. This means that in the past there have been all types of places, from temporary tide pools to inland seas, where evaporation would slowly concentrate the salts and organic compounds and thereby increase the likelihood of occurrence of new and complex chemical reactions.

Natural Selection, Chemical Level. As both Darwin and Oparin have emphasized, before any living things existed on our planet, complex compounds which today would be quickly metabolized, i.e., eaten up, by microorganisms of various kinds, would simply remain lying around. There would be no decay in the usual sense because the organisms which cause decay would not exist. Under these conditions there would be a natural selection among the various organic compounds mixing in the primeval seas and pools. Compounds that were less stable or were more difficult to form would become less abundant, while the more stable ones would increase. Compounds which had the ability to imprint their own organization on other compounds would be favored over those which lacked such an ability. Those well fitted to organize more molecules into configurations like themselves would be favored over those which did so only slowly. The slow ones would be "outbred," so to speak, and might even cease to exist.

Emergence of Life. By the time complex compounds had appeared which had the property of organizing, or of catalyzing, the formation of other compounds like themselves, we are already in the shadowy borderland between the clearly nonliving and the obviously living. In considering the probable events during this early period of life's origin, it is important to remember that many of the materials present in the primordial "soup," although relatively simple themselves, are nonetheless the substances out of which the highly complex macromolecules of life are built. Phosphoric acid, H_3PO_4, for instance, is an essential part of the structure of all nucleic acids and also essential in most energy transfers within living systems. Glycine, composed of one carbon, one $—NH_2$, and one $—COOH$ group, plus two hydrogens, is the simplest possible amino acid. Acetic acid, CH_3COOH, is almost the simplest possible organic acid. Yet glycine and acetic acid combine to form porphyrin. Porphyrin forms the skeleton of the vitamin B_{12} molecule which plays a central role in many metabolic processes including the formation of nucleic acids. Porphyrin also is a key part of the cytochrome, chlorophyll, and hemoglobin molecules!

The existence of complex, more or less self-duplicating compounds and aggregates of compounds would not prevent natural selection from taking place. If anything, it would be intensified. At first the energy for the synthesis of these compounds would have been supplied primarily by ultraviolet light from the sun and by lightning. But once complex compounds had been formed in some abundance, any molecular species of such a configuration that it could obtain the energy needed for its synthesis by causing the breakdown of other compounds, rather than depending on solar radiation, would clearly have an adaptive advantage. There was probably no free oxygen present; if there was, it was certainly very little, so that these first energy-yielding reactions would have to be anaerobic. At precisely what point these self-duplicating, energy-utilizing molecular entities can be said to be alive is a semantic question, that is, a question of precise definition of the terms used.

The view that the first energy-yielding reactions to appear in the history of life were anaerobic is supported not only by the astronomical and geological evidence that there was no free oxygen in the atmosphere of our planet in its youth; it is also supported by the fact that the initial stages in the utilization of foodstuffs to provide energy in animals, plants, and bacteria are always anaerobic. In other words, the Embden–Meyerhof glycolytic pathway—fermentation, if you will—which does not depend on free oxygen, precedes the Krebs citric acid cycle which does require free oxygen. In fact, as will presently become evident, there are good reasons for believing that the Krebs cycle evolved much later than the glycolytic pathway and that it was tacked on to the end of it, so to speak.

Very few and perhaps no biologists any longer believe that the first living things must have been green plants, purple bacteria, or other autotrophs. Obviously an autotroph must begin with a far more complex set of synthetic enzymes than a heterotroph, which depends on picking up and utilizing already existing compounds of some complexity. To begin with an autotroph, is to begin at the wrong end.

The Great Dichotomy of Life. Once many of these self-duplicating units had come into existence they would begin to compete with each other for the dwindling supply of complex nutrients. Two very different lines of selection then would become operative. Natural selection would favor a unit that required fewer complex molecules in its "diet" over one that required more. For example, an organism that required compounds A, B, C, D, and E, but could make its own F by transforming E, would have an obvious advantage over the organism which also required F. This line of selection leads to the photosynthetic plants, the autotrophs which can build themselves up from simple inorganic salts, CO_2, and water. Water was of course abundant from the start of life and the fermentations carried out by such organisms as existed would assure a supply of CO_2. No completely new world of mutations would be necessary to establish photosynthesis because, as has been recently discovered, photosynthesis is essentially one aspect of anaerobic respiration run backwards rather than an entirely new and different thing. Also, porphyrins themselves are light-sensitive compounds.

Fortunately for us there is another possible evolutionary answer to the food crisis of those remote times. The second line of selection would favor those units which could either move around and so get into a place where the necessary materials for their growth were present, or else could engulf other organized units and secure the essential materials that way. This line of selection clearly leads to the animals. Once photosynthesis became widespread, it would provide a supply of free oxygen. This would make aerobic respiration possible for plants but it would be of even greater importance for the evolution of animals which characteristically depend on vigorous activity, a highly energy-dependent trait.

It will be noted that the nutritional crisis just discussed would arise on any planet where life arose in the manner described. It would also be true that the same two possible answers would exist on any planet whatever. Hence it would seem reasonable to suppose that there would be both plants and animals on any planet where there was an abundance of living things.

Laboratory Confirmations. To some of these general arguments, Harold Urey and his student, Stanley Miller, have added laboratory proof. They set up a device in which they circulated a sterile atmosphere of water vapor, ammonia, methane, and hydrogen past an electric discharge to simulate lightning. The water vapor was then condensed into water, and in this water they found after some weeks a variety of complex substances including the amino acids glycine and alanine, two of the commonest in proteins, and others besides, probably aspartic acid. This experiment clearly ranks with the synthesis of urea by Wöhler as a landmark in understanding the chemistry of life. The work of Urey has been confirmed and extended in other laboratories.

Strong support for the concept that successive mutations increase the synthetic abilities of primitive organisms has been obtained by students of mutations affecting the nutritional requirements of bacteria and fungi, especially the

Fig. 10–11. Urey-Miller apparatus simulating conditions on earth before the appearance of life. Many complex substances including amino acids were found in the condensed vapor in the trap.

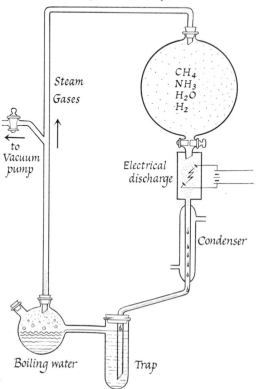

Steam
Gases

to
Vacuum
pump

CH₄
NH₃
H₂O
H₂

Electrical
discharge

Condenser

Boiling water   Trap

pink bread mold *Neurospora*. Essentially, mutations are occasional errors which occur in the duplication of the genic nucleic acids, and there is no reason to suppose that such events were any rarer in the remote past than they are now.

The Role of Chance. Does all this mean that the origin of life is a matter of chance? This often-asked question can easily lead into an exercise in semantics and scientific double-talk. In the sense that the particular time, place, and manner in which the first self-duplicating unit appeared would be no more and no less predictable than when the number five will turn up in a series of throws of dice, the origin of life is clearly a matter of chance. There is no necessary reason why the first living unit should be formed from compounds carried down by raindrops after synthesis by lightning rather than from molecules formed just under the surface of the sea by ultraviolet radiation. At the same time, the potentialities for combining into amino acids and more complex self-duplicating units must be present in the original methane, ammonia, and other molecules. If none of the dice used has a side with five dots on it, five will never come up regardless of how many times the dice are thrown. Obviously a five must be present if there is to be a chance for it to turn up. The appearance of life was a matter of chance, but the dice were loaded.

THE HISTORY OF LIFE ON THE EARTH

Fossil Remains. The vast drama of the evolution of life on this planet is at least partially recorded in the form of fossils in the rocks. Most fossils consist of either the actual body of an organism which has been gradually mineralized or of an imprint left by an organism. The sandstone of the Connecticut River valley is famous for fossilized footprints left by dinosaurs. Very similar dinosaur footprints of great size have more recently been discovered in the sandstone bed of the Paluxy River in Texas.

Many fossils have not been completely mineralized and still retain traces of organic matter. All the coal in existence is derived from forests from an age tens of millions of years before the dinosaurs flourished. All the oil and all the chalk cliffs are deposits formed from the oil droplets or skeletons of protozoans or algae. By contrast, some remains of extinct and prehistoric life are so recent they have scarcely been changed enough to be called fossils. In many parts of the United States there are bones of extinct animals. Preserved in ancient tarpits and in dry caves in the southwest are the remains of sabre-toothed tigers, small and large species of elephants, and other animals no longer in existence. In the far north in both Alaska and Siberia the frozen remains of several woolly elephants known as mammoths have been found. Not only was the fur preserved but even the flesh was still recognizable as meat and was eaten by dogs.

Fossils are found only in sedimentary, that is, in stratified, rocks. These are formed in two principal ways. One is the slow accumulation of sand or other sediment on ocean or lake bottoms. The other is the accumulation of material on the land, perhaps in extensive bogs and marshes, which in later ages becomes submerged beneath the ocean by the slow changes in the continents that seem always to be taking place. Igneous rock, which is spewed out of volcanoes and presumably formed the original crust of the earth, never contains fossils. Granite is such a rock.

New Methods of Chronology. The new ways of forcing the earth to reveal the age of her rocks and their fossils are continually becoming more precise. At the same time the older methods are still valuable. The rate at which Niagara Falls moves upstream, cutting its gorge as it goes, can be measured. By simple arithmetic it is then possible to estimate how long it has taken Niagara Falls to cut its gorge. Correcting for the probability that more water flowed over the falls in the past when the last glaciers were melting, the answer comes out to somewhat over 10,000 years, an estimate that agrees with estimates made by other methods.

Another method that gives reliable results in determining chronology of the recent past is to count varves in clay. **Varves** are layers of sediment formed where a river runs into a body of quiet water. This is especially true of rivers running down from snow-capped Alps or melting glaciers. Spring flood-waters wash down

Fig. 10–12. Varves in clay. *(Kindness of F. T. Thwaites)*

coarse sediment. As the runoff slows down during the summer, the sediment becomes finer and finer. In the winter it is finest of all, to be followed the next spring by another coarse layer. A long hot spring and summer with much melting ice will leave a coarse, thick layer. An unusually cool spring and summer, with little melting, result in a thin layer of finer clay. Consequently, by counting the varves in a deposit of clay it is as easy to determine the number of years it was in forming as it is to tell the age of a tree by counting the annual rings revealed by a cross section of the trunk. By comparing the pattern of successive varves in one lake with those in another it is possible to correlate their dates of origin.

Longer periods are dated by measuring the radioactivity of various materials imbedded in the different strata. Each kind of radioactive material has a different **half-life,** that is, the time before 50 per cent of its radioactivity is lost. A crystal of uranium-238 will be half lead after 4.5 billion years. By determining the percentage of lead in such a piece of uranium, it is possible to tell its age. The greater the proportion of lead, the older the crystal. Although such crystals form only in molten igneous rock as it cools, it is possible to use them to date strata of sedimentary rock which has been formed by the gradual deposit of silt or other material on the ocean floor. In volcanic convulsions molten igneous rock sometimes breaks through strata of sedimentary rock. Obviously all the strata through which such molten rock breaks must antedate the volcanic action. The molten rock often spreads out on top of the uppermost strata, forming an enormous pancake of igneous rock. Any sedimentary rock above this pancake must of course be younger. Obviously this method is only useful in measuring long periods.

A similar method is the recently introduced radio-carbon technique. This provides an accurate clock for periods ranging from a few thousand to about 35,000 years ago, since the half-life of radioactive carbon-14 is $5,568 \pm 30$ years. This carbon is being formed in the earth's atmosphere by the action of cosmic rays on nitrogen, and is also continually disintegrating, so that an enduring equilibrium exists age after age. Radioactive carbon built into plants by photosynthesis will not be replenished after they die. Consequently, the longer a piece of wood or of any animal that ate plants lies around, the less radioactive carbon it is found to contain.

1. The Archeozoic: The Origin of Life. The Archeozoic Era, during which life's nonliving precursors accumulated and interacted, and in which life finally took form, was an immense stretch of time, probably some 2,000 million years. Geological evidence in rocks of this age indicates a period of intense volcanic activity, mountain building, and extensive erosion with the formation of some sedimentary rocks. Columns of steam are thought to have arisen where molten rock flowed into the sea or violent rains fell on hot rocks. It was presumably the age of the primordial heterotrophs and the time when the animal and plant kingdoms first became differentiated. There are no recognizable fossils in the rocks of this age but there are deposits which may have been made by iron-, sulfur-, and carbon-utilizing bacteria.

2. The Proterozoic: The Origin of Phyla. Following the Archeozoic came another era lasting some 1,000 million years, the Proterozoic. Fossils occur in rocks of Proterozoic age, but are few in number and extremely difficult to

decipher. The time has been too long and the pressures and shearing of the rocks too severe. This also must have been a period of mountain building and erosion with consequent sedimentation. In Glacier National Park there are cliffs of about 50,000 feet of sedimentary rock laid down during this era and yet they represent the deposits of only a small fraction of its duration.

Life was still limited to the sea. Despite the poverty of fossils, it seems quite certain that during this immense stretch of time the major phyla were differentiated, because in the earliest strata of the next era, the Paleozoic, representatives of all the major animal phyla are already present. Lost in the tortured rocks of the Proterozoic is the record of how the first metazoans developed. Were they coelenterates, sponges, or flatworms? The record in the rocks is silent. Nor does the record tell how the animal kingdom came to be divided into the two great branches—the deuterostomes (composed of the vertebrates, the echinoderms, and their relatives), and the protostomes (composed of the annelids, the arthropods, the mollusks, and their kin).

3. The Paleozoic: Era of Invertebrates and Fishes. When the Paleozoic began, about 500 million years ago, nearly five-sixths of the entire time during which life originated and has evolved had already passed. Nevertheless, stupendous events in the history of life were yet to come—the rise of the insects, the higher mollusks like the octopus, and the vertebrates, including the dinosaurs, the birds, and, of course, man himself.

The Cambrian Period. The earliest division of the Paleozoic era is known as the Cambrian Period, because rock strata laid down then were first intensively studied in Wales (Cambria). The Cambrian rocks are the oldest in which fossils are abundant. So sharp is the distinction in this respect that all earlier strata are commonly referred to merely as pre-Cambrian. The Cambrian is not, however, a beginning in the history of life. It is rather a beginning in the fossil record of that history. Already present at the beginning of the Cambrian are representatives, small and generalized but unmistakable, of all the major invertebrate

Time-Table of Life on Earth

ERA AND DURATION (IN MILLIONS OF YEARS)	MILLIONS OF YEARS AGO (FROM START OF PERIOD OR EPOCH)	PERIOD AND EPOCH AND DURATION (IN MILLIONS OF YEARS)	CHARACTERISTIC LIFE
Cenozoic 70	0.025 1	Quaternary 1 Recent epoch Pleistocene epoch	Age of man
	10 25 40 60 70	Tertiary 69 Pliocene epoch Miocene epoch Oligocene epoch Eocene epoch Paleocene epoch	Age of mammals and insects Flowering plants
Mesozoic 130	130	Cretaceous 60	Modern birds appear Age of reptiles
	165	Jurassic 35	Age of reptiles Mollusks abundant
	200	Triassic 35	Age of reptiles Mammals appear in numbers
Paleozoic 350	230	Permian 30	Insects common Reptiles appear in numbers
	250	Pennsylvanian 20	Coal beds formed
	280	Mississippian 30	Sea lilies abundant Coal beds formed
	325	Devonian 45	Amphibians appear
	360	Silurian 35	Jawed fishes appear Land plants abundant
	450	Ordovician 90	Age of jawless fishes Corals abundant Land plants appear
	550	Cambrian 100	Representatives of all major animal phyla except chordates
Pre-Cambrian 2,500 Proterozoic Archeozoic	3,000		

phyla of animals: protozoans, sponges, coelenterates, annelids, echinoderms, mollusks, arthropods, and several others. The most abundant larger animals were trilobites, a kind of arthropod. Several kinds of animals living in the Cambrian are still present today almost unchanged, at least in general form. This is true of some of the jellyfish and some brachiopods. The only major phylum not represented was the chordates, of which the vertebrates are a subphylum, and these appear in the next period.

The Ordovician Period. The next period of the Paleozoic, the Ordovician, saw two events of paramount importance, the appearance of fresh-water and probably land plants and the appearance of the vertebrates. The two events were very possibly connected, since the fossil evidence indicates that the first vertebrates were jawless fishes, ostracoderms, which arose in fresh water. They are supposed to have come from primitive oceanic chordates, probably larval tunicates, that took to swimming up estuaries and rivers where they lived on the rich organic detritus coming down with the current. Until there were land plants, or at least fresh-water plants, there could of course be no nourishing debris washed down from the land, so the theory assumes an abundant land vegetation at this time. These ostracoderms were evidently bottom feeders, for their jawless mouths were on the underside of their flattish heads. This character fits the theory that they obtained their food, like so many invertebrates today, by ingesting large quantities of mud mixed with organic matter.

The most abundant animals still seem to have been trilobites; at least they left the most fossils. Perhaps they had the hardest shells or lived where fossils were most likely to be formed. Eurypterids, something like scorpions and something like lobsters, abounded. Notable also were the mollusks and echinoderms. Among mollusks were both well-developed snails and cephalopods living in long conical shells. All five of the living groups of echinoderms: starfish, sea urchins, sea lilies, and the rest were present, plus three additional classes of echinoderms now extinct.

The Silurian and Devonian Periods. The following two periods of the Paleozoic, the Silurian and Devonian, are memorable for the first conquest of the land by both plants and animals. By the end of the Devonian, there were forests of tree ferns, giant club mosses, and giant horsetails covering much of the formerly barren continents.

In the sea were still of course the invertebrate hordes, but there were now also vertebrates with jaws. These jawed fishes had evidently come down the rivers and reentered the sea. Sharklike fishes were numerous and the first really big vertebrates, such as the armored *Dinichthys* (*dinos,* terror-striking, + *ichthys,* fish) which grew to be 30 feet long, a "dinosaur" among fishes.

More important in the evolution of life was the appearance in fresh waters of muscle-finned fishes (Sarcopterygii), a group which includes the lungfishes and coelacanths. They formed the population from which in the Devonian the amphibians evolved. Until recently the coelacanths were thought to have been extinct for at least 75 million years, for there are no known fossils of them after the end of the Mesozoic (the age of the dinosaurs). However, a small group has been located living in deep water around some small islands along the east coast of Africa north of Madagascar. Specimens are now undergoing intensive study. Small populations of lungfishes are still living in Australia, Africa, and South America.

The way in which the muscle-finned fishes became adapted for terrestrial life in the process of becoming adapted for survival in regions subject to drought, and thus gave rise to the amphibians, has been discussed previously as a case of pre-adaptation.

The vertebrates were not the only forms to exploit the opportunities of terrestrial life in the Devonian. Several groups of arthropods also became terrestrial. These included centipedes, scorpions, which had already attained a terrifying size in the sea, and primitive insects somewhat like cockroaches.

The Mississippian and Pennsylvanian Periods. The two next periods were the earlier Mississippian and the more recent Pennsylvanian. Together they endured a total of about 50 million years and are often called the carboniferous periods because particularly during these times there flourished the great forests which formed our present coal. The climate must have been warm and moist, and much of the land low-lying and swampy to support those lush growths of the same general kind of non-flowering plants — giant club mosses and ferns — that characterized earlier eons. Abundant primitive seed plants were to be found, clearly modified ferns.

New animal groups also arose. The first small reptiles appeared, scarcely distinguishable from the now common amphibians, and certainly giving no hint of what they would become in a later era. In Pennsylvanian times living things first became able to fly, a remarkable evolutionary achievement 250 million years ago. The first flyers were either cockroaches or large dragonflies, very similar in structure to our present-day species. What they ate is a problem. Today dragonflies live in the water as larvae but catch other insects on the wing as adults. Perhaps the presence of these dragonflies indicates that there were other insects that have not left fossils. It seems more likely that the first wings had the same function as the wings of most insects today, namely, to disseminate the species and enable the adults to find new ponds or other suitable places to lay their eggs. The catching of other insects on the wing probably came much later. In the seas, the Pennsylvanian was a great age of echinoderms, especially of sea lilies.

The Permian Period. The Permian Period closed the Paleozoic era. It was a period of great climatic and geological changes. Due to shrinkage of the earth's crust, or perhaps other causes, the Appalachian Mountain range along eastern North America was thrust up, carrying with it Paleozoic sediments which had been pressed into fossil-bearing rock strata thousands of feet thick. The climate was dry and cold. In many parts of the world — South America, India, and Australia — there are unmistakable marks of a Permian glaciation apparently longer and more severe than the comparatively recent Pleistocene glaciation from which we are still emerging. All these changes are commonly called the Appalachian Revolution. The lush carboniferous forests of the two preceding periods dried up. The tree ferns all but disappeared. The last of the trilobites, which had been dominant animals since the Cambrian some 350 million years earlier,

finally died out. The sea lilies, those strange stalked echinoderms, dwindled to a few isolated populations. Generalized reptiles resembling heavily built salamanders and modern-looking insects became the dominant land animals. The most important event from the human point of view was the appearance of the forerunners of the mammals. These were the cynodont (*kynos*, dog, + *dont*, tooth) or dog-toothed reptiles, in which the teeth were not merely a row of sharp pegs as in the dinosaurs and reptiles generally, but were differentiated into incisors, canines, and cheek teeth with several cusps. Palatine teeth were missing. The best known genus is *Cynognathus* (*kynos*, dog, + *gnathus*, jaw), a lizardlike creature that flourished into the following era and grew to be about 8 feet long. For some species, like the "lamp-shells" or brachiopods which had flourished at the beginning of the Paleozoic and throughout its entire duration, this period was not different from any other. They continued to flourish.

4. The Mesozoic: The Great Age of Reptiles. After the Appalachian Revolution of mountain building and glaciation that ended the Paleozoic, the world entered an era that was more uniformly dry and warm, the Mesozoic. This period saw the rise of the first mammals, probably egg-laying creatures, even as the most primitive mammals today — the spiny anteater and the duckbilled platypus of Australia — lay soft-shelled eggs like those of reptiles. During the Cretaceous at the end of the Mesozoic, Australia became separated from the great land mass of Eurasia and so became a sanctuary for the primitive egg-laying and marsupial mammals. The Mesozoic also saw the origin of the first birds and the first flowering plants. The birds were equipped with two things no living bird possesses — teeth, and long tails of many vertebrae, as in a lizard or a dog.

The Mesozoic era is divided into three periods, the *Triassic,* the *Jurassic,* and longest and most recent, the *Cretaceous.* The predominant terrestrial animals during this span of about 130 million years were the dinosaurs. Like other groups of animals before and since, these reptiles experienced one of those evolutionary explosions known as **adaptive radiation.** The reptiles began in the previous era as lizardlike creatures which could lay their eggs on land, relatively safe from the teeming predators of the water. The development of an amnion was the key step here, along with a protective leathery shell for the egg. Hence reptiles and their descendants, birds and mammals, are known as the amniotes. From this generalized basic population, the reptiles spread out by becoming specialized for many different modes of life in many environments. Biped carnivores like *Tyrannosaurus* preyed on herbivorous dinosaurs like *Triceratops,* which had three horns. In the swamps was the gigantic *Brontosaurus,* attaining a length of 80 feet. In the sea, marine reptiles competed with sharks and other fishes, and in the air were flying pterodactyls.

The Problem of Extinction. A question of great interest, and one that even carries definite though, let us hope, remote implications for man himself, is this: why did the reptiles become extinct? For over 150 million years the reptiles flourished in abundance of individuals and diversity of structure, and ranged from giant dinosaurs to delicate little flying creatures. They dominated the sea, the fresh-water swamps, the land, and the sky; yet except for a small remnant lurking in obscure places, they have disappeared.

The problem of extinction is a general one, and there is at least one general principle which applies. Natural populations continually undergo fluctuations. This is quite normal and depends on many factors: the number of predators and parasites, the food supply, the variations of the seasons. A prolonged cold rainy spell at the time deer give birth to their young can have drastic effects on the deer population. When a population is large, the normal fluctuations do not threaten it with extinction. When a population becomes very small, there is always danger that in the course of the normal ups and downs, one of the depressions will reach the zero point. This means that it is not necessary for any single factor to destroy every breeding pair. It is only necessary for it to lower the population to the danger level. Excessive hunting probably did this to the destructive but edible and now extinct passenger pigeons.

To return to the most massive and spectacular case of extinction in the history of life, what factors may have brought the level of all the different reptile populations down within the danger zone? One possibility is the general change of climate which historical geologists believe occurred at the close of the Mesozoic Era, the age of reptiles, some 70 million years ago. But although the cooling and drying of the regions near the poles may account for the lack of the great reptiles in those areas, it is difficult to see why, on this basis, many of them could not still flourish in the tropical regions of Central and South America, Africa, and South Asia, or in the ocean.

A second possibility is competition with the primitive mammals. At the close of the Mesozoic the only mammals that had yet appeared were small, generalized animals, much like small mongrel dogs or opossums. They are supposed to have contributed to the downfall of the dinosaurs and other reptiles by eating reptile eggs. Perhaps—but such primitive mammals would have had to be ubiquitous and extraordinarily effective to eat all the eggs in all the many environments.

A third possibility is that some epidemic viral, bacterial, or even protozoan disease wiped out the great reptile populations. This possibility is as hard to prove as to disprove. It is known that the tsetse fly, which transmits the trypanosome of African sleeping sickness, has made it impossible to keep domestic cattle in large areas of Africa, but—and this is equally important—the native relatives of cattle, like the various gazelles and antelopes, have enough immunity to flourish in these same regions and serve as "reservoirs" of the disease.

The most interesting suggested explanation is a modern version of the old theory of **racial senescence.** No zoologists any longer hold that time, simply as duration, produces some inevitable racial aging. Too many different kinds of animals have existed unchanged, or with only the most trivial changes, for hundreds of millions of years—sharks, lungfish, some echinoderms, and others. But the natural course of evolutionary change resulting from mutation and natural selection tends to make animals more and more narrowly specialized. And **excessive specialization** can act as a trap. When an animal becomes so highly specialized that it loses the versatility needed to meet changing conditions, in either the living or the nonliving environment, then the highly specialized group loses out to the more generalized.

Another common result of evolution, which is very obvious in the mammals as it was in the reptiles, is an increase in size. What evolutionary forces lead to increased size? One obvious factor is competition, especially between males of the same species. Perhaps this leads to a disastrous spiral, in which only the largest males can win females but in which individuals become too large to function efficiently in food-getting and other ways. A similar type of disaster may have overtaken the big herbivorous dinosaurs such as the three-horned *Triceratops* and the 47-foot-long carnivore, *Tyrannosaurus*. A small *Triceratops* got eaten, but a big one couldn't eat enough to keep healthy. A small *Tyrannosaurus* couldn't overpower the average *Triceratops,* but a big one was too ponderous to make a kill. Here indeed was a predicament! There is evidence today that large male lions are partially dependent on the more agile females to obtain their food.

One, all, or none of these four factors may have been important. All we can be certain of is that the evolutionary deployment of the reptiles was remarkably like that of the mammals at a later time. Both began with a small, generalized form, and both gave rise to hundreds of extremely diverse types—the mammals to tigers, rabbits, giraffes, bats, and baboons. The reptiles produced a corresponding diversity, but except for a few relicts, they have disappeared.

The case of *Sphenodon,* lone survivor of its order and found only in remote New Zealand, is instructive in showing at least one of the most important factors causing extinction at the present time. Perhaps it throws some light on the extinction of so many groups of reptiles toward the end of the Cretaceous Period some 70 million years ago. With the settling of New Zealand by Europeans, sphenodons became rarer, until they were found only on a few small islands. Protective laws against killing them seemed only to slow the decline, not to stop it. Recently sheep-grazing on the islands where sphenodons live was stopped, the vegetation quickly returned to its original condition, and the tuataras, as the natives call them, have

greatly increased. In many similar cases in modern times a change in the environment—cutting down a forest or polluting a stream, for example—has resulted in the disappearance of its native populations.

5. The Cenozoic: The Age of Mammals. The final era of geologic time is the Cenozoic. This is the age which saw the evolution of the primates, including at the end man, and other mammals. The climate became progressively more temperate and drier. Hence the Cenozoic became the age of grass as extensive prairies, steppes, pampas, and veldts developed in many parts of the world. The evolution of the horse, camel, and other grass-eating animals was attuned to this spread of grass-covered prairies. It is probable that the thinning of the forests was an important factor in bringing man's precursors down out of the trees, though firm proof of this is lacking. The Cenozoic was also the age of birds and of modern insects and flowering plants.

The Cenozoic began only about 70 million years ago, so that it is by no means coordinate with the Mesozoic or Paleozoic Eras in duration, but rather with one of their subdivisions. The Cenozoic Era is divided into the Tertiary and Quaternary Periods. The Tertiary, in turn, is divided into five epochs: Paleocene, Eocene, Oligocene, Miocene, Pliocene. The Quaternary is divided into the Pleistocene and Recent epochs.

By the Paleocene at the beginning of the Cenozoic, the old ruling reptiles of the Mesozoic were extinct. Most of the mammals were small and generalized, vaguely doglike. However, there were a number of species of large and fairly specialized forms. The primitive elephants, for example, were larger than a large hog and probably provided with a well-developed and downward-bending snout. *Hyracotherium (Eohippus),* the remote ancestor of the horse, was vaguely suggestive of a miniature horse with four toes on its front feet and three on the hind. Its future course of evolution as a running herbivore seems to have been already set. By the end of the Paleocene there was one order of great ugly beasts that were roughly midway between a rhinoceros and an overgrown hippopotamus.

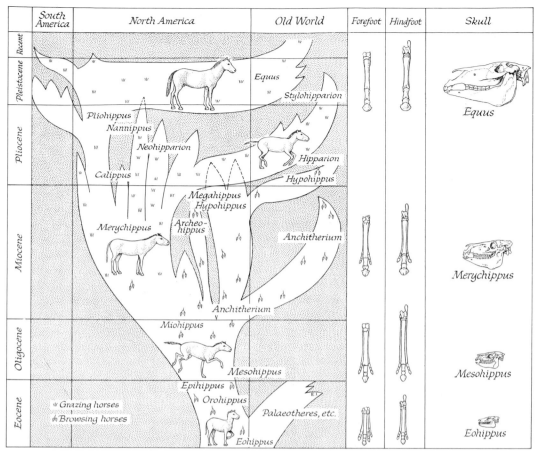

Fig. 10-13. Evolution of the horse. *(Adapted by permission from* Horses, *by G. G. Simpson. Copyright 1951 by Oxford University Press)*

During the rest of the Cenozoic the mammals underwent the same kind of explosive evolution or adaptive radiation that the reptiles had experienced in the Mesozoic. Like the reptiles, some of the mammals returned to the sea and became our present whales and porpoises. Later the seals and seacows followed. Others, the bats, became adapted for flying, like the pterosaurs. On land, the mammals diversified into a bewildering variety of species adapted for many kinds of life. One of the most spectacular and best studied cases is the evolution of the horse. *Hyracotherium*, the 18-inch-long "horse" of the Eocene, was followed by a whole series of populations of descendants. Some were more and some were less horselike, but in the long run natural selection favored those with the most elongated bones in the "hands" and feet and fewer toes, and with heavy corrugated grinding molar teeth; in other words, those better adapted for running on the prairie and eating grass. Toward the end of the Eocene, the larger *Orohippus* had not only larger feet, but a third toe larger than the other toes. This genus was followed in the Oligocene by *Mesohippus*, the first recognizable "horse," with a single toe on each foot carrying most of the weight. Its second and fourth toes scarcely touched the ground.

In the later Miocene and the following Pliocene several genera of horses appeared, again larger in body and more specialized in legs and teeth, *Merychippus*, *Pliohippus*, and others. The genus *Equus*, which includes as separate species the contemporary horse, the ass, and the zebra, actually first appeared in the late Pliocene. The members of this genus possess only "splint" bones on either side of the foot as tell-tale evidence of their many-toed ancestry. Horses spread widely in Eurasia, Africa, and North and South America. The charred bones of extinct horses are found in the fireplaces of

257

Stone Age men in California, but long before Europeans arrived on this continent the native horses had become extinct. We do not know why this happened.

The fossil record of the evolution of horses from fox-sized creatures in the Paleocene was the first fossil record worked out with any degree of completeness. This was largely the achievement of the paleontologists Kowalewsky in Europe and O. C. Marsh in the United States. Marsh dug his fossils out of the extensive Cenozoic deposits exposed in the "badlands" of the Big Horn River basin of Wyoming and the White River Badlands of South Dakota.

More or less fossilized remains of Pleistocene mammals have been found in many locations in North America. Typical species include the Columbian elephant or mammoth, the low-browed mastodon, the saber-toothed tiger, the stag-moose, a giant sloth, and primitive horses. Most exciting, in California there are "fossil fireplaces" containing the charred bones of mastodons. Evidently, early man on this continent killed, cooked, and ate mastodons. Either that, or these small elephants were in the habit of walking into fireplaces and getting burned up.

For several hundreds of years elephant tusks, "ground ivory," have been found in Siberia. Over 20 frozen, flesh-and-blood remains of mammoths have been found in northern Siberia, and in 1948 the frozen body of a baby mammoth was found during placer mining near Fairbanks, Alaska.

Fig. 10–14. Some of the more characteristic North American Pleistocene mammals, reduced to a uniform scale, with a pointer dog (in the ruled box) to show relative sizes. *1*, American mastodon. *2*, saber-tooth tiger. *3*, giant ground sloth. *4*, stag-moose. *5*, giant beaver. *6*, Columbian elephant. *7*, Texas horse. (*After Scott*)

The Origins of Man. Man's ancestry extends back to the origin of life, but his evolution as something very special among mammals began not earlier than sometime in the Paleocene, roughly 60 million years ago. At that time there was no distinction between the shrewlike insectivores and the monkeylike primates. But this primitive insectivore-primate stock possessed two characteristics which have left their marks on us to this day. These small mammals were generalized and they were tree-living.

They were generalized in their teeth, which were diversified into cutting incisors, piercing canines, and crushing molars, fitting their possessors for a varied omnivorous diet. Other mammals came to develop specialized teeth for chewing grass (a tough material to eat), tearing flesh, or gnawing. The primitive insectivore-primate group was also generalized in limbs, and in their five-toed feet, their skulls, and general bodily form.

The fact that these mammals were tree-living is equally important or even more so. For arboreal animals jumping from branch to branch, an ability to see well and especially to judge distance is of paramount importance. A misplaced jump can eliminate the jumper and his genes altogether. There was a premium on the possession of binocular vision, which confers depth perception. In contrast, a sense of smell becomes far less important to an arboreal animal. Here is the evolutionary explanation for the contrast in sensory abilities between a man who can see well but cannot follow a scent, and his dog who can follow a scent but whose vision is often deplorable by human standards.

Arboreal life is also associated with color vision. So far as is known, all mammals except the primates are color-blind and condemned to live in a world of greys. Not even the bravest bull can see the red of a red flag. Primates, however, like birds, have color vision, which gives an added "dimension" to seeing and confers an increased ability to identify objects at sight. It is also worth noting that color vision is useful only during the day. Significantly, this is the time when birds are about. Most mammals are primarily nocturnal, and both the herbivorous hunted and the carnivorous hunter are most active at dusk and just before dawn. In the trees and in the air life is relatively safe, animals can remain active during the day, and the ability to see in color is a useful accomplishment. Apparently we owe both our poor powers of smell and our remarkable powers of vision to our tree-living forebears.

The early arboreal environment is also believed to have been partly responsible for primates bringing forth but one young at a birth instead of a litter, as do ground-living species of insectivores. If the mother is to climb and jump among the boughs, as do many of the monkeys, one baby is about all that can be managed either *in utero* or clinging to the mother's body after birth.

When did the primates separate from the insectivores? The fossil record is missing, and even today it is impossible to make any clean-cut distinction between these two orders which span the enormous gulf between a man and a mole. Modern insectivores include not only moles but also shrews, which are common almost everywhere though seldom seen because of their small size and nocturnal habits. The primates include man and the anthropoid apes, the Old World monkeys, the New World monkeys (which alone possess prehensile tails), and the lemurs, now largely restricted to Madagascar and adjacent lands. The lemurs range from the size of a small rat to the size of a small dog, and range in appearance from a mouselike shrew to a monkey.

The most ancient monkeylike fossils so far discovered were found in lower, i.e., earlier, Oligocene strata in Egypt. *Parapithecus,* as this creature was named, was perhaps close to the base population from which both Old and New World monkeys diverged; but no one can be sure. Our broad shoulders and well-developed collar bones are clearly adaptations' for what anatomists call **brachiation,** i.e., swinging from branch to branch. But exactly when man's ancestors forsook the trees for the ground is unknown, although it is practically certain that they were fairly large, since the habit of swinging from branch to branch in contrast to climbing and jumping like the little lemurs is limited to the larger primates.

It does not seem too surprising that man's immediate subhuman predecessors left few fossils. Apparently they lived either in forests or grasslands where opportunities for fossilization are scanty, except for swamps, river quicksands, and tar pits. Evidently primitive man was too smart or too agile to get caught in these. However, anatomists have made some informed and plausible guesses about our early history.

The evolution of man took place during the end of the Cenozoic. This was a period when over large areas of the earth, forests were giving way to grasslands as the climate became drier. With the succulent leaves and buds of forest plants and the diverse animal life of forests vanishing, many animals were faced with a harsh choice: to eat grass or to eat other animals that ate grass. Grass is full of silica and not easy to eat. Hence the evolution of the complex corrugated grinding surfaces on the molars of horses and the extinct elephants, the mammoths. It was no accident that the evolution of grinding teeth and elongate hoofed legs in the horses went along together. Both are adaptations for life on prairies.

It is reasonable to suppose that these profound environmental changes affected the predecessors of modern man. The spread of the grasslands would necessitate either a changed way of life, with emphasis on hunting the animals (horses, deer, and mammoths) which ate the grass and shrubs, or a migration southward to keep within the dense forests. Perhaps both happened. Hunting of this kind would put an evolutionary premium on running and communication. Natural selection would then favor the further development of the upright posture and long straight legs, a good brain, and ability to speak and use weapons and other tools. It would also favor the kind of disposition that makes for mutual cooperation. The breeding units were certainly small. Populations of many millions are found in insects, fishes, and marine invertebrates, but surely did not exist in primates until man became industrialized.

Under these changing conditions the primary evolutionary forces of mutation and natural selection produced as much change in the primates as they did in the horses. This must have been the period when genetic factors building on the juvenile form with its proportionately much larger brain and prolonged period of willingness to learn must have come into play. This is the neoteny discussed earlier. In very small populations such as existed in the past, random genetic drift would come into play and produce changes regardless of adaptive significance. Perhaps the nonadaptive differences, if there really are any, between different races of men are to be explained in this way.

The most ancient remains of man-apes, or ape-men, or primitive man have been found in the Olduvai Gorge east of Lake Victoria at the southern end of the Rift Valley in Tanzania. The anthropologist Louis S. B. Leakey and his coworkers have unearthed an abundant deposit of bones, primitive stone tools, and other evidence of a primitive culture. The skeletons in this East African site resemble others found in South Africa and in Australia but are different enough to be given a new name, *Zinjanthropus*. The character of the stone tools dates this settlement about 500,000 – 600,000 years ago. However, the potassium-argon dating method places the material at the Olduvai site as about 1,750,000 years ago. Certainty will have to wait until further data can be obtained. The related forms, *Australopithecus*, both from Taung in Bechuanaland in Africa and from Australia may be as ancient as *Zinjanthropus* or even more so. No one really knows.

Dating back into the Pleistocene some 500,000 years ago are the remains of another extremely primitive man or manlike creature called variously the Java man or *Pithecanthropus* or *Homo erectus*, and also the Peking man or *Sinanthropus pekinensis*. When the fossils of these forms were first found in Java and a bit later near Peking they seemed different enough to merit separate generic rank. It will be recalled that there are no objective criteria for determining how different two organisms must be to deserve separate generic ratings. In the years since these discoveries, more remains of both have been found which are intermediate so that it seems the Java and Peking groups represent only slightly different forms of the same population. *Homo (Pithecanthropus) erectus* had a brain capacity of close to 1000 cc, about intermediate between a gorilla and a modern man. Plaster casts of the interior of the skulls reveal that the areas of the brain associated with speech were well developed, but, of course, proof of any spoken language is lacking. These Java men averaged well under 6 feet in height. The forehead was low, there was a heavy bony ridge over the eyes, and a heavy chinless jaw with large teeth. The skulls found in the deep limestone caves outside Peking had somewhat larger brains on the average.

Was *Homo (Pithecanthropus) erectus* truly human? If man is defined as a tool- and fire-using primate, the answer is clearly yes. Along with the humanoid remains are many stones, apparently chopping stones, which seem shaped to fit into the right hand. In the Chinese cave there are also circular charred areas, some deeply burned, which indicate the use of man's greatest tool, fire. And there are many bones—as someone has said, too many bones of the wrong kind. There are many bones of extinct deer and other animals split open so as to expose the marrow. There are also far too many human skulls in proportion to the scarcity of other human remains. And these skulls have all been broken open. This rather disquieting fact is also evident in the caves of prehistoric man in Europe. The implication of cannibalism is strong. Cannibalism is not a distinctive human trait but is found among many species; it may be of adaptive value, as when a population of rats expands when food is abundant and then subsists by cannibalism in times of famine.

Evidently early man, on both sides of the great Eurasian land mass, gave the skulls a special treatment. This fact is taken by some to mean that for these cavemen cannibalism possessed some symbolic or mystic significance. Perhaps so, but this is a question for the social anthropologist rather than the zoologist.

Neanderthal and Cro-Magnon Man. In marked contrast to all these early men who are known from a few scattered bones are the Neanderthals and Cro-Magnons. The latter people have left numerous remains widely distributed over Europe and extending east into Palestine and the Crimea.

The Neanderthal remains were first discovered in the Neander Valley near Düsseldorf in 1856. At the time some experts thought these bones merely represented a pathological maldevelopment of the skeleton of a modern man. But as similar bones were discovered deep in Pleistocene deposits in caves located in many different regions, it became clear that *Homo neanderthalensis* had indeed existed as a widespread population. The skull capacity and hence brain size (1300 to 1700 cc) falls within

Pleistocene Glaciations and Forms of Man

GLACIATION	NONGLACIAL PERIOD AND DURATION	MAN POPULATION
	Post-glacial 10,000 to 15,000 years	Contemporary man
Fourth, or Würm-Wisconsin		Cro-Magnon man
	Third interglacial 120,000 years	Neanderthal man
Third, or Riss-Illinoian		
	Second interglacial 300,000 (?) years	
Second, or Mindel-Kansan		
	First interglacial 100,000 years	Homo erectus (Java and Peking populations)
First, or Gunz-Nebraskan		
		Australopithecus; Zinjanthropus

the same general size range as that of modern man, but the proportions of the brain were slightly different. With the bones of Neanderthals have been found numerous hearths, chipped stone axes, flint spear tips and possibly other tools. There is evidence that Neanderthal man buried his dead with stores of food and implements. These men flourished for over 100,000 years during the third interglacial period and into the fourth and most recent glaciation, the Würm-Wisconsin. This is a long time indeed, compared with the trivial 5,000 to 7,000 years of written history. How did they end? Perhaps they were exterminated by their successors, the Cro-Magnons. Perhaps they merged with them. No one yet knows.

The Cro-Magnon people appeared in Europe and the Near East as the Neanderthals disappeared 25,000 to 50,000 years ago. Whether the Cro-Magnons had been pushed out of other regions by the increasing cold, or actually evolved on location under the stress of the ice age, they were physically a superb race, with a brain capacity on the average equal to or greater than our own. They were tall and straight of limb and have left truly magnificent works of art on the walls of caves, so that we flatter ourselves in identifying them as *Homo sapiens*.

Fig. 10–15. Cro-Magnon man (restored). *(American Museum of Natural History)*

Fig. 10–16. Drawings of an extinct elephant (the mammoth) by a Cro-Magnon. *(Field Museum of Natural History, Chicago)*

The culture of the Cro-Magnons was a Paleolithic, or Old Stone Age, culture in which they chipped but did not grind their stone axes, spear points, knives, lamps, and other implements. In many places they made such extensive use of reindeer bones and antlers that they are sometimes referred to as the reindeer men. From the bones around their fireplaces and deep in their caves, it is clear that they also ate horses, waterfowl, fishes, shellfish, and at least in some localities, probably other men.

The most remarkable fact about their culture is the great number of magnificent wall paintings they have left illustrating reindeer, extinct mammoths, extinct bisons, and extinct types of horses. These people drew pictures of animals now limited to the far north, like the reindeer, on caves in Spain and Palestine. They also left engravings and carvings in bone, soapstone, and ivory. They appear to have invented the bow and arrow, perhaps as a development of a stick with a leather thong attached to one end and used to throw a small javelin.

Exactly when man first arrived in North America is unknown, but it appears to have been during or even before the last glaciation.

There is abundant evidence of a flourishing Stone Age culture in the southwestern United States on the shores of prehistoric lakes that have not held water since glacial times. On the coast of California there are the prehistoric fireplaces containing charred bones of extinct elephants, camels, and horses. Only future investigation can tell who the firebuilders were and what was their relationship to Stone Age men in Europe and Asia.

Review and References

REVIEW TOPICS

1. What four theories and groups of facts formed the basis of Charles Darwin's theory of evolution? How does his theory differ from Lamarck's? From Saint-Hilaire's? From Owen and Hertwig's?

2. According to present ideas, what are the four major factors in evolution? Discuss.

3. In what senses are mutations chance events? In what sense are they not?

4. What are the three types of selection? What is genetic drift? What is the relationship of these factors to the Hardy-Weinberg law?

5. What are allopatric and sympatric species or races? What is a "rassenkreis"? What bearing do they have on evolutionary theory?

6. What is meant by the statement that neoteny is a means of escape from the evolutionary blind alleys of excessive specialization? What are some examples?

7. What are Dollo's, Cope's, Bergmann's, and Allen's rules? On what principles are they all explicable? How?

8. How do the kinds of animals and plants on the Galápagos, Cape Verde, and Madagascar islands support the theory of evolution?

9. What is the evidence for evolution presented by embryology, vestigial structures, homology? Why are embryonic structures conservative?

10. What experiments in the 17th, 18th, and 19th centuries established the principle that "All life comes from life"? Why did this problem require so many reinvestigations?

11. Describe the heterotroph theory of the origin of life. Present five lines of supporting evidence.

12. What are three different ways of computing geological time?

13. Characterize the life of the Paleozoic, Mesozoic, Cenozoic eras.

14. What is the modern theory of the origin of vertebrates? Of the first terrestrial ones?

15. What may have been the evolutionary effects of arboreal life on man's precursors? Of increasing grasslands?

16. Compare our knowledge of *Homo erectus* (the Java-Peking man) with what we know about the Neanderthals and the Cro-Magnons.

USEFUL REFERENCES

Anfinsen, C. B., *Molecular Basis of Evolution*, New York, John Wiley & Sons, 1959.

Berrill, N. J., *The Origin of Vertebrates*, Oxford, Clarendon Press, 1955.

Darwin, Charles, *Autobiography*, ed. F. Darwin, New York, H. Schuman, 1950.

Darwin, Charles, *The Origin of Species by Means of Natural Selection*, London, J. Murray, 1859.

Darwin, Charles, *The Voyage of the Beagle* (1831–1836), London, Dent, 1950.

Huxley, J., A. C. Hardy, and E. B. Ford, *Evolution as a Process*, London, Allen and Unwin, 1954.

Huxley, J., and H. B. D. Kettlewell, *Charles Darwin and his World*, New York, The Viking Press, 1965.

Lack, D., *Darwin's Finches: An Essay on the General Biological Theory of Evolution*, New York, Harper & Row, 1961.

Mayr, E., *Animal Species and Evolution*, Cambridge, Mass., Harvard University Press, 1963.

Oparin, A., I., *The Origin of Life*, 2nd ed., New York, Dover Publications, 1953.

Romer, A. S., *The Vertebrate Body*, 3rd ed., Philadelphia, W. B. Saunders Co., 1962.

Simpson, G. G., *The Major Features of Evolution*, New York, Columbia University Press, 1953.

Simpson, G. G., *The Meaning of Evolution*, New Haven, Conn., Yale University Press, 1949.

Stebbins, G. L., *Process of Organic Evolution*, Englewood Cliffs, N. J., Prentice-Hall, 1966.

Teilhard de Chardin, P., *The Phenomenon of Man*, New York, Harper & Brothers, 1955.

Part IV

Protostome Branch of the Animal

Kingdom

Except for relatively simple animals such as the protozoa and the sponges, the animal kingdom consists of two great divisions, the Protostomia and the Deuterostomia. The protostomes are united by a series of traits which at the same time separate them from deuterostomes such as echinoderms and vertebrates.

1. As the name implies (*proto*, first, + *stoma*, mouth), in protostomes the mouth is formed from the first opening into the embryonic gut; i.e., the mouth is usually formed from the blastopore.

2. The main axis of the central nervous system runs along the ventral or under side of the body. Hence in French the protostomes are called *hyponeuriens*.

3. The cleavage of the egg is usually spiral. Each cell is part of a rigidly fixed pattern so that its destiny in the embryo is clearly predictable. If the first few cells into which the egg cleaves are artificially separated, each produces only a partial embryo.

4. The body cavity or coelom is formed from a split within the middle layer of cells, the mesoderm.

5. If a tiny ciliated larva is present, it is usually a trochophore or trochophore-like organism. A trochophore is shaped like a spinning top with a tuft of cilia on its apex and a circular band of cilia around the equator.

The protostomes are an immense group divided into many important phyla. The arthropods are the most numerous of these, with 750,000 species, followed by the mollusks with about 95,000 and the nematodes with about 15,000, although current estimates of the total number of as yet unnamed species raise the total for nematodes to 500,000. There are several smaller phyla, notably the annelids and the flatworms.

Evidence is accumulating that suggests that the coelenterates belong among the protostomes. The "mouth" of a sea anemone, for example, develops from the blastopore. The coelenterates as a group may have evolved from the flatworms, which are clearly protostomes. There is, however, no certain proof.

Chapter 11

Flatworms, or Platyhelminthes

The flatworms or Platyhelminthes (*platy,* flat, + *helminthos,* worm) are a moderate-sized phylum of some 6,000 species divided into three classes. The free-living flatworms, or **turbellarians,** which make up the first class, have been recognized as a separate group since the time of the American Revolution. They are common, harmless animals, living in both fresh and salt water. Scientifically they are important as research material. One school of zoologists believes that the turbellarians were the first group of metazoans and that they evolved directly from the protozoans and gave rise to all the rest of the animal kingdom.

The parasitic flatworms fall into two classes, the flukes, or **trematodes,** and the tapeworms, or **cestodes.** Known from extremely ancient times, these parasites still present a serious challenge both to the animal breeder and the physician.

Flatworms, whether free-living or parasitic, are **bilaterally symmetrical.** They consequently possess the three primary anatomical axes found in all the higher animals, vertebrates included. The **anterior-posterior** axis is the head-tail axis; the **dorsal-ventral** axis is the back to belly, or upper to under, axis. The **right-left** axis completes the triad of dimensions. Bilateral symmetry seems to be the expression in structure of the habit of moving about. Sessile animals all tend to become radially symmetrical, like trees. For a moving animal, natural selection has favored a specialized anterior region with sense organs, nerve cells, and a mouth—in other words, a head—and also a specialized lower surface to present to the substrate on which the animal crawls or otherwise moves.

Flatworms are composed of three major layers of cells, the **germ layers.** The ectoderm covers the external surface. The mesoderm, or middle layer, makes up the main bulk of the body. The digestive endoderm lines the gut. These three layers are found throughout the animal kingdom, except in the protozoans and possibly the sponges.

Flatworms possess no coelom, or body cavity, no anus, and no circulatory, respiratory, or skeletal system. The excretory system in this phylum consists of **flame cells.** Most flatworms are hermaphroditic.

Flatworms are typical protostomes. The mouth forms from the embryonic blastopore, the main axis of the nervous system runs along the ventral side of the body, the cleavage of the egg is spiral, and the larva is a trochophore in the primitive marine species.

Flatworms and the Origin of Metazoa. Few questions have puzzled zoologists more than the problem of how the multicellular animals or metazoans evolved from the single-celled protozoans. This is one of the historic problems of zoology. The classic theory, advocated by the German evolutionary theoretician and champion of Darwinism, Ernst Haeckel (1834– 1919), held that the many-celled animals evolved from colonial flagellates like *Volvox*. Other investigators proposed other colonial flagellates as the probable ancestral form. And it is indeed possible to pick out a beautiful series of flagellates beginning with *Euglena* and ending with *Volvox* which, as has already been explained, does exhibit some cell specializations.

However, there have always been serious difficulties with this theory. The flagellates involved are clearly phytoflagellates, that is, plants producing cellulose, chlorophyll, and starch. They live in fresh water, while most basic animal groups live in the sea, especially the coelenterates to which Haeckel supposed *Volvox* had given rise. Even more damaging to his theory is the fact that in *Volvox* and similar organisms, meiosis is post-zygotic, that is, it takes place immediately after the zygote is formed. The body of the volvox is consequently haploid. In animals, by contrast, meiosis is pre-zygotic, that is, it takes place during the formation of gametes, and hence just prior to the formation of the zygote. The body cells of animals are diploid. The only metazoans which are extensively flagellated are the sponges, and they are universally admitted to be an aberrant side-branch of the animal kingdom, one which led nowhere. The collar cell of a sponge with its single flagellum is in fact widely different from the biflagellate cell of a volvox. It has also been pointed out that if the coelenterates really evolved from a volvoxlike type of organism, the coelenterate embryo would be expected to be a hollow sphere, which it is not.

In recent years a far more plausible theory, proposed half a century ago by the English zoologist Adam Sedgwick, has been revived and greatly strengthened by a Yugoslavian investigator, Jovan Hadzi, and his followers. This view is based on the many fundamental resemblances between multinucleate ciliates among the protozoans and the simplest of the flatworms, the acoelous turbellarians. Included in these basic resemblances are the following features:

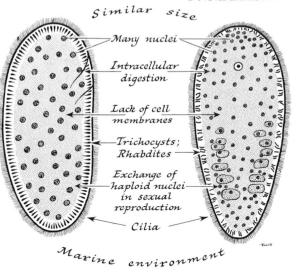

Fig. 11–1. A multinucleate ciliate and a primitive acoelous turbellarian flatworm.

1. Both live in the ocean, where life first arose and where the most primitive forms of animals are to be expected.

2. Both are of the same size, about 1 mm long, gigantic for a protozoan, minute for a metazoan.

3. Both are free-living heterotrophs. They ingest solid food and are dependent on other organisms for complex organic foodstuffs.

4. Both are anatomically very similar, with external ciliation and tiny protective vesicles just below the body surface. These are the trichocysts of the ciliates and the rhabdites and sagittocysts of the turbellarians.

5. Both lack a gut as well as a body cavity. Food is ingested through a mouth at or near the anterior end, and then digested intracellularly.

6. Especially noteworthy is the almost complete lack of cellulation in many species of the acoelous flatworms. The epithelium over the surface of these flatworms has large areas with many nuclei not separated from each other by cell membranes. Likewise, most of the interior of the acoelous flatworms is composed of an undivided mass of multinucleate cytoplasm. In fact, it is chiefly in the gametes that cellulation is well developed in this group of turbellarians.

7. Lastly, as a contemporary London zoologist, G. R. de Beer, has emphasized, the ciliates possess "the indispensable requisite for ancestors of the metazoa" in their habit of conjugation with exchange of gamete nuclei, rather than complete fusion of male and female organisms as in flagellates. Conjugation in ciliates can be homologized with the mating of multicellular animals in a way the cell fusion of the flagellates cannot. With many of the simple acoelous flatworms, copulation is very simple. Each partner injects sperms anywhere into the mesoderm of the other. In some highly specialized ciliates, such as the ophryoscolecids, the migrating nucleus in conjugation actually resembles a sperm complete with flagellum. All that is lacking in some multinucleate ciliates to make their sexual reproduction essentially metazoan in character is the enclosure of the stationary or female nucleus in its own special cytoplasm to form an egg cell. The pre-zygotic timing of meiosis in ciliates and flatworms has already been mentioned.

Probably we will never have final proof for this or any other theory of the origin of the many-celled from the one-celled animals. No fossil record exists. At present the evidence that the flatworms originated from multinucleate ciliates is undeniably impressive and adds up to the most plausible theory so far proposed.

There is a small group of minute ciliated animals called mesozoans which has sometimes been regarded as a possible link between the protozoans and the metazoans. This appears unlikely because all the so-called mesozoans are parasitic, and usually have complex life cycles involving two hosts. Most zoologists regard them as degenerate flatworms.

If the acoelous flatworms are truly the original metazoans, is there any evidence that flatworms in turn gave rise to higher forms? It has often been pointed out that a cross section of a free-living flatworm, a common planarian, for example, made through the extruded proboscis, resembles the body plan of a jellyfish with the flatworm proboscis corresponding to the manubrium of the jellyfish. The usual assumption has been that the coelenterate was the ancestor, but the series can be read equally well in the reverse direction. It will be recalled (see page 133), that Hyman pointed out basic anatomical

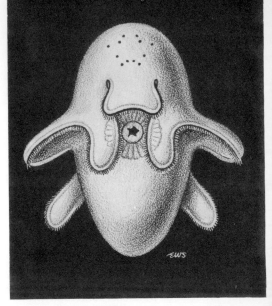

Fig. 11–2. Müller's larva, the semi-microscopic form that is characteristic of marine turbellarians.

similarities between flatworms and sea anemones and that Hadzi has pointed out additional cogent lines of evidence indicating that the coelenterates are in fact descended from the flatworms.

Ctenophores likewise seem to have arisen from flatworms. Marine turbellarians pass through a larval stage known as **Müller's larva.** The most noteworthy fact about this creature is that it has eight elongated ciliated lobes and in other ways resembles a ctenophore. This was once interpreted as meaning that ctenophores had given rise to flatworms. It now seems more plausible to read this series too in the opposite direction and to suppose that flatworms gave rise to the ctenophores by neoteny, that is, by the acquisition of sexual maturity in the larval stage.

TURBELLARIANS: CLASS TURBELLARIA

Turbellarians are free-living, non-parasitic flatworms. Externally they are ciliated, especially on the ventral and lateral surfaces. It is from the turbulence of this ciliated surface that they derive their name. The ciliated epithelium covering the body of the worm contains minute rod-shaped vesicles called **rhabdites.** The rhabdites resemble the trichocysts of *Paramecium* and are believed to have a protective function, but this has never been proved. Like

Fig. 11–3. Living marine polyclad turbellarian, *Stylochus zabra,* approximately life size. *(Kindness of William H. Amos)*

the worm to regenerate a new right half, and vice versa. As a result, turbellarians have been extensively used in the experimental analysis of animal development.

Evolutionary Relationships. Although there is disagreement about the origin of the turbellarian flatworms, there is general agreement that they gave rise to the two other groups of platyhelminthes — the trematodes or flukes, and the cestodes or tapeworms. The turbellarians are free-living, while the other two classes are parasitic. Furthermore, transitional forms exist and it is not very difficult to postulate a series of mutations which, under the pressure of natural selection, would have produced the parasitic groups.

Taxonomy. The turbellarian flatworms are divided into five orders depending on the structure of the gut.

1. The **acoelous** turbellarians, just described as possibly ancestral to the metazoans, lack a gut completely.

2. The **rhabdocoels** are a group characterized by a straight rod-shaped gut. These turbellarians are widespread in fresh-water and marine environments and are a familiar sight under a dissecting microscope in material collected

other flatworms, the turbellarians are hermaphroditic, but unlike the trematodes and cestodes, they have very simple life histories. Some also reproduce asexually, by fission, dividing themselves transversely several times until a chain of individuals is produced.

Turbellarians are famous for their spectacular powers of regeneration, which not only enable the body to grow a new head but a left half of

Fig. 11–4. The five types of turbellarians. Left to right: acoel, rhabdocoel, alloeocoel, triclad, and polyclad.

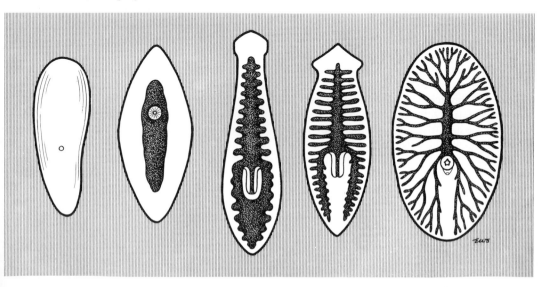

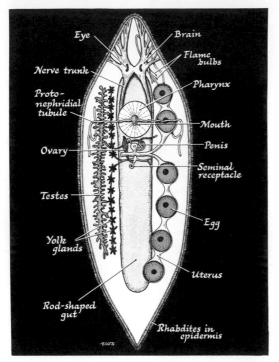

Fig. 11–5. *Mesostoma ehrenbergii*, a translucent rhabdocoel turbellarian. Ventral view showing the internal organs. Only male structures are shown left of the gut and only female structures right.

from ponds. The formation of chains of individuals by asexual fission is common. Some species are transparent and hence favorable material for study. (See Fig. 11–5.)

3. The **alloeocoels** constitute a small order in which the intestine usually resembles an elongate but more or less irregular sac.

4. The **triclads** are the order which includes the familiar fresh-water planarians commonly used in laboratory experiments. The gut has three main branches, one running from the pharynx anteriorly towards the head and two extending posteriorly, one on either side of the pharynx. Each main branch has side branches.

The commonest turbellarian in most parts of North America is a mottled brown and white triclad usually called a planarian, *Dugesia tigrina* (formerly called *Planaria* or *Euplanaria maculatum*). A very similar species occurs in Europe. A very dark, almost black triclad, *Dugesia dorotocephala,* is frequently found in spring-fed ponds and is used in laboratories. The principal ecological niches of both these flatworms are among pond weeds, stones, and on the under surfaces of dead leaves.

Some triclad turbellarians are marine, and a very few are terrestrial, living in semi-tropical regions and in greenhouses.

5. The polyclads form an exclusively marine order. The intestine has numerous branches radiating to all parts of the body. Some species possess hollow tentacles.

The **nemertines** are a widespread group of marine worms which are sometimes placed in the phylum Platyhelminthes, and sometimes are considered a separate phylum, Nemertinea. They are flat, unsegmented, and commonly attain a length of 3 feet. As in other flatworms, no body cavity is present. They live under the sand of tidal flats and below the low-tide line, feeding on *Nereis* and other marine annelids. There is at least one fresh-water species in the United States. It is a translucent, flattened, and ciliated worm living among pond weeds, where it may reach an inch in length. All nemertines have an anteriorly placed mouth from which they throw out a long wormlike proboscis with which they paralyze their prey.

Skeletal and Locomotor Systems. Flatworms keep their slithery ribbon shape by virtue of a mass of specialized mesoderm cells that fill the body between the ciliated epithelium of the body surface and the centrally placed three-branched intestine. These irregularly shaped mesodermal cells that give support are known as **mesenchyme.** Mesenchyme cells permeate and strengthen virtually every organ in the human body.

The gliding motion of flatworms is due to the coordinated beating of the cilia on the ventral surface. The structure of the cilia appears to be essentially the same as in the protozoans. The mechanism of their coordinated beat is very little understood.

Turning and similar motions of turbellarian flatworms are made possible by using two antagonistic sets of muscles. Just under the epidermis is a layer of transverse muscle fibers encircling the animal. Under this is a layer of longitudinal muscles extending from head to tail. Antagonistic pairs of muscles have been seen earlier in the coelenterates, and are found throughout the animal kingdom.

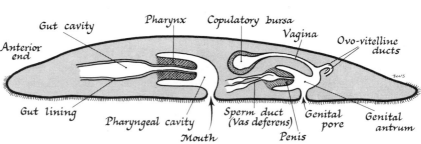

Fig. 11-6. A turbellarian flatworm. Above: cross section, pharynx protruded. Below: longi-section, pharynx retracted.

Digestive System. The three-branched gut of the common turbellarian flatworms leads into the muscular pharynx, a conspicuous tubular structure lying, when retracted, in a pharyngeal cavity. (See Fig. 11-6.) In feeding, the pharynx is protruded through the mouth located in the midline on the under side of the body. Particles of food, small animals, bits of liver, meat, or egg yolk are sucked up by the pharynx and then these are passed along into the intestine, where much, and perhaps all, of the digestion is intracellular within the cytoplasm of the gut cells.

Excretory System. As in many of the lower invertebrates, the excretory apparatus consists of tubules ending in **flame cells.** In the parasitic trematodes to be discussed later, the patterns of these excretory tubules supply an important means of accurate species identification. In most free-living flatworms there is an anastomosing, i.e., interconnecting, row of such tubules along each side of the body. Each flame cell consists of a single cell bearing a long waving tuft of cilia resembling a flame. The cytoplasm of the cell is drawn out into a long tubule around the "flame." This tubule connects with others, commonly in groups of three, which ultimately lead to the exterior.

The ciliary flame pushes water down the tubule and creates a slight negative pressure within it. As a result, water from the surrounding tissues is drawn into the tubule. As with most excretory systems, including those of vertebrates like ourselves, the primary function is the elimination of excess water. This is indicated by the relative lack of flame cells in marine flatworms, which live in an environment having an osmotic pressure high enough to prevent much water from entering the tissues.

Fig. 11-7. Flatworm excretory system. The magnification increases from *A* to *C*.

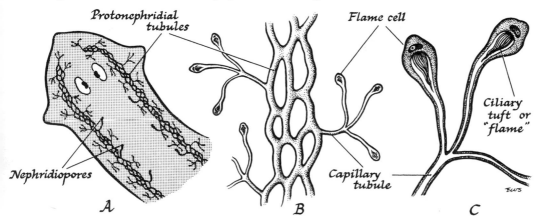

Reproductive System. With rare exceptions, the flatworms are hermaphroditic. In the simplest turbellarians, the reproductive system consits of little more than paired groups of egg and sperm cells and a protrusible organ, the penis, to inject sperms into the mesenchyme of another individual. In the common triclad turbellarians a complete set of reproductive structures of both sexes has been evolved. A short distance behind the eyes lies a pair of ovaries. From each ovary there extends posteriorly an ovo-vitelline duct which connects with many small yolk glands. The two **ovo-vitelline ducts** join near the hind end of the body and then enter a cavity known as the **genital antrum.** From near this point extends a long tube, usually called the **vagina,** ending in a sac, the **copulatory bursa.**

Fig. 11 – 8. Turbellarian reproductive system. Male structures shown on the left, female on the right.

The male reproductive system consists of two rows of **testes,** each with its own **vas deferens** running parallel to the ovo-vitelline duct on the same side of the body. Near the posterior end each vas deferens has an expanded portion where sperms are stored. The vasa deferentia join within the muscular **penis,** which protrudes into the genital antrum.

In reproducing sexually, each worm inserts its penis into the genital antrum of the other and deposits sperms in the copulatory bursa. The sperms soon pass from the bursa up the ovo-vitelline ducts to the ovaries, probably by muscular action of the ducts. Fertilization takes place as the eggs leave the ovary. As the eggs pass down the ovo-vitelline ducts, they are joined by large numbers of yolk cells. Fertilized eggs and yolk cells collect in the genital antrum, where droplets from the yolk cells form a proteinaceous capsule around the mass of yolk cells and the two or three up to a dozen zygotes. The egg capsules of many species are stalked. In different species there are many variations of this anatomical pattern.

Fig. 11 – 9. Turbellarian flatworms on a rock with stalked egg capsules; approximately life size. (*Kindness of William H. Amos*)

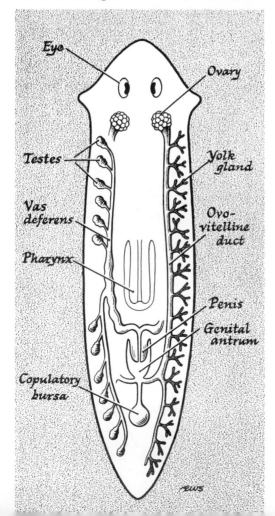

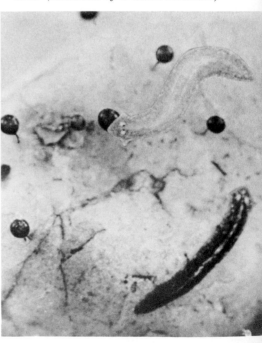

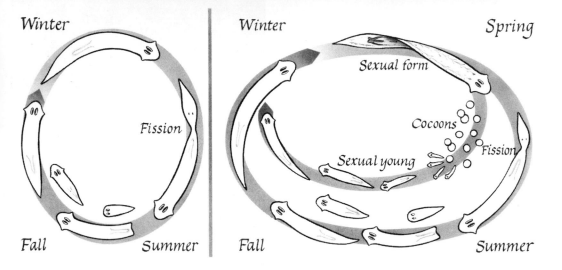

Fig. 11–10. Life cycles of turbellarian flatworms. Some species (left) appear to reproduce entirely asexually. Others (right) combine asexual with sexual reproduction. The fertilized eggs are enclosed in proteinaceous cocoons which may be attached to rocks.

Most of the common turbellarian triclads deposit egg capsules during the winter and spring. In some localities there are said to be entirely asexual races of the common planarian *Dugesia tigrina.* Hyman has shown that this species can usually be made to develop sexual reproductive apparatus and to lay capsules with viable eggs at any time of the year by keeping the worms at a low temperature for several days and then returning them to a warm room.

The cleavage of the eggs is known as spiral because of the beautifully precise spiral pattern in which the early cell divisions take place. In fact, so precise is this pattern that in flatworms, annelids, mollusks, and other protostomes, every cell up to the 24th cleavage has a special name and a fixed destiny.

Like most fresh-water invertebrates, the common triclad turbellarians have no larval stage. The marine polyclads develop into Müller's larvae (see page 268).

Nervous System. The two most conspicuous sense organs of the common genus of triclad turbellarians, *Dugesia,* are the **auricles,** little earlike points on the sides of the head, and the **eyes.** The auricles are not ears, but olfactory organs. If the auricles are removed, a flatworm can no longer locate food by detecting its odor in the water.

The eye consists of a pair of black pigment cups, each located against the medial margin of a circular area devoid of pigment, so as to give the worms an extravagantly cross-eyed look.

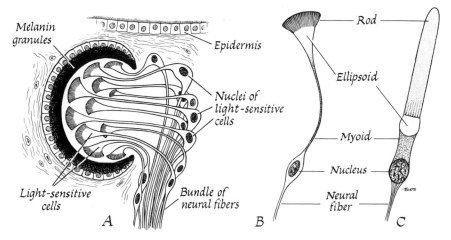

Fig. 11–11. *A,* the cellular structure of the eye of a flatworm. *B,* flatworm light-sensitive cell. *C,* vertebrate light-sensitive cell.

The light-sensitive cells dip into these cups with their photosensitive ends pointing away from the source of light. This amounts to an inverted retina, something found elsewhere only in vertebrates and a few mollusks.

What is the function of the melanin pigment cups? Without such shields, light from every direction, except perhaps from directly behind the worm, would reach the light-sensitive cells. Hence the worm could merely tell whether it was in the light or the dark, but would have no way of "knowing" from what direction the light was coming. The opaque cup of the right eye shuts out light rays from all directions except from the animal's right. The left eye acts in the same way. Thus purely by virtue of their anatomy, these eyes are highly selective and can be stimulated by light from a single direction only. This makes it possible for a worm to turn toward or away from a light source. Such are the simple anatomical beginnings of discriminating, intelligent behavior.

Some species of turbellarians possess **statocysts,** that is, small vesicles containing a concretion of some sort. The statocysts enable the worm to distinguish up from down. Many turbellarians also have patches of long protoplasmic hairs that detect water currents.

The brain is a bi-lobed structure close to the eyes. From it a dozen or more nerves extend out into the head and two, or in some species four, main nerve cords pass toward the tail.

Natural History. The natural history of any group of animals includes the study of their whole lives. It involves the web of relationships between each individual and other animals of the same species and of other species and includes the interrelations of the animals with their nonliving environment. Prominent among the problems of natural history are those of geographical distribution and of particular habitat. Why, for example, is a given species found only east of the Rocky Mountains, or why is its habitat limited to acid bogs? Equally important are the problems of population dynamics. What makes a population increase or decline? What sets the upper limits of population size? These are questions of obvious theoretical and practical importance. They cannot be fully answered without a knowledge of life cycles,

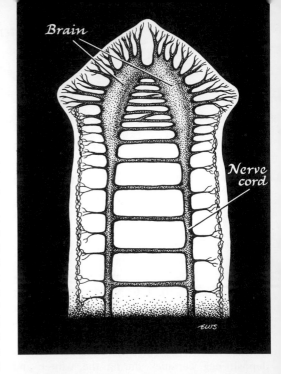

Fig. 11–12. Brain and paired nerve cords of a flatworm. (Diagrammatic, anterior end)

behavior, and evolution—usually a great deal more knowledge than is at present available.

Turbellarian flatworms are animals of shallow water, where they may be found among pondweed and seaweed, under stones and debris. Some fresh-water species are characteristic of ponds and lakes, others of streams and cold springs. They may be collected in a pond by placing a piece of raw beef in a submerged container. As the oxygen concentration falls, flatworms appear at the surface. Apparently flatworms have few enemies. Little is known of the way they are disseminated. Presumably the eggs and cyst stages are carried on the feet of water birds and other animals that step in mud. They are surely transported by water currents.

Regeneration. The remarkable powers of regeneration of the flatworms have long fascinated modern investigators. If a flatworm is cut in half crosswise, the head end forms a new tail, the hind end forms a new head and pharynx. More remarkable, because less like their normal asexual reproduction, if a flatworm is cut in half lengthwise, the right half will regenerate a new left half and the left half a new right. Moreover, flatworms appear virtually immortal. If starved, they absorb their reproductive

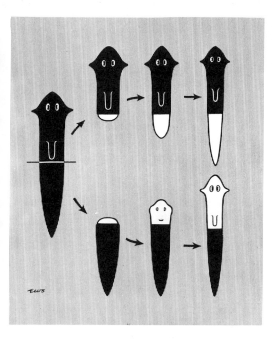

Fig. 11–13. Posterior and anterior regeneration in a flatworm from one transverse cut.

structures, and if further starved simply grow smaller and smaller. It is important to note that the size of the cells does not undergo reduction. The diminution is one of cell number. There seems to be a limit smaller than which no cell can go. As in a starving man or rat, the nervous system seems the last to be affected.

Such powers present great and far-reaching scientific problems. How is it possible for animals to do all this? When a flatworm is cut in half transversely, how does the cut surface of the anterior end "know," so to speak, that it should grow a new hind end? How does the cut surface of the hind end "know" that it should regenerate a new head and pharynx? Where do the cells come from that form these new structures?

The first principle to emerge from a study of these facts is that the kind of structures regenerated depends on the position of the regenerating surface relative to the rest of the animal. If a worm is cut in two along line *AB* in Figure 11–14, the tissues just anterior to the cut somehow mobilize and form a mass of embryonic cells known collectively as a **blastema.** This blastema then develops into a new hind end. But suppose the worm had been cut along line *ab.* In such a case the very same cells, that is,

those shown in the light area between the lines *AB* and *ab,* would now be somehow involved in the regeneration of a new anterior end with head and pharynx! To this extent, then, the developmental behavior of the individual cells depends on their relationship to the rest of the organism. (See also page 122 for a comparison with hydra.)

Another aspect of this principle is shown by the regenerative behavior of small pieces of flatworms. Such fragments usually regenerate complete individuals with the original anterior-posterior axis of the piece maintained. The original anterior edge of the piece will regenerate the new head, and the original posterior edge the new hind end.

Such facts have led, in the work of Child (1869–1954) and his students at the University of Chicago, to the theory that animal growth and form are controlled by **axial gradients,** that is, by properties gradually changing along the anterior-posterior axis of the animal. The head end is regarded as exerting a dominance over the rest of the body and as both inhibiting the development of other heads and controlling the

Fig. 11–14. Flatworm regeneration experiment to show that the nature of regenerating tissue after a cut depends upon its relation to the animal as a whole. See text for details of procedure.

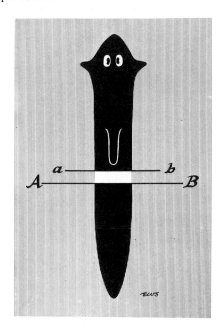

nature of the parts which form. This theory has been very useful in correlating many diverse facts in animals of widely different kinds and in suggesting many new experiments. However, "dominance" has remained little more than a convenient word to describe what happens. What dominance means in terms of some physical or chemical mechanism has so far eluded us. It has been possible to demonstrate an axial gradient of respiration and of susceptibility to various poisons. The dominant head end respires faster and is more sensitive to poisons than more posterior levels. Child showed that narcotics which depress respiration will cause animals to regenerate abnormally small heads. But how the head region exerts its dominance in terms of physics and chemistry has never been clarified. Moreover, there are some extremely awkward facts. Child himself showed that very small pieces cut from the most anterior region of the worm will often form a head at each end. Much attention has been given to the question of exactly which cells of the old part go to form the cells of the new regenerated part. Are the new muscles, nerves, gut, etc., formed from cells derived from the same tissues in the old part, or are there special embryonic formative cells in the old part that function in regeneration? The balance of evidence at present favors the latter alternative. Regeneration is completely blocked by X-rays, which tend to destroy undifferentiated cells capable of mitotic cell division but have much less effect on specialized, nondividing cells.

Fig. 11–15. Head regeneration in flatworms. Left: Two heads formed from a small piece near the head end. Right: New head formed from amputated head: "Janus" form.

Behavior. The behavior of turbellarian flatworms has been extensively explored by American, German, Russian, and Japanese investigators. This behavior is of two basic types. The first is a rather general response, usually an increased "random" motion following a generalized increase in some stimulus. For example, a general increase in illumination will cause a quiescent flatworm to glide actively around its dish. Such a nondirected response to light is termed **photokinesis.** A similar effect, **thermokinesis,** can be produced by heat.

The second type of reaction is highly specific and directed. As explained, the anatomy of a flatworm's eyes is such that the right eye can be stimulated only by light reaching it from the animal's right side, and vice versa. With this equipment, plus, of course, a nervous system and some muscles, a flatworm will turn away from a source of light. Such a directed reaction in response to an impinging stimulus is termed a **tropism** or a **taxis,** in this case a **phototropism** or **phototaxis.** Although this concept has been criticized as implying a much too simple underlying physiological mechanism, tropism remains a very useful term. The danger is that a descriptive word may be taken as explanation.

Flatworms usually show negative phototropism. In fact, they can be driven around in a bowl of water like a flock of sheep retreating from a strong light source. The larvae of marine species respond positively to light. This reaction keeps them swimming near the surface and thus allows ocean currents to disseminate the species.

Flatworms which live in streams show a positive **rheotropism,** i.e., they turn towards and move into the current. Most flatworms exhibit a positive **thigmotropism** after gentle mechanical stimulation. That is to say, if touched gently on one side of the head, the worm will turn toward the side touched. Likewise they will turn and move into a gentle current. If the intensity is increased, the sign of the stimulus changes to negative, as the worm now turns away from the stimulus. One of the most easily observed tropisms is the positive **chemotropism** of flatworms in the presence of diffusing food juices. Notice (Fig. 11–16) that this is essentially a trial-and-error process. It also bears certain resemblances to the feedback mechanisms of self-guided missiles and cybernetics.

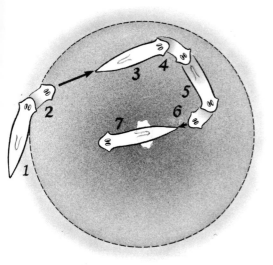

Fig. 11–16. Flatworm reaction toward a piece of food. The area of diffusing molecules from the meat is shown by the circle. At position *7* the pharynx of the worm is directly over the meat.

Can all the behavior of turbellarian flatworms, including their feeding and reproductive activities, be described in terms of either generalized responses like photokinesis or in terms of tropisms? This question cannot be answered at present. Nor do we really understand the mechanisms of these responses. How, for example, can a weak stimulus elicit a positive response, while a stronger one of the same type evokes a negative response?

It has recently been shown that flatworms can learn a simple T-maze and can be conditioned to respond in a certain way to a particular stimulus.

Incredible as it seems, worms will "remember" what they have been taught after their heads have been removed and new ones regenerated! This is in partial contrast to earthworms, where the amputation of the first several segments, including the brain, does not erase learning until a new brain is regenerated. When that happens, the worm has a "clean" brain and must learn again.

Some investigators have found that flatworms fed on the brains of trained worms learn faster than controls. These workers believe that memory is somehow stored in an RNA (ribose nucleic acid) code and can be transmitted by cannibalism. Other investigators have been unable to confirm these results.

TREMATODES: CLASS TREMATODA

Trematodes, or flukes as they are often called, are parasitic flatworms. They have been a serious health problem for man and his domestic animals since the dawn of history. Some of the oldest Egyptian mummies contain embalmed trematodes and their eggs, yet our knowledge of their rather complex life histories has been achieved only within the past 75 years.

In body conformation and internal structure trematodes resemble free-living turbellarians, but with a difference. Adult trematodes lack the external ciliation of the turbellarians but instead wear a flexible cuticle often armed with minute spines. Locomotion, and adhesion to their victims, is aided by two or more muscular suction disks, usually one around the mouth and a second on the mid-ventral line. The mouth is at the anterior end of the worm. The gut, after a short pharynx and esophagus, forks into two long branches. The reproductive apparatus is hermaphroditic and somewhat more elaborate than in turbellarians. The medically and agriculturally important species have a life cycle involving two hosts, one often a snail and the other a vertebrate.

Evolutionary Relationships and Taxonomy. From anatomical evidence, trematodes seem to have arisen from the turbellarians and become specialized for a parasitic life.

Taxonomically they fall into two groups: the **monogenetic** trematodes, which are external parasites sometimes found on the gills of fishes or the bodies of other aquatic animals; and the **digenetic** trematodes, which are internal parasites. The monogenetic species usually attack only one host and have a simple life history. The digenetic trematodes have two hosts and often six or more distinct stages in their life history, if egg and adult are counted.

From the medical and veterinary point of view trematodes may be classified according to the part of the vertebrate body they infest: external (or semi-external) monogenetic flukes, and the internal digenetic liver flukes, lung flukes, intestinal flukes, and blood flukes.

The most readily found monogenetic trematodes are species that live in the mouths, noses, or urinary bladders of fresh-water frogs and turtles, although various species can often be found on the gills and in the mouths of fresh-water fishes, from trout to carp. *Polystomoides oris,* from the mouth of the fresh-water painted turtle, bears a conspicuous rosette of six suction disks and a number of hooks at its extreme posterior end.

The sheep liver fluke, *Fasciola hepatica,* was the first trematode known, and the first to have its life history worked out. It is prevalent in sheep-raising regions but fortunately is rarely found in man. The Chinese liver fluke, *Opisthorchis (Clonorchis) sinensis,* regularly infests human beings and is widespread in China, Japan, Korea, and Formosa. Infection is contracted by eating raw, pickled, smoked, or dried but uncooked fish.

Many frogs which appear in vigorous health harbor a lung fluke, *Pneumoneces medioplexus.* This is the most generally available species for

Fig. 11 – 17. Chinese liver fluke, *Opisthorchis sinensis,* a trematode. Dorsal view of adult. About 3×.

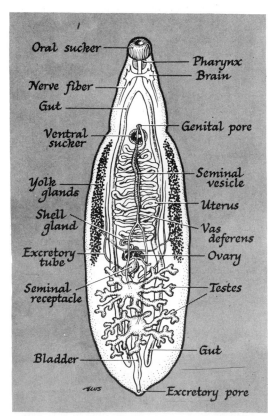

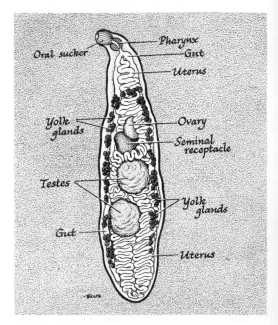

Fig. 11 – 18. Frog lung fluke, *Pneumoneces medioplexus.* About 3×.

laboratory study in the living condition. The flukes are conspicuous objects to the naked eye when the frog's lungs are cut open. In life the fluke uterus is usually filled with dark brown, almost black eggs; the ovary, seminal receptacle, and the two testes are white. Curiously, the Oriental lung fluke, *Paragonimus westermani,* was discovered in the lungs of two Bengal tigers which died in Hamburg. It is frequently found in man. A similar species, *P. kellicotti,* infests dogs, cats, muskrats, pigs, mink, and other North American mammals. Infestation is contracted by eating raw crayfish.

Most digenetic trematodes live in the intestines of their **definitive host,** i.e., the host in which the parasite becomes sexually mature. The most common is the giant intestinal fluke, *Fasciolopsis buski,* found widely throughout the Orient. The adults grow to be over 7 inches long and produce an intestinal ulcer at each point of attachment. In addition to the physical injury they do, they produce toxic substances which are absorbed by the bloodstream. Infection is incurred especially by children eating uncooked aquatic plants.

The blood flukes, or schistosomes, have been the scourge of the Nile valley from time out of mind and remain so today in Egypt and over much of Africa and large parts of Asia and

South America. Schistosomes live chiefly in the small blood vessels of the mesentery of the lower intestine; snails are the intermediate hosts. The three species of *Schistosoma (Bilharzia)* infecting man differ only slightly in structure, life history, and symptoms of the disease, schistosomiasis (bilharziasis), that they cause.

Functional Systems. The anatomy of the organ systems of both monogenetic and digenetic trematodes is essentially the same. The digestive system consists of a mouth surrounded by a muscular suction disk followed by a short muscular sucking pharynx which leads into a short esophagus that immediately forks into two branches, one passing down each side of the body to the posterior end of the worm. In the Chinese liver fluke, a very favorable object for laboratory study, the two branches of the gut bear no side branches. In the sheep and human liver fluke, *Fasciola,* blind side-branches of the gut branch again and again until they seem to fill the body. In freshly collected frog lung flukes, frog red blood cells are usually conspicuous in the gut.

The excretory system consists of flame cells similar to those already described for the turbellarians, and a system of tubules ending in a straight canal along the midline and called the **bladder.** The bladder opens to the exterior via a small pore near the posterior end.

The nervous system of trematodes is greatly reduced. The brain is a small pair of ganglia on either side of the gut just anterior or posterior to the pharynx, depending on the species. From the brain several nerve fibers extend out along the animal. Natural selection has eliminated sense organs in adult trematodes, as in most parasites.

On the other hand, the reproductive system has almost taken over the entire animal, likewise typical of parasites. The male organs consist of a pair of testes, one anterior to the other and usually located in the worm's posterior half. In the frog lung fluke the testes are disk-shaped, in the Chinese liver fluke somewhat branched, and in the sheep liver fluke elaborately branched. A vas deferens conducts sperms from each testis to a seminal vesicle leading into a muscular penis.

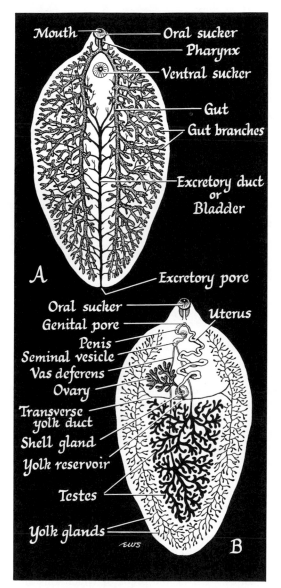

Fig. 11–19. Human and sheep liver fluke, *Fasciola hepatica,* shown slightly enlarged. *A,* digestive and excretory systems. *B,* reproductive system. Ventral views.

The female system consists of a disk-shaped or branching ovary anterior to the anterior testis. A short oviduct leads into a muscular uterus, a long irregularly coiled tube. In some species, such as the frog lung fluke, the uterus nearly fills the body. Along each side of the worm are numerous small yolk glands, or vitellaria. The vitelline ducts which drain these yolk-secreting glands lead into the oviduct at

279

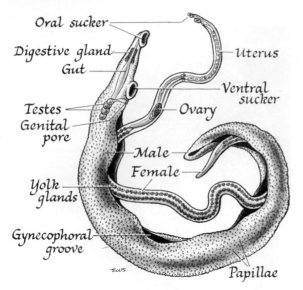

Oral sucker

Digestive gland

Gut

Uterus

Testes

Ventral sucker

Genital pore

Ovary

Male

Female

Yolk glands

Gynecophoral groove

Papillae

Fig. 11-20. Adult male clasping female blood fluke, *Schistosoma* (also called *Bilharzia*). About 20×.

about the place where it becomes the uterus. Entering the oviduct at about the same point is a duct from the seminal receptacle, an organ which receives sperms, usually from another worm — although if other worms are not available, self-fertilization is known to occur and produce viable offspring. In this same region the oviduct also receives one or more ducts from a shell gland. Consequently when the eggs start down the uterus they are successively fertilized, provided with yolk, and covered by a shell.

Natural History. The natural history of parasites like the trematodes presents special features, some of which are reflected in their life histories. Unlike the predator which kills and eats its prey within a short time, the parasite continues to live with its victim for long periods. The more perfect the parasite, the less quickly does it kill its host. This is an obvious advantage to the parasite, because it must usually die when the host dies.

The enormous development of the reproductive system in parasites of all types is plausibly explained as reflecting the great difficulty young parasites have in finding a suitable host. A worm living within the liver or lungs of its host has no way of knowing when a new host, which its offspring might infest, is near. Natural selection has evidently favored parasites that

went through life pouring forth eggs or larval offspring and thereby increased the probability that some of them would find the suitable kind of host.

Life Cycles. The digenetic trematodes living deep within the lungs, intestine, blood, or other tissues of their victims commonly alternate between a vertebrate and an invertebrate host. They usually pass through six stages in their life histories.

1. The **eggs** are laid almost continually and in enormous numbers during adult life in whatever definitive vertebrate host within which the worm becomes sexually mature. The size and shape of trematode eggs enable the species infesting a man or an animal to be diagnosed. The eggs are passed to the exterior with urine, feces, or sputum.

2. If the egg falls into water, a microscopic ciliated larva called a **miracidium** hatches. To survive, the miracidium must penetrate the tissues of a snail or other small invertebrate within 24 hours.

3. Within the snail the miracidium loses its cilia and grows into a **sporocyst**. This is a small wormlike creature lacking mouth and gut but containing eight or ten groups of embryonic cells. Each group of cells forms a worm that may become another sporocyst or a larger worm formed by the sporocysts and having at least a rudimentary gut.

4. The worms so formed are called **redias** for their 17th century discoverer, Francesco Redi (1626–1697), the Italian poet and naturalist known for his pioneer work on the origin of insects from eggs. A redia never leaves the body of the snail but produces, by a process of internal budding, tailed worms called cercarias.

5. A **cercaria** (*kerkos,* tail) superficially looks like a minute tadpole. The body is a small worm with a simple gut and no reproductive structures, but with several adaptations for its life. These include a pair of eye spots, the muscular tail, which is forked in many species, and either some cyst-producing glands or glands which pour out a powerful digestive enzyme that enables the cercaria to penetrate the host's skin. The cercarias break out of the redia in which they were formed, pass through the tissues of the snail, and finally swim away in

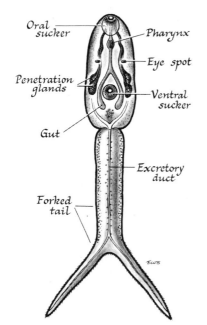

Oral sucker

Pharynx

Eye spot

Penetration glands

Ventral sucker

Gut

Excretory duct

Forked tail

Fig. 11-21. Cercaria of a fluke. Semi-microscopic.

schistosomes reach the blood vessels of their victims by directly penetrating the skin of persons who work in irrigated rice fields or walk through puddles. If the proper host of a given kind of cercaria is not a man but a bird or other animal, the cercarias may still penetrate the human skin but are killed on the spot by a local inflammatory reaction called swimmers' itch in fresh-water regions, and clam-diggers' itch around salt water.

In many species such as the sheep liver fluke, *Fasciola,* and the giant intestinal fluke, *Fasciolopsis,* the cercarias become encysted on some plant in or near the water and must wait until eaten by the sheep or man. The cercarias of the Chinese liver fluke encyst within the muscles of fishes and there wait to be eaten. The cercarias of the frog lung fluke encyst in dragonfly larvae and other small aquatic animals until they are lucky enough to be eaten by a frog.

6. Once within the definitive host the cercaria develops directly into a sexually mature adult. Usually some migration through the body of the host is first necessary to reach the favored spot. The ingested cercarias of the sheep liver fluke burrow across the intestinal wall and into the coelom, whence they reach

the water. Cercarias are positively phototactic and will collect on the lighted side of an aquarium, but they will turn and swim toward any dark object.

The cercarias reach the definitive vertebrate hosts in a variety of ways. The cercarias of

Fig. 11-22. Life cycle of the sheep liver fluke.

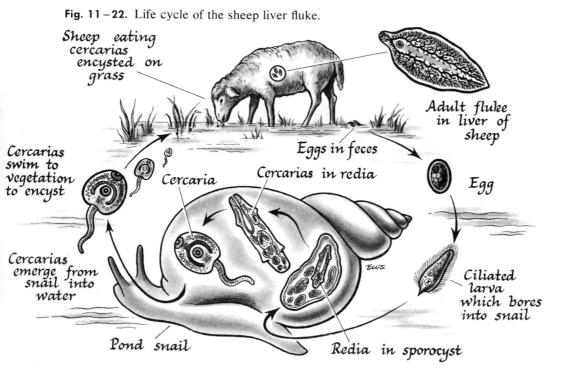

Sheep eating cercarias encysted on grass

Adult fluke in liver of sheep

Cercarias swim to vegetation to encyst

Cercaria

Cercarias in redia

Eggs in feces

Egg

Cercarias emerge from snail into water

Ciliated larva which bores into snail

Pond snail

Redia in sporocyst

the surface of the liver, which they enter to lodge in the bile ducts. The schistosomes are carried around by the bloodstream before they lodge in the capillaries of the inferior mesenteric and rectal veins.

The human cost of trematodes is great in terms of money and in terms of chronic ill health, death, and sheer misery. Control measures include eradication of snails as intermediate hosts, care not to eat uncooked food or drink unboiled water in regions where these plagues are endemic, and rigid enforcement of sanitary codes to prevent raw human excreta from contaminating bodies of water. Intestinal flukes are usually treated clinically with carefully measured doses of hexylresorcinol. Other chemotherapeutic agents, administered either by mouth or injection into the veins, are effective in eradicating infections, at least in the early stages.

TAPEWORMS: CLASS CESTOIDEA

Tapeworms, or cestodes, can be easily defined as flatworms which lack both external ciliation and a digestive system, and which possess a **scolex,** or head, provided with suckers, hooks, or other adhesive organs. The fully mature adults vary according to the species from small worms an inch or less in length to giants over 30 feet long. The scolex is very small; the elongate, ribbonlike body is usually composed of three or four to three or four thousand segments called **proglottids.** With almost no exceptions, the sexually mature adult lives in the intestine of a vertebrate; and no group of vertebrates from fish to man is immune.

The immature bladder worm or **cysticercus** stage is found in the muscles, livers, brains, and other organs of cattle, pigs, rabbits, men, and a wide variety of other animals. Until about a century ago it was believed that tapeworms arose spontaneously from eating too much of the wrong kind of food or from other vague causes. Mankind is indebted to a gynecologist named Küchenmeister for demonstrating the actual origin of tapeworms. He showed that if you feed bladder worms from raw pork to dogs, tapeworms will appear in the dogs' intestines. He even showed this for human beings by feeding bladder worms to a condemned criminal.

The adult tapeworm is a debilitating parasite for man and his domestic animals and for commercially valuable fish and game. The bladder worm stage of some species is extremely dangerous because of its propensity for lodging in the human eye or brain. Fortunately, in most parts of the world such ugly tragedies are rare.

Fig. 11–23. Living scolices ("heads") of tapeworms. These are shown approximately life size. (*From Faust,* Animal Agents and Vectors of Human Disease, *Lea & Febiger*)

Fig. 11–24. Tapeworm cysts in human brain. (*From* Animals Without Backbones *by Buchsbaum by permission of The University of Chicago Press. Copyright 1948 by The University of Chicago*)

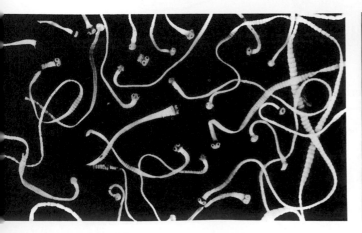

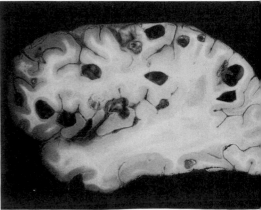

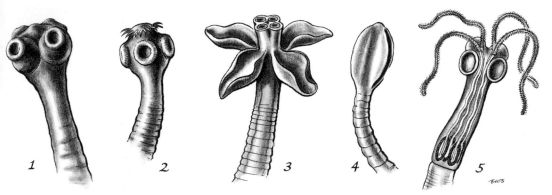

Fig. 11–25. Scolices of five species of tapeworms. *1*, beef tapeworm, *Taenia saginata*. *2*, pork tapeworm, *Taenia solium*. *3*, sting-ray tapeworm, *Myzophyllobothrium rubrum*. *4*, fish tapeworm, *Dibothriocephalus latus*. *5*, shark tapeworm, *Gilquinia squali*.

Evolutionary Relationships and Taxonomy. Tapeworms are clearly derived from digenetic trematodes. In fact, there are a number of intestinal parasites, often placed in a special class, the Cestodaria, that are in several respects intermediate between tapeworms and trematodes. In their musculature and lack of a gut they resemble tapeworms, while in the character of their suckers and in their lack of segmentation into proglottids, they resemble trematodes.

Over 2,000 species of tapeworms have been described. Apparently the tapeworms have undergone an extensive evolution of their own. Presumably this has more or less paralleled the evolution of their vertebrate hosts. Certainly no tapeworm could exist with its immature stages in sheep and its adult stage in wolves before herbivores and carnivores themselves had evolved.

The formulation of a satisfactory system of classification for tapeworms continues to baffle the specialists. The most recent monograph on tapeworms, a volume of nearly 800 pages, recognizes 11 orders. The classification is based largely on differences in the holdfasts on the scolex and in the reproductive organs. The eggs also show characteristic differences and furnish a means of diagnosis when present in the feces. The six most important species of tapeworms will be considered individually in the section devoted to life histories, later in this chapter.

Functional Systems. The heads or scolices of tapeworms are provided with a variety of holdfast organs. The commonest type is a group of cup-shaped, muscular suckers, as on *Taenia saginata*, the beef tapeworm, or, more accurately, the beef-human tapeworm, contracted from eating insufficiently cooked beef. Many tapeworms wear a crown of hooks, or rostellum, on the protruding top of the head. Other species are provided with lateral suction grooves, four long retractile and hook-covered tentacles, or four ear-shaped or petal-shaped lobes.

Next to the scolex is the neck, a proliferative region in which new proglottids, or segments, are continually being formed.

The major part of the adult worm is the **strobila,** composed of proglottids. The anatomy of a mature proglottid varies greatly from one species to another, especially in the details of the reproductive structures. We will take the beef tapeworm, *Taenia saginata*, as an illustrative example.

Externally, there is a thin cuticle overlying an epithelium, below which is a thin layer of transverse muscles and then one of longitudinal muscles. The body is filled with mesenchyme, as in other flatworms, but a peculiar feature of tapeworm musculature is a layer of circular muscle about midway between the body wall and the central axis of the worm. This layer divides the mesenchyme into an outer **cortical** and a central or **medullary** zone.

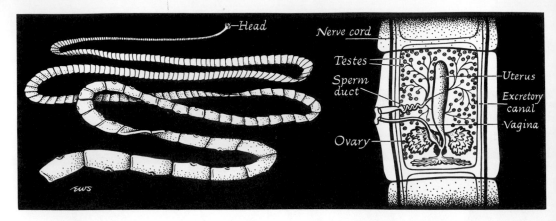

Fig. 11–26. Beef tapeworm, *Taenia saginata,* adult and single proglottid. *(From Pauli, The World of Life, Houghton Mifflin)*

The nervous system consists chiefly of a pair of nerve cords extending along each edge of the worm and running continuously through all the proglottids. The excretory system, more accurately called the **osmo-regulatory** system, consists of flame cells connected with one member of a pair of long excretory ducts extending along each edge of the worm and connected in each proglottid by a transverse duct.

The male reproductive system consists of numerous rounded testes that fill most of the medullary or central portion of the proglottid. They are connected by a branching system of ducts which conduct the sperms to a vas deferens leading to a genital pore on one edge of each proglottid. In some species there is a short muscular penis.

The female system consists of a bi-lobed ovary, also in the medullary zone. The oviduct begins at the isthmus of the ovary and leads to the exterior through an elongate vagina. Joining the oviduct, near its point of origin from the ovary, is a duct from the yolk or vitelline glands and another from some shell glands. The eggs are presumably fertilized in this location—before the shell is deposited, of course.

After the shells are formed around the eggs, they pass into the uterus. The uterus, at first rod-shaped, develops side-branches as more and more eggs are formed. As the proglottid itself elongates, the uterus with its side-branches comes to occupy most of the space. The number of lateral branches in a gravid, or "pregnant," proglottid is an important diagnostic trait. There are about 18 in *Taenia saginata,* the beef tapeworm, and only 8 to 10 in *Taenia solium,* the pork tapeworm.

Life Cycles. The tapeworm contracted from eating infected, insufficiently cooked beef, *Taenia saginata,* averages about 15 to 20 feet in length when mature, though much longer ones have been recorded. The mature proglottids separate from the worm and pass out with the feces to crawl away. In locomotion a proglottid looks like an albino planarian. The average gravid proglottid contains 80,000 eggs.

The eggs contain an embryo called an **oncosphere** or **hexacanth** embryo, from its three pairs of hooks. Cattle grazing on soil polluted by sewage pick up the eggs, which hatch in the intestine, penetrate into the mesenteric veins or lymphatics, and are carried to the liver, heart, and body muscles. There the oncospheres lodge and transform into the second stage in the life history, the **cysticercus** or bladder worm.

Fig. 11–27. *A,* embryonated tapeworm egg. *B,* newly hatched oncosphere or hexacanth embryo.

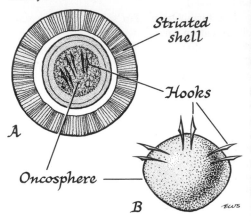

284

Any of the various stages after the oncosphere stage through which a tapeworm may pass in an intermediate host, i.e., a host in which it does not become sexually mature, are called **metacestode stages.** In the beef tapeworm the metacestode stage is the bladder worm or cysticercus. The cysticercus is a little bladder with an inverted scolex projecting in from one side. When insufficiently cooked beef is eaten, the scolex of the bladder worm everts in the human intestine and growth begins. Within three to six months after exposure, the complete tapeworm, with ripe proglottids, will be present. Control necessitates sanitary disposal of sewage so that it does not reach swamp ground where cattle might graze. Heating meat to 65°C (about 150°F) or storing it for 48 hours in a deep freeze is said to kill the bladder worms in beef.

The pork tapeworm, or, more accurately, the pork-human tapeworm, *Taenia solium,* so named by Linnaeus in 1758, resembles the beef tapeworm but is shorter, seldom exceeding 10 feet in length, and unlike *T. saginata* is provided with a circle of hooks on top of the scolex. The difference in gravid proglottids has already been described.

The pork tapeworm is world-wide in distribution, but fortunately is everywhere declining as the importance of the thorough cooking of pork becomes understood, and as sanitary measures become more widespread. The real danger from this tapeworm lies in the fact that if eggs are ingested by a man, they hatch as readily as in a pig, and the oncospheres migrate through the body and develop into the cysticercus or bladder worm stage. Except for the superficial tissues just under the skin, the eye and brain are reported to be the most frequent sites for oncospheres to lodge and bladder worms to grow. This may merely reflect the obvious fact that even a small nodule under the skin or in the eye can be detected, and a cyst the size of a marble in the wrong part of the brain can produce dramatic symptoms, while a much larger bladder worm in some other organ can go unnoticed for years. Self-infection from unclean habits is a serious danger. Over 25 per cent of 284 British troops in India with cysticercosis of the brain harbored *T. solium* in their own intestines.

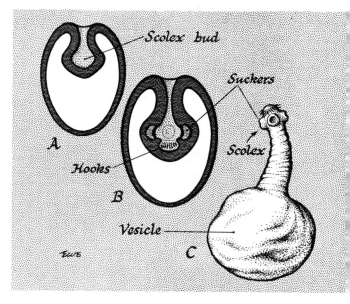

Fig. 11-28. Three stages in development of bladder worm or cysticercus, shown greatly enlarged.

The commonest tapeworm of the southeastern United States is the dwarf tapeworm *Hymenolepis nana,* although it is also world-wide in distribution. It commonly has only one host in its life cycle, usually a child with unclean habits. The proglottids disintegrate within the intestine so the feces are thoroughly mixed with eggs. When swallowed, the eggs hatch and the oncosphere embryos become attached to the villi of the human intestine, go through a brief bladder worm stage there, and then become adults.

The fish tapeworm, *Dibothriocephalus latus,* also called *Diphyllobothrium,* attains a length of 30 feet and has an elongate scolex lacking hooks but provided with two long suction grooves. It is contracted by eating raw or improperly cooked fish from fresh water. There are normally three hosts. The oncosphere burrows into a water "flea" or other small crustacean. This in turn is eaten by some fish in whose muscles the equivalent of the bladder worm develops. Bears, otters, cats, and dogs, as well as men, are the definitive hosts.

The **hydatid** tapeworm, *Echinococcus granulosus,* is the most dangerous of all. This is extremely small and never has more than three or four proglottids. It lives as a sexually mature adult in the intestines of dogs, foxes, and other carnivores. Almost any mammal which happens to pick up and swallow *Echinococcus* eggs is a suitable host for its bladder worm. The oncosphere develops into a bladder with multiple invaginated scolices and cysts within cysts. The hydatid cysts grow to a very large size. Cysts the size of grapefruit have been reported. Moreover the cysts are dangerous to remove because of the loose secondary bladders within them, "hydatid sand," which if spilled into the patient will start new cysts. Sheep, swine, and men are the chief intermediate hosts. Infestations are common in parts of the world where dogs have a chance to eat parts of sheep or swine carcasses.

The dog tapeworm, *Dipylidium caninum*, lives as an adult in the intestines of dogs, cats, and similar animals. It is a medium-sized worm. The intermediate host is a flea or louse. Infections that are found in the intestines of children are presumably due to the swallowing of infected fleas.

Review and References

REVIEW TOPICS

1. What traits unite the protostomes, and what phyla constitute this group?

2. What is the evidence for and against the theory that flatworms arose from multinucleate ciliates?

3. Describe the digestive, excretory, reproductive, and nervous systems of turbellarians.

4. What is meant by an inverted retina? What is the function of the pigment cup of the turbellarian eye, in terms of behavior?

5. What happens after cutting a flatworm crosswise? Lengthwise? What principles of regeneration emerge from such experiments?

6. Cats, pigs, and minks may contract a digenetic lung fluke by eating raw crayfish. Assuming this trematode passes through six stages, what is a probable life history of this parasite?

7. Define: cercaria, redia, *Schistosoma*, miracidium, statocyst, scolex, proglottid, flame cell, bladder worm, *Taenia*.

8. What control measures can be taken against *Schistosoma* (*Bilharzia*)? Against beef and pork tapeworms? Hydatid tapeworms?

9. In what ways do the anatomy and life history of trematodes and of tapeworms adapt each of them for parasitism?

10. Compare and contrast the structure of a planarian flatworm and a jellyfish; of a turbellarian and a trematode.

USEFUL REFERENCES

Best, J. B., "Protopsychology," *Scientific American*, vol. 208, 1963.

Bronsted, H. V. "Planarian Regeneration," *Biological Reviews,* vol. 30, Cambridge, England, The University Press, 1955.

Cheng, T. C., *The Biology of Animal Parasites,* Philadelphia, W. B. Saunders Co., 1964.

Child, C. M., *Patterns and Problems of Development,* Chicago, University of Chicago Press, 1941.

Dawes, B., *The Trematodes,* Cambridge, England, The University Press, 1946.

Faust, E. C., *Animal Agents and Vectors of Human Disease,* Philadelphia, Lea & Febiger, 1955.

Hyman, L. H., *The Invertebrates: II, Platyhelminthes and Rhynchocoels,* New York. McGraw-Hill Book Co., 1951.

Morgan, A. H., *Field Book of Animals in Winter,* New York, G. P. Putnam's Sons, 1939.

Pennak, R. W., *Fresh-Water Invertebrates of the United States,* New York, The Ronald Press Company, 1953.

Taliaferro, W. H., "Reactions to Light in *Planaria Maculata,*" *Journal of Experimental Zoology,* vol. 31, 1920.

Wardle, R. A., and J. A. McLeod, *The Zoology of Tapeworms,* Minneapolis, University of Minnesota Press, 1952.

Chapter 12

Nematodes and

Other Aschelminthes

The Aschelminthes (*ascus*, sac, + *helminthos*, worm) is a phylum made up of six subphyla of more or less wormlike animals which differ so widely among themselves that many competent zoologists rank them as six independent phyla. Of the six, only the nematodes are of any importance, but their importance is enormous. Many of the most serious diseases of plants, animals, and man are caused by nematodes. In addition, when the final count is in, it will probably be found that there are more species of nematodes than of all other kinds of animals combined, including the arthropods. The other five subphyla of the aschelminthes are: the nematomorphs, the rotifers, the gastrotrichs, the kinorhynchs, and the priapulids; for most of them there are no common names.

All aschelminthes are united by the following common traits:

1. They are constructed on the tube-within-a-tube plan, i.e., a body wall, a body cavity, and a gut extending from an anterior mouth to a posterior anus.

2. The body cavity is a pseudocoel, so called to distinguish it from a true coelom such as is found in vertebrates and annelids. A true coelom is formed in the development of the animal in a different way and is lined by a special layer of epithelial cells which is not present in a pseudocoel.

3. The aschelminth body is covered with a cuticle which in some species appears to be segmented in a series of rings. These are entirely superficial and there are no other traces of segmentation. The cuticle prevents growth, so that the animals must molt as their size increases. As in insects, the stage between each molt is called an **instar.**

4. The anterior end is radially symmetrical, this being especially noticeable in nematodes, kinorhynchs, and priapulids.

NEMATODES: SUBPHYLUM NEMATODA

No group of animals that is so little known to the general public has anything like the economic, medical, or scientific importance of the nematodes, or roundworms. They are second only to insects in the damage they do to agriculture. They cause numerous debilitating and fatal diseases of man and animals, both wild and domestic. They live in the widest possible environments: around the roots of grass and within the human eye; in the depths of the oceans and in glacial pools in the high Alps; and in all types of soils, from swamps to sandy deserts. No vertebrate is known that does not harbor parasitic nematodes, nor are crustaceans, mollusks, insects, or centipedes free from them. The United States Department of

287

Agriculture estimates the annual nematode damage to our agriculture as about 2 billion dollars. The list of crops seriously injured by them includes beets, carrots, chrysanthemums, cotton, mushrooms, peanuts, potatoes, rice, tobacco, tomatoes, wheat, and many others. Nematology deserves to rank with entomology in agricultural and medical importance.

Over 15,000 species of nematodes have been named, and conservative estimates place the probable number of species in excess of half a million. The abundance of individuals is also enormous. Some 300 million nematodes of a single kind, mononchs, have been estimated to occur per acre in sugar beet fields of Utah and Idaho. At least 3,000,000 people in the United States alone suffer with ascaris infections.

Nematodes are easily characterized and identified. They are cylindrical worms encased in a flexible but inelastic cuticle. This means that they cannot change either their length or their thickness, but in moving lash around like animated whips forming C's and S's. They are built on the tube-within-a-tube plan, with an anterior mouth, a straight gut, and a ventral anus, located a short distance anterior to the tail tip. Between body wall and gut is a cavity, the **pseudocoel.** In size nematodes range from microscopic to over 2 feet in length. Most soil and water-living species are semi-microscopic, many parasitic species grow to be an inch or so

Fig. 12 – 1. Living nematodes, as seen under the dissecting microscope. Note the characteristic S curves and C curves. (*Courtesy, General Biological Supply House, Inc., Chicago*)

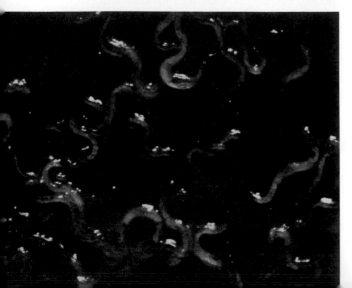

long, while some, like the common *Ascaris* which inhabits the intestine of man and many of his domestic animals, grow to be a foot long.

The sexes are separate except in rare instances. The gonads are the only organs lying in the body cavity. The worms usually pass through five stages or instars, separated by four molts of the cuticle.

Evolutionary Relationships and Major Groups. During their long evolutionary history the nematodes have undergone the familiar process of adaptive radiation in many directions. This vast assemblage of species is now usually divided into two big groups, the Class Phasmidea and the Class Aphasmidea.

The **Phasmidea** includes most of the soil-living and parasitic species, as well as many aquatic and free-living ones. The typical genus is taken as *Rhabditis.* Over 100 species of *Rhabditis* have been described, three of which are commonly found either living in the nephridia or encysted as juveniles in the brown bodies lying in the coelom in the posterior segments of earthworms. They are easily cultured on agar with a few scraps of beef when kept at cool temperatures. They furnish far better material for study than another phasmid commonly used, *Turbatrix* (formerly *Anguillula*) *aceti*, the much smaller nematode commonly found in crude vinegar. Most species of *Rhabditis* are found in soil or in decaying animal or vegetable materials. Other important phasmid nematodes include the hookworms, pinworms, ascaris, various lung, eye, and intestinal worms, the famous Guinea worm, and numerous parasites of plants and insects.

The **Aphasmidea** include only a few parasites, but they are important ones like the pork muscle worm *Trichinella*, the intestinal whipworm, and the giant red kidney worm. Most species are free-living and many are aquatic in both fresh and salt water. *Plectus* is taken as the "typical" genus. About 40 species of *Plectus* have been described living in soil, in fresh water, in damp leafy debris, and among moss and lichens.

The **phasmids,** which characterize the Phasmidea, are a pair of unicellular glands or sense organs, or (such is our ignorance of nematodes)

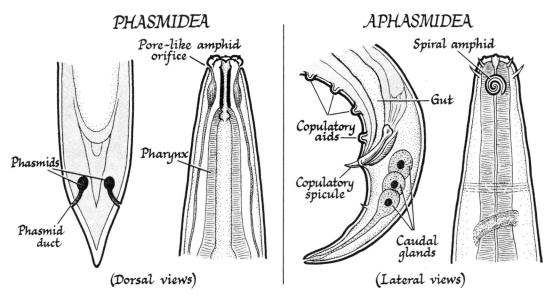

PHASMIDEA

APHASMIDEA

Pore-like amphid orifice

Spiral amphid

Gut

Phasmids

Pharynx

Copulatory aids

Copulatory spicule

Phasmid duct

Caudal glands

(Dorsal views)

(Lateral views)

Fig. 12 – 2. Posterior and anterior ends of typical phasmidean and typical aphasmidean. The phasmids must be stained to be readily seen.

perhaps glandular sense organs, located on either side of the body close to the tail tip. (See Fig. 12 – 2.) In a living, unstained nematode the phasmids, like most other nematode structures, are translucent and hence almost invisible. Consequently, the only sign of the phasmids in a living worm is a pair of very small holes in the cuticle through which these organs open to the exterior. Located on either side of the body at some distance behind the anus, each one looks like an eyelet for a shoestring. **Caudal glands,** on the other hand, characterize the Aphasmidea. These are composed of three or four large cells in the very tip of the tail. They probably secrete an adhesive material, and should be distinguished from anal glands, which are situated more anteriorly, opening near or in common with the gut, and are present in both groups. Both groups likewise have **amphids,** which are cuticular pits on either side of the head, but these sense organs are characteristically different in the two classes. In the Aphasmidea the amphids are commonly disk-shaped or spiral, while in the Phasmidea they usually open by pores. The males of the Aphasmidea are usually provided with accessory copulatory organs in the form of a special row of modified bristles on the ventral side. The differences between the two groups are summarized in the table.

Comparison of the Two Nematode Classes

TRAIT	PHASMIDEA	APHASMIDEA
Phasmids	Present	Absent
Caudal glands	Absent	Present
Amphids	Porelike	Disks or spirals
Excretory system	With lateral canals	Without lateral canals
Accessory copulatory structures	Usually absent	Usually present
Habits	Many parasitic	Few parasitic
Typical genus	*Rhabditis*	*Plectus*

Functional Systems. Judged by their success, nematodes must possess one of the most efficient bodily organizations known. The skeletal, muscular, excretory, and, to a large extent, the nervous systems are all built into the body wall. The **cuticle** is virtually an exoskeleton providing both protection for the worm and support for the muscles of locomotion. It is a noncellular layer composed of a horny material, **keratin,** that is extremely resistant to many solvents, including digestive enzymes. In parasitic species the cuticle is organized of five or six specialized layers. In many nematodes the cuticle externally bears various spines, plates, striations, annulations, punctations, copulatory papillae, ambulatory bristles resembling feet, oral excrescences, pre-anal suckers, and various forms of amphids, and of wing-shaped **alae** or tail shields. Immediately beneath the cuticle is the **epidermis** (sometimes termed hypodermis or subcuticle) which secretes the cuticle. Beneath the epidermis are the muscles.

The **muscular system** of a nematode is very different from that found in any other phylum. The muscle cells lie immediately under the epidermis and are divided into four quadrants by four cords, a mid-dorsal and a mid-ventral nerve cord, and a right and left excretory duct. All the muscle fibers are longitudinal; there is no antagonistic set of circular muscles. The muscle cells are giant cells of a fixed and rela-

tively small number, usually about 24 per quadrant, although the large parasitic genera like *Ascaris* may have a total of 150 muscle cells per quadrant. The contractile fibers lie in the periphery of the cytoplasm of these big muscle cells, always on the side adjacent to the epidermis and in many species extending well up on the sides of the cells, making a U-shaped or even hairpin-shaped structure in cross section. (See Fig. 12–3.)

The common relationship between muscles and nerves is reversed in the nematodes. From each muscle cell a long protoplasmic fiber extends out to the nerve cord. The processes of the muscle cells in the two dorsal quadrants extend to the dorsal nerve cord, those of the two ventral quadrants to the ventral nerve cord. The dorsal and ventral muscle cells act as a pair of antagonists. There is evidently no neural mechanism making it possible for the two right or the two left quadrants to contract together. Consequently nematodes can bend and lash only in a dorso-ventral plane, although as soon as they begin to do so it causes them to lie on their sides unless they are in a fairly thick medium. There is, however, some mechanism enabling anterior muscle cells to contract separately from posterior ones. Consequently an undulatory motion is possible and can easily be seen in nematodes from earthworms as they move around on the surface of an agar plate.

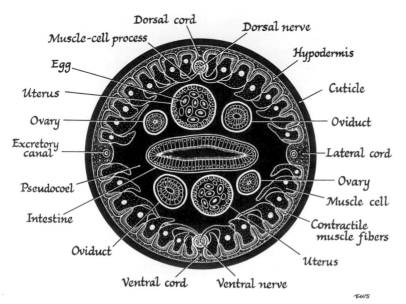

Fig. 12–3. Cross section of generalized female nematode. Each muscle cell has a long process reaching to a nerve cord. The entire length of most such processes cannot be seen in a single section.

The **nervous system** of a nematode is rather complex and evidently plays an important role in the nematode way of life, for more than 50 per cent of the cells of the entire animal are nerve cells. In *Turbatrix*, the common vinegar eel, 251 cells are nerve cells out of a grand total of 432 cells in the entire body.

The only part of the nematode nervous system that can be seen in a living worm is the **circumpharyngeal nerve ring.** This encircles the pharynx or esophagus and looks like a doughnut worn at a jaunty angle. In properly stained specimens it can be seen that the nerve ring consists of nerve fibers. Most of the cell bodies are located in various **ganglia.** Close beside the nerve ring on either side is a large lateral ganglion from which a large nerve extends forward to its amphid. Near the nerve ring are various other pairs of ganglia, postlateral, ventral, postventral, and papillary. Four or more nerves extend from the ring to sensory papillae on the "face," and two main nerves, the dorsal and ventral nerve cords, plus four or more smaller nerves, extend from the ring back to the

Fig. 12–4. Nematode nervous system, side view. Most structures, except the nerve ring and the dorsal and ventral cords, are paired.

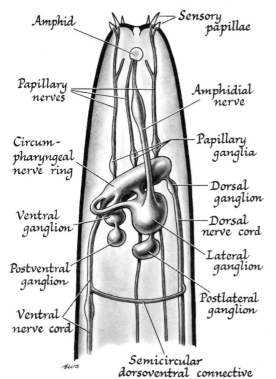

tail. At intervals there are half circles of nerve fibers which connect the longitudinal nerves. Near the posterior end of the animal is a pre-anal ganglion and nerves to sensory papillae and other structures.

The **sense organs** include the amphids, situated like ears on either side of the head, various sensory papillae and bristles, a pair of eye spots in a few species, and possibly the phasmids in the Phasmidea.

The **excretory systems** of nematodes are extremely simple. In the midventral region, at about the level of the nerve ring, there is a single giant excretory cell dubbed the **renette.** It opens to the exterior via a midventral pore. In the larger parasitic Phasmidea, there is in addition a pair of excretory tubules running the length of the worm, one in each of the lateral cords and connected to the excretory pore by a cross tube.

The **digestive system** follows a similar pattern in all nematodes. The mouth, however, shows considerable variation. As with insects and mammals, this is correlated with the diet. Some species have relatively smooth lips and merely suck in their food. Others have three or more strong chitinous jaws, still others have sharp spears with muscles to push them out of the mouth and into plant or animal tissues.

The first part of the gut is a muscular sucking region called by some workers the **pharynx,** by others the **esophagus.** It may have one or two muscular bulbs which are sometimes provided with teeth. The intestine is usually a straight tube without bends or attached glands. There are no circulatory or respiratory systems.

Reproduction and Development. The reproductive system is one of the most efficient known. A female *Ascaris*, for example, lays eggs at the rate of about 200,000 per day. The nematode reproductive system has also proved extremely useful to investigators interested in the behavior of chromosomes. The reason is that the testis and vas deferens form a narrow continuous tube. At the inner end of the testis, primordial germ cells proliferate continually by mitosis. A bit further down the tube are primary spermatocytes in the first meiotic division, still further down are secondary spermatocytes of the second meiotic division, and

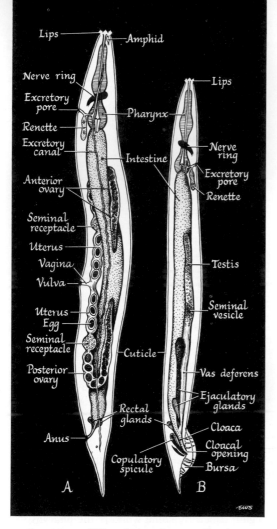

Fig. 12–5. Side views of generalized nematodes. *A*, female. *B*, male.

below them are maturing sperms. Nematode sperms differ from those of other animals in being amoeboid rather than flagellated.

The events in the ovary can likewise be observed in serial order: primordial germ cells first, then primary and secondary oocytes undergoing meiosis, mature eggs, the process of fertilization which occurs well up the oviduct (from this point on called the uterus), and then the various stages in the cleavage of the egg and the development of the embryo. The fact that many nematodes have a very small number of chromosomes also makes them favorable for research.

The vas deferens enters the hind gut and the two form a **cloaca.** In the males of most species there is a pair of conspicuous **copulatory spicules** and one or more **prostatic glands.** In the females of most species there are two ovaries and two uteri, one extending anteriorly and the other posteriorly. The uteri unite in a very short vagina which opens to the exterior via the vulva, on the midventral line about midway between head and tail.

The behavior of the chromosomes during the cleavage of the nematode egg supports Weismann's concept of the primacy of the germ-plasm or reproductive cells as contrasted with the body or somatic cells. In the two-cell stage it can be seen that one cell, called P_1, has normal chromosomes but that in the other cell, termed *AB*, large chunks at the end of each chromosome are lost into the cytoplasm (Fig. 12–6). At the second cleavage the process of

Fig. 12–6. Chromatin diminution during cleavage of nematode *Ascaris* egg. *1, 2*, two-cell stage; diminution in cell *AB*, normal division of chromosomes in cell P_1. *3*, four-cell stage. *4*, rearrangement of cleavage cells; diminished nuclei in cells *A* and *B*, diminution occurring in cell S_2, normal division in cell P_2. *L* = lost chromatin. (*After Boveri*)

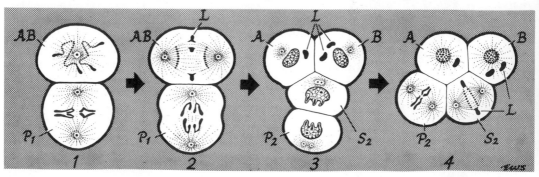

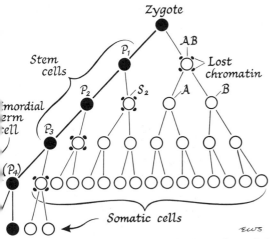

Zygote

Stem cells

P_1

P_2

P_3

(P_4)

S_2

AB

Lost chromatin

A

B

Primordial germ cell

Somatic cells

EWS

Fig. 12–7. Segregation of the primordial germ cell in *Ascaris*. *(After Boveri)*

chromosome diminution again occurs so that of the two cells formed by P_1 only one, P_2, contains a full complement of chromatin. Chromosome diminution continues in this way until by the 16-cell stage only one cell possesses DNA representing all the DNA in the original zygote. This cell gives rise to the reproductive cells, i.e., the eggs and sperms and the walls of the reproductive tract, but to no other parts of the body. This remarkable fact was discovered by

a brilliant student of Hertwig, Boveri, who also predicted that chromosomes imply the linkage and crossing-over of genetic factors, though few believed him at the time.

The most notable feature of embryonic development is that the blastocoel, instead of being obliterated as in most other animals, remains as the body cavity or pseudocoel.

The eggs usually contain embryos or small worms when laid. Commonly, the larvae or juveniles pass through five instars or stages separated by four molts or **ecdyses,** but there is little change in bodily form.

Natural History and Life Cycles. Nematodes are among the most adaptable animals known, from an ecological standpoint. Not only are there some species that can live in almost any conceivable environment, but many single species live in widely different habitats, from ponds in northern Alaska to jungle lakes in Brazil, in both waters and soils of many types. In a few cases it has been shown that a single species may have physiologically differentiated races which, although anatomically indistinguishable, nevertheless flourish under different conditions. Perhaps it is a matter of adaptive enzymes; nobody knows. Beyond the simple facts that their reproductive powers are prodigious, and that

Fig. 12–8. Some nematodes. Left to right: adult gourd-shaped female of *Heterodera,* the rootknot nematode; a carnivorous nematode; lateral view of the female *Achromadora minima.*

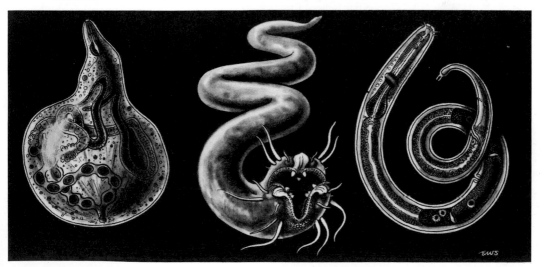

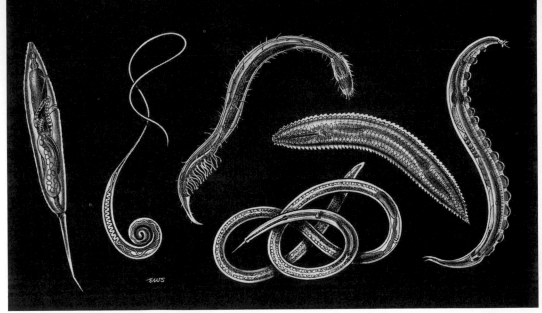

Fig. 12–9. Another group of nematodes. Above, left to right: *Hammerschmidtiella diesingi, Trichuris ovis, Draconema, Criconema, Bunonema.* Below: *Xiphinema.*

nematodes occur in enormous numbers, little is known concerning their population dynamics.

In diet many are carnivorous, eating protozoans, small annelids, rotifers, tardigrades, and even other nematodes. Many are herbivorous, living especially on roots; many live on decaying material; and many are parasitic.

Among the best known and most destructive of the nematodes injurious to crops is the root-knot nematode, *Heterodera,* belonging to the Phasmidea. It produces swellings on the roots of potatoes, turnips, tobacco, sugar beets, and some 75 other field and garden crops, vegetables, fruits, and weeds. The second-stage juveniles penetrate young roots, which respond by

Fig. 12–10. Roots of squash plants from untreated plots, showing heavy infestation with nematodes. *(U.S. Department of Agriculture)*

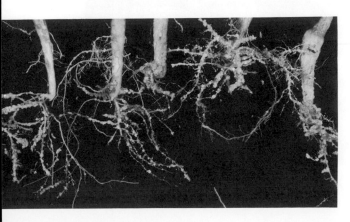

forming a swelling in which the worms mature. The females swell up and when sexually mature become pear-shaped or egg-shaped though only about a millimeter long. They never leave the gall, but merely spread their eggs in the soil when the root dies and disintegrates. The males resemble normal nematodes and wander about. In hot weather the life cycle requires less than a month. The eggs and second-stage juveniles within old galls can withstand drying but fortunately are killed by freezing.

The citrus nematode, *Tylenchus semipenetrans,* and the onion nematode, *Tylenchus devastatrix,* are both widespread wherever citrus fruits or onions, tulips, or other bulbs are grown. The worms are provided with a sharp dagger that can be protruded out of the mouth to penetrate small roots, from which they suck the juice. They are extremely difficult to eradicate. Living with them is usually a cannibalistic nematode of the genus *Mononchus.* The mononchs catch other nematodes which they swallow whole, since their three teeth are grasping organs. Since the mononchs eat species of nematodes that infest plant roots, they are beneficial to agriculture.

Hookworm. The most widespread and important parasitic nematode is the hookworm, three species of which infest mankind, and several other species various other mammals. The

294

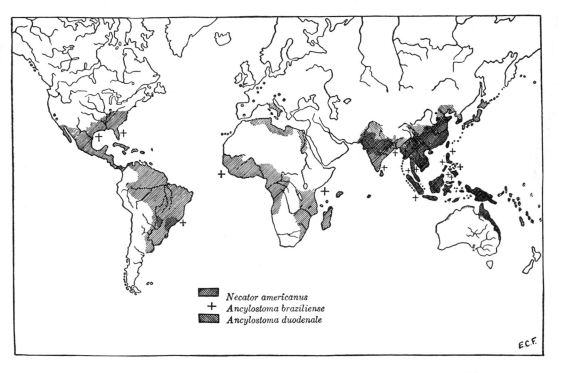

Fig. 12–11. World distribution of hookworms. *(From Faust,* Human Helminthology, *Lea & Febiger)*

Legend on map:
- ///// *Necator americanus*
- + *Ancylostoma braziliense*
- ▓▓ *Ancylostoma duodenale*

E.C.F.

adult hookworms live in the human intestine, and are attached by their mouths to the villi. They ingest blood and secrete a poisonous anticoagulant that causes anemia and general weakness. The females are slightly over a half inch long, the males appreciably smaller. The mouths of both sexes have small or obscure lips but are armed with teeth. The posterior end of each male bears a pair of flipperlike expansions that form a copulatory bursa supported by six or more pairs of ribs or rays. A mature female lays 5,000 to 10,000 eggs daily and usually lives a year or two.

The eggs already contain embryos when laid, and pass to the exterior in the host's feces. The eggs hatch in the soil, releasing **"rhabditiform" larvae,** so-called from their resemblance to *Rhabditis.* These larvae eat, grow, and molt twice in the soil before becoming infective. Optimum conditions are well-aerated top soil, moist but not wet, absence of direct sunlight, and a temperature of about 90°F (33°C). The

Fig. 12–12. The hookworm, *Necator americanus.* Left: male and female adults. Right: rhabditiform larvae. *(Kindness of William H. Amos)*

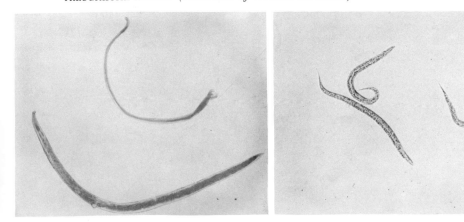

infective larvae appearing after the second molt are long, thin, so-called **filariform larvae.** The mouth is closed; they penetrate the skin of the feet, hands, or any other parts of a human body which come in contact with infected soil, and thus cause "ground itch."

Within the human body the larvae are carried by the bloodstream to the lungs, where they may cause appreciable damage. From the lungs the growing worms make their way up the windpipe to the throat and thence down into the intestine.

Many people in the United States, mostly in rural areas in the south, are still afflicted with hookworm, *Necator americanus.* The number in Mexico, South America, and Africa also infected is said to run into the millions. Around the shores of the Mediterranean is found a slightly different species, *Ancylostoma duodenale.* In the Orient both species flourish. A United Nations report estimates a world total of over 600,000,000 cases. Control consists in sanitary disposal of human feces, wearing of shoes, and the general avoidance of contact with contaminated soil.

Trichina. *Trichinella spiralis* is also a very serious threat to human health in the United States and in many other areas. A total of approximately 30,000,000 people are supposed to be afflicted by these parasites. The infection is contracted by eating insufficiently cooked meat of some omnivorous or carnivorous animal, almost always pork. Severe cases, however, have followed eating bear steaks, and it would be a hazard of cannibalism. The larvae lie encysted in muscles or other tissue—brain, for example. When eaten and the cyst digested, the larvae burrow into the host's intestinal mucosa, where they grow and mature. Each female worm deposits about 10,000 larvae, which migrate via the bloodstream and encyst in muscles and other sites. It is this encystment that causes most of the damage, especially when the site is the heart or brain. Prevention is possible simply by the thorough cooking of the meat. This not only protects the human beings concerned; it prevents continuing the cycle because it eliminates the possibility of infected garbage which might be eaten by pigs, rats, or other animals.

Fig. 12–13. *Trichinella spiralis.* Left, above: *Trichinella* larva encysted in striated pork muscle; below: *Trichinella* larva in brain surrounded by leucocytes. Right: worms in brain of patient dead of trichinous encephalitis. *(Merck Sharp & Dohme)*

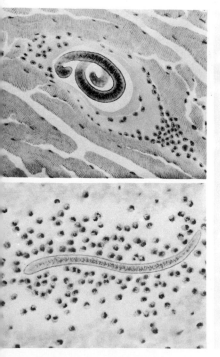

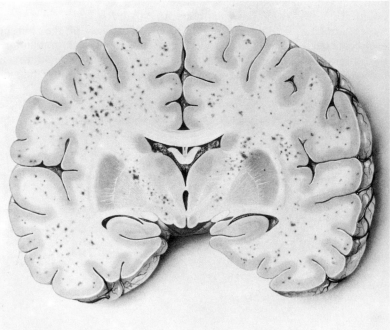

Other Parasitic Nematodes. *Ascaris* is a genus of many species adapted for living in the intestines of men, horses, hogs, and many other hosts. Because of its extremely large size — some species are over a foot long — *Ascaris* is frequently used for laboratory dissection. The embryonated eggs are usually swallowed with dirt and hatch in the stomach. The larvae penetrate the intestinal villi, enter the bloodstream and, as with hookworms, enter the alveoli of the lungs, whence they migrate up the trachea. After being swallowed a second time, they mature in the intestine about two months after the egg was swallowed.

Two of the most interesting nematodes, and perhaps the largest known, are the bright red kidney worm, usually found in dogs, and the Guinea worm of man. The kidney worm, *Dioctophyma renale,* is widely distributed in dogs, wolves, raccoons, minks, skunks, seals, and many other animals who might swallow one of the little ectoparasitic branchiobdellid annelids that infest crayfish and teleosts and harbor the larval stages of the kidney worm. The worm grows to be nearly 2 feet in length and is the diameter of a lead pencil. Its eggs escape with the host's urine. Rarely found in man, it may cause extreme renal colic.

The Guinea worm, *Dracunculus medinensis,* is contracted by drinking water containing very small crustaceans harboring the larvae. Within the body cavity of its human host the larvae grow to mature worms two or more feet in length. The gravid female then migrates through the tissues, causing severe allergic reactions in the host, until she comes to lie under the skin, with the anterior end just protruding from a small ulcer, usually on the ankle or wrist. When the ankle is immersed in water, the female lays eggs. This worm has been known from ancient times. The classic method of treatment is to wind the worm up slowly on a stick, an inch or two a day, in order to avoid breaking it.

Elephantiasis, in which the legs swell with a puffy edema to enormous proportions, has been recorded from remote antiquity in India and is described by such famous medieval Persian physicians as Rhazes and Avicenna. In the 19th century several investigators discovered microscopic worms in such patients. Finally

Fig. 12 – 14. *Dioctophyma renale,* the kidney worm. Compare its length with the 6-inch ruler. *(From Faust,* Animal Agents and Vectors of Human Disease, *Lea & Febiger)*

Manson demonstrated that these microfilariae, minute nematodes (*Wuchereria bancrofti*) that caused this swelling by multiplying in the lymph spaces, are transmitted by a night-biting mosquito, *Culex fatigans.* It may be recalled that this discovery helped lead to a similar one for malaria. Like a number of other parasitic nematodes, *Wuchereria* shows a marked rhythm

Fig. 12 – 15. Elephantiasis of the legs due to a small nematode living in the lymph spaces.

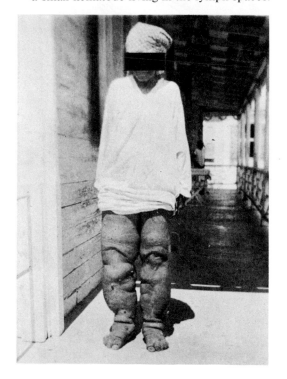

within its host. In this case the microfilariae appear in the peripheral blood mostly at night between 8 P.M. and 8 A.M. when mosquitos are most active.

Most domestic animals, including fowls, are afflicted with nematodes having life cycles similar to those outlined above. Embryonated eggs pass to the exterior with the host's feces, and the larvae hatch in the intestine and mature there either directly or after an excursion through the lungs. Some parasitic nematodes are beneficial. Such a one is *Agamermis*, some species of which afflict grasshoppers.

One of the most easily available parasitic nematodes for laboratory study alive is *Rhabdias* (*Rhabditis*), which is frequently found in the lungs of frogs as well as toads, garter snakes, and other cold-blooded vertebrates. Its life cycle was discovered by Metschnikoff, who found that the worms in the lungs are protandrous hermaphrodites, i.e., the young worms pass through a transient male stage. Their sperms are stored in a seminal receptacle and used to fertilize the eggs which are produced when the individual eventually transforms into an adult female! The developing eggs are coughed by the frog into the mouth, swallowed, and pass to the exterior with the feces. The rhabditiform larvae develop into small males or females in wet soil around the edges of ponds. The females produce filariform young which hatch within the mother, whom they consume. They then escape as infective juveniles ready to penetrate the skin of a frog host. This life cycle is similar to that of the hookworm, for there are rhabditoid and filariform larvae, but the sexually mature adults in one case are in the intestine and in the other outside in the soil.

Fig. 12–16. Life cycle of *Rhabdias* (*Rhabditis*) *bufonis,* a common lung parasite of frogs, snakes, and other cold-blooded animals. *A,* protandrous adult in the lung of a frog. *B,* rhabditiform larva on wet earth beside a pond. *C,* adult female, free-living. *D,* adult male, free-living. *E,* filariform juvenile which penetrates the skin of a frog and becomes the protandrous adult in the lungs.

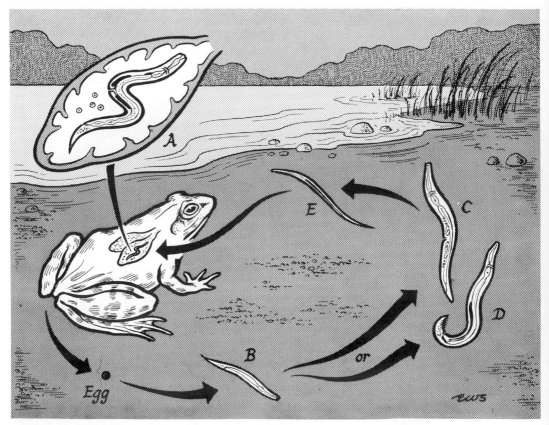

HORSEHAIR WORMS: NEMATOMORPHA

Horsehair worms are not uncommon in shallow puddles, along the shores of lakes, or under stones in swampy places. They appear like yellowish or blackish animated wires or horsehairs moving stiffly around and forming tangled knots whenever two or three are together. It was this behavior that gave them the name, used by Linnaeus, of gordians. The familiar species are a foot or more in length but some are minute, others over a yard long.

In general anatomy nematomorphs are closely similar to the nematodes. They possess a flexible but inelastic cuticle, a subcuticular epidermis, and below that a layer of longitudinal muscles without an antagonistic circular set. However, unlike the nematodes, the longitudinal muscles are not divided into four quadrants by dorsal, ventral, and right and left neural and excretory cords.

The body cavity is a pseudocoel, but it is provided with various mesodermal partitions.

The nervous system consists of a circumpharyngeal nerve ring and a single ventral nerve cord. The gut in adults is degenerate.

The sexes are separate. The reproductive system consists of a pair of elongate tubular ovaries or testes filling the entire body and opening via a posterior cloaca. The strings of minute eggs may be over 6 feet long and are spread over grass and weeds in wet locations. The larvae which hatch are aquatic and bear a general resemblance to nematodes because of their short piercing stylets protruding from the mouth. They either penetrate insects or encyst on grass or weeds. The definitive hosts are grasshoppers or other insects.

ROTIFERS: SUBPHYLUM TROCHELMINTHES

Rotifers are long-time favorites of the amateur microscopist. Their lively manners, their diversity and beauty of form, and their ubiquitous distribution have all served to insure their popularity. They can be found in all sorts

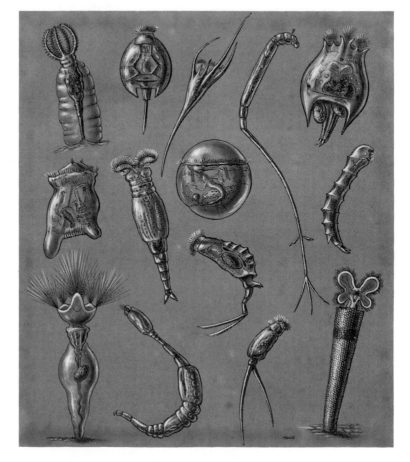

Fig. 12–17. Various species of rotifers showing typical diversity of form. They also exhibit variation in size. The one shown in upper left is barely visible to the naked eye; most are easily seen with a hand lens.

of odd places—rain barrels, cemetery urns, acid sphagnum swamps, as well as among the pond weeds of any lake. Like their cousins the nematodes, rotifers are great internationalists. The same species found in a pond in Kansas will be found in Kurdistan and in New York City parks, provided only that the conditions, especially the pH of the water, are the same. Likewise, the rotifer fauna of two ponds only a mile apart can be very different, if the conditions in them differ.

Rotifers or trochelminthes have been used in scientific investigations into the problems of life cycles and of aging. They were first seen by the 17th century microscopists and have been described and studied by a long line of naturalists, Leeuwenhoek, Linnaeus, Müller, Cuvier, Lamarck, Dutrochet, Huxley, and others.

Rotifers can be defined as microscopic, bilateral, pseudocoelomate, nonsegmented animals having an anterior end provided with a ciliated corona, a pharynx provided with movable jaws, and flame cells as the excretory structures.

The most conspicuous feature of rotifers, and an easy diagnostic mark, is the presence of a pair of ciliated lobes like wheels borne on the head. In fact, so deceptive is their appearance that Leeuwenhoek thought they actually did rotate. They create a stream of water which carries food particles to the mouth of a fixed rotifer, and which enables a free rotifer to swim.

A second characteristic of rotifers is possession of a "foot" or tail, which in many species has external segmental rings and a forked end. This is an organ both of attachment and of walking, inchworm fashion.

Externally, rotifers are provided with a nematode-like cuticle secreted by an underlying epidermis. The body cavity is merely the space between body wall and gut, and hence a pseudocoel. The straight gut is differentiated into a pharynx, a stomach with digestive glands, and an intestine. The pharynx is provided with a muscular bulb containing teeth, and called the **mastax**. It is reminiscent of similar structures in nematodes. Leeuwenhoek mistook these chewing jaws for a heart (like many a student today). In some carnivorous species the jaws are hooked like ice tongs and reach out of the mouth to seize prey.

The rotifers are provided with a fairly complex set of discrete muscles very different from the arrangement in any nematode. Some of the muscles are retractors for the "foot" or head. Others are circular muscles that elongate the animal. The excretory flame cells resemble those of flatworms, and lead into a pair of tubules which empty into a urinary bladder. There is a bi-lobed brain astride the pharynx, two main ventral nerve cords, often a pair of eye spots, and a short, thick, sensory tentacle like an oversized collar button on the back of the neck.

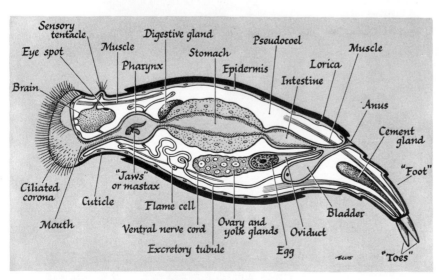

Fig. 12–18. Diagram of a generalized rotifer, longi-section.

As in nematodes, the number of cells, or strictly speaking the number of nuclei, in any individual of a given species is rigidly fixed and rather small, less than 1,000. It is interesting to note that it is again the nervous system that boasts the largest number of cells. For a common species, *Epiphanes* (formerly *Hydatina*) *senta,* the nervous system ranks first with 280 cells, the coronal apparatus has 172, the body epidermis 108, the muscles 82, the gut 74, etc. In the "foot" there is usually a pair of cement glands enabling the rotifer to attach itself to some object.

The sexes are separate. The males are much smaller than the females, and in many species have never been seen or do not exist. The ovary and yolk glands are often conspicuous.

Life Cycles. The life cycles of rotifers have long puzzled zoologists. There are two kinds of females, the so-called **mictic** and **amictic.** They are anatomically alike but show different reproductive behavior. Under continuously favorable conditions the amictic females lay eggs which develop without fertilization, i.e., parthenogenetically, into more amictic females like themselves. The amictic females and their eggs are diploid. Diploidy is maintained because only one meiotic division is completed. When conditions change, the amictic females lay eggs which develop parthenogenetically into mictic females. The eggs of the mictic females undergo complete meiosis and are therefore haploid, and the mictic females themselves are capable of mating. If they are not fertilized—and of course the first to appear are not fertilized because there have been no males in the population for generations—the unfertilized haploid eggs that the mictic females lay develop into males. If the eggs are fertilized and thereby rendered diploid, the mictic females secrete a heavy shell around each one, thus making the so-called winter or drought eggs. With the return of favorable conditions the diploid winter eggs hatch into the first of another series of generations of diploid, amictic females.

After decades of confusing attempts by many investigators to control sexuality by diet, temperature, oxygen, and other factors, it has recently been discovered that the appearance of mictic females and of males is responsive to the proper photoperiod in some species and to a dietary factor, probably a carotenoid or a compound related to chlorophyll, in other species. If the rotifer *Brachionus rubens* is kept under continuous illumination at 25°C, reproduction is by generation after generation of parthenogenetic, i.e., amictic, females. Exposure of such a culture to a minimum of 42.5 hours of darkness followed by at least 30 minutes of light results in the appearance of males. Drastic changes in temperature or exposure to the same photoperiod of the algae on which the rotifers were fed were ineffective.

Many puzzles remain. How does light trigger this result? At 25°C the life span of rotifers of this species is about two weeks for parthenogenetic females, about 24 to 48 hours for males. Males appear in a culture for about four days after exposure to the light, but a second crop of males cannot be elicited for at least three weeks. What is the meaning of this refractory period? Why may males appear again spontaneously after about 36 days? Is the same basic mechanism at work in all species but triggered by different environmental factors? If so, what is that basic mechanism?

Evidently rotifers have undergone a long evolution though there is no fossil record to tell the story. Like other groups they show adaptive radiation in several directions. Among the commonest rotifers in miscellaneous laboratory cultures of protozoans and other microorganisms are the bdelloid species, which crawl around like leeches, as their name suggests. Others are free-swimming and wear a protective lorica, like a Spanish conquistador's cuirass. Still others are sessile and live in tubes, or are colonial; and a few species have substituted long radiating protoplasmic threads for coronal cilia.

MINOR ASCHELMINTHES

The gastrotrichs, kinorhynchs, and priapulids are tiny groups of negligible importance from any point of view except perhaps in pointing to the lack of a truly satisfactory and objective system of classification. Although all three seem more closely related to the nematodes than to any other group of animals, still they are

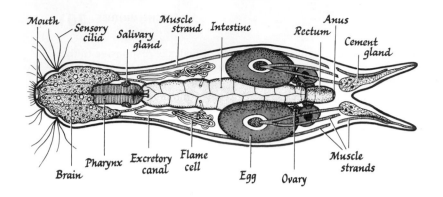

Fig. 12–9. A gastrotrich, dorsal view. (Semidiagrammatic)

so different from them that many zoologists feel justified in elevating each of them to phylum rank. But it seems absurd to make a phylum out of a mere handful of species.

The gastrotrichs are extremely small for metazoans, smaller than parameciums. Both marine and fresh-water species are known. They are commonly seen in old culture dishes where mixed protozoans or other small aquatic animals have been living. Like rotifers, gastrotrichs lay two kinds of eggs. One type begins cleavage as soon as laid and cannot survive freezing-thawing or drying. The second type must undergo a dormant period and can survive freezing and desiccation. Whether one or both types are parthenogenetic is unknown.

Review and References

REVIEW TOPICS

1. What is the economic and medical importance of nematodes?

2. Describe the digestive, locomotor, excretory, reproductive, and nervous systems of nematodes.

3. What is the life history of the hookworm? Of *Trichinella*? Of *Ascaris*? Of the kidney worm? Of the Guinea worm? Of the citrus fruit nematode? Of the frog-lung nematode?

4. The parasitic way of life is often accompanied by increased complexity of life cycle and decreased complexity of structure. To what extent is this true of nematodes? What factors might make nematodes differ in degree from flatworms in this respect?

5. What is unusual about the nematode neuromuscular system? Body cavity? Reproductive system?

6. Contrast the Phasmidea and Aphasmidea in structure and general habits.

7. What are horsehair worms?

8. How do different species of rotifers differ in structure? To what extent are these differences reflected in habits?

9. How is sexuality determined in the rotifers or trochelminthes?

USEFUL REFERENCES

Chitwood, B. G., and M. B. Chitwood, *An Introduction to Nematology,* Babylon, N.Y., M. B. Chitwood, 1937–1949.

Cobb, N. A., *Contributions to a Science of Nematology,* Baltimore, privately published, 1914–1935.

Faust, E. C., *Animal Agents and Vectors of Human Disease,* Philadelphia, Lea & Febiger, 1955.

Filipijev, I. N., and J. H. S. Stekhoven, *A Manual of Agricultural Helminthology,* Leiden, E. J. Brill, 1941.

Goodey, T., *Soil and Freshwater Nematodes,* New York, John Wiley & Sons, 1951.

Hyman, L. H., *The Invertebrates: III, Acanthocephala, Aschelminthes and Entoprocta,* New York, McGraw-Hill Book Co. 1951.

Laderman, A. D., and H. N. Guttman, "Induction of Sexuality," *Journal of Experimental Zoology,* vol. 152, 1963.

Noble, E. R., and G. A. Noble, *Parasitology,* Philadelphia, Lea & Febiger, 1964.

Pennak, R. W., *Fresh-Water Invertebrates of the United States,* New York, The Ronald Press Company, 1953.

Sasser, N. J., and W. R. Jenkins, eds., *Nematology,* Chapel Hill, University of North Carolina Press, 1960.

Chapter 13

Spiny-Headed Worms, Bryozoans, Brachiopods, and Other Minor Protostomes

There are four or five small phyla of doubtful relationships that nevertheless seem to belong with the protostomes. We will review them briefly here.

THE SPINY-HEADED WORMS: PHYLUM ACANTHOCEPHALA

The most important of the minor protostomes are the spiny-headed worms. This is a group of parasites which live as adults in the intestines of vertebrates, mostly fishes, but some species infest rodents, pigs, and, now and again, man. The adults vary, according to the species, from a quarter of an inch to about 4 inches in length. The larval stages live in crustaceans or the grubs of insects.

As the name Acanthocephala suggests (*acanthos*, spine, + *kephale*, head), this group is characterized by a cylindrical proboscis which can be retracted into the anterior end of the body, and which is covered with recurved spines. This structure enables the worm to cling to the lining of the gut of the host. There is no mouth or intestine in these worms. Food is merely absorbed through the dermomuscular body wall. There is no circulatory or respira-

tory system. Two branched and ciliated nephridia serve as excretory organs. The nervous system consists of a single ganglion at the inner end of the proboscis. The coelom is capacious and in the male contains a pair of testes. In females, eggs are produced from a ligament which serves as an ovary and is connected to the proboscis.

The eggs pass to the ground with the feces of the host. If ingested by an arthropod they hatch as elongate larvae. These burrow through the intestine and then merely lie quiescent in the body cavity of the crustacean or insect host. They furnish no clue to the relationships of the group. The lack of segmentation and the rounded shape have induced some zoologists to place the spiny-headed worms with the nematodes, but they show as many points of resemblance with various aberrant annelids, in so far as they have a dermomuscular body wall with both circular and longitudinal muscles, and a capacious coelom. Yet histologically the muscles are different from those of annelids. A possible but still doubtful relationship to the cestodes is suggested by the retractable proboscis with hooks, the complete absence of a gut, and other traits.

BRYOZOANS: PHYLUM BRYOZOA

The bryozoans are utterly unfamiliar to most people, yet they are extremely common in both marine and fresh-water environments. As their name implies (*bryon,* moss), these animals bear some resemblance—extremely superficial, of course—to moss. They are found covering rocks and shells along the sea coasts, and covering submerged logs and twigs in clear, quiet fresh-water ponds. Some of the fresh-water colonies secrete large jelly masses a foot or more in diameter within which the colony lives. Other species grow in a branching, almost vinelike, manner. They are not found in highly polluted water and are rare when the dissolved oxygen falls below 30 per cent of saturation. Most species are rarely found growing in bright sunlight, and many can grow in complete shade, as under ledges or in water pipes. The marine species form either a tightly packed and very fine mosaic over the rocks or a very finely branched growth resembling seaweed. They are of almost no importance to man, although in some places the large jelly masses of fresh-water species have clogged the intake grates

Fig. 13–1. *A, B, E,* and *F* are adult colonies of fresh-water bryozoans. *A* is shown life size. *C* and *D* are statoblasts. *(From Pennak,* Fresh-Water Invertebrates of the United States, *copyright 1953, The Ronald Press Company)*

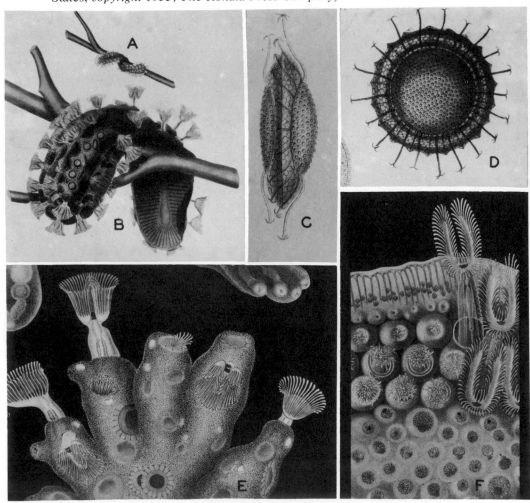

of hydroelectric plants or created problems by growing in water pipes.

The most conspicuous feature of bryozoans is their crown of ciliated tentacles. In most marine species this is a single circle, in fresh-water species usually a double row arranged like a horseshoe. The whole crown can be rapidly jerked into the protective tube or caecum within which the animal lives. The cilia of the tentacles sweep algae, protozoans, small crustaceans, and the like into the mouth at their base. The alimentary canal is U-shaped or Y-shaped, with the anus outside the crown of tentacles. Hence in some countries these animals are called **ectoprocts** (*ecto,* outer, + *proktos,* anus). There is a true coelom, one or more retractor muscles, and an ovary and testes, since most species are hermaphroditic. In many of the marine forms some individuals develop into minute structures resembling a bird's head, but consisting merely of a pair of sharp beaklike jaws, and muscles to move them. These **avicularia** protect the colony from being overgrown by barnacles, tunicates, and other encrusting animals.

The colonies grow by forming stolons. Most colonies are permanently fixed to their substrate, but some creep slowly about, like *Cristatella,* which has been known to move as much as 4 inches in 24 hours. Sexual reproduction leads to the formation of a rounded to elongate ciliated larva which has a very general resemblance to a trochophore. It forms directly one to several individuals with crowns of tentacles. Asexual reproduction by the formation of **statoblasts** is also common among fresh-water species, especially late in the summer. These button-shaped semi-microscopic structures are formed at the inner end of the animal, within the wall of the tube in which the animal lives. Each statoblast consists of a central mass of germinative cells surrounded by a protective sclerotinized coat. Outside this is usually a layer of vacuolated gas-filled cells that make the statoblast float. In some species there is a fringe of elongated hooks about the structure. Statoblasts enable the species to endure the winter and periods of drought, and are important in the dissemination of the species. They have been recovered from the mud on ducks' feet and are capable of germination after pass-

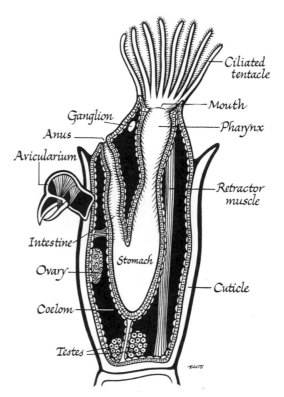

Fig. 13–2. Body plan of a marine bryozoan. Semi-diagrammatic and greatly enlarged. (*From Pauli,* The World of Life, *Houghton Mifflin*)

ing through the alimentary canal of ducks, turtles, or frogs. They are common objects among material collected from ponds. Fossil bryozoans are abundant and are found in very ancient rocks, first appearing in the Ordovician over 400 million years ago.

Kamptozoa. A small group of marine and fresh-water animals called the Kamptozoa (*kamptein,* to bend) is often grouped with the bryozoans. These are very small animals, usually found in small branching colonies. Each individual possesses a circle of ciliated tentacles which, however, are nonretractile but can be rolled up into a protective cavity. The gut is U-shaped, with the anus located within the circle of tentacles; hence the kamptozoans are termed entoprocts. The coelom is filled with gelatinous mesenchyme, and there is an excretory system in the form of a pair of flame cells.

BRACHIOPODS: PHYLUM BRACHIOPODA

The brachiopods are notable because they are so abundant as fossils in extremely ancient rocks. In fact, they are widely useful as indicators in typing rocks and identifying the period to which they belong. There are a number of virtually unique features about brachiopods that have made them useful to the geologist. One is that they are abundant in rocks of all ages, from the earliest Cambrian to the present. Another is that in each age there is a characteristic brachiopod fauna. From age to age some species became extinct, others appeared, others that were rare became abundant, and vice versa. Another remarkable fact is that the two very different present-day forms have existed almost unchanged, at least in shell type, during the entire course of evolution from the beginning of the Paleozoic Era.

Brachiopods look superficially like mollusks, specifically, like bivalves, but on opening the shells, instead of the muscular foot and fleshy visceral mass of a clam, the interior of the shell seems empty except for a pair of ciliated arms called **lophophores,** which resemble watch springs when seen from above. The name (*brachium,* arm, + *pod,* foot) is derived from these structures. Furthermore, the pair of **shells** on a brachiopod are dorsal and ventral, while in clams one shell is on the right and one on the left. In other words, if you cut a clam in the

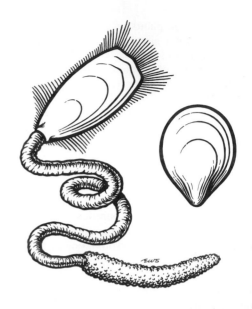

Fig. 13–4. The two types of brachiopods. Left: more primitive *Lingula* type, with horny shell and long body stalk. Right: calcareous shell type.

plane passing between the two shells, the clam will be cut into a right and left half which are mirror images of each other. To cut a brachiopod into two symmetrical halves, it is necessary to cut each shell in half and through the attachment stalk as well. Lining the shell of a brachiopod is a **mantle** which secretes the shell. The structure of the shell is different from that found in mollusks, and in one group of brachiopods it is largely chitinous. Protruding from the edge of the mantle are golden chitinous **setae** like those of the polychaetous annelids.

In one of the two major groups of brachiopods the upper and lower shells are calcareous and hinged, and the upper shell is smaller in such a way that the lower one protrudes at the posterior end of the animal and gives rise to an attachment **stalk** or **peduncle.** Consequently this type of brachiopod resembles one of the oil lamps of classical antiquity, with the stalk in the place of the wick. This resemblance has given rise to the popular name for these organisms, the lampshells. Lampshells usually live in cold water well below low-tide lines; no fresh-water species has been recorded, living or fossil.

Fig. 13–3. Body plan of a brachiopod, life size. Semi-diagrammatic. *(From Pauli,* The World of Life, *Houghton Mifflin)*

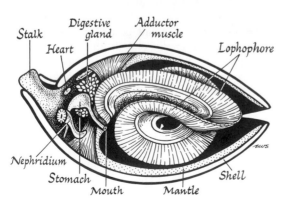

Stalk

Digestive gland

Adductor muscle

Heart

Lophophore

Nephridium

Stomach

Mouth

Mantle

Shell

In the other major type of brachiopod the two shells are equal in size. The stalk is very long and is buried vertically downwards 5 or 6 inches into the sand or mud. *Lingula* is the oldest known animal genus since it has existed since the beginning of the Paleozoic. It can be found living just below the low-tide line along the coasts of the United States, off the Virginia Capes, for instance.

Feeding is of the ciliary type found in the bryozoans. The intestine is short and U-shaped. Lampshells lack an anus. There is a coelom surrounding a digestive gland, a pair of annelid-like nephridia, a tubular heart, and two gonads. A nerve ring surrounds the esophagus. There are no special sense organs. The brachiopod fertilized egg develops into a trochophore-like larva.

PHORONIS: PHYLUM PHORONIDEA

It has been the custom for many decades to place the single genus *Phoronis* in a phylum by itself. *Phoronis* thus occupies an isolated position among the protostomes comparable to that of *Sagitta,* the arrow worm, which similarly constitutes a one-genus phylum among the deuterostomes.

All the dozen or so species of *Phoronis* are marine. They vary in size from a few millimeters to over a foot in length. They live in tubes sometimes buried vertically in the mud, sometimes more or less encrusted and intertwined on submerged objects. Each bears a horseshoe-shaped crown of ciliated tentacles, coiled like a scroll at each end of the horseshoe. From ciliated gills to U-shaped intestine, the feeding mechanism resembles that of bryozoans and brachiopods. The coelom is divided into compartments by longitudinal mesenteries passing from body wall to gut and by a transverse septum. There is a well-developed vascular system with red blood cells containing hemoglobin. The ciliated nephridia suggest annelid affinities. Both an ovary and a testis are found at the hind end of the body. The larva is somewhat like a trochophore. The nervous system consists of a subepithelial ring around the mouth, and nerves going from the ring to tentacles and other body regions.

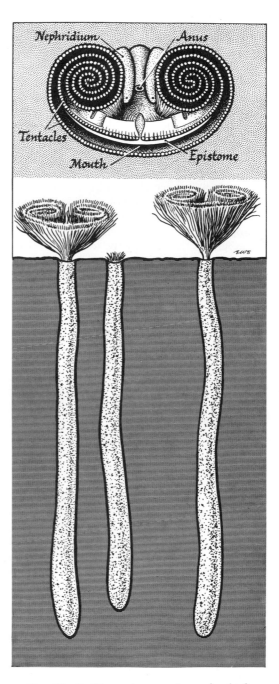

Fig. 13–5. *Phoronis*, a marine animal of unknown relationships but possessing a puzzling mixture of nematode, bryozoan, and annelid traits. Shown life size. The upper drawing shows the free end.

TARDIGRADES: PHYLUM TARDIGRADA

These are minute, even microscopic animals, which are sometimes placed with the nematode worms and sometimes with the arthropods near the mites and spiders. They have four pairs of stubby legs bearing hooks on the end and a stout little body that gives them their popular name, the water bears. Their scientific name has a different meaning (*tardus,* slow, + *gradi,* step). Their internal anatomy somewhat suggests that of a nematode or other aschelminth, although the ventral chain of ganglia, one ganglion per pair of legs, resembles the situation in arthropods, as do their Malpighian tubules.

Tardigrades are extremely tough little animals. Most of them are cosmopolitan, ranging from the poles to the equator and also around the world from east to west. Within their ranges they occupy surprising ecological niches: among wet moss and lichens, on roof tiles and tree bark, or, for marine species, in the capillary water between sand grains on the beach.

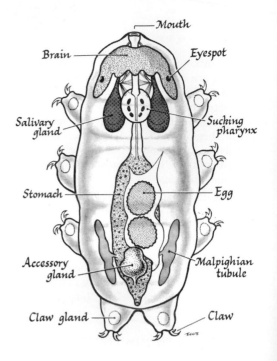

Fig. 13–6. A tardigrade, dorsal view. (Semidiagrammatic)

Review and References

REVIEW TOPICS

1. What are the spiny-headed worms? What is their importance?

2. If you found small animals bearing tentacles and growing from stolons spreading over a submerged rock, how could you tell whether they were bryozoans or coelenterates?

3. In what ways are brachiopods different from clams? Why are brachiopods of special interest?

4. Where do tardigrades and *Phoronis* live? What are the possible relationships of these animals to other phyla?

5. Define: statoblast, ectoproct, lophophore, Malpighian tubule, Cambrian.

USEFUL REFERENCES

Moore, R. C., C. G. Lalicker, and A. G. Fischer, *Invertebrate Fossils,* New York, McGraw-Hill Book Co., 1952.

Pratt, H. S., *A Manual of the Common Invertebrate Animals*, Philadelphia, P. Blakiston's Son & Co., 1935.

Pennak, R. W., *Fresh-Water Invertebrates of the United States*, New York, The Ronald Press Company, 1953.

Chapter 14

Annelids

The annelids are a well-known phylum of very modest size. The 8,000 or so described species include the familiar earthworms and leeches, the "bloodworms" and clamworms of coastal fishermen, and some rather elaborate and beautiful marine forms.

The phylum was named by Lamarck and defined as segmented, coelomate worms. Except for some peculiar species of uncertain affinities, all annelids have the following traits:

1. The body is serially segmented. The segments, which are also termed **metameres** or **somites,** usually show externally as rings encircling the body and internally as partitions or septa dividing the body cavity into compartments.

2. The body cavity is a true **coelom** lined with a mesodermal epithelium, the peritoneum, and providing a spacious cavity between the gut and the body wall. The gut is a straight tube within the tube of the body wall and extends from the mouth at the anterior end to the anus at the posterior.

3. The nervous system is of the type found in protostomes, i.e., there is a ganglionic brain dorsal to the anterior part of the gut and connected to a ventral nerve cord by a pair of circumpharyngeal or circumesophageal nerves.

4. When a larva is present, as it is in the marine species, it is a **trochophore.** The cleavage of the egg is of the spiral, determinate type.

5. The body is covered by a thin, flexible, proteinous cuticle and is armed with glistening chitinous bristles termed **chaetae** or **setae.**

6. In most annelids there is a partial preoral segment called the **prostomium** (*pro,* before, + *stoma,* mouth). In earthworms the prostomium resembles a kind of nose guard, and is useful in identifying species.

Ever since Charles Darwin wrote his famous book on the formation of vegetable mold (by which he meant topsoil) through the action of earthworms, their role in the cultivation and formation of soil has received considerable attention. Their precise importance is difficult to evaluate, but it is certainly considerable.

Both earthworms and marine annelids have been widely used in research. In a few parts of the world earthworms and some of the swarming marine annelids are used as food by man.

The harmful effects of annelids are slight. Leeches may be so abundant in northern lakes and in tropical swamps that they discourage swimmers, but, although they are unpleasant to think about, it cannot be claimed that they are dangerous. Earthworms are intermediate hosts to several parasitic worms. They harbor the bladder-worm stage of *Amoebotaenia,* a tapeworm of chickens and other birds. Earthworms also carry nematodes, e.g., *Metastrongylus* which becomes adult in the lungs of pigs, and *Syngamus* which causes gapes in fowl.

EVOLUTIONARY RELATIONSHIPS AND MAJOR GROUPS

The origin of annelids from simpler forms is unknown. Although attempts have been made to show a relationship between the simplest annelids and primitive ctenophores, most zoologists remain unconvinced. The fact is that the relationships among present-day annelids and annelidlike animals are uncertain.

There are five classes of annelids plus three additional groups which are sometimes regarded as aberrant annelids but sometimes as three independent phyla, although one of these three groups is sometimes thought to be arthropod. This last is the terrestrial creature *Peripatus*, which presents a mixture of annelid and arthropod traits and somewhat resembles both a clamworm and a centipede. Classes and groups are:

1. The archiannelids, Class **Archiannelida** (*archi*, first, + *annellus*, little rings), are a very small group of tiny marine worms that develop from typical trochophore larvae but never develop very far. Some zoologists hold that they are ancestral to the rest of the annelids, specifically the polychaetes, while others read the series in the opposite direction and derive the archiannelids from the polychaetes.

Fig. 14–1. *A,* trochophore. *B,* trochophore metamorphosing into an adult. *C,* adult of a primitive annelid. *(From Pauli,* The World of Life, *Houghton Mifflin)*

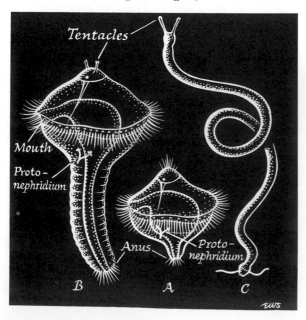

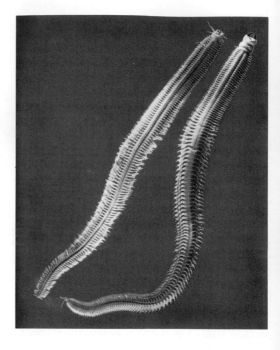

Fig. 14–2. *Nereis (Neanthes),* the clamworm, a polychaete. Note chitinous jaws in these medium-sized individuals. *(Kindness of P. S. Tice)*

2. The polychaetes, Class **Polychaeta** (*poly,* many, + *chaeta,* bristle), are a large group that contrast markedly with the earthworms and other oligochaetes. Whereas the earthworms and their allies are either fresh-water or terrestrial in habitat, the polychaetes, with very few exceptions, are marine. Where the earthworms are drab and plain, the polychaetes are sometimes brightly colored and frequently bear feathery gills either from the head or from the sides of the body. As the name indicates, the polychaetes are well provided with long bristles, usually protruding in golden bundles from fleshy, leglike appendages, the **parapodia,** along the sides of the body. The sexes are separate in polychaetes, the gametes are shed into the sea water, and the spirally cleaving egg develops into a trochophore.

3. The oligochaetes, Class **Oligochaeta** (*oligo,* few, + *chaeta,* bristle), include the earthworms and their fresh-water relatives. As noted earlier, the oligochaetes contrast with the polychaetes in many ways. With few exceptions

they live on land or in fresh water. They lack parapodia completely and have relatively few setae. Except for fingerlike projections from the posterior end of some small fresh-water species, they lack gills. They are hermaphroditic, and the eggs are deposited in a cocoon secreted by a swollen glandular ring around the body called the **clitellum.** There is no trochophore or other larval form.

4. The leeches, Class **Hirudinea** (*hirudo,* leech), are a predominantly fresh-water group of annelids, although there are both marine and terrestrial species. They are probably closely related to the oligochaetes, among which some of the nais-like species, as well as the branchiobdellids so commonly found on crayfish, have a general leechlike character. Leeches have 32 segments, and lateral nerves. Externally there are usually three to five grooves per segment, so that the number of segments appears greatly increased. There is a muscular suction disk at each end of the body. The skin is often brightly colored, but the evolutionary advantage of this is unknown.

5. The Class **Myzostoma** (*myzein,* to suck, + *stoma,* mouth) is composed of curious disk-shaped parasites found on starfish and their relatives, the sea lilies. Their taxonomic position is uncertain. They possess five pairs of parapodia bearing setae.

The three groups commonly regarded as related to the annelids but different enough to warrant elevation to phylum status are the Echiuroidea, the Sipunculoidea, and the Onychophora.

FUNCTIONAL SYSTEMS: EARTHWORM

Because of its ready availability for study both by dissection of preserved individuals and by vivisection of anesthetized ones, an earthworm will be used to illustrate the way in which the functional systems of an annelid are organized. The most conspicuous aspect of the external anatomy is the serial segmentation.

It was once believed that earthworms grew by the gradual addition of new segments at the hind end throughout the life of the worm. However, it has recently been shown that the familiar earthworms of both North America and Europe emerge from their egg cocoons with the full adult complement of segments. As in the backbone of a man, growth in an earthworm occurs strictly by the enlargement of the units present at birth. The number of segments varies with the species. *Lumbricus terrestris,* the night crawler, commonly has about 150; *Eisenia foetida,* the barnyard earthworm, about 95. In a sexually mature worm, there is a raised glandular belt, the clitellum (*clitellae,* pack saddle), extending from the 25th through the 32nd segment in *E. foetida* and from the 32nd through the 37th in *L. terrestris.* The position of the clitellum is an important trait in identifying the species. The function of the clitellum is to secrete a proteinous ring, which then slides off the end of the worm and forms a cocoon for the eggs.

Just above the mouth of an earthworm is a small projecting prostomium. This structure is also helpful to the zoologist in identifying the species, and serves the worm as a sensitive probing organ.

Setae. Like other annelids, earthworms are well provided with setae, largely chitinous in composition. Each seta is embedded in a sac formed as an invagination of the surface epithelium and is provided with both retractor and protractor muscles. In an earthworm these are visible in cross sections, and in the naids they can be seen through the transparent body wall pulling the seta back and forth like an oar. Apparently the setae do not grow continually, like hairs or fingernails, but fall out and are replaced. In native North American earthworms there are normally eight setae per segment, arranged in four pairs. In many oriental earthworms, some of which have become naturalized in various parts of the United States, there are many setae arranged in a ring completely around each segment. Any robin can testify to the effectiveness with which setae can hold a worm in the ground.

Epidermis and Muscle Layers. The body wall consists of a cuticle secreted by the epithelial cells which underlie it. The epithelial cells form the epidermis. Under a microscope four types of cells can be observed in the epithelium. Most of the cells are tall columnar epithelial cells, but between them are many

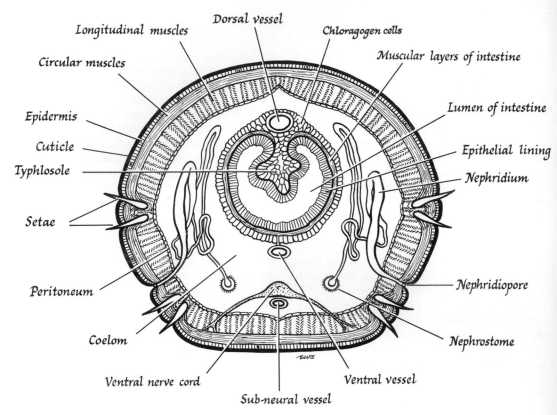

Longitudinal muscles
Dorsal vessel
Chloragogen cells
Circular muscles
Muscular layers of intestine
Epidermis
Lumen of intestine
Cuticle
Epithelial lining
Typhlosole
Nephridium
Setae
Peritoneum
Nephridiopore
Coelom
Nephrostome
Ventral nerve cord
Ventral vessel
Sub-neural vessel

Fig. 14–3. Cross section of an earthworm. (Diagrammatic) *(From Pauli,* The World of Life, *Houghton Mifflin)*

mucus-secreting cells usually filled with granules or globules. In certain regions of the skin there are sensory cells of various types. Some, which are photoreceptors, have a reticular cytoplasm containing a clear body which seems to act as a lens. These cells are short and rounded and most abundant on the prostomium and the first and last two or three segments. Others are small clusters of very tall, thin cells with minute sensory hairs. Lastly, scattered along the base of the epithelium there are small basal cells which may be replacement cells comparable to the germinative or replacement layer found in the human skin.

Under the epidermis is a layer of circular muscles and below this a much thicker layer of longitudinal muscles. Here is the familiar pattern of a pair of antagonistic muscles, common throughout the animal kingdom from coelenterate to vertebrate. The circular muscles contract to make the worm longer and thinner, the longitudinal to make it short and stout. The pigment in the body wall is present in amoeboid

cells in very young worms, but later only crowded granules can be found. Like hemoglobin and chlorophyll, this pigment, with a spectroscope, gives the absorption bands which indicate that it is a porphyrin.

Digestive System. The alimentary canal begins with a tough muscular **pharynx** richly provided with glandular cells which secrete a mucus into the lumen or cavity of the pharynx. The pharynx is the chief digging and eating organ. Posterior to it, the gut narrows to a straight tube, the **esophagus,** which conducts the food past the five pairs of hearts and the reproductive organs. The esophagus is notable for the presence of **calciferous glands.** These are a series of leaflike folds, or **lamellae,** making a series of deep parallel grooves on each side of the esophagus. For most of their length they are separated from the lumen of the esophagus by a membrane. Darwin was very much interested in the functional meaning of these structures and wrote, nearly a century ago, "Almost as many theories have been advanced for their use as there have been observers." This statement remains true today. The fact that they are heavily vascular argues that they may be glandular, and they frequently form crystals of calcium carbonate. It may be that this $CaCO_3$ aids digestion by rendering the anterior portion of the digestive system sufficiently alkaline for the digestive enzymes to act. The leaf mold that worms eat is certainly very acid. The mechanism may also be a way of excreting excess calcium and carbon dioxide.

Posterior to the esophagus is a thin-walled **crop,** usually occupying segments 15 and 16. There is no evidence as to its precise function. The **gizzard** follows immediately. It is a thick-walled muscular zone, lined with cuticle, in which food is ground. The **intestine** extends as a straight tube without differentiation from the gizzard to the anus. The intestine is lined with a ciliated epithelium. The absorptive surface is increased by a longitudinal dorsal fold, the **typhlosole** (typhlos, blind, + solen, channel), which hangs down into the lumen of the intestine. Surrounding the intestinal epithelium is a thin muscular layer, and, outside that, a thick layer of **chloragogen cells.** These are large cells full of yellowish, greenish, or brownish granules. They are not amoeboid; hence the function of the chloragogen cells is supposed by some workers to be the absorption of wastes from the blood. Others have held that chloragogen cells store glycogen and fat which is then distributed when the cells break loose and disintegrate. There is some evidence for this view, but really none for the theory that chloragogen cells control growth and regeneration.

The diet of earthworms varies with the species. Many eat fallen leaves and are especially fond of lettuce. Others live principally on the organic matter in soil.

The capacious coelom is lined by a peritoneal epithelium, or **peritoneum,** as it is usually called in both annelid and human anatomy. The peritoneum is of two parts, the parietal peritoneum which is a thin layer of flattened epithelial cells pressed against the inner surface of the body wall, and the visceral peritoneum which is pressed against the viscera, chiefly the intestine. While in a mammal the visceral peritoneum is also of thin flattened cells, in earthworms it is composed of the very large chloragogen cells. The septa or partitions which extend from the body wall across the coelom to the gut are perforated with one or more porthole-like openings so that coelomic fluid and cells can pass from one segment to another.

Two principal types of cells are suspended in the coelomic fluid. The first are amoeboid cells which are **phagocytic** (phagos, eating, + cyte, cell) and ingest foreign particles, parasites, etc., that get into the coelom. They are thus comparable to the amoeboid white cells of human blood. The "brown bodies" often found within the coelom of earthworms, especially in the hinder segments, are massed aggregations of these phagocytic cells and contain encysted

Fig. 14–4. Internal anatomy of an earthworm. *(From Pauli, The World of Life, Houghton Mifflin)*

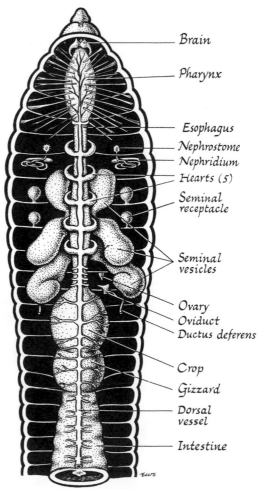

Brain

Pharynx

Esophagus
Nephrostome
Nephridium
Hearts (5)
Seminal receptacle

Seminal vesicles

Ovary
Oviduct
Ductus deferens

Crop

Gizzard

Dorsal vessel

Intestine

nematodes, worn-out setae, protozoan cysts, and large amounts of pigment granules from chloragogen cells.

The second type are rounded cells called **eleocytes** (*eleos*, olive, + *cyte*, cell). These cells are bright yellow in *Eisenia foetida*. They are usually yellowish and are always filled with minute lipoid droplets. When an earthworm is irritated, the coelomic fluid, along with eleocytes, is pressed out through the dorsal pores and gives off a characteristic acrid or fetid odor. The dorsal pores are minute openings, one in each intersegmental groove, that connect the coelom with the exterior.

Circulation. The vascular system of an earthworm is a true closed system, just as in vertebrates, with a pulsating region, arteries which conduct blood away from this region, microscopically fine capillaries with walls so thin that oxygen, carbon dioxide, food, and wastes are exchanged between blood and tissues, and veins which conduct return blood.

The pulsating region is a complex structure consisting of the **dorsal** blood **vessel** which runs the entire length of the worm immediately above the gut, and five pairs of **aortic arches** lying in segments 7 through 11. Both the dorsal vessel and the aortic arches are provided with flap valves which allow blood to flow only in one direction — toward the head in the dorsal vessel and downward in the aortic loops, which are often called "hearts." The blood is pushed forward and then downward by peristaltic contractions of the dorsal vessel. These rhythmic contractions begin near the posterior end of the worm and progress forward. This rhythmic action is affected by the same drugs that affect the human heart and must therefore be under nervous control. The peristalsis of the dorsal blood vessel and the vigorous contractions of the five pairs of aortic arches or "hearts" can be easily seen either in an earthworm opened under anesthesia or, in a very small worm, through the skin.

The main artery carrying blood to the body is the **ventral vessel,** which runs under the gut and above the nerve cord. It receives blood from the five pairs of hearts and carries it back toward the tail. In each segment it gives off a pair of small arteries called **segmental vessels;** these curve upward and deliver blood to the muscles of the body wall. The main ventral artery also gives off small branches in each segment to the nephridia, to a lateral neural artery which extends along each side of the nerve cord, and directly upward to the underside of the intestine.

In the body wall and its musculature, in the nephridia, nerve cord, and intestine, the arteries break up into **capillaries,** through the thin walls of which physiological exchanges of materials occur between blood and the tissue fluids.

The main venous return is through the **subneural** blood **vessel,** which is the principal vein. It receives blood from capillaries around the nerve cord and sends it back toward the tail and upward through parietal veins, a pair of which

Fig. 14–5. Vascular system in the anterior end of the earthworm. Note the five aortic loops, or "hearts."

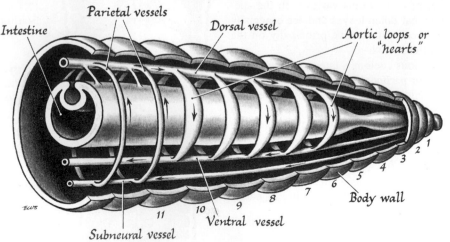

Intestine

Parietal vessels

Dorsal vessel

Aortic loops or "hearts"

Body wall

Subneural vessel

Ventral vessel

occur in each segment. The parietal vessels receive blood not only from the subneural vein but also from the body wall, and pour it into the dorsal vessel.

In addition, a circulation which absorbs food directly from the intestine also carries oxygen and carbon dioxide to and from the gut. In each segment the dorsal vessel gives off an artery directly into the typhlosole, and receives a pair of veins from the intestine.

The **plasma** or fluid of the blood is red from dissolved **hemoglobin,** formed of an iron-porphyrin combined with a protein, but not identical with vertebrate hemoglobin. Its function is to transport oxygen. The circulating blood cells are colorless. Oxygen is absorbed and carbon dioxide given off through the capillaries in the skin. In various polychaetes a wide variety of conditions can be found. In some, there is no respiratory pigment. In others, like *Nereis* and *Arenicola,* the hemoglobin is dissolved in the bood plasma. In a few, the hemoglobin is in the cells in the coelom, and in a few there is a green iron-porphyrin compound.

Excretory System. The chief interest in the excretory system of earthworms arises from the striking resemblance between an earthworm nephridium and the functional unit, the **nephron,** of a vertebrate kidney. Earthworms lack the flame cells and solenocytes of the polychaetes and retain only the tubular nephridium. Each nephridium begins with a fan-shaped ciliated funnel, the **nephrostome** (*nephros,* kidney, + *stoma,* mouth). In all vertebrate embryos the nephron likewise begins with a nephrostome. In the adult vertebrate each nephron has the physiological equivalent of a nephrostome, that is, a glomerulus, which is a device to obtain fluid without discrimination of waste or useful components. From the nephrostome or glomerulus the fluid passes down a long, coiled, and highly vascular tubule that changes along its course in diameter and in the character of its cell membranes.

In native American earthworms there is a pair of nephridia, one on each side of the midline, in every segment except the first two or three and the last one or two. The nephrostome of each nephridium projects into the coelom of one segment, and the long, coiled tubule lies in the immediately posterior segment. The evolutionary explanation of this curious phenomenon has not been uncovered.

Examination under a dissecting microscope shows that the body of the nephridium consists

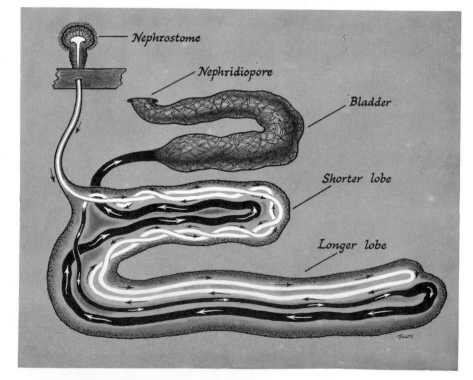

Fig. 14-6. Kidney (nephridium) of the earthworm. Arrows show direction of flow of fluids.

Nephrostome

Nephridiopore

Bladder

Shorter lobe

Longer lobe

of three fingerlike parts. Strangely enough, the uriniferous or urine-forming tubule passes twice through each of these lobes except the last, which serves as a urinary bladder. The fluid drawn from the coelom into the nephrostome by its cilia passes first along a straight, narrow, ciliated tubule which pierces the septum and continues a short way into the posterior segment. This tubule then enters the shorter lobe, loops into it, then out into the longer lobe and back again, and into the short lobe again. At the base of the short lobe the tubule turns again to the longer lobe, where it now becomes somewhat wider and brownish. At the tip of the long lobe the tubule suddenly becomes much larger and remains so as it passes back to the base of the long lobe, loops out the short lobe for the third (and last) time, and then forms the third fingerlike lobe which is a wide, muscular-walled, U-shaped tube that serves as a urinary **bladder**. It opens to the exterior via a **nephridiopore**. The nephridiopores are extremely difficult to see, but are located just posterior to the intersegmental furrows in a ventro-lateral position.

Since each nephridium receives blood from the segmental artery almost immediately after the artery leaves the main ventral artery of the body, much as in the human kidney, a blood supply under high pressure is assured. Blood is returned from the nephridium to the dorsal blood vessel via the parietal vein. The first two lobes of the nephridium, in which the tubule makes so many loops, are very richly vascular, a condition indicating a very active secretory or absorptive function — perhaps both — in the tubule cells.

Since the structure of an earthworm nephridium is so similar to that in a vertebrate kidney, it is not unreasonable to suppose that they function similarly. Although a full discussion of the physiology of the vertebrate kidney will be postponed until the chapters on the vertebrates and the excretory system, it can be said here that there is good evidence that uric acid and other nitrogenous wastes are secreted into the lumen of the earthworm nephridial tubule and that water is reabsorbed back into the bloodstream as the coelomic fluid passes down the tubule. In this manner the wastes are concentrated.

In some oriental and tropical earthworms there are variations in the character and arrangement of the nephridia that are astonishing to anyone whose experience is limited to the earthworms of Europe and North America. In the dry regions of India there are species in which the nephridia empty their wastes into the intestine, where all the available water can be absorbed back into the body. This is an adaptation suggestive of the birds. In some species there are very small **micronephridia**. These may be attached in large numbers and regularly arranged like a design against both sides of the septa and against the body wall. In one giant Australian earthworm each nephridium has 40 or 50 nephrostomes instead of a single one.

Reproduction. The earthworm reproductive system consists of both male and female structures. There are two pairs of testes, one in the 10th and one in the 11th segment of *Lumbricus,* attached to the anterior septum of each segment low down and near the midline. They can be found only with a dissecting microscope, but each pair is enclosed in a large conspicuous testis sac. The sac of the first pair has four large extensions called **seminal vesicles;** the sac of the second pair, two seminal vesicles. The vesicles store sperms which reach the exterior by a pair of vasa deferentia, one on each side, opening by a conspicuous pair of pores on the ventral surface of the 15th segment.

The female structures consist of a single pair of ovaries on the anterior septum of the 13th segment. Each ovary is small and pear-shaped, with its narrow end projecting into the coelom in which ovulation occurs. Facing each ovary, but on the opposite (posterior) wall of the segment, is a funnel which leads into a short oviduct that penetrates septum 13/14 and opens to the exterior through the ventral surface of the 14th segment on a line with the opening of the vas deferens. (See Fig. 14–4.)

The seminal receptacles that receive sperms transferred from another worm, and the clitellum, must be regarded as part of the female system. There are two pairs of seminal receptacles, small round structures lying in the 9th and 10th segments, and connected to the exterior by small pores in intersegmental furrows 9/10 and 10/11.

Mating differs in detail according to species. *Lumbricus terrestris,* the big night crawler, mates on the surface of the ground at night, commonly after a rain. Some species, such as *Eisenia foetida,* the barnyard earthworm, mate in moist debris or underground. The two worms come to lie with their ventral surfaces together and their heads in opposite directions. In this position they become more or less covered with mucus. It is reasonable to suppose that they would lie with the sperm openings on segment 15 of each individual opposite the openings of the sperm receptacles of the other worm, which are in intersegmental grooves 9/10 and 10/11. But the facts are quite different. The clitellar region of each worm lies over the openings of the sperm receptacles of the partner. It is not clear why, and there are conflicting accounts in the literature. The clitellum partly grasps the sperm receptacles zone of the other earthworm. Sperms are discharged through the sperm openings on segment 15 and are pushed by muscular contraction in a visible groove on the surface of the worm back to its own clitellum, where they enter the sperm receptacles of the opposite individual. The worms then separate.

After this exchange of sperms, each individual in isolation may continue for weeks to produce **cocoons** containing eggs fertilized with sperms from the sperm receptacles. The cocoon or egg-case is secreted by the clitellum and hardens on contact with the air into a band encircling the worm. This cocoon fits the worm rather loosely at its anterior edge, much more tightly at its hinder edge. Eggs and sperms are discharged into the space between the cocoon and the body wall. The worm pulls itself backward out of the cocoon, which slips off over its head. As it does so, each end contracts so as to make a capsule. These cocoons are about the size of a grain of wheat in *Lumbricus,* somewhat smaller in *Eisenia,* and 3 inches long by 1½ inches in diameter in *Megascolides australis,* the largest known earthworm. The eggs cleave in a modified spiral manner as in other protostomes. From each cocoon will hatch from one to six or even more wormlings.

Nervous System. The earthworm nervous system is closely similar to that of polychaetes, except that the brain is relatively smaller and there are no eyes. The bi-lobed brain of an earthworm lies just above the pharynx in the 3rd segment, and from it numerous sensory nerves extend forward to the prostomium and 1st segment. The brain is connected by stout connectives encircling the pharynx to the ventral nerve cord, which swells slightly to form a ganglion in each segment.

The nerve cord gives rise in each segment to three pairs of lateral nerves. One pair arises a short way from the anterior septum, the other two from the ganglion in the middle of the segment. These are mixed nerves carrying both motor and sensory nerve fibers. There are nerve fibers in the cord from the three main types of nerve cells or neurons. Each **motor**

Fig. 14 – 7. Gross anatomy of anterior portion of the earthworm nervous system.

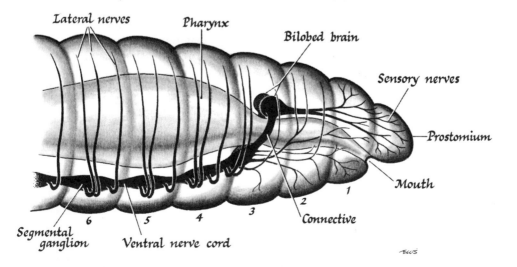

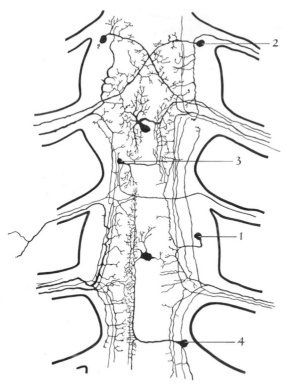

Fig. 14–8. Ventral nerve cord of earthworm, showing the course of individual nerve fibers. Note the complexity of interrelationships. *(From Pauli,* The World of Life, *Houghton Mifflin)*

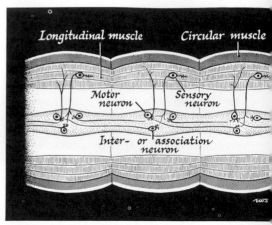

Fig. 14–9. Diagram of neural basis of crawling reflexes in earthworm.

nerve cell has its cell body with the nucleus located in a ganglion. The interneurons or **association nerve cells** which conduct impulses from one nerve cell to another are also located within the nerve cord. The third type, the **sensory nerve cells,** are located in the body wall and send their fibers into the nerve cord. As can be seen in Figure 14–8, which is a greatly simplified diagram, these fibers make a very intricate system.

It is easy to see how this system functions in ordinary crawling. Within the muscles are stretch receptors which are stimulated when the segment is stretched. These sensory nerves send impulses in to the motor neurons in the cord, which in turn send impulses out to the longitudinal muscles and cause them to contract. This is a simple **reflex arc.** In the propagation of waves of contraction along the worm,

these reflex arcs work in conjunction. One segment, contracting, pulls on the adjacent segment and stretches it. The stretch receptors in the second segment are then stimulated and the second segment contracts. This stretches a third segment, and the cycle is repeated.

This interpretation found support long ago in the famous experiment of Friedlander, in which the worm was cut completely in two but held together with sewing thread but without direct contact between the two pieces of the worm. Waves of contraction were able to pass across this gap purely through the mechanical action of the pull on the threads. It is also possible to show that the waves of contraction will pass through a region where the muscles are completely missing but the nerve cord is intact. This is called "double assurance"—two ways of achieving the same end.

One of the best-known features of the earthworm's nervous system is the set of three **giant fibers** that run the length of the nerve cord. These are conspicuous in any cross section of the worm which includes the nerve cord. Their function is basically the same as the giant nerve fibers in the mantle of the squid. In both, the giant fibers are part of an escape mechanism which permits the animal to make a quick getaway. The rate of conduction through the regular neurons of the nerve cord of the earthworm is about 50 cm per second, while in the largest of the three giant fibers it is 300 cm (about 100 feet) per second. The larger central

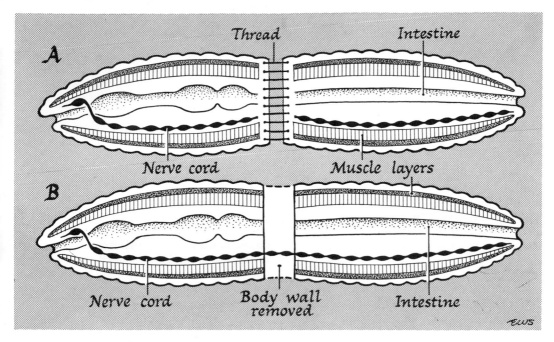

Fig. 14–10. The mechanism of contraction in an earthworm was proved by (*A*) the Friedlander experiment with the two parts of a cut worm connected solely by thread, and (*B*) removing section of body wall, leaving ventral nerve cord intact. See text for details.

fiber conducts toward the tail, the two lateral fibers toward the head. This apparatus assures that whenever an earthworm is over-stimulated at either end – by a robin at the head or a mole at the tail – every segment in the body can be simultaneously contracted within a few milliseconds and the worm jerked out of danger.

The anatomy of these giant fibers has several unusual features. Cell bodies with their nuclei are found all the way along the fibers, and not just at one end. The fibers in each segment are separated from those in adjacent ones by an oblique membrane, which is, of course, a synapse. Whether because such a large surface is afforded by this oblique contact or for some other reason, these synapses do not delay transmission as synapses normally do. The two lateral, forward-conducting fibers are connected at intervals by transverse nerves.

The brain of an earthworm is not very different from the ventral ganglia. It does, however, contain a great many **neuro-secretory cells** which quite clearly have an endocrine function. These cells have the same staining reactions as neuro-secretory cells in the brains of other animals, including insects and mammals. Their function is in some doubt but injury or other types of stress will produce changes in them.

The sense organs of earthworms are limited to relatively simple sensory nerve endings in skin and muscles. The most complex appear to be the photosensitive cells in the head end. These are oval cells containing a clear lens-like body and each having a long nerve fiber.

NATURAL HISTORY OF EARTHWORMS

The chief popular interest in earthworms centers in their role as cultivators of the soil and in their powers of regeneration. On the first topic, Charles Darwin wrote,

When we behold a wide, turf-covered expanse, we should remember that its smoothness, on which so much of its beauty depends, is mainly due to all the inequalities having been slowly levelled by worms. It is a marvellous reflection that the whole of the superficial mold [topsoil] over any such expanse has passed, and will again pass, every few years through the bodies of worms. The plough is one of the most ancient and most valuable of man's inventions; but long before it existed the land was in fact regularly ploughed and still continues to be thus ploughed by earthworms.

319

In recent years large and perhaps greatly exaggerated claims have been made about the benefits conferred by earthworms upon agriculture. The precise extent of these benefits is difficult to evaluate because soil conditions which favor plant growth also favor earthworms. There can be no doubt, however, that their burrows, which extend a foot or two into the soil in summer and six or more feet in winter, aid in aerating the soil and in facilitating the penetration of water. It is also clear that earthworms bring large amounts of soil from lower layers, including at times even the subsoil, to the top of the ground, where they eject it as castings.

Darwin collected the castings over sample square yards of surface in different kinds of localities. After drying and weighing the material collected, he estimated values ranging from 7.5 to 18 tons of soil per acre per year brought up to the surface. This is enough to make a layer from somewhat less than an inch to about two inches in depth every ten years. Darwin also showed how, by this action of earthworms, objects varying from broken glass to the stones of Roman ruins become gradually buried deeper and deeper in the soil as worms occasionally burrow under them and carry out the earth. Within the past few years very accurate measurements at the Rothamsted Agricultural Experiment Station have given values of 2 to 3 tons per acre per year in light dry soil where earthworms are not abundant, 11 tons

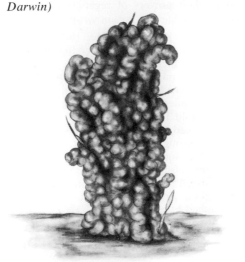

Fig. 14 – 11. Earthworm casting in the botanical gardens of Calcutta. *(From Charles Darwin)*

per acre per year in pasture land, and up to 100 tons in certain tropical localities.

Population size in earthworms is difficult to determine. One method is to dig, another to try to force the worms to the surface by massive soaking of the soil with potassium permanganate solution or with an alternating electric current. Most species are tolerant of a wide range of soil pH, though some prefer acid soils and others do not. The distribution of the small aquatic fresh-water oligochaetes like *Nais, Dero,* and *Stylaria* is virtually world-wide, perhaps because they can be transported long distances in the mud on birds' feet. The large terrestrial earthworms are limited geographically, but perhaps as travel and trade between continents become more frequent more earthworms will be cosmopolitan.

The behavior of earthworms was intensively studied by Darwin and more recently by Yerkes, better known for his work on apes. Earthworms are nocturnal in emerging from the soil. A number of species are luminous. Even *Eisenia foetida,* the common brandling, is said to exude a luminous material through its dorsal pores if roughly handled. The chief visible signs of earthworms are castings of earth brought to the surface, and stuffings of decaying leaves, twigs, and debris over the entrances to their burrows. Darwin thought this kept the interior moist and kept out cold air. Yerkes and others have shown that *Lumbricus* can learn to take the correct turn in a T-maze in some 20 to 40 "lessons." It has only recently been discovered that they learn much faster between 8 P.M. and midnight than they do in the morning. An interesting and unanswered question concerns species recognition. In a garden or barnyard where half a dozen or more species live side by side, mating pairs always seem to belong to the same species. Perhaps each species carries a characteristic odor.

REGENERATION IN EARTHWORMS

The ability of earthworms to regenerate lost parts has been an object of popular interest and scientific investigation ever since it was discovered by Trembley in the 18th century. In addition to pure curiosity, there has been a practical aim back of these investigations.

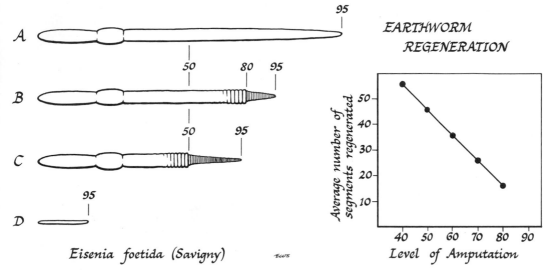

Eisenia foetida (Savigny)

Fig. 14–12. The number of segments regenerated in an earthworm is correlated with the level of amputation. If the level of cut is moved 10 segments toward the tail, the number of segments regenerated will decline by 10. *A,* intact worm. *B,* worm after amputation at segment 80. *C,* after amputation at segment 50. *D,* newly hatched juvenile with adult number of segments.

Spallanzani in the 1790's was very explicit about this. If enough could be learned about the regeneration of lower animals, it ought to be possible to enable higher organisms, including man himself, to replace lost parts. Yet despite the very extensive work of T. H. Morgan (1866–1945) and many other able investigators in the United States, Europe, and Asia, the problem remains unsolved.

The salient facts can be briefly summarized. To the common question, "If an earthworm is cut in two, can each half form a complete worm?" the answer is, "No." Planarians among flatworms can do this, and some species of South Asian earthworms, but not ours. If any number of segments up to 10 is cut off the head of a common earthworm, a new head of four or five segments will form. If more than 15 segments are amputated, the wound does little more than heal over.

Regeneration of a new tail can take place at any level from about the 35th segment back to the hind end of the worm. Although tail regeneration has been known since the 18th century, it was never intensively studied until recently, and then a remarkable fact came to light. Earthworms have some way of counting their segments, so to speak. Every time the level of amputation is moved 10 segments farther from

the head, the average number of segments regenerated declines by 10. This means that there is a linear relationship between level of cut and number of segments regenerated. Why do earthworms stop adding new segments at the regenerating tip when the correct number has been formed? It is at least possible to say that the formation of new segments does not stop because nutrition has run out, for starving worms regenerate in almost exactly the same way as well-fed ones. It is also well established that the nerve cord must be present at the cut surface for regeneration to occur.

POLYCHAETES

Major Groups. Polychaetes fall into two groups distinguished by very different types of anatomy which, in turn, are correlated with very different ways of life. The less specialized and therefore probably the more primitive group is composed of the errant or wandering polychaetes (Order **Errantiformes**). They crawl on and through the mud and sand. The most familiar example is *Nereis* (*Neanthes*), the clamworm. In this group the gills are limited to the sides of the body and usually sprout from 20 or more of the parapodia. The parapodia themselves are usually well developed. Some

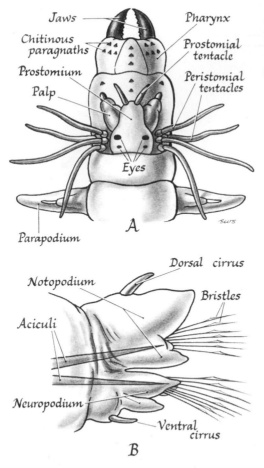

Fig. 14–13. *Nereis (Neanthes)*, the clam-worm. *A*, dorsal view of head region with pharynx everted. *B*, parapodium, lateral view.

species are armed with a strong pair of curved chitinous jaws capable of inflicting a painful bite. Many species swim freely, especially when about to spawn.

The second type of polychaete is the seden-tary or tube-living form (Order **Sedentari-formes**). In these species the parapodia are reduced in size, though present, and from the head there extends a crown of tentacles or gills. Some species resemble flowers, others snaky gorgon heads of writhing tentacles. A small but common and beautiful species is illustrated in Figure 14–14. When an enemy approaches, the feathery crown of tentacles is jerked back into the tube, which is blocked by a plug, the **operculum**. The worms eat very small particles caught in the gills and driven by a ciliary cur-rent into the mouth.

Fig. 14–14. *Hydroides*, a tube-living poly-chaete with circle of varicolored gills and clublike operculum. ×3. *(American Mu-seum of Natural History)*

A very different but spectacular species is *Chaetopterus*, which grows to over 6 inches long, and lives its adult life within a U-shaped tube buried in the mud and sand except for the two tips of the tube. The worm possesses flap-like parapodia which produce a current of water through the tube that carries in oxygen and food particles. *Chaetopterus* is brilliantly lu-minescent, though the function of that trait is uncertain.

Fig. 14–15. *Chaetopterus* in its parchment-like U-tube with ends opening into the sea water. Shown one-third life size. *(American Museum of Natural History)*

Over a dozen species of fresh-water polychaetes belonging to several families have been reported, but most of these are extremely rare. Several nereis-like species have been found in lakes and streams of California close to the sea, and two species in Lake Baikal in Siberia, a very large lake over 1,000 miles from the ocean and geologically ancient. The first-known fresh-water polychaete is *Manayunkia,* named after a Philadelphia suburb near which it was discovered by Joseph Leidy, a prominent 19th century naturalist. It has more recently been discovered in the Great Lakes. *Manayunkia* is a very small, gill-bearing species which lives in tubes applied to stones. The blood of this fresh-water polychaete is bright green from chlorocruorin.

Organ Systems. The **digestive system** of a polychaete consists of a straight tube. In the seaweed-eating, free-crawling species, there is usually a pair of digestive glands opening into the esophagus.

The **circulatory system** consists of a contractile dorsal blood vessel running just above the intestine. It pumps blood toward the head by a series of peristaltic waves of contraction which begin at the hind end of the worm and pass forward. The rhythmical waves of pulsation of the dorsal blood vessel appear to be under the same kind of nervous control as vertebrate hearts.

At least, chemicals like acetycholine and eserine (to be discussed in connection with the vertebrates) have the same kinds of effects on these pulsating annelid blood vessels that they have on vertebrate hearts. Blood returns to the posterior end of the worm by a noncontractile blood vessel ventral to the intestine. In every segment the dorsal and ventral blood vessels are connected by smaller vessels that pass through the gut walls and the parapodia.

As the blood passes through the gills it absorbs oxygen and gives off carbon dioxide. Most polychaetes have hemoglobin dissolved in the blood plasma. This is true hemoglobin, composed of an iron-containing porphyrin combined with a protein. Although not identical with vertebrate hemoglobin, its function as an oxygen carrier can be accurately confirmed, since it can be made incapable of carrying oxygen by exposing it to carbon monoxide and the fall in the worm's respiration can then be

Fig. 14–16. *Chaetopterus* luminescing in total darkness. *(Kindness of E. N. Harvey)*

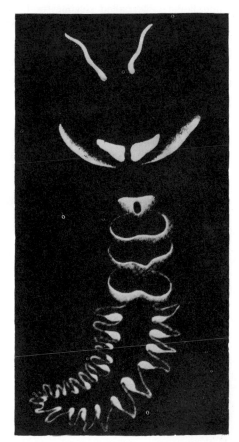

measured. A few species, like *Glycera,* contain the hemoglobin within red cells. Several species contain iron-porphyrin proteins of extremely high molecular weight which are green in the dilutions found in the worm (although red in very concentrated solutions). These green respiratory pigments are called **chlorocruorins** (*chloro,* green, + *cruor,* blood). Their evolutionary significance is unknown.

The **excretory organs** of polychaetes have long been a subject of discussion; many problems of their physiological, anatomical, and evolutionary aspects remain unsolved. There are at least four types of structures. In the trochophore larva, the excretory organs are typical flame cells like those of the flatworms. In the adults the nephridia are tubes lying in the coelom and leading to the exterior by small pores. Usually there are two nephridia, one on the right and one on the left, in every segment except the first two or three. In many species each nephridium is a tube with several short branches on its inner end. These branches do not open into the coelom but carry clusters of modified flame cells called **solenocytes** (*solen,* pipe, + *cyte,* cell). Each solenocyte looks like a hatpin, whose "head" is the rounded cell body with the nucleus. A long flagellum extends down the hollow stem which enters the blind inner end of one branch of the nephridial tubule. Presumably they function in essentially the same way as flame cells in pushing excess water and wastes to the exterior. The relationship of this type of kidney to the flame cells of the flatworms has presented no problem. The puzzling fact is that the solenocyte kidney is the kind found in the most vertebrate-like of all the primitive chordates, *Amphioxus.* Does this mean that *Amphioxus,* and with it the vertebrates, are derived from annelids? Or that both are derived from flatworms? Are there other possibilities?

In many other species of polychaetes the nephridia open into the coelom by a ciliated funnel, the **nephrostome** (*nephros,* kidney, + *stoma,* mouth). The second and third types of nephridia are of this kind. In most species the nephridium is a long coiled tubule, often lined with cilia along most of its length and ending in a smooth and somewhat wider section before it

opens to the exterior via a nephridiopore. In some species the entire nephridium lies within a single segment, but in others the inner opening of the tubule, the nephrostome, opens into the segment anterior to the one holding most of the tubule, just as in earthworms. No explanation for this curious arrangement is available.

In the fourth type of polychaete nephridium, the tubule is very short and thick. This is true in *Arenicola,* called by fishermen the lugworm. This type of kidney serves as an exit for the eggs. There are many different relationships between the kidneys and the ducts which carry eggs and sperms to the exterior. In some species there are entirely separate genital and excretory ducts; in others the same ducts serve two purposes. In some species the nephridial ducts become enlarged and modified during the breeding season.

Spawning in polychaetes is sometimes a conspicuous event. Since the gametes are merely shed into the ocean, the problem is to insure synchronous shedding so that the eggs and sperms will have a good chance of meeting. This is often timed in some way by the moon. The best-known case is that of the palolo worm, a nereis-like species that lives in the crevices of the coral reefs of the South Pacific. At the dark of the moon in October and November, the sexual forms of these worms emerge from the coral reefs. At dawn on two successive days the worms swarm in incredible numbers on the surface of the sea, where they are caught as food by the local inhabitants. A similar species found in the West Indies spawns in May and June. In a Bermuda species the females appear in the dark of the moon and attract the males by luminescence and by swimming rapidly in tight, bright circles.

In the reef-dwelling species, like the palolo worm, an asexual generation, called the **atoke**, alternates with a sexual generation, the **epitoke**. Atokes have small eyes, or none, and sturdy leglike parapodia enabling them to crawl among the corals. They continue to grow in length by the formation of new segments in a zone of cell division just anterior to the anal segment. After some time a new head with large eyes forms roughly in the middle of the worm. The parapodia from the new head to the tail become

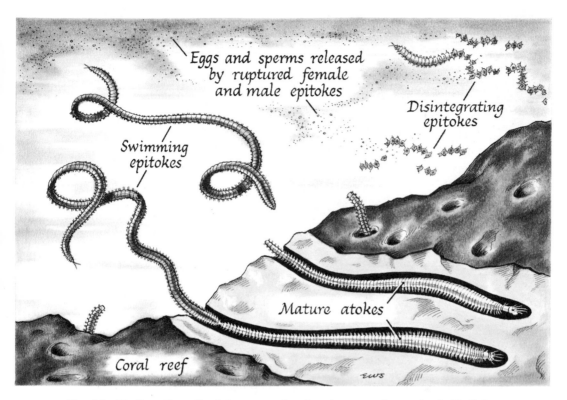

Eggs and sperms released
by ruptured female
and male epitokes

Disintegrating
epitokes

Swimming
epitokes

Mature atokes

Coral reef

Fig. 14–17. Breeding of palolo worm showing the asexual anterior half of the worm or atoke, and the posterior sexual half, the epitoke.

flattened swimming plates; in some species eyes develop on each of the parapodia, and in all species many pairs of gonads develop. The posterior half with the new head then breaks away from the anterior portion and swims off as a sexual epitoke, either male or female.

The time of reproductive swarming is determined by an annual rhythm limiting it to one or perhaps two months in the year, a lunar periodicity placing the activity within a certain day, and a diurnal rhythm placing it within a specific time after sunset. It has been claimed that approximately 90 per cent of the palolo worms that swarm do so within a two-hour period once a year. The physiological control of all this is poorly understood, but the formation of the epitoke is somehow controlled by a brain hormone. If the brain is removed from an atoke, epitoke characters appear. Likewise if the brain of a young worm is implanted into a mature one, epitoke characters are inhibited.

The asexual atoke crawls back into the recesses of the reef to grow a new sexual portion. Even though the anterior part of a worm does not produce gametes and reproduces asexually, it is nevertheless either male or female in its chromosomal complement. This means that a given individual will produce only male or only female sexual individuals. It will be recalled that a similar situation exists in coelenterates, where a given hydroid will bud only male or only female jellyfish.

The **central nervous system** of polychaetes consists of a pair of cerebral ganglia constituting the brain and lying dorsal to the anterior part of the gut. This brain gives off many nerves to the head and sends connecting nerves to the ventral nerve cord, which in some species is double. The **sense organs** are especially notable. The free-swimming sexual forms have two or four prominent eyes on the head. They are complex structures with lens, retina, and

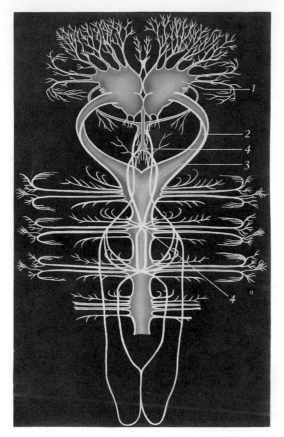

pigmented cup, striking to see. Many of the tube-dwelling polychaetes possess eyes, perhaps a dozen or more on their gills plus a pair on the anal segments. Presumably these serve to warn the worm against backing completely out of its tube, which may have been broken at the hind end. Some crawling species have otocysts in the prostomium.

OLIGOCHAETES

The oligochaetes are divided into three orders based on the position of the male pores. The Order **Plesioporiformes** includes many small aquatic species, mostly world-wide in distribution. They are well suited for study and experimentation because their transparency makes it possible to see all the organs in the living animal, and because of the ease with

Fig. 14–20. Translucent body of a living fresh-water oligochaete, *Stylaria*. Note dark gut, transverse septa, bundles of setae, and nephridia within the coelom. *(Kindness of William H. Amos)*

Fig. 14–18. Nervous system of the free-swimming polychaete, *Eunice sanguinea*. *1*, brain. *2*, circumpharyngeal connective. *3*, sub-esophageal ganglion. *4*, intestinal nerve complex. *(From Pauli, The World of Life, Houghton Mifflin)*

Fig. 14–19. Complex eye of the polychaete *Alciope*. *1*, visual cells of retina. *2*, light-sensitive rods. *3*, optic nerve. *4*, lens. *5*, lens muscle. *6*, accessory retina. *(From Pauli, The World of Life, Houghton Mifflin)*

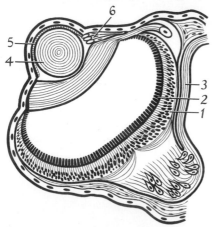

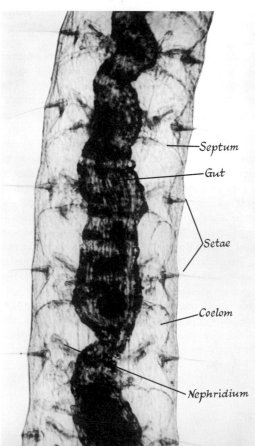

which they can be cultured in the laboratory. Their remarkable manner of growth and of asexual reproduction were discovered in the 18th century by Abraham Trembley, who performed the pioneer experiments on hydra. Ever since, annelids have been used in attempts to analyze the factors that control cell division and cell growth. In these transparent aquatic forms new segments are continually formed in a zone of proliferation just in front of the anal segment. In this region, and in this region only, cells are continually undergoing mitosis. Thus the farther a segment is from the tail, the older the segment is.

Reproduction is almost exclusively asexual by means of formation of **fission planes.** In this process, a single segment about two-thirds of the way back from the head undergoes a profound change. The intestine, the most opaque structure in the body, becomes completely translucent in this single segment. The cells of the segment undergo an explosive series of mitoses. Why this happens, no one knows, nor why it stops when it does. After the requisite number of new cells has been produced, those in the anterior part of the segment begin to form a new tail complete with growth zone and anal gills (if the species has them) while the posterior part forms a new head complete with prostomium, mouth, eye spots, and head bristles. Subsequently the worm breaks in two. The

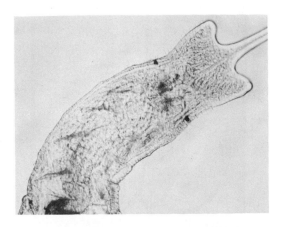

Fig. 14–22. Living fresh-water oligochaete, *Stylaria*. Note black eye spots on either side of head and long "style," i.e., prostomium. (*Kindness of William H. Amos*)

anterior part crawls off with the old head and a new tail, the posterior part with a new head and the old tail.

Among the more familiar genera are *Stylaria*, which has a long flexible prostomium, probably sensory in function; *Dero*, which has three fingerlike tail gills in which the circulation of the blood can be observed; *Aulophorus*, which adds to the gills a pair of nonciliated sensory filaments; and *Nais*, perhaps the commonest of all, which lacks both gills and elongate prostomium.

Fig. 14–21. The fission plane in a fresh-water oligochaete. The new tail is on the left and the new head on the right, in the shaded area of the lower figure. The heavy diagonals show the zone of cell division.

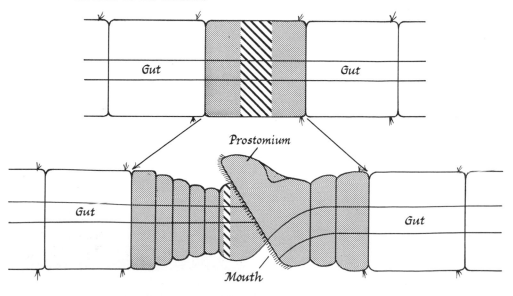

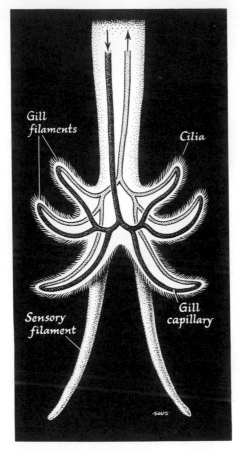

Fig. 14–23. Posterior gills of a fresh-water oligochaete, *Aulophorus*. Note the direction that the blood flows.

In this order also are *Enchytraeus,* a genus of small, opaque, milk-white worms which inhabit moist soil and are commonly raised as food for tropical aquarium fishes; and *Tubifex,* a red worm which lives with its head in the mud and its tail waving vertically in the water. *Tubifex* may be so abundant in ponds and along the edges of slow streams that many square yards of bottom will be red. It is an indicator of streams and ponds polluted with organic matter from cattle or other sources.

A second order, the **Opisthoporiformes,** includes the various kinds of earthworms. Most of those in North America belong to the family Lumbricidae. *Lumbricus terrestris,* the big "night crawler," is easily identified by its flattened tail end and by a prostomium which extends back to touch the furrow between the first and second segments. *Eisenia foetida,* the barnyard earthworm long used in regeneration experiments, is the species Isaak Walton called the "brandling." It is characterized by alternating light and dark cinnamon rings, giving it a tigerlike appearance when extended. This is the "California tiger" of the "earthworm farms." *Helodrilus (Allolobophora) caliginosus* is one of the commonest of the half dozen or so species usually found in gardens. *Octolasium lacteum* is often found under dead logs or piles of leaves. This is an unusual looking species. The first few segments are pink, the body as a whole a blue grey, the clitellum a reddish brown, and on the dorsal side of the extreme posterior tip there is usually a bright yellow spot, probably chloragogen cells showing through the skin.

Only a few American earthworms belong to other families, although on other continents there is a rich and varied earthworm fauna. Perhaps the most interesting are some of the India species already mentioned, and the 6-foot earthworms native to tropical Australia, the Malaya region, and South America.

The third order of oligochaetes, the **Prosoporiformes,** includes some small semi-transparent species that are common ectoparasites on crayfish. Some species are usually found among the gills, others crawl about the face. From their leechlike manner of walking (inchworm fashion), they are called branchiobdellids (*branchia,* gills, + *bdella,* leech). A remarkable anatomical fact about them is their small and constant number of segments, 15.

Fig. 14–24. Giant earthworm from tropical Australia and a full-grown North American *Lumbricus,* the night crawler or dew worm. *(Courtesy, General Biological Supply House, Inc., Chicago)*

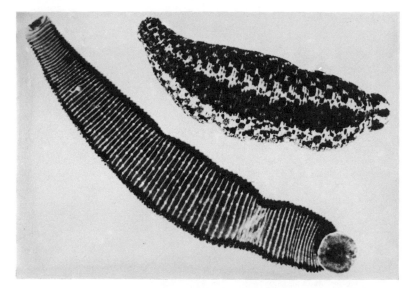

Fig. 14–25. Leeches, *Hirudo medicinalis*, useful in blood-letting, once a medical cure-all. *(Kindness of P. S. Tice)*

LEECHES

Leeches are very different from either oligochaetes or polychaetes and show adaptations for blood sucking. Internally the gut consists of a heavy muscular sucking pharynx. In the blood-sucking species its walls are richly provided with unicellular glands which secrete an anticoagulant, **hirudin,** which prevents the blood of the victim from clotting either in the wound or in the gut of the leech. Back of the pharynx is an elongate crop with ten or more diverticuli (paired blind outpocketings) which fill much of the body. The stomach-intestine is short and straight.

The rest of the internal structure of leeches is difficult to dissect. The coelom is said to be reduced to a vascular sinus containing a fluid with hemoglobin in solution. The space between the muscular body wall and the gut is filled with connective tissue, muscles, and other cells. The excretory system consists of paired nephridia in the form of ciliated funnels varying with the species from simple to complex.

Leeches are hermaphroditic. The male part of the system consists of ten pairs of testes, one pair to a segment, opening into a pair of ducts regarded as a vestigial coelom. One pair of ovaries in the 11th segment connects via short ducts to the exterior. As with most hermaphrodites, cross fertilization is the rule. The eggs are deposited in a cocoon formed by a clitellum.

The nervous system resembles that of other annelids. There are cerebral ganglia above the pharynx, and connectives from these to a ventral ganglionic nerve cord. Many species have several small eyes on the head. Most North American leeches belong either to the order **Rhynchobdelliformes** (*rhynchos*, snout, + *bdella*, leech), which have no teeth, a very small mouth, and an eversible proboscis, or to the **Gnathobdelliformes** (*gnathos*, jaw, + *bdella*, leech), characterized by three semicircular chitinous teeth set in a large mouth with no proboscis. Most small leeches found on snails, fishes, turtles, or merely scavenging are toothless. The toothed group includes *Hirudo medicinalis*, once used in blood letting, the big horseleech, *Hemopsis*, and others which attack men, cattle, frogs, fishes, and invertebrates.

RELATED PHYLA

The phylum **Echiuroidea** is made up of 50 or so genera of rather short fat worms having a capacious coelom, scanty septa, obscure segmentation, a few setae at each end, and a very large proboscis which may represent a prostomium. The best known genera are *Bonellia, Echiurus,* and *Urechis.*

A female *Bonellia* has a body approximately the size of a somewhat flexible walnut and a very long extensible proboscis bifurcated at the end. She feeds by collecting semi-microscopic particles in a ciliated groove on the proboscis. The male is a minute ciliated organism that lives in the female's reproductive tract. This case of sexual dimorphism has attracted much

Fig. 14–26. *Macroperipatus geayi.* Adult female with young. *Peripatus* is sometimes classified with the annelids, sometimes with the arthropods, and sometimes in a special phylum. *(Photo by L. J. and M. J. Milne)*

attention because the sex of the individual is determined by the environment. If the free-swimming larva settles down alone, it develops into a female. If, however, it chances upon a female, it settles on her proboscis, and then develops into a male. Extracts of the proboscis and many other substances such as copper ions and glycerol prevent development into females.

Echiurus and its relatives are bloated-looking creatures about the size of a man's thumb. They are sometimes abundant in muddy sand and have been much used as bait in the codfish industry. *Urechis* is even larger and lives in more or less U-shaped tubes in the sand.

The phylum **Sipunculoidea** consists of *Phascolosoma* plus some 250 other wormlike animals with a spacious coelom which resembles that of the echiuroids. The anterior quarter of the body is called the introvert and can be pulled back into the rest of the body. The mouth is surrounded by a circle of ciliated tentacles. The larva is a trochophore. In some places where conditions are just right, sipunculoids are so abundant in muddy sand below low-tide lines that every shovelful of sand will contain a dozen or more.

The phylum **Onychophora** (*onychos*, claw, + *phoros,* bearing) is remarkable because of its combination of annelid and arthropod characters. The best-known genus is *Peripatus.* This animal resembles a caterpillar with a pair of antennae, a warty and transversely wrinkled skin, and short fleshy legs provided with claws. These creatures are found in many tropical and semi-tropical parts of the world, under stones, bark, fallen logs, and other moist places.

The general body plan and the arrangement of most of the organ systems of *Peripatus* resemble those of annelids. Specifically, the segmentally arranged nephridia are of the annelid type. The presence of cilia in the reproductive ducts is also an annelid trait; for some unknown reason the arthropods have no cilia. The eyes resemble those of polychaete annelids.

The most conspicuous arthropod trait, and one which has caused some zoologists to place the Onychophora high among the arthropods, is the system of air ducts, or **tracheae,** like those of centipedes and insects. The jaws of *Peripatus* appear to be modified legs, and this is also a typical arthropod trait. The young "worms" have a blood vascular system much like that of earthworms, but as they grow larger the blood vessels expand until they obliterate the coelom. Thus the body cavity of the adult is a hemocoel, as in arthropods.

The sexes are separate, fertilization is internal, and the young are born from the mother as miniature adults. It seems improbable that *Peripatus* was the actual ancestor of any living group of arthropods, but it may show the kind of animal which formed the bridge.

Review and References

1. What six traits characterize annelids? What are the major groups of this phylum?

2. What is the ecological importance of earthworms? Their importance as intermediate hosts of parasites?

3. It has been claimed that if an annelid is turned upside down it exhibits the same basic body plan as a vertebrate. To what extent is this true of the coelom, body wall, and digestive, vascular, and nervous systems?

4. By what neuro-muscular mechanisms does an earthworm crawl? What is the function of the three giant fibers?

5. Describe the flame cell, solenocyte, nephrostome, and nephrostome-gonoduct types of nephridia. How is the earthworm nephridium like the vertebrate kidney?

6. Compare and contrast the reproductive structures and methods of earthworms and small aquatic naids. What is a fission plane and how does it function?

7. How do polychaetes differ from oligochaetes in external anatomy, respiratory and circulatory systems, reproduction?

8. What is scientifically notable about *Peripatus? Bonellia?* The palolo worm?

9. Define: coelom, nephrostome, clitellum, parapodium, porphyrin, prostomium, trochophore, hemocoel.

10. How are leeches like other annelids? How are they adapted for blood sucking?

USEFUL REFERENCES

Dales, R. P., *Annelids,* New York, Hillary House, 1963.

Dixon, G. C., *Tubifex,* Liverpool, University of Liverpool Press, 1915.

Hartman, O., "Marine Annelids of North Carolina," Duke University Marine Station Bulletin #2, Durham, N. C., Duke University Press, 1945.

Kevan, D. K. McE., ed., *Soil Zoology,* New York, Academic Press, 1955.

Laverack, M. S., *The Physiology of Earthworms,* New York, The Macmillan Company, 1963.

Olson, H. W., "Earthworms of New York State," American Museum Novitates, #1090, New York, American Museum of Natural History, 1940.

Olson, H. W., "The Earthworms of Ohio," *Ohio Biological Survey,* IV (2) #17, Columbus, Ohio State University Press, 1928.

Pennak, R. W., *Fresh-Water Invertebrates of the United States,* New York, The Ronald Press Company, 1953.

Pratt, H. S., *Manual of the Common Invertebrate Animals Exclusive of Insects,* Philadelphia, P. Blakiston's Son & Co., 1935.

Stephenson, J., *The Oligochaeta,* Oxford, Clarendon Press, 1930.

Chapter 15

Mollusks

The mollusks are a well-defined but extremely diverse and very large phylum of some 70,000 living and 25,000 fossil species. They are bilateral with rudimentary or no segmentation and a soft body (*molluscus,* soft). The molluscan body is typically made up of four parts: (1) a visceral mass containing the digestive and reproductive organs, (2) a ventral muscular foot, (3) a head and mouth in which there is a flexible muscular tongue, called the **radula,** bearing long parallel rows of minute teeth, and (4) a **mantle.** The mantle is like a cloak of skin enfolding the animal. On its outer surface the mantle secretes the characteristic calcareous shell. The coelom is small.

There are exceptions to this general scheme. In bivalves like clams, there is no head and hence no radula. In oysters even the foot is missing. The basic structure of all six classes of mollusks can easily be understood in terms of the body plan of the chitons or amphineurons, which will be described below.

Mollusks have been important as food since well before the beginning of written history. This is shown by the enormous piles of shells making up the kitchen middens or refuse piles of many Stone Age peoples in Europe. The American Indians, who were living in a Stone Age culture before the arrival of Europeans, also left huge piles of clam and oyster shells along the coasts of North America. Along San Francisco Bay there are enormous Indian shell mounds, estimated to represent an accumulation extending back over 3,000 years. In North Carolina some mounds are so large that they serve as a source of road-building material.

The royal purple of the ancient Greeks and Romans was obtained from a yellow pigment which turns intense purple upon exposure to light, and which is secreted by a so-called mucus gland in a Mediterranean snail, *Murex.* Huge piles of these shells are still to be seen on the shores of Syria and adjacent regions.

The use of mollusks for food has continued steadily from prehistoric times. The United Nations Economic Yearbook records the total world catch of mollusks at about 2,000,000 metric tons annually. (A metric ton is 2,205 lb.) The annual haul of oysters in the United States is now about 450,000 tons.

Fig. 15–1. Shell of *Murex,* the snail which furnished the royal purple dye of ancient Greece and Rome. (*By permission of Trustees of the British Museum, Natural History*)

EVOLUTIONARY RELATIONSHIPS
AND MAJOR GROUPS

Mollusks are clearly members of the proto-stome branch of the animal kingdom. The egg, in most species, undergoes a beautiful spiral cleavage, the larva is a typical trochophore, and the mouth is formed from the blastopore. The coelom is not formed by budding off from the gut; the nervous system consists of a ring around the esophagus and, at least in the simpler mollusks, a ventral nerve cord.

The relationship of the mollusks to other protostome phyla was uncertain until 1957. Some zoologists believed with Anton Dohrn, founder of the famous Naples biological station, that mollusks had evolved from turbellarian flatworms, chiefly because of their soft, unsegmented bodies and creeping muscular foot. Others held that mollusks are derived from annelids because of a slight amount of segmentation in some very ancient groups. The pearly nautilus, for instance, has four pairs of gills and four pairs of kidneys. Until recently there was little definite evidence to support either theory. But the dramatic discovery of a hitherto little-known group of mollusks, the monoplacophorans, to be described below, strongly supports the theory of annelid relationship. For these mollusks are segmented and possess well-developed coeloms.

There are now six known **living classes** of mollusks: the Monoplacophora, the Amphineura or the chitons, the Scaphopoda or elephant tusks, the Gastropoda or snails, the Pelecypoda or bivalves, and the Cephalopoda or squids and octopuses.

Newly-Found Primitive Mollusks. To the amazement of zoologists, a population of living monoplacophorans, Class Monoplacophora (*mono*, single, + *plakos*, something broad and flattish, + *phora,* bearing), was discovered in 1957 in very deep water (3,590 meters or roughly 2 miles) off the west coast of Mexico. This discovery outdoes the case of the coelacanth fishes found two decades ago in deep water north of Madagascar off the east coast of Africa (see Chapter 20). The coelacanths were supposed to have been extinct since the end of the Mesozoic, the Age of Reptiles, 70 million years ago. The most recent fossils of the primitive monoplacophoran mollusks date from the Silurian, over 300 million years in the past. No wonder there is no popular name for them.

As the word monoplacophoran suggests, these ancient animals bear a single, broad, rounded shell somewhat like the shield of a classical Greek warrior. Under this shell the animal is bilaterally symmetrical with an anterior mouth, a strong radula in the pharynx, and a posterior median anus. On each side of the flat, rounded, snail-like foot is a row of gills, five pairs in all. Internally there are five pairs of nephridia and five pairs of gill hearts. There are five pairs of strong retractor muscles for the foot plus three more pairs in the "head." The body is clearly in five segments and the head evidently represents three more segments. The coelom is well developed and the sexes are separate, as in polychaetes. No copulatory organs have been found; presumably gametes are shed directly into the water. The specimens collected are of the genus *Neopilina* and are in the Zoological Museum of the University of Copenhagen.

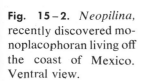

Fig. 15–2. *Neopilina,* recently discovered monoplacophoran living off the coast of Mexico. Ventral view.

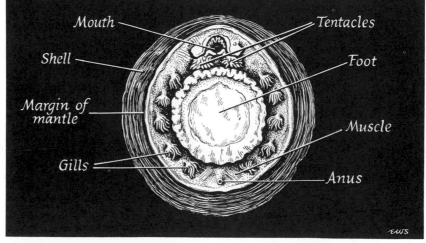

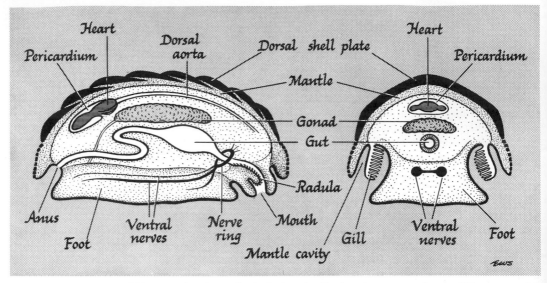

Fig. 15 – 3. Chiton, a simple mollusk, in longitudinal and cross sections. (Diagrammatic)

The Chitons. Members of the Class Amphineura (*amphi,* double, + *neuron,* nerve) are usually found on rocks along the sea coast in shallow water. The adults vary, according to species, from about a half inch to 10 or 12 inches in length. The oval body is protected dorsally by eight transverse shell plates which give the chitons a segmented appearance. Encircling the dorsal plates is a marginal girdle composed of numerous tiny calcareous platelets. The body plan of a chiton may be taken as typical of mollusks.

As seen in longitudinal section (Fig. 15 – 3). the entire body is covered by the **mantle,** which hangs down around the edges and lies immediately under the **shell plates** it has secreted. Extending along the lower surface of the chiton is a thick muscular **foot.** The space between the mantle on one side and the visceral mass and foot on the other is known as the **mantle cavity.** It opens freely to the sea water. At the anterior end is a short **proboscis** with a **mouth** containing the characteristic **radula.** The ribbon of fine **teeth** on the radula act like a flexible file to rasp off algae growing on rocks and other objects. Within the body above the gut is the **heart,** lying in a small cavity, the **pericardium,** which is in fact the **coelom.** The **gonad** lies above the gut and opens into the mantle cavity via a pair of ducts that end above the edge of the foot near the posterior end of the body. The sexes are separate. The larvae are free-swimming trochophores.

The nervous system consists of a **circumesophageal ring** from which a pair of **ventral nerve cords** extend back through the foot and a pair of **lateral nerves** extend back on either side of the body. The **gills** can be seen by turning the animal upside down or by examining a cross section. They hang down in the mantle cavity between the mantle and the visceral mass and foot. This is the normal position of the gills in clams and other mollusks. Chitons have from 6 to 80 pairs of gills.

The muscular foot on the large species of chitons found in the West Indies is eaten as "sea beef."

The Elephant Tusk Shells. These are of the Class Scaphopoda (*skaphe,* boat, + *podos,* foot), and are the least important group of mollusks although their shells were extensively used as money and ornaments among West Coast American Indians, where a 1⅞-inch shell was the equivalent of 25 cents and must have represented well over a dollar in present-day purchasing power. Along the East Coast of the United States scaphopods are known to occur only on the bottom in quiet deep water in a few Maine coves.

The edges of the mantle of scaphopods are fused together along the midventral line, thus enclosing the animal in a tube open at both ends. The mantle tube is slightly curved and just enough smaller at the posterior end to make the shell it secretes resemble a miniature ivory tusk.

The somewhat knoblike foot protrudes from the larger end along with several sensory ciliated tentacles which conduct food to the mouth. There is a radula. Gills are lacking and there is only one gonad for which the right nephridial duct serves to conduct the gametes to the exterior.

The Gastropods: Snails and Others. The snails and their relatives, Class Gastropoda (*gaster*, belly, + *podos*, foot), are an enormous and important group of animals. Anyone who wishes to make a complete collection of snail shells from all the world will have to accumulate some 50,000 varieties. In Japan, China, and France snails are regarded as edible delica-

Fig. 15 – 4. Snail shell as seen by X-ray. *(Kindness of Pat Cook)*

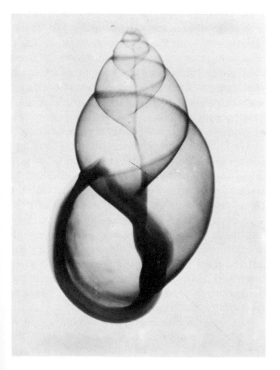

cies. In semi-tropical regions several species can become very destructive to citrus fruits and other crops, while in oyster beds a small carnivorous snail, *Urosalpinx,* the oyster drill, is an expensive, unsolved problem. A few gastropods are parasitic on holothurians; some species are reduced to little more than a blood-sucking proboscis and a visceral mass which is mostly gonad.

The structure of a typical gastropod is essentially like that of a chiton in which the main body mass—the visceral mass containing the intestine and gonads—along with the heart and nephridia, has been pulled up into a great hump, usually coiled. Within the mantle cavity is a gill-like organ of taste and smell, called the **osphradium.**

In the more primitive snails and their bizarre relatives, the intestine is more or less straight and the anus and gills posterior in position (Fig. 15 – 5, *A*). However, in the overwhelming majority of gastropods the larva undergoes a curious asymmetrical growth known as **torsion.** The left side of the visceral mass grows more than the right. The result is that the visceral mass rotates with respect to the head and foot through 180° in a counterclockwise direction viewed from above. It is almost as though the left side of your neck grew so much more than the right that your face was turned farther and farther to the right, until your head faced backwards. In the end, the visceral mass, with the intestine, is twisted around a half circle so that the anus is brought up on the right side along with the gills. The nerve cords are also thrown into a crossed loop. The evolutionary advantage of this curious maneuver, may involve bringing the gills forward in an animal living within a shell.

The **coiling** of the visceral mass, as seen in the familiar coiled snail shell, is a separate process. It occurs mostly later in development than the torsion through 180°. Instead of growing higher and higher into a long top-heavy point, the visceral mass merely winds around an axis at right angles to the axis of the torsion. In many gastropods the trochophore stage is passed before the snail hatches. In such species there may be a larger swimming larva, the **veliger,** with two rounded, ciliated lobes on the head. Gastropods fall into three orders.

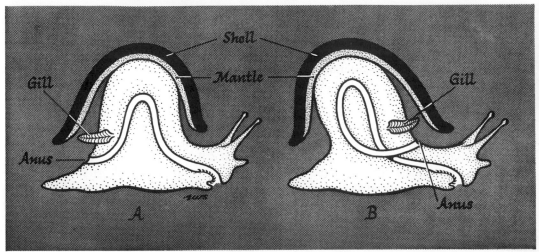

Fig. 15–5. One-sided growth results in the torsion of snails, placing the originally posterior gills *(A)* in an anterior position *(B)*.

The Prosobranch Gastropods. The Order Prosobranchiformes *(proso,* in front, + *branchia,* gill) is an enormous group in which, as the name suggests, the gills are anterior in position due to the torsion of the larval body. The nerves and intestine are twisted. The overwhelming majority of marine snails are prosobranchs. The sexes are separate, the head is provided with a pair of nonretractile tentacles and a pair of eyes which may or may not be on the tentacles. The mouth and radula are usually on the end of a long proboscis.

The anterior edge of the mantle is commonly prolonged into a tubular siphon which the snail waves around in front of it as it moves, testing the water first in one direction and then in another. Most prosobranchs are carnivorous, and nothing will bring snails gliding from all corners of a tide pool faster than a piece of crushed clam. The eggs are usually deposited in transparent or leathery capsules, which may be connected in long strings.

The most important prosobranchs economically (now that royal purple is no longer fashionable) are the big conchs like *Strombus* and *Busycon.* These are extensively used as bait in the cod-fishing industry and are ground up to make chowder for human consumption. Their shells are prized either entire or cut as cameos. The most harmful species is the oyster drill, *Urosalpinx.* Other species include the beautiful tropical cowries and the edible periwinkle, *Littorina,* introduced into Nova Scotia from Europe in 1857 and now the commonest snail along the east coast as far south as New Jersey. The abalone, the limpet or "Chinaman's hat," and the boat shell, *Crepidula,* are all snails with visceral masses so flat there is no coiling.

The Opisthobranch Gastropods. The Order Opisthobranchiformes *(opistho,* back, + *branchia,* gill) is an extremely heterogeneous group containing only about 2,000 species of snails plus the nudibranchs and pteropods, strange and sometimes lovely creatures. As the name opisthobranch indicates, the gills are posterior in position. The nerve cords are uncrossed.

The facts are extremely puzzling. Most opisthobranchs undergo the same kind of torsion found in the prosobranchs. The left side of the visceral mass grows relatively far more than the right. Indeed the right gill, kidney, and right side of the heart usually atrophy completely. Yet these gastropods undergo enough secondary detorsion in later development to bring the gill and anus to or near the posterior end. Unlike the prosobranchs, the opisthobranchs are hermaphroditic, a trait they share with the fresh-water and terrestrial snails.

The opisthobranch most commonly seen is the Florida sea hare, a soft animal about the size and shape of a smallish football, with no

Fig. 15–6. Living nudibranchs, *Hermissenda*, eating marine hydroids. *(From Ricketts and Calvin,* Between Pacific Tides, *3rd ed., rev. by J. W. Hedgpeth, Stanford University Press)*

visible shell. It swims by means of fleshy folds which extend along each side of the body, and it emits a dark purple ink when annoyed. The nudibranchs are brown or gaily colored, with branching dorsal frills and fringes. They crawl over seaweed-eating hydroids. The sea butterflies or pteropods are translucent blue or pink creatures, an inch and a half or so in length, which swim in the open ocean by means of a pair of winglike extensions of the foot. They are carnivorous, preying on smaller animals. In the polar seas, sea butterflies swarm in numberless billions and at certain seasons constitute a major item in the diet of the large whalebone whales.

The Pulmonate Gastropods. The Order Pulmonatiformes (*pulmonis,* lung) comprises the fresh-water and terrestrial snails and slugs. In place of gills, they possess a lung in the form of a more or less vascular lining of the mantle cavity which communicates with the exterior by a small opening. Pond snails can be seen to expel a bubble through this pore from time to time. Torsion has brought the hind end of the gut forward. Aquatic species have one pair of nonretractile tentacles, at the base of which are the eyes. Terrestrial pulmonates have two pairs of retractile tentacles; near or at the tip of the hinder pair are the eyes.

Like the opisthobranchs, the pulmonates are hermaphroditic, although mutual cross fertilization is the rule. Most species are herbivorous though a few are carnivores and even cannibalistic. The common edible snail of the gourmets, *Helix,* is a pulmonate.

Some snails coil in what is called a dextral manner and others in a sinistral manner (see Fig. 15–7). The interest of zoologists has been challenged by the discovery that in some completely unknown way, the direction of coiling is determined by the genes in the diploid set of chromosomes during the growth of the egg cell in the ovary. This means that this particular character of the adult is determined before the egg is fertilized; and although the sperm will carry factors for direction of coiling they will produce no effect on the embryo, but only on the developing eggs which that embryo will eventually produce when it becomes an adult.

To illustrate: let R = a dominant gene for dextral and r = a recessive gene for sinistral coiling. Then a snail of genotype RR or Rr will lay eggs which will all develop into dextral type snails irrespective of whether these eggs are fertilized by R- or r-bearing sperms. Apparently paradoxical results can readily be explained on this basis. Suppose that a snail of genotype Rr is crossed with one known to be homozygous for r. All the eggs of the Rr snail

Fig. 15–7. Dextral and sinistral coiling of snail shells.

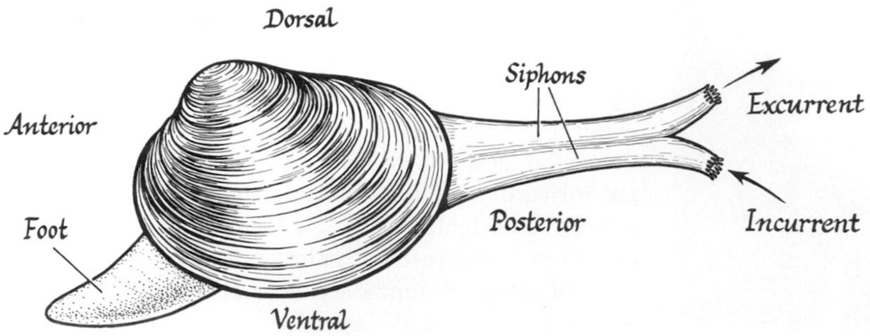

Dorsal

Anterior

Siphons

Excurrent

Foot

Posterior

Incurrent

Ventral

Fig. 15-8. Pelecypod with foot and siphons extended.

will receive some kind of information from the *R* gene which will make them coil in a dextral manner. At meiosis 50 per cent of the eggs will retain the *R* gene and lose the *r* in a polar body, and 50 per cent will retain the *r* gene and lose the *R* in a polar body. Since all the sperms carry an *r* gene, 50 per cent of the fertilized eggs will be homozygous *rr* and according to the usual process of heredity should be sinistral in coiling. However, they are all dextral. Any eggs which develop from the dextral *rr* snails will be sinistral even though fertilized by *R*-carrying sperm. This case is famous partly because it involves the first gene known to act before fertilization.

The Bivalves. The bivalves or pelecypods, Class Pelecypoda, include the clams, oysters, mussels, shipworms, and scallops. It is a highly specialized class, and economically the most important group of mollusks.

The mantle, and consequently the shell, is divided into a right and left half hanging down from the back or dorsal side of the animal. In most clams the right and left shells are closely similar, so the only way right and left can be easily distinguished is by the siphons, which are posterior, and by the hinge ligament, which is dorsal. Therefore, when the hinge is uppermost and the siphons toward you, the clam's left is to the holder's left. The head and radula are completely missing. The mouth is merely a hole into the intestine at the anterior median edge of the visceral mass. The soft visceral mass hangs down in the mantle cavity between the two valves of the shell. At the lower edge of the visceral mass is the more or less hatchet-shaped muscular foot. On either side of the visceral mass, and hanging down into the right and the left mantle cavities, are the ciliated gills. In many species the posterior edge of the mantle

has evolved into a double tube, the **siphons,** which conduct water into and out of the mantle cavity. The cilia of the gills produce a current of water in through the lower or incurrent siphon, over and through the gills, where minute food particles are trapped, and into the space above the gills, the **epibranchial cavity.** From there the water passes out through the upper or excurrent siphon.

Most marine pelecypods are **protandrous,** that is, they are males while small, and grow up into females when they attain full size. The larva is a trochophore. In the large fresh-water clams the sexes are separate and the larva is known as a **glochidium,** which is a temporary but obligatory parasite on fishes. The edge of each valve of the shell of the glochidium is provided with a sharp hook or tooth with which the animal fastens itself to the gills of the fish. Later the glochidium drops off and matures in the stream bed. The fingernail clams of quiet ponds are hermaphroditic and brood their young in their gills until the adult form is attained.

Fig. 15-9. Cross section of a clam (pelecypod). Details of organs within the visceral mass have been omitted.

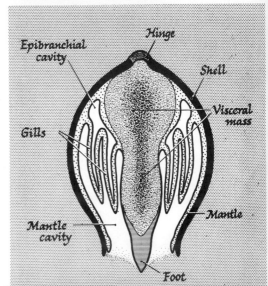

Epibranchial cavity

Hinge

Shell

Gills

Visceral mass

Mantle cavity

Mantle

Foot

Economically the most important clams are the fresh-water forms like *Unio* and *Anodonta* which are sought as food and for mother-of-pearl, and the marine hard clam or littleneck clam, *Venus mercenaria*. The latter was much used by East Coast American Indians as food and for the manufacture of purple wampum. The common name of "quahog" is from the Algonquian language. Various other species are nearly as important, especially the soft shell, long-neck, or steamer clam, *Mya arenaria*. In the rivers of the Mississippi drainage there are 15 or 20 species of fresh-water clams which form the basis of a profitable pearl button industry. True pearls are found in fresh-water clams as well as in oysters. These are formed when a minute foreign particle, perhaps a fine grain of sand, becomes surrounded by a covering of mantle epithelium which secretes the pearl.

The various species of *Sphaerium*, the little fingernail clam, can be found crawling around over pond weeds and dead leaves. It is an instructive sight under a dissecting microscope because its transparency makes it possible to see most of the organ systems.

Perhaps the only destructive pelecypod is *Teredo*, the "shipworm." This elongate clam uses its modified bivalve shell to bore tunnels into wood. Wharfs and ships that are unprotected by tar products soon become completely riddled by these animals.

The Squids and Octopuses. The Class Cephalopoda (*kephale*, head, + *podos*, foot) includes the squids and octopuses. This is today a small class of only about 400 living species, though there are some 10,000 fossil ones. The cephalopods comprise the only invertebrate group which can boast large dangerous animals on the vertebrate scale of size. The giant squid of the cold waters of the northernmost Atlantic attains a body length of 20 feet, and has a pair of grasping tentacles over 30 feet in length and eight shorter ones of about 10 feet. Fifteen feet in diameter is probably maximum size for an octopus. Most octopuses are extremely shy animals.

The body plan of a cephalopod can be easily understood by imagining a snail in which the mouth with the radula has been moved back into the center of the foot, and the foot itself drawn out around the mouth into eight or ten or more tentacles. The visceral mass in the squids has a stiff internal shell, while in an octopus the body is a mere bag. The body axes of a cephalopod are compared with those of a clam in Figure 15 – 10. Note that the siphons of both clam and squid are posterior.

There is no reasonable doubt that cephalopods are mollusks. Everything about their adult anatomy is molluscan: the mantle cavity with its contained gills, the siphon formed from the mantle edge, the radula, the visceral mass, even the ink sac. Their development is very

Fig. 15 – 10. Comparison of the body axes of a clam and a squid. The squid normally swims in a horizontal position with the anatomically anterior surface uppermost. (*From Pauli,* The World of Life, *Houghton Mifflin*)

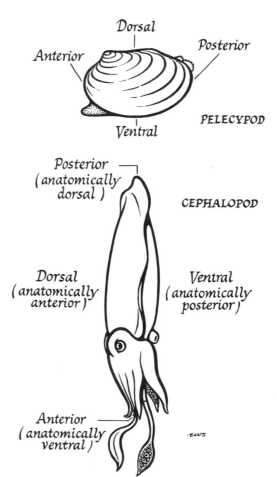

different from that of other mollusks. There is no true trochophore or other larval stage. The young develop directly into the adult form.

Living cephalopods fall into two major groups:

1. The nautilus group, Order **Tetrabranchiformes** (*tetra*, four, + *branchia*, gill), has many fossil genera but only one living genus, *Nautilus pompilius*, the pearly nautilus of song and story. It is edible and is found chiefly in the Indian and Pacific Oceans. Members of this group have four gills (two pairs), two pairs of kidneys, numerous tentacles without suckers, and a well-developed calcareous shell. The jaws are armed with a pair of chitinous bills, much like the beak of a parrot. The tongue is a radula.

2. The octopus and other octopod cephalopods, and the squids and other decapod cephalopods, Order **Dibranchiformes** (*di*, two, + *branchia*, gill), have only two gills (one pair), one pair of kidneys, eight or ten tentacles provided with powerful suction disks, and either no shell at all or a more or less reduced internal one. The mouth is always armed with a formidable parrot-like beak, and the tongue is a radula. The saliva is rich in serotonin, an amine normally present in minute amounts in vertebrate brains and other tissues, but a potent poison in large amounts. Both squids and octopuses vary in size from species a few inches long up to true giants. The paper nautilus (*Argonauta*) is a rather small octopus-like creature. The female secretes a shell as an egg case.

Fig. 15-11. *Nautilus pompilius*, the pearly nautilus of tropic seas. (*American Museum of Natural History*)

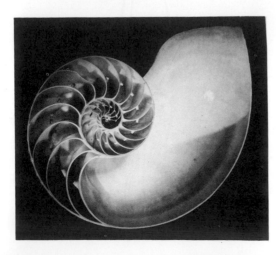

Fig. 15-12. A living octopus. Note the eyes on raised knobs. (*Douglas P. Wilson*)

FUNCTIONAL SYSTEMS OF MOLLUSKS

The organ systems of clams and other pelecypods are organized so differently from those of cephalopods that the two groups will be discussed separately.

Pelecypods. Aside from the connective tissue cells, the **skeletal system** of clams consists of a three-layered shell formed of two valves or halves. The outermost layer is a black or brown horny **periostracum** which protects the limy shell from external erosion. Once it is worn away it cannot be renewed because it can be secreted only by the mantle edge of the shell where increase in size takes place. Within the horny periostracum is a prismatic layer of tightly packed columns of calcium carbonate, and within this the layer of mother-of-pearl. This is composed of extremely thin alternating layers of calcium carbonate and horny material. It can continue to increase in thickness throughout the life of the clam, since it is immediately adjacent to the mantle. The enzymatic mechanism responsible for the secretion of the shell is currently under investigation. New information about it may throw light on the manner in which bones and egg shells are secreted.

At the upper edge of the shell is a hinge and a proteinous hinge ligament so constructed that it constantly tends to pull the shells open. The shells of most bivalves can be kept closed only by the action of muscles. This is why, at death, the shells gape.

The **muscles** which close the shells are known as **adductors,** anterior and posterior. They are short rounded columns of muscle connecting the right and left shells. A remarkable fact about them is that each muscle is really double. The crescentic region of each, toward the ends of the shell (see Fig. 15–13), is known as the locking muscle. The main part of the adductor muscle, usually pink in color, is the closing muscle. It can snap the shells shut, but rapidly fatigues. The locking muscle can close the shells only very, very slowly, but it has great strength and endurance and can hold the shell closed against the pull of the hinge ligament and the pull of enemies indefinitely. If the locking muscle is cut, the closing muscle soon tires and the shells open.

Another remarkable feature of the muscles is that they gradually change their position as the shell grows. As the shell grows longer, the muscles not only become larger but also move apart, keeping well out near the anterior and posterior ends of the shell. In adult oysters there is only one adductor muscle. It moves down the shell from the hinge as the oyster grows, and very often it is possible to see the scar of the old muscle attachment marking a path leading from the muscle back toward the hinge. The growth mechanism involved is little understood, but one is reminded of the way the interior of the long bones in man is eroded away as the marrow cavity enlarges, while at the same time new bone is deposited on the outside. The anterior and posterior **retractors** are small muscles which pull in the foot. In many species there is also a **protractor** muscle which helps extend the foot. The foot itself is muscular and is protruded in part by forcing blood into it.

The **foot** functions in digging the clam into the mud and sand and in "walking." Oysters, which have no foot, are completely stationary and usually lie stuck to a rock by the left shell. Scallops, which also lack a foot, swim vigorously by allowing the mantle cavity to fill with water and then vigorously clapping the shells

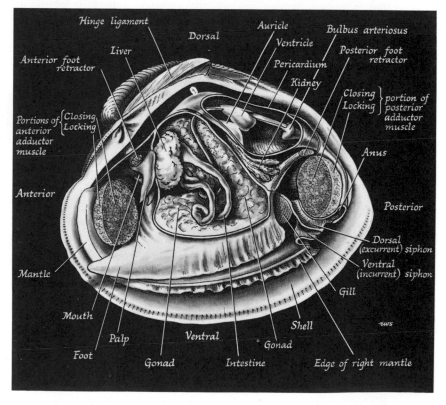

Fig. 15–13. Anatomy of a hard-shell clam or quahog. Shell, mantle, and gills of the left side have been removed.

together to squirt the water out dorsally. The single adductor muscle of the scallop is the part that serves as human food.

The **gills** of clams are their key specialization, and the respiratory, digestive, circulatory, and, in many species, reproductive systems are all tied in with the gills. The current of water pulled in through the incurrent siphon by the action of the cilia on the gills carries both dissolved oxygen and food particles. The food is entangled in cilia and mucus, passes down the gill filaments to the lower edge of the gill, and then forward in a continual stream to the mouth and into the stomach and intestine, which makes a loop or two in the visceral mass above the foot before ending near the excurrent or dorsal siphon. Near the stomach is a digestive gland, the liver, and a long blind tube opening into the stomach. This blind tube secretes a glistening, translucent rod of protein called the **crystalline style.** It is slowly pushed into the stomach and there the protein breaks up, releasing a starch-digesting enzyme. An anatomical peculiarity of the intestine of the clam is that it passes directly through the ventricle of the heart.

The slow beating of the heart may be readily observed after one shell and the mantle have been removed. The ventricle lies in a small pericardial cavity and receives blood from a right and a left auricle. The auricles receive aerated blood from the gills and mantle. From the ventricle an anterior aorta carries blood to the stomach, foot, and visceral mass, and a posterior aorta to the intestine, siphons, and mantle. Blood returning from the visceral mass passes through the kidneys, then the gills, and finally to the auricles. The blood of most mollusks contains a copper-containing protein, blue in color. It is the respiratory oxygen-carrying pigment, and is called **hemocyanin.** However, the red in the muscles of the radula is due to a hemoglobin.

The functioning of the **kidneys** has been little investigated and may be very different from that in vertebrates. However, it is worth noting as a striking triple instance of convergent evolution in a physiological trait that marine snails (prosobranchs) which live above high-tide lines where their principal source of moisture is occasional rain and spray, and the terrestrial pulmonate snails alike excrete waste nitrogen in the form of uric acid. And among vertebrates the birds, which are the most completely adapted for a life away from water, also excrete nitrogen as uric acid.

Fig. 15 – 14. Structure of a fresh-water clam.

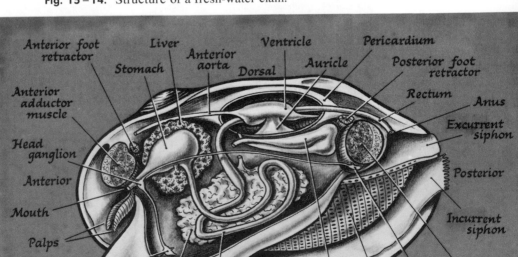

Fig. 15–15. Close-up photo of edge of shell of living scallop, *Pecten,* showing the beadlike eyes along the margin of the mantle. *(Kindness of William H. Amos)*

The **reproductive system** of clams and pelecypods generally is extremely simple and effective. A single oyster may produce 60 million eggs a year. The gonad lies in the visceral mass among the coils of the intestine. A short genital duct empties the gametes, eggs or sperms, into the mantle cavity. In many fresh-water clams and in some marine species—the European oyster, for example—the gills are used as brood sacs for the developing embryos.

The **nervous system** consists of a pair of head ganglia encircling the esophagus near the anterior adductor muscle. From the head ganglia nerve cords extend down into the foot, where there is a pedal ganglion, and also back toward the posterior adductor muscle, where there is a posterior ganglion controlling that muscle and the siphons. Probably all pelecypods have light-sensitive cells at the ends of the siphons. The best-known and certainly the most beautiful sense organs of these mollusks are the eyes which adorn the edge of the mantle of the scallop like a row of luminous pearls. The remarkable fact about these eyes is that the retina is inverted, like that in a vertebrate eye. In an inverted retina the light-sensitive nervous structures point away from the source of light. This case of convergent evolution of an anatomical trait has been discussed by several philosophers, notably Henri Bergson.

Cephalopods. In squids the **skeleton** is of two radically different kinds. The pointed body is given rigidity by an elongate bladelike structure imbedded in the upper (anatomically anterior) side of the body. In the common American *Loligo* this blade is of chitin and is popularly known as the **pen.** In *Sepia,* the European cuttlefish, it is largely calcareous. These structures are secreted by the mantle in which they lie. The other division of the skeleton is composed of cartilage and forms a kind of skull around the brain. This cartilage represents another remarkable case of convergent evolution, for its histological structure, showing pairs and quartets of cells lying scattered through a rather homogenous matrix, is like that of vertebrate cartilage. The biochemical composition of cephalopod cartilage is incompletely known, but it appears to be a complex starch bound to a protein, much like vertebrate cartilage.

Squids are covered externally by a very thin epidermis, which may be part of the reason they are so difficult to keep alive in aquariums, where they readily injure themselves. Below the epidermis are complex **chromatophores,** color-bearing structures. These make it possible for a squid to change from its customary speckled brownish pink to a livid purple within a few seconds, and just as quickly to become a pale silvery white. A freshly caught and thoroughly "frightened" squid makes a spectacular

Fig. 15–16. Molluscan eyes. *A,* eye of a limpet, *Acmaea. B,* pinhole camera eye of *Nautilus. C,* eye of a snail, *Helix,* showing lens virtually filling vitreous chamber. *D,* eye of the squid, *Sepia.* Note close resemblance in gross anatomy to the vertebrate eye. *E,* eye of the scallop, *Pecten.* The retina in *Pecten* is inverted as in vertebrates.

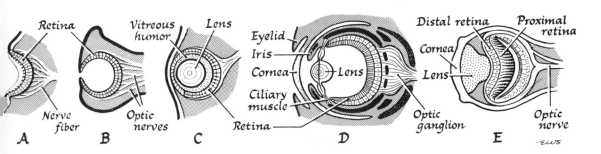

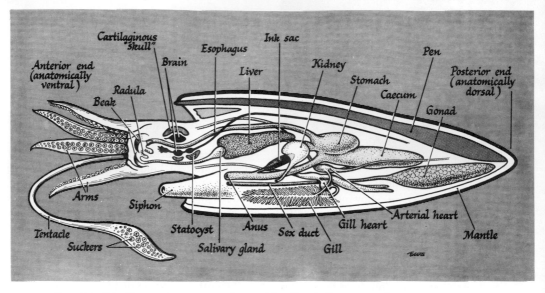

Fig. 15 – 17. General anatomy of a squid. (Semi-diagrammatic)

sight. Each chromatophore is a multicellular structure consisting of an elastic sac of pigment which can be pulled out by a dozen or more radiating muscle bands. Obviously cephalopod chromatophores are very different from the amoeboid single-cell melanophores so common among vertebrates.

The tentacles with their muscular suction disks are specialized in three general ways. One pair is much longer than the others and serves to catch crabs and other prey. The shorter arms hold the victim while it is crushed by the parrotlike beak and shredded by the radula. In adult males the lowest left arm is modified for the transfer of sperm capsules to the female. In squids the modification involves chiefly the suckers, but in some species of octopus the end of the arm is enlarged and breaks free from the body of the male with its load of sperm capsules. Hasty observers over a century ago discovered these detached arms still alive in the mantle cavities of females, and supposing them to be parasitic worms named the "worm" **hectocotylus.** The name stuck, and the lowest left arm of the mature male is still said to be hectocotylized. Hectocotylization of this arm is a secondary sexual character, since it is found only in males. Recent castration experiments show that this trait is not dependent on a hormone from the testis because hectocotylization develops fully after the gonads have been removed.

Locomotion is accomplished by two mechanisms. For ordinary swimming either forward or backward, the squid uses its lateral fins, which are muscular extensions of the mantle. In emergencies a squid is jet-propelled. The water within the mantle cavity is forcibly expelled through the siphon and causes the squid to zip through the water in the opposite direction. At the same time the squid often emits a black cloud of ink and changes color abruptly. These tactics are confusing even to man. The ink or sepia is a form of melanin.

The **digestive system** consists of a long narrow esophagus leading into a saccular stomach. The stomach opens into a large blind pouch or **caecum,** which extends out into the hind (anatomically dorsal) end of the squid. The intestine ends in the mantle cavity near the siphon, an arrangement similar to that in clams. There is a salivary gland and a liver "below" the esophagus.

The **circulatory system** consists of three hearts and a network of veins and arteries. There is a venous heart at the base of each gill which receives blood from the body and pumps it through the gill. Blood returns from the gills to the arterial heart, which is an asymmetrical muscular structure lying between the bases of the two gills. It pumps blood all over the body. In mammalian terms, this is as if we had a special heart at the root of each lung to push blood through the lung and then a third purely arterial heart which received blood from the lungs and pumped it throughout the body. The paired **kidneys** are closely applied to the great veins as they approach the gill hearts.

The **reproductive system** consists of a single gonad, which, when mature, largely fills the pointed "hind" end of the squid, and, in the male, an extremely complex system of glands which package the sperms into intricate cartridgelike capsules. These **spermatophores,** as the capsules are called, are thrust by the male into the mantle cavity or between the arms of the female. Here each spermatophore expels a sac of sperms. The sac sticks to the body of the female and slowly discharges sperms for a day or more. Females have large **nidomental** glands which secrete a jelly in which the eggs are embedded. The eggs in their jelly are pressed out through the siphon of the female and become attached in clumps of elongate "dead man's fingers" on submerged rocks.

Development is direct; the young hatch as miniature adults, although the bodily proportions are somewhat different. Like adults, newly hatched squids have a strong schooling tendency and if separated in an aquarium by stirring, will immediately close ranks again to form the school.

The **brain** consists of several large ganglia connected in a ring around the esophagus. On either side of the body, just under the inner surface of the mantle near the head, are a pair of stellate, i.e., star-shaped, ganglia. From each radiates a series of giant nerve fibers to the muscles of the mantle. These nerve fibers are so large that it was a long time before anyone suspected they could be nerves. The diameter of a single fiber is as large as an entire vertebrate nerve made up of hundreds of nerve fibers. Since their rediscovery in modern times they have become famous among neurophysiologists, because it is possible to insert a fine electrode inside a single nerve fiber and, with a second electrode on the outside, measure the electrical characteristics of the fiber as an impulse passes over it. These giant fibers conduct with extreme rapidity and thus enable impulses from the brain to reach all parts of the mantle simultaneously. The mantle then contracts rapidly and as a unit in the escape reaction, and forces out the jet stream of water.

The **eye** of a squid or octopus is closely similar to a vertebrate eye in gross anatomy. There is a transparent cornea over the front of the eye, a pigmented iris, a spheroid crystalline lens, a large vitreous chamber behind it, and a retina. There is even a cartilaginous sclerotic coat. The retina, however, is direct; that is, the light-sensitive rods face into the source of light, instead of away from it as in the scallop, *Pecten,* planarians, and vertebrates.

If various kinds of mollusks are considered, a complete evolutionary series showing the origin of complex eyes can be seen. The simplest of their eyes are merely open cuplike depressions on the heads of certain marine gastropods. The eyes of the abalone are likewise cup-shaped, but the cup is a deep goblet drawn together at the top so the opening is restricted and the cavity filled with a clear jellylike secretion. In the pearly nautilus the eye cup has only a minute opening to the exterior. Hence a clear image is focused on the retina, as in a pinhole camera. In most cephalopods, evolution has taken a different turn, and instead of a pinhole as focusing device, a crystalline lens has developed.

Within the cartilaginous skull of a squid there is a pair of **statocysts,** cavities containing a small concretion. These structures serve as sense organs of equilibration.

NATURAL HISTORY AND BEHAVIOR

In the course of their evolution mollusks have undergone a successful radiation into many diverse environments. With arthropods and vertebrates they share the conquest of the land; snails cover the land everywhere except in the driest and coldest regions. On the rain-swept islands of the south Pacific nearly every valley has its unique variety of land snail. In fact, several zoologists have speculated as to why no octopus has become terrestrial. Perhaps this is something evolution has in store for the future. In any case, inasmuch as crabs are a favorite food of the octopus, there is no obvious reason why an octopus, which can move over land, should not chase beach and land crabs, especially on small islands where such crabs swarm and octopuses lurk along the shore. Anyone who has ever watched the deadly efficiency of a "wolf pack" of squids shooting back and forth and catching the fishes attracted to a strong light held over a ship's side must have wondered why squids were not the predominant large animals of the sea, instead of fishes.

The behavior patterns of cephalopods are very imperfectly known even on the descriptive level. In his *Historia Animalium,* Aristotle over 2,000 years ago gave a partially correct account of mating in the squid, but the subject lay almost neglected until it was reinvestigated at the Woods Hole Laboratory on Cape Cod at the beginning of this century. A sexually excited female swims in a characteristically jerky manner, with peculiar trembling movements of the arms. The male swims parallel to the female with his head in the same direction as hers, occasionally spreading his arms and touching the female. The chromatophores of the male are active, especially in producing a conspicuous spot which appears and disappears at the base of each third arm. These spots are probably what are now known as "sign stimuli," and in this case are effective in influencing female behavior. There is also a good deal of blushing on the part of the male, sometimes involving the head and sometimes the entire body.

Mating is extremely rapid and is over within ten seconds or less. It is of two types. In one, described by Aristotle, the two sexes clasp each other face to face with arms intertwined. With his left fourth arm the male places the spermatophores against the skin of the female near the mouth between the bases of her arms. In the other type, not observed by the Greeks, the male grasps the female around the opening of her mantle and places the sperm cartridges within her mantle cavity. In either case, both sexes are extremely pale during clasping. The male inserts the penis into the inner end of his siphon and then pulls a bundle of spermatophores from its external end by means of his left fourth arm.

Egg-laying takes place some time later. The female partly squeezes and partly pulls out through the siphon a long pencil of soft jelly containing the eggs. This pencil is twirled between the extended arms of the female which form a closed sheath over it. During this period the eggs are fertilized from the supply of sperms near the female's mouth. The female then assumes a vertical position and attaches the egg pencil, known by coast-dwellers as a "dead man's finger," to a rock.

A revealing fact about this behavior pattern is that if the egg pencil is taken away from the female as it is extruded from the siphon, she will nevertheless go through the entire routine, including the motions of attaching a nonexistent egg mass to a rock. This rigidity of an instinctive behavior pattern, once started, is also seen in orb spiders and in many insects.

The behavior of pelecypod mollusks such as clams and oysters is near the simple end of the

Fig. 15 – 18. The two mating positions of *Loligo,* the squid.

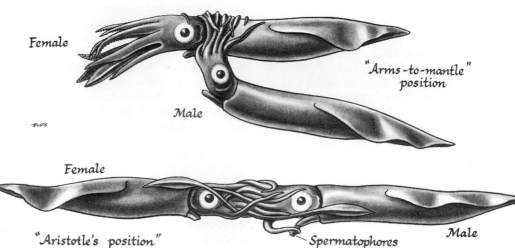

Female

"Arms-to-mantle" position

Male

Female

"Aristotle's position"   Spermatophores   Male

Fig. 15–19. Stages in squid egg-laying. Female in foreground is reaching for egg string with dorsal arms. Female in background is attaching egg string to a rock.

Egg string or "pencil"

Egg strings attached to rock... "Dead man's fingers"

spectrum of complexity. It is important for sedentary species like oysters to shed their gametes synchronously, so that eggs and sperms will meet. This is insured by two mechanisms. Oysters will not spawn until the temperature of the water reaches a certain critical level. Furthermore, the gametes give off a chemical which stimulates other individuals to spawn.

The factors which control populations of certain mollusks have been much studied. Oyster beds are complex communities of oysters and their predators and commensals or associates. Starfish and oyster drill snails eat the oysters; a species of miniature crab lives within the mantle cavity; while around, on, and boring into the shells are many kinds of protozoans, the scarlet sponge *Microciona* and the yellow boring sponge *Cliona*, a large variety of hydroids and other coelenterates, flatworms, nematodes, bryozoans, annelids, a multitude of crustaceans from tiny copepods to large crabs, and finally representatives of the chordates, the sea squirts or tunicates. The waters over the oyster bar often teem with ctenophores and teleosts. Little wonder that some overenthusiastic marine ecologists have argued in all seriousness that a natural oyster bar represents a super-organism.

Population problems of terrestrial mollusks have been less studied than those of the marine ones. The most interesting case is the attempt to control the citrus-eating snail, *Helix,* by introducing the African cannibal species, *Gonaxis.*

Fig. 15–20. Cannibal snail *Gonaxis* (left) eating the citrus snail *Helix. (Kindness of Ken Middleham)*

347

Review and References

REVIEW TOPICS

1. What is the justification for placing animals as diverse as clams, snails, and octopods in the same phylum?

2. Compare the structure of a snail and a squid.

3. How are the gross and microscopic anatomy of a clam's gills adapted for the two major functions they perform?

4. Compare the reproductive habits of a clam and an octopus. What is the explanation for the enormous difference in number of gametes produced by these two mollusks?

5. Two snails, known to be homozygous, one dextral, the other sinistral in coiling, are crossed and yield all dextral type offspring. One of these hybrid dextral males is crossed with a homozygous sinistral female. All the offspring turn out to be sinistral. Explain this result.

6. Define: radula, protandry, trochophore, epibranchial, mantle, wampum, adductor, chromatophore, torsion, pulmonate.

7. Mollusks and vertebrates have closely similar eyes, retinas, serotonin, and cartilage. How exact is this convergent evolution? How would you attempt to explain it?

8. Contrast prosobranch and opisthobranch snails in structure, reproductive habits, and economic or ecological importance.

USEFUL REFERENCES

Abbott, R. T., *American Seashells,* Princeton, N. J., D. Van Nostrand Co., 1954.

Drew, G. A., "Sexual Activities of the Squid (Loligo)," *Journal of Morphology,* vol. 22, 1911.

Morris, P. A., *A Field Guide to the Shells of Our Atlantic and Gulf Coasts,* rev. ed., Boston, Houghton Mifflin Company, 1951.

Morris, P. A., *A Field Guide to the Shells of the Pacific Coast and Hawaii,* Boston, Houghton Mifflin Company, 1952.

Pennak, R. W., *Fresh-Water Invertebrates of the United States,* New York, The Ronald Press Company, 1953.

Pratt, H. S., *A Manual of the Common Invertebrate Animals Exclusive of Insects,* Philadelphia, P. Blakiston's Son & Co., 1935.

Wilbur, K. M., and C. M. Yonge, *Physiology of Mollusca,* New York, Academic Press, 1964.

Chapter 16

Spiders, Ticks, and Other Chelicerate Arthropods

All arthropods are characterized by the following traits:

1. Jointed legs, as their name indicates *(arthron,* joint, + *pod,* leg).

2. Serial segmentation in the annelid manner. Indeed, it has been said that arthropods are essentially annelids that knew what to do with segmentation.

3. A chitinous exoskeleton. A result of this feature is the necessity for periodic molting or ecdysis during growth.

4. A protostome type of nervous system consisting of a dorsal brain or pair of cerebral ganglia, a pair of circumpharyngeal connectives around the anterior part of the gut, and a ventral nerve cord consisting of a chain of more or less fused ganglia.

5. A greatly reduced coelom and an "open" vascular system, that is, the arteries do not empty into capillaries but into intercellular cavities or hemocoels.

The chelicerate arthropods form so large and important a group, and differ so markedly from other (i.e., mandibulate) arthropods, that they are often regarded as constituting a subphylum. Among the chelicerate arthropods are to be found the famous "living fossil" *Limulus* (the horseshoe crab), the weird sea-spiders, and finally a large class of animals that includes scorpions, spiders, disease-transmitting ticks and mites, and a variety of other creatures.

Definition. This large division of the arthropods is set apart by the following traits:

1. Chelicerates lack mandibles or jaws. Instead, immediately adjacent to the mouth, is a pair of jointed appendages, the **chelicerae,** ending in claws. It is this trait that gives the group its name, Chelicerata. The lack of proper jaws able to chew seems to be related to the fact that chelicerate arthropods commonly live on liquid food which they suck up.

2. All chelicerate arthropods lack antennae.

3. As can be seen easily in a horseshoe crab or a spider, these arthropods possess only six pairs of appendages, i.e., four pairs of legs, a pair of palps (properly called **pedipalps**), and, next to the mouth, the pair of chelicerae.

Structure. The head, thorax, and abdomen of a chelicerate arthropod are not necessarily the precise equivalents of the same regions in other arthropods. Consequently careful arachnologists use the words **prosoma** for the head region, and **mesosoma** and **opisthosoma** for the thoracic and abdominal regions, respectively. However, the words head and abdomen can be used without embarrassment provided it is remembered that these terms do not denote exactly the same regions as in mandibulate arthropods. After all, head and abdomen are words of rather broad application. One speaks of the abdomen of a man or the head of a worm without implying

349

precise anatomical correspondence between man, worm, and arthropod.

In the chelicerate arthropods the head or prosoma consists of seven segments. The first bears eyes, the second the chelicerae, the third the palps, while the fourth, fifth, sixth, and seventh bear the walking legs. The thorax, or mesosoma, bears the genital opening and the gills or book lungs. The abdomen, or opisthosoma, bears no appendages (except perhaps a spine, sting, or spinnerets at its posterior end).

THE CLASS MEROSTOMATA

The merostomates are chelicerate arthropods with abdominal gills and a long spikelike **telson** (tail). This class contains *Limulus,* the horseshoe crab, and the fossil sea scorpions called eurypterids.

Limulus. The genus *Limulus* (or *Xiphosura* as some zoologists prefer to call the horseshoe crab) first appears as a fossil in the Triassic rocks dating from 175 million years ago. Its close relatives and contemporaries were the still older sea scorpions known as eurypterids. Some of these apparently formidable creatures, which have been extinct for hundreds of millions of years, grew to 9 feet long. *Limulus* continues to flourish.

Horseshoe crabs first became known to Europeans in 1590 through the writings of Thomas Harriot on the fauna and flora of Virginia. *Limulus polyphemus* L. lives in moderate abundance, plowing through the sand and mud of the continental shelf of the eastern coast of North America, from Nova Scotia to southern Mexico. Three other species live along the eastern and southern coasts of Asia. They are all bottom-feeders living on marine worms and mollusks.

Limulus is famous among biologists for several reasons. The first is its peculiar position among the arthropods, together with the fact that it has undergone virtually no evolutionary change in some 175 million years. A second notable feature is the structure and innervation of its heart, which make it favorable material for research. A third is the biochemistry of its blue blood. Finally, the eyes and optic nerves are so constructed as to make possible precise

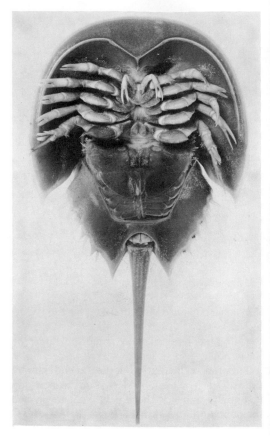

Fig. 16–1. *Limulus (Xiphosura) polyphemus.* Ventral view showing the six pairs of appendages on the cephalothorax.

investigations into the physical basis of vision. An additional advantage of *Limulus* as a research animal is that it is virtually without economic use and is therefore very inexpensive. Fortunately it can be shipped long distances, for it is able to live indefinitely out of water provided it is kept damp and cool. Evidently it would not require profound modifications for such an animal to become adapted to terrestrial life, perhaps after passing through a stage of living on tidal flats.

Evolutionary Relationships. What is *Limulus* anyway? This question has puzzled many a zoologist. For long after its discovery along the Virginia coast in 1590 it was regarded as a crustacean, as its common name of "horseshoe crab" implies. Two centuries later a French zoologist pointed out its peculiar anatomy and in 1808 created the class Xiphosura especially for *Limulus*. Twenty years later still, a German observer noted that *Limulus* possesses many traits in common with spiders and scorpions. Nevertheless *Limulus* was still placed among the Crustacea until the work of Ray Lankester (1847–1929) at the end of the last century established beyond all possible doubt its relationship to the spiders.

Unlike crustaceans, but like spiders, *Limulus* (1) possesses chelicerae, that is, claws, instead of chewing jaws, immediately adjacent to the mouth; (2) completely lacks antennae; and (3) has only six pairs of appendages—four pairs of legs, a pair of palps (pedipalps), and the pair of chelicerae. This does not take into account the gills on the abdomen, but even these leaflike structures find a counterpart in the book lungs of spiders.

The larva of *Limulus* is known as a **trilobite larva** because it bears some resemblance to a trilobite. This rather superficial resemblance is borne out by a more basic one in the *Limulus* embryo. However, trilobites possessed antennae and jaws, plus biramous appendages, so the trilobites seem much more closely related to the crustaceans and hence to the mandibulate branch of the arthropods. Perhaps trilobites, which appeared in the Cambrian Period some 500 million years ago, were ancestral to both divisions of arthropods.

Around the turn of the century Patten in the United States and Gaskell in England attempted to show that some animal resembling *Limulus* was the ancestor of the vertebrates.

THE CLASS PYCNOGONIDA

The Pycnogonida are marine chelicerate arthropods in which the abdomen is reduced to a mere knob. They are called sea-spiders. These strange, sinister-looking creatures seem to have walked slowly—they never hurry—right out of science fiction. Fortunately, most of the 500 or so living species do not average over an inch in length. They are moderately abundant in the sea, crawling over sea weed, hydroids, sea anemones, and other objects from the low-tide line down to great depths. In fact, in the abyssal zone of all the oceans at depths of a mile or

more, from the Arctic to the Antarctic, there can be found the giant sea-spider, *Colossendeis,* a pycnogonid.

What strange convergence of evolutionary factors produced these anomalous animals we can only guess. Perhaps they are adapted for living on minimal amounts of food. They certainly have the appearance of animals living in the depths of the sea, where meals are a long time apart. The loss of an abdomen has necessitated compensating modifications. The intestine has diverticula extending into the basal segments of the legs; the gonads also are located in the legs.

The eight walking legs, the chelicerae, and the palps serve to place the pycnogonids clearly in the same subphylum with the spiders and *Limulus*. Between the palps and the first pair of walking legs there is an additional pair of legs with which the males carry the eggs.

This "extra" pair of legs presents a problem for the taxonomist. The fact, all but unique in the animal kingdom, that it is the males who carry the eggs, presents a problem to both the evolutionist and the student of animal behavior.

Each pycnogonid has four minute eyes, mounted on a small mid-dorsal tubercle near the anterior end of the animal. The nervous system consists of a dorsal brain connected to a ventral chain of five ganglia. The mouth is at the end of a proboscis. There is no respiratory or excretory system. Pycnogonids are of no economic importance and their role in the general economy of the oceans appears to be a minor one.

THE CLASS ARACHNIDA

The terrestrial Arachnida—the scorpions, spiders, ticks, and their relatives—are easily the most abundant and important of the chelicerate arthropods. The spiders, of course, possess the greatest popular interest, because of their remarkable behavior patterns. But the ticks and mites are of most human importance, because many either transmit serious diseases of man and his domestic animals, or else are themselves the cause of such disease. There are a dozen or more recognized orders of arachnids, of which we will consider here only the most outstanding.

ARANEIFORMES: THE SPIDERS

The spiders compose the Order Araneiformes. Modern biological science is notable for making important advances in two very different, almost opposite, directions. One is on the biochemical level; the other is on the level of the behavior of entire animals. These two levels of organization are connected, and one of the connections is by way of the ancient science of anatomy.

Few animals show more clearly than spiders this tie-in between behavior and anatomy. Few show more undeniably the dominant role that unlearned or instinctive behavior can play in animal life. The kind of web a spider spins is as truly an innate part of the animal as the number and arrangement of its eyes. But first it is necessary to consider what spiders are and how they are put together.

Like other arachnoid (spiderlike) arthropods, spiders lack antennae and mandibles or jaws. In place of antennae, spiders use their palps as feelers. These pedipalps are leglike, six-jointed

Fig. 16–2. Face of a lycosid or wolf spider from sand dunes. Six of the eight eyes are visible above the shaggy down-hanging chelicerae at the lower ends of which the fangs can be seen. *(Kindness of W. H. Amos)*

appendages held in front of the face. In place of jaws spiders have a pair of chelicerae bearing fangs. Each of these consists of a strong, roughly cylindrical basal segment bearing a sharp, curved tooth at its end.

Posterior to the pedipalps are four pairs of legs. In all this, spiders are, in general, like other chelicerates. But unlike their close relatives—horseshoe crabs, scorpions, ticks, and the like—spiders have a distinct abdomen sharply separated from the cephalothorax by a very narrow waist. Furthermore, the spider's abdomen has no external segmentation. All other spiderlike animals, even the familiar daddy longlegs or harvestman, have a broad waist and show external abdominal segments, although ticks, which can scarcely be confused with spiders, lack abdominal segments. The characteristic specialization of spiders is, of course, the battery of **silk-producing glands** and the teatlike **spinnerets** through which the silk is extruded. The glands and the webs are described on pages 355–358. Some 20,000 species of spiders have been described.

External Anatomy. The most conspicuous external feature of the spider's cephalothorax is the set of **eight simple eyes** on the antero-dorsal angle of the head. These eyes present a striking, almost frightening, appearance when viewed with a strong light under a dissecting microscope. Moreover, they peer in various directions, so that it is impossible to look a spider in all eight eyes at once. On the under side of the cephalothorax is a breast plate or **sternum,** around which are the basal segments of the eight legs and of the palps. Between the sternum and the leg bases is a relatively thin skin. It is here that the arch enemy of spiders, the female mudwasp, inserts her sting.

On the under side of the abdomen, in the midline at the posterior tip, there is a small **anal tubercle.** Immediately anterior to it is a clump of three pairs of teatlike spinnerets. Immediately anterior to these is a small **tracheal spiracle** that permits air to enter or leave the system of **tracheae** or respiratory passages. The reproductive opening lies on the midline of the under side of the abdomen, up near the cephalothorax. In females this opening is covered by a chitinous plate, the **epigynum,** of

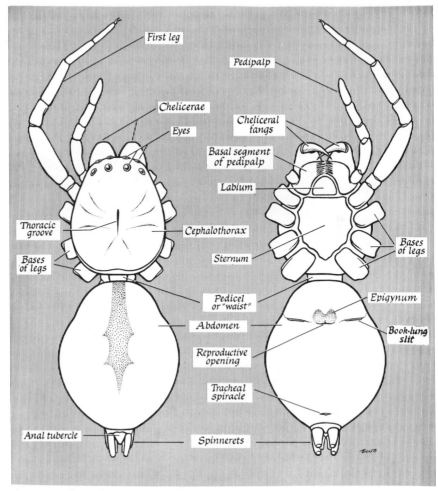

Fig. 16-3. External anatomy of a spider. Left: dorsal view. Right: ventral view.

First leg
Pedipalp
Chelicerae
Eyes
Cheliceral fangs
Basal segment of pedipalp
Labium
Thoracic groove
Cephalothorax
Bases of legs
Sternum
Bases of legs
Pedicel or "waist"
Epigynum
Abdomen
Book-lung slit
Reproductive opening
Tracheal spiracle
Anal tubercle
Spinnerets

various and, in some species, complicated design. On either side of the reproductive opening lie the openings of the book lungs. Even apparently smooth spiders like the black widow are covered with fine hairs. Each hair is said to have its own nerve fiber!

Internal Anatomy. The internal anatomy of spiders is similar to that of other arthropods. In the head are poison glands, probably modified salivary glands. The "saliva" they secrete contains a neurotoxin, or, in some cases, a hemotoxin that destroys red blood cells. Fortunately, of some 20,000 described species, very, very few have enough of either type of poison to produce more than a slight irritation in a human being. In the United States virtually the only spider at all dangerous is the famous black widow, *Latrodectus mactans.* Although its venom is about 15 times as toxic on a dry weight basis as prairie rattlesnake toxin, so little is injected by a spider that fatalities are extremely rare. Most of the deaths are of small children. Similar black-and-red species of *Latrodectus* are found in most warm countries around the Mediterranean, across Iran and southern Asia, in the East Indies and beyond to New Zealand.

The various hairy wolf spiders, or lycosids, including the tarantulas, have a vicious reputation. However, none in North America is very poisonous, and there are many reasons to doubt that the original tarantula, the local wolf spider of Taranto in southern Italy, is responsible for the dancing mania attributed to it. In fact, there is evidence that the type of group dancing

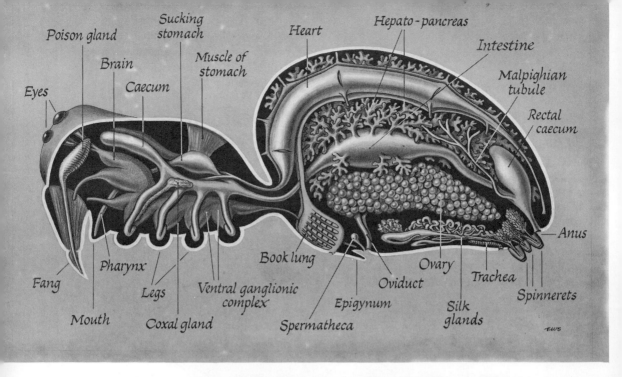

Fig. 16-4. Internal anatomy of a female spider. (Semi-diagrammatic)

found in the area can be traced back to pre-Christian religious rites. Various volunteers bitten by these spiders experienced symptoms similar to but less intense than from a bee sting. In tropical South America there is a *Lycosa* whose bite may produce a nasty sore.

The pharynx and stomach of a spider are beautifully constructed as sucking devices. The tubular pharynx and esophagus have heavy reinforced walls which prevent their collapse when the internal pressure is reduced. The walls of the stomach are provided with stiff plates attached by muscles to the walls of the cephalothorax. Clearly, when these muscles contract, the walls of the stomach are pulled apart so as to enlarge its lumen and thus create the low pressure which sucks in the juices of the spider's victims. Surrounding the intestine is a large, branched **hepato-pancreas**, a digestive gland similar to that of the crustaceans.

Spiders enjoy a double respiratory system. Like insects they possess **tracheae.** In addition, recessed into the antero-ventral part of the abdomen is a pair of **book lungs.** Each of these consists of a series of platelets something like the leaves of a book set within a recess in the under surface of the abdomen. The structure suggests the gill flaps found on the ventral side of *Limulus.*

The excretory system is likewise double. In the abdomen are **Malpighian tubules** similar to those of insects. In the cephalothorax is a pair of **coxal glands** opening at the bases of the first pair of legs. Such glands are at least reminiscent of the excretory "green" glands in the heads of crayfish. The heart is a long tubular structure dorsally placed in the abdomen, and is reminiscent of the heart in the horseshoe crab.

The female reproductive system consists of a pair of large ovaries with a short oviduct and uterus ending just above the epigynum. There also is a spherical **spermatheca** where sperms are stored. Each ovary may produce up to 250 eggs. The male gonads consist of a pair of long tubular testes, each with a vas deferens. These unite to open at the genital aperture.

There is a complex nervous system consisting of a bi-lobed ganglion or brain above the esophagus. The brain is connected by a thick pair of nerves to a very large ventral complex of ganglia. Nerves run from this ventral complex into the abdomen, but there is no ventral ganglionic chain as in more primitive arthropods. It is worthy of note that a similar if less extreme concentration of the nervous system has evolved independently in the social insects such as bees. The eyes and the sensitive hairs have already been described.

The Spider's Web. The battery of **silk-producing glands** found within a spider's abdomen is extraordinary.

1. Two large **ampulliform glands** *(ampulla,* flask) secrete the famous drag line that web-making spiders habitually spin out after them wherever they go. It is used also to construct the frame, the guy-lines, and the spokes of an orb web. That spiders produce such a non-sticky, dry line was not known until 1890, when a student of spiders named Warburton discovered it. This is certainly one of that long list of discoveries that could have been made by the ancient Greeks. No microscope or other apparatus unavailable to them would have been necessary.

2. There are many, up to 200, small pear-shaped or **pyriform glands** which secrete a silk that acts as a glue. It is used to anchor the dry drag line when a spider drops from the ceiling to the floor, or to cement together the framework of the web.

3. There are from ten to several hundred small, round or **aciniform glands** closely adjacent to the pyriform glands. They secrete the silk that forms the elastic spiral lines of an orb weaver's web and also swathing bands thrown around a struggling insect caught in the web.

4. **Cylindrical glands** secrete a special silk used in wrapping the eggs in a cocoon.

5. In the orb weavers and several other spiders, aggregate or **arboriform glands** secrete a type of silk that does not harden upon contact with air but remains as viscid drops along the lines of the webs.

6. Spiders having a special comblike device, called a **cribellum,** for spreading out swathing bands of silk also have special silk glands which supply the cribellum.

Chemically the silk is a protein, secreted as a liquid, which hardens in the air. Spider silk is used for dividing lines in optical instruments like transits because it is exceedingly fine and strong and of uniform diameter. A reel of 1500 cm, approximately 50 feet, sells for about $20.

Behavior and Anatomy. No one will deny that the structure of an animal is inherited. In spiders it is evident (1) that behavior patterns are also inherited, and (2) that the structure of a spider and its behavior fit each other as a hand fits a glove.

Most spiders die in the fall. They leave behind them masses of eggs neatly protected inside waterproof silk cocoons. These silken bags can easily be found hanging near the site of the mother's old web. By the time the spiderlings emerge by the hundreds the following spring, the winter's storms have destroyed the old web. The spiderlings have never seen a

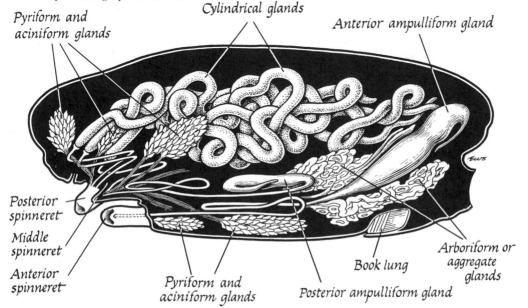

Fig. 16−5. Silk glands and spinnerets of the left half of the abdomen of the orb weaver spider, *Argiope aurantia.*

Pyriform and aciniform glands

Cylindrical glands

Anterior ampulliform gland

Posterior spinneret

Middle spinneret

Anterior spinneret

Pyriform and aciniform glands

Book lung

Posterior ampulliform gland

Arboriform or aggregate glands

spider's web. Much less have they had a chance to study the complexities of construction methods. They have never witnessed so much as a fly snared, trussed up, injected with poison, and carried away to a lair. They have never observed the intricacies of that dangerous business (dangerous, that is, for the male), spider courtship and mating. In brief, they have never seen another spider. The eyesight of many spiders is so poor and their mode of living so solitary that the chances are high that, once the brood swarm has dispersed, the majority of spiders will never see another spider until the time of mating.

Nevertheless, as these spiders grow up, their behavior is predictable, as predictable as the number of molts they will undergo. In most web-making species the infant spiders climb to the top of some object, a fence post or a blade of grass, turn so that they face into the wind, and then spin out into the breeze a long silk thread. As the silk strand becomes longer it pulls more and more on the tiny spider until, like a small boy hanging onto a kite string he can no longer control, the spiderling goes sailing off into the wide world. Large flights of such ballooning infant spiders are often responsible for the glistening sheets of gossamer that are sometimes seen in the air or draped over shrubs in meadows. For this first important act after hatching from the cocoon, there are probably very few essential components. First, a "drive," a "desire" to climb upwards. Perhaps this tendency should be described as a "negative geotaxis." Second is a turning to face into the wind. The third essential is the spinning of the thread of silk.

The kind of web each spider will construct, once established in a suitable spot, can again be predicted if the species of spider is known. The various orb weavers inevitably construct the type of web familiar on the covers of mystery stories. The funnel spiders always construct a horizontal platform, perhaps in the corner of a window ledge or on the grass. Down from one side of this platform runs the tunnel at the bottom of which lurks the owner of the web. It is even possible to make a shrewd bet as to the genus of the spider by noting the web's location. If it is on a hedge or in grass, the spider responsible will be *Agelena;* if it is in a corner

of your cellar, the spider will be *Tegenaria.* But if the spider is some species of *Theridion,* the housewife's spider, it is as inconceivable that it construct either an orb or a funnel web as that a cow should lay an egg. Instead, in some convenient place, under a chair or where walls and ceiling meet, a member of the genus *Theridion* will make a very loose, irregular, tangled web of no apparent design. One of the most remarkable and beautiful is the web of a common spider of shady woods, *Linyphia.* This spider makes a handsome dome or inverted bowl about the size of a man's cupped hand. And so it is with each kind of spider. Different species of orb weavers reveal themselves by slight but characteristic differences in the orbs they make. (See Fig. 32–3.) If you know the kind of spider, you can predict the web. If you know the web, you can tell what spider spun it—spun it out of its own inner nature—in a not too fanciful sense, out of its own chromosomes.

The dramatic correlation between anatomy and behavior can easily be seen by comparing a wolf spider like the common *Lycosa* with an orb weaver like the yellow and black garden spider, *Argiope.* The wolf spider, which does not catch its victims in a web but walks on the ground stalking its prey, has large eyes. *Argiope,* which lives in a web (and merely waits until the tugging on the silk signals that a victim has been caught), has, by contrast, very small eyes scarcely visible without a magnifying lens. The legs of a wolf spider are robust and muscular, very different from the long thin legs of *Argiope,* which are not adapted for running and jumping over rough terrain and holding struggling prey but rather for running delicately over the spokes of a web. The color of the body of each fits its mode of life. The bright yellow and black garden spider looks enough like a flower to mislead insects, at least sufficiently for some to fly into the web. The grays, browns, and blacks of the hairy lycosids help them blend into their background and so serve the same function as the stripes of a tiger which help it disappear into the sunlight and shadows of the jungle.

Both wolves and orb weavers among spiders contrast markedly with the crab spiders in behavior and, as is to be expected, in structure. These spiders do not stalk their prey, neither do

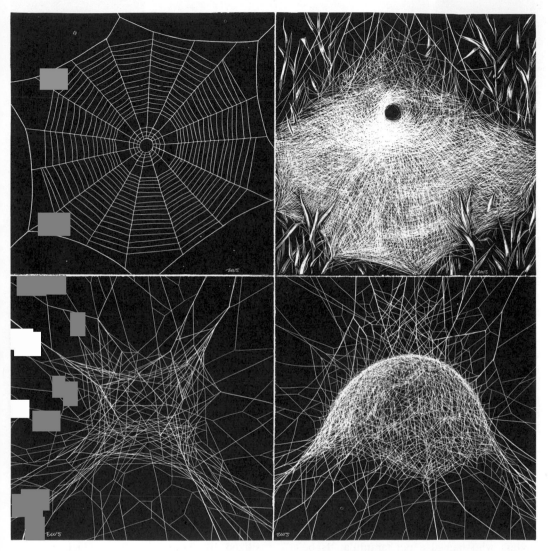

Fig. 16–6. Four types of webs. Above: orb of *Tetragnatha*; funnel of *Agelena*. Below: three-dimensional mesh of *Theridion*; dome of *Linyphia*.

they spin a snare. Instead they climb to a brightly colored flower, where they take up a position waiting to pounce on any insect that pays a visit. Untaught, they not only wait on a flower, they hold their long legs far to each side so as to give them a crablike appearance and prepare them to grasp their food. Most spiders are dark in coloration, but the crab spiders wear bright colors—white, lemon yellow, or orange. For a hunter that lurks in flowers, the advantage of this coloration is again obvious.

Two areas of very intimate correlation between spider anatomy and behavior concern web-making and reproduction. The construction of an orb web regularly follows a set pattern. First (Fig. 16–7), the framework is laid down. This is made of dry silk from the big ampulliform glands. The framework is glued in place by secretions from the pyriform silk glands. Second, the radii are put in. These are also of nonadhesive dry line glued to the frame. Third, the spider constructs a small inner spiral

Fig. 16–7. Four stages in the construction of an orb web.

that acts as a scaffold to give some solidity to the spokes while the spider puts on, fourth, the definitive or main spiral. This spiral is not of dry line but of highly elastic silk spun from the hundreds of little aciniform glands. Moreover, it is covered, as it is spun out, by a sticky silk solution from the aggregate glands. Finally, a garden spider like *Argiope* will make a zigzag band of silk over the center of the orb where the spider will take up its post, in the orthodox spider position, head down.

Concerning the series of stimuli and responses that produce this true marvel of nature we know almost nothing. There are other questions to which we have only partial answers or none at all. How does a spider keep from becoming caught in its own web? This one is easy—it is "careful" to step on the dry line radii, not the sticky and elastic spirals! The question is still with us: How is an untaught spider so clever—?

Reproductive Behavior. The sex of a spider is extremely difficult to discover until after the final molt. Indeed, there is a story (a true one) about one of the world's leading authorities on spiders who named a pet tarantula "Isabella" in honor of one of his students. After the tarantula's final molt it became necessary to change its name to "Ferdinand." After the final molt, a male spider is conspicuous because of a complex bulbular apparatus on the end of its palps. Any spider that looks as though it were wearing boxing gloves is a mature male. The bulbous palps can be seen in Figure 16–8.

Before mating the male spins a small flat web on which he deposits a drop of semen. He then turns around and carefully fills the bulbs on the ends of his palps with this sperm-laden fluid. Thus equipped, he sets out seeking a female. Male spiders have a number of signs which act as stimuli for the female, conveying the "information" that here is a potential mate, not a meal. Some species signal the female by fantastic posturings with the legs. Other males begin by striking the female with their legs, while in still other species the males commence by tentatively and gingerly touching the tip of one of the female's legs. Many orb weavers begin by tweaking the web of the female. In some species the males may live in the same web with the females, who accept the advances of the males readily. In other species males are very likely to be eaten by the females, if not before mating, then afterwards.

In the act of copulation, if in spiders it can be called that, the male places the seminal bulb at the end of his palp against the epigynum at the genital opening of the female. Here the transfer of sperms takes place. Figure 16–8 shows four of the six or more mating positions. Most positions are not "optional" but characteristic of the species.

Enemies of the Spider. Spiders are eaten by various birds, shrews, frogs, toads, and other animals, including other spiders. They are parasitized by ichneumon flies, which lay their eggs on the spider. The eggs then hatch into grubs that proceed to grow fat on the body fluids of the host.

Probably the most serious enemies of spiders are the solitary mud wasps. In fact, one of the most convenient ways to collect spiders is to break open the mud nests of these wasps. A single mud nest on the side of an old barn may contain from 10 to 100 or more paralyzed spiders. The way a wasp overcomes a tarantula much larger than itself has been very carefully studied. The wasp sees well; the spider at best has poor eyesight. The wasp stands in front of the spider, touches it lightly, induces the spider

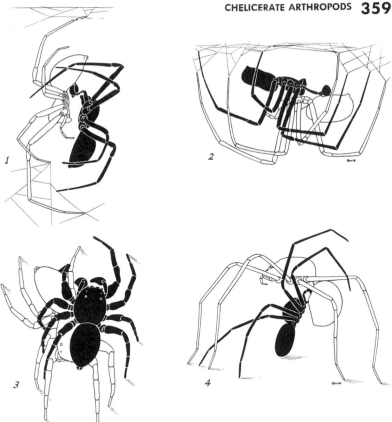

Fig. 16–8. Four of the mating positions in spiders. The black figures represent the males; the outlined ones, the females. 1, *Chiracanthium*. 2, *Linyphia*. 3, *Phidippus*, 4, *Scytodes*. (*After J. B. Kaston*)

to "stand on its toes," dives under the spider, and touches it from behind. Some investigators have thought the wasp gives the spider false mating signals. In any case, it must all be very confusing for the spider, which in the end gets a paralyzing sting on the under side in the soft place between its sternum and the leg bases.

Wasps catch web spiders by flying into the web. If the spider doesn't rush to the wasp at once, the wasp moves slightly. When the spider approaches close enough, the wasp grasps it and flies off. Once the spider is safely paralyzed and within the mud nest, the wasp lays an egg on the unfortunate arachnid which is doomed to provide fresh food for the wasp larva. From beginning to end this wasp-spider relationship is another remarkable instance of a complex, unlearned behavior pattern.

Fig. 16–9. Mud wasp, *Sceliphron cementarium*, with captive spider just paralyzed. (*Kindness of W. H. Amos*)

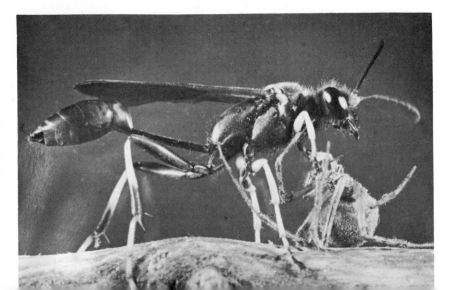

SCORPIOIDIFORMES: THE SCORPIONS

Structure. The scorpions, members of the Order Scorpioidiformes, are arachnids in which the abdomen forms a tail bearing a terminal sting. Scorpions have attracted human attention from remotest antiquity. Indeed, the scorpion is one of the signs of the zodiac. There is no mistaking a scorpion, with its long tail-like post-abdomen tipped by a sting, and its large clawed pedipalps. In fact, the pedipalps give the scorpion a lobsterlike appearance.

The legs and other appendages of scorpions bear a one-to-one correspondence with those of both the horseshoe crab and the spiders. It is the relative size and shape that differ. Scorpions even crush their food with specialized bases of their legs, the so-called **gnathobases,** much as *Limulus* does. A unique feature of scorpions is a conspicuous pair of combs or **pectines** on the under side just posterior to the last pair of legs. The function of these structures is little known. Jean Henri Fabre (1823–1915), who kept a group of scorpions enclosed in his garden, believed the pectines helped steady scorpions during their mating, but the evidence was insufficient. Most contemporary students believe the pectines have some sensory function. Also prominent are the **stigmata,** or openings into the gillbooks; a pair is found on the under side of the anterior abdominal segments.

Distribution and Varieties. Of the forty-odd species of scorpions found in the United States, only two are dangerous to man, though most can deliver a nasty sting. The two dangerous ones are *Centruroides sculpturatus* and *Centruroides gertschi.* Both are found principally in southern Arizona. Both inject a neurotoxin with an effect similar to that of strychnine. In Egypt and other tropical or semi-tropical countries there are species virulent and common enough to have made the development of an antitoxin a medical necessity. Although most of the 500 known species of scorpions inhabit warm climates, one North American species (*Vejovis boreus*) extends its range into North Dakota. The largest American scorpion, *Hadrurus hirsutus,* attains a length up to about 5 inches. Fortunately this species is not especially poisonous.

Behavior. The known behavior of scorpions centers on eating and reproduction. Most of their hunting is done at dusk or during the night. Insects and spiders are caught by the big claws of the pedipalps, torn, and crushed, while the body juices are sucked up. In tearing and crushing with the gnathobases of the legs, scorpions resemble *Limulus;* in sucking the body juices of their prey, they resemble spiders. Thus is the behavior of an animal correlated with its anatomy and so in turn with its taxonomic position. The scorpion stings very large

Fig. 16–10. A scorpion. (*Kindness of P. S. Tice*)

prey by whipping its abdomen up over the back and down onto the victim as it struggles to escape from the clawed pedipalps.

Mating is preceded by a "formal" dance. The male grasps the big claws of the female in his own. The pair may advance and retreat several times, pull each other back and forth and roundabout, seeming to fence the while with their tails crossing each other high over their backs. Finally they find protection under a rock or other object where copulation takes place. The female then usually kills and eats the male and thus insures his maximum contribution to the development of his offspring. The eggs hatch within the female, and the young when born climb on their mother's back, where they remain for a week or so until their first molt. This is also true of the wolf spider, *Lycosa,* and of the opossum. Recently there has been a revival of speculation about such similarities of behavior. What is the nature of the connection between them? Homology? Analogy? Convergent evolution? Or is there no meaningful connection at all?

ACARINIFORMES: THE TICKS AND MITES

The Order Acariniformes includes the ticks and mites, arachnids in which head, thorax, and abdomen are fused into an unsegmented ovoid. The direct human importance of ticks and mites is so great and the number of known species so large (at least 15,000) that their study has been given a special name, **acarology.** Their importance derives from the fact that some ticks and mites transmit the microbes responsible for serious diseases, and that many species of mites are themselves serious and sometimes fatal parasites of plants, animals, and man. There is even a particular mite that ruins cheese.

Despite their small or even minute size, ticks and mites can be readily identified by their eight legs and ovoid unsegmented body. It is surprising to note, however, that the egg hatches into a six-legged larva which does not develop eight legs until its first molt.

Diseases. The most famous of the diseases transmitted by the bite of a tick, and in this sense caused by it, is Texas cattle fever. The discovery that Texas cattle fever is tick-borne

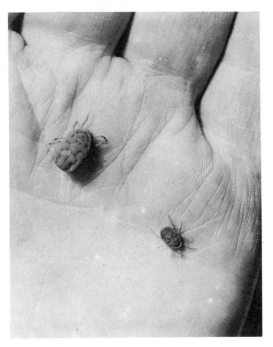

Fig. 16–11. Ticks, carriers of relapsing fever, tularemia, and other diseases. *(Science Service)*

was made in 1893 by Theobald Smith (1859–1934), then of the U.S. Department of Agriculture. This was an epoch-making discovery, for it was the first time that an arthropod had been found to transmit a disease. After Smith's work, Ronald Ross demonstrated that malaria was transmitted by the bite of a certain species of mosquito (see pages 92–95), and then Walter Reed and his research team showed a similar situation for yellow fever.

The tick that transmits Texas cattle fever is *Margaropus annulatus* (also known as *Boophilis bovis*). The causative agent is a sporozoan, *Babesia bigemina,* that lives in red blood cells and appears somewhat like the malarial parasite. Spotted fever in man, often called Rocky Mountain spotted fever although it occurs in most parts of the United States, is transmitted by both the dog tick, *Dermacentor variabilis,* and by Anderson's tick, *Dermacentor andersoni.* The causative agent is a **rickettsia,** i.e., an intracellular viruslike organism, and one closely allied to that which causes typhus fever.

Among human diseases transmitted by acarids are the following:

1. Spotted (Rocky Mountain) fever, mentioned above.

2. Scrub typhus, or tsutsu-gamushi disease. This fever was responsible for over 7,000 American casualties in the South Pacific region during World War II. How prevalent it is among the natives of this area is unknown. The acarid responsible is a minute "chigger," *Trombicula,* which harbors the rickettsial organisms.

3. Tularemia or rabbit fever. The bacterium causing this disease is transmitted not only by the common ticks *Dermacentor variabilis* and *D. andersoni* but also by the bites of fleas, lice, and horseflies.

4. A central American relapsing (recurrent) fever and a similar though different relapsing fever in Africa.

5. Oroya and Verruga fevers. These are probably two forms of a disease due to the same agent. The fevers have been scourges in Peru from ancient times.

6. St. Louis encephalitis. The virus of this disease has been recovered from chick and pigeon mites.

The damage done to man and domestic animals by the direct action of mites is large.

1. Chiggers. These are usually the larvae of mites of the *Trombicula* group, barely visible as minute red dots. Some persons are immune, but in others a blister several inches in diameter may be raised at the place of the bite. In most persons chiggers produce red welts with excruciating itching. They are a nasty problem for campers, sportsmen, troops on maneuvers, and persons whose employment takes them into woods and fields in summertime.

2. Mange in dogs, cats, and other animals. This skin disease is due to the activities of female mites of the genus *Sarcoptes.* The fertilized females burrow into the skin and eat a small tunnel in which they lay a succession of eggs. Several species are said to be characteristic of certain hosts, e.g., man, hog, dog, cat. In Australia there is a serious sheep mange due to a trombiculid mite something like a chigger.

3. Poultry mites. There are a number of different mites that attack chickens, turkeys, pigeons, and other birds. *Dermanyssus gallinae* (discovered by DeGeer in 1778) is the most important and is world-wide in distribution. When present in enormous numbers, they can cause the death of the bird and can easily lower egg production in hens. A trick of their behavior, which also allows a method of control, is that these mites attack almost entirely at night. During the day they leave the host and may be found in cracks and crevices on the under sides of perches, in nesting boxes, and similar locations. Consequently they can be controlled merely by regularly painting these locations in the daytime with waste oil or some other insecticide. An interesting case recorded by Baker and Wharton is that of a household where a baby was being attacked; in the same house an electric clock was heavily infested. Presumably the mites had been attracted by the warmth of the clock.

The reason for attraction to a warm object is obvious enough in any parasite of a warm-blooded host. But how could the curious habit of leaving the host bird during the day have arisen in the course of evolution? What meaning does it have in terms of the mites' life? No such behavior could become established except with a host that returned often to the same roost. One might venture the guess that mites (among other things) are what the dust baths of birds are about. Leaving the bird in the daytime would allow the mite to escape the bath.

4. Numerous other mites attack other animals and animal products. There are mites that infest the insides of the ears of dogs, that parasitize houseflies, that live on potato beetles, that attack cheese, leather, and other substances of animal origin.

5. A long list of mites attack useful plants. *Tetranychus* and its relatives are the common spider mites, so-called because they spin out silk. The silk is emitted from an opening near the mouth. Under certain conditions a heavily infested plant may have its leaves covered with cobweb from mites. Spider mites are especially injurious to fruit trees, both citrus and deciduous ones like the apple, peach, plum, etc., but are extremely catholic in taste and will use their chelicerae to pierce the leaves of almost any plant, from cotton to peas, in order to suck the juices. Some species lay so many red eggs that wintering twigs look red. Other species overwinter as larvae or adults. The adult is often

rcd, but may be green, yellow, orange, or brown. Spider mites are very small, averaging less than half a millimeter in length.

Lastly, the water mites (hydrachnids) should be mentioned, because they are a large assemblage of species and are commonly observed swimming in and around water weeds in fresh-water ponds, lakes, and slow streams. Though small, they are large enough to be noticeable on account of their vivid scarlet, yellow, or other colors. They have the distinction of being the only arachnids that have colonized fresh water. They are predacious and parasitic, attacking small crustaceans, the larvae of aquatic insects, aquatic worms, and, in some species, dead animals. Not rigidly conditioned by temperature, they are active the year round even under the ice.

Anatomy. Ticks and mites both possess a typical arachnid anatomy. They differ from each other largely in size. Ticks are larger. They possess the customary four pairs of walking legs, the pair of palps, and the pair of chelicerae. Like most arachnids, mites and ticks suck liquid food. Even species that eat something as dry as feathers are thought to suck up tiny bits in their own saliva.

Although head, thorax, and abdomen are fused into an unsegmented globular or ovoid mass, the most anterior part of what corresponds to the head in most arthropods is more or less marked off from the rest of the body. It bears the palps and chelicerae, which may or may not bear claws, and is referred to as the **gnathosoma.** On some species of ticks the female bears a shield or **scutum** that covers the anterior third or so of her back. The male either lacks such a shield or it covers his entire back.

Most mites have a muscular (sucking) pharynx and a long, thin, tubular esophagus. In all but the very smallest species, respiration is through spiracles or **stigmata** opening into tracheae. According to the suborder, there are one, two, or four pairs of stigmata.

The central nervous system consists of a consolidated ganglionic mass (the "brain") surrounding the esophagus. From it nerves extend to the chelicerae, palps, eyes, legs, and other parts of the body. The eyes, of which there may be four or more, are tiny and probably detect merely the degree of light. Numerous sensory hairs, some of specialized structure, are present.

Ticks carry a **Haller's organ** on each tarsal segment of the first pair of legs. These are rounded depressions containing specialized hairs and are partially covered with a thin membrane. It is believed that Haller's organs help ticks find their hosts.

Life History. The eggs of ticks and mites hatch into six-legged larvae. After feeding, these molt into the nymphs. This first molt is followed by two more, producing larger nymphs, and a final one giving the adult: total, four molts and five instars or stages. In all but a few varieties the nymphs closely resemble the adults. One or more nymphal instars may be omitted in some species, and other variations occur also.

The full life history has been carefully worked out for the common dog tick, *Dermacentor variabilis.* The egg hatches into the usual six-legged larva, in this case called a **seed tick.** This stage feeds on small mammals, possibly field mice. When replete with blood from the rodent, it drops to the ground and molts into a nymph with eight legs. The nymph feeds on a larger mammal, drops off, and molts into the adult. The adult climbs high up on a stalk of grass or on a shrub, holds on with its third pair of legs, and extends its first pair with the Haller's organs, either to catch the odor or perhaps sense the warmth of some passing mammal. The second and fourth pairs of legs are also extended to aid in attaching the tick to a suitable passing host. That ticks are not very discriminating is shown by the effectiveness of one of the standard techniques for collecting them—just drag a white woolen blanket slowly over grass and bushes.

There is no special stage in which ticks overwinter.

The life histories of other ticks and mites are similar to that just described. In some species one of the nymphal stages is adapted for clinging to an insect, a millipede, or even a piece of dust. Such a stage is called a **hypopus,** may last up to two weeks, and serves to identify the species.

Fig. 16-12. A terrestrial mite, much enlarged. *(Kindness of P. S. Tice)*

Mites live in almost every conceivable ecological niche, from the reindeer moss of the polar regions to the tropical rain forests. Under the bark of an oak, in the flour barrel, on the fruit fly *Drosophila,* between the gills of mushrooms, on the gardener's tulip bulbs, in the florist's greenhouse as on the rancher's cattle, almost everywhere some species of mite has found itself a home.

ARACHNIDA: MISCELLANEOUS ORDERS

In addition to the spiders, the scorpions, and the ticks and mites, there are some ten additional, less important orders of arachnids. Three will be briefly considered.

1. The **Opilioniformes,** composed of the daddy longlegs or harvestmen, is probably the most widely known of the minor orders. Even without a hand lens it is easy to see the orthodox arachnid traits, especially the eight legs, the pair of palps, and the chelicerae which bear claws. Of course, there are no antennae. The segmentation of the abdomen can be clearly distinguished. Their food consists of small insects, spiders, mites, and the like, or, in an emergency, plant juices. The role of the daddy longlegs in the economy of nature cannot be very great. Strange as it may seem in such innocuous and apparently effete creatures, the males are said to fight fiercely for the females every autumn. They spin no webs and merely deposit their eggs in crevices.

2. The **Solifugiformes,** made up of the wind scorpions, is a small order of arachnids found in most of the warmer parts of the world. In the United States its range extends from Florida to California and north into Kansas and Colorado. In general appearance the solifuges resemble hairy spiders with ten legs and segmented, elongate abdomens. They frequent sandy places, where they become active at dusk and are greatly feared, partly, no doubt, because of their extremely hairy, spiderlike appearance and their lightning-fast movement. They are extremely dangerous, but only if you are less than an inch long. They have no poison but crush and tear their prey with their immense pair of clawed chelicerae.

The appearance of ten legs results from the large size and leglike structure of the palps. Attached to the under side of the proximal three segments of each of the most posterior legs is a row of conspicuous fan-shaped "**raquet organs,**" a total of five on each leg. Their function is unknown. The numerous long hairs covering the body and appendages are sensory. The eyes are extremely small. Both these anatomical traits seem fitted for the nocturnal life of the animal.

3. The **Pseudoscorpioidiformes,** or pseudoscorpions, resemble their venomous namesakes except that the posterior part of the abdomen is not elongated into a thin tail with a sting at its end. Biologically one of the most interesting facts about pseudoscorpions is that they produce silk, which they spin out from the movable finger of each chelicera. The silk is used to make "nests" in which the animal retires to molt or hibernate. Most are small.

Pseudoscorpions are retiring in disposition and live among old books and furniture, under bark, leaves, or stones. There they feed on small insects or unresisting larvae.

Review and References

REVIEW TOPICS

1. How do chelicerate differ from mandibulate arthropods?

2. In what ways is *Limulus* more like a spider than a crab? What is scientifically notable about *Limulus?*

3. How are the color and the external and internal anatomy of spiders correlated with their methods of catching their prey? Of reproducing?

4. What different kinds of webs do spiders spin and how do they construct them?

5. How is it possible to know that stereotyped inherited behavior patterns are predominant in the lives of spiders? Document your answer.

6. What human and animal diseases are transmitted by ticks and mites? What is the causative agent of each disease?

7. What direct damage is caused by mites to plants, animals, and man?

8. When first hatched, ticks possess only three pairs of legs. What structures would you look for to distinguish newly hatched ticks from insects?

9. What is the life history of a dog tick, *Dermacentor variabilis*?

10. What anatomical traits mark daddy longlegs (harvestmen) as chelicerates? Distinguish them from spiders.

USEFUL REFERENCES

Baker, E. W., and G. W. Wharton, *An Introduction to Acarology,* New York, the Macmillan Company, 1952.

Cloudsley-Thompson, J. L., *Spiders, Scorpions, Centipedes, and Mites,* New York, Pergamon Press, 1958.

Fabre, J. H., *The Life of the Scorpion,* trans. A. T. de Mattos and B. Miall, New York, Dodd, Mead & Co., 1923.

Savory, T. H., *The Arachnida,* London, Edward Arnold and Company, 1935.

Snodgrass, R. E., *A Textbook of Arthropod Anatomy,* Ithaca, N. Y., Cornell University Press, 1952.

Spiders:

Comstock, J. H., *The Spider Book,* rev. and ed. W. J. Gertsch, Ithaca, N. Y., Comstock Publishing Associates, 1948.

Crompton, J., *The Life of the Spider,* Boston, Houghton Mifflin Company, 1950.

Fabre, J. H., *The Life of the Spider,* New York, Dodd, Mead & Co., 1913.

Gertsch, W. J., *American Spiders,* New York, D. Van Nostrand Co., 1949.

Kaston, B. J. and E., *How to Know Spiders,* Dubuque, Iowa, William C. Brown Company, 1953.

Savory, T. H., *The Spider's Web,* New York, Frederick Warne & Co., 1952.

Woodson, T., *The Black Widow Spider,* Chapel Hill, Univ. of North Carolina Press, 1945.

Chapter 17

Crustaceans, Insects, and Other Mandibulate Arthropods

The mandibulate arthropods are the most important group of animals after the vertebrates, and are certainly the largest group that exists with the possible exception of the nematodes. The insects alone account for over 700,000 described species, and other mandibulate arthropods for some 35,000 more, most of which are crustaceans.

The economic damage inflicted by these arthropods, chiefly the insects, is staggering. The U.S. Department of Agriculture estimates that the loss due to grasshoppers alone has amounted in the United States to over $100 million annually in years when control measures have been neglected. Loss from the tobacco worm (moth larva) averages around $80 million a year, and from the European corn borer (also a moth) to $350 million a year, although these figures have recently been drastically cut by control measures. No crop—from onions to forest trees—is immune. To all this must be added the substantial losses caused by various cattle and sheep flies which have maggot stages that live under the skin or in the nasal passages of the animals. The transmission of human diseases by insects is a constant threat, and in the past has wrecked armies, debilitated entire nations, and wrought countless personal tragedies to the old and the young, the ignorant and the learned alike.

On the positive side, the United Nations Economic Yearbook records the world catch of crustaceans at over 460,000 metric tons (about 500,000 U.S. tons). About 20 per cent of this is shrimp landed in the United States. The scientific importance of insects as research tools in the study of heredity, behavior, and many other problems rates extremely high.

General Characteristics. The mandibulate arthropods, of course, exhibit all the distinctive arthropod traits: (1) Jointed legs. (2) Serial segmentation. (3) A chitinous exoskeleton resulting in the necessity for periodic molting or ecdysis during growth. (4) A protostome type of nervous system consisting of a dorsal brain or pair of cerebral ganglia, a pair of circumpharyngeal connectives around the anterior part of the gut, and a ventral nerve cord consisting of a chain of more or less fused ganglia. (5) A greatly reduced coelom and an "open" vascular system, i.e., the arteries empty into intercellular cavities or hemocoels rather than into capillaries.

In contradistinction to the spiders and other chelicerate arthropods, the mandibulates are characterized by the following traits:

1. They possess **mandibles** or jaws. The mandibles are crushing and chewing structures that do not end in a claw. Even in a mosquito,

where the mouth parts are adapted for piercing and sucking, the modified jaws can be seen. It will be recalled that in a spider, or in *Limulus* the horseshoe crab, the mouth is a mere hole and the first pair of movable structures ends in a claw. Consequently, spiders and their close relatives are condemned to a liquid diet, while *Limulus* stuffs and perhaps sucks food into its mouth and grinds it up later in a gizzard.

2. Mandibulate arthropods possess **antennae.** There are two pairs in crustaceans, and one pair in centipedes, millipedes, and insects.

3. Where the chelicerates have six pairs of appendages (four pairs of legs plus two pairs of appendages close to the mouth, the pedipalps and chelicerae), the mandibulates commonly have many pairs of appendages, as in centipedes and crustaceans. In insects, where the number of legs is reduced, the pattern of appendages is quite different from that found in the spiders. Instead of two pairs of mouth parts, insects possess three, including, of course, mandibles, and three pairs of legs instead of four.

The general body plan of both branches of the arthropod phylum is basically alike and like all arthropods, the mandibulates differ from the more primitive protostomes in lacking a trochophore larva. The larval stage is a **nauplius** among crustaceans, and a wormlike caterpillar or maggot among insects.

THE CRUSTACEA

Crustaceans, Class Crustacea (*crusta,* shell), are easily defined as gill-breathing mandibulate arthropods with two pairs of antennae, and, generally, **biramous** (*bi,* two + *ramus,* branch) or two-branched **appendages.** In fact, in contrast with annelids and even with other arthropods, crustaceans may be thought of as the animals who best knew how to take advantage of segmentation. A crayfish, for example, has a total of 19 segments, each with a pair of appendages. Of the 19 pairs of appendages, only three pairs are alike. This is because in different regions of the body the appendages are specialized for different functions: feeling out the environment, manipulating food, fighting, breathing, walking, reproducing, swimming, or escaping enemies.

Crustaceans inhabit oceans and fresh water everywhere; a few species, like the various land crabs and the "pillbugs," are terrestrial. The great economic importance of shrimps, lobsters, and crabs has already been noted. The ecological importance of the very small crustaceans is even greater, for these minute animals form a crucial link in the major food chains of both fresh and salt water. Because they eat unicellular algae and are in turn eaten by animals, they stand between the unicellular algae, which form the nutritive foundation of all aquatic life, and the larger animals such as the fishes and the whales.

Evolutionary Relationships and Major Groups. The crustaceans are clearly protostomes and appear to be related to the polychaetes. Unfortunately, the fossil record tells virtually nothing about their origin, because they appear already well developed in the Cambrian strata, the oldest rocks that contain fossils in any abundance. A study of the cross sections of a polychaete and a crustacean will reveal a basic similarity. Not only are the nerve cord and main pulsating blood vessel in the same positions, but the parapodia of the polychaete are really biramous, that is, two-branched, and bear gills on the dorsal branch. (See Fig. 17 – 1.)

The Crustacea falls into several natural groups, ranked as subclasses. The first four, known as branchiopods, ostracods, copepods, and barnacles or cirripedes, are often grouped together because they are composed of small, often minute, animals with a relatively large number of segments, and no abdominal appendages except a single pair of more or less spikelike structures at the very tip of the tail. A fifth group, the malacostracans, is composed of the familiar lobsters, crabs, "pill-bugs," and many other larger to medium-sized animals usually having five head, eight thoracic, and six abdominal pairs of appendages.

The **branchiopods,** as their name implies (*branchia,* gills, + *poda,* feet), have thin, flat, leaflike appendages which serve both as gills and as swimming organs. The fairy shrimps are probably the most primitive of the branchiopods, because they have no carapace or shell covering the thorax, each segment being free as in the annelids. These beautiful, glasslike, and

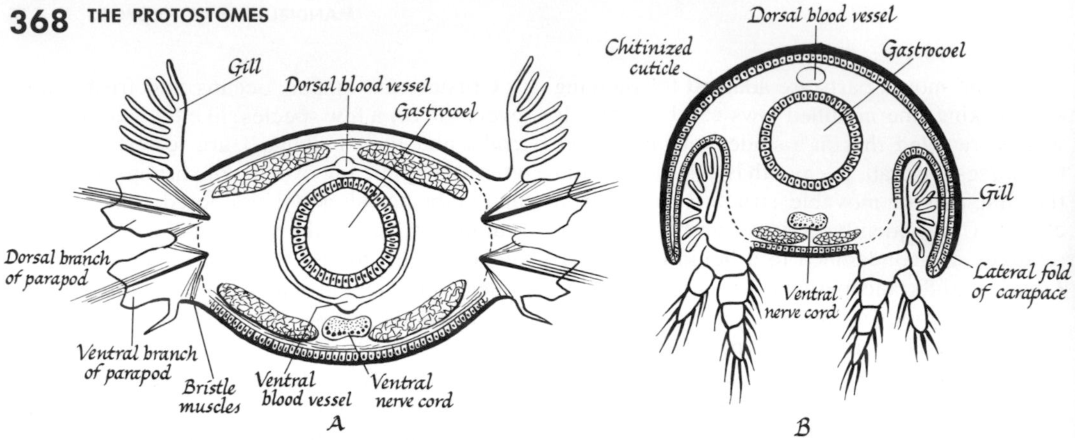

Fig. 17–1. Cross sections of *(A)* a polychaete annelid and *(B)* a crustacean. Diagrammatic. *(From Pauli,* The World of Life, *Houghton Mifflin)*

iridescent little shrimps vary in size, according to time and place, from less than half an inch to well over an inch in length. They are found in ponds all over the United States, especially in early spring. One of their curious habits consists in swimming upside down—or at least with the neural side up and the gut side down, which would be upside down compared with other crustaceans. *Artemia*, the brine shrimp found in the Great Salt Lake of Utah and other salty waters in North America and Europe, is a fairy shrimp. Its eggs can be bought dried and will hatch readily in the laboratory. The anatomical form and life history of *Artemia* can be varied by changing the salinity of the water in which it is raised. Moreover, races from different places appear to be different in these respects, even though the salinity is about the same. Consequently these animals have been extensively studied cytogenetically in attempts to untangle hereditary from environmental effects and perhaps throw light on evolution in action. Some races are parthenogenetic, some are diploid, and some tetraploid (possessing four sets of chromosomes). Those in the Great Salt Lake are diploid and males are common. The eggs hatch into a nauplius larva, a tiny creature with three pairs of limbs which may be biramous. (It should be noted that the term *shrimp*, like *bug*, is commonly applied to several very different kinds of animals.)

Another branchiopod is the common water flea, *Daphnia*. In this creature a carapace or shell covers most of the body. *Daphnia* swims by means of a large pair of biramous second antennae which in appearance suggest a deer's antlers. Daphnias are commonly raised in laboratories both for study and as food for other small animals, such as hydras, tropical fishes, and salamander larvae. The anatomy and life history of *Daphnia* will be discussed below.

A spectacular branchiopod, which attains about three-quarters of an inch in length and invariably calls forth surprise from all but the callous specialist, is *Leptodora*. This is a carnivorous species that lives on smaller crustaceans and rotifers and is very common in larger lakes. It is little known because it comes to the surface chiefly at night.

The **ostracods** *(ostrakodes,* having a shell) are sometimes called seed shrimps because the carapace is hinged and shaped much like a little clam shell that can completely enclose the animal and make it resemble a seed. Most species are marine, although ostracods are very common in fresh water, too, and usually flourish among pond weeds kept for some time in the laboratory. Because of their small size and opaque carapace they are difficult to study. There is no heart, and the number of appendages is reduced. Many species are parthenogenetic, males being unknown.

The **copepods** *(kope,* oar, + *poda,* foot) are one of the largest subclasses of crustaceans, and probably the most important. They have been called "the insects of the ocean," for they are the most abundant metazoans in the sea and usually in any body of fresh water except rapid streams. They form a major link in the food chain—in fact, *the* link between the phytoplankton, or floating plant life, and the zooplankton, or small floating and swimming animal life, of the ocean. They inhabit the open sea far from land as well as bays and estuaries. They are found at the surface, on the bottom, and at most intermediate levels. Most are free-living and subsist on unicellular algae and other such material; but many are commensals invariably found in association with certain larger animals, some are ectoparasites, popularly called fish lice, and some highly modified forms are internal parasites in the eyes, gills, heart, or other structures of fishes.

The body of a copepod is typically elongate, with a carapace covering the more anterior part. The stouter forepart of the body narrows to a segmented region which narrows again to form a segmented abdomen ending in a pair of branched spikelike appendages. The females carry the developing eggs, like two compact clusters of grapes, attached to each side of the body where the abdomen begins. In many species the second antennae are extremely long and are used to propel the copepod through the water in rapid jerks.

The parasitic copepods are so highly modified that they are practically unrecognizable as copepods or even as crustaceans. Their bodies are reduced to pale whitish or dark red irregular bags, but when they are mature, the two hanging masses of eggs are indicative of the copepod nature of these animals. So also is the copepod type of nauplius larva which develops from the eggs.

Barnacles, or **cirripedes** (*cirrus,* curl, + *pedis,* of the foot), have been known from antiquity, but until a surprisingly recent date everyone had supposed them to be mollusks because of their heavy calcareous shells. A little over a century ago an English army surgeon and amateur naturalist took them out of the Mollusca, where they had been placed by Linnaeus and Cuvier, and showed that they are truly arthropods. Their arthropod nature can be verified by anyone who observes a barnacle in an aquarium or who dissects one. The most conspicuous features are the biramous jointed and curly legs, with which the barnacle kicks food particles into its mouth. Further proof that barnacles are indeed crustaceans is to be seen in the typical nauplius larvae that develop from their eggs. The nauplius swims freely for a short time, then affixes itself to a rock, a ship's bottom, or some other object, and undergoes a metamorphosis into the adult.

The cirripedes fall into three groups. There are the familiar sessile barnacles crowding rocks and wharf pilings at varying tide levels the world around. There are the goose barnacles which are attached to some object, often a

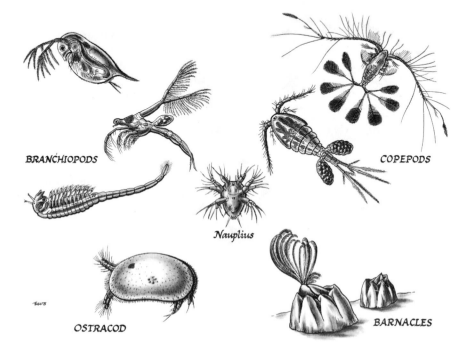

Fig. 17–2. Representatives of the four most important groups of smaller crustaceans, and the nauplius larva common to them all. (Not drawn to scale)

BRANCHIOPODS

COPEPODS

Nauplius

OSTRACOD

BARNACLES

floating one, by a flexible stalk often an inch or more in length. Lastly, there are parasitic forms like *Sacculina* in Europe and *Peltogaster* on this side of the Atlantic. In these, the nauplius settles on a crab and develops into a parasite with rootlike processes extending into the body of its victim and a baglike body hanging outside that consists of little more than body

Fig. 17–3. Nauplius larvae (left) and adults (right) of four crustaceans. Top to bottom: a copepod parasitic in fish gills, a shrimp, a goose barnacle, and a free-living copepod. Note the three pairs of legs in the larvae. (*From Pauli,* The World of Life, *Houghton Mifflin*)

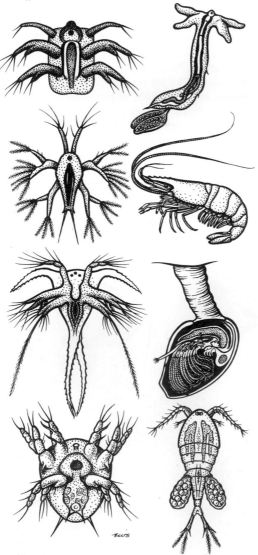

wall and gonads. The evolutionary development of such a parasitic habit is not surprising. Various species of barnacles regularly grow on crabs, whales, and sharks, and some have holdfasts which penetrate into the host's flesh.

No discussion of barnacles would be complete without including some mention of Charles Darwin's monumental work on the cirripedes (1854). For eight years he worked steadily on barnacles, and only on barnacles. The resulting two volumes, published a full decade before the *Origin of Species,* changed Darwin's status from that of amateur to professional. Of more importance, these eight years of intensive study of barnacles gave him a deep and first-hand knowledge of a single and remarkable group of animals that his earlier survey of many species could not provide.

Barnacles present many puzzling features even today. In a few species the sexes are separate, but most are hermaphroditic. In certain species there are small "supplemental" males.

The final group of living crustaceans, the **malacostracans,** is a very large one and includes all the larger species. With few exceptions malacostracans possess five more or less fused head segments, eight thoracic segments, and six abdominal ones which are usually well supplied with appendages. Of the ten or more orders, we will describe briefly only the five most important. These are the mysids, the amphipods, the isopods, the decapods, and the euphausids.

The **mysids** are usually less than an inch in length, although one species grows to nearly a foot long. They are elongate, shrimplike animals found along the shores of most oceans. There are three points of interest about them. Their thoracic legs are biramous, a very primitive trait. The statocysts or balancing organs, consisting of a cyst containing some kind of "stone," are located in the tail instead of the head, as in lobsters and commercial shrimps. Thirdly, lobsters and commercial shrimps pass through a stage when they resemble a mysid and have biramous thoracic appendages.

The **amphipods,** often called beach fleas, are usually somewhat under an inch in length, and so flattened in a right-left plane that they cannot stand up but always fall over on their sides. They are very common among masses of seaweed on beaches and in the ocean, although

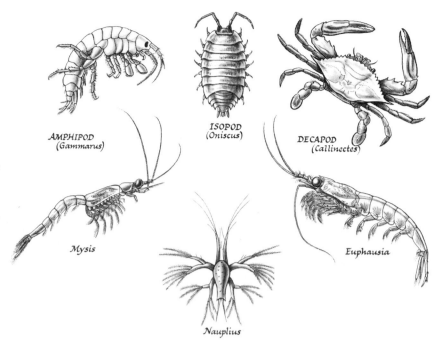

Fig. 17–4. Representatives of the five major groups of large crustaceans. The nauplius shown is the typical shrimp larva.

AMPHIPOD (*Gammarus*)

ISOPOD (*Oniscus*)

DECAPOD (*Callinectes*)

Mysis

Euphausia

Nauplius

there are a few fresh-water species. Their big claws are relatively enormous and of a type called **subchelate.** The two "prongs" of the claw do not serve as pincers, as in a lobster's claw, but the "thumb" swings back to lie against the next proximal segment of the appendage.

Many amphipods show the famous "sun compass" response. If removed from a beach which extends north and south, with the ocean on the east, and placed in a dish from which they can see only the sky, when they begin to dry up they will move towards the east. If removed from a beach which runs east and west with the sea water on the north, under the same conditions they will move north. To elicit this response, the sand and air of the container must be very dry and the sky must be clear. Amphipods will orient themselves correctly regardless of the time of day, i.e., regardless of the position of the sun. It follows that they must possess a biological clock which permits them to compensate for the motion of the sun across the sky.

The **isopods** include marine, fresh-water, and terrestrial forms. Isopods are flattened, but at right angles to the plane of flattening in the amphipods. In other words, they are flattened in the dorsal-ventral plane. The common terrestrial genera, such as *Armadillidium, Porcellio,* and *Oniscus,* are familiarly known as pill-

Fig. 17–5. *Caprella,* an amphipod, showing the characteristic subchelate claw. (*Kindness of William H. Amos*)

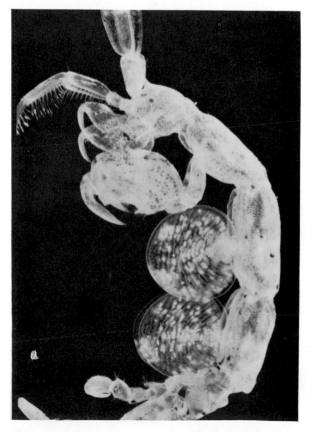

bugs and sow-bugs and are common under damp wood and leaves or in cellars. One of their most strikingly crustacean characters is possession of small but clearly biramous tail appendages, or **uropods** (*oura*, tail, + *poda*, feet).

The **euphausids** have gained notoriety recently because they appear to be the animals primarily responsible for producing false depth readings on modern marine instruments. Apparently in many regions of the ocean they form a layer dense enough to reflect sound. The depth varies from 200 to about 1,000 meters, since these euphausid shrimps, like most other pelagic or sea-living animals, move closer to the surface during the night. Euphausids form most of the "krill," a favorite food of the gigantic baleen whales in polar waters. The euphausids differ from other shrimps in that they have but a single row of gills and lack maxillipeds. Their eyes are very large, and there are luminous areas on the eye stalks, the leg bases, and the under side of the abdomen.

The **decapod** crustaceans, as their name implies (*deka*, ten, + *poda*, feet) have ten feet, although the first pair is usually a greatly enlarged pair of aggressive claws. Included in the group are: *Homarus,* the northern lobster; *Panulirus,* the southern or spiny lobster; *Cambarus,* the crayfish; *Cancer,* the rock crab; *Callinectes,* the blue crab; *Uca,* the fiddler crab; *Palaemonetes,* the transparent freshwater shrimp; *Pagurus,* the hermit crab; and many other famous names. A fiddler crab showing the enlarged claw is shown below.

Fig. 17–6. Male fiddler crab with greatly enlarged claw. (*Kindness of William H. Amos*)

FUNCTIONAL SYSTEMS OF CRUSTACEA

Daphnia. *Daphnia magna* or *D. pulex* may be taken as an illustration of the smaller (non-malacostracan) crustaceans. The chitinous exoskeleton of daphnia is molted usually about 17 times. The first three to five instars, or periods between molts, are juvenile. Growth occurs rapidly immediately after each molt and before the new exoskeleton has had time to harden.

The segmentation of the body is vague. The appendages are as follows. The first antennae (antennules) are extremely small, unsegmented sensory structures situated just under the pointed **rostrum** or "nose." The second antennae are large, biramous swimming organs. The four mouth parts consist of a median labrum or "upper lip," a pair of stout mandibles, a pair of pointed maxillae to push food between the mandibles, and a median labium or "lower lip." Five foliaceous (leaflike) pairs of legs produce a respiratory current of water that also brings in food particles. The big muscles which move the swimming antennae are worth examination under a compound microscope because striated muscle can be seen in the living state.

The gut is a fairly straight, easily observable tube, bearing a digestive gland, sickle-shaped as it curves back of the eye. The dorsal heart is shaped like a tangerine and forms a conspicuous, rapidly pulsating object. The ovaries are a pair of elongate structures in the thorax on either side of the gut. Most reproduction is by parthenogenetic females. The eggs develop in a dorsally located brood pouch. Males appear rarely, usually when the conditions are in some way unfavorable.

The nervous system consists of a cerebral ganglion (brain) just dorsal to the esophagus and a paired ventral chain of ganglia. There is a single compound eye with 22 **ommatidia,** or visual units (*ommatos,* eye), and muscles which rotate the eye. There is also a single minute simple eye at the anterior end of the brain. Various small bristles around the head and two long bristles near the end of the abdomen are believed to be sensory. Daphnia behavior is easily observed in the laboratory. In acid water daphnia are markedly and positively phototropic.

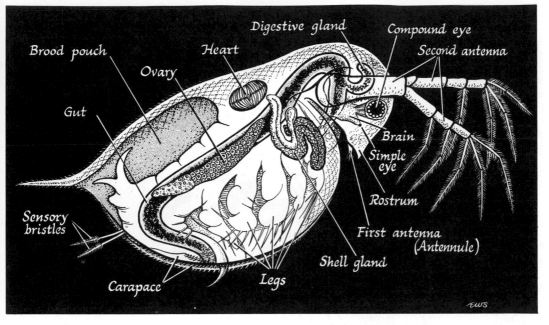

Fig. 17–7. Anatomy of *Daphnia*, the common water flea (female).

The Crayfish. Ever since the time of Darwin and T. H. Huxley, the crayfish has been the animal used to typify the larger or malacostracan crustaceans. No large crustacean is as readily available, as cheap, or as satisfactory for dissection. Although some 130 species of crayfish have been described in the United States alone, they are all so closely alike and so similar to the northern lobster, *Homarus*, in everything except size, that a single description will serve for all.

The exoskeleton covering the cephalothorax forms a• carapace that hangs down over the sides of the body and covers the gills, which are attached to the bases of the legs. In many species there are several so-called pleurobranch gills which are attached to the body just dorsal to the basal segments of the legs. The six segments of the abdomen and the terminal piece, or **telson** (*telson*, the limit), are covered dorsally by a hard **tergum** and ventrally by a softer **sternum**. The exoskeleton is notable for three reasons, which will be considered in order: the serial homology of the appendages, the physiology and control of molting, and the ability to regenerate lost parts.

Fig. 17–8. General anatomy of male crayfish, with a portion of the carapace cut away so as to show the gills. (*From Pauli, The World of Life, Houghton Mifflin*)

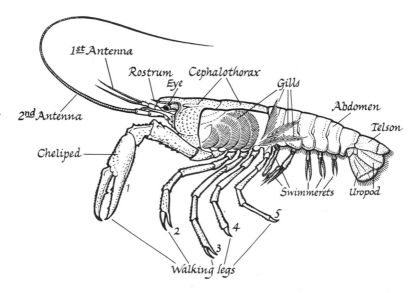

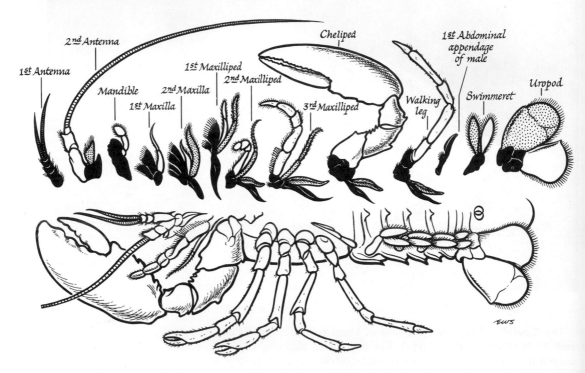

Fig. 17–9. Lobster or crayfish, showing serial homologies of appendages. In the upper half of the drawing, black represents the protopod; stippled, the outer branch or exopod; and white, the inner branch or endopod. *(After* Animals Without Backbones *by Buchsbaum by permission of the University of Chicago Press. Copyright 1948 by The University of Chicago)*

Appendages. In the juvenile and certainly in the ancestral condition, each appendage is biramous, and consists of three parts: the **protopod** or basal portion from which arise two branches, the **exopod** or more lateral branch, and the **endopod** or more medial branch, i.e., nearer the midline of the body. In an ancient and extinct group of crustaceanlike animals called trilobites, there were similar biramous appendages upon each of the approximately 30 segments.

The appendages of these crustaceans are serially homologous.

In an adult crayfish or lobster, a remarkable series of adaptations can be seen in different regions of the body, where the appendages have become so modified that their originally biramous character is often lost. Briefly, the first two pairs of appendages are modified as sense organs, the antennae. The six pairs of mouth parts, viz., the mandibles, two pairs of maxillae, and three pairs of maxillipeds, are modified for handling food. In addition, the second maxilla on each side is modified to form a kind of scoop which pulls a current of water forward under the side of the carapace and over the gills. The five pairs of thoracic appendages are called walking legs. In larval lobsters the exopods are present, but as molting takes place the exopods on these legs are lost. The protopod of the third walking leg bears the opening of the oviduct. The protopod of the fifth has the opening of the sperm duct.

The six pairs of abdominal appendages are modified for mating, swimming, or escape. The first two pairs in the male are modified for the transfer of sperms. In a female the first pair of abdominal appendages is vestigial, and the second is biramous like all the rest in both sexes, except the last pair. The 19th segment bears a pair of flat uropods. Together with the telson the uropods can give the tail a mighty flip and send the animal speeding backwards.

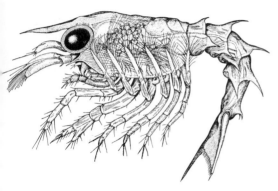

Fig. 17–10. Larval lobster with exopods, which are later lost, on the thoracic legs.

Molting. Increase in the size of a lobster, a crab, or a crayfish is possible only immediately after the molt. Interest in molting has been stimulated by the crabbing industry. Soft crabs—that is, crabs which have recently molted—are prized as delicacies and bring the highest prices. Soft crabs are quiescent, rarely come to bait, and are therefore seldom caught. Consequently it is necessary to keep large quantities of crabs waiting in enclosures to molt. The mortality and consequent loss is very high. A practical method of inducing molting is obviously desirable. Enough is now known to make such control seem a possibility in the foreseeable future.

In the actual process of molting the calcium is absorbed from the exoskeleton, which becomes soft, and is deposited instead in the large hepato-pancreas or liver and, at least in crayfish, in the **gastroliths** (*gaster*, stomach, + *lithos*, stone) secreted by the gastric epithelium of the anterior wall of the stomach between the epithelium and the chitinous lining of the stomach. After molting, the two gastroliths are exposed to the gastric juice, dissolve, and the absorbed lime is made available for redeposition in the new exoskeleton. When about to molt the animal seeks a sheltered corner, arches itself, and pulls out of the old shell first its thorax and head and then its abdomen. In the spiny lobster, *Panulirus*, the process requires three to ten minutes, depending on the lobster's size.

Adult crayfish usually molt twice a year, once in the spring and once in the fall. If the eyestalks of a nonmolting individual are removed, calcium begins to be withdrawn from the exoskeleton, the gastroliths begin to enlarge, and in about 15 days molting occurs. The mortality is heavy, but those crayfish that survive molt again within about 15 days. Molting can be inhibited by implanting eyestalks from nonmolting donors into eyestalkless animals. The responsible organ in the eyestalk is the **sinus gland,** an inconspicuous body close to the optic nerve, and an associated structure, the X organ. Neurosecretory cells in the X organ and in the brain form a molt-preventing hormone which is stored in the sinus gland. The sinus gland itself is mostly a mass of nerve-fiber endings. Similar results have been attained in other species of crustaceans.

A second pair of glands, the Y organs, are located in the anterior part of the thorax, in most crustaceans near the base of the jaw muscles. The Y organs secrete a hormone, probably closely similar to ecdysone of insects, which induces molting. During most of the life of the animal the hormone of the Y organ is held in check by the sinus gland hormone. When the brain and X organ fail to produce the sinus gland hormone, molting occurs under the action of the Y organ.

It is worth noting that extracts of mammalian pituitary, when injected into crustaceans, produce results that are similar to those of eyestalk extracts.

Fig. 17–11. Diagram showing anatomical and functional relationships of the endocrine system that controls molting in a crustacean.

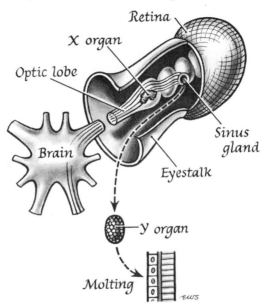

Regeneration. Crustaceans possess moderate powers of regeneration. If a leg is injured sufficiently at any point, it will be broken off by the animal itself at a special breaking point by the action of a special muscle. This **autotomy** (*autos,* self, + *tomo,* to cut) occurs close to the base of the leg, specifically, in a predetermined line through the basal segment of the endopod of the first walking leg (the big claw) and between the second and third segments in the other legs. At these places there is a preformed membrane that lessens hemorrhage when the limb breaks off. A small regenerated limb appears after the next molt.

If the end of an eye is amputated, a new eye will regenerate. If, however, the entire eyestalk is removed, not an eye but an antenna is regenerated. Such an event is termed **heteromorphosis** (*heteros,* other, + *morphos,* form), but its actual meaning in terms of either evolution or developmental mechanics is very obscure.

Two essentially unexplained phenomena of regenerative growth concern asymmetry. If the big claw of a crab or lobster is removed, in subsequent molts the remaining smaller claw will become the big one and the amputated great claw will be replaced by a small one, thus reversing the asymmetry. The second phenomenon is known as **Bateson's rule,** named for an early English exponent of Mendelian heredity. Bateson observed that whenever double limbs are produced, as may happen when the bud of a regenerating limb is injured, the reduplicated limbs are always mirror images of each other, "thumb" facing "thumb" or perhaps palm facing palm, but never in series with thumb facing little finger. Behind these curious facts lie only dimly perceived laws of animal form.

Organ Systems. The **muscles** of arthropods, like those of other animals, are arranged in antagonistic sets of flexors and extensors. The chief muscle mass of the body is composed of the flexors of the abdomen, which account for most of its bulk. These are the muscles which produce the vigorous escape flips of the "tail." Dorsal to them there is a much thinner layer of extensors which straighten out the abdomen.

The **digestive system** of a crayfish consists of a foregut, which includes an esophagus and a two-part stomach; a midgut or intestine, to which the hepato-pancreas is attached; and a hindgut, making up the remainder of the intestine. Foregut and hindgut are ectodermal in origin, and secrete a thin chitinous lining which is shed during molting. The esophagus is short and almost vertical, opening into the cardiac portion of the stomach. This part of the stomach is provided with a gastric "mill," a complex apparatus including a dorsal and two lateral teeth which grind up food. The anterior wall of the cardiac stomach secretes the calcareous gastroliths mentioned above. After being chewed in the gastric mill, food passes into the smaller pyloric stomach where further digestion takes place. The hepato-pancreas, like the vertebrate liver, is a gland with several functions, including the secretion of digestive enzymes, storage of food, regulation of the sugar concentration in the blood, and reduction of waste nitrogen compounds to simple ammonia, which is easily excreted by aquatic organisms.

The **vascular system** is an open one, that is to say, the arteries do not finally end in capillaries which themselves pass into veins. Rather, the arteries merely pour out blood into the tissue spaces where, after bathing the cells, it collects

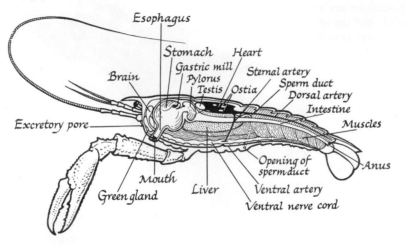

Esophagus

Stomach   *Heart*
Gastric mill   *Sternal artery*
Brain   *Pylorus*   *Sperm duct*
Testis   *Ostia*   *Dorsal artery*
Intestine
Excretory pore   *Muscles*
Opening of sperm duct   *Anus*
Mouth
Green gland   *Liver*   *Ventral artery*
Ventral nerve cord

Fig. 17–12. Internal organs of a crayfish (male). (*From Pauli, The World of Life, Houghton Mifflin*)

in a large midventral or sternal sinus. From this sinus the blood passes into the gills and thence up to the pericardial sinus surrounding the oblong dorsal heart. Blood enters the heart through three pairs of openings, or **ostia.** From the heart a median ophthalmic artery carries blood to the head and eyes, right and left antennary arteries carry blood to the antennae, a posterior artery running just above the intestine carries blood to the abdomen, and a sternal artery passes straight down (ventrally), either to right or left of the intestine, and pierces the nerve cord to supply a ventral artery that runs the length of the animal and supplies blood to the legs.

The **excretory system** consists of a pair of "green glands" located in the head, one at the base of each of the second, larger antennae. Each consists of a thin-walled sac which funnels through a nephrostome into a labyrinth of intercommunicating passages in the green gland. The cells here appear to be secretory in structure. From each green gland there is a tubule — long in fresh-water species, short in marine ones — leading to a bladder that opens to the exterior by a pore on the protopod of the second antenna.

In crayfish the single **gonad,** either a testis or an ovary, is roughly Y-shaped, lying below the heart and with the arms of the Y on either side of the intestine. In the female, the oviducts open on the basal segments of the third pair of walking legs. In the male, the vas deferens on each side opens at the base of the fifth walking leg. The male copulatory appendages have already been described. In mating the female lies on her back, and the male holds her big claws in his and deposits sperms in a depression on her under side, close to the openings of the oviducts on the third legs. The eggs are laid and fertilized some days after mating. In fact, the sperms of lobsters are believed to remain viable, adhering to the seminal receptacle, for over a year. During egg-laying the female curls her abdomen up tightly over the under side of her body so that the eggs become attached by a mucilaginous secretion to her abdominal appendages, the **swimmerets.** Newly hatched crayfish remain attached to their mother's swimmerets for some time. The young of many marine crustaceans pass through several larval stages, beginning with a nauplius and ending with a mysis-like form in which the walking legs have exopods.

The **nervous system** follows the annelid-protostome pattern. There is a brain or a pair of cerebral ganglia between the eyes and above the esophagus, a pair of connectives, and a ventral chain of ganglia, clearly one ganglion per segment in the abdomen, but with more or less fusion in the thorax. The chief sense organs are the tactile and probably also olfactory first and second antennae, the eyes, which are compound, being composed of many visual units or ommatidia, and the statocyst in the base of each second antenna.

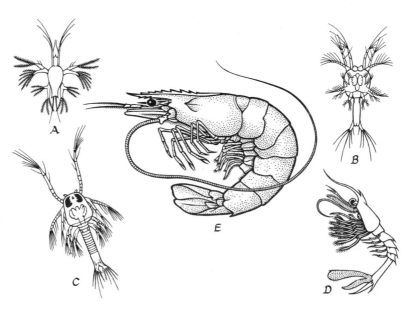

Fig. 17–13. Life history of the shrimp. *A*, nauplius. *B*, protozoea. *C*, zoea. *D*, mysis (note exopods on the thoracic legs). *E*, adult. (*From Pauli,* The World of Life, *Houghton Mifflin*)

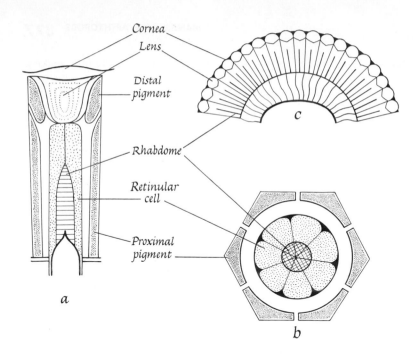

Cornea

Lens

Distal pigment

Rhabdome

Retinular cell

Proximal pigment

a

b

c

Fig. 17–14. The compound eye of an arthropod. *a*, ommatidium in longitudinal section. *b*, ommatidium in cross section. *c*, many ommatidia organized into an eye.

The Compound Eye. Compound eyes are common to both crustaceans and insects. Many attempts have been made to imagine what the world looks like through compound eyes. The results are learned guesses; and it is a safe assumption that without an arthropod brain to go with the compound eyes, learned guesses are all we will have for some time.

There is no doubt, however, that compound eyes are powerful and precise instruments — witness the ability of a dragonfly to outmaneuver and catch other insects in flight. Even a butterfly can be a tricky thing for an adult man to capture. Compound eyes not only are adept at detecting motion, they also can furnish precise information about distance. This is the result of binocular vision, as can be proved by blinding one eye. It has recently been shown that the compound eyes of bees and of *Limulus*, the horseshoe crab, can analyze polarized light. This ability probably is important in using the light from the sky as a compass. Since each ommatidium of a compound eye points in a slightly different direction, compound eyes can serve as precise detectors of the angular position of the sun in relation to the head. This ability seems to be a clue to the remarkable homing abilities of ants and other arthropods.

The structure of compound eyes is strikingly similar in crustaceans and insects. Apparently these complex organs have arisen in almost exactly the same form twice in the course of evolution. The explanation lies in the action of natural selection on the possibilities of arthropod mutations in the face of the requirements imposed by the physical nature of light. Each ommatidium is a cylindrical, pencil-shaped structure capped on the exterior by a transparent cornea which serves as a lens. Immediately beneath the cornea is a layer of translucent epithelial cells which form a new cornea when the old one is lost at molting. Below these is a large crystalline cone, formed of four cone cells which make the major lens, and below that, making up the greater part of the ommatidium's length, is a core of crystalline material called the **rhabdome** (*rhabdos,* rod) surrounded by six or seven cells which have secreted it. These cells are called the **retinular cells** because they are the actual photosensitive cells which continue out of the eye as nerve fibers. At the base of the ommatidia is a basement membrane. Each ommatidium is surrounded by a distal collar of pigment cells around the crystalline cone and by a second collar of proximal pigment cells around the retinular cells at the base of the ommatidium. From one species to another there is considerable variation in the length of the rhabdome and other details of eye structure.

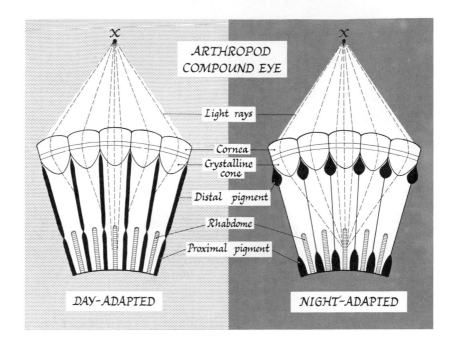

ARTHROPOD COMPOUND EYE

Light rays
Cornea
Crystalline cone
Distal pigment
Rhabdome
Proximal pigment

DAY-ADAPTED

NIGHT-ADAPTED

Fig. 17–15. Migration of pigment in the ommatidium for day and night vision.

The pigment in the eyes of most arthropods migrates according to the amount of light, and makes two different forms of vision possible. In the daytime or light-adapted compound eye, the pigment is dispersed so as to form a collar completely surrounding each ommatidium. In this condition each ommatidium is stimulated only by light rays coming in parallel to its long axis. The image on the eye is a mosaic or apposition image, as each optic unit "sees" only what is directly opposite it. In the nighttime or dark-adapted eye, the pigment is concentrated out of the way so that each ommatidium can be stimulated by light entering the adjacent corneas as well as its own. Night vision of this kind is supposed to be much less precise but to require much less light.

The number of ommatidia varies from several dozen to many thousands in different species. The nerve fibers from all the retinular cells of each ommatidium form the optic nerve. In many species, there are four ganglia within the optic nerve; each of the four is itself composed of two or three subganglia. Between some of the optic ganglia there are optic **chiasmata** in which optic nerve fibers cross from each side of the nerve to the other. As a pioneer in the study of nerve pathways, Ramon y Cajal, put it, complexity of the nerve fiber tracks behind a compound eye "staggers the imagination."

Other Functions in Crustacea. In the basal segment of each first antenna there is a cavity, the **statocyst,** opening to the exterior by a small pore and containing many sensory hairs and sand grains. The statocysts are organs of equilibration. This can be demonstrated by the classical 19th century experiment of Kreidl. If a crayfish is allowed to molt in an aquarium containing iron filings, some iron filings instead of sand will get into the renewed statocyst. Such an animal will make postural responses to a magnet, especially if the eyes are covered.

Fig. 17–16. The nocturnal compound eyes of *Ocypode*, the white beach crab. (*Kindness of William H. Amos*)

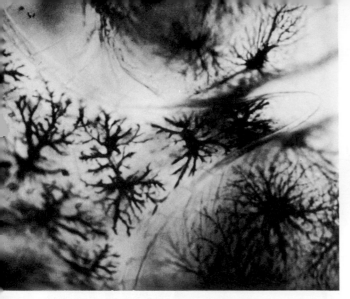

Fig. 17–17. Melanophores in a living shrimp. *(Kindness of William H. Amos)*

In recent years it has become increasingly evident that special **neurosecretory cells** in the brain and various ganglia control a number of functions in crustaceans. The role of the sinus gland in the eyestalks in controlling molting is such a case; color pattern is another. Crustaceans possess chromatophores containing several pigments, black and brown melanins, red and yellow carotenoids, white guanin, and a blue pigment that is thought to be a carotenoid combined with a protein. It is this blue pigment which becomes red after boiling. The degree of dispersion of these various pigments, and hence the color of the animal, is controlled by hormones, three from the sinus gland, and one or two from neurosecretory cells in the brain. In lobsters and shrimps of various kinds removal of the eyestalks leads to darkening. In the various crabs, removing the eyestalks produces paling, whereas injection of extracts of eyestalks produces darkening. In addition, the migration of pigment in the eye during light and dark adaptation of the ommatidia has been shown to be under the control of hormones from the sinus gland.

NATURAL HISTORY OF CRUSTACEA

Most crustaceans are nocturnal, or at least light-shy. This is well authenticated for the fresh-water crayfish, the spiny lobster *Panulirus,* the white beach or ghost crab *Ocypode,* and many other species. Most of the pelagic crustaceans living far from land, like the euphausid shrimps, perform a vertical migration twice daily, down into darker water during the day, up closer to the surface at night. Fiddler crabs often swarm on muddy tidal flats at low tide in the bright sun, but they are exceptions.

An analysis of population dynamics has been begun in relatively few species. As indicated earlier, the abundance of small fresh-water and marine crustaceans is a determining factor and possibly the key factor in controlling the growth rate and size of population among fishes. Marine populations are notoriously difficult to estimate and virtually impossible to count. This is especially true of crustaceans, which molt and are thus unsatisfactory animals to band.

Some of the larger crustaceans are known to migrate. *Callinectes,* the blue crab of Chesapeake Bay, moves down the bay to the Virginia Capes into saltier water every year to breed, and returns several hundred miles up the bay to feed during the rest of the year. Land crabs migrate to the sea to breed. The spiny lobster, *Panulirus,* forgets its fear of light and can be seen crawling over the bottom in broad daylight on its way to deeper water at breeding season.

In many of the fresh-water species, the size of the population and even the form of the body depend partly on the life history and partly on the time of year. The common fairy shrimp of northern states, *Eubranchipus vernalis,* hatches from dry and dormant eggs late in the fall when rains fill up the ponds. The nauplii swim under the ice during the winter, metamorphose, and grow rapidly in the spring, reaching full maturity and producing thick-shelled, over-summering eggs within two weeks after the ice is off the ponds. Other fairy shrimp, commoner in the south, remain active throughout the year.

The situation with *Daphnia* is similar but with important differences. In temperate climates the population attains two maxima or peaks, one in the spring and, after a midsummer slump, another in the fall. In the far north there is but one maximum, and the size of the population at that point depends largely on the number of winter eggs that have lasted over. This is because the growing season for *Daphnia* is very short, and winter—probably sheer cold—stops further increase. In warmer regions the population can fully exploit its living space and at-

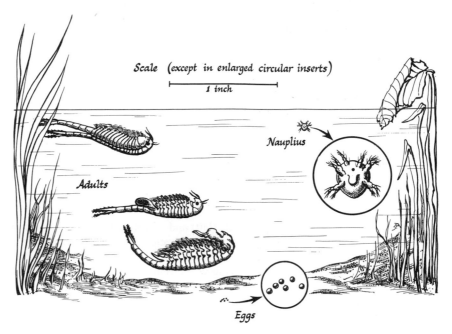

Fig. 17–18. Seasonal cycle in *Eubranchipus*, the fairy shrimp found in fresh-water ponds. Adults flourish in late winter and early spring. The eggs survive the dry summer. Nauplius larvae hatch when fall rains fill the ponds.

Scale (except in enlarged circular inserts)

1 inch

Nauplius

Adults

Eggs

tain a maximum set by food supply and other more subtle factors. The change in body form at different months of the year has attracted much attention, but its causes remain obscure.

MINOR MANDIBULATE ARTHROPODS

The only important minor mandibulate arthropods are the millipedes and the centipedes. They are sometimes grouped together as the Class Myriapoda (*myrios,* numberless, + *poda,* feet), but this is now regarded as not quite as fair a representation of their relationship as to make each of them a separate class, coordinate with insects and crustaceans. The millipedes form the Class Diplopoda, so named because each "segment" bears two pairs of legs; and the centipedes form the Class Chilopoda, named from the Greek *cheilos,* a lip, because of a fancied resemblance of the mouth parts to lips.

Millipedes and centipedes have many features in common: a body composed of a small head with antennae and jaws, and a long trunk consisting of many essentially similar segments. The arrangement of the organ systems follows the typical arthropod character: a dorsal brain, a pair of neural connectives around the esophagus, and a ventral chain of ganglia. The heart is a long tube extending along most of the dorsal side of the intestine. The excretory and respiratory systems resemble those of insects, in particular. Instead of the ciliated tubular nephridia of the annelids and *Peripatus* or the green glands (which appear to be highly modified nephridia) of crustaceans, both millipedes and centipedes have a pair of long malpighian tubules extending nearly the entire length of the body cavity and emptying into the intestine. The respiratory system consists of a system of air ducts, or tracheae, ramifying throughout the body and opening to the exterior as in insects by porthole-like spiracles, one on each side of each segment. A millipede and a centipede are shown in Figure 17–20.

Fig. 17–19. Change in form in *Daphnia cucullata* at various dates in the year.

7/30 8/15 9/7 10/2 10/21 11/16 12/17 2/7 3/22 4/11 4/25 5/21 6/5 6/17 7/11 8/3

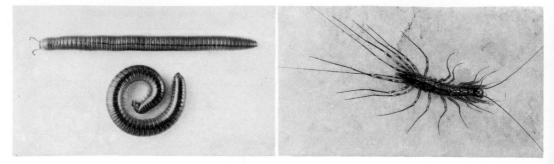

Fig. 17–20. A millipede (left) and a centipede (right), both shown life size. There are also much larger and much smaller species. (*U.S. Department of Agriculture, H. S. Conard*)

The millipedes are slow-moving vegetarians. Probably they are very close to the stock from which insects arose. Not only do they possess malpighian tubules and tracheae, but the larval millipede has only three pairs of legs like an insect. The eyes seem to show an intermediate stage in the formation of compound eyes from simple eyes, for on each side of the head near the base of the antennae is a cluster of simple eyes or **ocelli.** Curiously, each "segment," except the first six or seven, appears to be composed of two segments fused together. This seems an absurdity, and it is difficult to see what advantage it confers. However, the facts are that each "segment" bears two pairs of legs, has two pairs of spiracles, two ganglia in the ventral nerve cord, and even two pairs of ostia in the heart tube. The stepping rhythm of the legs is regulated by impulses which arise near the hind end of the millipede and move toward the head as a wave of stepping. Several of these waves can be observed passing forward in different parts of the body at the same time. Cooling the animal slows the waves; pressing on the head reverses their direction. The gonads and the openings of the gonaducts lie in the anterior end of the body.

The centipedes, by contrast, are swiftly moving predacious animals with a sharp pair of jaws connected to poison glands. Some of the tropical species attain a length of about a foot and can inflict a painful bite, though rarely if ever is it fatal to a human adult. Each segment bears but one pair of legs. The gonads are dorsal to the gut, in the posterior half of the body, and open near the anus. The larvae hatch with at least seven pairs of legs.

INSECTS

Insects are easily defined as mandibulate arthropods which have three pairs of legs when adult. The body is divided into head, thorax, and abdomen. The thorax bears both the three pairs of legs and the two pairs of wings.

Flight has been attained independently in the course of evolution by several groups of animals, the prehistoric reptiles, the birds, a group of mammals (the bats), and at last artificially by the chief of the primates, man himself. But few have the sure and easy mastery of the air possessed by insects. This ability, plus many other ingenious adaptations, have made insects the dominant animals of the land, with only one serious rival, man. Over 700,000 species have been described. The number of individuals is beyond estimation.

Importance. The economic importance of insects was documented at the beginning of the chapter, where the damage done to certain crops was given in dollars. The damage inflicted is extremely widespread and often appears in unexpected ways. Wooden foundations may be eaten by termites. Museum specimens in their glass cases are liable to be reduced to powder by dermestid beetles. Bee moths enter bee hives at night when the bees are asleep and lay eggs on the comb; these hatch into ravenous grubs that eat the wax. Bot flies lay eggs on the legs of cattle; each egg hatches into a maggot that penetrates the skin, migrates through the tissues, and finally becomes a large grub in a swollen cyst opening through a hole in the skin of the back. These holes lessen the value of the hides and result in an annual loss of some $50 million.

The role of insects in the transmission of disease is equally important, and as long as the insects responsible remain alive, will constitute a major threat to mankind. Fleas carry the bacteria of bubonic (black) plague, which threw the Roman world in the reign of Justinian (565 A.D.) into confusion. Whole towns and countrysides were deserted, crops rotted in the

Some Important Diseases Transmitted by Arthropods

DISEASE	CAUSATIVE AGENT	CARRIER	DISCOVERERS OF CARRIER
	PROTOZOA		
Texas cattle fever	Pyrosoma bigeminum	Margaropus (Boophilus), tick	Theobald Smith, 1889-1893
Malaria	Plasmodium vivax	Anopheles, mosquito	Ross, 1897; Grassi, 1898; Manson and Sambon
African sleeping sickness	Trypanosoma gambiense	Glossina palpalis, tse-tse fly	Bruce, 1895; Castellani, 1903
Chagas fever	Trypanosoma cruzi	Rhodnius, bloodsucking bug	Chagas, 1909
	BACTERIA		
Bubonic plague (Black Death)	Bacillus pestis	Pulex irritans, common flea Xenopsylla cheopsis, rat flea	British Indian Plague Commission at Bombay — best proof, 1907; others
Typhoid	Bacillus typhosus (Eberthella typhosus)	Musca domestica, house fly	Vaughan and Veeder, 1898
Tularemia	Pasteurella	Ticks	
	VIRUSES		
Yellow fever	Yellow fever virus	Aedes aegypti (Stegomyia), mosquito	Reed, Carroll, Lazear, Finlay, others, 1900
Typhus fever	Typhus virus (Rickettsia bodies) ?	Pediculus, the human louse Polyplax, the rat louse	Nicolle, Comte, and Conseil, 1909
	WORMS		
Elephantiasis	Filaria bancrofti	Culex, Aedes, and Anopheles, mosquitos	Patrick Manson, 1878

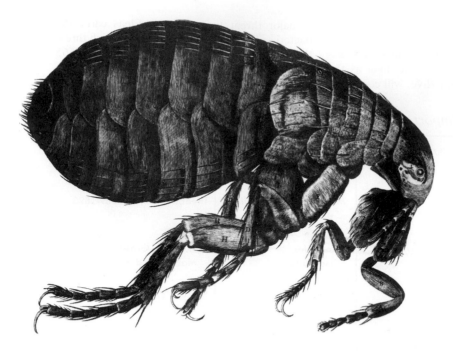

Fig. 17–21. A flea, from Robert Hooke's famous *Micrographia*, published in 1665.

fields, and it is estimated that at least half the population of the Western world died, most after suffering so intense that many people threw themselves from housetops to escape their agonies. No cure was known. The black plague wrought havoc and misery a dozen times in Europe during ancient and medieval times. The most important pandemic was the Black Death of the 14th century, which spread over the entire world. In Oxford two out of every three students died. Everywhere there were depopulated towns and farms. The resulting

Fig. 17–22. Plague in the 16th century. From an engraving by Sabatelli. (*The Bettmann Archive*)

economic crisis led directly to the political and religious turmoils of the 14th and 15th centuries. There has been no such epidemic in modern times, but the threat continues. As recently as 1941 plague appeared in Los Angeles, where it may have arrived on ship from the Orient.

Plague is primarily a disease of fleas and small rodents, especially both wild and house rats. The bacteria are sucked up by the flea with the blood, multiply in its digestive tract, and are either regurgitated or defecated on the skin of man, where they easily enter any small scratch or the puncture wound made by the flea. Regions where rodent plague is continuously endemic and which are consequently possible sources of plague occur in many parts of the world—around the Caspian Sea, in southeast Asia, Morocco, central Africa, parts of Argentina and Brazil, and certain parts of southwestern United States.

Despite all the control measures malaria still rates on a world basis as the foremost human disease in number of victims per year. The story of how Ross discovered that it is transmitted by the bite of a particular mosquito, of the genus *Anopheles,* has already been told (pages 92-95). The impact of malaria has been felt in many times and places, in classical Greece, in medieval Italy, in the South Pacific in World War II.

The conquest of mosquito-borne (*Aedes*) yellow fever made possible the construction of the Panama Canal. The fate of several armies—Napoleon's, Kaiser Wilhelm's, and others extending back into the mists of history—has been sealed by the louse which transmits typhus.

No gift of science to mankind has been greater than the knowledge that insects can carry human diseases. It is for this reason, combined with the vast importance of insects in agriculture, that **entomology,** the study of insects, has attained its high rank among the biological sciences. The table on page 383 lists the important insect- and tick-borne diseases. For many people insects are important as objects of scientific and general interest. Their behavior, their complex societies, their beauty, or merely their strange diversity—often like creatures from another planet—have long fascinated mankind.

Evolutionary Relationships. The evidence at hand very strongly suggests that insects arose from millipede-like ancestors by neoteny. As indicated in Chapter 10, neoteny (the attainment of sexual maturity by a larval stage which thereby becomes the adult) appears to have led to extremely important advances in several evolutionary lines, including perhaps our own. In any case, the millipede larva has three pairs of legs, tracheae, malpighian tubules, and also several other traits that make it closely resemble an insect.

Insects are an extremely ancient group. Fossil cockroaches are found in Carboniferous strata laid down some 300 million years ago, tens of millions of years before the appearance of dinosaurs. Many fossil insects are beautifully preserved in amber (fossil resins), and in ancient deposits of volcanic ash and sand in what must have been lake bottoms. Many genera present in this 50-million-year-old material are still extant, and some of the ants and other species are indistinguishable from present-day forms.

During their evolution insects have undergone an explosive adaptive radiation which has carried them into virtually all parts of all continents and every environment from desert sands to polar snows.

ANATOMY OF INSECTS

One of the best ways to gain insight into the nature of the efficient machines for living that insects really are, is to compare a relatively generalized insect like a grasshopper with a specialized species like a honeybee.

External Anatomy. Both of these insects show the typical tripartite division into head, thorax, and abdomen. The head carries the chief sense organs and the mouth. The compound eyes occupy prominent, bilaterally symmetrical positions. Three simple eyes, or ocelli, form a triangle with one corner near the top of each compound eye and the third in the middle of the "forehead." The antennae are organs of touch, smell, and chemoreception. The mouthparts consist of seven elements. (1) A median, unpaired **labrum** forms an "upper lip." (2 and 3) Immediately behind this is the pair of hard

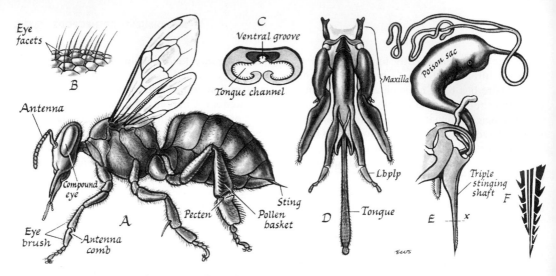

Fig. 17–23. Anatomy of worker honeybee, representative of endopterygotous insects. *Lbylp,* labial palp. *(From Pauli,* The World of Life, *Houghton Mifflin)*

stout **mandibles.** (4 and 5) Posterior to the mandibles are the **maxillae.** In the grasshopper each maxilla has two basal segments which bear three appendages. The most conspicuous and most lateral is a five-segmented maxillary **palp.** Medial to the palp is the long rounded **galea,** and medial to that is the **lacinia,** really a jawlike structure. (6) Just posterior to the maxillae is the **labium,** a sort of lower lip which bears a pair of labial palps very similar to the maxillary palps. (7) In the center of all these mouthparts is a more or less cylindrical tongue,

or **hypopharynx.** In bees the same mouthparts are present, but both the maxillae and the labial palps are elongate and fit together to make a sucking tube within which the tongue moves up and down.

The thorax is divisible into prothorax, mesothorax, and metathorax. The **prothorax** bears legs; the **mesothorax** and **metathorax,** both legs and wings. The six segments of a leg are a short **coxa** and **trochanter,** followed by a long **femur,** a long **tibia,** and a shorter **tarsus** and **pretarsus,** the latter equipped with a pair of

Fig. 17–24. External anatomy of a (female) grasshopper, representative of exopterygotous insects.

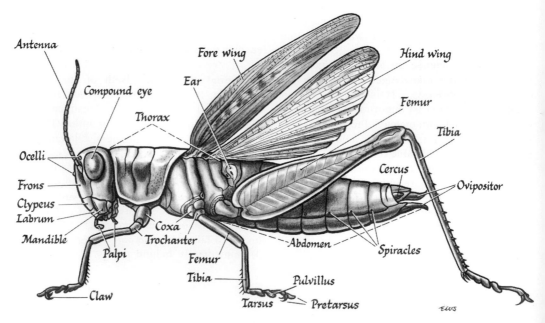

claws to hold onto rough surfaces and between them a flaplike **pulvillus** to adhere to flat surfaces. Insects' legs show remarkable adaptations. The prothoracic legs of bees are provided with a semicircular brush and a hinged scraper which work together as an antenna cleaner. The mesothoracic leg has a spur used to pick off the scales of wax that are secreted between the abdominal segments. The metathoracic legs bear pollen baskets composed of the concave broad side of the leg, plus surrounding long bristles. The metathoracic legs of grasshoppers are highly modified for jumping.

The segments of the abdomen are covered dorsally by **terga,** the under sides by **sterna.** Along each side is a row of small holes, one pair to a segment. These are the **spiracles,** which open into the **tracheae.** Both alimentary canal and reproductive organs open in common at the posterior end of the abdomen. In males there are usually clasping organs, while in females the external genitalia take the form of a pair of dorsal and a pair of ventral leaflike structures forming an ovipositor. In some species the ovipositor is longer than the rest of the body, and in many of the hymenopterous species is a sting. Thus drones are unarmed.

Respiratory System. The respiratory system consists of spiracles and a network of tracheae ramifying throughout the body. In grasshoppers the more anterior spiracles are open at inspiration, when the body expands, and the posterior ones are closed; at expiration the situation is reversed. Consequently there is a current of air moving in via the anterior and out via the posterior openings. In grasshoppers, bees, and other insects there are a number of **air sacs** in the thorax and usually a pair in each abdominal segment. It was in the wing muscles of honeybees that Keilin rediscovered a forgotten pigment, cytochrome, an all but universally present and important respiratory pigment in plants and animals. (See Chapter 3.)

Digestive and Excretory Systems. The alimentary canal consists of three main divisions: an ectodermal **stomodeum** or foregut, an endodermal **mesenteron** or midgut, and an ectodermal **proctodeum** or hindgut. The **foregut** begins with the **buccal** or **mouth cavity** and **pharynx** followed by an **esophagus,** then a **crop,** and then

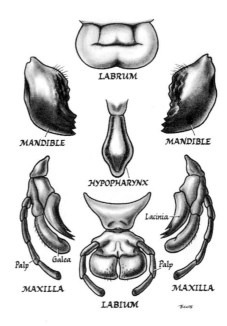

Fig. 17–25. Mouthparts of a grasshopper, the basic generalized type for insects.

a thicker-walled **proventriculus** or **gizzard** that contains six chewing **teeth.** In many insects crop and gizzard are separate structures; in others, a single tube. A pair of **salivary glands** empties into the buccal cavity.

The gizzard opens into a relatively short **midgut** which bears eight **mesenteric** or **hepatic caeca** at its anterior end. If the remainder of the midgut is thick, it is called the **stomach;** if small, the **anterior intestine.**

The **hindgut** or **posterior intestine** bears from two to over 70 pairs of **Malpighian tubules** at its anterior end. Usually long and threadlike, the tubules in many insects are orange or white from the urates they contain. In many species they empty their excretory products into the intestine whence they are voided with the feces. The hindgut usually ends in a large **rectum.**

Circulatory System. The heart is a tubular, crustacean type of structure lying dorsal to the gut in the abdomen. The body cavity is a blood cavity (hemocoel), as in other arthropods, and there are no capillaries or veins. The colorless blood contains phagocytic white blood cells which ingest bacteria. The blood itself transports food and wastes. In most larval insects there is a conspicuous lacework of giant fat-rich

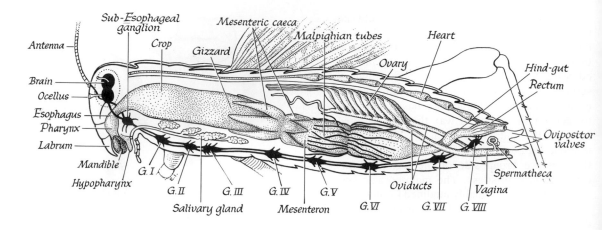

Fig. 17–26. Internal anatomy of a (female) grasshopper. The ganglia are numbered.

cells, which are probably storage bodies. In most insects this fat-body is composed of at least two kinds of cells. The most numerous contain granules of fat, glycogen, and protein. Others contain spherical crystals of uric acid.

Reproductive System. The female reproductive system consists of two ovaries, each made up of strings of eggs arrayed in ovarian tubules. At the distal end of each tubule are primordial germ cells, while farther down the tubule one finds oocytes in various stages of meiosis and of yolk accumulation. The oviducts enter a vagina which is connected with a spermatheca or sperm receptacle. In the spermatheca the sperms are stored from a mating which may immediately precede egg-laying. However, in the bee, sperms are stored for the lifetime of the queen, who makes but one nuptial flight.

The male system consists of a pair of testes, each connected to a somewhat coiled vas deferens leading into an enlarged sperm storage cavity, the seminal vesicle, which in turn leads to the ejaculatory duct ending in a short penis. In both sexes there are usually accessory mucus glands.

Nervous System. The nervous system consists of the typical arthropod dorsal brain connected to a double ventral chain of ganglia. The ganglia in the thorax are usually enlarged and more or less fused. In addition to the eyes and antennae, many insects possess both ears and the means of producing characteristic

sounds. In grasshoppers the ear drums can easily be seen on the sides of the first abdominal segment above the hind legs. In the katydids and crickets a tympanum, or ear drum, is ingeniously placed within the tibia of each front leg. Noctuids, the night-flying owlet moths, and some others possess an ear on each side of the thorax. An air-filled cavity is covered by a tympanic membrane from which stretches a sensory cord containing only two nerve cells. It has been shown by Roeder and others that these ears enable moths to avoid bats which hunt at night by a vocal radar. It is probable also that here is the answer to the old puzzle as to why so many moths have such downy coats. Natural selection has favored those in which the scales were fluffy rather than like shingles on a roof, as in butterflies. A soft surface does not reflect sound clearly.

Sounds may be produced, as in katydids, by rubbing special filelike ridges on the wings, by special vibrating blades in the wing base, as in mosquitos, or by rapidly pulling a drum or tympanum in and out, as cicadas do. This last device works on the same principle as making a noise by snapping in the bottom of an empty tin can with pressure from a thumb.

One special kind of sense organ is the **haltere** of the flies, mosquitos, and other members of the Dipteriformes. These structures look like short sticks with a knob on the end, and from their position and innervation are modified hindwings. Without them normal flight is impossible, but their exact function is unknown.

CLASSIFICATION OF INSECTS

Bases of Classification. The classification of insects into orders brings a manageable system to this stupendous array of animals and reveals their evolutionary kinship. There are four major bases of insect taxonomy.

1. The first criterion for insect classification is whether or not **wings** are present (or, as in the case of lice and fleas, appear to have been present in the ancestors). Several small orders of very primitive, i.e., crustaceanlike, insects constitute the Subclass **Apterygota** (*a,* not, + *pteryon,* wing). All other insects belong to the Subclass **Pterygota,** in which the character of the wings forms an important and easily usable taxonomic feature.

2. Among the pterygotous or winged insects the type of **metamorphosis** is a major taxonomic trait. Again there are two major groups, commonly called divisions.

The first division consists of the **Exopterygota** in which the wings develop on the outside of the body. Here are found the cockroaches, grasshoppers, and termites, among others. The egg hatches into a form resembling a miniature adult with small wing pads. These larval forms are called **nymphs** and undergo a series of molts gradually becoming more and more like the adult until the adult or **imago** is reached. Because the differences between each stage or instar are small, this type of metamorphosis is often called gradual, direct, incomplete, or hemimetabolic. The nymphs in most species have large compound eyes.

The second division consists of the **Endopterygota** in which the wings develop within the body of the larva. Here are found the butterflies, beetles, flies, ants, bees, and many others. The larval form is usually a wormlike grub or caterpillar with tiny eyes or none. The next to the final molt commonly produces a quiescent stage, a **pupa,** from which the adult or imago will emerge. This type of metamorphosis is often termed indirect, complete, or holometabolic.

3. A third important basis for insect classification is the nature of the **mouthparts.** They are easily studied under a dissecting microscope; they reveal evolutionary relationships of the various species; and, not least important, they furnish important clues about the food of the insect. The basic, primitive pattern of

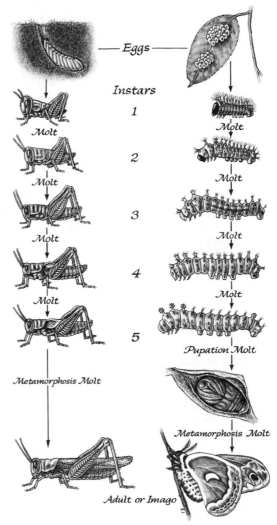

Fig. 17–27. Exopterygotous development (left) as in a grasshopper, and endopterygotous development (right) as in a moth.

mouthparts can be seen in grasshopper or cockroach but even in a mosquito all the parts present in a grasshopper can be identified highly modified as a stiletto for withdrawing blood.

4. A fourth commonly useful basis is the nature of the **external genitalia.** In fact, differences of this kind seem to have been important in evolution by making the exchange of genes impossible between sympatric species.

Many other traits are useful in taxonomy, especially those concerned with the eyes, antennae, legs, and surface bristles.

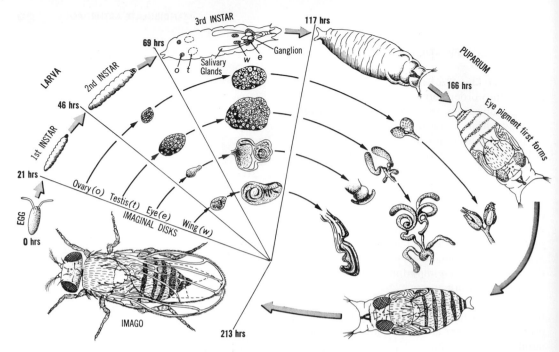

Fig. 17–28. Life cycle of *Drosophila melanogaster*, showing the development of several internal organs. (*From D. Bodenstein*, Biology of *Drosophila*, *Wiley*)

Orders of Insects. The subclasses and divisions of insects are further subdivided into more than 20 orders. Some are of such general importance that every informed person should know of them, others are of minor or limited importance. The numbering of the list here is largely arbitrary. The evolutionary deployment of the insects is a three-dimensional branching bush, not a single-track highway.

Subclass Apterygota. Primitive insects without wings.

1. The **Proturiformes** (*protos,* first) have no metamorphosis, no wings, and chewing mouthparts. These small primitive insects are found in most parts of the world under bark or in damp soil. They are interesting chiefly because their three pairs of small leglike abdominal appendages link them to more primitive forms like the millipedes.

2. The **Collemboliformes** (*kolla,* glue, + *embolon,* peg), the springtails, have no metamorphosis, no wings, and chewing mouthparts. These minute primitive insects sometimes cover wet logs or the surfaces of quiet ponds like animated sand grains. The abdomen is equipped with a peg-and-lever jumping device.

3. The **Thysanuriformes** (*thysanos,* fringe or tassel, + *oura,* tail), the silverfish and firebrats, have no metamorphosis, no wings, and chewing mouthparts. These primitive, wingless insects have the ability to digest cellulose, and frequent old wood, old books, and long-forgotten lecture notes.

Subclass Pterygota. Insects with wings or winged ancestors.

Division Exopterygota. Wings develop on the outside of the body. Metamorphosis gradual. Larvae commonly with compound eyes.

4. The **Orthopteriformes** (*orthos,* straight, + *pteron,* wing) include the grasshoppers, crickets, cockroaches, walking sticks, praying mantids, etc. They have gradual (exopterygotous) metamorphosis; the forewings are leathery, the hindwings are thin; there are generalized chewing mouthparts. Cockroaches are extremely ancient animals, and appeared long before the dinosaurs. Modern cockroaches are not much changed. They are omnivorous insects and may injure food or clothing and possibly transmit polio and hepatitis, but they are useful laboratory animals. The orthopterans called grasshoppers in North America are called locusts in

most other parts of the world, and are a serious menace to crops in regions where they swarm. The praying mantis is a carnivorous and very beneficial member of the Orthopteriformes. Some entomologists divide the Orthopteriformes into several orders.

5. The **Isopteriformes** (*isos*, equal, + *pteron*, wing) are the termites. They have gradual (exopterygotous) metamorphosis, two pairs of equal-sized wings with a fine lacework of veins, and chewing mouthparts. Termites are at least as different from ants as cows are from horses. Ants (order number 19 in this list) have a complete or endopterygotous metamorphosis, the anterior pair of wings is markedly larger than the hind pair, and the veins are few in number and generally run from the base of the wing to the outer edge with a very small and definite number of cross veins. In termites the thorax is very broadly joined to the abdomen, whereas ants have a very narrow wasplike waist. Ter-

mite social organization is more complex than that of ants, for termites have four castes and various subcastes: a winged reproductive caste, a wingless reproductive caste, workers, and soldiers. Unlike ants and bees, where all workers are undeveloped females, with termites there are males and females in every caste.

The ability of termites to digest wood is due to symbiotic flagellated protozoa which they harbor in the gut. These can be eliminated from the termites by various means, after which the termites continue to eat but produce fecal pellets of undigested wood and eventually starve. The species of termites found in most parts of the United States require contact with the earth to maintain themselves. South of a line beginning at the Virginia Capes, running down the coast roughly 200 miles inland, then swinging west across the southern edges of the Gulf states, and turning north again to run up along the California coast to a point well north

Fig. 17–29. Representative orders of exopterygotous insects. *(From Pauli,* The World of Life, *Houghton Mifflin)*

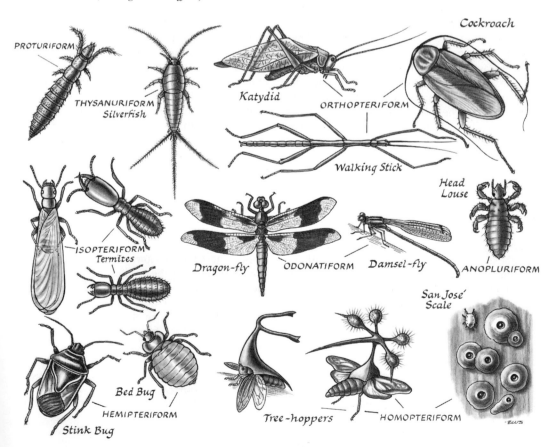

of San Francisco, there are dry-wood, or non-subterranean, termites that can live without contact with the soil.

6. The **Odonatiformes** (*odontos*, tooth) are the dragonflies and damselflies. They have gradual (exopterygotous) metamorphosis with aquatic larval (nymphal) stages, two pairs of long net-veined wings, and chewing mouthparts. Both nymphs and adults are carnivorous, preying largely on other insects. The economic importance of these insects is negligible.

7. The **Ephemeriformes** (*ephemeros*, of a day) are the mayflies. They are characterized by gradual metamorphosis and flimsy wings with the forewings very much larger than the hindwings. Mouthparts in the adult are vestigial. The aquatic larva has paddle-shaped gills along the sides of the abdomen. Mayflies are the flies of fly-fishermen. In the Great Lakes and other parts of North America and in some of the Swiss lakes, mayflies hatch in such immense swarms that their crushed bodies cause autos to skid and may completely obscure windshields on highways near the lakes.

8. The **Homopteriformes** (*homos*, the same, + *pteron*, wing) are the aphids, cicadas, tree-hoppers, plant lice, and scale insects. They have exopterygotous metamorphosis, both pairs of wings are translucent, and there are piercing and sucking mouthparts. This order includes many insects that injure crops. The aphids or plant lice and the 17-year cicadas (or, as they are also called, "locusts") are the best known. The San José and other scale insects which suck sap from fruit tree stems are the most destructive. The tree-hoppers are among the most grotesque.

9. The **Hemipteriformes** (*hemi*, half, + *pteron*, wing), the true "bugs," include such groups as the stink bugs, bedbugs, water striders, and water bugs. There is exopterygotous metamorphosis; half of each forewing is leathery, half membranous; there are piercing and sucking mouthparts. Many of the true bugs are harmful to garden crops; the famous chinch bug is extremely destructive to grain in the Mississippi valley. A so-called "kissing bug" is responsible for transmitting the trypanosome of Chagas disease in South America.

10. The **Anopluriformes** (*anoplos*, unarmed, + *oura*, tail), are the blood-sucking lice. There is slight if any metamorphosis, no wings, and mouthparts are adapted for piercing and sucking. The fact of overwhelming importance about lice is that they transmit viruses of typhus and of relapsing and other fevers. Lice have received many common names, such as cootie, etc. In World War II lice were effectively controlled by dusting persons and underclothing with DDT.

11. The **Mallophagiformes** (*mallos*, a lock of wool, + *phagein*, to eat) are the chewing lice and the bird lice. They have slight if any metamorphosis, no wings, and chewing mouthparts. These lice eat hair, feathers, or dermal scales, and can become a serious pest for poultry.

12. The **Thysanopteriformes** (*thysanos*, a fringe or tassel, + *pteron*, wing) are the thrips. They have exopterygotous metamorphosis. There are two pairs of wings like little toothpicks covered with a long fringe of fine bristles, and piercing and sucking mouthparts. Thrips are very tiny but can nonetheless be ruinous for many crops, especially onions, strawberries, and pears. A few genera are beneficial and feed on aphids.

Division Endopterygota. Wings develop within the larval body. Metamorphosis complete. Larvae without compound eyes.

13. The **Neuropteriformes** (*neuron*, nerve, + *pteron*, wing) are the dobson flies and the ant lions. They have endopterygotous metamorphosis, lacelike (finely "nerved") wings, and chewing mouthparts. This is a small order interesting chiefly to fishermen, who use the big hellgramite, as the aquatic larva of a dobson fly is called, for bait, and to zoologists who are interested in the behavior of the ant lion, *Myrmeleon,* which constructs a funnel-shaped hole in the sand to trap ants and other small pedestrians. The big-jawed ant lion larva hides under the sand at the bottom of the pit with its head facing away from the sun.

14. The **Coleopteriformes** (*koleos*, sheath, + *pteron*, wing) are the beetles. They have complete, i.e., endopterygotous, metamorphosis. The forewings are horny sheaths not used in flying, which is accomplished by the membranous hindwings. There are chewing mouthparts. The beetles are an enormous order, including both carnivorous and herbivorous families. There are more species of beetles than of any other order of insects except perhaps the Dipteriformes. Among the carnivores

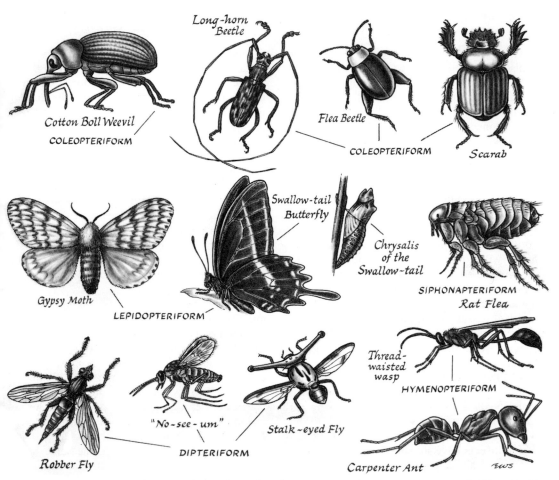

Fig. 17–30. Representative orders of endopterygotous insects. *(From Pauli,* The World of Life, *Houghton Mifflin)*

are the bright metallic blue and green tiger beetles, a host of predacious water beetles (often with social habits), various ground-beetles, the glow-worms and fireflies, and the useful ladybird beetles which eat aphids. The herbivorous groups include the cotton boll weevil and other weevils in which the mouth is on the end of a prolonged snout.

15. The **Lepidopteriformes** (*lepis,* scale, + *pteron,* wing) include the butterflies and moths, which have complete, i.e., endopterygotous, metamorphosis. Their large wings are covered with microscopic, often brightly colored scales. Mouthparts of the adult are elongated for sucking. The pupal instar is commonly called a **chrysalis.** The pupa (chrysalis) of a moth is usually enclosed within a silken cocoon; that of a butterfly is unprotected and merely supported around the "waist" by a silken thread spun by the caterpillar just before it molts.

The 150,000 or more species of moths and butterflies are among the most beautiful and destructive of insects. Moths (suborder Frenatae) are generally nocturnal, with threadlike or plumose antennae, while butterflies (suborder Rhopalocera) are diurnal and have antennae with a knob or swelling at the end.

Neither the adaptive, that is, the evolutionary, significance of the handsome colored wing patterns nor the developmental chemistry that produces them, is well understood. Species differ in wing pattern, and within some species the males and females differ. Consequently it is a safe guess, but still largely a guess, that species- and sex-recognition are important functions of these designs. Many moths and butterflies are protectively colored on the sides of the wings which show when at rest, so that they blend into their surroundings. So-called mimicry by which the wing patterns of two kinds of butterflies resemble each other is discussed in the chapter on evolution.

Moths can be collected at night in specially constructed traps consisting of a light behind an arrangement of wide funnels. Holland, the great pioneer in the study of North American moths, recommended baiting a series of trees just before dusk with a mixture of honey and rum, plus a dash of glue, and then sitting down to smoke a cigar while the moths collected. Butterflies usually require a net.

16. The **Trichopteriformes** (*trichos*, hair, + *pteron*, wing), the caddis flies, have endopterygotous metamorphosis. The wings are finely hairy, with long scales somewhat like those of moths. There are chewing mouthparts in the larva and vestigial mouthparts in the adult. The aquatic larvae are known for beautiful little cylindrical cases, made out of tiny stones or pieces of wood, in which they live. Some of the species living in streams spin cup-shaped nets to catch algae and small crustaceans.

17. The **Dipteriformes** (*di-*, two, + *pteron*, wing) are the flies, mosquitos, and gnats. Metamorphosis is endopterygotous, forewings are membranous, hindwings are reduced to **halteres**, i.e., short rods with a knob on the end. These insects have sucking mouthparts, and the larva is usually a legless maggot.

Fig. 17–31. Asilid fly, a predacious robber. Note the haltere at lower right, resembling a miniature tennis racket. (*Kindness of William H. Amos*)

The Dipteriformes are an extremely successful order of between 80,000 and 100,000 species, and have a geological history extending back into the late Paleozoic, before the time of the dinosaurs. As already noted, many flies and mosquitos transmit diseases. *Drosophila,* the fruit fly, is a jewellike little creature that has proved extremely useful in the study of heredity. Robber flies have taken to catching and eating other insects much in the manner of dragonflies. In the far north of Canada and Siberia tiny biting gnats and midges, called "no-see-ums," can make human life almost unbearable. The Hessian fly, which feeds on wheat stems, is extremely harmful. The larvae of various other species of this group feed on decaying wood or on mushrooms.

18. The **Siphonapteriformes** (*siphon*, tube, + *apteron*, no wings) are the fleas. These have endopterygotous metamorphosis and no wings. Mouthparts are modified for piercing and sucking. The major fact of significance for mankind about fleas is their role in the transmission of bubonic plague. There are only about 1,000 species of fleas, each with a fondness for a special kind of mammal. However, the human flea, *Pulex irritans,* will readily attack cats, dogs, rats, and other mammals; and the same holds true for *Ctenocephalus felis,* the cat flea, and *C. canis,* the dog flea. The maggots live modestly in cracks in the floors, among straw or dirt, and subsist on organic debris.

19. The **Hymenopteriformes** (*hymen*, membrane, + *pteron*, wing) include the bees, wasps, ants, and ichneumons. These have endopterygotous metamorphosis. Their wings are membranous. The forewings are much larger than the hindwings, and are united with them by a row of hooks. They have chewing or chewing and sucking mouthparts.

The hymenopterous insects form a world among themselves and yet are quite varied. Apparently social organization has developed independently a number of times in different groups of ants, hornets, and bees, yet its genetic basis always has certain features in common. Workers are undeveloped females. The only adult reproductive individual in a colony is typically a fertilized female. Males are haploid and are produced parthenogenetically. This astonishing discovery was made about a century ago by a German beekeeper who had a hive in which all the brood was hatching into drones. He found that the queen was so old she had run out of sperms, which are stored following the original mating flight in sperm receptacles within the female's abdomen. In primitive bees and ants new colonies are founded by single fertilized queens, but most bees and some of the familiar species of ants found new colonies by the emigration of a young queen and a group of followers. Some of the new discoveries about the behavior of bees will be discussed in Chapter 32 on Animal Behavior. The ichneumons, or ichneumon "flies" as they are often called, are parasitic on other insects on whose larvae they lay their eggs.

A number of minor orders of extremely limited importance need not be mentioned.

NATURAL HISTORY, BEHAVIOR, AND METAMORPHOSIS OF INSECTS

Common Characteristics. The ways of life of insects are so numerous and varied, their habitats so diverse, and their life histories and population characteristics so very different in so many ways that it seems almost impossible to consider the natural history of insects as a whole. Yet they do have one common trait. Group after group of insects has been a resounding success. Theirs is in fact *the* great biological success story. Are there features common to all insects which form the basis of this evolutionary achievement?

One trait all insects possess is an **exoskeleton composed largely of chitin.** Many entomologists have extolled the advantages of this protective armor. Chitin has the properties of an ideal plastic. It is strong, wear-resistant, waterproof. It does not soften with heat nor become brittle at freezing temperatures. It will stand up against alcohols and other organic solvents. It is not injured by any acids or alkalis found in the natural environment. In fact, boiling in strong acid is one of the few treatments that will destroy the chemical integrity of this remarkable substance. The chitin molecule is a polysaccharide containing nitrogen, and consists of a long chain of glucose molecules with added acetyl groups (from acetic acid) and amines, i.e., simple nitrogen-containing groups.

It must be remembered that some other organisms can also form chitin. The cell walls of some molds, the jaws and setae of polychaete annelids, and the "pen" of a squid are all formed of chitin. But perhaps none of these other groups have used chitin so well and in such a happy combination with other advantageous traits. Over the chitin in many arthropods is a waxy layer of protein and lipid material giving a double protection.

A second trait common to all insects is **small size.** The very largest insects scarcely attain the size of the smallest mammals. Small size is no doubt connected with the limitations imposed on growth by an exoskeleton which must be molted for increase in size to occur. This is not only physically more difficult in large than in small organisms, but a really big animal by vertebrate standards would be crushed by its own weight after molting and die a helpless mass suffocated from crushed lungs or tracheae, just as a stranded whale suffocates because its short ribs cannot support the lungs.

The small size of insects has sometimes been written down as a limitation and a disadvantage, but smallness may well be one clue to the success of the insects. On the scale of things on this planet, small size may greatly increase the availability of cracks, crannies, and protective niches. A level field for a fox or a rabbit is a veritable jungle for an ant or a beetle.

A second important effect of smallness is that it greatly increases the strength of an insect in relation to objects in its environment. A man begins to have serious trouble in lifting and moving objects only slightly heavier than himself. An ant or a wasp can move objects ten or more times its own weight. This is not because insect muscle is stronger than vertebrate muscle, but because of the geometry of size. The weight of a muscle (or any other object) increases with the cube of its dimensions, while its strength increases with the cross-sectional area. In other words, for any increase in size the weight of a muscle increases in proportion to the cube of its dimensions, while the strength increases only in proportion to the square.

A third and perhaps most important trait of insects is the **ability to fly.** Insects have been enjoying the advantages of living in the air age for at least 250 million years. In many ways, such as escaping enemies, overcoming obstacles, and dispersing the species into new and distant environments, flight much more than compensates for lack of size. A rabbit may run and hop two or three miles in a day, although all the evidence indicates that rabbits cover that much ground only under the most unusual conditions of crowding. But a winged ant, once it attains some height above the ground, may easily be carried ten miles by the wind.

Instinctive Behavior. A fourth feature of insects which seems to have been important in their success is the character of their **nervous system** and the type of **behavior** that goes with it. The important fact about insects is that they have a complex nervous system but almost no intelligence. Many other invertebrates lack intelligence—jellyfish and flatworms, for example—but they have simple nervous systems. Vertebrates, especially the higher mammals, have complex nervous systems but of a type that permits, and indeed necessitates, a highly flexible type of behavior. Learning plays a dominant role in their lives. By contrast, insects are like spiders; their behavior is predominantly instinctive, that is, it is based primarily on innate, more or less stereotyped reaction patterns. Learning and experience play a role, but a minor one.

In the insects, behavior patterns are almost as diagnostic of the order, or family, or even species, as are anatomical characters. This is true of the kind of plants on which a given species of beetle will lay its eggs, the shape of the mud nest built by a wasp, the shape and location of the cocoon spun by a moth caterpillar, the way a dragonfly mates and then lays its eggs under water, or the way a female cricket approaches a chirping male. In fact, it is possible to call a mature female cricket to the telephone merely by holding a chirping male at the speaking end, although he may be in another city. Male mosquitos will fly toward a tuning fork vibrating at the same frequency as the wings of females of their own species. The list of such

acts based on inherited responses, perhaps on single key reflexes but much more probably on chains and complexes of built-in reflexes, could be extended to fill many volumes.

Some of these instinctive responses are relatively simple, and knowledge of them can be of economic importance. For example, males of many species of moths will travel upwind for long distances to reach a female. The large feathery antennae of the males of these species reflect this behavior. The females secrete a special sex attractant in the form of a highly volatile chemical. These odoriferous substances have been isolated and analyzed in several cases. They are long-chain molecules of simple construction. The formula of the sex attractant of the silk moth, as worked out by Butenandt, is shown at the bottom of the page. A similar molecule has been found as the sex attractant of the female cockroach and the female gypsy moth. The attractant of the latter, manufactured and sold under the name Gyplure, is used to entice males into death traps.

One classic case of instinctive behavior was described in 1872 by an entomologist named Riley, and has been carefully confirmed and restudied recently. It is the case of the flowering yucca or Spanish bayonet and the yucca moth, *Pronuba*. These moths emerge from their cocoons at the time of year the yucca blooms. Mating occurs at dusk, and the impregnated female lights on a yucca flower from the anthers of which she collects a ball of pollen with the aid of specially modified mouthparts. She then flies to another flower, and head downward thrusts her ovipositor into the base of the pistil (which will develop into the seed pod) and lays an egg or two. She then goes to the top of the pistil where she pushes her load of pollen into the funnellike stigma at the pistil's end, thus insuring the development (and cross fertilization) of the seeds. The grubs which hatch from her eggs damage the yucca only slightly.

Another case which has been studied both in Europe and North America relates to the habits

$$H_3C-CH_2-CH_2-\overset{\overset{\displaystyle H}{|}}{C}=\overset{\overset{\displaystyle H}{|}}{C}-\overset{\overset{\displaystyle H}{|}}{C}=\overset{\overset{\displaystyle H}{|}}{C}-CH_2-CH_2-CH_2-CH_2-CH_2-CH_2-CH_2-CH_2-CH_2-CH_2OH$$

sex attractant of the silk moth

of various species of mud wasps which have been described by the famous French country school teacher, Jean Henri Fabre. The common mud dauber, *Sceliphron cementarium,* plasters its nests in deserted parts of buildings everywhere. The females are creatures possessing a rather special slim elegance and strength. They are the wasps which catch spiders, paralyze them with an expertly placed sting, and fly with them to their mud nests. Taking apart mud daubers' nests is a common practice among collectors of spiders. Of course, if the collector is too late, the wasp's egg will have hatched and the grub will have eaten the unfortunate spider. The shape of the *Sceliphron* nest is shown in Figure 17–32. It consists essentially of a series of mud cylinders built side by side and cemented into a single mass.

Another solitary wasp is *Eumenes fraternus,* the potter wasp. Instead of constructing a group of cylindrical jars all stuck together, the potter wasp makes a roughly spherical flask, about the size of a small cherry with a short flanged neck. These flasks are attached singly to small twigs or stems. *Eumenes* fills them with paralyzed caterpillars on which she lays her egg.

Other species of solitary wasps have the same general behavior but always there are differences in detail. *Perionyx* digs tunnels in the ground and stocks them with grasshoppers to feed her grubs. Such wasps seize grasshoppers by the antennae, and sitting astride the paralyzed prey, fly home with it while grasping it with their legs. Still other species clean out cavities in the pith of stems and there store up paralyzed prey for their grubs.

None of these behavior patterns—from the flight of a male mosquito toward a tuning fork humming like a female of his species to the behavior of the yucca moth or the mud wasp—depends on learning in any ordinary sense of the word. The most dramatic proof of this assertion can be seen in the sexual behavior of decapitated insects. An immature male praying mantis will begin correct and vigorous copulatory movements immediately after the head has been removed. In fact, if placed beside a female, a decapitated male will mount and successfully mate. Apparently the brain keeps the copulatory centers in the abdominal ganglia continuously inhibited. Neither previous experience nor even a brain is necessary. In nature, females sometimes eat the head and part of the thorax of the male before copulation, without detriment to the reproductive act.

The advantage of this general type of behavior is that it furnishes its possessor with a complete set of rules, as it were, to meet the expected events of life. The insect does not waste much time learning and making mistakes; most species lose no time at all this way. A male mosquito responds to the wing vibration of a female mosquito. If for any reason either in his hereditary make-up or in his environment, he fails to respond, he also fails to leave descendants, and so the unresponsive nervous

Fig. 17–32. Left: *Sceliphron cementarium,* the mud wasp, holding a ball of mud in her jaws. Right: mud nest of *Sceliphron.* (*Edward S. Ross*)

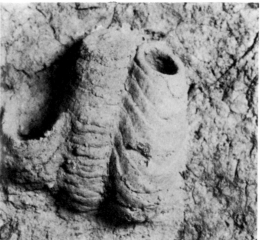

system fails to be perpetuated. In the vast majority of insects, the parents die shortly after egg-laying, so that there is no possibility of imitation or other forms of learning in the young. For most insects, life is short, and it is evidently an advantage—a very great advantage—to be provided with a ready-made built-in response mechanism.

Of course, it must be remembered that this contrast between insects and vertebrates is quantitative rather than absolute and qualitative; it is a matter of degree. Insects, at least some of them, do learn, and many vertebrates (fishes and birds especially) show many innate responses. For example, both ants and bees find their way around, in part, by the position of the sun in the sky. An ant can learn a maze. If she learns it with the light on a certain side, when the light is moved to the opposite side she will attempt to run the maze in reverse. Bees learn their way to and from the hive and become conditioned to a particular color or kind of flower in which to seek nectar. If a bee has discovered a rich source of supply, when she returns to the hive she performs certain motions. (See Chapter 32.) Exactly what motions will depend on the direction in which the supply of nectar is located, and how far away it is. Other bees leave the hive and fly in the correct direction and for the correct distance. This amazing behavior seems highly intelligent, yet there is something strangely rigid and mechanical about it from the vertebrate, or at least the mammalian, point of view. No bee has to be taught what motions to make on returning to the hive. No bee has to be taught how to respond to a particular motion. It is an innate or instinctive response composed of reflex patterns somehow built into the nervous system. Indeed, the blind "trial and error" behavior of a paramecium in the face of an unknown obstacle seems more human than this so-called language of bees.

Fishes, birds, and probably even mammals show innate responses to varying degrees. The females of any species of duck do not have to be taught what the drakes of their own species look like, and will resist the approaches of drakes of other species. Birds do not have to be taught what kind of nest to build, nor how to build it, nor where. The common North American robin lines its nest with mud and then covers this with an inner lining of dried grass. And all without any lessons, without any chance of imitation, for the nest is made before the eggs are laid. Yet even here the vertebrate shows some glimmerings of intelligence in the sense of benefitting by experience, for later nests are constructed somewhat better than the first tries.

Metamorphosis. A fifth notable and almost universal feature of insect life is **metamorphosis.** What is its adaptive meaning? Primarily it is a device to provide a single organism with two bodies, one the larval, specialized for eating and growing, and a second the imaginal or adult, specialized for reproduction and disseminating the species. One investigator calls the adult "a flying machine for reproduction." Very often the two bodies are adapted for entirely different environments. The larva may be aquatic, may live inside a tree trunk, or even in the nasal passages of a sheep, while the adult flies freely in the air.

The two major types of metamorphosis have already been described. Neither the gradual, exopterygotous type exemplified by grasshopper and dragonfly, nor the complete, endopterygotous type exemplified by bee and butterfly should be regarded as more advanced. They are rather two somewhat different ways of achieving the same ends.

The anatomical facts in both types are basically similar, but much more drastic changes take place between the last pupal instar and the imago or adult in the case of the complete type. In this type the next to the final molt yields the pupa. During the quiescent pupal instar certain organs are broken down, digested by phagocytic white blood cells, and used to build the new adult. This is true of the muscles and salivary glands, which are very different in caterpillar or maggot than in the adult. Other structures remain, or merely continue their growth. This is true of parts of the gut, the nervous system, and the gonads, although the nervous system and other organs are extensively modified. Lastly, many structures are formed anew. The wings, legs, eyes, and mouthparts of the imago are formed from clusters of cells called **imaginal disks,** because they form structures characteristic of the adult or imaginal instar. These disks can be removed from one larva and implanted into the body of another, where they will develop into extra organs.

The mechanism of metamorphosis has been known only in recent years and is by no means completely understood. The first clues came from tying ligatures around caterpillars a short time before metamorphosis. If this is done at different body levels, the part of the body in which the brain is located molts to the pupal stage while the part on the other side of the ligature from the brain remains in the caterpillar stage. Figure 17–33 shows a similar experiment using the readily available bluebottle fly maggot. Implanting certain glands into the part of the larva that has been constricted off from its own brain results in that part metamorphosing also.

Metamorphosis has been analyzed in this country using *Platysamia* (*Hyalophora*) *cecropia,* the large American silk moth, *Drosophila,* and *Periplaneta,* the cockroach, and in England using a blood-sucking bug, *Rhodnius.* At first it seemed as though each insect might be different, but as has happened with respiration and many other matters, the underlying mechanisms turned out to be remarkably alike. Large cells in the brain, so-called **neurosecretory cells,** se-

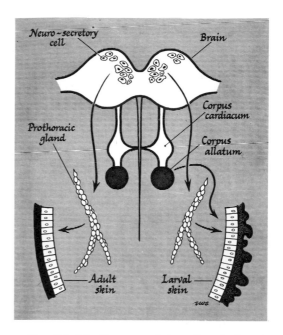

Fig. 17–34. Hormone interaction in insect metamorphosis.

crete a growth and differentiation hormone. This hormone functions, as do the hormones of the pituitary gland at the base of the brain in vertebrates, by stimulating a second gland. This is the prothoracic gland, in moths and bugs located in the prothorax; in flies, close beside the brain. The hormone of the **prothoracic glands, ecdysone,** acts on the skin and other structures, inducing them to grow and molt. Thus ecdysone seems to correspond to the hormone of the Y organ in crustaceans. Chemically it is an unsaturated ketone. But this system is regulated by a hormone from a pair of small glands, the corpora allata, located a short distance from the brain. Each **corpus allatum** (*corpus,* body, + *allatum,* brought to) is connected to a **corpus cardiacum** (*cardiacum,* heartlike), the whole making up a so-called **"ring gland,"** which in turn is connected to the brain by a pair of nerves. The hormone of the corpora allata is known as the **juvenile hormone** because, as long as it is abundant, larval molts occur but not metamorphosis. If the corpora allata are surgically removed, the following molt will result in metamorphosis into the adult form. If extra corpora allata are implanted before the final molt, the molt will not yield the adult but another juvenile or larval form.

If such a hormonal control of metamorphosis exists, then it should be possible to produce

Fig. 17–33. The basic constriction experiment to demonstrate the role of hormones in insect metamorphosis. The brain is represented in the illustration by a pair of rounded ganglia. Note that the portion of the maggot that turns dark (adult) is always the part that contains the brain.

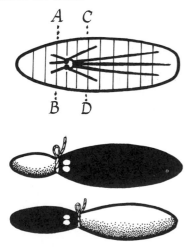

dwarf insects by removing the source of the juvenile hormone, the corpora allata, and to produce giant insects by adding such bodies. These feats have been achieved. By extirpating the corpora allata of a silkworm caterpillar in the next to the last larval instar, a Japanese worker has obtained dwarf adults, *B* in Figure 17–35. By extirpation in the next to the next to the last larval instar he has obtained still smaller dwarfs. Similar results have been attained by American workers with cockroaches. Similarly, giant-sized walking stick insects, grasshoppers, and bugs (*Rhodnius*) have all been produced by implanting extra corpora allata. (See Fig. 17–36.)

How are these three hormones regulated in the normal insect? Much remains to be learned here, but a beginning has been made. The nervous system plays an important role, as is shown by the direct connection of the corpora allata with the nervous system and the dependence of both these and the prothoracic glands on the neurosecretory cells in the brain. Work on the American silkworm, *Platysamia* (*Hyalophora*) *cecropia,* has shown that the brain must

Fig. 17–36. Above: normal adult walking stick. Below: giant produced after three extra molts caused by implantation of nymphal corpora allata into last instar nymph. (*From Roeder,* Insect Physiology, *Wiley*)

be chilled for a certain time before it will release the hormone that activates the prothoracic gland. This is an important mechanism in the life history of any insect which has but one generation per year, because it prevents an individual from developing through metamorphosis and hatching in the late summer or fall. Since the brains of these moths must be exposed to at least two weeks of cold, a sudden cold spell in the early fall will not set the insect off to a premature start.

The action of the juvenile hormone from the corpora allata and the growth and differentiation hormone of the prothoracic glands seems to be in an antagonistic balance. Implanting extra prothoracic glands in early larval stages has a similar but less dramatic effect than extirpation of the corpora allata. There is also evidence that the act of molting in some way, through the nervous system or through the body fluids, influences the endocrine activity of the brain, thus constituting a feedback system. In some insects, like the bug *Rhodnius,* nervous impulses from the stomach after a full meal appear to be an important stimulus to set off the neurosecretory activity of the brain. Recent studies on *Platysamia* (*Hyalophora*) *cecropia* have shown that brains which are not secreting a hormone are electrically silent (that is, send out no brain waves) and that choinesterase, an enzyme essential for nervous function, is absent.

Fig. 17–35. Artificially produced dwarf silkworm moths. *A,* very small cocoon and moth produced when corpora allata were removed in the third larval instar. *B,* small cocoon and moth produced when corpora allata were removed in the fourth larval instar. *C,* normal cocoon and moth.

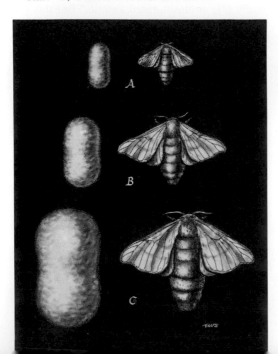

Review and References

REVIEW TOPICS

1. Characterize the four chief groups of mandibulate arthropods.

2. Describe the ecological or economic importance of five groups of crustaceans.

3. Discuss the evolutionary meaning of the correlation between form and function in the appendages of a lobster or a crayfish.

4. What mechanisms control molting and regeneration in crustaceans?

5. What types of metamorphosis are found among insects and what physiological mechanisms are involved? What advantage is metamorphosis to the insect?

6. Compare and contrast the respiratory, excretory, nervous, and vascular systems of crustaceans and insects.

7. Describe the structure and discuss the function of compound eyes.

8. Contrast the structure and habits of millipedes and centipedes.

9. Document the economic and medical importance of insects.

10. On what criteria are the orders of insects separated?

11. Give the diagnostic traits, life histories, and ecological, economic, or medical importance of any ten orders of insects.

12. Define: exoskeleton, nauplius, exopterygotous, instar, endemic, malpighian tubule, ommatidium, mandible, corpora allata, prothoracic gland.

13. What facts seem chiefly responsible for the great biological success of insects?

14. Discuss insect behavior as contrasted with the behavior of vertebrates.

USEFUL REFERENCES

Crustacea and General

Faust, E. C., *Animal Agents and Vectors of Human Disease*, Philadelphia, Lea & Febiger, 1935.

Green, J., *A Biology of Crustacea*, Chicago, Quadrangle Books, 1961.

Pennak, R. W., *Fresh-Water Invertebrates of the United States*, New York, The Ronald Press Company, 1953.

Pratt, H. S., *Manual of the Common Invertebrate Animals*, Philadelphia, P. Blakiston's Son & Co., 1935.

Waterman, T. H., ed., *The Physiology of Crustacea: I, Metabolism and Growth; II, Sense Organs, Integration, and Behavior,* New York, Academic Press, 1961.

Insects

Barrass, R., *The Locust (Grasshopper), A Guide for Laboratory Practical Work*, London, Butterworth, 1964.

Bates, M., *The Natural History of Mosquitoes*, New York, The Macmillan Company, 1949.

Brues, C. T., A. L. Melander, and F. M. Carpenter, *Classification of Insects*, Cambridge, Mass., Museum of Comparative Zoology, Bull. 108, 1954.

Ehrlich, P. R., and A. H. Ehrlich, *How to Know the Butterflies*, Dubuque, Iowa, William C. Brown Company, 1961.

Fabre, J. H. C., *Insect World* (1914), E. W. Teale, ed., New York, Dodd, Mead & Co., 1949.

Jaques, H. E., *How to Know the Beetles*, Dubuque, Iowa, W. C. Brown Company, 1951.

Jaques, H. E., *How to Know the Insects*, Dubuque, Iowa, W. C. Brown Company, 1951.

Klots, A. B., *A Field Guide to the Butterflies*, Boston, Houghton Mifflin Company, 1951.

Lutz, F. E., *Field Book of Insects*, 3rd ed., New York, G. P. Putnam's Sons, 1935.

Macy, R. W., and H. H. Shepard, *Butterflies*, Minneapolis, Univ. of Minnesota Press, 1941.

Michener, C. D., and M. H. Michener, *American Social Insects*, Princeton, N. J., D. Van Nostrand Co., 1951.

Patterson, J. T., and W. S. Stone, *Evolution in the Genus Drosophila*, New York, The Macmillan Company, 1952.

Roeder, K. D., *Nerve Cells and Insect Behavior*, Cambridge, Mass., Harvard University Press, 1963.

Roeder, K. D., ed., *Insect Physiology*, New York, John Wiley & Sons, 1953.

Snodgrass, R. E., *Anatomy of the Honeybee*, Ithaca, N. Y., Comstock Publishing Associates, 1956.

Wheeler, W. M., *Foibles of Insects and Men*, New York, Alfred A. Knopf, 1928.

Part V

Deuterostome Branch of the Animal

Kingdom

Compared with the protostomes, the deuterostome branch of the animal kingdom is small, but since man is clearly a deuterostome we can hardly regard them as unimportant. The 80,000 or more species of deuterostomes are divided into about 55,000 chordates, mostly vertebrates, and about 26,000 echinoderms, mostly extinct, plus one or more minor phyla of uncertain affinities.

Deuterostomes are united by five basic developmental and anatomical characteristics. In recent years biochemical evidence of their relationship has also been found.

1. As the name implies (*deutero,* secondary, + *stoma,* mouth), the mouth is formed as a second opening into the gut of the embryo, and not from the blastopore, which is the first opening and which in this branch of the animal kingdom becomes the anus.

2. The main axis of the nervous system runs close to the surface and, in the chordates, it runs along the upper or dorsal side. Hence in French the deuterostomes are called *epineuriens.*

3. The cleavage of the egg is radial rather than spiral, and the first few cells, if separated from each other, are each capable of developing into a complete embryo in most species.

4. The body cavity or coelom is budded off from the gut of the early embryo.

5. If a small ciliated larva is formed, it resembles the pluteus larva of a sea urchin.

The biochemical evidence for the distinction between protostomes and deuterostomes concerns two compounds important in energy cycles of muscular contraction. Muscles of vertebrates contain creatine phosphate; those of invertebrates utilize arginine phosphate for the same function. If echinoderms and the most primitive chordates, the acorn worms or enteropneusts, really belong in the same division of the animal kingdom as the vertebrates, they should use creatine phosphate in their muscles. They do, although not in all species. Many groups of invertebrates have been tested — coelenterates, flatworms, mollusks, crustaceans, and others. The only organisms found using creatine phosphate except chordates and echinoderms are a few polychaete annelids.

The two great divisions of the deuterostomes, echinoderms and chordates, seem at first so utterly different that a close relationship appears fantastic. In mode of life and in bodily design the two are far apart indeed. Yet a second look at a dog and a starfish will reveal not only the anatomical, developmental, and biochemical points of agreement listed above, but more. Alone among the phyla, these two have a dermo-muscular body wall with an inner endoskeleton that is largely calcareous.

Chapter 18

Echinoderms and Minor Deuterostomes

The nonchordate deuterostomes are exclusively marine. The echinoderms constitute the major phylum. Also included among deuterostomes are two minor groups, the chaetognaths or arrow-worms and the pogonophors.

THE ECHINODERMS

Importance. Echinoderms constitute a well-defined phylum of moderate size, having about 6,000 living and 20,000 fossil species. They are exclusively marine and are found from tide lines to great depths. The economic importance of echinoderms is chiefly negative. Sea stars, better known as starfish, are destructive to clams and oysters, on which they prey. The long slender spines of tropical sea urchins are a menace to divers. On the positive side, *Arbacia*, the commonest sea urchin along the western shores of the Atlantic, from Cape Cod to Yucatan and throughout the West Indies, has become a standard laboratory animal for the cell physiologist. The eggs of sea urchins and starfish are favorite experimental material for embryologists. In the Orient and in the Mediterranean, sea cucumbers are eaten, as trepang in Singapore, bêche-de-mer in Marseilles. Sea urchin eggs are also edible.

Echinoderms have been known from ancient times. Aristotle himself described the beautifully precise and complex jaw apparatus of sea urchins over 2,000 years ago. About 1800 Lamarck brought together in one group most of the animals we know as echinoderms, and by a half century later they were regarded as constituting a separate phylum.

Characteristics. Echinoderms are characterized in five ways.

1. They possess a calcareous endoskeleton, commonly with spines. It is this trait that gives them their name (*echinos,* hedgehog [spiny], + *derma,* skin). Even the longest spines of a sea urchin, those which appear like exoskeletal structures, are in fact actually covered by a thin layer of living cells which have secreted the bony spine.

2. Adults show a conspicuous radial symmetry. Usually it is a five-rayed symmetry, although there are some exceptions. From the St. Lawrence River northward there is found a common species of starfish which normally has six arms, and from Puget Sound northward there is a very different species which also possesses six arms. In many seas occur the solasters, which may have 20 or more rays.

404

3. A third and completely unique feature of echinoderms is their water-vascular system. This is a locomotor system consisting of a circular duct, the **ring canal** around the esophagus, and five long water-filled ducts, the **radial canals,** that extend out from it, one along each ray. There is also a calcified canal that extends from the ring canal up to the aboral surface, i.e., the surface away from the mouth. On the aboral surface this **stone canal** ends in a sievelike disk, the **madreporite,** often called the "eye." It is thought to serve as an intake valve for the water-vascular system. Arranged in pairs along the five radial canals are the **tube feet.** These are hollow muscular tubes. On the inner end of each is an expanded bulb and on the protruding end, a suction disk. By contracting the muscles of the bulb and simultaneously relaxing those of the protruding tube, the foot can be greatly extended, and by contractions of the musculature on one or another side of the tube, the foot can be bent in any direction.

4. Most echinoderms have a capacious coelom into which project the bulbous inner ends of the tube feet, the alimentary canal, and the gonads.

5. The echinoderm egg develops into a bilateral larva; in sea urchins a **pluteus,** in starfish a **bipinnaria.** The larvae bear a more or less complicated but bilaterally symmetrical pattern of ciliated bands on the surface. The adult is always formed by a profound metamorphosis.

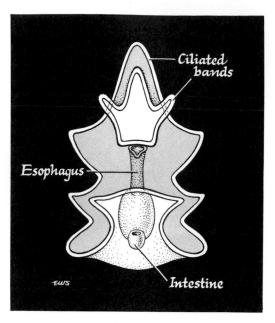

Fig. 18–2. Semi-microscopic bilateral larva of an echinoderm.

Evolutionary Relationships. Except that echinoderms are clearly deuterostomes and hence related to the chordates, their evolutionary relationships, either to other animals or among themselves, are obscure. From their development it may be inferred that the original ancestor was a bilaterally symmetrical creature called a **dipleurula.** While this seems plausible, there is no definite evidence to support the idea,

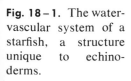

Fig. 18–1. The water-vascular system of a starfish, a structure unique to echinoderms.

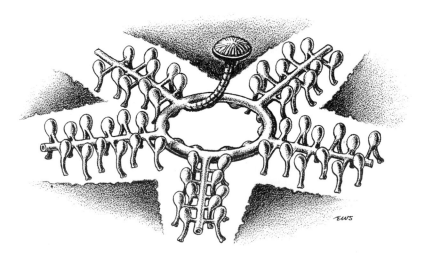

so the dipleurula remains, in the words of Hyman, a contemporary student of echinoderms, "merely a name for features common to present echinoderm larvae."

The rich fossil record of the echinoderms takes all five of the living groups plus seven extinct ones back to or well within the Cambrian, the most ancient rocks with appreciable numbers of fossils. The only conclusion that can be drawn from these earliest representatives is that the most ancient and generalized echinoderms were sessile, like present-day sea lilies. Apparently the ancestral dipleurula became attached and in the course of ages evolved a calcareous endoskeleton, and tentacles formed from fingerlike protrusions of the coelom. These coelomic tentacles became converted into the tube feet. In any case the entire water-vascular system develops from an embryonic coelomic sac.

Major Groups. There are two subphyla of echinoderms.

1. The more primitive is the **Pelmatozoa** (*pelmatos*, foot, + *zoa*, animals), in which the animal is attached to the bottom, usually by an aboral stalk, at least during youth. The mouth faces upward, and the tube feet are primarily feeding tentacles. The food consists of minute particles of dead or dying microorganisms falling from upper levels of the ocean. This detritus is collected in the ciliated **ambulacral grooves** (called ambulacral because they are the alleys where the feet or ambulatory organs are) between the double rows of tube feet and is swept by the ciliary current into the mouth.

The sea lilies, Class Crinoidea (*krinon*, lily), are the only living class of Pelmatozoa. Crinoids are usually found today growing in deep cold water. At widely separated spots on the ocean floor, where conditions are exactly right, there must be small forests of crinoids up to 3 feet high, for on rare occasions a dredge will bring up thousands of stalked crinoids from a single haul. A commoner group of crinoids, known as comatulids, break off from their stalks as adults and slowly, very slowly, wander about. From the body or calyx of a crinoid extend five arms, each of which branches dichotomously one or more times to produce ten, twenty, or more divisions each provided

Fig. 18-3. Photo of a living crinoid, a sea lily. Life size. *(Science Service)*

with a ciliated ambulacral groove leading ultimately into the mouth at the center of the body disk. From the sides of the stalk and sometimes of the arms are commonly minor branches. Most of the time crinoids, whether stalked or free, lie quiescent with their ambulacral grooves facing upward to catch food particles. Four fossil classes of Pelmatozoa have been discovered.

2. The second subphylum is composed of the free-living echinoderms, or **Eleutherozoa** (*eleutheros*, free, + *zoa*, animals), which include four living groups of echinoderms. At no time in their lives are they stalked, the mouth faces downwards or sideways, and the tube feet are used for locomotion rather than food gathering. Fossil evidence tends to relate the starfish to the brittle stars, and the sea urchins to the holothurians (sea cucumbers). The evidence from embryology, however, places the starfish with the holothurians, and the sea urchins with the brittle stars. Recent biochemical evidence, based on the type of sterols present, supports the embryological evidence. The starfish and holothurians form a special kind of sterol called stellasterol while the sea urchins and brittle

stars form cholesterol in much the same manner as do the vertebrates.

(a) The sea stars (starfish), Class **Asteroidea** (*aster*, star), are the most familiar. The arms are broad at the base and taper toward the distal end. A large coelom extends into the arms and contains the gonads and digestive glands. The madreporite is usually conspicuous on the aboral surface. With the subjacent stone canal it establishes a plane of bilateral organization. The two arms adjacent to the madreporite are referred to as the **bivium**, the remaining three as the **trivium**.

Sea stars vary greatly in color and form, although the vast majority have five arms. The mud-eating starfish have such short broad rays that they are virtual pentagons.

(b) The brittle stars, Class **Ophiuroidea** (*ophis*, snake), are common just below low-tide lines nearly everywhere, but are much less familiar than starfish because they are strongly and negatively phototropic as well as strongly and positively thigmotropic. Consequently they remain in the dark, in close physical contact with some solid object. If you uncover one by turning over a rock, it will quickly slither under another or a bit of sea weed. The disk is round and the wormlike arms are sharply demarcated from it.

Fig. 18–4. A sea star righting itself. *(Kindness of Ralph Buchsbaum)*

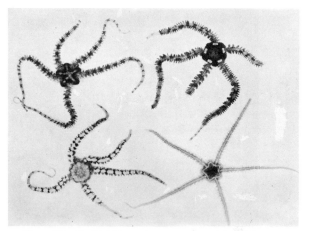

Fig. 18–5. Brittle stars, or ophiuroids, one-fourth life size. No two have identical color patterns.

In contrast to starfish, in brittle stars the arms are almost solid and composed of a series of calcareous ossicles called, with questionable accuracy, vertebrae. The snakelike writhing of the arms is brought about by intervertebral muscles. The coelom in the arms is greatly reduced. The tube feet have no inner bulbs or suction disks and are used merely as sense organs, not for locomotion as in the starfish. The gonads are located in pouches that swell out from the edges of the disk between the bases of the arms.

(c) The sea urchins and sand dollars, Class **Echinoidea** (*echinos*, spiny), may be thought of as starfish in which the upper or aboral body wall of the arms has been cut away and the five arms then pulled upward to meet over the center, making the starfish into the shape of an onion. The body of an actual sea urchin is a somewhat flattened sphere with a mouth on the under side at the lower pole and, at the upper pole, a centrally placed anus surrounded by four or more calcareous plates (four in *Arbacia*). Around these are five genital plates with openings through which the gametes reach the exterior. One of the genital plates serves also as a madreporite. (See Fig. 18–6.)

The body wall consists of a very thin epithelium overlying a shell or test, composed of tightly fitting calcareous plates like tiles on a floor. After death, if both the spines and the flesh are removed, the shell reveals five double

Fig. 18–6. Left: shell, life size, of *Arbacia*, the sea urchin, widely used in research. Aboral (upper) side with spines removed. Right: close-up, slightly enlarged, of living sea urchin showing mouth, tube feet, and spines on oral (under) surface. *(Kindness of E. B. Harvey, William H. Amos)*

rows of paired holes extending from the mouth up along five meridians and converging in between the five genital plates at the aboral pole. In sea urchins each tube foot connects with its bulb on the inner side of the shell by two small tubes passing through the calcareous plate. Consequently a single row of tube feet is represented by a row of paired holes. Visible also on the sea urchin shell are five double rows of plates with knobs for the attachment of spines.

Sand dollars and heart urchins have a structure resembling a sea urchin, except that they are flattened, the movable spines are very small, and the five double rows of tube feet are reduced to a petallike pattern on the upper or aboral surface. The anal opening is frequently at one edge of the shell. Many sand dollars have oval holes called **lunules,** regularly placed like so many keyholes, through their disks. Apparently these lunules aid the sand dollar to bury itself in the sand. Some Japanese investigators have found that if the lunules are filled with paraffin, righting and burrowing in the sand become very difficult. Sea urchins are found in oceans everywhere, usually on rocky bottoms; sand dollars, on sandy bottoms.

(d) The sea cucumbers, as they were called by Pliny, Class **Holothuroidea** (*holothurion*, a water polyp), are a widely distributed class of echinoderms, although not as well known to the general public as most of the other groups. They may be thought of as greatly elongated sea urchins with soft flexible bodies bearing a circle of ten highly branched tentacles around the mouth. The dermal skeleton, instead of forming a rigid shell, has been reduced to scattered ossicles in the form of minute perforated wheels, anchors, and spicules. The five rows of tube feet extend from one end of the body to the other. Commonly three of these rows crawl along the substratum while two rows wave in the water. The ten branched tentacles around the mouth are hollow and are part of the water-vascular system. Apparently they have evolved from tube feet. A few aberrant species are wormlike and lack tube feet, and a few deep-sea species are very short, with rows of pointed projections along their sides and backs that make them resemble prickly slugs.

The typical holothurian resembles a big black or dark brown cucumber slowly crawling along the bottom or adhering to the side of a wharf

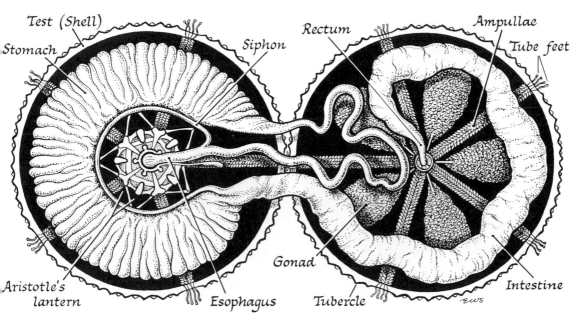

Test (Shell)
Stomach
Siphon
Rectum
Ampullae
Tube feet
Gonad
Aristotle's lantern
Esophagus
Tubercle
Intestine

Fig. 18–7. General structure, life size, of *Arbacia,* the sea urchin. The shell, or test, has been cut horizontally and the oral half laid to the left. The spines are omitted.

pile. From time to time one of the ten oral tentacles is bent over and pushed down inside the mouth. The small animals that have fallen on the tentacles or have been swept up by them are scraped off as the tentacle is slowly pulled out of the mouth. The opening at the opposite end of the animal serves both for the egestion of indigestible particles and for respiration.

Opening from this cloaca are two long branching systems of tubes, called **respiratory trees,** which ramify through the spacious coelom. A regularly alternating respiratory current of water is maintained in and out of the trees.

Aside from their use as food in the Orient and in southern France, holothurians are perhaps best known for their remarkable powers of

Fig. 18–8. Sand dollars. *(Kindness of Ralph Buchsbaum)*

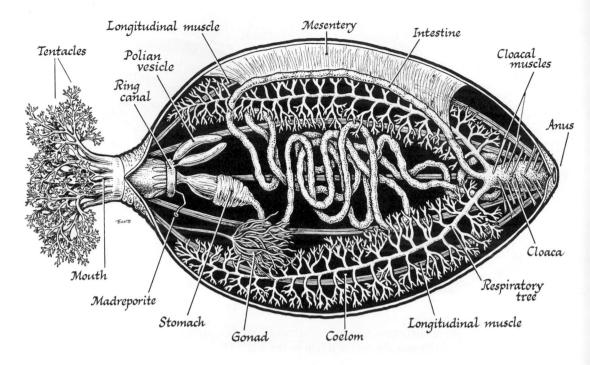

Tentacles · Longitudinal muscle · Polian vesicle · Ring canal · Mesentery · Intestine · Cloacal muscles · Anus · Cloaca · Respiratory tree · Longitudinal muscle · Coelom · Gonad · Stomach · Madreporite · Mouth

Fig. 18–9. Internal anatomy of a holothurian, or sea cucumber, shown life size. (Semi-diagrammatic)

regeneration. When attacked by an enemy such as a lobster or fish (or when immersed in 0.1 per cent ammonium hydroxide in sea water), most sea cucumbers eviscerate themselves, spewing out intestine, respiratory trees, tentacles, muscles, and even gonads. All these structures are later regenerated from the torn stumps which remain within the otherwise empty body. During the process the entire animal grows smaller, since the various organs are regenerated at the expense of the body wall.

FUNCTIONAL SYSTEMS OF ECHINODERMS

Effector Systems. The primary effectors of echinoderms are the muscles, which are organized around three kinds of structures: the water-vascular system, the skeleton, especially the spines, and the pedicellarias. The water-vascular system, already described, is much the same in all echinoderms.

The muscles of starfish extend between the skeletal plates or ossicles in the body wall and are responsible for the slow, bending move-ments of the arms. In sea urchins the large movable spines are connected to the shell by a double circlet of muscles. These muscles enable a spine to point in any direction within a wide circle. The inner circlet of muscle maintains a firm constant tonus, holding the spine rigid in a set position. Physiologically it has a "locking" function similar to the crescent-shaped locking adductor muscle in a clam. The other circle of muscles moves the spine in various directions.

The **pedicellarias** are sinister-looking little structures consisting of a longer or shorter flexible and muscular neck bearing two or three sharp little jaws. Many bear a poison sac. Pedicellarias are found scattered over the aboral surface of starfish and between the spines of sea urchins. Their function seems to be to keep the surface of the animal free of small parasites and of sessile animals that might grow on it the way barnacles, sponges, hydroids, bryozoans, and other such creatures foul ships' bottoms and cover rocks and pilings along seashores.

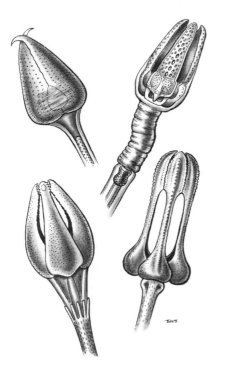

Fig. 18–10. Types of pedicellarias, as seen under a compound microscope. Above: left, bidentate (sand dollar); right, tridentate *(Arbacia).* Below: left, globiferous *(Eucidaris, a sea urchin);* right, tridentate *(Clypeaster,* a sand dollar).

Fig. 18–11. Aristotle's lantern.

Aristotle's Lantern. The most remarkable effector in echinoderms is the jaw apparatus, which Aristotle described as resembling a "horn lantern with the panes of horn left out." "Aristotle's lantern" is one of the most intricate and beautiful structures in the entire animal kingdom, vertebrate or invertebrate. Each of the five white calcareous teeth resembles the elongate incisor of a rat, and like these it grows from a persistently growing root which, in the sea urchins, can be seen curving inward over the top of the lantern. Each tooth is held in a triangular pyramid of bone. The five pyramids are firmly held together in a pentagonal lantern by short, strong muscle fibers which unite them side by side and pull the five teeth together. The entire lantern and hence the teeth are protruded from the shell by five pairs of protractor muscles extending from the top of the lantern to the edge of the shell. Five pairs of antagonists, the retractors of the lantern, pull the lantern into the shell. They extend from the bottom of the lantern to raised, earlike bases called **auricles** on the edge of the shell. Other muscles account for fine movements of the teeth. In all, there are 40 skeletal parts in a lantern.

Digestive and Circulatory Systems. Except for Aristotle's lantern, the most notable fact about the echinoderm digestive system is the way in

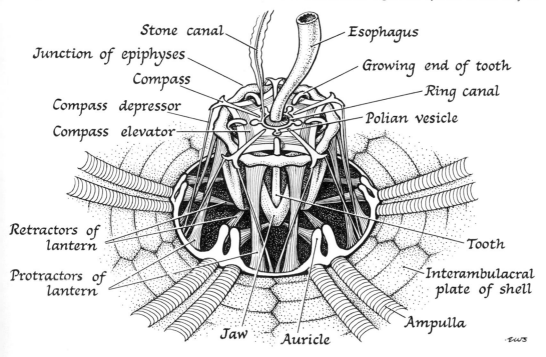

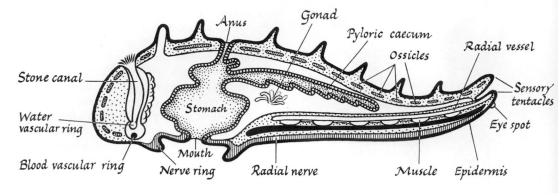

Fig. 18–12. Interior of a starfish (longi-section of an arm). Note the superficial position of the nerve ring around the mouth and on the under side of the arm. *(After MacDougall and Hegner,* Biology, *McGraw-Hill Book Co. Copyright 1943. Used by permission)*

which starfish pull open the shells of clams and oysters and then extrude their stomachs out of their mouths to enclose and digest the unfortunate bivalve.

The blood-vascular system of echinoderms is poorly developed except in holothurians, where an extensive system of blood vessels including a pulsating "heart" is present in some of the larger species. *Thyone,* a common mud-living species, is almost unique among invertebrates because it possesses blood cells containing hemoglobin. Invertebrate hemoglobin is usually merely dissolved in the blood plasma. Special excretory organs are absent unless tiny pimples on the surface of starfish serve such a function.

Nervous System. The nervous system consists of three divisions. The main division, called the **ectoneural** because of its superficial position, is made up of a ring of nervous tissue around the mouth or esophagus plus five radial nerves, one along each arm. In the sea stars these nerves are actually in contact with the sea water in the ambulacral grooves on the under (oral) side of the arms. The **hypodermal** and the **aboral** divisions parallel the ectoneural, the hypodermal beneath the skin and the aboral close to the aboral (upper) surface.

The most remarkable activity of the ectoneural system is the coordination of the direction of stepping of the tube feet (see page 418). Each foot acts independently of all the rest in the timing of its steps so that, when viewed as the animal climbs the side of an aquarium, the wildest confusion seems to reign. But all the tube feet on the same arm will step in the same direction with respect to the long axis of the arm even though they have to make a very different angle to that axis from the stepping feet in the adjacent arms.

The chief sense organs are small tentacles and eyespots close to the tips of the arms. Each eyelet consists of a lens, a vitreous chamber, and a retina with both light-sensitive and pigment cells. Some species have 200 such eyespots while others have virtually none.

Pigments. The black pigment of echinoderms is the familiar melanin, which, like adrenalin, is a derivative of the amino acid tyrosine. The red pigment is a naphthoquinone called echinochrome, with a structural formula of two benzene rings side by side and a short side chain of carbon and hydrogen. It was first studied and named by MacMunn, the discoverer of cytochrome. Echinoderms also produce steroids and large amounts of the carotenoid vitamin A pigments.

Reproductive System. The sexes are separate in echinoderms. The gametes are usually squirted out in innumerable millions into the sea water, where fertilization occurs at random. Virtually nothing is known about any mechanism which insures synchronous spawning, but

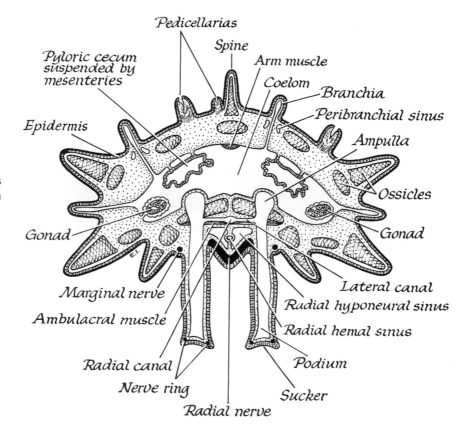

Fig. 18–13. Cross section of a starfish arm.

Pedicellarias

Spine

Pyloric cecum suspended by mesenteries

Arm muscle

Coelom

Branchia

Peribranchial sinus

Epidermis

Ampulla

Ossicles

Gonad

Gonad

Marginal nerve

Ambulacral muscle

Lateral canal

Radial hyponeural sinus

Radial hemal sinus

Radial canal

Podium

Nerve ring

Sucker

Radial nerve

Fig. 18–14. Longi-section of a single eye-spot of *Asterias*, as seen under a compound microscope.

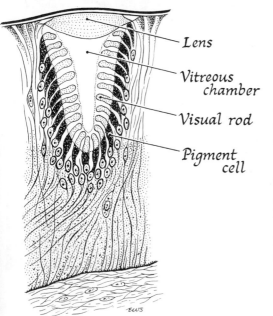

Lens

Vitreous chamber

Visual rod

Pigment cell

many kinds of injury and shock will induce almost immediate shedding of gametes in a ripe sea urchin. The best method of obtaining fully ripe eggs or sperms is that devised by the late Ethel B. Harvey. As shown in Figure 18–15, she applied to the sides of a sea urchin electrodes carrying alternating current of the strength used to ring doorbells. Within about a minute, from the five aboral genital pores, five streams of eggs or sperms appear.

In the summer of 1875 the great German embryologist and humanitarian, Oskar Hertwig, discovered that he could follow in detail all the events of fertilization in the eggs of starfish. Ever since, starfish and sea urchin eggs have been favorites of students of development and cell physiology. They are easy to obtain and handle, and develop rapidly.

The common echinoderm egg cell, before becoming haploid by meiosis, has a very large nucleus with a prominent nucleolus. This large

Fig. 18–15. Electrical stimulation of spawning in *Arbacia,* a common sea urchin, shown life size. The male is shown in the left photo and the female in the right. The dark rods are electrodes from a transformer delivering doorbell current. Note the white masses of sperms and the elongate piles of (reddish) eggs. *(Kindness of Ethel B. Harvey)*

diploid nucleus was long ago named the **germinal vesicle.** In the process of maturation it breaks down and its contents mingle with the egg cytoplasm. The two meiotic divisions produce the first and second polar bodies (see page 153), which appear at the upper or animal pole of the egg. The lower pole was named the **vegetal pole** many years ago from its supposed vegetative or plantlike functions. The egg is now haploid and ready for fertilization.

The sea urchin sperm has a short, conical head with a sharp point. The head contains the haploid set of chromosomes, for *Arbacia* 18 or 19 — the chromosomes are so small that it is extremely difficult to be certain of the number. The midpiece is fairly prominent and contains two spheres, probably centrosomes which act as division centers in the first cell division. The tail is long and threadlike.

Fertilization may be seen by placing ripe eggs in a watch glass of sea water, adding a sea water suspension of sperms with a medicine dropper, and then observing under a compound microscope. As soon as the head of a sperm has entered the cytoplasm, a fertilization, or vitelline, membrane appears around the egg. This

Fig. 18–16. Albino female sea urchin that has been cut open to reveal the ovary filling most of the animal. *(Kindness of Ethel B. Harvey)*

membrane keeps other sperms out and holds the cleaving cells of blastomeres together. It is now a zygote by the fact of fertilization. The head of the sperm slowly enlarges within the egg cytoplasm to form a nucleus, the so-called male **pronucleus.** It comes to lie alongside the female or egg pronucleus, also haploid. Thus the zygote becomes diploid, with two sets of chromosomes, one of maternal and one of paternal origin. The first subsequent cell division, being a normal mitosis, will apportion a set of maternal plus a set of paternal chromosomes to each of the first two cells.

Cleavage. Cleavage, which is a succession of mitotic cell divisions, is of the typical deuterostome type called radial. Each of the first several blastomeres are **totipotent;** that is, if separated from each other, each blastomere can develop into a complete though small embryo. This amazing discovery was made by Hans Driesch in the closing years of the last century and promptly went to the heads of some zoologists who could not imagine how any scientifically comprehensible mechanism could have such remarkable powers of self-regulation. No machine, they said, can be cut in four parts, and each part form a whole.

The egg cleaves into a ball of cells, the **morula,** which by further mitotic cell divisions produces a hollow ball of cells, the **blastula.** The blastula is converted into a **gastrula** by gastrulation, a process whereby cells from the lower or vegetal pole invaginate to produce a tubular cavity, the primitive gut or **archenteron** (*archi-,* first, + *enteron,* gut). The original opening of the archenteron to the exterior is the **blastopore,** which in echinoderms, as in deuterostomes generally, becomes the anus. A new mouth is later formed at the opposite end of the gut. At the inner end of the archenteron, in late gastrula stages, there can be seen a pair of outpocketings from the primitive gut. These will form the coelom and the water-vascular system. The gastrula develops into the larva.

Larvae. The larvae of echinoderms are minute and so very different from the adults that without observation of their metamorphosis a relationship would never be suspected. The larvae are bilateral with a symmetrical pattern

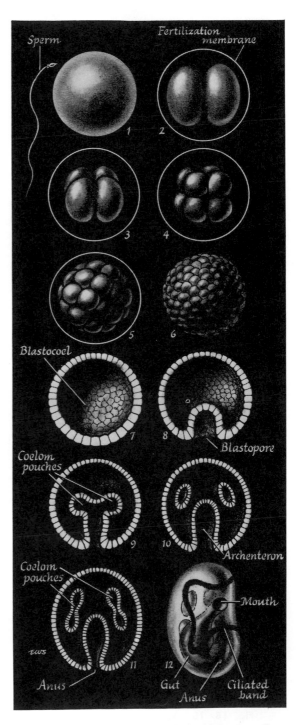

Fig. 18–17. Cleavage and development of an echinoderm egg. Note budding of coelom pouches (sacs) from the archenteron.

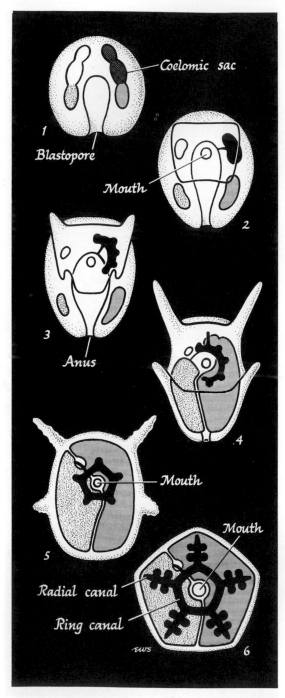

Fig. 18–18. Development of a starfish, as seen from below. One of the coelomic sacs becomes the water-vascular system (black) while the others form the coelom.

of ciliated bands over the surface. Internally their anatomy is extremely simple. There is a roughly C-shaped gut extending from a broadly open mouth to an anus. On either side of the gut is a coelomic sac, each of which consists, in early development, of three pouches—anterior, middle, and posterior. The two posterior pouches form the coelom of the adult, the left middle one becomes the water-vascular system. The rest degenerate very early in the development of the larva. In some classes of echinoderms the bilateral larva develops several pairs of rod-shaped "arms" which may contain calcareous skeletal rods.

The larvae of the five living echinoderm classes differ considerably in external appearance. The asteroid larva, which metamorphoses into a starfish, is known as a **bipinnaria**. Its structure is close to the supposed ancestral form and it lacks long arms. However, it changes into a second larval form known as a **brachiolaria** which has long, more or less flexible arms (*brachium*, arm). The brachiolaria becomes attached to a rock or some other object by its anterior end. The free posterior end then forms the starfish. This metamorphosis is so profound it almost amounts to an alternation of generations.

The best-known echinoderm larva is the **pluteus** of the echinoids because sea urchins are so much used in research. The larvae of ophiuroids, or brittle stars, are also plutei. A pluteus is basically like a bipinnaria but becomes roughly triangular in shape with the growth of two or more pairs of long thin arms with calcareous skeletons. The adult develops from part of the left side of the fully grown pluteus. (See Fig. 18–21.)

The larva of a holothurian or a crinoid is called a **doliolaria** because of its barrel-shaped body (*doliolum*, a small cask). This kind of larva also closely resembles a bipinnaria, but is perhaps even simpler. The body is shaped like a short fat cigar which the ciliated bands encircle like so many cigar bands. Because the fossil evidence indicates that the crinoids are the oldest class of echinoderms, the resemblance of the larvae of holothurians to those of the crinoids suggests that the sea cucumbers are the second most ancient and primitive echinoderm group.

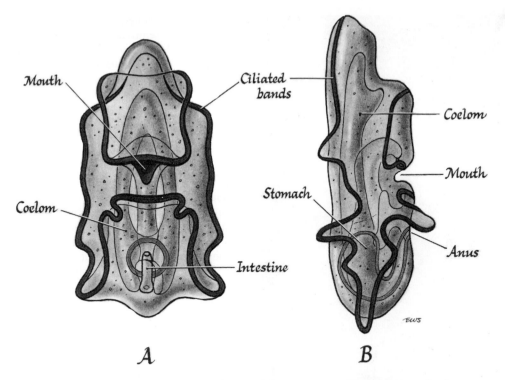

Fig. 18–19. Bipinnaria (larva) of a starfish, as seen under a compound microscope. *A,* ventral view. *B,* lateral view. Note the elaborate ciliated bands, simple gut and coelom.

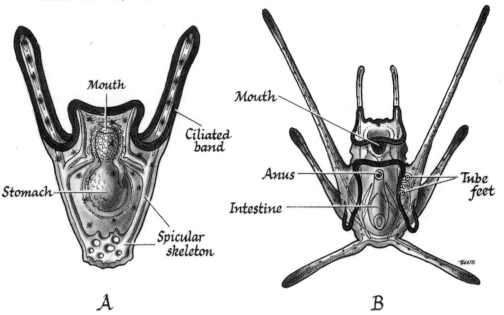

Fig. 18–20. Pluteus (larva) of a sea urchin. *A,* dorsal view of a young pluteus. *B,* ventral view of a mature pluteus.

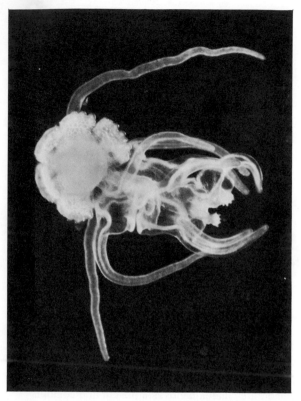

Fig. 18 – 21. Starfish in process of metamorphosis from a larva into an adult, a rare sight. Note the rudiments of the five arms on the disk-shaped adult bud. *(Roman Vishniac)*

ECOLOGY AND BEHAVIOR OF ECHINODERMS

Like other animals, echinoderms fit their environment. Sea urchins, living on the outside of a reef where the surf thunders, possess short thick spines. The sea urchin from which were obtained the pencils once used to write on school slates was such a species. In the water on the inner side of any coral reef lives the black *Diadema,* whose exceedingly long needlelike spines make a beautiful sight against the white tropical sand, but are the enemies of divers. On ordinary rocky shores live species like *Arbacia,* with spines of intermediate length and thickness.

Not very much is known about the population dynamics of echinoderms. *Arbacia* has become scarce around Cape Cod, supposedly from continuous heavy use for experimental purposes. However, over 40,000 bushels of starfish were removed in a single year from Long Island Sound oyster beds, but the benefits were difficult to evaluate. Data for several species of sea urchins indicate that full adult size is attained by the fourth or fifth year.

Compared with arthropods or vertebrates, the behavior of echinoderms is unexciting. Yet it presents some problems of general interest in the reactions of the spines of sea urchins, and a baffling phenomenon in the unidirectional stepping of the tube feet.

The easiest way to see a sea urchin's spines in activity is to turn one upside down. The spines then make frantic and ultimately successful efforts to right the animal. If a single spine is touched by a finger, it will be found that the locking muscles at the base of the spine hold it almost immovable. However, if the surface of the shell nearby is touched, the spine becomes freely movable and bends in the direction of the stimulus. This means that the second stimulus has inhibited the locking circlet of muscles at the base of the spine, and at the same time has produced a directional contraction of the outer circlet of muscles. By scraping away a narrow line between the base of the spine and the point of stimulation, it can be readily shown that impulses to the spine muscles travel in the epithelial nerve net on the surface of the shell.

When a starfish walks, the stepping of the tube feet is unidirectional but lacks unity of phase. In other words, all the thousand or so feet are out of step with each other but all step in the same direction! If one arm points in the direction of progress, all the feet step in a direction parallel to the long axis of that arm. But the feet on the four other arms must step at some angle to the long axis of their arms. How do they achieve this tricky piece of trigonometry? No complete answer has been found, although it has been discovered that if you amputate the arm of a starfish without including any of the nerve ring, all the feet step toward the cut base. If you cut deeply enough into the central disk to include a piece of the central nerve ring, then all the feet step toward the distal tip of the severed arm. However, in both cases the stepping is parallel to the long axis of the arm.

Fig. 18–22. Two types of sea urchins adapted to different habitats. Left: *Podophora* (shown life size), with short heavy spines, lives on surf-beaten rocks. Right: *Diadema* (shown about one-third life size), with long spines, inhabits quiet waters inside a coral reef. *(Courtesy, General Biological Supply House, Inc., Chicago; photograph copyright 1966 Jerry Greenberg).*

MINOR DEUTEROSTOMES

In the open ocean in all parts of the world are swift-swimming, glass-clear animals shaped like arrows. They are voracious killers and would be far more dangerous than sharks were it not for the fortunate circumstance that they are only 2 or 3 inches long. These strange animals constitute a phylum of their own, the **Chaetognatha,** so called from their rapacious jaws, armed with curved spikes or chaetae.

Zoological interest in the Chaetognatha centers on two facts. At certain times and places these arrow-worms are among the most abun-dant animals in the plankton—the floating and feebly swimming life in the sea. Consequently they must form a critical link in the great food chains of the oceans.

The other interesting point about the arrow-worms is, "What are they?" In some ways ar-row-worms suggest annelids. The body is built on the tube-within-a-tube plan, the coelom is divided by transverse septa into three divisions, the head is provided with setae, and the animal is hermaphroditic. There is a long post-anal tail, a feature characteristic of chordates. The nervous system is subepithelial. The tail fins are horizontal, like the flukes of a whale. The

Fig. 18–23. *Sagitta,* an arrow-worm or chaetognath, as seen under a dissecting microscope. (Diagrammatic.) These glass-clear, voracious animals hunt in the open sea.

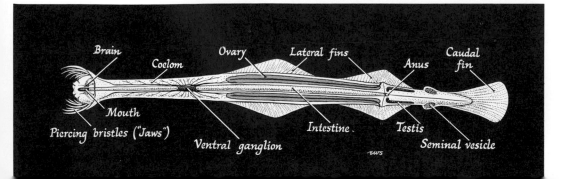

Brain   Coelom   Ovary   Lateral fins   Anus   Caudal fin

Mouth   Piercing bristles ("Jaws")   Ventral ganglion   Intestine   Testis   Seminal vesicle

mouth is a second opening into the embryonic gut, and the coelom is budded off from the gut; hence the arrow-worms are placed with the deuterostomes.

Another puzzle is the phylum **Pogonophora** which has only about 80 known species, all living at great depths in the ocean. They are wormlike animals living in parchmentlike tubes and with enough resemblances in nervous and vascular systems and in general body form to the hemichordates for some zoologists to assign them to that group. A digestive tract is com-

pletely lacking but a circle of tentacles forms a cylindrical tube which is thought to act as a digestive cavity. It is remarkable that this group of animals was completely overlooked by explorers of the ocean floor until very recently. The joke is that they are the size of earthworms and were often obtained in large numbers by dredging, but thrown overboard as nonliving debris.

Some zoologists regard three additional phyla as deuterostomes—the brachiopods, the bryozoans (except the entoprocts), and *Phoronis*.

Review and References

REVIEW TOPICS

1. What characteristics mark both echinoderms and vertebrates as deuterostomes? What other animals belong to the deuterostomes?

2. Why are echinoderm eggs especially favorable for research? How are they obtained?

3. Compare and contrast starfish (asteroids) and brittle stars (ophiuroids); starfish and sea urchins (echinoids).

4. Compare holothurians with sea urchins (echinoids); starfish (asteroids) with crinoids.

5. Describe the water-vascular, nervous, and reproductive systems of echinoderms.

6. What biochemical evidence tends to unite the various deuterostomes?

7. Define: pluteus, Aristotle's lantern, madreporite, respiratory tree, aboral, crinoid, pedicellaria, echinochrome, tube foot, chaetognath.

8. Discuss regulation and regeneration in echinoderm eggs and in adult starfish and sea cucumbers (holothurians).

9. What did the following contribute to our knowledge of echinoderms: Aristotle, Lamarck, Hertwig, Driesch, Ethel B. Harvey?

10. What is the economic and scientific importance of echinoderms?

USEFUL REFERENCES

Chadwick, H. C., *Asterias*, Liverpool, England, Marine Biological Committee, Memoirs No. 25, 1923.

Chadwick, H. C., *Echinus*, Liverpool, England, Marine Biological Committee, Memoirs No. 3, 1900.

Galtsoff, P. S., and V. L. Loosanoff, *Natural History and Method of Controlling the Starfish*, Washington, D.C., U.S. Bureau of Fisheries, Bull. 49, 1939.

Grassé, P. P., *Traité de Zoologie, XI, Échinodermes—Stomocordes—Protocordes*, Paris, Masson et Cie., 1948.

Harvey, E. B., *The American Arbacia and Other Sea Urchins*, Princeton, N.J., Princeton University Press, 1956.

Hyman, L. H., *The Invertebrates, IV, Echinodermata*, New York, McGraw-Hill Book Co., 1955.

Nichols, D., *Echinoderms*, New York, Hillary House Publishers, 1962.

Smith, J. E., "Some Observations on the Nervous Mechanisms Underlying the Behavior of Starfishes," *Symposia of the Society for Experimental Biology*, No. 4, New York, Academic Press, 1950.

Chapter 19

Tunicates and Other

Primitive Chordates

The Chordata, the phylum to which man himself belongs, was established taxonomically in 1874 by the great German evolutionary theorist, Ernst Haeckel, largely on the basis of the epoch-making investigations of Alexander Kowalevsky (1840–1901) on *Amphioxus* and the tunicates.

Chordate Characteristics. All chordates, from the simple wormlike hemichordates to the most sophisticated of the vertebrates, possess at some stage in their life histories the same basic set of anatomical features. In the primitive forms it is possible to see the original evolutionary meaning of many structures that man himself still possesses.

1. The long axis of the body of every chordate is strengthened by a fairly stiff but flexible rod, the **notochord.** The functional significance of the notochord can scarcely be exaggerated because it confers on the chordates a swimming ability that enables them completely to outclass the segmented worms in locomotion. Although a segmented worm may be similar to a chordate in size, shape, and even activity, when a worm swims it moves forward much more slowly. Its undulations make S's in the water, but they are comparatively ineffectual because there is no rigid support which can deliver a real thrust. The difference between a chordate and a seg-

mented worm is like that between two men each standing in the stern of a boat and trying to propel it forward, one by moving a rigid oar back and forth, the other a rope. The vertebrates improve on the notochord by converting it in the adult into a series of bony disks, the **vertebrae.**

2. A second feature common to all chordates and not found in any other phylum is a set of pharyngeal **gill slits** or clefts. These are paired openings on either side of the pharynx or throat, so placed that water taken in at the mouth can pass to the exterior again through these slits. In the nonvertebrate chordates the gill slits remain functional throughout life; in some groups like the urochordates and in *Amphioxus* they become greatly elaborated and serve both as organs of respiration and for food-catching. Among the vertebrates the gill slits remain throughout life only in the fishes. But even in mammals and birds they are easily seen in embryonic stages. In man, they are present when the embryo is about 30 days old. In land animals, of course, the gill slits grow closed, though the first pair forms the Eustachian tubes of the ears and others help form some of the endocrine glands.

3. A third common feature of chordates is a **dorsal tubular nervous system.** This tube is made up of nerve cells and their extensions. It

421

runs the length of the animal just dorsal to the notochord (see Fig. 9–20). In vertebrates it develops into the central nervous system, composed of the brain and spinal cord. This dorsal neural tube presents a marked contrast to the ventral chain of ganglia characteristic of nonchordates like the insects and other protostomes, or to the nerve nets of the coelenterates.

4. The three characteristics listed above are diagnostic for chordates. Members of no other phylum possess them. A number of other important traits characterize chordates but are not diagnostic because chordates share them with other groups. Like the flatworms and the annelids, chordates are bilaterally symmetrical, with right and left, anterior and posterior, and dorsal and ventral sides. Like annelids and arthropods, many chordates are serially segmented. Even in man this segmentation is clearly evident in the backbone, ribs, nervous system, and body musculature. Like annelids, most chordates have a spacious coelom or body cavity between the body wall and the alimentary canal.

THE HEMICHORDATES

The hemichordates (*hemi,* half, + *chorda,* rod) or enteropneusts (*enteron*, gut, + *pneuma*, breath) are a small subphylum of chordates, entirely marine, that show a curious mixture of chordate and echinoderm characteristics. In fact, many zoologists rank the hemichordates as a separate phylum. The body is divided into three parts, a **proboscis,** which seems to be a burrowing organ, a **collar,** in which there is a kind of notochord underlying a nerve tube, and a **trunk,** bearing gill slits in the anterior part.

The enteropneusts are moderately common sand-burrowers along the coasts of most continents. They reveal that animals very different from ourselves can have deuterostome and specifically chordate anatomy.

The body plan of a common enteropneust like *Saccoglossus kowaleuskii,* which is found along the west coast of the Atlantic Ocean, is shown in Figure 19–2. The so-called notochord is a fingerlike outpocketing or diverticulum extending anteriorly from the collar into the proboscis. Except for connective tissue there is no other skeletal system.

Organ Systems. The digestive system of the enteropneusts consists of a long, straight tube. The mouth is at the anterior edge of the collar and ventral to the protruding proboscis. In the anterior third of the trunk are dozens of small gill slits. The anus is terminal. The most interesting feature of the digestive system is that the anterior part of the gut is divided into dorsal and ventral portions by a horizontal partition. The food particles, mixed with mucus, pass posteriorly in the ventral half of the esophagus, while the oxygen-bearing water enters the mouth, passes along the dorsal portion, and out through the numerous gill slits. This arrangement is seen again in the lamprey eels, except that in them the esophagus is dorsal to the gill slit region.

The vascular system consists primarily of a dorsal and ventral longitudinal blood vessel with a **glomerulus** in the proboscis. The glomerulus is a tuft of small vessels thought to be excretory in function.

The sexes are separate. Multiple gonads are located in pairs throughout somewhat more than the middle third of the trunk. Each gonad extrudes its gametes through a separate pore to the exterior, where fertilization takes place.

Fig. 19–1. *Saccoglossus,* the acorn worm, a sand-living hemichordate, shown approximately life size. (*From Pauli,* The World of Life, *Houghton Mifflin*)

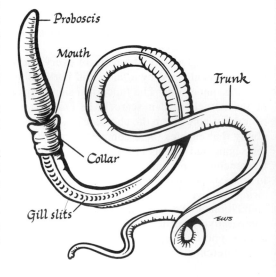

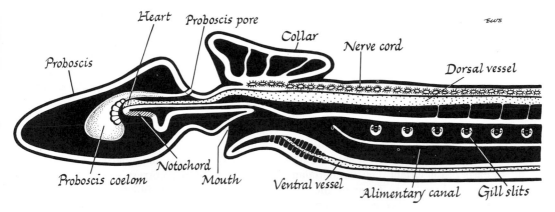

Fig. 19–2. Longitudinal section through the anterior end of *Saccoglossus*. *(From Pauli, The World of Life, Houghton Mifflin)*

The larva of most species is called a **tornaria.** It is a tiny creature with bands of cilia and a general organization very closely resembling the larvae of the echinoderms.

Another feature of the enteropneusts that relates them to the echinoderms is their coelom. The coelom is divided into the same three parts as the body—proboscis, collar, and trunk. The coelom in the proboscis, like that in the trunk, opens to the exterior through a tiny pore. These coeloms consequently become filled with water and supply turgidity to the anterior end of the animal. Such a system bears a marked resemblance to the otherwise unique water-vascular system of the echinoderms.

The nervous system along most of the body follows the echinoderm pattern and consists of a dorsal cord of nerve cells and fibers located just beneath the epithelium. In the collar zone the nerve cord becomes tubular, as in all chordates. An important feature of this tubular portion of the nervous system foreshadows the situation in the vertebrates. Nerve cells in each side of the tube give rise to nerve fibers which cross over to the other side and innervate structures on that side. In vertebrates, nerve fibers cross from one side of the brain to the other in such a way that an injury to the left side of the brain causes paralysis on the contralateral (i.e., right) side of the body.

Most enteropneusts smell strongly of halides, a curious medicinal odor between the odor of iodoform and that of chlorine. The biochemical and functional meaning of this is obscure.

THE PTEROBRANCHIATES

The Pterobranchia are marine sedentary forms seldom seen. Some taxonomists regard them as constituting a separate phylum, others as a subphylum of the chordates, and still others as a class of the hemichordates. There are, of course, no objective tests by which such differences of opinion can be settled.

As in the enteropneusts, the body is tripartite, with proboscis, collar, and trunk. The entire body is bent on itself, i.e., U-shaped. From the collar extend a number of feathery gills. The animals secrete a protective housing. Small colonies are formed by asexual budding, but the pterobranchs also reproduce sexually.

THE CEPHALOCHORDATES: AMPHIOXUS

The subphylum Cephalochordata (*cephalon*, head, + *chorda*, cord) is so called because the notochord extends not only into the tail but anteriorly into the tip of the head. For nearly a century these sharply pointed little animals, the lancelets, have been famous because they appeared to represent the most primitive and generalized type of chordate.

The first individual described scientifically was taken near Penzance on the southwest coast of England; in 1774 it was named *Limax lanceolatus* by Pallas, who supposed it was some kind of slug. The familiar name *Amphioxus lanceolatus* was conferred some 50 years later, but it was not until the monumental researches of Kowalevsky in the 1860's and 1870's that the animal's true nature was really understood.

Most species live in the sand, from the low-tide level down to moderate depths, wherever the water is not too cold. On the North Atlantic coasts they are found from the Virginia capes southward and from southern England south into the Mediterranean Sea. In the eastern North Pacific *Amphioxus (Branchiostoma) californiense* occurs from San Diego southward. In parts of the Òrient they are abundant enough to be used for food. Those on the east coast of North America average about an inch in length. In life they make spectacular use of the advantages conferred by possession of a notochord. They swim with great rapidity and can bury themselves in wet sand in a matter of milliseconds. Their translucency makes them difficult to see. In repose they lie buried in the sand with only the head exposed. There are two families and several genera of lancelets.

Amphioxus (amphi, both, + *oxys,* pointed) has no paired fins as in fishes though there is a ventro-lateral finfold extending along each side of the animal, plus a dorsal fin running along the back and around the tail.

Segmentation. The main mass of the body consists of muscles arranged on either side of the notochord. The most significant feature of the muscles is that they are segmented, that is, arranged in a series of units or segments from head to tail. Each muscle segment is separated from those next to it by a partition, or septum, of connective tissue. Such a series of muscle segments along each side of the long axis of the body will be seen again in all vertebrates, from fish to man. In *Amphioxus* and in many vertebrates the muscle segments are shaped like V's or W's lying sideways. This arrangement affords greater strength and smoothness in action.

In *Amphioxus* the original adaptive evolutionary significance of this segmentation can be clearly seen. If there were but one continuous, undivided muscle on each side of the body, the muscle would have to contract as a unit. As a result, even with a notochord to prevent the animal from shortening, when one of the muscles contracted *Amphioxus* would merely bend into the form of a C. By alternately contracting first one and then the other of such a pair of muscles an animal could thrash around but would tend to get nowhere. Segmentation into a series of separate muscles makes it possible for the muscles at the anterior end to contract first, and to be followed in regular order by muscles farther and farther toward the tail. Thus a wave of contraction can pass back along the animal in such a way that a forward motion results. This type of motion can be seen in fishes, salamanders, and other vertebrates. It is made possible by a corresponding development of anatomical and functional segmentation within the nervous system. This is the evolutionary origin of the segmentation of the human nervous system.

Other Anatomical Characteristics. Ventral to the notochord is the gut, which serves both for respiration and for the capture and digestion of food. The mouth is just ventral and posterior to the extreme anterior tip of the animal. It is protected by an **oral hood** (*oris,* mouth). From the edge of this hood project **buccal cirri** (*bucca,* cheek, + *cirrus,* lock of hair or tentacles). The circular mouth, a short way in under the oral hood, is protected by a series of **velar tentacles** (*velaris,* curtain) which project inward from the edge of the mouth like the spokes of a wheel with a rim but no hub. They prevent large particles from entering the mouth.

Posterior to the mouth is the pharynx (*pharynx,* throat). As in all chordates, the pharynx is pierced by **gill slits,** of which *Amphioxus* has about 200. In fact, they occupy about half the total body length. The narrow **gill bars** of the gill slits are ciliated and drive water out through the slits on either side of the body. This action continually pulls more water into the pharynx through the mouth. The water passing out through the gill slits on either side of the pharyngeal region does not go directly to the exterior, because the delicate ciliated gills are protected by a covering of body wall which encloses them in such a way as to form a cavity or **atrium** (*atrium,* room), much as an oversized coat encloses a space between itself and a man's body. The water which enters the atrium from the gill slits leaves by an opening, the **atriopore,** on the ventral side of the body near the hind end of the pharynx.

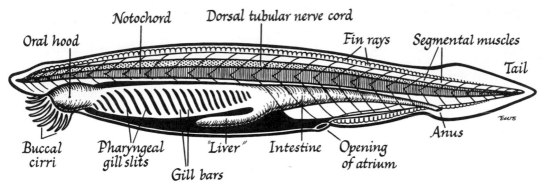

Oral hood — Notochord — Dorsal tubular nerve cord — Fin rays — Segmental muscles — Tail

Buccal cirri — Pharyngeal gill slits — Gill bars — "Liver" — Intestine — Opening of atrium — Anus

Fig. 19–3. Longitudinal section of *Amphioxus*. (Diagrammatic.) See Figure 19–4 for additional structures. *(From Pauli,* The World of Life, *Houghton Mifflin)*

Its peculiar manner of feeding is characteristic not only of *Amphioxus* but also of the urochordates, or tunicates, and of the larval forms of the most primitive vertebrates, the lampreys. Like clams they are all "filter-feeders" because they strain out minute particles of food on their ciliated gills. Mucus is copiously secreted by the cells lining the pharynx, especially those along the ventral midline. Semi-microscopic particles of food become entangled in this mucus. By the beating of cilia on the inner sides of the gills the mucus is pushed forward and upward on both sides of the pharynx to the dorsal midline. Here its direction of flow is reversed and the mucus, now impregnated with food, passes posteriorly into the intestine.

In *Amphioxus* there is a deep and ciliated **hypobranchial groove** (*hypo*, below, + *branchia*, gills) or **endostyle** extending the length of the pharynx in the ventral midline. It secretes a major portion of the mucus and by its long cilia aids in pushing it forward. When a larval lamprey eel, which resembles *Amphioxus*, metamorphoses into an adult, part of its endostyle becomes the thyroid gland. Since a lamprey is a vertebrate, this fact led to the belief that the thyroid gland is in some way the homolog of the endostyle. Proof of this is now at hand. It is well known that the thyroids of frogs and mammals concentrate iodine in their cells, where it is incorporated into the molecules of hormone secreted by the gland. Recent studies using radioactive iodine show that the endostyle of *Amphioxus* does indeed concentrate iodine. Even more convincing is the additional discovery that anti-thyroid drugs like uracil likewise inhibit the accumulation of iodine by the endostyle of *Amphioxus*.

In *Amphioxus* there is another major mucus-secreting structure, the so-called **"wheel organ,"** which consists of a pattern of ciliated bands on the lining of the oral hood. Inside the pharynx, along the mid-dorsal line of the gill region, is an **epibranchial groove** (*epi*, above, + *branchia,* gills) along which the stream of mucus passes posteriorly to the intestine.

The intestine is short and straight, and opens to the exterior by an anus a moderate distance anterior to the end of the tail. Thus the tail is post-anal in position, a characteristic of most chordates and especially of vertebrates but virtually unknown among invertebrates.

A short distance from its anterior end the intestine gives off a blind sac or **diverticulum** (*diverticulum,* bypath), which extends still futher to the anterior like the finger of a glove. It lies in the atrial cavity between the gill slits and the body wall. Since it secretes digestive enzymes and serves as both a liver and a pancreas, it may be called a hepato-pancreas.

Circulation and Excretion. The character of the blood vascular system in *Amphioxus* also gives a preview of the general vertebrate scheme. (See Fig. 19–4.) Ventral to the endostyle in the gill region is a long ventral artery, called the **ventral aorta.** Waves of contraction pass forward along it and push the colorless blood anteriorly and up through many pairs of small arteries that run through the gill bars between the gill slits and carry the blood up to the dorsal side of the gill slits. These small arteries that curve upward around the pharynx and carry the blood from the ventral aorta to the dorsal aorta are called **aortic arches.** Small pulsatile bulbs, one at the ventral end of each aortic arch, aid in pushing the blood up through the aortic arches. These bulbs, together with the ventral aorta itself, function as a heart. In passing through the gill bars the blood exchanges carbon dioxide for oxygen.

Along the dorsal side of the pharynx is a pair of dorsal aortae which receive the freshly oxygenated blood from the gills and carry it in a posterior direction. Posterior to the gill region they fuse into a single **dorsal aorta** which carries blood toward the tail and gives off branches to the intestine, the muscles, and other parts of the body. There the arteries break up into microscopic capillaries, through the thin walls of which oxygen is lost to the tissues and carbon dioxide is taken up.

The venous system, which returns the blood to the gills, is also basically like that of vertebrates. Blood from the body—mostly from the muscles, since they constitute most of the body—is carried in right and left **precardinal veins** from the head region, and a similar pair of **postcardinal veins** from the posterior part of the body. The pre- and postcardinals on each side meet and fuse to form on each side of the animal a **duct of Cuvier,** which carries the blood inward to a cavity or **sinus** at the beginning of the ventral aorta, whence it is again pushed through the gills.

Another important feature to be seen again in all the vertebrates is the **hepatic portal system.** Blood capillaries in the intestine absorb digested food and carry it to a vein to the liver, i.e., to the hepato-pancreatic diverticulum. The vein that does this is the **hepatic portal vein.** It breaks up into capillaries in the liver, where food is removed and stored or processed and returned to the circulation as needed. Blood is then taken from the liver back to the sinus at the beginning of the ventral aorta.

The excretory system of *Amphioxus,* on the other hand, does not foreshadow the vertebrate

Fig. 19–4. *A,* circulatory and excretory systems of *Amphioxus.* Arrows indicate the direction of blood flow. Note the nephridia opening into alternate gill slits. An enlarged view of this is shown in *B,* and still further enlargement in *C.*

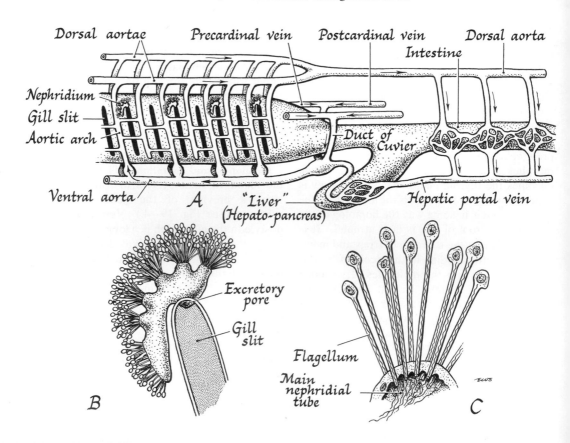

plan. Instead, it is very similar to a system found in certain marine polychaetous annelids, although not in the earthworms. This curious system consists of a series of short curved tubes situated at the dorsal ends of the gill slits, and closed at one end but opening at the other into the gill slit. The curved portion bears five or six tufts of specialized cells somewhat resembling little hatpins. These elongated cells project into the small coelom or body cavity and, by means of a long flagellum which extends from the rounded head of the cell down its long slender stalk and into the main curved tube, they transfer, i.e., excrete, excess fluid and dissolved wastes from the coelom to the exterior.

Reproduction. In *Amphioxus* the sexes are separate. The gonads are closely similar in males and females and consist of a row of about 25 more or less oblong structures along both sides of the animal, in the pharyngeal region. The exact number is diagnostic of the various species. The ripe gametes pass to the exterior through the atriopore. The development of *Amphioxus* has been the object of many elaborate studies, beginning with the classic work of Kowalevsky. The small but yolky egg develops into an elongate larva swimming by means of external cilia. How it develops into an adult has puzzled several generations of zoologists, because the mouth, the gill slits, and other structures form at first in very asymmetrical positions.

Nervous System. As in all chordates, the central nervous system consists of a tube immediately dorsal to the notochord. There is no brain at the anterior end, although the central canal within the neural cord enlarges into a small anterior vesicle.

The nerve cord is connected to the muscles by pairs of ventral nerves which run out, one to each muscle segment. From the dorsal edge of the nerve cord extend pairs of sensory nerves, which pass between the muscle segments and innervate the skin or pass ventrally to the gut.

The sense organs are extremely rudimentary. A ciliated and innervated pit on top of the "head" is probably a chemoreceptor. Distributed along and within the neural cord are photosensitive cells protected on one side or the other by black pigment cups. The head end, which is normally exposed, is insensitive to light, but any light striking the rest of the body leads to rapid swimming movements, the only reaction of which *Amphioxus* seems capable.

THE UROCHORDATES: TUNICATES

The subphylum urochordates or tunicates is composed of some of the strangest animals known. They secrete a tough protective tunic (whence Lamarck's name, tunicate). This tunic is composed of a kind of cellulose! The tubular heart is notable because it pulses first in one direction and then in the opposite one, reversing itself every few minutes.

The blood cells do not contain hemoglobin but many of them are bright green, yellow, blue, red, or purple—from the various oxidation states of the vanadium they contain. Certain species lack vanadium-containing cells entirely yet live successfully alongside those which do. The vanadium is linked into pyrrole rings but the pyrroles do not seem to be joined together into porphyrin molecules and there is no evidence that the vanadium compounds play a part in respiration. The puzzle is all the greater because vanadium is so scarce in sea water that it cannot be detected by the ordinary chemical procedures.

Although tunicates are found nearly everywhere in the oceans, their practical importance is slight. They are included in what navigators called fouling organisms which form undesirable growths on ships' bottoms. They were the first animals in which alternation of generations was discovered. This was the achievement long ago of a German poet and naturalist, Chamisso. It led directly to another discovery that did have a very important practical application, an understanding of the life history of tapeworms.

As indicated in the chapter on evolution, a plausible but necessarily unproved (since fossils are as yet missing) case has been made for the theory that the vertebrates arose from tunicate tadpoles. Presumably they took to swimming up rivers where, as filter feeders, they could exploit the rich organic detritus coming down into the sea after fresh-water and land plants became established. In such an environment the development of a backbone to aid in swimming would confer a great advantage. A mutation which produced neoteny, that is, attainment of sexual maturity in the larval stage, would eliminate the sessile adult. *Amphioxus* is then to be regarded as derived from such a neotenous form.

Tunicates have undergone extensive deployment of species in their own right. There are three classes. The **Ascidiacea** (*ascus*, sac) are sessile, living singly or in complex colonial aggregations attached to submerged rocks, wharfs, ships, etc. Many members of this class are conspicuous animals. Among the solitary species some resemble black, velvety bananas, others are rounded and pink and are called sea peaches, others look like scarlet thumbs, while still others have the appearance of gnarled potatoes. A common colonial species, *Botryllus,* grows as a glistening black or purple mat studded with rosettes of yellow and pink openings like the petals of a flower. The second class, the **Thaliacea** (*Thaleia,* one of the three graces), comprises pelagic, usually glass-clear animals, more or less barrel-shaped. The third class, the **Larvacea,** are minute animals with long tails.

A Typical Tunicate. *Ciona,* a solitary ascidiacean, may be taken as typical of tunicate structure, since it is relatively simple and is regarded by specialists as probably representative of the most primitive and generalized type. *Ciona* is cylindrical, with two funnels or siphons at the free end. The one at the tip is the mouth, or incurrent siphon, while the one just beside it but lower down is the excurrent atrial siphon. When handled, the animal contracts the entire body and squirts water from the siphons—hence the name "sea squirts."

In the mouth is a circle of tentacles reminiscent of *Amphioxus.* Below this is an enormous pharynx or branchial sac that occupies most of the space within the tunic and is pierced by a grillwork of ciliated gill slits. Water passes into the pharynx through the mouth, out through the gill slits into a spacious atrial cavity, again like that of *Amphioxus,* and thence to the exterior via the excurrent siphon. The method of feeding is also similar to that of *Amphioxus.* A well-developed ciliated hypobranchial groove, or endostyle, extends along the anatomically ventral side of the pharynx. A stream of mucus forms here and passes toward and finally around each side of the mouth and then back along a dorsal epibranchial groove which is marked by the dorsal lamina that extends along its length. From this dorsal groove the stream of mucus carrying entrapped detritus, both minute food particles and much indigestible material, passes into the short esophagus. This leads into a rounded stomach and then an intestine, that curves up alongside the gill slits and ends in an anus emptying into the atrial cavity not far from the excurrent siphon.

The heart is a translucent, U-shaped tube alongside the stomach. It pumps blood through

Fig. 19–5. *A,* external view of a solitary tunicate contracted. *B,* three juvenile colonies of six "individuals" each, encrusted on a leaf of eel grass. Note the six separate openings of the incurrent siphons and the single excurrent opening in the center. *A* and *B* are both life size. *(After Wolcott, Animal Biology, McGraw-Hill Book Company. Copyright 1943. Used by permission)*

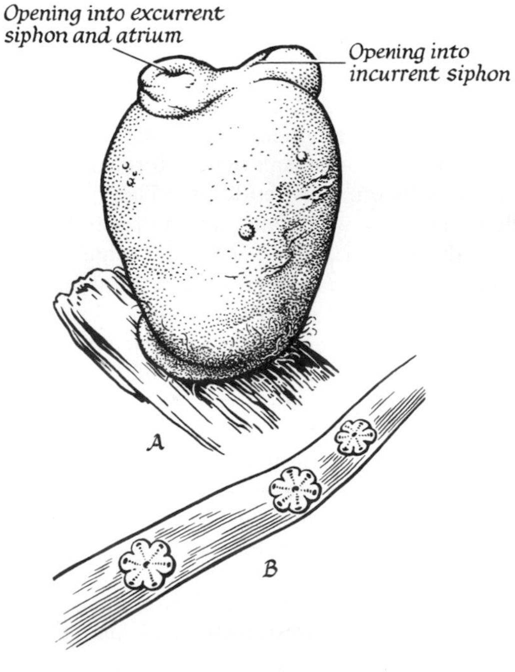

Opening into excurrent siphon and atrium

Opening into incurrent siphon

A

B

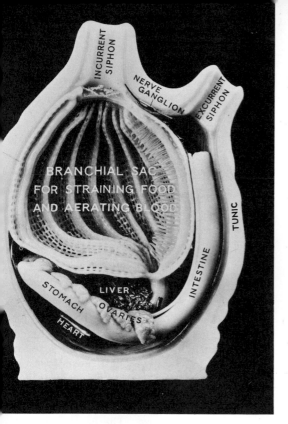

the gills, mostly through a ventral aorta "beneath" the endostyle. The colored vanadium-carrying blood cells have previously been mentioned. The function of the vanadium compounds is still obscure. They do not seem to transport oxygen, like hemoglobin. An excretory system is lacking except in a few species which possess masses of cells in the loop of the intestine which store nitrogenous wastes.

True to its chordate and deuterostome nature, *Ciona* possesses a **coelom** or body cavity, although some zoologists prefer to call it a perivisceral sac or even an **epicardium.** But the body cavity of *Ciona,* in typical chordate fashion, is formed from a pair of diverticula or outpocketings from the gut. In the adult these cavities surround the stomach, heart, and other viscera with an empty, epithelium-lined cavity. As in the vertebrates, the coelom can be likened to an inflated balloon fitting into the space between viscera and body wall, but itself empty. In colonial tunicates the wall of the coelom forms a stolon that buds off new individuals.

The reproductive system consists of one or a pair of gonads lying beside the stomach. Gametes are shed into the atrial cavity. Hermaphroditism is the rule. The eggs develop with determinate (mosaic) cleavage. The destiny of the various parts is much the same as in the egg of a frog. The embryo hatches as a tiny tadpole. (See Fig. 19–7.) Its tail consists of a central

Fig. 19–6. Adult solitary, sessile urochordate cut to show internal organs. The enormous branchial sac leads into a short esophagus which disappears behind the liver before entering the stomach. The tunic is of cellulose. (*American Museum of Natural History*)

Fig. 19–7. Longisection of a tunicate or urochordate tadpole. (Semi-diagrammatic)

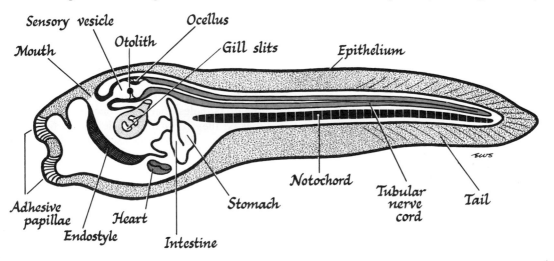

notochord flanked by muscles, a dorsal tubular nerve cord, and an epithelial sheath over the whole. Its body carries a conspicuous sensory vesicle containing both an organ of equilibration, the **otolith,** and a light-sensitive structure, the **ocellus.** The gut, with pharynx, endostyle, one pair of gill slits, and intestine, is poorly developed and so is the ventral heart. The tadpoles swim near the surface for a day or two, then become fixed on some solid object where they metamorphose into the sessile adults. By this means the species is disseminated and the new individuals become located in suitable environments.

Nervous System. The movements of so sessile an animal are extremely limited and amount to little more than closure of the siphons and general contraction of the body. The nervous system is correspondingly reduced to a single cerebral ganglion situated between the bases of the siphons. From it extend several nerves.

The Subneural Gland and the Pituitary. Immediately under the cerebral ganglion and in contact both with it and with a ciliated pit or funnel that opens into the dorsal part of the pharynx, is a **subneural gland.** Thus the subneural gland of a tunicate has the same anatomical relationships as the pituitary gland of a vertebrate. On these anatomical grounds, it has been thought probable for many years that the tunicate subneural gland and the vertebrate pituitary gland were homologous structures. Recently it has been shown that extracts of the tunicate gland will indeed do most of the things that pituitary extracts will do, such as stimulate the growth of ovaries in adolescent mice, cause male toads to discharge sperms, stimulate contractions in uterine muscles, and control pigment cells. Evidently the rather surprising relationship between the pituitary gland at the base of the brain and the gonads in a distant part of the body began in the tunicates.

What is the function of the subneural gland in the tunicate? Extracts both of subneural gland and of its mammalian equivalent will induce a tunicate to ovulate. If tunicate gametes, either eggs or sperms, are imbibed with water by a mature tunicate, they induce the animal to shed its own gametes. Thus synchronous spawning, necessary to insure fertilization in sessile animals, is achieved. For this to happen both the subneural gland and the ganglion must be physiologically active. Apparently the ciliated pit acts as a sense organ which detects the gametes and transmits a stimulus to the gland and its ganglion. It is beginning to appear as though the vertebrate pituitary, with its strange double origin — part from the brain, part from the roof of the throat — first began as a mechanism to produce synchronous spawning.

Other Tunicate Classes. The Thaliacea are glass-clear, barrel-shaped, pelagic forms found in all oceans. The barrellike body is open at both ends and bears about a dozen muscle bands which contract in sequence, thus pushing the animal through the water by a kind of jet propulsion. The endostyle extends along the inner side of the barrel. The heart, stomach, and other viscera lie ventrally near the posterior end. There is a stolon which buds off other individuals.

The life history of a tunicate is more complex than Chamisso thought when he made his original discovery of the alternation of generations. In general, groups or chains of individuals break off from the stolon and move through the ocean as a unit for a considerable time before breaking apart. After breaking apart, each produces and self-fertilizes a single egg which develops within the parent. When the offspring reaches a certain size it escapes through the atrial opening as a stolon-bearing individual.

The Larvacea, like all the tunicates, are exclusively marine. They clearly seem to be ascidian tadpoles that have become neotenous, that is, they reproduce while still in the larval condition. Unlike the ascidian tadpoles, the larvaceans secrete an extensive cellulose "house" in which they live and which serves as a trap for food. They are filter-feeders like primitive chordates in general.

Review and References

REVIEW TOPICS

1. Characterize the chordates, and give distinguishing traits of the four chordate subphyla.

2. What is the functional advantage of a notochord? Of segmented body muscles?

3. What are "filter-feeders," and by what mechanisms do they eat?

4. What is the anatomical and physiological evidence that the subneural gland of tunicates corresponds to the pituitary of vertebrates?

5. What is the evolutionary explanation for the connection between the pituitary gland at the base of the brain and the gonads in a distant part of the body?

6. What is the evidence for an evolutionary relationship between the endostyle and the thyroid gland?

7. Describe the reproductive and vascular systems of a tunicate; of *Amphioxus*.

8. Define: pharynx, endostyle, enteropneust, tornaria, atrium, Eustachian tube, hepatic portal system, hypobranchial, epibranchial.

USEFUL REFERENCES

Berrill, N. J., *The Origin of Vertebrates,* Oxford, Clarendon Press, 1955.

Bigelow, H. B., and I. P. Farante, "Lancelets," in *Fishes of the Western North Atlantic,* New Haven, Yale University Press, 1948.

Grassé, P. P., *Traité de Zoologie, XI, Echinodermes — Stomocordes — Procordes,* Paris, Masson et Cie., 1948.

Willey, A., *Amphioxus and the Ancestry of Vertebrates,* New York, Columbia University Press, 1894.

Chapter 20

Fishes: Jawless and Jawed

The Subphylum Vertebrata is commonly divided (there is nothing like a consensus here) into six classes: (1) jawless fishes, or Agnatha, (2) jawed fishes or Ichthyognatha, (3) Amphibia, (4) reptiles, (5) birds, and (6) mammals. The basic chordate traits—a notochord, gill slits in the pharynx, and a dorsal tubular nerve cord—are, or course, present in the vertebrates as in the tunicates and other lower chordates. In addition, in this subphylum, a backbone develops around the notochord, which is relegated to a purely embryonic structure. The backbone is the key advance because it raises the ability of vertebrates to move around to an entirely new level of achievement.

The only living representatives of the very primitive jawless fishes or the **Agnatha** are the cyclostomes, which are also limbless. They are not only primitive but parasitic. Especially in larval form, they resemble *Amphioxus*. Lampreys are the best-known examples.

The jawed fishes fall into three major groups. The first, the **elasmobranchs** or cartilaginous fishes, include the sharks and rays. The second and largest group of fishes are the **ray-finned fishes,** or Actinopterygii. They constitute the first great deployment of vertebrates, with thousands of species and a fantastic array of adaptations—electric organs capable of delivering up to 500 volts, winglike fins enabling the fish to be airborne, even light-producing organs on the ends of movable rods!

Lastly there are the **muscle-finned fishes,** the Sarcopterygii. Here are the lungfishes and the famous coelacanths supposed to have been extinct for 70 million years but now caught by local fishermen off the east coast of Africa. By developing lungs and nostrils, muscular leglike paired fins, and eggs that could be laid on land, the ancestors of these fishes were responsible for the evolutionary breakthrough that made life on land—and man himself—possible.

THE CYCLOSTOMES: AGNATHA

The cyclostomes (*cyclos,* circle, + *stoma,* mouth), or lampreys and hagfishes, are the only living representatives of the Agnatha and differ radically from all other vertebrates.

1. They completely lack jaws, and instead have a round, sucking mouth. In the commonest group, the lampreys, the mouth is provided with a rasping tongue and is surrounded by a fleshy "hood" so that the entire anterior end of the animal resembles a plumber's suction cup. With this the lamprey holds on to a fish, rasps a hole in its flesh, and sucks the blood. The complete lack of jaws, which are so essential in all other vertebrates, is what sets the cyclostomes and other agnatha apart as a separate class.

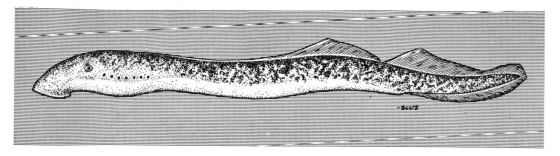

Fig. 20 – 1. *Petromyzon,* the lamprey eel. Note the row of rounded openings from the internal gill slits, and the complete lack of paired fins.

2. Cyclostomes also differ, even in embryonic stages, from all other vertebrates in the entire absence of paired limbs, either fins or legs.

3. The **ammocoetes** larva of a cyclostome bears a close and striking resemblance to *Amphioxus.*

4. There is but one nostril, centrally located high on top of the head. It connects by a long tube with the pituitary, just ventral to the brain.

Lamprey eels are very different from the true eels, which are highly modified bony fishes, essentially like a codfish slimmed down and pulled out into a snakelike form but still possessing a pair of bony jaws, a pair of anterior and a pair of posterior fins, two nostrils where nostrils are usually found in vertebrates, and no amphioxus-like larval stage. There are many additional differences. True eels possess a complex bony skull which lampreys lack. Their gill structure also is very different.

Adult lampreys grow to about a meter in length. Their importance is twofold. They are regularly sold for food and are considered a great delicacy by gourmets. Unfortunately, the destruction of other fishes which they have wrought in the Great Lakes in recent years has far overbalanced the value of lampreys as food. In 1829 the Welland Canal around Niagara Falls opened the Great Lakes to *Petromyzon marinus,* the sea lamprey. The lampreys did not thrive in Lake Erie, perhaps because it is shallow, but once they had passed through it into the deep lakes beyond, serious trouble began. Lake trout and other commercial fishes were found in increasing numbers with lamprey scars. The number of fishes that were caught fell precipitately. In Lake Huron, for example, 1,743,000 pounds of lake trout were caught in 1935, against 940,000 in 1940, only 173,000 in 1945, and a negligible 1,000 pounds in 1949. These lake-dwelling sea lampreys migrate up

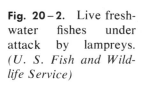

Fig. 20 – 2. Live freshwater fishes under attack by lampreys. (*U. S. Fish and Wildlife Service*)

streams and rivers to spawn. Consequently, control measures are possible at those points, but have proved difficult. Various types of dams to block the upstream migration have been tried but are very expensive to build and maintain. Killing the larvae in their sand and mud beds is accomplished without killing other species of fishes in the stream by specific poisons. So successful has this method been that the lake trout fishing industry is on the way to full recovery.

Life History. All lampreys, whether they live in the ocean or in lakes, are called **anadromous** (*ana,* up, + *dromos,* running) because they migrate up rivers and streams to breed, usually early in the spring, though some species do so in the fall. Almost nothing is known about the neural and physiological basis of this behavior, but when the water in the stream warms up to about 50°F (10°C) the migration begins. Male and female lampreys work together to clear a spawning site in some shallow part of the stream by pulling away stones from a roughly circular area with their sucking mouths. Eggs and sperms are shed simultaneously into the water as the pair twine around each other. A single female lays between 50,000 and 100,000 eggs. After spawning the adults die.

The eggs become mixed with sand and gravel on the bottom, and each egg cleaves into a ball

Fig. 20-3. Lampreys nest-building in a stream. (*U. S. Fish and Wildlife Service*)

of cells very much as a frog's egg does. The elongate larva is a little transparent creature much like *Amphioxus.* When first discovered, the cyclostome larva was thought to be a distinct genus and was named *Ammocoetes.* It is now over 250 years since a fisherman of Strasburg named Balder, otherwise unknown to history, discovered that ammocoetes metamorphoses into a lamprey, but the name is still retained.

Like *Amphioxus,* an ammocoetes larva lives buried in the sand with only a bit of the anterior end projecting, the mouth protected by an oral hood. A current of water continually passes in through the mouth and out through the eight to ten pairs of gill slits. Along the ventral midline of the pharynx is a ciliated groove, as in *Amphioxus,* and opening into this groove is a ventral diverticulum, the **endostyle,** which contains ciliated mucus-secreting cells. The cord of mucus passing back into the intestine somehow catches food particles, as in *Amphioxus,* but the water current is produced by muscular contractions of the pharynx, not by ciliary action.

After four years in the bed of a stream, and after attaining some 5 inches in length, the ammocoetes completes its metamorphosis into an adult lamprey and swims downstream. During metamorphosis part of the endostyle develops into the thyroid gland, the gland which controls the general metabolic rate. Actually, the endostyle may function as a thyroid even before metamorphosis, for it has been shown to concentrate radioactive iodine in the larva, and iodine is an essential part of the thyroid hormone. There is no doubt that the lamprey thyroid is a true thyroid gland. Its development and position in the floor of the throat is the same as in all other vertebrates. Furthermore, its histology or cellular anatomy is the same, and when fed to frog tadpoles it induces precocious metamorphosis. These facts make it seem probable that the gland controlling metabolic rate arose first in connection with the feeding mechanism.

There are, of course, many other changes in the ammocoetes at metamorphosis. Paired eyes appear, muscles and horny "teeth" develop, and cartilaginous plates form in a segmental series along the dorsal side of the persistent notochord and enclose the nerve cord in a canal of rudimentary vertebrae.

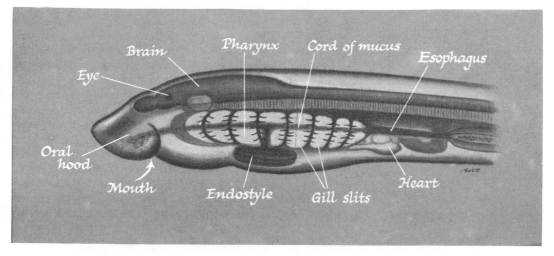

Fig. 20–4. Ammocoetes larva of a lamprey. Note the resemblance to *Amphioxus*.

Evolutionary Relationships. Are cyclostomes degenerate animals or truly primitive in character? This old puzzle has been debated for many years. There can be no doubt about their relationship, if not to *Amphioxus* directly, at least to some common stock from which both arose. The ammocoetes larva is enough to establish that. Somewhat over a decade ago a fossil animal named *Jamoytius* was discovered in fresh-water deposits in extremely ancient Silurian rocks. *Jamoytius* is intermediate in structure between *Amphioxus* and the oldest known vertebrates, the jawless ostracoderms (*ostracon*, shell, + *derma*, skin). There was considerable variety among the ostracoderms but most were encased in bony armor plate over the anterior part of the body, and many were evidently bottom feeders with flattened heads

Fig. 20–5. Ammocoetes and *Amphioxus* in cross section.

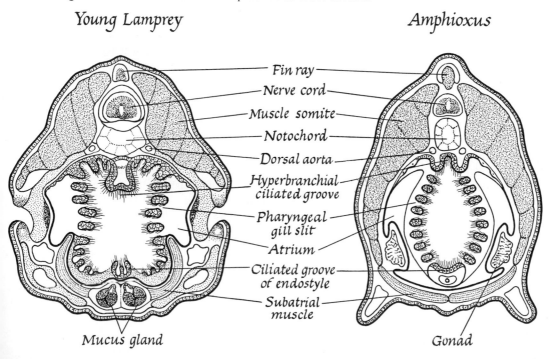

and a single nostril far back on the top of the head. It would seem possible that an amphioxus-like creature gave rise to *Jamoytius,* which in turn led to the ostracoderms. The unarmored ostracoderms, or the armored ones by losing their armor, could then have evolved into the cyclostomes with relatively minor modifications.

On the other hand, parasitism commonly results in an evolutionary loss of structures. This is easily seen in parasitic crustaceans, some of which, like *Sacculina,* are reduced to little more than a bag of gonads with nutritive extensions penetrating the body of its victim. Cyclostomes do show some specializations for their semi-parasitic life. The strongly muscled sucking mouth and the rasping tongue fit them for attacking fishes. The single nostril far back on the top of the head makes it possible to smell while the head is buried in the body of its prey, although this feature may have been carried over from a bottom-living ancestral ostracoderm. In any case cyclostomes could not have been parasitic on other fishes until other fishes had evolved.

Consequently, although no cyclostomes like those of today can have been the ancestors of the rest of the vertebrates, cyclostomes seem closely related to the ostracoderms which probably were those ancestors.

THE SHARKS, SKATES, AND RAYS

The name elasmobranch given to this group means plate-gilled (*elasmos,* plate, + *branchia,* gill) after the flat, platelike character of the gills which is well known to anyone who has ever slit open a shark's throat. **Elasmobranchs** are also called cartilaginous fishes or Chondrichthyes (*chondros,* cartilage, + *ichthyes,* fish) because their skeletons are composed of cartilage rather than bone. Elasmobranchs may be distinguished from other fishes in a number of important ways.

1. Unlike cyclostomes but like all other vertebrates elasmobranchs possess jaws.

2. The skeleton of elasmobranchs is cartilaginous, rather than bony as in other fishes.

3. Externally the five gill openings are visible as vertical slits on either side of the throat or the pharynx. In other kinds of fishes the gill slits are protected by a flaplike **operculum,** so that only one slit is visible externally.

4. The tail is asymmetrical, the dorsal lobe being larger than the ventral.

5. The body is covered by a characteristic type of **placoid scale.** These scales resemble teeth in structure, and in elasmobranchs show transitional stages from typical scale to typical tooth at the edges of the mouth.

Commercially, sharks are valuable for their skins, which are sold under the name shagreen, and for their oil, found chiefly in the liver. The small dogfish sharks commonly used for laboratory dissection are called "sweet williams" in England and are regularly sold for human consumption. Sharks vary from giants like *Rhinodon,* the whale shark, which grows to be over 50 feet long, to small species like *Squalus,* the dogfish, which seldom exceeds 3 feet in length.

Sharks are commonly regarded as the wolves of the sea. They certainly are rapacious carnivores, and there are well-authenticated cases of attacks on people. This question was carefully investigated during World War II. Apparently one of the most important factors in precipitating an actual attack on a man is blood in the water. A skin diver who cuts himself on a sharp object is in special danger. Several shark repellents have been described, using copper acetate and other substances, but none is very effective against hungry sharks.

The small sharks have proved to be very useful animals for the scientific study of kidney action, a topic which will be discussed more fully in the section on bony and rayfinned fishes (Actinopterygii). Sharks are also extremely useful for dissection because they have only a cartilaginous skeleton, and because they reveal the basic vertebrate structure with an almost diagrammatic simplicity.

According to the fossil record, the earliest vertebrates with jaws were not elasmobranchs but armored fishes, the Placodermia (*placo,* plate, + *derma,* skin). The skeleton of a placoderm was bony, and that of the gill arches simple and generalized. All available evidence indicates that the placoderms lived in fresh water and were the ancestors of both the elasmobranchs and the present-day bony fishes. In fact, the physiology of the shark kidney makes sense only in terms of the shark's descent from

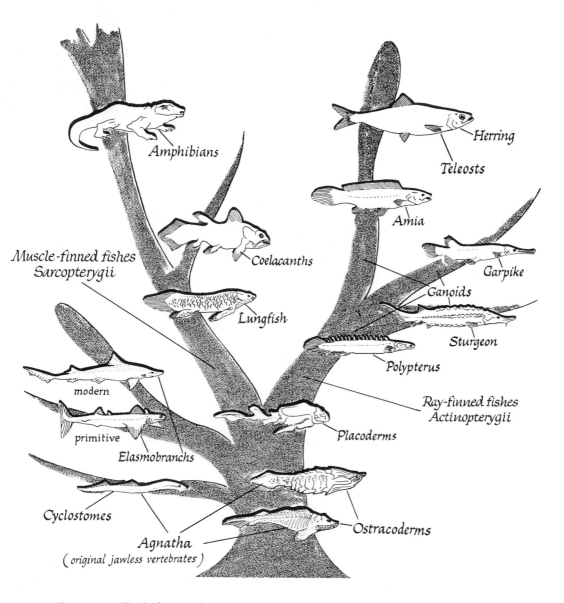

Fig. 20-6. Evolutionary deployment of the fishes.

a fresh-water ancestor (see page 567). The cartilaginous aspect of the elasmobranch skeleton is consequently not a primitive but rather a specialized or, if you prefer, a degenerate characteristic.

The flattened rays and skates are modified for bottom-living and subsist chiefly on mollusks and other invertebrates.

Skeletal System and Gill Arches. The skeleton of a shark clearly reveals the basic plan found in all vertebrates, including man. There is an **axial skeleton** composed of the backbone, the skull, and gill arches; and there is an **appendicular skeleton** composed of the **pectoral girdle** and its appendages, the anterior paired fins (or front legs), and the **pelvic girdle** and its appendages, the posterior paired fins (or hind legs).

The **backbone** consists of the usual series of vertebrae. As in all fishes, these are in the form of biconcave disks built around the old notochord. On their dorsal surfaces the vertebrae support cartilaginous neural arches that form a protective arcade or canal for the dorsal tubular

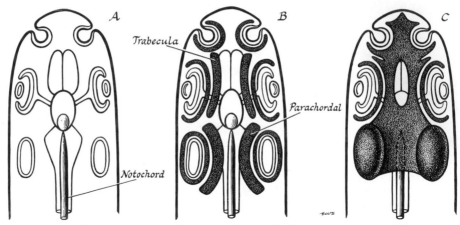

Fig. 20 – 7. Stages in the development of the primitive vertebrate skull from cartilaginous capsules around the nose, eyes, and inner ears, plus trabecular and parachordal bars along the brain and notochord. These stages can be seen most easily in the development of elasmobranchs. (*After Wilder,* History of the Human Body, *Holt, Rinehart & Winston*)

spinal cord, which is anatomically a posterior continuation of the brain.

The **skull** consists of an elongate cartilaginous box which supports and protects the brain, plus three pairs of sense capsules protecting the major sense organs. The most anterior is a pair of cartilaginous **nasal capsules** enclosing the olfactory epithelium. The most posterior is a pair of **otic capsules** enclosing the semicircular canals and the associated **sacculus** and **utriculus,** organs governing equilibration. Both the otic and the nasal capsules become permanently fused to the rest of the skull. Between the nasal and the otic capsules lie the

optic capsules that surround the eyes. These remain free from the skull and thus make it possible for the eyes to move. In some big bony fishes the optic capsule actually becomes ossified, but in most vertebrates it remains cartilaginous and forms the whites of the eyes or the sclerotic coat.

The **gill arch** cartilages extend from the skull and backbone on either side, in between the gill slits, down to the ventral midline of the pharynx. These arches have undergone an extraordinary evolution. The first gill bar on each side bent in the form of a V with its apex pointing towards the fish's tail. The apex of the V be-

Fig. 20 – 8. Evolution of the gill arch cartilages from the primitive jawless condition as in cyclostomes, shown on the left, to the jawed state on the right. The *h* represents the hyoid arch still unmodified in the placoderms (center) but thickened as a support for the jaws in the higher fishes (right). Note that the first gill slit, *s,* of the placoderms has become a small spiracle in the higher fishes. It becomes the Eustachian tube in man. (*After* Vertebrate Paleontology *by Romer by permission of The University of Chicago Press. Copyright 1945 by The University of Chicago*)

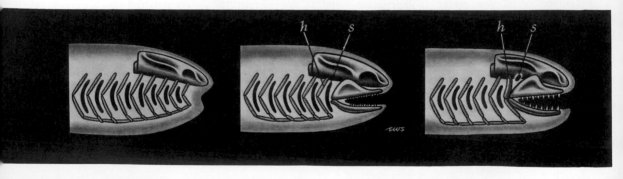

came attached to the skull on each side and formed the hinges of the jaws. The upper arms of the V's on each side fused under the snout and became the upper jaw. The lower arms of the V's on each side fused at their ends forming the lower jaw and the chin. The nerves that innervate the upper and lower jaws of a man are exactly those one would expect from this interpretation of the origin of jaws. The importance of jaws for the life of a vertebrate can scarcely be overestimated. They not only aid greatly in food-catching, as in fishes; they also make chewing possible in the higher animals, and are important in fighting, nest-building, speech production, and other ways. In short, they confer power over the environment.

But this is not all that came ultimately out of these gill arches. The inner ends of the upper and lower jaws in the higher reptiles and the mammals have become transformed into tiny bones which transmit vibrations to the inner ear! The upper end of the lower jaw or mandible became the **malleus,** the adjacent end of the upper jaw became the **incus,** and the upper end of the **hyoid** or second arch (counting the jaws as the first arch) formed the **stapes.** As Figure 22–7 shows, these homologies can be found in man and other mammals. The ventral parts of the second and third arches form the hyoid bone, which can be felt at the base of the tongue by pressing two fingers up under the chin above the "Adam's apple" or larynx. The thyroid cartilages of the larynx in turn are formed from the fourth and fifth gill arches. The first gill slit in many sharks is so poorly developed that it is only a small tube leading from the exterior above the angle of the jaw past the ear region and opening into the throat. In the higher vertebrates this so-called **spiracle** becomes the Eustachian tube leading from throat to ear. Thus does man bear in his skull and throat the stamp of his aquatic ancestors.

The pectoral and pelvic **limb girdles** in all fishes are imbedded in the body wall and give support to the front and hind paired fins, but are very loosely, if at all, connected to the axial skeleton. Of course, in the higher vertebrates, where the pelvic limbs are used in running and jumping, the pelvic girdle is firmly anchored to the backbone.

Muscular System. The muscles of a shark also reveal the basic vertebrate plan with great simplicity. The body muscles are divided, as in *Amphioxus,* into a series of more or less zigzag segments, or **myotomes.** It will be recalled that this makes it possible for waves of contraction to pass down the animal and to push the body and tail against the water effectively.

Beginning a short distance behind the eye and extending along each side of a fish almost to the tail is a **lateral line.** Along this line is a series of small sensory pits which probably detect changes in water pressure. Extending from this lateral line along its entire length and inward to connect with the backbone is a partition of tough connective tissue. This separates the muscles into a dorsal, **epaxial,** and a ventral, **hypaxial,** group. The epaxial and hypaxial muscles together constitute the **axial muscle system.**

In the terrestrial vertebrates the external lateral line disappears, but the anatomical and functional distinction between epaxial and hypaxial muscles remains even in man. The epaxials are extensors of the spine. When they contract they make a man sit up straight. The hypaxial muscles are flexors of the spine, and their contraction causes the body to bend forward. These are basic sets of muscle antagonists in the vertebrate body. All the motor nerves in shark and man branch soon after leaving the spinal cord. One branch goes to the epaxial and the other to the hypaxial muscles.

Three other muscular systems are of importance in the dogfish. One is composed of the **limb musculature.** This is derived entirely from the hypaxial muscles and consists of extensors or elevators of each paired fin, and their antagonists, the flexors or depressors. The principal difference between the musculature of a dog and a dogfish is that in the dog (as in man), the limbs have become relatively enormous and the muscles that connect them to the body no longer occupy only a small part of the trunk immediately adjacent to the paired fins. Instead, the muscles which move the limbs in relation to the body fan out to cover most of the trunk.

The other muscle systems are the **branchial** or **gill arch muscles,** which move jaws and gills,

Fig. 20–9. Diagram illustrating the anatomical relationship between a dog and a dogfish. Note that the chief external differences lie in the head and the paired limbs and their musculature which is greatly enlarged in the dog and spread out over the body surface.

and the **visceral muscles,** which cover the stomach and intestine. Many anatomists consider both of these muscle groups as visceral. The innervation of the jaw muscles is the same in a man and a shark.

Vascular and Excretory Systems. The vascular system of an elasmobranch resembles that of *Amphioxus*, yet is basically like that of any embryonic vertebrate. The heart is located at the back of the throat, ventrally placed just beneath the muscles between the pectoral fins. This is its embryonic position even in mammals. The heart is not divided into right and left chambers, as in higher vertebrates, but is constructed of a single **sinus** (cavity) **venosus** which receives blood from the veins and empties it into a single auricle that in turn delivers it to the single ventricle. The thick-walled muscular ventricle squeezes, i.e., pumps, blood anteriorly into a tube, the **conus arteriosus,** and on into the **ventral aorta.** From the ventral aorta it passes upward, i.e., dorsally, to the gills in five pairs of **afferent branchial arteries.** In the gills the blood passes through capillaries where carbon dioxide is exchanged for oxygen. Oxygenated blood is

carried away from the gills in five pairs of **efferent branchial arteries** to the **dorsal aorta.** The dorsal aorta carries blood posteriorly all the way to the tail, and gives off as branches: the **subclavian** arteries to the pectoral fins, the **coeliac** and **mesenteric** arteries to the stomach, liver, intestine, and other viscera, the **renal** arteries to the kidneys, and the **iliac** arteries to the pelvic fins. All the arteries ultimately break up into capillaries. Through the thin walls of the capillaries the blood loses oxygen and food and picks up carbon dioxide and other wastes.

Blood is returned to the heart much as in *Amphioxus*. A right and a left precardinal vein carry blood from the head back to the heart and a pair of right and left postcardinals take blood forward to the heart from the hind part of the body. Blood carrying absorbed food from the intestine goes to the liver through a **hepatic portal vein,** as in all vertebrates. After passing through the cavities of the liver the blood is again collected in a vein, the **hepatic vein,** which returns it to the heart.

The excretory system consists of a pair of thin, elongate **kidneys** running along the entire length of the coelom or body cavity on eith

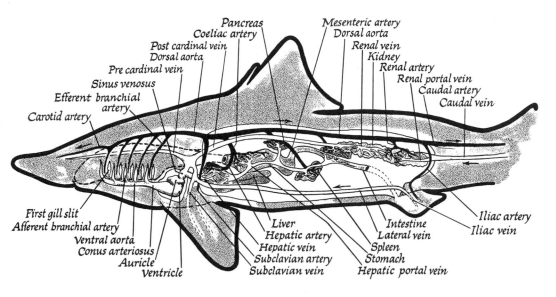

Fig. 20–10. Vascular system of an adult shark. This is very similar to the situation in any vertebrate embryo, including the human embryo.

side of the dorsal aorta and just beneath the thin peritoneal membrane which lines the coelom. The function of the kidneys will be discussed later in the section on the ray-finned bony fishes.

Reproductive System. The reproductive system of elasmobranchs is anatomically very simple. Males can be distinguished from females because the pelvic fins of the male are provided with elongated "claspers" which aid in transferring sperms into the body of the female. Internally the gonads, whether ovaries or testes, are placed close to the anterior end of the kidneys. The sperms pass to the exterior by the urinary duct, which exits through a median urogenital papilla.

In females there is commonly but one ovary. The eggs are extremely yolky and range in size from that of a hen's egg upward. The eggs break out of the ovary and fall into the coelom, a process known as **ovulation** and common to all vertebrates. From the coelom the eggs enter the large funnel-shaped openings of the paired oviducts. These openings are located at the anterior end of the coelom. Fertilization is always internal.

In many species of sharks and rays the yolky egg, as it passes down the oviduct, becomes surrounded by a watery albumen and then by a tough horny case with curly hooks. Many other species of sharks are **ovoviviparous** and some are truly **viviparous**, depending on the degree of vascular intimacy between fetal and maternal bloodstreams. Not only are the fertilized eggs retained within the oviduct, now worthily termed a **uterus**, until a well-developed

Fig. 20–11. Egg case of a skate, which has been opened to show the embryo with umbilical cord attached to yolk. (*Kindness of William H. Amos*)

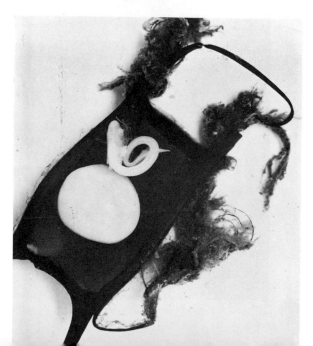

young shark is formed; but there is even a vascular area of the yolk which presses against the lining of the uterus and constitutes a true if primitive **placenta**. This remarkable fact was known to Aristotle over 2,000 years ago, but was not studied again until the work of the great German physiologist, Johannes Müller (1801-1858).

Nervous System. The nervous system of elasmobranchs is also basically like that of other vertebrates and, because of the ease with which the cartilaginous skull can be dissected, makes favorable material for study. The brain is formed as a series of five swellings and thickenings of the anterior end of what was a simple tube in the embryo. Most of the tube remains tubular and constitutes the spinal or neural cord, extending down the back just dorsal to the round centra of the backbone. The same five divisions of the brain are found in all animals with backbones.

The most anterior part of the brain, the **telencephalon** (*telos*, end, + *enkephalos*, brain), consists of a right and a left lobe which are concerned with smell. In higher vertebrates, parts of them become the cerebral hemispheres.

The next anterior division of the brain is the **diencephalon** (*dia*, through, + *enkephalos*, brain). Through it pass nerve fibers from the telencephalon to more posterior portions of the brain, but it is an important structure in its own right. Its thickened sides form the **thalamus**, which contains nerve centers controlling general emotional tone, if not in sharks (about whose emotional life little is known) yet certainly in men and in most mammals and birds. In the lower part of the diencephalon, i.e., in the **hypothalamus**, are centers controlling appetite, thirst, sex drives, and sleep. The diencephalon is also the region of the brain into which pass the optic nerves from the eyes. On the midline just below the diencephalon and connected with it is the **pituitary**. This gland is controlled by neurosecretory cells in the hypothalamus and it in turn regulates growth, reproduction, and several other activities of the organism.

Posterior to the diencephalon is the **mesencephalon** (*mesos*, middle). On its dorsal surface are a pair of large optic lobes. These have to do with vision in sharks and other vertebrates all the way to man, although in the mammals there are also important visual centers in the cerebral hemispheres.

Immediately posterior to the mesencephalon is the **metencephalon** (*meta*, after). The dorsal part of it is an oval structure, the **cerebellum**, a

Fig. 20–12. The five basic divisions of the vertebrate brain as seen in a human embryo approximately one month after conception.

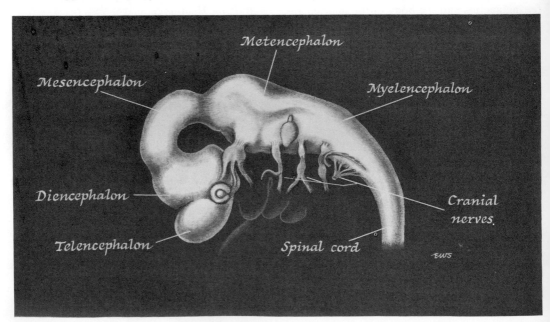

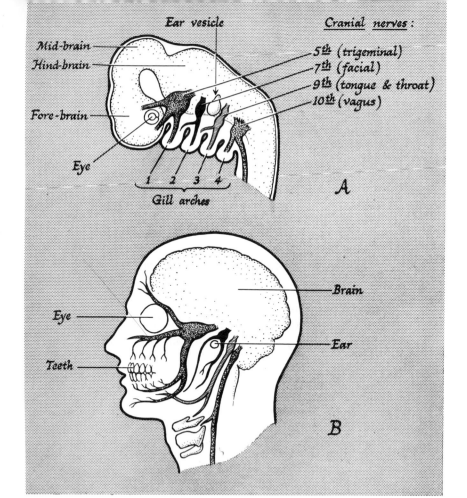

Fig. 20–13. Some of the cranial nerves of a man *(B)*, drawn to show their relationship to the gill arches of the embryo *(A)*.

center concerned with equilibrium. The ventral part of it forms the **pons.**

The fifth and last division of the vertebrate brain is the **myelencephalon** (*myelos,* marrow). This is a tapering cylindrical structure which passes into the cartilaginous vertebral canal as the spinal cord. All the nerve fibers connecting the brain and the spinal cord pass through the myelencephalon, which is usually referred to as the **medulla oblongata.** In higher vertebrates it contains an important nervous center regulating breathing. Other reflex centers located here include those for swallowing, vomiting, and vasoconstriction.

The spinal cord of the shark, as of all vertebrates, contains a small canal which is continuous with the cavities, or ventricles as they are usually called, of the brain. This canal and the ventricles of the brain are filled with **cerebro-**

spinal fluid. Brain and spinal cord make up the **central nervous system,** abbreviated as CNS.

From the brain extend ten pairs of **cranial nerves** (twelve pairs in mammals). These are as follows:[1]

1. Olfactory nerves to the olfactory epithelium of the nose.

2. Optic nerves to the retinas of the eyes.

3. Oculomotor nerves to four of the six muscles which move each eyeball.

4. Trochlear nerves to the most dorsal of the eyeball muscles.

5. Trigeminal nerves (the toothache nerve). each with three branches, one to the face, one to the upper, and one to the lower jaw.

[1] One of the best-known mnemonic rhymes in anatomy is associated with the names of the cranial nerves. One version is: On old Olympus' towering top a Finn and German valse and hop.

6. Abducens nerves to the most posterior of the six eyeball muscles.

7. Facial nerves to the face.

8. Auditory nerves to the ears.

9. Glossopharyngeal nerves to tongue and throat.

10. Vagus nerves to heart, gills or lungs, stomach, and other organs.

The two additional pairs in mammals are:

11. Accessory nerves, in fishes a part of the important vagus but in higher vertebrates separate, innervating the shoulder muscles.

12. Hypoglossal nerves to the tongue and adjacent structures.

Three of the pairs of cranial nerves are purely sensory, the olfactory (1st), the optic (2nd), and the auditory (8th). Three other pairs, the oculomotor (3rd), the trochlear (4th), and the abducens (6th), are primarily motor (the oculomotor carries some sensory fibers), and all three innervate the muscles which move the eyeballs. The remaining four pairs of cranial nerves are mixed motor and sensory and reveal a close relationship with the gill arches. The trigeminal (5th) innervates the upper and lower jaw, as though it agreed with the theory that they are derived from a gill arch. The facial (7th) innervates all the muscles and cartilages derived from the second or hyoid arch, and sends a branch on either side of the spiracle or first gill slit. This is the gill slit that becomes the Eustachian tube in man, and in man the facial nerve accordingly innervates essentially the corresponding structures as in the shark. Specifically, it innervates all the facial muscles which are derived in the human embryo from the muscle mass of the hyoid arch. The glossopharyngeal (9th) innervates the third gill arch and its muscles. The vagus (10th) innervates the fourth and all succeeding gill arches.

The parts of the brain and the various cranial nerves of a shark can be easily seen after dissecting away the cartilaginous roof of the skull. Most of the cranial nerves can be readily identified, although the big trigeminal with its three branches and its common origin with the facial confuses the picture.

The spinal nerves leave the spinal cord in pairs, one pair to each muscle segment. This segmentation of the nerves is a conspicuous feature of the human as well as the shark nervous system. Each spinal nerve has three main

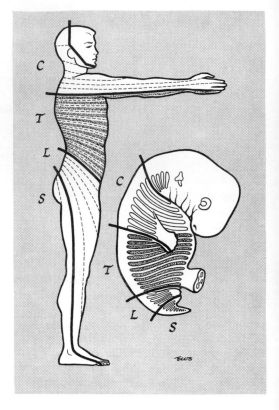

Fig. 20–14. Left: segmentation of the spinal nerves to the skin in man. Right: a human embryo, showing segmentation of the muscle and skin-forming tissues. *C,* cervical; *T,* thoracic; *L,* lumbar; *S,* sacral.

branches, one going to the epaxial muscles, one to the hypaxial muscles, and a third to the viscera. Each spinal nerve also innervates its own narrow zone of the skin. Immediately before a spinal nerve enters the spinal cord it divides into two roots. The **dorsal root** is afferent or sensory, carrying impulses into the central nervous system. The **ventral root** is efferent or motor, carrying impulses away from the central nervous system, to the muscles and glands.

The cranial and spinal nerves are often spoken of as constituting the **somatic** division of the **peripheral nervous system.** The second division is the **autonomic nervous system,** which innervates the smooth muscles, especially of the viscera, heart, blood vessels, etc. The vagus or 10th cranial nerve is part of the autonomic system. Because this system is well developed in mammals, further discussion of it will be postponed until the chapter dealing with the nervous system of that class.

The central and peripheral nervous systems, and the divisions of the latter, are often discussed as though they were separate and distinct, but it must be remembered that all the parts of the vertebrate nervous system constitute a single and integrated whole. The divisions are matters of semantic and methodological convenience.

The Sense Organs. The three most important vertebrate sense organs are the familiar nose, eyes, and ears.

In elasmobranchs, as in most fishes, the **nostrils** are blind pits containing a sensory epithelium and provided with a small flap so placed that when the shark swims, a continuous current of water will flow over the sensory epithelium.

The structure of the **eye** is in all essentials uniform in all vertebrates. The eyeball is moved within its socket by six extrinsic muscles running from skull to eyeball. There are four **rectus muscles,** dorsal, ventral, anterior, and posterior. In man the anterior rectus is beside the nose and is known as the medial rectus, while the posterior rectus is called the lateral rectus. There is also a dorsal or superior and a ventral or inferior **oblique muscle.** These tend to pull the eyes forward and toward the nose and possibly produce a slight roll. Because of their large size in sharks, a feature combined with a cartilaginous skull, the eye muscles are studied more easily in elasmobranchs than in any other vertebrates.

The eyeball consists of a fairly stiff layer, roughly spherical and composed of a glass-clear area in front called the **cornea,** which is continuous with an opaque, white, sometimes cartilaginous area called the **sclerotic layer** that makes up the remainder of the eyeball. The part of the sclerotic layer that is visible externally is the familiar white of the eye. As the illustration shows, within the eyeball is a crystalline **lens.** In fishes this is relatively larger than in most other vertebrates. The commonest kind of cataract is due to opacity of the lens. Between the lens and the cornea is a circular diaphragm, the **iris.** The hole in the center of the iris is the **pupil.** The iris has a sphincter muscle encircling the pupil. When it contracts, the pupil becomes smaller and the amount of light entering the lens is reduced.

The lens is held in position by the **ciliary body,** which connects the edge of the lens to the eyeball not far from the zone where the transparent cornea becomes the opaque sclerotic coat. The ciliary body carries a muscle, the ciliary muscle, which focuses the eye by changing the shape of the lens.

Within the vertebrate eyeball are three chambers. Between the cornea and the iris is the **anterior chamber.** In communication with it through the pupil is the **posterior chamber,** lying between the iris and the lens with its ciliary body. Both anterior and posterior chambers contain a watery **aqueous humor.** The main chamber of the eye is the large **vitreous chamber,** filled with the vitreous body, a clear gelatinous substance between the lens and the retina at the back of the eyeball.

The wall of the eyeball opposite the transparent cornea consists of three layers. Outermost is the aforementioned white and stiffened **sclerotic** layer. Immediately within it is the pigmented and vascular **choroid** layer. Pressed tightly against it is the **retina.** The retina contains the actual photosensitive **rods** and **cones** plus other nerve cells which connect with the rods and cones and with each other and carry impulses to the brain.

Fig. 20-15. A typical vertebrate eye in cross section. Note that the posterior chamber is merely the space between the iris and the lens and its ligaments.

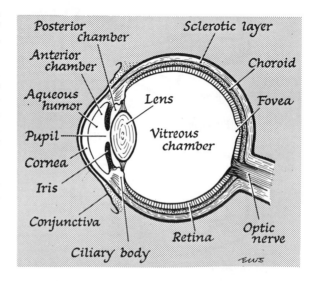

The elasmobranchs are also what anatomists call the animal of choice for dissection of the **inner ear,** i.e., semicircular canals, sacculus, and utriculus. The incomparable superiority of sharks for this purpose lies in the combination of large size and ease of dissection. As in all vertebrates (except the cyclostomes), there are three **semicircular canals,** roughly one in each of the three dimensions of space. One is anterior and one posterior, both vertical and almost at right angles to each other. A third is horizontal and thus at right angles to the other two. Swollen **ampullae** at the ends of the canals contain nerve endings. The canals connect with the **utriculus** and **sacculus,** which in many kinds of fishes contain a hard **otolith.** In the higher vertebrates the organ of hearing develops as an outgrowth of the sacculus called the **lagena.** A narrow **endolymphatic duct** leads from the sacculus up to the top of the shark's head where it opens to the exterior through a minute pore. A well-dissected inner ear of a shark is one of the most beautiful objects in anatomy.

Fig. 20–16. Two views of the inner ear of a shark, showing the three semicircular canals.

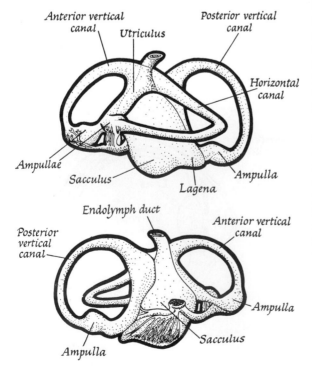

THE RAY-FINNED FISHES: ACTINOPTERYGII

As we said earlier, the ray-finned fishes as a group represent the first great deployment of the vertebrates. There are only about 3,000 species of elasmobranchs, but the described number of species of ray-finned fishes is in excess of 20,000. Their scientific name, Actinopterygii (*actinos,* ray, + *pteron,* wing or feather) derives from the fact that the projecting portion of their paired fins is supported only by dermal rays. The elasmobranchs have a well-developed cartilaginous skeleton extending out into the paired fins; and members of the remaining major group of fishes, the muscle-finned fishes or Sarcopterygii (lungfishes and coelacanths), have muscular paired fins strengthened virtually to their tips by a bony internal skeleton.

The ray-finned fishes are commonly divided into three groups. The more primitive groups are the **chondrosteans,** which include the sturgeons and the paddlefishes of the Mississippi and *Polypterus,* the bichir of Central Africa, and the **holosteans,** which include the garpike and *Amia,* the fresh-water dogfish. Both groups have their scales set in the skin like tiles on a floor which do not overlap as do shingles on a roof. Moreover, the scales are thick with a bony base and a covering of shiny material called **ganoine.** In many present-day chondrosteans scales are absent from many areas of the body. The cladisteans are somewhat less sharklike than the chondrosteans in that their tail does not turn up nor does their mouth tend to be ventral. Also, the cladisteans flourished in somewhat more recent geological times.

The third group, the **teleosts,** are the dominant group of fishes today. The scales of teleosts easily identify them for they are thin and flexible, lacking the bony base or the ganoine covering, and are imbricated, that is, overlapping like shingles. The scales of all fishes are formed within the mesoderm and hence are covered with a thin layer of living tissue, in marked contrast to the epidermal scales of reptiles, birds, and mammals. The latter type of scales grow on their inner surfaces and lie naked, with their outer surfaces exposed rather than covered with living cells as in the fishes. Thus the scaly surface of a fish is moist while scales of a reptile, bird, or mammal are dry.

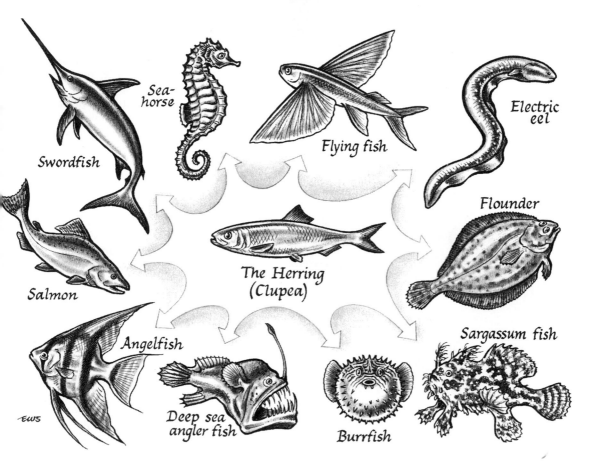

Fig. 20–17. Adaptive radiation in teleosts, the bony fishes.

The social and economic importance of fishes is great everywhere except in desert regions, and is especially so for maritime countries like Norway, England, and Japan. One of the great complications in the fishing industry, and one felt quite keenly in small countries like Norway and Japan where fisheries represent a large proportion of the total national income, is the erratic nature of fish populations. One year fishes are superabundant and there is a glut, while perhaps the next year there are very few. Despite prolonged investigations, the migrations and the rise and fall of fish populations are still very poorly understood.

The Great Deployment. Even fishermen seldom realize the bewildering extent of the variation found among the teleosts. For the first time among vertebrates they exhibit an evolutionary pattern followed by all the major subse-

quent groups, the pattern of **adaptive radiation.** Beginning with a generalized body form like that of *Clupea,* the herring (Fig. 20–17), evolutionary adaptation has carried the teleosts in many different directions and fitted them for many ways of life in diverse environments. In the great depths of the sea teleosts live in eternal night, illuminated only by light which they themselves carry in specialized luminous organs. Above the surface, flying fishes skim through the air propelled by the strike of their tails against the water and suspended by their greatly developed winglike pectoral fins.

Equally noteworthy are the adaptations of thousands of other species. Half hidden on the bottom sands lie the flounders. Each begins its development as a normal-looking symmetrical fish. Then differential growth sets in; either the right or the left side of the head, depending on the species, grows faster than the other side,

Fig. 20-18. Flying fishes spotted at night by a photo flash camera at Catalina Island, California. Actual size about 1 foot long. (*Harold E. Edgerton*)

twisting the skull around until both eyes come to lie on the same side of the body. In addition to this gross anatomical adaptation to a life of ambush on the bottom, flounders possess a remarkable ability to change their color pattern to match the background. These changes depend on the expansion or contraction of melanophores, amoeboid cells containing the black pigment melanin. The electric eel of the Amazon, *Electrophorus,* generates an EMF (electromotive force) in excess of 500 volts, with enough current to disable a horse. The little sargassum fish so closely resembles the ragged sea weed among which it lurks that other animals almost swim into its mouth. The 1,000-pound swordfish is equipped with a formidable weapon 3 feet long and has eyes larger than a whale's. Puffer fishes of various kinds swell up by swallowing water, thus making themselves hard to catch. The list of such special adaptations is virtually endless.

Classification Problems. For generations zoologists have tried to make order out of this assemblage of over 20,000 species. There is an old saying among zoologists that no man who went into teleost taxonomy ever came out. There is no better group of vertebrates in which to see the difficulties of constructing a rational system of classification.

The great French comparative anatomist Cuvier (1769–1832) made a primary division of teleosts into those with soft fins and those with spiny fins; he called them malacopterygians and acanthopterygians, respectively. Later the German physiologist Johannes Müller (1801–1858) made the same attempt, but chose to divide the teleosts into those in which the air-bladder retains an open connection to the gut throughout life and those in which it becomes closed. Thus Müller erected the Physostomi, or the physostomous fishes with open swim-bladders, and the Physoclisti, or the physoclistous fishes in which the swim-bladder is closed off and has no opening whatsoever. Working with the same group of fishes, Müller's contemporary, Louis Agassiz (1807–1873), sometimes called the "father of American zoology," divided teleosts on the basis of their scales into the Cycloidei and the Ctenoidei (see Fig. 20–20). Of course, all teleost scales are the thin flexible type which lack a bony layer. The only difference between cycloid and ctenoid scales is that the exposed edge of the cycloid scale is smooth while the exposed edge of the ctenoid scale has minute teeth. Both cycloid and ctenoid scales show annual growth rings that reveal the age of the individual fish. Later still, the famous American ichthyologist and university president David Starr Jordan (1851–1931) labored at the same problem. He ended by dividing teleosts into the Abdominales, in which the pelvic fins are in a posterior position, much as in the sharks, and the Thoracices and Jugulares, in which the pelvic fins are far forward, in the thoracic or even the throat region.

What could better illustrate our lack of objective criteria on which to base taxonomic divisions? None of these four methods gives the same results in detail. At the same time it is important to note that the four criteria do give the same general result. Most of the fishes with

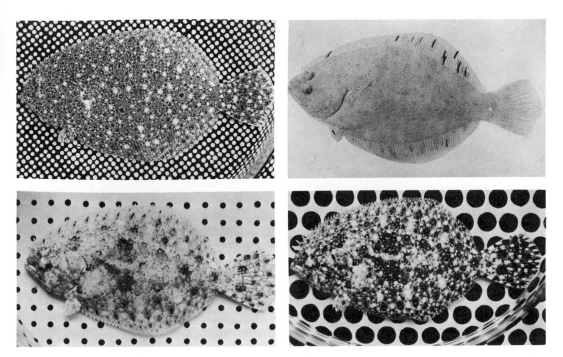

Fig. 20–19. Pattern changes in flounders in response to different backgrounds. (*U.S. Fish and Wildlife Service*)

soft-rayed fins have open air-bladders, and most teleosts with open air-bladders also have cycloid scales and pelvic fins in the abdominal position. These are the primitive and relatively unspecialized teleosts such as the herring, the salmon, and the trout. Perch and bass are representatives of advanced teleosts.

Major Adaptations: Swim-Bladder and Kidneys. Why have teleosts been so very successful, compared to their 'nearest rivals the elasmobranchs? No certain answer can be given. Perhaps the fin rays combined with their thin cycloid or ctenoid scales give them an agility in the water that no other fishes can match.

Fig. 20–20. Scales of teleosts, showing growth rings. Left: cycloid scale of herring. Right: ctenoid scale of perch. ×2 (*U.S. Fish and Wildlife Service*)

They have assumed a far greater variety of body forms than any other group of fishes, but there is no evidence that they have a higher mutation rate and thereby present to natural selection more material to work with.

Teleosts possess two general adaptations worthy of study, the swim-bladder and, more important, improved kidneys. The kidneys of both elasmobranchs and teleosts have been much used in research on kidney function; this work will be discussed in the chapter on excretion. The **swim-** or **air-bladder** serves as a hydrostatic organ which regulates the specific gravity of the fish as a whole, so that it can remain at any particular depth without continual effort. This is something sharks lack. In the more primitive — that is, generalized — species the swim-bladder opens into the dorsal wall of the pharynx. This is true of the sturgeon and other ganoids, as well as of primitive teleosts. The evolutionary origin of these structures is obscure. They develop in somewhat the same way as lungs, but the arteries to these air-bladders come from the dorsal aorta, whereas lungs always receive their arterial blood supply from the sixth pair of gill arteries.

In fishes with physoclistous (closed) bladders one or more highly vascular glands project into the bladder. These glands secrete or absorb gas and, in response to different conditions, change the volume of the bladder. When the hydrostatic pressure of the water is decreased, as happens when a fish swims near the surface, more gas is secreted into the swim-bladder. This enlarges the bladder and decreases the specific gravity of the fish as a whole. Artificially increasing the pressure within the swim-bladder results in violent reactions of the fins plus depression of the heart beat. Presumably these responses would take the fish into deeper water, where the hydrostatic pressure would balance the increased air-bladder pressure. This does not happen if the autonomic nerves to the bladder are cut, a fact showing that these responses are mediated through the autonomic nervous system.

One of the most important of all the adaptive organs of the vertebrates is the **kidney.** It is the organ primarily responsible for maintaining the constancy of the internal environment, that is, of the blood and fluids in which the cells are bathed. This, the "milieu intérieure" of the famous French physiologist Claude Bernard (1813–1878), confers on vertebrates their ability to live in such diverse external environments. This primary function of the kidney is to control the osmotic concentration of the blood.

The problems presented to the vertebrate kidney can be properly understood only in the light of the curious evolutionary history of the vertebrates themselves. According to fossil evidence, the first vertebrates arose in fresh water, presumably in bays and river mouths not far from the sea where life originated. Marine invertebrates, and the primitive chordates from which the first vertebrates sprang, have blood that is in osmotic equilibrium with the sea water in which they live. Hence they have no osmotic problem. But a fresh-water vertebrate needs a kidney for the same reason that a fresh-water amoeba needs a contractile vacuole, to pump out excess water as it enters the tissues. The blood and the cells have a relatively high concentration of salts and other osmotically active substances. In fresh water the cells would swell and burst unless there were some means of removing that water.

The earliest kidneys, designed primarily for elimination of excess water, were tubules with a funnel-shaped open end where coelomic fluid entered and was then passed along to the exterior. Very early in piscine evolution the open funnel or nephrostome became secondary and then disappeared. Its place was taken by a knot or tuft of capillaries carrying blood under high pressure. This capillary tuft is known as a **glomerulus.** It is pushed into the thin-walled, expanded end of the tubule. This thin-walled and expanded end is known, from its discoverer, as **Bowman's capsule.** The glomerulus pushes into one side of Bowman's capsule in much the way you might push your fist into a thin rubber balloon. Bowman's capsule plus the glomerulus are together known as a **renal corpuscle.** The entire functional unit of a vertebrate kidney, the renal corpuscle plus the uriniferous tubule leading off from it, is known as **nephron.**

How the nephron functions has been the subject of a brilliant series of investigations extending over a century and continuing today.

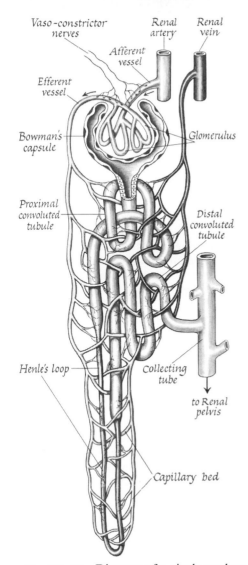

Vaso-constrictor nerves

Renal artery

Renal vein

Afferent vessel

Efferent vessel

Bowman's capsule

Glomerulus

Proximal convoluted tubule

Distal convoluted tubule

Henle's loop

Collecting tube

to Renal pelvis

Capillary bed

Fig. 20 – 21. Diagram of a single nephron.

In the primitive fresh-water fishes the capillaries of the glomerulus exude a watery fluid through their own walls and those of Bowman's capsule into the renal tubule. As this fluid (essentially merely a filtrate of the blood) passes down the tubule, food and other molecules are reabsorbed by the tubule walls, and what remains to pass to the exterior is excess water.

As geological time passed the kidney took on other functions, primarily the elimination from the blood of nitrogenous wastes. However, even today, fresh-water fishes eliminate most of their waste nitrogen in the form of simple ammonia via their gills. If such a fish is placed through a tightly fitting rubber partition so that

its head and gills are on one side and its urinary opening on the other, almost all of the waste nitrogen will be found in the water on the head side of the partition.

In the course of evolution some of these well-adapted fresh-water fishes invaded the sea. This would have presented no osmotic problem to the fish kidney if the oceans had remained as they were when the prochordate ancestors first entered the estuaries and rivers. However, due to a cosmic distillation cycle — evaporation from the sea, distilled water falling on the land, and this fresh-water in the rivers washing down more salts into the sea — the sea itself had, in the course of millenia, become more salty.

The problem for an animal in a medium of higher osmotic concentration than its own body fluids is not how to eliminate excess water but how to conserve water against the osmotic pull from outside which would dehydrate it and concentrate the salts in blood and lymph. The primary loss of water is through the capillaries in the gills but these structures obviously cannot be dispensed with because they are essential for respiration.

How do fishes solve this problem? Sharks and other elasmobranchs do so by allowing urea to accumulate in the blood until the osmotic concentration equals that of sea water. Urea is a harmless product manufactured by the liver from two waste products, ammonia and carbon dioxide. Any excess salt, ingested with the food, is excreted by a rectal gland. Apparently elasmobranchs gradually developed these adaptations while living in the sea throughout the hundreds of thousands of years during which it has become more salty. In marine rayfinned fishes there are several probably less efficient methods. In some, like the ugly little toadfish, *Opsanus tau,* commonly found guarding its eggs in the old tin cans of a harbor, there is an anatomical adaptation. The glomeruli, where most of the water enters the nephron from the blood, are missing. Their aglomerular kidneys possess only the tubules which secrete metabolic wastes. Other marine bony fishes swallow large quantities of sea water which is absorbed through the intestine and compensates for the water continually lost through the gills. Unfortunately salts, especially sodium, potassium, and chloride ions, are also absorbed by the intestine. These salts are excreted by special cells in the gills! If this salt were not excreted the osmotic concentration of the blood would increase to equilibrium with the sea water and apparently beyond the tolerance of the cells of the fish. While the kidneys of the sharks were becoming adapted to maintaining a relatively high level of urea in the blood, the cells of the shark must have developed a tolerance for a higher osmotic environment. The bony fishes took a different path.

Minor Adaptations. Of the so-called minor adaptations none is of greater interest than the **electric organs.** A common laboratory experiment in marine biological stations is to make an electric fish light electric signs, ring doorbells, and accomplish similar feats. As already mentioned, the electric organ in the tail of the Amazon eel, *Electrophorus (Gymnotus) electricus* generates over 500 volts.

Electric organs are known to have arisen independently several times in evolution, because they are found among both elasmobranchs and teleosts. And in both groups they are found in widely separated species. The stargazer is a teleost, like the Amazon eel, but has its electric organs on top of its head. The two commonest electric elasmobranchs are *Torpedo,* a heavy-set medium-sized ray, and *Raia,* the large sting-ray. In the genus *Torpedo,* the rounded electric organs occupy a large area on each side just back of the head; in sting-rays the electric organs are elongate structures in the tail.

The ancient Egyptians and Romans knew that various electric fishes possess strange powers, but it was not until 1773 that the electrical nature of these fishes was established. They have been studied by Michael Faraday (one of the inventors of the dynamo) and many others to the present day. With one questionable exception, the electric organs in all these unrelated fishes are modified muscles. This is obvious from their position, their innervation, and their development. Every muscle emits a slight electric discharge on contraction. This is what makes electrocardiographs possible. The electrical changes of the heart muscle are strong enough to be picked up by suitable apparatus

and recorded. Hence it is not too surprising to find that electric organs are modified muscles, although the case of *Astroscopus,* the stargazer fish, does verge on the fantastic, for in this animal the electric organs are innervated by the oculomotor nerves and they develop from a primordium that in other fishes forms eye muscles.

In structure electric organs consist of a series of **electroplaxes,** each representing a highly modified muscle. Each electroplax begins as a multinucleate structure which in other locations would develop into muscle. Instead, it forms a flattened structure innervated on one side, usually the electronegative side. The whole electroplax somewhat resembles an enlarged motor end-plate, that is, the structure with which a motor nerve ends on a muscle. Each electroplax produces from 0.05 to 0.15 volts. Since these electroplaxes are connected in series, the total voltage produced is the sum of the voltages of the individual electroplaxes, just as the total voltage produced by a series of dry cells is the sum of that produced by each.

In recent years the electric organs of fishes have become important research material to help solve problems in nerve-muscle physiology. Curare, an extremely potent poison used by South American Indians on arrow tips, paralyzes by inactivating the motor end-plates of the victim's muscles. It also completely inactivates electric organs. Chemically, electric organs are similar to motor end-plates. Two chemicals are involved in the excitation of a muscle by a nerve, acetylcholine and an enzyme which destroys it, cholinesterase. Electric organs are rich sources of these substances. The most potent war "gases" known are nerve poisons which are anti-cholinesterases.

The special adaptations seen in fishes seem endless in number. The **light-producing organs** on deep-sea fishes appear to have arisen independently many times in evolution, because they are very different in location and pattern in fishes belonging to different families. In both elasmobranchs and teleosts the light-producing organs often are arranged as a pattern of spots on the head or along the sides of the grotesque bodies of these black fishes of the eternal darkness. They are specialized mucus-secreting

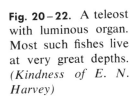

Fig. 20–22. A teleost with luminous organ. Most such fishes live at very great depths. (*Kindness of E. N. Harvey*)

structures filled with luminous bacteria. In two or three cases they are on the ends of tentacles above the mouth and appear to act as lures for food. A not improbable function for these patterns and colors of lights is as markers for species recognition, which must be as difficult as it is important to propagation. Not only man is fearfully and wonderfully made.

The brilliant and varied **colors** of teleosts, especially tropical reef fishes, are due to several mechanisms. Most important are irregular, more or less amoeboid cells called **chromato-phores** (*chroma,* color, + *phore,* to carry). Like amphibians, fishes have **melanophores** carrying the black or brown tyrosine derivative, melanin. Many fishes may also possess yellow **xantho-phores** (*xanthos,* yellow), red **erythrophores** (*erythros,* red), and white **leucophores** (*leuco,* white).

A vast amount of research has been directed toward understanding how these and other elements produce the changing colors of fishes. Not only tropical fishes change color, but even common flounders can make spectacular changes in response to different backgrounds. In fact, all fishes seem able to become lighter or darker. In many elasmobranchs and some teleosts the melanophores appear to be controlled entirely by hormones from the pituitary. In the lampreys and certain sharks and rays the posterior lobe of the pituitary produces a melano-phore-expanding substance. Removal of this gland results in a permanent paling of the fish. Injection of pituitary extract, on the other hand, produces darkening.

In some elasmobranchs and most teleosts there is both a hormonal and a nervous control of coloration. In these species, response to light and dark backgrounds will continue, though in a lesser degree, after removal of the pituitary. Electrical stimulation of certain nerve roots will produce either a blanching or a darkening over the entire area innervated by the nerve stimulated.

Many essential adaptations in fishes are **behavioral,** often closely tied in with special structural adaptations. The asymmetrical head and pancake-shaped body of a flounder are meaningless without a specific type of behavior to go with them. The remora or shark sucker is provided with a flattened oval suction disk on top of its head. This structure seems purpose-less until the remora uses it to affix itself to a passing shark; then it is evident that the suction disk is used to provide a free ride and a seat under the shark's table, where the remora is ready to grab the crumbs.

The remarkable **migrations** of fishes are of three kinds. **Anadromous** (*ana,* upwards, + *dromos,* a running) species like salmon, shad, and lampreys migrate upstream out of large lakes or the sea to breed. **Catadromous** (*cata,* downwards, + *dromos,* a running) species like the common teleost eels live most of their lives in fresh-water lakes and migrate downstream into the ocean to reproduce. Within the ocean itself many of the commercially important species of fishes make long annual and as yet little-understood migrations, or at least mass movements.

THE LUNGFISHES AND COELACANTHS: SARCOPTERYGII

The most notable fact about the muscle-finned fishes is that they quite clearly gave rise to all the terrestrial vertebrates — amphibians, reptiles, birds, and mammals. Their scientific name, **Sarcopterygii**, refers to the flesh or muscles on the fins *(sarcos,* flesh, + *pteron,* wing or feather). The muscles on the paired fins are supported almost to the tip by a jointed bony skeleton. These fishes are also sometimes called Choanichthyes (*choane,* funnel, + *ichthyes,* fish) to refer to the nostrils which only fishes of this group possess. The nostrils of elasmobranchs and of teleosts and other ray-finned fishes are merely little blind sacs lined with an olfactory epithelium. The nostrils of the muscle-finned sarcopterygians are like those of air-breathing terrestrial vertebrates and connect the opening on the snout or nose with the inside of the throat. These nostrils are indeed funnels.

Three genera of **lungfishes** (dipnoids) survive today. The Australian lungfish, *Epiceratodus,* living in northeastern Australia, is a rather heavy-set, longish fish, known locally as a Burnett salmon. *Protopterus* in Africa and *Lepidosiren* in South America are almost eellike in appearance. The wide geographical distribution of these fishes is typical of extremely ancient forms. It is notable that all three live in regions of seasonal drought, when air-breathing is a necessity. The fossil evidence strongly indicates that legs evolved first to enable animals to get to water, not to conquer the land. In a dry season a fish that could crawl up- or downstream to a remaining pool of water would be favored by natural selection.

The development from egg through larva is almost indistinguishable from that of a salamander. For many years lungfishes were considered the actual ancestors of the Amphibia, but the lungfishes have very strange teeth, adapted for crushing, and various skeletal specializations which make that unlikely.

The **coelacanths** were supposed to have been extinct ever since the Cretaceous Period, ending at least 70 million years ago. But in 1938 a strange fish caught off the east coast of Africa came to the attention of J. L. B. Smith, an African zoologist who recognized the specimen as a coelacanth. Then followed a 14-year search up and down the coast to discover others. It was finally found that they live in extremely deep water off the Comoro islands north of Madagascar. To date several dozen have been caught, and an international group of investigators has been organized to study different aspects of their form and function.

Smith has named the recently found coelacanth *Latimeria chalumnae.* It is a big fish, attaining over 5 feet in length and weighing up to 180 pounds. It is certainly a specialized form adapted for living at depths of 1,000 to 3,000 feet, and it is not surprising to find that both the lungs and internal nostrils are undeveloped.

Review and References

REVIEW TOPICS

1. Distinguish between cyclostomes, elasmobranchs, ray-finned fishes, and muscle-finned fishes.

2. What is the economic importance of cyclostomes? Elasmobranchs? Ray-finned fishes?

3. What is the structure and life history of the ammocoetes larva? What evolutionary relationship do they suggest? Why?

4. Show how the skeletal and muscular systems of elasmobranchs are basically like those of mammals but in simpler form.

5. What are the cranial nerves? What structures does each pair innervate in the shark and in man?

6. Describe the function of each part of the eye. Of the inner ear.

7. Discuss adaptations in fishes.

8. What is the coelacanth story?

9. Define: Bowman's capsule, epaxial muscles, antagonistic muscles, dorsal aorta, diencephalon, electroplax, acetylcholine, melanophore, catadromous, glomerulus, ovoviviparous, viviparous.

USEFUL REFERENCES

Axelrod, H. R., and L. P. Schultz, *Handbook of Tropical Aquarium Fishes,* New York, McGraw-Hill Book Co., 1955.

Bigelow, H. B., *Fishes of the Western North Atlantic,* New Haven, Yale University Press, 1948.

Breder, C. M., *A Field Book of Marine Fishes of the Atlantic Coast from Labrador to Texas,* New York, G. P. Putnam's Sons, 1929.

Brown, M. E., ed., *The Physiology of Fishes, I, Metabolism; II, Behavior,* New York, Academic Press, 1957.

Carlander, K. D., *Handbook of Fresh-water Fishery Biology,* Dubuque, Iowa, William C. Brown Company, 1955.

Daniel, J. F., *The Elasmobranch Fishes,* Berkeley, Univ. of California Press, 1934.

Hubbs, C. L., and K. F. Lagler, *Guide to the Fishes of the Great Lakes and Tributary Waters,* Bloomfield Hills, Mich., Cranbrook Institute, 1941.

Innes, W. T., *Exotic Aquarium Fishes,* Philadelphia, Innes Publishing Company, 1955.

Lagler, K. F., J. E. Bardach, and R. R. Miller, *Ichthyology,* New York, John Wiley & Sons, 1962.

Longley, W. H., *Fishes of Tortugas, Florida, with observations on color, habits and local distribution,* Washington, D.C., Carnegie Institution, 1941.

Williamson, H., *Salar the Salmon,* Boston, Little, Brown & Co., 1936.

Chapter 21

Amphibians

Frogs, toads, salamanders, and other living members of the Class Amphibia are sharply separated from the fishes on one side and from the reptiles, birds, and mammals on the other. They are separated from the fishes by having **pentadactyl,** i.e., five-toed, legs instead of paired fins. They are separated from the scaly reptiles by a lack of external scales, and by laying eggs which have to develop in water or at least in a very damp place. This is because the amphibian embryo does not grow a membrane, the amnion, around itself. In reptiles, birds, and mammals the amnion encloses the embryo in a sac of water that makes it unnecessary for the egg to be laid in a pond. So important is the amnion as a basic adaptation for terrestrial life that the reptiles, birds, and mammals are grouped together as amniotes.

The egg, embryo, and larva of the amphibians are almost indistinguishable from those of the lungfishes. Prominent among the fishlike traits of the larval or tadpole stage characteristic of amphibians are the functional gills and gill slits, the lateral line of sense organs along each side of the body, and a tail fin that usually extends well forward along the back. The fin never has rays as in fishes, but is important in swimming. Tadpoles excrete nitrogenous wastes as simple ammonia as fishes do, instead of converting them to urea like frogs and mammals.

Relatively abrupt metamorphosis from the aquatic larva into a gill-less adult is characteristic of amphibians. The anatomy and physiology of metamorphosis will be discussed in the final section of this chapter.

The frogs, and to a lesser extent the salamanders, have proved to be extremely useful animals for biological teaching and research. They are clean, cheap, and readily available, and certainly far outrank the proverbial guinea pigs as laboratory animals. The economic importance of the amphibians is negligible.

EVOLUTIONARY RELATIONSHIPS AND TAXONOMY

The ancestors of the amphibians were clearly muscle-finned fishes (i.e., Sarcopterygii), probably closely related to our present-day lungfishes which, when first hatched, so resemble larval salamanders that only an expert can distinguish them. As already discussed in the chapter on evolution, the amphibians represent a striking case of pre-adaptation because their three major adaptations for terrestrial life — legs, lungs, and eggs that can be laid on land — were all adaptations developed by aquatic ancestors which enabled them to survive better in the water, but which also opened the way for the new terrestrial existence. The only confusing thing about it is that our familiar amphibians of north temperate regions lay small aquatic eggs. The fossil record indicates that this is a relatively late modification. The earliest amphibians (the stegocephalians) laid much larger reptilelike eggs with protective coats. This type of egg is still found in some tropical species.

The only three living orders of Amphibia are so dissimilar that they cannot be very closely related to each other. About 2,500 species have been described. The fossil record reveals that the first Amphibia were scaly and so were those that led to the reptiles. Since our contemporary Amphibia are scaleless or nearly so, they are presumed to be in a blind alley off to one side of the main line of vertebrate evolution. This is certainly true of the frogs and toads, which are very highly specialized. The three living orders follow.

1. The **Caudatiformes** (*cauda*, tail) are characterized by the possession of tails in the adult as well as the larva. These are the salamanders. The caudate amphibians are frequently referred to as the urodeles (*oura*, tail).

2. The **Salientiformes** (*saliens*, leaping) lack tails in the adult but possess them in the larval or tadpole stage. These are the frogs and toads. They are often called anurans from their lack of a tail (*an* + *oura*, no tail).

3. The **Gymnophioniformes** are a very small group of wormlike amphibians found only in tropical regions. These animals are completely without legs.

FUNCTIONAL SYSTEMS

External Anatomy and Skeletal System. Externally frogs show a very common vertebrate adaptation, that of countershading, a device frequently employed in military camouflage. The dorsal surface is dark, the under surface light, a combination which makes a frog swimming near the surface inconspicuous to its enemies both above and below. Other external adaptations include details of coloration, webbed feet, and the dorsal position of the protuberant eyes. Toads and salamanders show countershading but lack the webbed feet.

The skeleton of the salamanders is an obvious modification from that of fishes. The paired limbs exhibit the basic pattern of all vertebrates, including birds and mammals. Articulating with the pectoral girdle is a single bone on each side, the **humerus,** from shoulder to elbow. The forearm from elbow to wrist has two bones, the **ulna** which makes a hinge joint with the humerus, and parallel with it the **radius.** Then follow **carpals** or wrist bones, elongate **metacarpals** in the palm of the "hand," and lastly the **phalanges** in the digits or "fingers."

The hind limb follows the same pattern. Attached to the pelvic girdle is a single bone on each side, the **femur,** followed at the knee by a pair of bones, the **tibia** and **fibula,** and these by the **tarsals** of the ankle, the **metatarsals,** and the **phalanges.**

Fig. 21–1. The limb skeletons of a salamander and a man show the same basic pattern. *A*, front limb of salamander. *B*, hind limb of salamander. *C*, arm of man. *D*, leg of man.

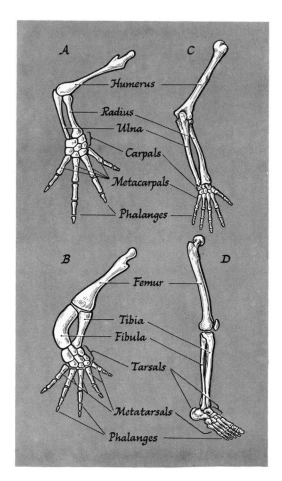

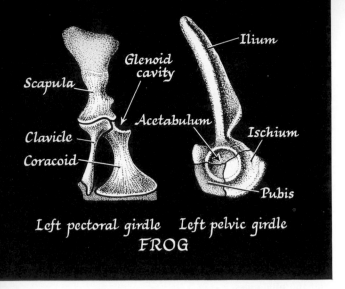

Scapula

Glenoid cavity

Clavicle

Coracoid

Ilium

Acetabulum

Ischium

Pubis

Left pectoral girdle   Left pelvic girdle

FROG

Fig. 21–2. The tripods of bones that make up each half of the pectoral and pelvic girdles of a frog. They are similar to the tripods supporting the limbs of reptiles, birds, and mammals.

Each leg is supported by a tripod of bones, the **scapula, clavicle,** and **coracoid** or their representatives for the front leg, and the **ilium, pubis,** and **ischium** for the hind leg. These tripods make a more or less firm connection with the back bone. The tripods for the front legs constitute the **pectoral girdle,** those for the hind legs, the **pelvic girdle.**

In the caudate amphibians, the backbone is long and the segmental muscles so arranged in series that the major means of locomotion is fishlike, by sinuous S-shaped waves passing back over the body.

In the frogs and toads, the skeleton is highly modified. The backbone is drastically shortened and the limbs are highly specialized for jumping. The radius and ulna are semifused and so are the tibia and fibula. Two of the tarsals are elongated until they appear like tibia and fibula. The pelvis is also highly modified. In short, the skeleton of a frog is so highly specialized that it is a very poor form in which to study the vertebrate skeleton.

Muscular System. The muscular system of a frog or a salamander can be most easily understood by imagining a modified shark in which the limb musculature has undergone a markedly greater development (see page 439). There are the same three primary divisions: (1) the axial, or trunk and tail, muscles; (2) the limb muscles; and (3) the gill-arch muscles.

The **axial muscles** of trunk and tail are especially fishlike in organization. Before metamorphosis there is a lateral line clearly marking the distinction between the epaxial and the hypaxial muscles. Throughout life this distinction remains though the lateral line disappears. The epaxial muscles, innervated by the dorsal branches of the spinal nerves, straighten the spine, while the hypaxials, innervated by the ventral branches of the spinal nerves, flex the spine. In amphibians as in human beings, the rectus muscles and the obliques over the abdomen belong to the hypaxial system.

The **limb musculature** is derived from the hypaxial system, but in the amphibians has become so important that it spreads out over both the hypaxial and epaxial muscles. In fact, the limb muscles meet over the back in the shoulder region. These are known as the **extrinsic muscles** of the leg because they move the leg as a whole in relation to the rest of the body. They become more and more important in terrestrial animals, where the limbs rather than a swimming tail and trunk are the primary locomotor organs. The **intrinsic leg muscles,** which move the various parts of the legs, also become more and more important, especially those which move the hands in primates.

Another way of defining extrinsic and intrinsic as applied to muscles is in terms of origin and insertion. The **origin** of a muscle is its point of attachment nearer the midline of the body; its **insertion** is its point of attachment farthest from the midline. An extrinsic muscle is one which has its origin on one structure and its insertion on another. An intrinsic muscle is one which has both its origin and its insertion on the same organ or structure. Thus muscles which have their origin on the shoulder over the back, such as the trapezius and the latissimus dorsi, and their insertions on the limb, are extrinsic muscles of the leg. Muscles with both origin and insertion on the leg, such as those which move the foot, are intrinsic leg muscles.

It is important to know something about the intrinsic leg muscles of the frog, because they have always been the most readily available for the study of muscle action. The **gastrocnemius** is the large muscle in the calf of the leg. Its origin is on the femur and its insertion is by the tendon of Achilles to the heel. Its contraction raises the heel and depresses the foot. It is asserted that during the Middle Ages noblemen used to "hamstring" minstrels whose services they wished to retain, by cutting the tendon of Achilles.

In frogs and salamanders, the **gill-arch musculature** is again present for the jaws, head, and throat; it is innervated by the same cranial nerves as in fishes and men.

As is true throughout the animal kingdom, the muscles of amphibians are generally organized in antagonistic sets or pairs. Flexors cause a limb to bend, extensors to extend. The heart, however, is but a single muscle. It contracts actively to pump blood out but fills again when the heart muscle relaxes. Sphincter muscles which surround openings, as in the gut between stomach and intestine, do not usually have antagonists.

Because of their easy availability and because they remain alive and functional for long periods after removal from the body, frog muscles and frog hearts are important research materials and have been such since the beginnings of physiology in the 18th century. Figure 21–4 shows the classic experiment of Galvani in which he demonstrated that a muscle will contract when it is touched by two different metals that are arranged as part of a complete electric circuit.

Fig. 21–3. Comparison of the muscles of a man and a frog.

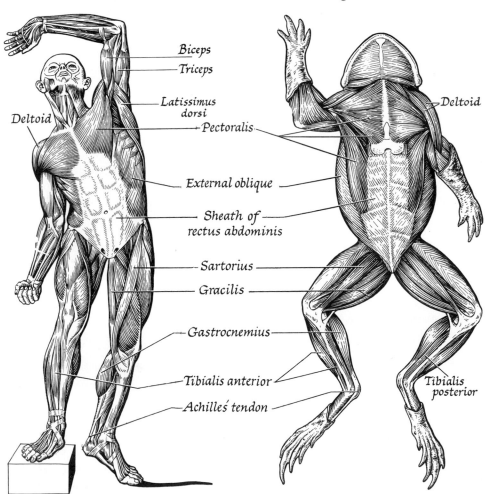

Biceps
Triceps
Latissimus dorsi
Deltoid
Pectoralis
Deltoid
External oblique
Sheath of rectus abdominis
Sartorius
Gracilis
Gastrocnemius
Tibialis anterior
Tibialis posterior
Achilles' tendon

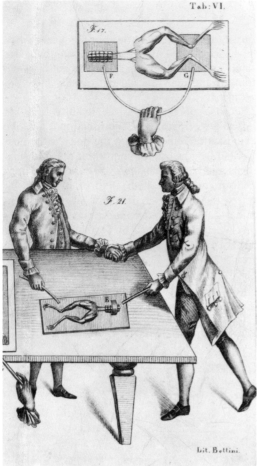

Fig. 21–4. The classic 18th century experiments of Galvani initiated the scientific study of muscle action and led to the first source of a continuous electric current in the battery of Volta. From Galvani's book of 1791. *(Library of Congress)*

Figure 21–5 shows an electron microscope photograph of **striated muscle** such as moves a leg. Three kinds of bands (actually, of course, they are disks) can be seen in this flattened fibril. The very narrow cross bands are called Z bands and the broad ones A bands. The thin bands showing fine longitudinal filaments are the I bands. The A and I cross striations can be seen in fresh muscle under high power of an ordinary light microscope. Heart muscle is also striated but the muscles of the gut and oviduct and other viscera lack striations and are hence termed **smooth muscles.**

Digestive System. The digestive system of the amphibian begins with a large mouth, as is usual in animals of carnivorous diet. The mouth leads directly into the stomach through an esophagus so short as to be almost nonexistent. The stomach is an elongate and enlarged portion of the gut or alimentary canal. The opening between the stomach and intestine is the **pylorus.** It is kept closed by a circular sphincter muscle, the pyloric muscle.

The two great glands or secreting organs of the digestive system, the **liver** and the **pancreas,** play much the same role in amphibians as in all vertebrates. Blood from the intestine carries digested food to the liver, where it is processed and stored as glycogen, or animal starch. The pancreas is an inconspicuous elongate gland lying between the stomach and a bend of the intestine. It pours potent digestive juices into the intestine a short distance below the pylorus.

The posterior end of the gut is a short enlarged passage known as the **cloaca.** It receives the openings of the excretory and reproductive systems.

Respiratory System. The respiratory system in frogs and salamanders begins with external nostrils on the surface of the snout and internal nostrils opening in the roof of the mouth. Air is drawn through the nostrils into the cavity of the mouth by a vacuum caused by depressing the floor of the throat. The mouthful of air is then swallowed into the lungs.

Fig. 21–5. Electron microscope photo of a striated muscle. Original magnification × 30,000. *(Kindness of Ralph W. G. Wyckoff)*

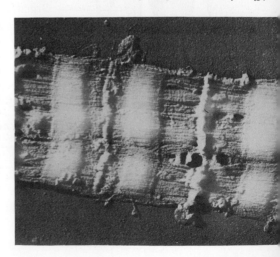

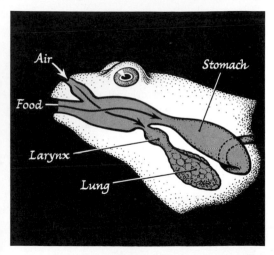

Fig. 21–6. Frog's head. Note the crossing of the routes of food and air in the pharynx of terrestrial vertebrates.

A peculiarity of the air-breathing vertebrates, from frog to man, is that the route of air from internal nostrils to lungs crosses the route of the food from mouth to esophagus. The **glottis,** a slitlike opening on the floor of the mouth well back towards the esophagus, leads into a squarish cavity, the **larynx,** which in turn opens into the lungs, one on either side.

The larynx is supported by cartilaginous rods, and from its inner sides arise a pair of horizontal membranous folds, the **vocal cords.** Thus begins the use of the sound-carrying properties of air. Correlated with the vocal cords, which produce sounds by their vibrations, is the development of a **tympanum** or eardrum to pick up these vibrations. In frogs and toads this tympanum is flush with the surface of the head and is stretched across the old first gill slit, the spiracle in sharks. The gill slit itself now becomes known as the **Eustachian tube,** named for the 16th century Italian anatomist who discovered it, Bartolommeo Eustachio.

Vascular System. Four features of the amphibian vascular system are of general interest: the aortic arches in the gill-slit region, the capillaries, the renal portal system, and the heart itself.

Possession of six pairs of **aortic arches** in the pharynx seems to have been the primordial vertebrate condition. This condition is found in all vertebrate embryos. The surprising fact that the embryo of a chicken or a man has gill slits

Fig. 21–7. Gill slits (arabic numbers) and aortic arches (Roman numerals) of some fishes and amphibians; side view. The situation in embryos of reptiles, birds, and mammals resembles that of the fishes and the salamander. *i.c.,* internal carotid artery; *e.c.,* external carotid artery; *s.a.,* systemic artery; *L,* lung.

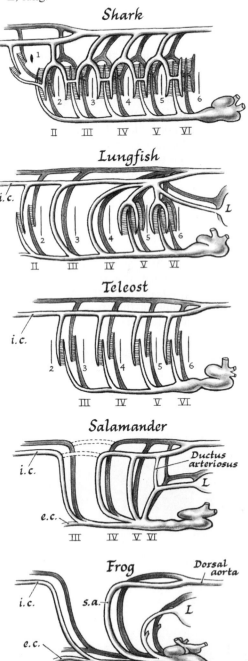

and aortic arches much like those of an embryonic fish was discovered only a little over a century ago by a young German embryologist, Heinrich Rathké. In the adult shark, it will be remembered, there are five aortic arches. The first, or most anterior one, is greatly reduced in size along with the reduction of the first gill slit into a mere spiracle.

In the salamanders all six aortic arches are, of course, present in the embryo, but in the course of embryonic development the first and second fail to maintain their growth and finally disappear. The third arch, however, becomes part of the internal **carotid arches** that carry blood to the head. The first three arches have the same fate in all the higher vertebrates. The fourth arch takes blood from the **ventral aorta** up to the dorsal side of the pharynx and there forms the **dorsal aorta** which conducts blood along the back towards the tail. This also is true of the fourth arch in all higher vertebrates.

The fifth pair of arches remains in salamanders, but is lost in frogs and higher vertebrates. The sixth pair, closest to the heart, gives off on

Fig. 21 – 8. Arterial system of a frog, viewed with the animal lying on its back. The Roman numerals indicate the three aortic arches remaining in the frog: III, carotid; IV, systemic; VI, pulmonary.

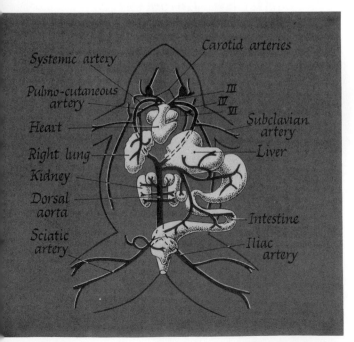

each side a branch to the lungs. This branch is the beginning of the **pulmonary artery.** It can be seen in the diagram of the situation in the salamander that the original sixth aortic arch continues, after giving off the pulmonary artery, upward to join the dorsal aorta. This short section of artery is known as the **ductus arteriosus,** or duct of Botalli in mammals. It plays an essential part in the prenatal circulation of man or any other mammal by enabling blood that enters the sixth arch to bypass the lungs and enter the dorsal aorta. In frogs and in all the higher vertebrates the dorsal part of the sixth arch, the duct of Botalli, atrophies so that it is not present in the adult.

In an adult frog it is possible to see three of the aortic arches. They are enclosed in a common sheath of connective tissue as they leave the heart, so that at first glance they look like a single pair of arches, one on each side, each with three branches. Actually the first of these three branches has developed from the third pair of aortic arches and carries blood to the head. It is known as the **carotid artery.** The middle branch is the largest, has developed from the fourth arch, and is known as the **systemic artery.** It carries blood around to the dorsal side of the gut. Here the two fourth arches, one from each side, meet to form the dorsal aorta. The third branch, closest to the heart, develops from the sixth arch and carries blood to the lungs and to the skin. In the frog this is the **pulmocutaneous** (*pulmo,* lung, + *cutis,* skin) **artery.** A long flap valve directs blood leaving the heart so that the most highly oxygenated blood from the lungs enters the third or carotid aortic arch to the head, while the least oxygenated blood enters the sixth or pulmocutaneous arch.

The distribution of the arteries leading from the dorsal aorta is much as in the elasmobranchs. A pair of **subclavian arteries** leaves the fourth or systemic arch and passes to the front legs. A large **coeliac artery** leaves the dorsal aorta at about the point where it is formed by the fusion of the two sides of the fourth arch. The coeliac artery carries blood to the intestine and other viscera. From the sides of the dorsal aorta extend a series of six or eight arteries, renal to the kidneys, gonadal to the gonads, etc. At its posterior end the dorsal

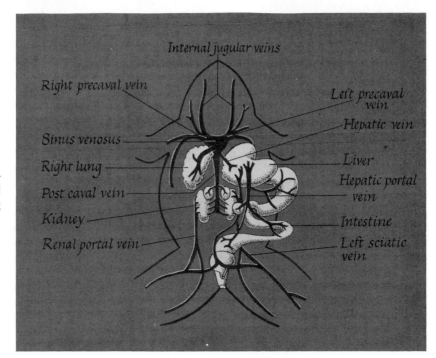

Fig. 21–9. Venous system of a frog, viewed with the animal lying on its back.

Labels: Internal jugular veins; Right precaval vein; Left precaval vein; Hepatic vein; Sinus venosus; Liver; Right lung; Hepatic portal vein; Post caval vein; Intestine; Kidney; Renal portal vein; Left sciatic vein

aorta divides into two common **iliac arteries** which pass to the hind legs.

The arteries break up into **arterioles** and finally these fan out into **capillaries.** Through the thin walls of the capillaries, and here alone, take place all physiological changes in the composition of the blood. Food is absorbed by the intestinal capillaries, and is distributed to the tissues through the capillaries in the rest of the body. Oxygen is absorbed by the capillaries in the lungs or close to the moist surface of the gills or skin, while the reverse occurs in the rest of the body.

Capillaries could not be discovered without microscopes. The classic place to observe capillary circulation is in the tail fin of a frog tadpole, although the gills of a larval salamander viewed under a dissecting microscope are perhaps the most spectacular. Leeuwenhoek, in 1686, tried to see capillaries in the comb of a young rooster, the ear of a white rabbit, and even the wing of a bat. This is what he wrote when he finally hit upon a tadpole's tail fin.

A sight presented itself more delightful than any mine eyes had ever beheld; for here I discovered more than 50 circulations in different places. . . . For I saw not only that in many places the blood was conveyed through exceedingly minute vessels, from the middle

of the tail toward the edges, but that each of the vessels had a curve or turning, and carried the blood back toward the middle of the tail, in order to be again conveyed to the heart.

From the capillaries the blood passes into **venules** and then into **veins** which carry it back to the heart. There are two main systems taking blood back to the heart, the **pulmonary veins** which carry freshly oxygenated blood to the left auricle of the heart; and the **systemic veins,** consisting of the right and left precavals from head and shoulders, plus a postcaval from the rest of the body and hind legs.

The Amphibia, like the fishes, possess two portal systems, a portal vein being one which carries blood to any organ other than the heart. Both portal systems are subsidiary to the post-caval vein. The **renal portal veins** carry blood from legs to kidneys. In birds the renal portal system is much reduced. In mammals it is lacking altogether. No one knows whether in amphibians it is an advantage, a disadvantage, or neither. It has, however, been useful to physiologists in investigating renal function.

The second portal system is the **hepatic portal system.** This carries blood from the intestine to the liver and is present in all vertebrates. Claude Bernard in Paris, in the middle of the last century, showed that the liver is the first great storage organ for food, particularly glycogen. The function of the hepatic portal vein is to transport digested food, especially glucose, to the liver where it is converted into glycogen.

The **heart** of amphibians is incompletely divided into a right and a left side. Blood returning from all over the body in the two precaval and the single postcaval veins enters a thin walled sac, the **sinus venosus**. This cavity or sinus is an extremely important part of the heart because it initiates the beat; it is the **pacemaker**. In the human heart, which like all mammalian hearts has no sinus, there is still in the wall of the right auricle a **sinus node,** the evolutionary remnant of the sinus venosus. The sinus node sets the pace for the mammal heart. If the beating of a frog's heart be observed, it will be seen that the sinus contracts first. It thus empties its blood into the right atrium or auricle, whereas the left auricle receives the pulmonary veins with freshly oxygenated blood. In all the higher vertebrates deoxygenated blood goes to the right side of the heart and oxygenated blood to the left side. The single ventricle of the frog is a heavy muscular structure which squeezes blood out through the short **truncus arteriosus** and into the aortic arches.

Excretory System. The kidneys of the amphibians are built up of the functional units already described (see page 450) and common to all vertebrates. These units are **nephrons,** consisting of a **Bowman's capsule** and a **glomerulus** at one end of a long **uriniferous tubule.** While in fishes the kidneys are elongate, almost ribbonshaped organs on either side of the midline just under the membrane lining the dorsal wall of the body cavity or coelom, in amphibians they are shorter and thicker but lie in the same position. Urine is conducted to the cloaca from each kidney by a duct which may be called a **ureter,** although it is not precisely the homolog of the ureter of a mammal.

Reproductive System. The reproductive system in amphibians is little different from that of fishes. The paired gonads, either testes or ovaries, are suspended from the body wall by thin folds of the peritoneal lining of the coelom (see Fig. 21–11). In the male, the sperms are conducted through many fine tubules, the vasa efferentia, into the ducts of the kidneys, whence they pass to the exterior via the ureters and cloaca. As in female mammals, the eggs break out of the ovaries and fall into the coelom. In female frogs the lining of the coelom, including that portion of it which covers the

Fig. 21–10. Diagram of the frog heart. *A,* dorsal view. *B,* ventral view. *C,* ventral view after slicing away part of the ventricle and part of the left atrium (auricle). Arrows indicate the direction of blood flow from the sinus venosus into the left atrium, then into the ventricle, and then out via the bulbus arteriosus.

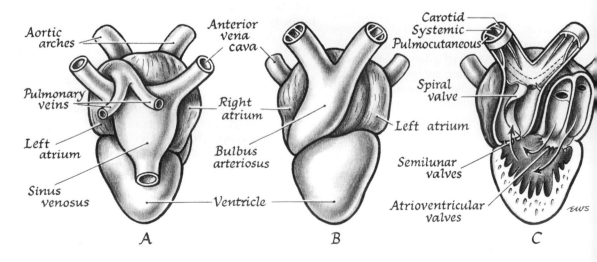

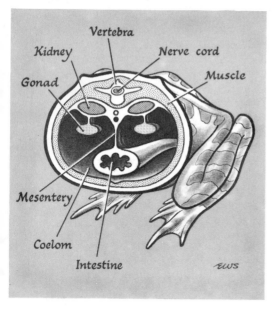

Fig. 21–11. Diagrammatic cross section of the body of a frog as a typical vertebrate.

liver, is ciliated. These cilia beat toward the heart and push the eggs forward to the mouths or **ostia** of the oviducts, which lie against the anterior end on the body cavity. The oviducts are much convoluted but are held to the body wall by their own mesentery. Before emptying

into the cloaca, each oviduct expands into a uterus, where eggs are stored before laying.

Ovulation from ovary into the coelom and thence into the oviduct can be artificially induced at any time of the year except for a month or so after a frog has ovulated, when the ovaries are empty of ripe ova. The method is to implant, under the skin or in the coelom, pituitary glands from other frogs or from mammals, or to inject pituitary extracts. Males can also be made to shed sperms by the same means. A common test for human pregnancy is the injection of some urine from the subject into the dorsal lymph sac of a frog or toad. The urine of a pregnant woman contains enough gonad-stimulating hormone from the placenta to cause a female frog or toad to ovulate within six to eight hours, or to cause a male to shed sperms promptly.

Nervous System. The nervous system of the Amphibia, as of all vertebrates, consists of two major and closely interdependent divisions. The **central nervous system** comprises the brain and spinal cord. The **peripheral nervous system** is further subdivided into the **somatic nervous system** of cranial and spinal nerves and the **autonomic nervous system.**

Fig. 21–12. Urogenital system of a frog. Left: male. The size of the vestigial oviduct varies with the species. Right: female. *(After Woodruff,* Foundations of Biology, *6th ed., 1941, The Macmillan Company)*

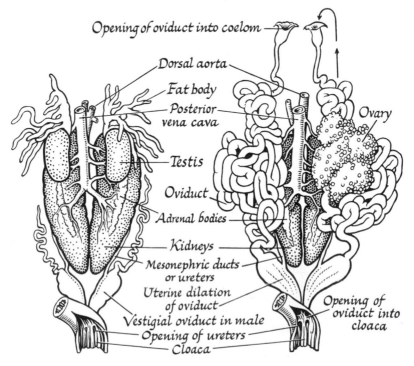

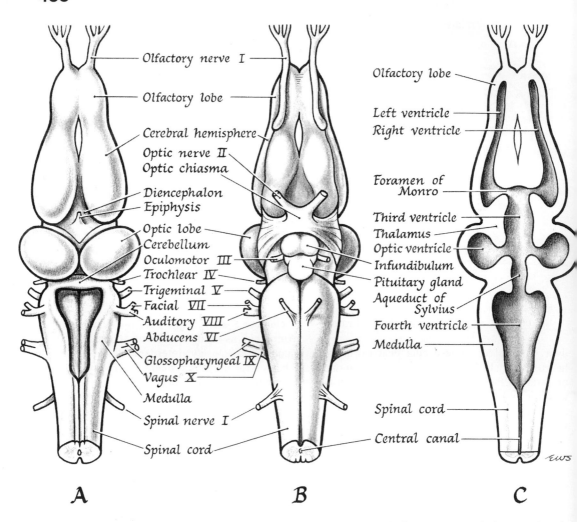

Fig. 21 – 13. Brain and cranial nerves of a frog. *A*, dorsal view. *B*, ventral view. *C*, longisection from dorsal side. The epiphysis or pineal body continues as a thin nerve through the skull roof and ends as a rudimentary eye under the skin in the top of the head.

The **brain** consists of the five basic parts which have been already noted in the shark and which are found in all vertebrates.

1. The **telencephalon** is composed of two elongate, hollow, cerebral hemispheres. The name hemisphere is applied to these essentially tubular structures because in the higher vertebrates they become actually hemispherical. Each hemisphere contains a cavity, or **ventricle,** which opens, at its posterior end, through an orifice known as the **foramen of Monro** into a common central cavity. Monro was a famous 18th century Edinburgh anatomist who discov-

ered these interventricular foramina in the human nervous system. The cavities within the cerebral hemispheres are the first (left) and second (right) ventricles. The central cavity which lies almost entirely in the diencephalon is the third ventricle. Although the "hemispheres" are separate throughout much of their length, they are joined at both ends.

2. The **diencephalon** in a frog contains a large cavity, the third ventricle, into which the foramina of Monro open. The thick side walls of the diencephalon are known in all vertebrates as the **thalamus.** Ventrally it carries an extension

forming the **hypophysis** or **pituitary**. When the brain of a freshly killed frog is removed by taking off the roof of the skull and lifting out the brain, the pituitary gland can usually be found adhering to the floor of the skull. It has two main parts: the anterior pituitary, which is formed in the embryo from a pocket growing up from the roof of the mouth; and the posterior pituitary, which forms from a downward growth protruding from the diencephalon. The anterior part of the pituitary produces gonad-, thyroid-, and growth-stimulating hormones.

A short distance anterior to the pituitary on the under surface of the diencephalon is the **optic chiasma** or crossing, where the optic nerves from the eye enter the brain. On the roof of the diencephalon is a small protuberance, the **epiphysis**. From this there extends a thin cord of nervous tissue which reaches up to the top of the head just under the skin, where it expands into a very small rounded structure, the **pineal body**. This appears to be a remnant of a third eye which was present in all the primitive jawless ostracoderms but is found today only in lampreys and some reptiles, and then poorly developed.

3. The **mesencephalon** of amphibians is the main visual center. On the dorsal surface are two conspicuous **optic lobes**. The cavity, or lumen, of the central nervous system is reduced in the mesencephalon to a narrow canal, called the **aqueduct of Sylvius**, named after a 17th century neuroanatomist of Leyden, Holland. The aqueduct opens anteriorly into the third ventricle and posteriorly into the fourth ventricle, the common cavity of the metencephalon and myelencephalon.

4. The **metencephalon** of frogs and salamanders is poorly developed. In both fishes and higher vertebrates this division of the brain develops a large dorsal lobe, the **cerebellum.** But in the amphibians, the cerebellum remains a small transverse ridge just posterior to the optic lobes.

5. The fifth division of the brain, the **myelencephalon,** is the elongate **medulla oblongata**, with a large, roughly triangular cavity, the fourth ventricle, under its dorsal surface. This cavity is continuous with the central canal of the spinal cord. Like all the ventricles of the brain, it is filled with cerebrospinal fluid.

The **peripheral nervous system** of the frog begins with the same ten cranial nerves found in sharks (see page 443). From the spinal cord come ten pairs of spinal nerves. The first three nerves on each side interconnect to form the **brachial plexus** in the shoulder before passing to the front leg. Spinal nerves four, five, and six are small nerves to the trunk. Seven, eight, and nine form the **sciatic** or **lumbo-sacral plexus** before passing into the hind leg, chiefly as the sciatic nerve. Ten is extremely small.

As each spinal nerve approaches the nerve cord it splits into two roots, a **dorsal sensory root** bearing a ganglion, and a **ventral motor root.** The sensory nature of the dorsal roots was proved independently over a century ago by Bell and Magendie. They severed the dorsal roots of the nerves to a leg while leaving the ventral roots intact. In a kitten so prepared they found that the limb would be without feeling but not paralyzed. When they also cut the motor nerves the limb became paralyzed.

Fig. 21 – 14. Frog nervous system, viewed from the ventral side. The Roman numerals denote cranial nerves; *S1, S2*, etc., paired spinal nerves. (*From Pauli*, The World of Life, *Houghton Mifflin*)

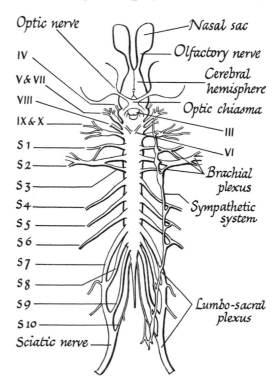

The nerves of the **parasympathetic** division of the **autonomic system** leave either the brain or the posterior, i.e., sacral, end of the spinal cord. The chief component from the brain is the tenth or **vagus nerve** which innervates the heart and many of the viscera. The parasympathetic nerves leaving the sacral region of the cord innervate the urinary bladder and reproductive structures. The **sympathetic** division of the autonomic system consists of a chain of small ganglia parallel to and on either side of the backbone, plus several unpaired ganglia, of which the solar plexus is the best known. The sympathetic ganglia are connected to the spinal cord by nerves at every level of the cord, and innervate most of the viscera: heart, lungs, intestines, bladder, etc. In frogs and salamanders the sympathetic nerves are not easily dissected.

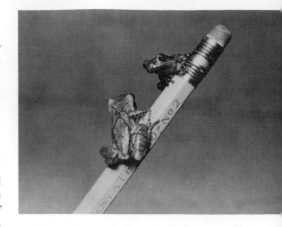

Fig. 21–15. *Hyla crucifer,* the spring peeper, on a pencil. (*American Museum of Natural History*)

ECOLOGY

The Challenge of the Environment. Present-day Amphibia, except primitive forms living in the tropics, are restricted to water for laying their eggs, which require an aqueous environment in which to develop and in which the larvae can live. The adults are also tied to water or moist locations by their scaleless moist skins which easily dry up. Only a few species like the toads have escaped this limitation.

Because amphibians must remain moist, and because they are "cold" blooded—that is, **poikilothermic** (*poikilos,* various, + *therme,* heat)— and cannot maintain a constant body temperature, hibernation is a necessity to meet, or rather to escape, the challenge of cold. Salamanders that live on land, like *Ambystoma maculatum,* the spotted salamander, hibernate during the winter in soil, usually deep in crevices between rocks or under logs. Other salamanders, such as *Diemictylus* (*Triturus*) *viridescens,* the common pond salamander, hibernate under mud and debris on the bottom of a pond. Most frogs migrate to ponds in the fall, and hibernate under mud on the bottom. Commercial harvesting of frogs makes good use of this fact. Toads usually bury themselves in earth or sand.

The stimuli responsible for these fall or spring migrations are little known. Changing temperature or length of day in the fall and again in the spring seem the two most probable factors. The common laboratory *Rana pipiens,* the leopard frog, will swim downward if placed in water at about 50°F (10°C), but will not remain on the bottom. If the temperature is lowered to about 40°F (4°C), leopard frogs swim to the bottom and remain sprawled there. In very cold water they are negatively phototaxic, but in warm water the phototaxism is reversed and they seek the light. What the physical basis in the nervous system of this behavior may be, no one knows, but its adaptive significance is obvious. The calling of frogs and toads certainly plays an important directional role in the spring, bringing individuals together.

Compared with other groups of vertebrates, the Amphibia show little diversity in body form within each order. All frogs and toads are built much alike, though there are spectacular differences in size between a spring peeper (see Fig. 21–15), and some of the tropical toads the size of a man's foot. The salamanders are likewise fairly alike in body form. This lack of diversity probably explains to some extent why the amphibians are not found in a vast number of habitats, as are successful groups such as insects and mammals.

The Problem of Food. Adult amphibians are primarily carnivorous. Samples of food taken from the stomach of *Necturus,* the river- and pond-dwelling mudpuppy that is frequently used for laboratory dissection, have shown the following average composition: 38 per cent crayfish, 18 per cent plants, 17 per cent insects, 12 per cent fishes, 7 per cent snails, 2 per cent leeches, and 6 per cent sticks and miscellaneous substances. The diet of frogs is much the same, except that insects form about 75 per cent of the food, plants and fishes very little.

The five commonest species of frogs east of the Rocky Mountains illustrate the important evolutionary principle of **competitive exclusion.** According to this principle, no two similar species that live in the same region (i.e., are sympatric) occupy precisely the same ecological niche. In other words, such species do not compete in all aspects of their lives. Their breeding times, nesting sites, diets, hunting methods, or any one or more of many factors may be different. As can be seen on the accompanying maps, the ranges of these five species coincide over most of the United States and Canada east of the Mississippi River. There are three notable ways in which these five species either avoid competition for food completely, or greatly lessen it.

The first method, which could be illustrated in many other kinds of animals, is to occupy different habitats within the same range. *Rana sylvatica*, the wood frog, roams the forest floor all its adult life, except when it comes to the ponds to breed. *Rana pipiens*, the leopard or meadow frog, frequents meadows and damp low fields. The very similar *Rana palustris*, the pickerel or swamp frog, is usually found in an actual marsh. *Rana clamitans*, the green frog, and *Rana catesbeiana*, the bullfrog, both live in ponds. *R. clamitans* will live in much smaller ponds and along streams in a way *R. catesbeiana* will not, but often they are found together.

A second method of avoiding direct competition for food that can be found in various kinds of animals is a marked difference in size. An adult bullfrog of either sex is very much larger than an adult green frog. Consequently these two species tend to catch and eat things of different sizes.

There is still a third way in which these essentially similar five species of frog avoid competition for food. This is by breeding at different times, so that the young do not compete. *Rana sylvatica*, the wood frog, is always the first to breed in any given locality. Ice may even return to the ponds after its eggs are laid. *Rana pipiens* lays its eggs next, usually about

Fig. 21–16. Ranges of the five most common North American frogs: *Rana sylvatica*, the wood frog; *R. pipiens*, the leopard or meadow frog; *R. palustris*, the pickerel or swamp frog; *R. clamitans*, the green frog; and *R. catesbeiana*, the bullfrog. Note that *R. sylvatica*, which breeds earliest in the spring, also extends farthest north, followed by the other species in the order in which they breed.

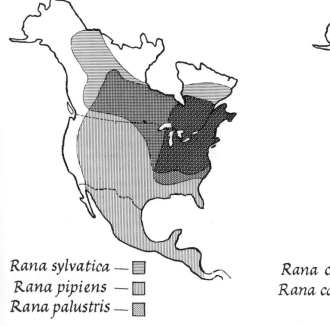

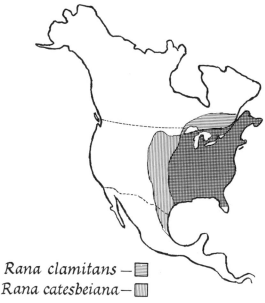

Rana sylvatica —

Rana pipiens —

Rana palustris —

Rana clamitans —

Rana catesbeiana—

Fig. 21–17. *Bufo,* the toad; male with inflated vocal sac. *(From Oliver,* The Natural History of North American Amphibians and Reptiles, *Van Nostrand, 1955)*

two weeks later. The pickerel or swamp frog, *R. palustris,* is third, followed by *R. clamitans* and still later by *R. catesbeiana.* In the northern part of its range the bullfrog does not breed until late June or early July, long after the *sylvatica* tadpoles have metamorphosed into frogs.

Avoidance of competition for food is a very important part of the environmental adjustments of any group of species, but it is only part of a much larger and more complex set of factors. Inspection of the maps showing the ranges of these five species will reveal that only two of them extend far to the west of the Mississippi River. These are the wood frog, *R. sylvatica,* and the leopard or meadow frog, *R. pipiens.* These two species, in the moist eastern part of their range which they share with the other three species, live in the relatively driest parts. The bullfrog, the green frog, and the swamp or pickerel frog are all limited to the east by their greater water requirements. It is also significant that the wood frog, which breeds first in any locality, is the species that extends farthest north, and that the northern limits of the other species follow the same order in which they breed. The same series appears in reverse for the southern limits, with the exception of *R. pipiens,* which has by far the largest range of any.

Rana pipiens, the common laboratory frog, forms a string of local races, a rassenkreis, ex-

tending from Great Slave Lake in Canada to Florida. Individuals from adjacent groups are interfertile but crosses between frogs at the ends of the chain result in a high mortality during embryonic development, apparently because they are each adapted for development at such different temperatures as to be incompatible.

Breeding Habits. The importance of the various peepings and croakings of frogs has to do chiefly and perhaps exclusively with reproduction. A lake or pond is a big place for a frog, and the chorus of calls serves to concentrate the dispersed individuals into a restricted zone. Species like *Rana sylvatica,* the common wood frog that wanders far from water, might often not find a woodland pond at all were it not for the brek-a-kek-kek of the first frogs lucky enough to find water.

Fertilization is external. The male, usually smaller than the female, remains on the back of his mate with his front legs tightly clasped around her body just behind her front legs. Male frogs have an enlargement at the base of the thumb which aids in maintaining this posture. The action of clasping the female in this way is known as **amplexus.** Little is known of the mechanism of sex recognition or of the mechanism which synchronizes the shedding of eggs and sperms. Frog eggs are laid in irregular masses of jelly. The story is closely similar for toads except that toad eggs are laid in strings of jelly rather than rounded masses.

Fig. 21–18. Mating position of *Rana pipiens,* showing the male on the back of the female. *(From Oliver,* The Natural History of North American Amphibians and Reptiles, *Van Nostrand, 1955)*

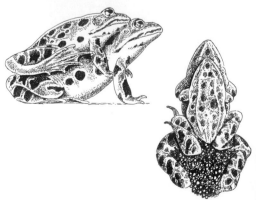

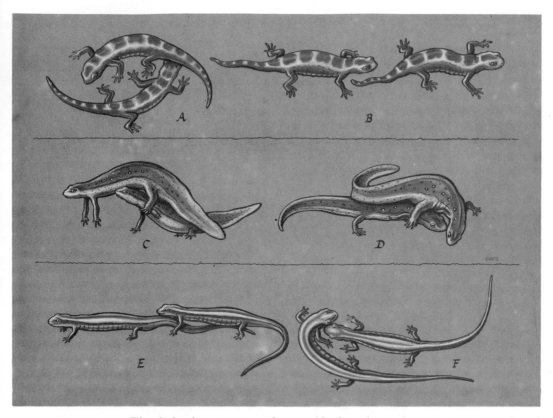

Fig. 21–19. The behavior patterns of courtship in salamanders are stereotyped and distinctive for each species. *A* and *B,* marbled salamander. *C* and *D,* spotted newt, *Diemictylus (Triturus) viridescens.* *E* and *F,* two-lined salamander.

In salamanders fertilization is internal, and in some species is preceded by an elaborate courtship. In other species the males and females may not even see each other. In the common North American spotted wood salamander, *Ambystoma maculatum* (also known as *A. punctatum*), often used in the experimental analysis of development, the males walk down to woodland ponds during the night of the first heavy rain after the first sufficient thaw in spring. The males congregate in dense milling masses and deposit spermatophores on sticks and dead leaves. Each spermatophore looks like a pinch of white cotton and contains thousands of sperms entangled in a proteinous jelly. With daylight the males disappear and gradually disperse into the woods again. On subsequent nights, the females migrate to the ponds, find the spermatophores and pick them up in their cloacas, where an enzyme dissolves the jelly and releases the sperms. The fertilized eggs are then laid in masses of jelly.

In marked contrast, the common yellow-brown pond salamander with the row of black-circled vermilion dots along each side, *Diemictylus (Triturus) viridescens,* has a definite courtship ritual. The male grasps the female with his hind legs around her shoulders. Males in this species can be distinguished from females by the greater thickness of the males' legs, which are ridged on their ventro-medial surfaces by transverse black glandular ridges. With the female held firmly, the male bends himself in the shape of a C, rubbing first one and then another of his cheeks against the nose of the female. The male then releases the female and walks slowly forward, depositing spermatophores on the floor of the pond or aquarium. The female follows, slowly picking up the spermatophores. An isloated female may continue to lay fertilized eggs over a period of several months. Each egg is deposited separately, enclosed in a jelly capsule which adheres to pond weed leaves or other objects.

METAMORPHOSIS

It has been common knowledge for centuries that tadpoles metamorphose into frogs, but it was not until just before World War I that an investigator named Gudernatsch found the key to the process in what now would be called a screening experiment. He fed bits of many different organs to tadpoles and discovered that thyroid gland induces precocious metamorphosis. This finding was soon confirmed by the reverse experiment, excision of the thyroid. Tadpoles so treated never become frogs. Both thyroid gland and various iodine-containing compounds will induce metamorphosis.

The physiological explanation of metamorphosis is still uncertain. **Tissue specificity** is certainly involved. If a piece of skin from the tail is grafted onto the side of a tadpole it will heal in so well that it cannot be detected. However, when the tail begins to be absorbed at the time of metamorphosis, the transplanted

Fig. 21–20. Precocious metamorphosis of frog tadpoles, *Rana catesbeiana. A,* untreated control at end of experiment. *B* through *F,* animals preserved at intervals during two weeks of thyroid feeding. *G,* precocious adult after two weeks of thyroid feeding. Note changes in tail, front and hind legs, and mouth. *(From Turner,* General Endocrinology, *3rd ed., W. B. Saunders)*

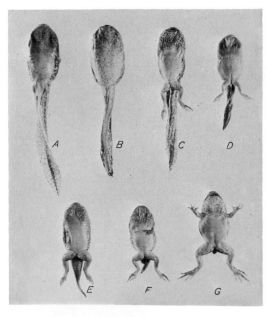

tail skin will disintegrate. Contrariwise, if an eye is grafted onto the tail it will not be absorbed but will slowly be pulled into the body so that a frog is produced with an eye where its tail used to be.

What triggers metamorphosis? The best hypothesis so far is as follows. The pituitary gland at the base of the brain secretes a thyroid-stimulating hormone. In response, the thyroid secretes thyroxin, which, however, inhibits the action of the pituitary. This much can be proved in various ways. The pituitary itself is stimulated by a neurosecretory hormone produced by the hypothalamus, the lower portion of the diencephalon. The evidence for this is good, and includes actual observation of hormone granules. At the same time the hypothalamus is thought to be stimulated by the thyroxin. This stimulation of the hypothalamus results in an overriding of the inhibitory feedback from the thyroid to the pituitary, very slowly at first and then faster and faster to a climax of a self-accelerating positive feedback. In the end, the great production of thyroxin is brought back to low levels because the hypothalamus becomes adult and loses its sensitivity to thyroxin. Thus the thyroid is once more under the inhibitory feedback control of the pituitary.

The evidence is far from complete. It has been shown that the hypothalamus, as well as the thyroid and pituitary, are essential for metamorphosis. How does thyroxin produce its dramatic results? In mammals thyroxin raises the metabolic rate. But that can hardly be the mechanism here because various substances which elevate respiratory rate, such as dinitrophenol and others, do not induce metamorphosis, while acetylated thyroxin, which does not increase respiration, does induce metamorphosis. Thyroxin is a rather simple compound, essentially two linked molecules of the amino acid tyrosine, each with two iodine atoms attached. How it acts we can only guess. Many basic questions still remain unanswered, including why certain tissues are sensitive and others not.

The anatomical and behavioral changes of metamorphosis are profound. In addition to the loss of the tail and the growth of the limbs, the pigmentation and character of the skin and its glands change. Internally lungs grow; gills and the operculum over them are absorbed.

The small rounded mouth of the tadpole, with its fleshy lips protected by rows of horny teeth and enclosing horny jaws resembling those of a turtle, is converted into the enormous, ear-to-ear mouth of the carnivorous adult. Algae and other plant materials are the main foods of the herbivorous tadpoles, though they are quick to act as scavengers. Like other herbivorous animals subsisting on a bulky plant diet, tadpoles have a long digestive tract; adult frogs have a short digestive tract. In fact, the coiled intestine of a grown tadpole is longer both relatively and absolutely than that of an adult frog.

Metamorphosis also brings a highly significant change in the physiology of the excretory system. In tadpoles, waste nitrogen is excreted as ammonia, which simply diffuses out into the water through the gills as it does in teleosts. In the adult terrestrial frog, waste nitrogen is converted into urea by the liver and then excreted by the kidneys as in mammals.

The visual pigment in the retina of tadpoles is porphyropsin, as in the eyes of freshwater fishes. After metamorphosis the visual pigment is rhodopsin, as in the terrestrial vertebrates.

The caudate amphibians undergo a similar, if less spectacular, change. The tail itself is not lost but the delicate tail fin around the tail is. The thickness, pigmentation, and glands of the skin become very different, gills are absorbed, and lungs developed. A few salamanders like the Mexican axolotl, *Ambystoma mexicanum,* are neotenous; they become sexually mature and breed while still in the larval state in other respects. The same holds true for the mudpuppy, *Necturus.* The axolotl can be induced to metamorphose by thyroid feeding. Neoteny occurs in many different and unrelated species of salamanders more or less regularly.

Review and References

REVIEW TOPICS

1. In what ways are amphibians different from fishes? From reptiles?

2. In what ways are amphibians like fishes? Like reptiles?

3. Distinguish smooth muscles from striated muscles.

4. Trace the course of the blood in a frog from the left auricle to the intestine and back to the left auricle. What capillary systems will it pass through and what happens in each?

5. Discuss the evolution of the aortic arches in vertebrates.

6. What are the functions of the five main divisions of the frog brain? How can these functions be discovered?

7. Distinguish fully the caudate from the salient amphibians.

8. What is the principle of competitive exclusion?

9. By what three different devices do the five most common North American species of frogs escape interspecific competition?

10. Discuss the anatomical, physiological, and behavioral aspects of amphibian metamorphosis.

11. What facts lead biologists to believe that present-day amphibians are a more or less degenerate evolutionary blind alley?

USEFUL REFERENCES

Bishop, S. C., *Handbook of Salamanders. The Salamanders of the United States, of Canada, and of Lower California,* Ithaca, N. Y., Comstock Publishing Company, 1947.

Conant, R., *A Field Guide to Reptiles and Amphibians,* Boston, Houghton Mifflin Company, 1958.

Francis, E. T. B., *The Anatomy of the Salamander,* Oxford, Clarendon Press, 1934.

Galvani, L., *Commentary on the Effects of Electricity on Muscular Motion, 1791,* Baltimore, Waverly Press, 1953.

Holmes, S. J., *The Biology of the Frog,* New York, The Macmillan Company, 1927.

Moore, J. A., ed., *Physiology of the Amphibia,* New York, Academic Press, 1964.

Oliver, J. A., *The Natural History of North American Amphibians and Reptiles,* Princeton, N. J., D. Van Nostrand Co., 1955.

Wright, A. A., and A. H. Wright, *Handbook of Frogs and Toads. The Frogs and Toads of the United States and Canada,* Ithaca, N. Y., Comstock Publishing Company, 1933.

Chapter 22

Reptiles

Reptiles can be easily distinguished from all the other living groups of vertebrates as **scaly tetrapods.** Birds, of course, have scales on their legs, but they also have feathers, which reptiles lack. Some mammals have scales, but mammals also have hair and produce milk, unlike any reptile. The only animals with which reptiles are sometimes confused are the urodeles, that is, the salamanders. But the urodeles are valid members of the Amphibia, and like all the living representatives of that class, have no visible scales.

Another important difference between amphibians and reptiles is that the reptiles, like their descendants the birds and mammals, develop a membrane, the **amnion,** around the embryo. The amnion encloses the embryo in its own "private pond," and hence makes it unnecessary for reptiles, birds, or mammals to lay their eggs in water. So important is this adaptation for life on land that reptiles, birds, and mammals are generally grouped together as **amniotes.** A human baby born with a piece of the amnion on its head is popularly believed to be endowed with good fortune.

Briefly, reptiles may be defined either as scaly tetrapods or as cold-blooded—that is, poikilothermic—amniotes.

Importance to Man. The reptiles are of little economic, medical, or even esthetic importance to man. Compared with the fishes, birds, mollusks, and many other groups, their human importance is negligible. The most valuable of all reptiles is easily the friendly green turtle, *Chelonia mydas,* of the warmer parts of the ocean. Both its eggs and its flesh find a ready market. The eggs make excellent cake. The average adult green turtle ranges between 300 and 500 pounds in weight, but individuals up to 850 pounds are known. The diamond-backed terrapin of brackish bays along the sea coast is the species most prized for soup. The pugnacious hawksbill turtle, *Eretmochelys imbricata,* like the green turtle, inhabits the warmer seas and is esteemed for its eggs and flesh. It is the species which provides natural tortoise shell. Alligators are valuable for their skins, and between 25,000 and 50,000 hides are imported annually into the United States from south of the Rio Grande. A great many of them are used to make shoes and handbags.

Some reptiles are harmful to man. Poisonous snakes in all the warmer parts of the world take an annual toll of human lives, but fortunately this means tragedy for only a very few individuals.

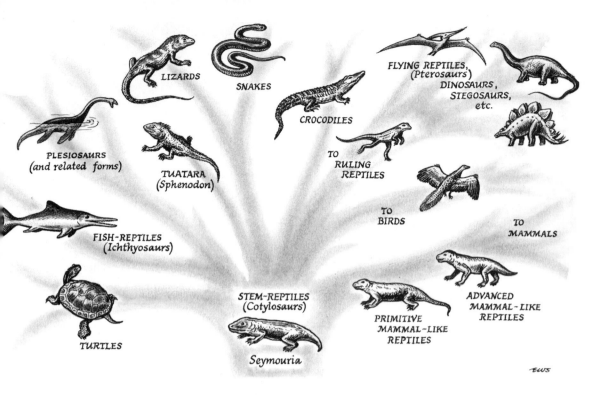

Fig. 22 – 1. Adaptive radiation during the evolution of the reptiles.

EVOLUTIONARY IMPORTANCE

In the evolution of the vertebrates, the reptiles hold a central position. From them arose both the birds and the mammals. The fossil record is unmistakable on this point. Beautiful fossil birds have been found dating from the Mesozoic Era, the age of reptiles. These birds bore a very close resemblance to many of the smaller dinosaurs. The fossil evidence of relationship between reptiles and mammals is even clearer. A group of fossilized vertebrates called **therapsids** contains many species for which it is impossible to be certain whether they had warm blood, hair, and milk and thus were mammals, or not. Moreover, their teeth and skulls are intermediate between the two groups. The fossil evidence is confirmed by the great similarities between reptiles, birds, and mammals in musculature, heart and blood vessels, and embryonic development.

In addition to the three basic adaptations for terrestrial life inherited from the amphibians — lungs, legs, and land eggs — the reptiles have developed others. The embryo within the egg became protected by an amnion, and the outside of the egg covered with a leathery coat. A new type of horny epidermal scales quite different from the dermal scales of fishes provides protection against drying. The leg muscles were greatly enlarged and the legs themselves brought in under the body, furnishing improved support on land. The sense organs were modified, notably the inner ear evolved to become much like that in mammals. The arterial and venous blood were more completely separated due to modifications inside the heart and in the aortic arches in the pharynx.

The reptiles themselves underwent **adaptive radiation** and assumed many diverse forms suitable to as many environments. Some developed the ability to fly, others resembled sharks, while on the land flourished a multitude of different species, carnivorous and herbivorous, large and small. The evolution of the flying reptiles did not culminate in the birds, but it did parallel bird evolution in a number of interesting ways. The bones became hollow, the bony tail became short, and in the most specialized forms, the teeth were lost. But in place of feathers, the flying reptiles possessed a skin membrane more like the

475

covering of a bat's wings. The history of the reptiles is best represented not as a tree but rather as a tree-sized bush, branching out in many directions.

What was the origin of the reptiles? Here too the fossil record is clear. There are dozens of fossil genera of animals called labyrinthodonts (*labyrinthos,* labyrinth, + *odontos,* tooth) because of the elaborate pattern of the enamel of their teeth. These animals are customarily grouped with the Amphibia, but this is recognized as rather arbitrary. They were all scaly, flat-headed, salamanderlike creatures, intermediate between undoubted amphibians and undoubted reptiles.

SURVIVING GROUPS

Of all the hordes of reptiles that have existed on this planet, only five groups now remain, and two are so closely related that they are placed in the same order. About 4,000 living species have been described.

1. The Order **Cheloniformes** *(chelone,* turtle), made up of the turtles both of the land and the sea, is the most primitive among the reptiles in skull structure, but in other ways, especially in the remarkable "shells," is highly specialized. The **carapace,** or dorsal part of the shell, is formed of fused ribs; the flat ventral **plastron,** of bony plates formed in the body wall. Teeth are lacking, and the jaws are encased in horny beaks. Some biologists try to reserve the term turtle for aquatic species, tortoise for terrestrial ones, and the Algonquin Indian word terrapin for all edible species except sea turtles.

2. The Order **Rhynchocephaliformes** *(rhynchos,* snout, + *cephale,* head) are the most generalized and hence presumably the most ancient of living reptiles. There is but one species, *Sphenodon punctatum,* the tuatara, formerly found on all the main islands of New Zealand, but now restricted to a few small islands. In general body form and in the possession of a parietal eye on the top of the head, *Sphenodon* resembles a lizard. But it differs from lizards in a number of important respects, especially skeletal. The lower jaw in *Sphenodon* is attached to the skull by a quadrate bone which is immovably fixed to the skull. In lizards the quadrate is movable, so that there are really

Fig. 22–2. A rattlesnake. *(U. S. Fish and Wildlife Service)*

two joints to the jaw. Other differences include the architecture of the skull, a persistent notochord with biconcave vertebrae like those of fishes, and a lack of copulatory organs.

3. The Order **Squamatiformes** *(squamatus,* scaly) is made up of two suborders. The lizards are the Lacertilia; the snakes are the Serpentes. Lizards and snakes resemble each other and differ from other living reptiles in having movable quadrate bones connecting the lower jaw to the rest of the skull. This device makes it possible to open the mouth wider than would otherwise be possible. The squamatiform reptiles are also distinguished by the possession of two copulatory organs in the male. There are many differences between the lizards and the alligators.

4. The Order **Crocodiliformes** is the most advanced, that is, the most like mammals, of all existing reptiles. A hard (bony) palate forms the roof of the mouth. The inspired air does not enter the mouth cavity only a short distance behind the front teeth, as in frogs and lizards, but is conducted in a closed passage above the palate to the back of the throat. The heart has four chambers as in mammals, although the ventricles are not entirely separate. The tongue is not protrusile nor the quadrate movable, as in lizards and snakes.

There are seven genera and about 25 recognized species of crocodiles. All are similar in size and habits, being amphibious with adaptations for both terrestrial and aquatic life. They are all truly vicious animals, whether gavials in southern Asia, crocodiles in Africa, or caimans, alligators, and crocodiles in tropical and semitropical America.

FUNCTIONAL SYSTEMS

Reptilian Scales. Reptiles are protected by a more or less flexible **exoskeleton** of horny scales. Reptilian scales are homologous (that is, basically alike in structure, position, development, and chemical composition) to the scales found on birds' legs and on the few mammals which have them, as beavers and rats do on their tails. These amniote scales are composed of **keratin,** a proteinous substance. They are formed by the cornification or hardening of the most external layer of the skin, a layer derived from the outermost embryonic germ layer, the ectoderm. In contrast, the different kinds of scales found in fishes are made of other materials, often a leathery, degenerate type of bone. Like bone, fish scales are formed within the dermal layer of the skin and lie completely covered externally by a layer of living tissue composed of mesoderm, which is itself covered externally by the ectoderm. This important embryological, anatomical, and biochemical difference between the scales of fishes and reptiles perhaps indicates that the actual amphibians which gave rise to the reptiles had passed through a scaleless stage. The important functional distinction is that the mesodermal scales of fishes, being themselves covered by an unprotected layer of living tissue, do not give protection against drying out. The new-type, ectodermal scales of the reptiles provide protection against drying because they lie on the actual surface of the body. Presumably the new ectodermal scales developed during evolution by an increasing hereditary ability of the superficial layers of the skin to become keratinized.

In some reptiles, such as snakes and lizards, this ectodermal covering of scales can be shed.

Turtles, however, merely keep adding new layers of keratin under the old ones. This produces the parallel lines around the "diamonds" on a terrapin's back.

The Inner Skeleton. The endoskeleton of a reptile is similar to that of a salamander. It is easier to see in reptiles that each leg is supported by a tripod of three bones and that the limb girdles are produced by the fusion of the tripods from the two sides of the body. The tripod for each hind leg consists of an **ilium** which is firmly fixed to the sacral region of the backbone, and two ventrally extending bones, a **pubis** which extends anteriorly and an **ischium** which extends posteriorly. In man, the ilia are frequently called the hip bones and can readily be felt at the belt line; the ischia are the bones pressed against a chair when sitting; and the pubic bones may easily be felt at the lower end of the abdomen on the front side. Together these bones form the **pelvic girdle.** Where the three bones of each tripod meet there is a rounded cavity, the **acetabulum,** into which fits the head of the femur or thigh bone, the first bone of the leg.

Each tripod of the **pectoral girdle** of the forelegs is also composed of three bones: the **scapula,** or shoulder blade, extends dorsally along the backbone; the **clavicle,** or collar bone, varies greatly among reptiles, but always supports the anterior part of the pectoral girdle; and the **coracoid** connects the girdle with the sternum ventrally. As in frogs, the scapula, clavicle, and coracoid all aid in supporting the forelimb. But they usually do not actually meet to form the **glenoid cavity,** homologous with the acetabulum, because in most reptiles additional bones help make up the shoulder girdle.

Fig. 22-3. Difference between the dermal scales of fishes, which are within the mesoderm and covered by a thin layer of living tissue, and the epidermal scales of reptiles, birds, and mammals, which are secreted on the surface of the epidermis.

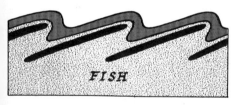

FISH *REPTILE-BIRD-MAMMAL*

 Scale   *Dermis*   *Epidermis*

The **skull** of the crocodile and alligator shows several important adaptations for breathing while almost submerged and with the mouth held open holding a drowning prey. The nostrils are dorsal on the snout, instead of anterior in position. The hard palate on the roof of the mouth enables air to pass from the nostrils far back to the internal nostrils at the back of the throat, just above the glottis opening to the lungs. A flap at the back of the tongue and a downward fold of the palate work together to close off the back part of the throat, so that a crocodile can continue to breathe even with its mouth open under water.

The skull of a snake is remarkably adapted for swallowing prey larger, sometimes very much larger, than the head of the snake itself. The two sides of the lower jaw are connected by a stretchable ligament at the chin, an arrangement allowing the two halves of the jaw to separate widely. As mentioned previously, the quadrate bone by which the lower jaw is attached to the skull is movable; in addition, it is elongated. In consequence, the lower jaw can open to swing down and back through some 125°. The teeth are strongly recurved and very sharp, so that the more a victim squirms, the farther back into the throat it slides. Moreover, the teeth on the upper jaw are arranged in two parallel rows on each side. There is one row along the **maxillary** bones at the edges of the

mouth, as in other vertebrates, plus an inner row on each side of the roof of the mouth, on the **pterygoid** bones. These bones are movable, and by working them alternately, a snake can literally walk his head over his prey.

In poisonous snakes the maxillary bones holding the teeth of the upper jaw are reduced in size, are movable, and hold the **fangs,** which are sharp, curved, hollow teeth. Normally a group of **replacement fangs** lies against the roof of the mouth. When the mouth is opened, the maxillary bones holding the fangs are swung forward by a thrust of pterygoid and other bones of the roof of the mouth. With the maxillaries thus rotated forward, a snake can strike and inject venom as though from a hypodermic needle, without having to close the jaws.

Muscular System. The most notable feature of the reptilian muscular system is its great resemblance to that of a mammal. Obviously there are differences, and these are overwhelmingly great in specialized forms like the snakes which have no limb muscles, or the turtles which have little except limb muscles. In general, the muscular system of reptiles, compared to that of fishes or amphibians, shows a reduction in the relative importance of the trunk muscles and a great increase in the limb muscles, including the extrinsic musculature which connects limbs with the rest of the body.

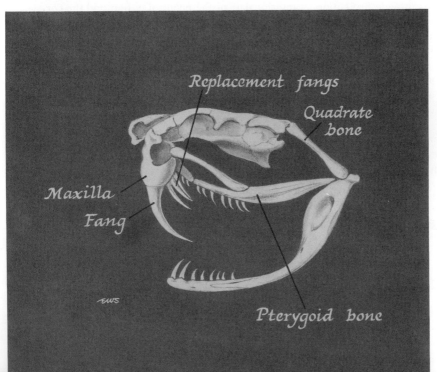

Replacement fangs

Quadrate bone

Maxilla

Fang

Pterygoid bone

Fig. 22-4. Rattlesnake skull, showing fangs, replacement fangs, and fang-erecting bones. Note the long movable quadrate bone attaching the lower jaw to the skull.

Digestive System. Except for some of the turtles, present-day reptiles are almost entirely carnivorous. They usually capture their prey with their teeth, although a few, like the chameleon, make quite dramatic use of an eversible tongue.

The most spectacular feature of the digestive system of the reptiles is the development of **poison glands** from salivary glands in some snakes and lizards. These are not homologous with the salivary glands of mammals, but are similar to them in secreting into the mouth a lubricating fluid containing digestive enzymes. The modified poisonous saliva contains two different kinds of toxin, depending on the kind of snake or lizard. The toxin of the rattlers and copperheads of North America is primarily a hemotoxin that attacks blood cells and blood vessels. The toxin of the cobras of Asia and the coral snakes is a neurotoxin that paralyzes the nerve centers. Both toxins are believed to begin digestion of the victim from within before it is swallowed by the snake. Anti-venoms are available but must be used with caution.

Respiratory and Vascular Systems. The lungs of reptiles are not only larger than those of amphibians and lungfishes, but are better provided with air chambers. The posterior portions are mere avascular sacs, and in breathing the fresh air is pulled in and out over the vascular portion of the lungs and most of the "dead" residual air remains in the nonvascular zone. In birds this scheme is further developed, with large nonvascular air sacs on the sides of the lungs away from the source of fresh air.

In reptiles the air is drawn into the lungs by the movement of the ribs, as in mammals. Crocodiles show a further advance, in the form of a muscular partition, the **diaphragm,** which separates the part of the coelom surrounding the lungs from that surrounding the other viscera. This is part of the anatomical structure which creates the loud roar of the male alligator.

The heart and aortic arches of reptiles present notable advances toward the mammalian condition. It will be recalled that there are six pairs of aortic arches in all vertebrate embryos, and that in the Amphibia the first and second arches degenerate, leaving the third on each side to form the beginning of the internal ca-

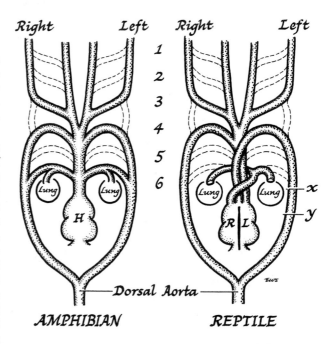

Fig. 22–5. Diagram of the aortic arches of an amphibian and a reptile. The view is in the conventional manner—as though the animal were lying on its back, with its right side therefore on the viewer's left.

rotids. The fourth arch on each side forms the dorsal aorta above the gut. The fifth degenerates, and the sixth sends branches to the lungs (see Figs. 21–7 and 22–5). The condition in reptiles is essentially the same.

In the lizard, turtle, and alligator, the arteries from the heart develop as shown in Figure 22–5. The heart is divided into right and left sides. The blood returning from most of the body enters the right side and passes through the sixth arch to the lungs. The ventral aorta has divided into three parts: one is the pulmonary artery (sixth arch) just mentioned; the other two lead to the dorsal aorta via the fourth arch, one on each side. In birds and mammals the fourth arch persists only on one side. Why have both remained in reptiles? Is their presence a disadvantage the reptiles have not overcome? Or is theirs even a better scheme than the mammalian one?

Recently two ambitious students set out to find answers to some of these questions. The left fourth arch in reptiles leaves the heart between the pulmonary arch and the right fourth arch at a point opposite a foramen between the

479

right and left ventricles where the partition between the two sides of the heart is not quite
complete. This is the **foramen of Panizza.** It is
not present in mammals or birds. The students
secured a small alligator and under ether anesthesia carefully and tightly ligated (tied off) the
left fourth arch at levels x and y in Figure
22 – 5. To be doubly sure, they cut out the section of artery between x and y and sewed up the
body wall again.

The alligator made an uneventful recovery.
So far as these students could detect, loss of
one of the fourth arches made no difference to
the alligator. Even after violent exercise, it
appeared normal. Reptilian hearts are notoriously hardy. This is no doubt the basis of the
myth that a snake will not die till sundown.
Physiologists have found this resistance useful,
and turtle hearts are standard objects for the
study of heart action.

Excretory System. There are two important
points to be noted about the reptilian excretory
system, one anatomical, one physiological. In
fishes and amphibians, the kidney is composed
of a longer or shorter strip of tissue on either
side of the midline just above the coelom. The
most anterior portion is the **pronephros.** The
pronephros characteristically has openings into
the coelom, called **nephrostomes,** that draw in
excess fluid from the coelom, in addition to the
typical nephrons with their renal corpuscles of
Bowman's capsule and glomerulus. (See page
451.) The long middle region of the kidney
strip is the Wolffian body, or **mesonephros.** The
nephrons in it are the same as in the pronenph-
ros, except that there are no nephrostomes.
The pronephros functions only in the embryo,
except in some cyclostomes. The mesonephros
is the functional kidney of fishes and amphibians. Its duct, called the mesonephric or Wolffian duct, or "fake" ureter, conducts both urine
and sperms to the cloaca.

In reptiles, birds, and mammals – that is, in
the amniotes – the mesonephros functions only
in the embryo. The kidney of the adult develops out at the extreme posterior tip of the strip
of kidney-forming tissue and is called the **meta-
nephros.** The functional units, the nephrons,
are the same as in the mesonephros, although
there are many more of them. The metaneph-
ros, or hind-kidney, develops its own duct,

the **ureter** proper, which carries urine to the
urinary bladder. The mesonephric duct degenerates in females, but remains to serve as the
vas deferens in males and to carry sperms to
the copulatory organ.

Reproductive System. The reproductive
system of a reptile is simple and not very different from that of any living amphibian. The
major differences obviously have to do with
the adaptation to life on land. These are, first,
the presence of the very large yolked eggs enclosed in shells; and second, the development
of intromittent organs in the males, inasmuch as
fertilization on land must be internal and must
take place before the shell is placed around the
egg.

The ovary of a reptile in the breeding season
resembles the ovary of a hen. In the ovum the
nucleus and its cytoplasm form but a minute
spot on top of the immense mass of nonliving
yolk. This enormous quantity of yolk is deposited within the egg cytoplasm by the cells of
the ovary.

Although the ova may be an inch or more in
diameter, they are ovulated into the coelom as
in frogs, and then enter the oviducts. Here they
meet the sperms and are fertilized and then
carried down the oviducts. The cells lining
each oviduct, instead of secreting around the
egg a layer of protein which swells on contact
with water, as in the Amphibia, here secrete a
more watery protein, the albumen of the egg.
Near the end of the oviduct the cells secrete the
leathery shell.

Most reptiles are oviparous, and lay eggs like
birds. Many species, however, are ovoviviparous, that is, they retain the eggs until after
hatching, so that they bring forth living young.
This is true of the Mediterranean chameleon
and many common snakes. Both the rattlesnake and the harmless gartersnake bear their
young alive. Most snakes, like the blacksnake
and the king cobra, lay eggs, but a few are now
known to be truly viviparous. This means that
their young not only develop in the oviduct,
which thereby deserves to be called a uterus,
but there is a true **placenta** – a highly vascular
structure pressed against the lining of the uterus
through which the young derive their nourishment. The sea snakes and some of the cobras
belong in this group.

Except for *Sphenodon,* all the reptiles have developed an eversible sac which can be protruded from the wall of the cloaca of the male and which serves to conduct the sperms into the female's cloaca. The unusual fact about snakes and lizards is that there is a pair of penes, one on either side of the cloaca. They are commonly mistaken for rudimentary legs when forced out of a snake by violent injury.

Nervous System. Much has been made of the relatively small size of the brains of reptiles, especially of the dinosaurs. While reptiles cannot be regarded as intellectual animals in any sense, nevertheless if the reptilian brain is compared not with that of a mammal or even a bird, but with that of a frog or salamander, it will be evident the reptilian brain is larger and more closely resembles the mammalian condition. Notable is the growth of the **cerebral hemispheres,** which are merely tubular in Amphibia but have become at least pear-shaped in the reptiles. The internal architecture of the brain also more closely resembles the mammalian pattern.

A most remarkable feature of the reptilian nervous system is the accessory **third eye** growing up from the dorsal surface of the diencephalon or second division of the brain. This is found in most lizards, and in the lonely New Zealand *Sphenodon.*

In the embryonic development of vertebrates there are usually two fingerlike outgrowths of the brain, one directly behind the other in the midline of the roof of the diencephalon. The anterior one is the **parietal organ,** the posterior one the **pineal organ** or body. Either or both may be called the **epiphysis.** The **hypophysis,** or pituitary body, is a stalked, downward growth from the floor of the diencephalon. In most lizards the parietal organ develops into an eyelike structure, with lens, retina, and nerve. It is noteworthy that the retina is not inverted, as in the ordinary paired eyes that grow out from the sides of the diencephalon; i.e., in the parietal eyes the rods and cones do not point away from the source of light but toward it. None of the median eyes, whether parietal or pineal, permit clear vision because the cornea over them is thick and clouded. In cyclostomes both the parietal and pineal bodies form eyes. A median eye on top of the head is found in the ostracoderms, the oldest known fossil vertebrates, and

Fig. 22–6. Chameleon. Note the remarkable ability to rotate the eyes through a wide arc. *(Kindness of Isabelle Hunt Conant)*

was generally present in the placoderms and the ancient amphibians and primitive Paleozoic reptiles. A parietal or pineal organ, or both, persists in birds and mammals. Recent evidence indicates that the pineal body is an endocrine gland that is influenced in its activity by the relative lengths of the light and dark periods experienced by the animal. The pineal body influences the sexual cycle in rats and other mammals.

The big Mediterranean chameleon· has an unusual ability to move its eyes separately. The right eye can look up and to the right while the left eye moves to look down and to the left. The neural mechanisms of vision within its brain must be very different from those found in mammals, where the eyes are functionally coordinated.

The ears of reptiles are intermediate between those of the lower vertebrates and the mammals. The inner ear shows the least change. The three semicircular canals connect with the **utriculus,** which opens into a lower chamber, the **sacculus.** From the side of the sacculus has appeared a new structure, the **lagena** or

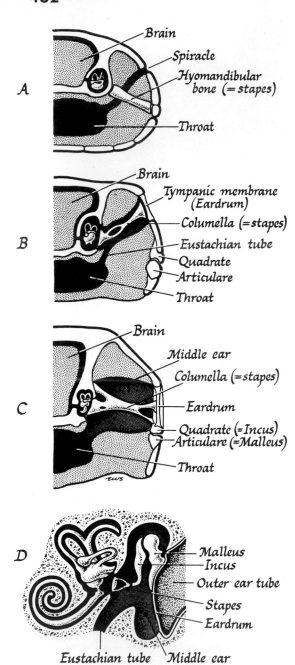

Fig. 22–7. Evolution of the bones of the middle ear. *A*, fish. *B*, amphibian. *C*, primitive reptile. *D*, man (ear region only, different scale). The labels indicate apparent homologies of the bones.

future **cochlea.** In reptiles this is scarcely more than a small knoblike extension containing the sensory epithelium of hearing. In birds and mammals the lagena is no longer flask-shaped, as its name implies, but is coiled like a snail shell, and hence the new name, cochlea.

In reptiles as in amphibians, the middle ear still contains a single bone, the **columella,** which transmits vibrations from the eardrum to the inner ear. But the **quadrate** bone at the hind end of the upper jaw, and its partner, the **articulare** at the hind end of the lower jaw, are both small in the mammal-like reptiles and come very close to both the columella and the eardrum. In mammals the columella is present but is called the **stapes** on account of its stirrup-like shape. The quadrate becomes the **incus,** and the articulare the **malleus.** This is the evolutionary origin of the chain of three little bones that is found in the middle ear of mammals and conduct vibrations from the eardrum to the inner ear.

ECOLOGY AND BEHAVIOR

Environmental Relationships. The primary fact about reptiles in relationship to their environment, both living and nonliving, is that they are terrestrial poikilotherms, animals whose body temperature closely follows that of their environment.

The lack of ability to maintain a constant and high body temperature has restricted the habitats of reptiles to warm climates and has rigorously necessitated hibernation in the winters of the temperate zone. Only the turtles and snakes are adept at hibernation, and these are the only reptiles that range very far north of the ground-frost line. Turtles that live in ponds burrow into the bottom mud; those that live in woods and fields sometimes enter ponds and sometimes bury themselves in the earth.

A most striking fact about snakes outside the tropics is that they commonly over-winter entwined in a ball of several up to 30 or more individuals. These clusters are similar to the balls of earthworms found during dry seasons, and in some regions serve similar purposes, the conservation of moisture or heat. Snakes form these hibernation masses deep in holes under cliffs and boulders, under logs, or in old burrows of mammals. Usually all the snakes in a single "den" are of the same species, but this is by no means always the case. Among species that hibernate in this way are: *Thamnophis,* the garter snake; *Coluber,* the black snake; *Agistodon,* the copperhead; and *Crotalus,* the rattlesnake.

Little is known about the stimuli that induce reptiles to crawl or dig into places of hibernation. Snakes hibernate year after year in the same dens. How this comes about no one knows. Once under the ground or within a crevice, turtles and snakes penetrate below the frost line, which is not more than about 3 feet under the surface even in very severe winters, especially if there is a blanket of snow. Moreover, it is highly probable that a ball of snakes can resist actual freezing temperatures by their own latent heat better than could single ones.

Breeding Behavior. Breeding behavior in reptiles is intermediate in complexity between that of the amphibians and that of birds and mammals. Factors concerned with sex recognition are still largely matters of conjecture. Many snakes and the alligators emit strong odors from cloacal glands. There is some evidence that males locate females by following a scent trail. Many snakes mate soon after emerging from hibernation, a habit which would facilitate the meeting of the sexes. In the southern parts of the United States the roaring of male alligators during the breeding season can be heard for long distances. Whether this serves to warn other males, attract females, or both is uncertain. Male alligators will answer the "challenge" of gunshot, or even thunder, with a roar. Experimentally it has been found that they will respond most readily to sounds having a frequency of about 57 vibrations per second, such as the B flat two octaves below middle C played on the French horn.

The problem of sex recognition merges with that of courtship. In reptiles courtship ranges from the simple in turtles to the elaborate in lizards. The male turtle merely claws the female gently on the side of the head with especially long toenails. A male snake usually rubs his chin along the back of the female, though some species grasp the female in their mouths. It has recently been discovered that two males

Fig. 22–8. "Combat dance" of two male snakes. (*Zoological Society of San Diego*)

of the same species of snake perform "combat dances" in which each appears to attempt to push the other backwards. The function of this behavior is unknown.

Lizards possess elaborate, if stereotyped, courtship rituals involving much bobbing of the head, prancing about, nudging of the female, and especially spectacular displays of colored areas and designs on the skin. The male of the common lizard or chameleon of the southern United States and the Carribean, *Anolis,* which is brown to bright bluish-green depending on the color of the background and its own "emotional" state, has a brilliant orange dewlap which is suddenly thrown out from under the throat when courting a female, challenging a male, or attempting to frighten off a boy or a dog. Many tropical species have even more colorful displays.

One interesting way in which male lizards anticipate the behavior of male birds is by becoming very "conscious" of a particular territory during the breeding season. Each male will defend a localized and clearly defined area from intrusion by other males or animals of any sort whatsoever, except females of his own species. Mating among snakes and lizards is a relatively simple, brief process with the two individuals placing cloacas in juxtaposition.

Most reptiles lay their eggs in nests dug into moist earth or sand. It has been shown that

Fig. 22–9. Leatherback sea turtle on the beach to lay its eggs. *(Kindness of J. Carver Harris)*

female sea turtles are guided onto the beaches by the white sand and that the young, when they hatch, race toward the white of the breakers guided by the pattern of ultraviolet light in the sky. The alligator and a few snakes like the cobra guard their eggs. *Anolis,* the Caribbean chameleon, lays its eggs singly, one every two weeks during the summer.

Growth and the Problem of Longevity. Knowledge about the growth and longevity of reptiles has a double importance. It must form the basis for any intelligent program of conservation and harvesting, and it is part of the general problem of growth common to all animals.

Authenticated data are available for only a few species. Very little is really known about the most economically valuable of all reptiles, the green sea turtle. More or less reliable data for common representatives of each of the four important groups of reptiles have been obtained. In the American alligator, males and females grow at the same rate during the first five years. Then sexual maturation begins, after which males grow faster. At the end of the first year after hatching, an alligator attains a length of slightly over 2 feet and a weight of about 4 pounds.

The growth of the box turtle, found over most of the eastern and central portions of the United States, is apparently extremely slow, at

least in the northern part of its range. A 3-inch individual was five years old, a 5-inch one 20 years old. They are said not to become sexually mature until 12 or 15 years of age.

In contrast, the American chameleon, *Anolis,* attains adult size and maturity within twelve months. As with the alligators, the males are larger than the females. The most plausible evolutionary explanation is that competition between males during the breeding season favors the larger ones. The growth of the Western rattlesnake, *Crotalus viridis,* has been determined by an extensive banding program in central California. This species attains about 2 feet in length in two years, 3 feet in four years. Sexual maturity is reached during the third year. Rattlesnakes are born with one rattle, the so-called button. Young snakes ready to enter hibernation at the end of their second summer usually have a string of four buttons. The following autumn they bear six or seven. Thereafter they apparently add an average of slightly more than one a year.

In general, the growth rate of any poikilothermic animal such as a reptile depends on the temperature of its environment. This temperature determines its metabolic rate which in turn determines its activity, including how much it eats. The onset of sexual maturity for any given species is determined by size rather than by age.

With human populations everywhere tending to become older and older as advances in medicine continue to extend life expectancy, the problems of aging will become increasingly important. Reptiles are famous for their long lives. How long do they really live? It is important to distinguish between two different meanings of this question. The first is a statistical one. It concerns life expectancy and the age structure of the population. The second meaning concerns the physiological life span, barring accidents. A recent study of the Caribbean chameleon, *Anolis,* illustrates this difference. By tagging these little lizards it was found that over 95 per cent of them live less than one year in the wild, but they live to be four years old if kept in protected cages.

The statistical questions are the ones that are important in conservation. The **life expectancy** means the number of years, months, or days, on the average, which the members of any particular group of animals will most probably live. If the group is selected at the time of hatching, then of course the life expectancy is the same as the average age of the members of the species at death. If a very old group of animals is taken, then the further life expectancy will be short. Among reptiles, life expectancy is likely to be much greater for animals a month or more old than it is at hatching. For example, as recently hatched sea turtles scramble down the beach toward the water they may be spotted by a flock of sea birds and all but a small percentage eaten. They may just happen to enter the water at the moment when a school of fishes, of just the wrong size from the baby turtle's point of view, is passing. Several days later, when they have become dispersed in the sea, the turtles' life expectancy will be much greater than it was at their birth. In some ways a knowledge of the **age structure** of a population is more useful than knowledge of life expectancy. This means knowing how many or what percentage of the individuals are less than one year old, how many in their second year, how many in their third, etc.

The second question, dealing with the natural or **physiological life span** of a species, is of even greater human import. Trustworthy data on the actual life span of various reptiles are difficult to obtain. Underpaid attendants in zoological gardens sometimes treat scientific accuracy rather lightly. So many box turtles have been found bearing the inscription "G. Washington 1751" that even the most gullible must doubt their authenticity. There are apparently valid records which indicate that some of the big land tortoises from the Galapagos Islands live to well over a century. Various alligators have attained great age. Why do some reptiles live so long while others, like the little chameleons, fail to do so? No one knows.

Review and References

REVIEW TOPICS

1. Characterize the living groups of reptiles.

2. How do reptiles illustrate the phenomenon of adaptive radiation?

3. What are the differences between fish scales and those of reptiles, birds, and mammals? What is their adaptive significance?

4. Distinguish between a salamander and a lizard.

5. What anatomical, physiological, and behavioral adaptations for terrestrial life are possessed by reptiles?

6. Define: amnion, diaphragm, nephrostome, ureter, extrinsic muscle, neurotoxin, foramen of Panizza, pentadactyl, cold-blooded, pineal eye.

7. What bones make up the pectoral girdle? The pelvic girdle?

8. Distinguish between life expectancy and physiological life span.

9. What patterns of reproductive behavior are found among reptiles?

10. What factors may have been responsible for the disappearance of the dinosaurs?

USEFUL REFERENCES

Carr, A., *Handbook of Turtles,* Ithaca, N.Y., Comstock Publishing Company, 1952.

Conant, R. *A Field Guide to Reptiles and Amphibians,* Boston, Houghton Mifflin Company, 1958.

Oliver, J. A., *The Natural History of North American Amphibians and Reptiles,* Princeton, N. J., D. Van Nostrand Co., 1955.

Chapter 23

Birds

Birds can be defined very simply as feathered bipeds. But while this definition is absolutely diagnostic, it tells little about the Class Aves, except by implication. Birds, like mammals, are homoiothermic amniotes, that is, they maintain a constant and high body temperature, and the embryo grows a protective amnion enclosing itself in a sac of fluid during development. Both the anatomy and the physiology of birds are profoundly modified by their dominant adaptation, the ability to fly.

Human Importance. From before the dawn of history birds have touched the life of man at many points. Stone Age men snared and shot them both for food and for their feathers. Ever since, the plumage, the songs, the migrations, and the behavior of birds have fascinated a large segment of mankind. The Egyptians, the Greeks, and other peoples of antiquity developed an extensive bird lore, part observation, part myth. Well over 100 different kinds were named, not only the familiar eagles, owls, swans, and ravens, but various kinds of wrens, swallows, flamingos, herons, ostriches, shearwaters, and even the Indian talking mynah bird. The famous birds of Diomedes, whose eerie wailing cries and nocturnal flights have shivered the spines of many an ancient mariner, were shearwaters. These are the birds that

St. Augustine, a native of the Mediterranean, mentions in his great book, *The City of God.* Caged song birds were as common in the marketplace of Athens in the age of Pericles as they are today in the little market under the shadow of Notre Dame of Paris.

Since World War II there has been a great resurgence of interest in bird behavior among zoologists. A series of challenging new theories has led to a host of new observations and the discovery of new facts. Many of these theories may turn out to be only partially true, but others are strongly founded and will probably exert a marked influence on the study of human behavior and psychology. The subject will be discussed again in Chapter 32 on Animal Behavior.

The most important bird economically is the domestic chicken, *Gallus*. No one knows precisely how or when it was domesticated. It is not mentioned in Homer or the Old Testament, but by the great age of Greek civilization it was commonly known as the Persian fowl. According to Chinese legend, the chicken was introduced into that culture about 1400 B.C. from the West. Today jungle fowl closely similar to the old-fashioned black-and-brown barnyard chickens roam the forests and thickets from eastern India to the Malay Peninsula. They travel in small flocks and lay eight to twelve creamy white eggs on the ground.

In relatively simple and rural economies domestic chickens add to the resources of the community by subsisting almost wholly on miscellaneous food which they find for themselves and which would otherwise be wasted. In most industrial economies, poultry-raising is big business and depends on cultivated grain.

EVOLUTIONARY RELATIONSHIPS AND MAJOR GROUPS

Birds have evolved from reptiles. Both the structure of living birds and the fossil record are very clear about this. The skeleton, the muscles, the heart, the character of the scales, and the manner of development, all point in that direction. Beautifully preserved fossil birds have been found dating from the Mesozoic, the age of reptiles, some 150 million years ago. *Archaeopteryx* and *Archaeornis* both possessed long reptilian tails but with feathers along each side, three prominent clawed fingers on each wing, solid bones, and a complete set of teeth. Their skeletons bear a very close resemblance to those of many of the smaller dinosaurs, with long hind legs adapted for running and jumping, shorter front legs, and a generally light body build. Other fossil birds have been found in later rocks. Some of these are transitional between the long-tailed *Archaeopteryx* and the stub-tailed modern birds.

Like reptiles and mammals, the birds have undergone adaptive radiation which fits them into many diverse environments and types of life. Living birds are sometimes divided into two groups. First is a flightless **ratite** group, in which the pectoral muscles of the breast which move the wings are poorly developed and in which the sternum or breastbone is flat and raftlike (*ratis,* raft). The second group is the **carinate** group, in which the pectoral muscles are well developed and the sternum has a prominent ridge or keel (*carina,* keel). These anatomical differences represent important adaptations for the lives of the birds, but it is no longer believed that all ratite birds are closely related. The ostriches of Africa, the kiwis of New Zealand, and the cassowaries of Southeast Asia are all ratites and have the same primitive jaw structure, but in other ways seem quite unrelated. Consequently, in accordance with the

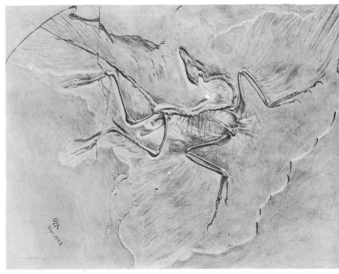

Fig. 23 – 1. Fossil evidence of the relation of birds to reptiles: *Archaeornis,* from the Jurassic rocks laid down during the Mesozoic, the Age of Reptiles. Note the imprint of feathers, the reptilian skull with small teeth, the long tail with many vertebrae (in marked contrast to birds today), and the claws on the wings. *(American Museum of Natural History)*

most recent practice, no distinction will be made between ratites and carinates in presenting the orders of living birds.

It is generally conceded by ornithologists that some rearrangements of genera, families, and orders may have to be made when more is known about the internal structure of different kinds of birds. Many species are known only from museum specimens consisting merely of skins with feathers. It is also conceded that the number of species will remain about as it is. For many animal groups—insects and nematode worms, for example—every large new collection turns up many species new to science. This is not true of birds. The last new species discovered in North America was found in 1918. There are now about 8,500 clearly distinguished species in the world. Many of these can be separated into several subspecies. If subspecies are counted, the number of kinds of birds reaches about 30,000.

The widespread and ever-popular song sparrow, *Melospiza melodia,* is the classic North American example of the way a species becomes slightly but nonetheless perceptibly

Fig. 23–2. Adaptive radiation in birds. Observe the contrasts in wings, tails, bills, and feet, as well as in body size and shape.

modified in different localities. In general, North American song sparrows follow Bergmann's rule of evolution that within a given genus or species the average size of the individuals increases in the northern part of the population. Such a progressive change in a character is referred to as a **cline**. The song sparrows living on the sand dunes of the Atlantic coast are paler and grayer than those in adjacent inland regions. Those in the Mississippi valley are a bit smaller and darker than those in the eastern states, while those of the drier parts of the southwest are paler and more rusty and have shorter wings and tail. In California there is a different subspecies in almost every river system. Stretching north along the Pacific coast and out into the Aleutians is a series of subspecies becoming larger and darker as the climate becomes colder and moister.

At present just fewer than 30 orders of living birds are recognized. While no one except a specialist would attempt to memorize all of them, every zoologist should have a general familiarity with the way in which birds have deployed in the course of evolution. A mere reading of the roster of orders confers a vivid realization of the true diversity of bird forms. The first four orders are the ratites; the remaining orders are the carinates. The ratites

are not only flightless but possess primitive, i.e., reptilelike, skulls. They are probably derived from ancient groups which became specialized for exclusively terrestrial life.

1. Order **Struthioniformes.** Ostriches. Natives of Africa and Arabia. A recent theory holds that they are essentially neotenous, i.e., overgrown immature birds breeding in a juvenile stage. At least their feathers resemble those of nestlings, though of giant size.

2. Order **Rheiformes.** Rheas. These are ostrichlike birds of southern South America.

3. Order **Casuariformes.** Cassowaries and emus. Flightless birds of Australia, New Guinea, and adjacent islands.

4. Order **Apterygiformes.** Kiwis. These nearly extinct flightless birds of New Zealand are peculiar in many ways. Little larger than a domestic hen, they lay eggs 5 inches long.

5. Order **Tinamiformes.** Tinamous. There are over 50 species of these strange partridge-like birds in Mexico and South America.

6. Order **Sphenisciformes.** Penguins. Although flightless, these birds swim with their wings, plunging into the surf and swimming much in the manner of porpoises, mostly under water but leaping up at regular intervals for air. The pectoral muscles and carina are both well developed. Found in southern hemisphere only.

7. Order **Gaviformes.** Loons. There are but four species of loons, all in the northern hemisphere. Excellent swimmers and divers.

8. Order **Podicipitiformes.** Grebes. These are ducklike birds, excellent swimmers but poor fliers. World-wide distribution.

9. Order **Procellariformes.** Albatrosses, petrels, and shearwaters. This order of birds is probably more highly specialized for a truly oceanic life than any other. Albatrosses have been measured with wing spreads of just under 12 feet, exceeding the maximum span recorded for any eagle or condor by at least a foot. The extremely long, narrow wings are adaptations for a special kind of soaring on air currents close to the surface of the sea. Shearwaters today are known for spectacular feats of homing over vast distances. One that was flown by plane from the coast of Wales to Boston and released there returned to its nest in Wales in 12½ days, having covered a distance of 3,200 miles, an average of 250 miles a day.

10. Order **Pelecaniformes.** Pelicans, cormorants, gannets, tropic birds, frigate birds. In this diverse group of water birds all four toes are connected by a web of skin.

11. Order **Ciconiformes.** Herons, egrets, flamingos, storks, and ibises. These are the long-legged waders.

12. Order **Anseriformes.** Ducks, geese, swans. In this order, the web of skin extends between three toes only.

13. Order **Falconiformes.** Falcons, eagles, hawks, kites, and vultures. The osprey is a remarkable member of this order because there is but one species and it is world-wide.

14. Order **Galliformes.** Jungle fowl, quail, pheasant, guinea fowl, turkeys. Mostly grain-eaters with short broad wings adapted for rapid flight of brief duration. Their jaw structure is different from that of both the flightless ratites and most other carinates. Evidently they diverged from other modern birds in the very remote past.

15. Order **Gruiformes.** Rails, coots, and a large variety of other marsh birds.

16. Order **Charadriformes.** Gulls, terns, plovers, sandpipers, phalaropes, and a large variety of other shore birds.

17. Order **Columbiformes.** Pigeons, doves. The extinct dodo was a member of this order.

18. Order **Psittaciformes.** Parrots, macaws, and their relatives, some 325 species.

19. Order **Cuculiformes.** Cuckoos and road-runners.

20. Order **Strigiformes.** Owls. The 140-odd species show remarkable adaptations for capturing prey at night. Like the falcons they possess hooked beaks and talons, but unlike them have binocular vision and retinas with rods but few if any cones.

21. Order **Caprimuligiformes.** Goatsuckers, potoos, frogmouths, whip-poor-wills.

22. Order **Micropodiformes.** Swifts and hummingbirds. About 325 species.

23. Order **Coliformes.** Mouse-birds. Found in Africa.

24. Order **Trogoniformes.** Trogons. Famous for brilliant colors and shimmery plumage. In tropical regions around the world. Best known is the quetzal, national bird of Guatemala.

25. Order **Coraciformes.** Kingfishers, bee-eaters, hornbills, many other curious species.

26. Order **Piciformes.** This is a heterogeneous order including the woodpeckers, honey-guides, toucans, jacamars, and others.

27. Order **Passeriformes.** Literally sparrow-like birds, these are the perching birds. There are about 70 families. Almost half the total number of bird species are members of this order: sparrows, thrushes, robins, crows, vireos, swallows, wrens, tanagers, and hosts of others. Their four toes are always arranged for gripping a perch. A well-developed song and elaborate nest are characteristics. The young are always helpless at hatching.

THE SKELETAL SYSTEM AND FLIGHT

Types of Flight. In recent decades aeronautical engineers have learned about flight from birds and in turn have taught zoologists the meaning of hitherto puzzling wing structures. Bird flight is of three main types:

1. **Gliding flight** is perhaps the most primitive. This is the kind seen in flying squirrels. It can easily be observed in ducks coming in for a landing on water. It is characteristic of quail, pheasants, and other gallinaceous birds which jump into the air, flap their wings violently but briefly, and then glide on in silence for some distance.

2. **Flapping flight** is the familiar flight of most birds. This is a complex type of motion in which the wings are extended maximally on the downward stroke and then partially folded on the upward stroke. In hummingbirds the wings may beat up to 75 times a second.

3. **Soaring flight** is familiar in hawks, vultures, and many sea birds. The best soaring birds have extremely long, narrow wings like those of shearwaters and albatrosses. In hawks, where heavy prey must be carried, the wings are wide as well as long.

There are three methods of soaring. The two most familiar depend on upcurrents, either thermal or deflective. The third type is known as dynamic soaring and depends primarily on horizontal winds. In **thermal** soaring hawks and vultures make use of warm air rising from sun-heated fields or rocks, the kind of updrafts that produce cumulus clouds. In this type of soaring the bird usually ascends in great circles. A mountain ridge also frequently creates upcurrents by deflecting winds. This is utilized in **deflective** soaring. One of the most famous migration routes for hawks lies for hundreds of miles along the eastern edge of the Appalachian Mountains where air masses striking the ridges are deflected upwards. At Hawk Mountain near Drehersville in eastern Pennsylvania, such ridges funnel migrating hawks into a narrow corridor of air. Bird census-takers have recorded at this point every known kind of eastern North American hawk and eagle, and often in large numbers during the southward migration in the fall. Hawks travel along this ridge for miles at speeds ranging from 20 to 40 miles an hour, yet without flapping their wings.

A very different and more ingenious type of soaring is the **dynamic** method employed by ocean birds like the albatross. As shown in the diagram, the bird moves against the wind in a series of undulations. The bird rides up at an angle of very roughly 40° against the wind until it stalls; it then turns and falls rapidly under the pull of gravity and the force of the wind, until it almost strikes the water. At this point it turns, banks sharply, and coasts up into the wind until it stalls at another crest, when it goes into another dive to pick up momentum.

Wings. Among the aerodynamic principles that act as factors in natural selection to mold the form of birds' wings are: (1) the relationship of the ratio of wing area to body weight and the speed of flight; (2) the relationship of the shape of the wing to the type of flight; (3) the camber or cross-sectional curvature of the wing; and (4) the presence of slots.

Because body weight increases roughly as the cube of linear dimensions, whereas wing area increases only as the square, it follows that a larger bird has to have wings relatively larger in comparison to its body than a smaller bird, if it is to have the same amount of wing surface for each gram of weight. Larger birds usually do not have quite as much wing area for their weight as smaller ones, and consequently fly with a smaller margin of safety.

Fast fliers requiring great maneuverability, such as quail, have short broad wings, as do high-speed airplanes. A long leading edge catches the wind and is an advantage in soaring, but offers undesirable resistance when speed is the primary aim.

Fig. 23–3. Dynamic soaring. By this method sea birds are able to fly against the wind with almost no flapping of the wings.

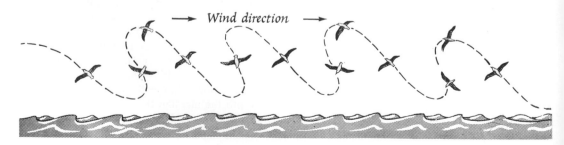

Wind direction

Fig. 23–4. A gannet braking its flight preparatory to landing. Note the black feathered alulae or bastard wings at the angle of the wings. *(Kindness of G. Harper Hall)*

The **camber** or curvature of the wing so guides the airflow over its surfaces as to produce a positive pressure on the under side, and a slight lessening of pressure above. The **alula,** or bastard wing, made up of a few feathers on the leading edge of the wing about half way to its tip, long puzzled students of birds. These feathers are attached to what looks like the thumb but is actually the second digit, or the index finger.

The marked tapering in the big primary feathers which produces **slots** between the feathers at the tip of the wings in many excellent flyers has likewise long puzzled zoologists. Aeronautical engineers now understand that both these devices play an important part in guiding air currents over the wing surfaces in such a manner as to minimize turbulence and stalling.

Feathers and Scales. Feathers form the chief exoskeletal parts of birds, but reptile-type ectodermal scales are found on their legs, and ectodermal horny bills take the place of teeth. The feathers seem to have been derived from ancestral ectodermal scales, and develop in the embryo from scalelike papillae. In addition to making flight possible, feathers provide the insulation which enables birds to maintain their high and constant body temperature of 104°F or higher. The very rapid metabolism indicated

by this high temperature is apparently necessary to exploit fully the ability to fly.

Feathers also play other important roles in avian life. Their color, form, and pattern serve to identify the species, not for the benefit of taxonomists but for the birds themselves. In many species the feathers also advertise the sex, and are used in courtship displays. Many birds, especially females, are protectively colored by their feathers.

There are three main types of feathers.

1. **Contour feathers** are the large familiar feathers of wings, tail, and much of the body. Each consists of a quill, or **calamus,** at whose proximal end there is a small opening, the **umbilicus,** through which blood vessels entered while the feather was developing. The main axis of the feather is the shaft, or **rachis,** from two sides of which extend the **barbs.** The barbs in turn bear smaller **barbules,** which end in a series of minute curled **hooks.** Close to the point where the shaft leaves the skin there may be an **aftershaft,** a miniature edition of the main feather.

In most birds the contour feathers are distributed over the body in definite feather tracts called **pterylae,** with naked intervening areas. The number of big flight feathers on wings and tail is extremely constant. Except when molting, a pigeon or a chicken with the wrong number of **rectrices,** or tail feathers, is as hard to

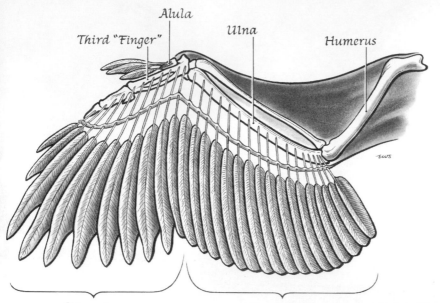

Third "Finger"   Alula   Ulna   Humerus

Primaries   Secondaries

Fig. 23–5. Wing of a bird showing the two major groups of flight feathers, the primaries attached to bones of the hand and the secondaries attached to the ulna of the forearm. Note the second or index finger bearing several feathers constituting the alula.

find as a man with the wrong number of fingers. The flight feathers, or **remiges,** of the wings are also fixed in number. Those which extend from the forearm, where they are anchored to the ulna, are called **secondaries.** Those which extend from the modified hand, where they are anchored to the three bones of the third finger, are the **primaries.**

2. **Down feathers** lack a shaft and consist of a tuft of many short fluffy barbs. Down feathers serve as insulation for nestlings and occur under the contour feathers of adults.

3. **Filoplumes** are hairlike feathers consisting of a threadlike shaft with an inconspicuous tuft of barbs at the end.

Plumage and Sex. The plumage of birds, whether gorgeous in color and design or merely drab, depends on many factors, the most important of which is sex. Charles Darwin devoted special attention to "sexual selection," which is an important evolutionary cause in the development of the dramatic differences between the sexes. However, there is a good deal more to the story than Darwin supposed. The brilliant plumage of the male is fully as effective in frightening away rival males as in impressing susceptible females.

Much modern research has been directed not at discovering the selective devices which have produced feather patterns in the course of evolution, but rather at attempting to analyze the genetic and biochemical bases for the colors and forms of feathers. On this molecular level

birds fall into two groups with respect to sexual differentiation of their feathers. There are (1) birds in which the feathers, or really the feather papillae from which the feathers grow, are genetically different in the two sexes, and (2) birds in which the feather papillae are genetically alike. In this second group, differences are determined by sex hormones.

The house sparrow, *Passer domesticus,* is an excellent example of the type in which the feather differences are genetically determined and are independent of sex hormones. If nestling house sparrows are castrated at such an early age that the two sexes have identical juvenile plumage, it will be found that later, when the birds assume adult sexually differentiated plumage, it is either that of a normal cock or of a normal hen sparrow. In this species the pigmentation of the bill is a sensitive indicator of the sex hormone level in the blood, although the feathers are not.

A breed of pheasant tested by transplanting skin between males and females showed that the formative cells from which the feathers grow were genetically different, but the feathers were nevertheless modified by the hormonal environment. Feathers grown out of male skin grafted onto a female were not hen feathers but they were definitely modified. The same was true of feathers growing from female skin grafted onto a cock.

Brown leghorn chickens are the classic example of a breed in which the feather germs (formative cells) are alike in both sexes. The difference in plumage between males and females is here due to the action of hormones. The feathers of both sexes are genetically male. This means that cocks, as well as capons and poulards, i.e., castrated males and spayed females, respectively, all have rooster-type plumage. Female sex hormones—estrogens—injected into males, capons, or poulards produce henlike plumage.

Very little is yet known about most birds in these respects. Some birds, such as blue jays, appear to wear male feathers in both sexes. No one knows why. Many questions arise to which there are still no answers. In the common herring gull, *Larus argentatus,* it is possible to induce cock plumage in females by injecting androgens (male sex hormones), but females cannot be made to act like males to the extent of staking out a claim to a nesting site and fighting off other males.

The colors of feathers are due partly to melanin, a pigment derived from the amino acid tyrosine. Special melanin-forming cells, the melanophores, deposit the black, brown, reddish, or yellowish forms of melanin in the feathers during their growth. Brilliant reds, as in the scarlet tanager, *Piranga erythromelas,* and the intense yellow of the goldfinch, *Spinus tristis,* are due to fat-soluble pigments called lipochromes. Blues are produced by physical properties of certain cells on the surface of the barbs. The deposition of these pigments is controlled not only by the hormones of the gonads but also by those of the thyroid.

Molting of feathers is also under hormonal control. Thyroidectomy inhibits molting, causes loss of pigmentation, and develops fluffy, barbless feathers. Anyone familiar with domestic chickens knows that the onset of molting and the cessation of egg-laying take place together and are accompanied by profound changes in behavior. Exactly what hormonal actions are involved is not known.

Endoskeleton. The bony endoskeleton of birds still shows a resemblance to that of the short-bodied little dinosaurs that hopped and skipped about on their long hind legs. Impressed on this basic pattern are special adaptations for flight. The forelegs are modified into wings and the sternum carries a prominent keel, which helps to support the pectoral muscles of flight. The humerus of the wings is a hollow tubular bone filled with air derived from air sacs connected to the lungs. In a freshly killed bird the lungs can be inflated by blowing air in through the humerus. Obviously the weight of the humerus is far less, when filled with air, than it would be if filled with blood and cells. At the same time, a relatively thin tube is far stronger than the same amount of material in the form of a solid rod of necessarily much smaller diameter.

Like a man and a reptile, a bird can drop its lower jaw, but a bird can also raise its upper jaw, a feat no man can perform because his upper jaw is immovably fused to the rest of his skull. This ability in the birds is made possible by an ingenious arrangement of bones on the roof and sides of the mouth. The bill is hinged to swing upward from what may be called the "bridge" of the nose. It is pushed upward by

Fig. 23–6. Bird skull showing upper bill in usual *(A)* and raised *(B)* positions. To raise the upper bill, the quadrate bone swings forward, pushing a triangle of bones at the base of the skull, which push forward on the bill.

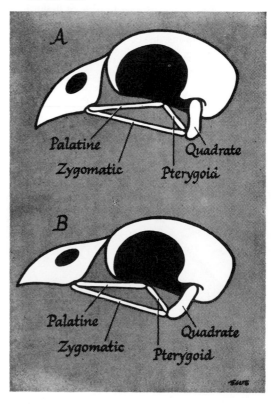

the forward thrust of a triangle of bones on each side of the head, the **zygomatic** or "cheek" bone laterally, and the **palatine** and **pterygoid** in the roof of the mouth. This triangle swings forward from a movable **quadrate.** It will be recalled that the quadrate in mammals is reduced to the tiny incus, the middle bone in the chain of three (malleus, incus, and stapes) that transmit vibrations from eardrum to inner ear.

What does this unusual ability mean in the life of birds? Mammals generally use their forepaws to hold food and for many other purposes. The forelimbs of birds are specialized for but one purpose. Presumably the increased mobility in the jaws of birds in some measure substitutes for paws or hands.

The **shoulder girdle** is composed of the familiar pair of tripods, one for each wing. The **scapula** is a long thin bone resembling a slightly curved sword blade laid back along the backbone. The second bone of the tripod, the **clavicle,** is a thin bone extending downward to the keel of the sternum, where it is fused with its mate from the opposite side. The two together are known as the **furcula,** or wishbone. By far the largest bone of the tripod is the **coracoid.**

This forms a sturdy column from the shoulder, where the wing is attached, down to the sternum. The tendon of the pectoralis minor muscle, which pulls the wing up after the down beat, runs over the top of the coracoid through the **foramen triosseum,** where the scapula, clavicle, and coracoid meet. The action of this arrangement will be explained more fully below.

OTHER FUNCTIONAL SYSTEMS

Muscular System. Because the body of a bird is essentially a rigid box, the muscles are limited almost exclusively to those concerned with the head, neck, and limbs. The large breast muscles, the engines of flight, are arranged in a beautifully ingenious way that was clearly demonstrated by Leonardo da Vinci in one of his famous dissections. The **pectoralis major** muscle, which pulls the wing down on the power stroke, is the very large superficial breast muscle having its origin along the keel of the sternum and its insertion onto the ventro-lateral surface of the humerus. The antagonist of the pectoralis major is the **pectoralis minor,** which raises the wing. This muscle lies underneath

Fig. 23 – 7. Breast muscle of flight dissected to show the foramen triosseum, which acts as a pulley through which the tendon of the pectoralis minor muscle raises the wing. This is a famous dissection first made by Leonardo da Vinci. *A,* lateral view of right shoulder girdle. *B,* medial view of left shoulder.

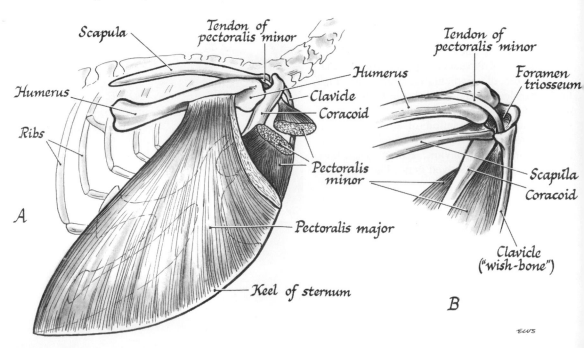

the pectoralis major in the long space, triangular in cross section, where the keel joins the rest of the sternum. As those who carve know, the fibers of these two muscles run roughly at right angles to each other. At the shoulder, where the wing joins the body, the pectoralis minor tapers into a tendon which passes up through the foramen triosseum and is inserted on the dorsal surface of the humerus. The bones of the shoulder girdle, the scapula, clavicle, and coracoid, as already explained, form this foramen where the sturdy coracoid acts as a column for the pulleylike action of the tendon of the pectoralis minor in raising the wing.

In perching birds and birds of prey, the gastrocnemius muscle of the calf of the leg, and other flexors of the toes, are well developed.

Digestive System. The alimentary tract of birds presents a number of special features. In gallinaceous and other grain-eating birds the lower end of the esophagus forms a capacious **crop** in which food hurriedly eaten can be stored. Birds of prey and fish-eating birds have a similar device. It is similar to the large rumen or first stomach in animals like cattle, an adaptation that enables them to bolt down a large quantity of food which can be chewed as cud later in a safer place. The birds do not regurgitate the food to be chewed, since they have no teeth. Instead the food passes on down into a muscular stomach popularly called the **gizzard.** There small stones aid in crushing hard kernels after they have undergone a preliminary softening by digestive enzymes in the crop.

It was from the crop of buzzards and chickens that René de Réaumur obtained copious samples of digestive juice in the middle of the 18th century and thereby placed the study of digestion on an experimental basis. His method was to induce these birds to swallow perforated metal tubes containing sponges to soak up the gastric juice, which he obtained when the birds regurgitated the tubes.

A second, even more remarkable adaptation of the gut of birds is found in pigeons and various members of the parrot family. In these birds both males and females have **milk-secreting glands** on the sides of the esophagus. Bird milk is a true milk formed by the breakdown of cells, just as in mammals. It is worth noting that **prolactin,** the hormone immediately responsible for stimulating milk secretion, is identical in birds and mammals and was, in fact, first discovered in pigeons. Prolactin is secreted by the pituitary gland at the base of the brain. Pigeon milk, like the milk of sea lions, is extremely high in fat content.

Owls and other birds of prey form in the crop characteristic pellets of the nondigested bones, fur, and feathers of their victims. These pellets are then ejected by mouth, and provide a ready means of studying the character of the owls' diet. Many berry-eating birds are responsible for disseminating plants that have seeds which resist the birds' digestive processes. This method of spreading a plant species may be very slow. If it takes the seed of a holly berry three hours to pass through a bird's digestive tract, and if the bird's average flying speed is 25 miles per hour—and there is evidence for both assumptions—the maximum distance holly seeds could be transported from a given locality would be 75 miles. There would have to be a period of a decade or more before the seedlings at the periphery of the 75-mile radius attained seed-bearing size.

Respiratory and Vascular Systems. The respiratory system of birds is notable physiologically for the extremely high rate at which metabolism takes place. Most birds have a normal body temperature of 104°F or higher, a temperature at which man is wretchedly ill.

Lavoisier, one of the discoverers of oxygen, predicted that the smaller an animal is, the more rapid must be its respiratory metabolism if it is to maintain a constant body temperature. This is because (1) an animal loses heat from its surface, and (2) the smaller a three-dimensional object is, the larger is its surface in proportion to its volume. Thus a mouse has far more surface in proportion to its weight than does a man, and hence must respire and also eat far more in proportion to its weight than a man.

In the 19th century this principle was tested on many mammals, from elephants to shrews. As can be seen in Figure 27–12 where oxygen consumption is plotted on the vertical axis and the logarithm of the body weight along the horizontal axis, chickens, pigeons, and those smallest of all birds, hummingbirds, fit well on the curve which includes the mammals. It will be noted from the shape of this curve that there is a minimum possible size for a homoiothermic, or warm-blooded, animal. At a body weight of 2 grams, its oxygen consumption would be literally sky high. How perilously close to the lower limit of size hummingbirds are is indicated by the fact that they lapse into a state of hibernation during the night, with a body temperature down almost to that of the environment and a correspondingly low oxygen consumption. Were this not so, such a bird would starve to death overnight.

The exchange of oxygen and carbon dioxide that makes this metabolism possible takes place in lungs which possess anatomical peculiarities thought to facilitate this rapid exchange, although precisely how is still in some doubt. There is no doubt, however, that the **trachea** carries air down into the thorax, and there branches into two main **bronchi**. Each bronchus continues through the mass of the **lung**, giving off four to six secondary bronchi that lead into a series of intricate passageways, many of which are **anastomosing**, i.e., interconnecting. The capillaries through which O_2 is absorbed and CO_2 lost are just under the surfaces of these anastomosing passageways. Thus the structure of a bird's lung is quite different from that of a mammal's. There are no blind pouches, or alveoli.

Furthermore, from the edges of the lungs away from the bronchi extend nine thin-walled and nonvascular **air sacs**. Eight of these are paired; they fill much of the body cavity and reach up into the neck. The median interclavicular air sac sends a branch into each humerus. Most investigators believe that the chief function of the air sacs is to eliminate the problem of what is called residual air in mammals. The air that a man breathes in and out in normal respiration is known as **tidal air**. It is truly fresh air. But because the mammal lung is a blind sac and cannot be completely freed of air even after forced expiration, there always remains some "dead" or **residual air** in such a lung. In birds most of the residual air remains in the air sacs, and the entire lung is washed with tidal air on both inspiration and expiration.

The vocal cords of birds are not located, as in mammals, at the upper end of the trachea in a larynx. Instead, the vocal cords of birds lie in a so-called **syrinx**, at the lower end of the trachea, at the point where the two main bronchi begin.

The **heart** of birds is four-chambered, as in mammals. For no known reason, it is the right fourth aortic arch that persists to form the dorsal aorta, instead of the left as in mammals. As in amphibians and reptiles, a renal portal system takes venous blood from the legs to the kidneys. In addition there is the universal hepatic portal system to take venous blood from the intestine to the liver.

Excretory System. Although entirely internal, the excretory system shows profound adaptations for flight. The kidneys are lobed structures above the coelom and immediately adjacent to the backbone. Ureters conduct the urine directly to the cloaca, for there is no urinary bladder in a bird. Such a structure, plus the contained fluid, would add appreciably to the weight of the body. The waste nitrogen is excreted as in reptiles in the form of uric acid. Uric acid precipitates out of solution very easily, as a whitish material. This means that very little water is necessary to carry away the waste nitrogen. There are thus correlated biochemical and anatomical adaptations here.

In dry climates, the feces of sea birds sometimes accumulate in great deposits over their nesting sites on islands and rocky cliffs. This material is called **guano** and is extremely rich in nitrates and phosphates. It is used for fertilizer and in the manufacture of explosives. The most important guano deposits, dating far back into prehistoric times, are located along the coast of Peru. At one time in the past the entire expenses of the Peruvian government were paid from the sale of guano which was shipped all over the world.

Reproductive System. The male reproductive system is extremely simple. The paired testes are internal. It is believed that one function of the abdominal air sacs in the male may be to lower the temperature of the gonads. In passerine or "perching" birds the sperms become lodged in a scrotumlike cloacal protuberance during the breeding season. In most mammals normal spermatogenesis does not take place if the testes are retained within the abdomen or their temperature is raised to that of the body as a whole. A vas deferens conducts sperms from each testis to the cloaca of the bird.

The female reproductive system is remarkable because only the left ovary and left oviduct develop. This again is an obvious adaptation for flight, in that it limits the essential organs to a minimum. The actual egg cell or ovum is commonly called the yolk of the egg. It is a single cell with a nucleus and spot of cytoplasm at one pole. The yolk is secreted into the egg by surrounding follicle cells. Fertilization occurs far up the oviduct near the ovary. The two layers of albumen, the two shell membranes, and finally the shell itself, are secreted around the yolk as it passes down the oviduct to be discharged into the cloaca.

Egg Production. Some birds, like the common herring gull, *Larus argentatus,* are **determinate layers.** Once such birds begin to lay, they lay a fixed number of eggs in a clutch — three in the case of this gull — regardless of any known external stimuli. Other birds are **indeterminate layers** and tend to continue to lay eggs until a given number is present in the nest. The eastern flicker, *Colaptes auratus,* normally lays five to nine eggs in a clutch. If, early in the series, an egg is carefully removed every time a new one is laid, a flicker will continue to lay eggs up to 60 or 70! Domestic fowls are indeterminate layers. Different breeds vary, but a common practice is for a hen to begin a series by laying an egg soon after dawn. Then each succeeding day an egg is laid, approximately an hour later than on the day before. This continues until the laying time falls late in the afternoon, when a day is skipped and the egg is laid early the following morning. Domestic chickens lay their maximum number of eggs the first year. Then, under comparable conditions of food and care, the number of eggs a hen lays in any year is roughly 75 per cent of the number laid the previous year.

The primary condition controlling bird reproduction, by controlling size of the gonads, is the number of hours of daylight. (See Fig. 23-16.) It is common practice to give domestic hens added hours of light during winter in order to increase egg production. This useful discovery was made by Rowan in northwestern Canada. He found that the gonads of migratory birds could be made to enlarge in the middle of winter, even in birds kept in outdoor cages, provided the birds were given additional hours of illumination. Many of the birds flew northward when released. Warmth will intensify the action of light, at least in some species. The mechanism is still in some doubt, but a great deal of evidence suggests that the primary factor is the pituitary gland, with the eyes acting as photoreceptors. A recent discovery, which may furnish an important clue to the physiological mechanism and which is already used by poultrymen, shows that it is possible to obtain enlargement of the gonads on only ten hours of light out of twenty-four, provided one hour is used to break the long period of darkness. Similar phenomena are known in photoperiodism in flowering plants.

The size, shape, color, and number of eggs laid present an interlocking series of adaptations which are, in turn, tied in with the life habits of the species. To all such questions as why some birds lay round, white eggs, while others lay pointed, speckled ones, there are always two very different kinds of answers. One is in terms of the physiology of the oviduct that shapes and colors the shell; the other is in terms of natural selection. A bird lays white or speckled eggs depending on whether or not the oviduct secretes pigment on the shell. The shape of the egg is determined by the nature of the contraction of the oviductal muscles at the time when and the place where the hard shell is secreted. These traits are inherited.

Why certain traits and not others are inherited is determined by their adaptive qualities, and hence by natural selection. In general, birds that lay their eggs in holes where they are protected both from predators and from rolling out, lay round, white eggs. This is true of such unrelated birds as woodpeckers, owls, and kingfishers. Birds that lay eggs on rocky ledges usually lay eggs that are very large at one end and narrow to a point at the other. Such eggs roll around in small circles and hence avoid the danger of rolling away. Many species, but by no means all, that lay eggs in rather sketchy nests on the ground and leave them when alarmed, like plovers, lay eggs that are heavily mottled.

The generally more primitive birds are called **precocial,** because their chicks hatch completely covered with down and are able to follow their parents and feed themselves almost immediately after hatching. Precocial species, such as ducks, chickens, or quail, usually lay large numbers of eggs. The passerine birds, like thrushes and warblers, hatch helpless and nearly naked. Such **altricial** (*altrix,* nurse) nestlings require prolonged parental care. Altricial birds typically build well-constructed nests and they lay few eggs.

Incubating the eggs may be done by the female alone, as in chickens, or by both parents, as in the majority of birds, or in rare cases by the male alone. **Broodiness** is a definite psycho-physiological condition dependent on the internal hormonal state. As long as a hen is laying eggs she will not incubate them. When a clutch of eggs is laid, broodiness sets in, but it can be brought to a premature end by preventing the bird from setting. During incubation a special **incubation patch** develops on the ventral surface of the bird's body. The down feathers over this region are molted and the skin becomes highly vascular. The result is a hot spot against which the eggs are pressed. Birds' milk has already been discussed (page 495).

Fig. 23–8. Extremely simple nest of a precocial bird, *Gelochelidon milotica,* the gull-billed tern. *(F. P. J. Kooymans)*

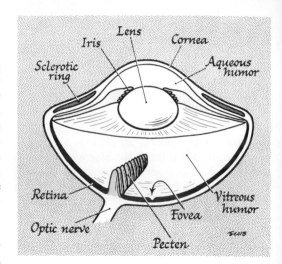

Fig. 23–9. Section through the eye of a swan; semi-diagrammatic. Note the conspicuous pecten extending into the vitreous chamber.

Nervous System and Eyes. The things a bird can do are determined by the executive organs—wings and tail, legs and bill. The executor is the central nervous system, which in birds follows the general reptilian pattern, although the brain is relatively larger than in reptiles. In mammals the great development of the brain is largely in the **pallium,** or roof of the telencephalon, which forms the cerebral hemispheres. In birds, however, the pallium remains thin, though not paper-thin as in teleosts. Most of the brain development is in the **corpus striatum,** which represents the thickened ventro-lateral walls of the telencephalon. Thus in the two highest classes of vertebrates, the birds and mammals, two different regions of the telencephalon have been elaborated to form the basis of an exceedingly complex behavior.

The most important sense organs are the eyes, probably keener than those of any mammal, including man. The sclerotic coat is strengthened by a ring of bone a short distance behind the transparent cornea. The two notable features are the pitlike fovea and the pecten. The **fovea** is the centrally placed area of keenest vision on the retina. Its steep sides magnify extremely slight movements of the image on the retina. For light from a point source to reach into such a narrow pit, the eye has to be turned *exactly* towards the source. This type of fovea is characteristic of hawks, kingfishers, and other birds of prey.

The **pecten** is a more puzzling structure. Large, heavily pigmented, vascular, and comb-like, it projects out into the big vitreous chamber from the retina at the point where the optic nerve leaves it. The most plausible of the many speculations on the function of the pecten is that in some way it makes possible the detection of extremely minute movements within the field of vision. Hawks, which detect the motion of mice far below them, have especially well-developed pectens. It has recently been suggested that the pecten enables birds to determine the position of the sun in the sky. Apparently birds do this in homing and probably during migration. In any case, the pecten casts a saw-toothed shadow on the retina which may provide a series of reference points for judging small displacements of the image.

The **retina** of nocturnal birds is made entirely of rods, that of diurnal birds, of cones. The density of cones is far greater than in man, and in the fovea of hawks reaches the almost incredible number of 1 million per square millimeter—i.e., within the area covered by a small o in newsprint.

ECOLOGY AND BEHAVIOR

Homing. Recent research indicates that there are three or more types of homing.

Type I homing is based on visual clues in familiar territory and random exploration in unfamiliar territory. It is what is called contact flying in aviation. This type of behavior has been observed in various ways, including the following of birds at a discreet distance in small airplanes. It appears to be a habit common to pigeons and also to wild species. In one famous series of experiments the gannet, *Morus bassanus*, was followed by a plane. The gannet is more easily followed than many birds because it is twice the size of the common herring gull and is pure white with black tips on its wings. Nesting gannets from Bonaventure Island in the Gulf of St. Lawrence were released far inland in northern Maine. The return flights of eight birds were followed for distances up to 230 miles. (See Fig. 23–11.) In this unfamiliar territory these birds wandered in irregular courses at a rate of about 100 miles a day. Ultimately most of them got home.

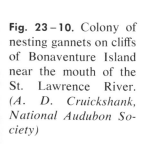

Fig. 23–10. Colony of nesting gannets on cliffs of Bonaventure Island near the mouth of the St. Lawrence River. *(A. D. Cruickshank, National Audubon Society)*

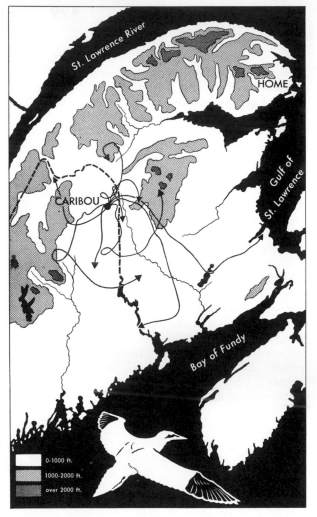

Fig. 23–11. Flights of homing birds as observed from an airplane. Adults were taken from their nests in the Gulf of St. Lawrence (upper right) and released in north-central Maine. Initial stages of their flight were followed and appear as random exploration, i.e., the first stage of Type I homing. Ultimately most of the birds got home.

Pigeons, experienced in flying home by going south from the southern end of a long narrow lake like Lake Cayuga in New York State, flew south when released for the first time at the southern end of a very similar long narrow lake. When the pigeons found that flying south did not bring them home, they returned to the release point and after considerable flying about, finally reached the home loft. When released a

second time at the southern end of the second lake they no longer flew south but directly home. This behavior is most plausibly explained on the basis of response to visual clues. The second time the birds were no longer fooled by the general topographical similarity. Nesting gulls can be temporarily confused by moving some conspicuous object, such as an old wreck, on a beach.

Type II homing occurs when birds fly in a certain compass direction after release in unfamiliar territory. This kind of homing ability may have been involved in the experiment with pigeons, just described. It is seen most often and most clearly when racing pigeons are trained to fly home in a given direction, say to the northeast. If such birds are taken north of their loft, they will still fly in a northeast direction, although, of course, this will take them farther away from home.

A massive German experiment with the migratory hooded crow is usually regarded as a case of Type II homing. Thousands of these birds were captured on the coast of East Prussia and banded. Those released there continued their normal migration to the northeast and were found later in Estonia, Latvia, Finland, and other regions northeast of East Prussia. An additional 500 birds were taken nearly 500 miles west and released in southern Denmark. These crows later showed up in Sweden, which is northeast of Denmark.

Type III homing occurs when birds take the correct way home from unfamiliar territory by flying in an unfamiliar direction. The case of the white-crowned sparrow is an instance of this type of homing. (See Fig. 23–12.) Shearwaters, which have returned home from Venice to the coast of Wales, some 3,700 miles by coast line, have been observed to fly off in the right direction when in a strange locality, provided the sky was clear, but to scatter at random when it was heavily overcast. In all such cases it is difficult to be certain that homing of Types I and II has been completely eliminated.

One of the fundamental discoveries in recent years is that birds can **orient** themselves **by the sun's position.** Various species, including the common starling (*Sturnus vulgaris*), can be trained to find food at any one of six identical windows around the periphery of a covered

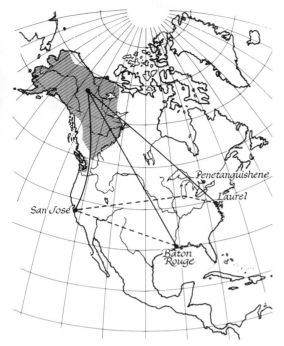

Fig. 23–12. Migration and homing of white-crowned sparrow. San José is the winter territory; shaded area, nesting territory. Dotted lines are route of airplane displacement of premigratory birds; solid lines, probable routes by which birds reached nesting territory. One from Laurel, Md., was recovered in Penetanguishene, Canada. *(After L. R. Mewaldt, Science, vol. 146, p. 941, Nov. 13, 1964)*

circular cage according to the position of the sun. When the sun is reflected by mirrors, the trained birds change the window of choice accordingly, choosing the window in all cases at, say, 60° to their left as they face the sun. Much more amazing, these birds somehow compensate for the time of day. If trained in the morning to find food in a window at a certain angle from the direction of the sun, they can still find the window in the afternoon even when the angle with the sun is quite different!

This experiment can be carried out in reverse, that is, by keeping the position of the "sun" constant by the use of a strong electric lamp. The birds then compensate for a movement that does not take place and go to the wrong window. Such compensation for time by an **internal clock** mechanism would be all but incredible except that similar internal clocks have been discovered to control the activities of fiddler crabs and other animals which live between tide lines. An ability of this kind could readily explain Type II homing. Type III is a more baffling problem, granted that it exists. Magnetic guidance seems ruled out in various ways. Tying magnets on pigeons' heads is without effect, although such a procedure would completely upset a ship's compass. Coriolis force, due to the earth's rotation, seems much too weak to have any effect, but cannot be ruled out.

Fig. 23–13. Orientation of birds to angle of sun. Dots represent position of birds in circular screened cages. Birds trained to find food at a certain angle to sunlight can be directed to go to any position of the sun with the use of a mirror. Dashed arrows indicate direction of sunlight; solid arrows, direction taken by the birds. *(From Wolfson, ed., Recent Studies in Avian Biology, The University of Illinois Press, 1955)*

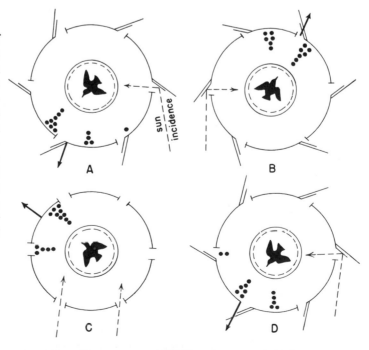

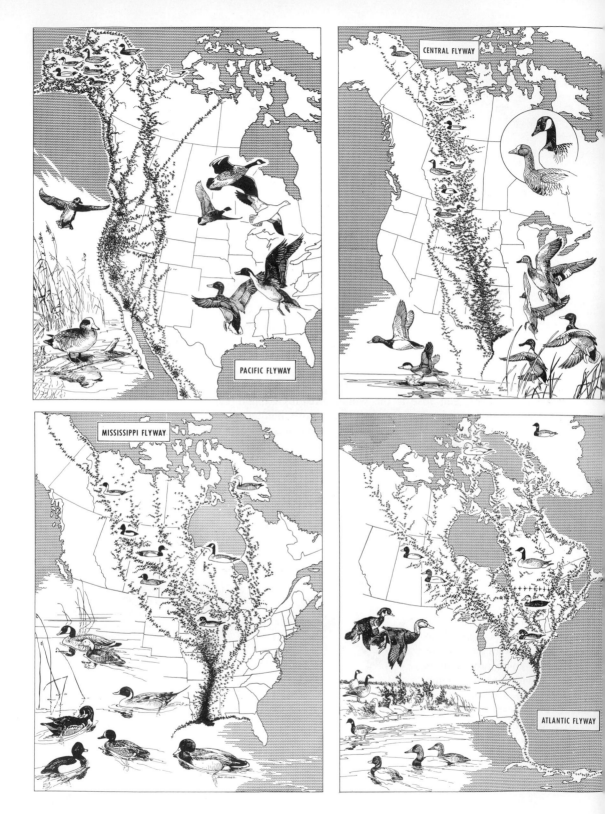

Fig. 23–14. The four major waterfowl flyways in North America. (*U.S. Fish and Wildlife Service*)

Migration. Annual migrations are crucial in the lives of many species of birds. Figure 23–14 shows the migration routes of some North American waterfowl. Four main flyways extend between the summer breeding grounds in northern Canada and Alaska and the winter ranges in the Caribbean area and Mexico. The Atlantic flyway follows the east coast from the tip of Florida north to Chesapeake Bay, where it fans out to reach from Greenland to the territory northwest of Hudson's Bay. The Mississippi flyway is concentrated along the river; the Central flyway runs roughly along the eastern edge of the Rockies; and the Pacific flyway extends from Alaska down through California into western Mexico. The north-south distance is between 5,000 and 6,000 miles.

The European stork, *Ciconia ciconia,* migrates over a route of comparable magnitude from northern Germany southeasterly along the Danube valley, through Turkey and Israel to Egypt, and then along the Nile and on to South Africa. All along this route hundreds of storks banded in Germany have been recovered. The famous flyway of the hawks along the eastern edge of the Appalachians has already been mentioned.

Not only large birds like storks, but many of moderate and even small size, migrate long distances and cross the equator twice every year. Many species of plovers, terns, swallows, and warblers do so. Many other species migrate only relatively short distances: bluejays, juncos, various sparrows, finches, and robins, for instance. In many species of birds males come north earlier than females. A large flock composed exclusively of males of the showy red-winged blackbird, *Agelaius phoeniceus,* makes a never-to-be-forgotten sight. In some species young and old birds migrate together, but in others first-year birds migrate alone—a startling fact, on first thought. Many species migrate at night. Such flights are studied quantitatively by patient observers watching the full moon through telescopes.

What is the **adaptive purpose** of migration? Very clearly migration takes birds from the crowded tropics or subtropics into otherwise largely unoccupied regions to breed where food is abundant and the days are longer than they are near the equator. Contrariwise, food is not available for most birds in the far north during the winter months.

The evolutionary history of annual migrations is obscure. Some suppose that the original home of the migrants was in the equatorial zone and that natural selection favored species endowed with a physiological mechanism that sent them north to breed. Others have held that the glaciation of much of North America in geologically recent times, the Pleistocene, must have pushed all North American birds far to the south. Many species with breeding habits adapted primarily for the long-day northern climates would be forced south. Consequently it would be advantageous for any which took to flying north to breed as the glaciers retreated.

The **physiological basis** of this behavior within the nervous, endocrine, and other systems is only beginning to be known. In such a complex process it is likely that quite different mechanisms are responsible for getting the bird ready, triggering the actual flight, orienting the bird during the migration, and finally locating it in its particular nesting site.

Fig. 23–15. Method of observing migration by counting birds as they fly past the moon. Note that when the moon is low, the area observed is larger.

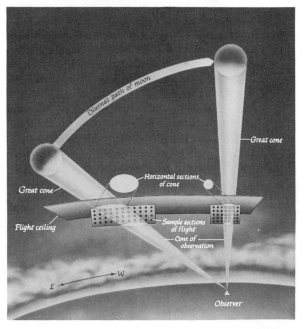

It has been known for over a century and confirmed by many recent studies that, unlike human athletes training for a race, birds deposit much fat, especially subcutaneously, in the premigratory period. On arrival at their destination this fat has been burned up, having been used as fuel during the journey. Many birds end a molt just before they start on their migration.

The basic experiment revealing the environmental factor chiefly responsible for migration was performed by Rowan in the middle 1920's. He showed that increasing the hours of light by artificial illumination, even on birds kept out-of-doors in subzero weather, would result in an increase in the size of gonads and a tendency to fly north. The well-studied case of the Pacific Coast white-crowned sparrow illustrates the almost unbelievable difference in size of the gonads when the hours of daylight are increasing in the spring and when the length of day is decreasing in the fall. Photographs of the large and minute testes are shown below.

There are many unsolved problems here, but one plausible theory is that the light acts via the eyes and the hypothalamus on the pituitary, which in turn stimulates the gonads and other glands, and this in turn sensitizes the nervous system, resulting in a general "migration disposition."

As already mentioned, in various species the young birds, which have never experienced migration, normally migrate well before or well after their parents. Rowan reproduced this experimentally by keeping first-year crows caged in Alberta in northwest Canada for a month after all the adults in the region had left for the south. After the young birds were released, over 50 per cent were recaptured in a direct line southward from Alberta.

Recent work in Germany has shown that caged migratory birds show a directional urge, persistently flying against the appropriate side of the cage, at the time of migration, provided they have a view of the sky. All this behavior fits in well with other facts already discussed about avian orientation to the direction of light (page 500). Perhaps birds migrate in a general northerly or southerly direction depending on whether they are responding positively or negatively to either sunlight or moonlight. The location of the particular nesting territory is then selected on the basis of visual recognition of topographical landmarks.

Breeding Behavior. For convenience breeding behavior may be more or less arbitrarily divided into (1) the establishment of a breeding territory, (2) courtship and mating, (3) nest-building and the laying and incubation of eggs, and (4) care of the young. Within this framework there is a high degree of diversity among different species of birds, as will be noted in the discussion below.

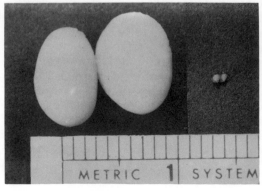

Fig. 23–16. Testes from a white-crowned sparrow. The two large testes were found just before start of migration time; the minute testes were found in the nonbreeding season. (*Kindness of William Kirsher, Donald Farner*)

The role of **territory** in bird life has been realized vaguely since the days of Aristotle, but its overriding importance and precise manifestations have been evident only since the epoch-making observations of H. E. Howard in the 1920's. It is a cause for scientific humility to recognize that any aspect of bird life as important and widespread as this, and as easily observed, should have escaped so many ardent observers for so many hundreds of years. A territory is usually defined as an area which is defended by a bird shortly before and during a sexual bond. The establishment and defense of the territory is the role of the male, except in a few species like the phalarope (*Phalaropus fulicarius*), where the female takes charge of the real estate. Territoriality in this sense has been observed in loons, ducks, gulls, and hawks, plus a very large number of passerine birds including thrushes, robins, wrens, song sparrows, and orioles.

Commonly the male arrives first and stakes out a claim by singing from conspicuous points close to the boundaries. To another male the song of his species is a warning and a challenge. This is the primary meaning of bird song. Chaucer, describing the crowing cocks answering each other from different barnyards, seems to have understood this better in 1375 than ornithologists writing prior to 1920. To a female, the male's song indicates the locality of a male, and if the song is particularly frequent, an unmated male. When one male enters the territory of another, he is immediately driven out. This is the meaning of male birds attacking their reflection in windows and the explanation of the stimulating effect of either a mirror or a noisy sewing machine on the singing of a male canary.

Territorial exclusiveness confers a number of advantages on the species. Most important, it spreads a species evenly over the available breeding area so that maximum use is made of the food supply.

Courtship and sex recognition are dependent on song, plumage, and behavior. Often the same brilliant display used to warn away other males serves as a courting signal for the female. The bowing and scraping of a courting male pigeon can be observed on any spring day in most city parks. In the common eastern flicker,

Colaptes auratus, the male differs from the female in possessing conspicuous black "moustache" marks. If these are painted on a female, the male will attack her as he would another male in his territory.

Copulation in birds is simple and brief. With his wings the male balances himself on top of the female and discharges sperms through his somewhat everted cloaca into that of his mate.

Almost every imaginable type of pairing can be found among birds. The overwhelming majority are monogamous. This habit has probably been favored by natural selection because it provides a coordinated team to care for the young. For many years it was believed that when penguins returned from their fishing trips at sea they merely fed any chick they happened upon. Recent banding experiments in the antarctic prove that this does not occur. Each penguin not only recognizes its own mate among thousands of others, but is most particular to feed only its own chick. A few species remain paired for life and stay together the year round—geese, swans, some parrots, probably eagles. Most sea birds appear to take the same mate in successive years, but the couple separates except during the breeding season. Most passerines pair for a single season. For some obscure reason birds which nest in holes, like wrens and bluebirds, sometimes change mates between broods. Polygamy is common among gallinaceous birds, ostriches, some blackbirds. The domestic rooster is so aggressive in this respect that two equally strong roosters in the same enclosure with hens will prevent each other from mating. A few cases of polyandry—where there are several males to each female—have been reported. It is probably significant that the cowbird, *Molothrus ater,* of which this may be true, does not build a nest nor incubate its own eggs, but deposits them in the nests of other species.

Birds' **nests** range all the way from the complex hanging structures of vireos, orioles, and tropical weaver birds to crude platforms of sticks or a mere depression in gravel. Some species dig a hole in a sandy bank or a tree trunk, or make a squat clay bottle stuck to the side of a cliff. In some species both sexes build the nest; in others the female builds the nest actually used while the male constructs several accessory nests in the neighborhood (which may be useful as decoys); in some species only the female makes the nest. The character and location of the nest is determined by instinct, that is, by factors resident in the nervous system. Birds reared by hand will build the correct kind of nest for their species, although even in the wild, young birds are less skillful than experienced ones.

Incubation in precocial birds like ducks and chickens is entirely the business of the female, as is the **care of the young.** In most birds, both parents take turns incubating, and both work strenuously in feeding the young.

Population Studies. Conservationists and sportsmen have a special interest in bird population studies. Within historic times a number of species have become extinct. The classic case of the dodo, *Didus ineptus,* was also an exceptional case — a large, flightless, pigeonlike bird on the island of Mauritius in the Indian Ocean, it fell an easy prey to hungry sailors. The total dodo population was confined to small islands. More puzzling is the complete disappearance of the passenger pigeon, *Ectopistes migratorius,* and the Carolina parakeet, *Conuropsis carolinensis,* in the United States. Both species were regarded as great nuisances by farmers; but undesirable animals of all kinds, including birds, are notoriously difficult to exterminate. The passenger pigeons travelled over the country in numbers running into the hundreds of millions. They nested in enormous colonies; one group in a Michigan forest covered over 100,000 acres. In the 1860's such pigeons were shipped to New York and Chicago from a single such nesting site at the rate of 100 barrels a day during the breeding season. No one could imagine that this bird might be seriously reduced in numbers, much less pushed to extinction.

Perhaps the complete answer will never be known. Excessive hunting seems unlikely as the sole answer though it may well have been the crucial factor in reducing the population to the point where other factors finished it off. Of great importance was the cutting of forests for lumber and for farmland. The case of the nearly extinct *Sphenodon* in New Zealand is one of a number which indicate that the most devastating catastrophe which can overtake a species is a radical change in its environment, especially one which destroys breeding or feeding grounds. A third possible factor has recently come to light. Certain colonial nesters do not nest successfully in colonies below a certain minimum size. For unknown reasons, the birds become restless, eggs are not properly incubated, the young are abandoned, and the colony fails to reproduce itself. Excessive hunting plus clearing the primeval forest may have combined to reduce the flocks to a point where few if any colonies reproduced themselves. With the population thus drastically shrunken, the normal ups and downs due to disease, variations in weather, and the like, which affect any population, could be counted on to deal the final blow.

Modern research concentrates on elucidating population dynamics and population structure both in game birds and in other species. Bird-banding combined with the type of mathematical analysis used by life insurance statisticians are the chief methods used. Four general conclusions emerge.

The age structure of populations of the California quail, *Lophortyx californica,* and of the very few other species which have been studied in these ways is heavily weighted in favor of very young individuals. As can be seen in Figure 23–17, the total population has an annual low every summer and an annual high every fall when the summer's hatch swells the ranks. But at any given time the vast majority of the birds are two years old or younger. This is true despite the fact that the potential or physiologically possible longevity of this species is ten years and probably longer. Further research may show that the age structure of the populations of other types of birds favors the middle-aged or even the old, but no such facts have yet come to light.

A second conclusion, which applies to some species but apparently not all, is that the mortality rate remains constant once the birds have become adult. This has been found true for the song sparrow, *Melospiza melodia,* the European blackbird, *Turdus merula,* and appears to hold generally for ducks, passerines, and gallinaceous species. This means, for example, that if in one year 50 per cent of the four-year-olds

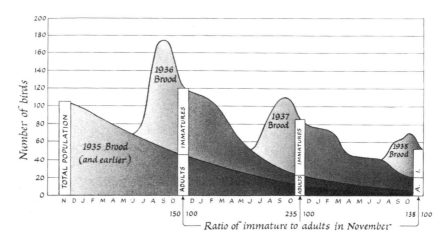

Fig. 23–17. Age structure of a quail population. Note that the vast bulk are young birds, with over 50 per cent of the population being immature juveniles and almost none over two years of age.

die, so will 50 per cent of the five-year-olds, the nine-year-olds, and so on. The most plausible explanation is that since birds' behavior is so largely governed by innate responses, experience is of little value in survival, and that since most birds die such a long time before they approach the end of their maximum genetically possible life span, senescence plays an insignificant role.

Much has been written about cycles in populations of animals, including birds. Some cycles have been demonstrated to exist, correlated with sun spots or various other factors, but convincing proof of the causes has been virtually impossible to obtain.

Finally, it is important to remember that the growth curve of any population tends to assume a logistic curve similar to that of the growth of money in the bank at compound interest. As will be discussed in the chapter on ecology, this means that if birds are "harvested" at the lower end of the population curve, the result can be disastrous, but at the upper end of the curve there is a "harvestable surplus" which can be trapped or shot without appreciably affecting the size of the population. In this country it is the job of the U.S. Fish and Wildlife Service to determine the population dynamics of game birds and thus to provide trustworthy information as a guide to action.

Review and References

REVIEW TOPICS

1. Name, characterize, and give examples of ten orders of birds.

2. What are the various types of flight, and what structural adaptations of wing size and shape are associated with each?

3. How do evolutionary and endocrine factors affect the colors and patterns of feathers?

4. In what ways is the skeletal system of birds adapted for flight? The reproductive system? The optical system? The respiratory and muscular systems?

5. What factors influence reproduction in birds, including the size, shape, color, and number of eggs laid?

6. What principles limit the minimum size of warm-blooded (homoiothermic) animals? How?

7. What is the evidence for three types of homing in birds? That some birds orient by the sun's position?

8. What is the role of territory and of song in bird life?

9. What factors may have been responsible for the extinction of various species of birds?

10. What is meant by "population structure"? What four conclusions have been reached about bird populations?

11. Define: alula, altricial, corpus striatum, foramen triosseum, dynamic soaring, pecten, prolactin, syrinx, primary feathers, bird territory.

USEFUL REFERENCES

Austin, G. R., *World of the Red-Tailed Hawk,* Philadelphia, J. B. Lippincott Co., 1964.

Bent, A. C., *Life Histories of North American Birds,* 6 vols., New York, Dover Publications, 1961 (paperback).

Forbush, E. H., and J. B. May, *Natural History of the Birds of Eastern and Central North America,* Boston, Houghton Mifflin Company, 1939.

Griffin, D. R., *Bird Migration,* New York, Doubleday & Company, 1965.

Griscom, L., *Audubon's Birds of America,* New York, The Macmillan Company, 1950.

Lincoln, F. C., *Manual for Bird Banders,* Washington, D.C., U.S. Fish and Wildlife Service, 1947.

Nice, M. M., *Watcher at the Nest,* New York, The Macmillan Company, 1939.

Peterson, R. T., *A Field Guide to the Birds,* 2nd ed., Boston, Houghton Mifflin Company, 1947.

Saunders, A. A., *A Guide to Bird Songs,* 2nd ed., New York, Doubleday & Company, 1951.

Sturkie, P. D., *Avian Physiology,* Ithaca, N.Y., Comstock Publishing Associates, 1954.

Tinbergen, N., *The Herring Gull's World,* New York, Frederick A. Praeger, 1953.

Welty, J. C., *The Life of Birds,* Philadelphia, W. B. Saunders Co., 1962.

Wolfson, A., ed., *Recent Studies in Avian Biology,* Urbana, University of Illinois Press, 1955.

Chapter 24

Mammals

Mammals (Class Mammalia) are defined zoologically as vertebrates with hair and subcutaneous mammary glands. All are viviparous; that is, they give birth to more or less well-developed young, except for a small primitive group, the monotremes, to which belong the Australian duckbilled platypus, *Ornithorhynchus paradoxus,* and its relatives. Like reptiles, the monotremes lay leathery, shelled eggs.

The mammalian heart is completely divided into four chambers, a right auricle and ventricle and a left auricle and ventricle. Blood is carried from the heart to the dorsal aorta by the left side of the fourth aortic arch, not by the right side as in birds, or by both sides as in amphibians and reptiles. In most mammals there is a placenta which serves as an organ for exchanges of food and wastes between mother and embryo before birth. In the marsupials the placenta is rudimentary and its function is performed by special adaptations like the pouch and the muscles that press milk into the mouths of extremely immature young.

The skeleton, especially the skull, has fewer bones than are found in the ancestral reptiles. A chain of three bones carries sound from eardrum to tympanum instead of one, as in the reptiles.

Because man himself is a mammal, the study of this group complies with the Socratic imperative, "Know thyself." Knowledge of the mammals illuminates human psychology and social anthropology; it is indispensable to the medical sciences; and because most of our domestic animals are mammals, their study is important to agriculture.

This chapter will consider the mammals as a taxonomic group, their adaptive radiation in the course of evolution, and what it is that primarily distinguishes them in their ecology and behavior from other animal groups. The study of their organ systems will be the subject of the next section of the book.

EVOLUTIONARY RELATIONSHIPS

The first mammals appear in the fossil record in rocks dating from the Jurassic Period during the Age of Reptiles (the Mesozoic Era), some 150 million years ago. These early mammals were all small and generalized, somewhat like a rather large shrew or a small mongrel dog. They can be distinguished from the closely related mammal-like reptiles by their skulls, cheek teeth, ear bones, and pelvis. The skull has a relatively larger brain case, and the lower jaw is composed of a single bone on each side instead of three or more. The cheek teeth of mammals are differentiated into complex molars and premolars, while those of reptiles

Fig. 24 – 1. A monotreme, *Ornithorhynchus,* the duckbilled platypus. Note the typical mammalian fur. The broad bill and webbed feet adapt the animal for life along streams. *(New York Zoological Society)*

form a row of mere conical pegs. The middle ear of the primitive mammals contains a chain of three bones, the stapes, incus, and malleus, between the tympanum and the cochlea, whereas the mammal-like reptiles have but a stapes (columella) and retain the other two as small bones at the angle of the jaw (the quadrate which is homologous with the incus, and the angulare of the lower jaw which is homologous with the malleus). The pelvis of mammals, while the same in basic structure as that in reptiles, has an elongated ilium, the element which connects the pelvis with the spine.

The fossil record reveals virtually nothing of the internal structures of these primitive mammals, nor of the evolution from scales to hair. It should be remembered that some mammals still possess reptilian epidermal scales, covering the tail in rodents and most of the body in one group of anteaters.

At the beginning of the age of mammals, the Cenozoic Era, some 70 million years ago, all the known mammals were still no larger than medium-sized dogs. Yet most of the major lines of mammalian evolution were at least foreshadowed, although there were no highly specialized forms. During the past 70 million years the mammals have undergone an explosive evolution, radiating outward in many

adaptive directions, much as did the reptiles before them. And in line after line – horses, elephants, cats, deer, etc. – the mammals have followed Cope's law that in the course of evolution, over millions of years, a race of animals tends to become larger in body size. In this too they resemble the reptiles. Note, however, that in both groups there are lines, like the rodents, where there has been little if any tendency to increase in size.

MAJOR GROUPS

Living members of the Class Mammalia fall into three subclasses, the monotremes, the marsupials, and the placentals.

1. The Monotremes (Subclass Prototheria). This is a very small group of egg-laying mammals limited to Australia, New Guinea, and adjacent islands. They are believed to have diverged from the main mammalian stock at extremely remote times. The body is covered by hair and is provided with subcutaneous mammary glands. There are no nipples, and the milk is merely exuded through innumerable tiny pores on the ventral side of the body. The skeleton is extremely reptilian, and so is the urogenital system, which opens to the exterior in common with the alimentary canal through a cloaca.

Overlying these very primitive traits are some specializations. *Ornithorhynchus paradoxus,* the Australian duckbilled platypus, is adapted for a semi-aquatic, semi-burrowing life along the edges of streams. In addition to the ducklike bill, the clawed toes are webbed. *Echidna* and *Tachygloss* are the genera of spiny anteaters found in Australia and adjacent regions.

2. The Marsupials (Subclass Metatheria). The marsupials are characterized by a pouch or **marsupium,** which is usually supported by a pair of **epipubic bones.** The young crawl into the marsupium immediately after birth, which takes place in a very much earlier stage of embryonic development than in placental mammals. A litter of 20 newborn opossums scarcely fills a teaspoon. The front legs are precociously developed to facilitate crawling into the pouch. Intrauterine life in a placental mammal like a cat lasts nearly 60 days; in an opossum of comparable size it lasts scarcely two weeks, but the young opossum spends about 50 days in the pouch. The sides of its lips grow together around the teat, which extends far down the throat of the young animal. Milk is squeezed into the infant by special muscles of the mother. All of this apparatus — marsupium, epipubic bones, special muscles to express milk into fetuses too young to suckle, precociously developed forelegs, and lips which grow together around the teats — is clearly a highly specialized and coordinated group of adaptations.

The brain is relatively smaller in marsupials than in modern placental mammals and, most surprisingly, there is no corpus callosum, the chief right-left connection between the cerebral hemispheres. The teeth are unspecialized, and the urogenital system is reptilelike in that both alimentary canal and urogenital system emerge together through a cloaca. A puzzling but characteristic feature of the female reproductive tract is a three-parted vagina. John Hunter, the 18th century Scottish anatomist, discovered this in the kangaroo. Such a construction was denied by Richard Owen, the

Fig. 24–2. Young marsupials lifted out of the pouch but still attached to the nipples. *(Courtesy, General Biological Supply House, Inc., Chicago)*

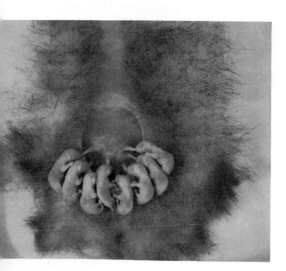

anatomist who opposed the views of Charles Darwin, but modern workers have at last fully confirmed Hunter. The sperms pass up through the lateral vaginal canals. The penis is bifurcated. The fetuses are born through the central vagina. The eggs are somewhat larger than those of placentals, but still minute. The yolk is surrounded by albumen and this by a shell membrane which is soon lost.

Clearly it was not the marsupials that gave rise to the placental mammals, but another, perhaps even more primitive trunk of the mammalian tree. There are only about 230 living species of marsupials, divided into three orders on the basis of their dentition, which, of course, reflects diet and coordinated adaptations.

a. **Carnivorous marsupials** (Order **Polyprotodontiformes**). This order possesses a carnivorous dentition and includes such species as the opossums, the Tasmanian wolves, the marsupial moles, the Australian "cats," and the insectivorous bandicoots.

b. **Rodent-like marsupials** (Order **Coenolestoiformes**). This group possesses an intermediate type of dentition. It includes small rodentlike and shrewlike marsupials found in South America.

c. **Herbivorous marsupials** (Order **Diprotodontiformes**). This order has herbivorous teeth — chisellike incisors, reduced canines, and crushing molars, sometimes ridged. The group includes the kangaroos, wallabies, wombats, and the popular koala bears.

3. The Placentals (Subclass Eutheria). In the placental mammals the epipubic bones, the marsupium, the precocious development of forelegs, and the whole cluster of marsupial adaptations are absent. The eggs are semi-microscopic and in many ways resemble the eggs of those other deuterostomes, the echinoderms. The embryo remains within the uterus until a relatively advanced stage of development when it can actively suckle. It is always nourished by means of a placenta having blood vessels derived from an embryonic membrane called the **allantois**. However, the placentas of different groups of Eutheria differ very greatly in both gross and microscopic anatomy. Evolutionary development among the placentals has involved most structures but especially the brain, which

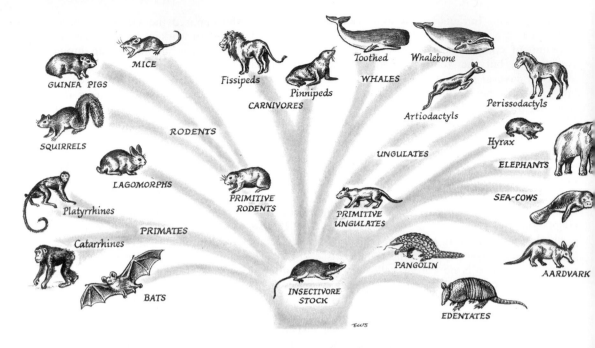

MICE

GUINEA PIGS

Fissipeds

Pinnipeds

CARNIVORES

Toothed Whalebone

WHALES

SQUIRRELS

RODENTS

Artiodactyls

Perissodactyls

Hyrax

UNGULATES

ELEPHANTS

LAGOMORPHS

PRIMITIVE
RODENTS

SEA-COWS

Platyrrhines

PRIMITIVE
UNGULATES

PRIMATES

Catarrhines

PANGOLIN

AARDVARK

INSECTIVORE
STOCK

BATS

EDENTATES

Fig. 24–3. Adaptive radiation in placental mammals. Note how the specializations of the feet give a clue to the manner of life.

has become relatively larger and has developed a **corpus callosum** connecting the two cerebral hemispheres; and the teeth and legs, which reflect the character of the animal's life with remarkable accuracy. Indeed, Sir Richard Owen is reported to have said (paraphrasing Archimedes when he announced the principle of the lever), "Give me a tooth and I will reconstruct the animal." The more important living orders of the subclass follow.

a. **Insectivores** (Order **Insectivoriformes**). The insectivores most nearly represent the original type of mammal that first appeared during the Mesozoic. They are small, with many sharp teeth in marked contrast to those of the rodents which they superficially resemble. Insectivores live on a carnivorous but varied diet of insects, earthworms, millipedes, eggs, etc. Living genera include the shrews, which are largely nocturnal, and although seldom seen are among the most abundant of all mammals in most temperate parts of the world. The moles are specialized for a life of burrowing; the hedgehog is notable for a coat of protective spines.

b. **Bats** (Order **Chiropteriformes**). The bats are the only mammals with actual flight, although several others can glide considerable distances. As in a bird, the sternum of a bat bears a keel to which the large pectoral muscles are attached. The fingers are elongated and help support the leathery wing instead of being reduced, as in birds. The shoulder girdle resembles that found in the brachiating primates, i.e., monkeys that swing from branches by their arms. The clavicles are very large and support the shoulder in much the way the large coracoid does in birds. Many species possess highly specialized ears which form part of a remarkable sonar system that enables bats to avoid obstacles in the dark by hearing the reflection of their own high-pitched squeaks.

There are three types of bats, insectivorous ones, which are most numerous and almost world-wide in distribution; fruit-eating ones, the "flying foxes," limited to tropical America and the Pacific; and blood-sucking bats, provided with sharp teeth which inflict almost painless razorlike cuts.

c. Primates (Order **Primatiformes**). The primates, the order which includes man and the various apes, monkeys, lemurs, and similar forms, are hard to separate from the primitive insectivores from which they arose. The technical distinction is based on apparently trivial features. The primitive number of incisors between the canines in placental mammals is six—as in modern insectivores, bats, and carnivores like dogs and cats. Primates have but four incisors.

The key fact about primates is that they evolved as an arboreal group and are still arboreal, with a few exceptions such as man and the baboons. In an arboreal environment, where one has to jump from branch to branch, natural selection would strongly favor the development of grasping forelimbs to catch on to the next bough. This requirement led to the famous **opposable thumb** and great **manipulative** ability in the **hand.** Once such a structure has evolved, natural selection would then favor mutations increasing brain size and hence increasing the ingenuity with which the versatile hand was used.

Life among the branches also places a high premium on the ability to judge distances correctly, and on spying things out by sight rather than tracking them by smell. Hence natural selection would press strongly in favor of the **visual centers** in the brain at the expense of olfactory centers, and in favor of mutations advantageous to **binocular vision.** There is a strong tendency evident among the primates for the eyes to face forward and for the snout to be reduced.

Except for some remarkable investigations by a handful of workers on three or four species, very little has ever been learned about man's closest relatives. The primates as a group are surely a rich field for future research. The suborders of the primates are:

(1) Lemurs. True lemurs are found only on Madagascar and nearby islands, but closely related animals, the loris and the bushbaby (*Galago*), are found from the East Indies across southern Asia and into Africa. They are all small nocturnal animals, arboreal and omnivorous, subsisting on insects, worms, birds' eggs, fruits, nuts, etc. The tail is long and bushy, but is never prehensile, that is, used as a grasping organ. Some species appear strangely human, others resemble cats or squirrels.

(2) Tarsoids. Tarsius is the only living representative of this suborder. Limited to the East Indies, it resembles a lemur but has a better developed brain, enormous anteriorly directed eyes resembling those of owls, and like owls it looks in different directions by turning its neck a full half-circle if need be. The retina

Fig. 24-4. The human skeleton, from Vesalius's great *De Humani Corporis Fabrica,* 1543. *H,* humerus; *R,* radius; *U,* ulna; *P,* pelvis; *Fe,* femur; *T,* tibia; *Fi,* fibula.

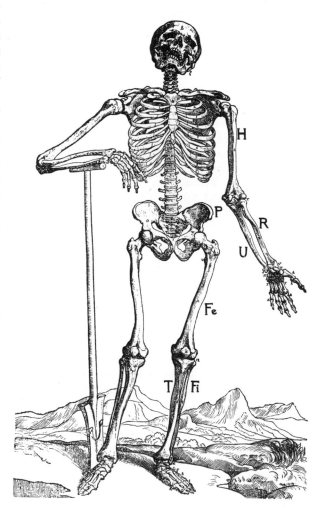

contains only rods and consequently is most useful at night.

(3) Anthropoids. This suborder includes the monkeys, apes, and man. The cerebral cortex is far more convoluted than in the more primitive suborders, the eyes face more directly forward, and the uterus is simplex, i.e., it lacks horns as in primitive forms. There are two major groups of anthropoids, the platyrrhines and the catarrhines, which have evolved separately from very primitive insectivore stock.

The **platyrrhine** (flat-nosed) monkeys live in tropical America. The nasal septum is broad and the nostrils face somewhat laterally. Unlike any of the Old World monkeys of Africa and Asia, the platyrrhines have **prehensile** tails. In this they agree with several other unrelated South American animals (opossums, for instance). Two families are recognized. The family Hapalidae, or marmosets, are very small monkeys. The family Cebidae includes, among others, *Cebus,* the organ-grinders' monkey, *Ateles,* the spider monkey, and *Alouatta,* the howler monkey. The latter lives in large "clans," and its social behavior has been extensively recorded.

The **catarrhine** (downward-nosed) anthropoids include the Old World monkeys, apes, and man. The monkeys and apes live in southern Asia and Africa. The nasal septum is relatively narrow. Three families are recognized: the Cercopithecidae *(cercopithecus,* a long-tailed monkey), the Simiidae *(simia,* an ape), and the Hominidae *(homo,* a man).

The family Cercopithecidae includes the baboons, mandrills, proboscis monkeys, the physiologists' macaque, and others. They are highly socialized animals often living in large colonies.

The family Simiidae includes the four great apes: *Hylobates,* the gibbon; *Simia,* the orangutan; *Pan,* the chimpanzee; and *Gorilla.*

The family Hominidae includes but one living species, *Homo sapiens.* The fossil record so far has revealed very little about the relationship of this family to other catarrhines.

d. **Lagomorphs** (Order **Lagomorphiformes**). In the past the rabbits, hares, and "conies" or pikas were placed in the same order as the rodents. It now seems to most students of these groups that such similarities as rodents and lagomorphs possess *(lagos,* hare) are due to convergent evolution adapting a small mammal to an herbivorous diet. The body of a lagomorph is adapted for speed in jumping. The tail is reduced to a button of fuzz. Rodents, by contrast, are adapted for running, and have long, usually scaly tails. The incisors in both groups are chisellike, but this is true in various kinds of mammals. Even in this respect there is a constant difference, for rodents have but two incisors in the upper jaw, while rabbits and hares have four. Also the cheek teeth are very different, and so is the jaw musculature. The fossil record shows that the lagomorphs and the rodents were separate from remote Cenozoic times.

e. **Rodents** (Order **Rodentiformes**). Rodents possess but two upper incisor teeth and not more than five cheek teeth. With few exceptions the tail is long and often scaly, the jaw musculature highly specialized. The rodents are the most successful of all mammals in number of species—about 3,000, divided roughly into three groups. The myomorphs *(myos,* mouse) are the mice, rats, and their allies. The hystricomorphs *(hystrix,* porcupine) include, besides the porcupines, the chinchillas and the capybara of South America. The latter is the largest of all rodents, reaching the size of a small pig. The sciuromorphs *(sciurus,* squirrel) include the squirrels, gophers, beavers, and similar forms.

f. **Carnivores** (Order **Carnivoriformes**). The chief carnivore specializations are sharp teeth, a keen nose, and somewhat forward-facing eyes. There are two major groups, **fissiped** *(fissi,* divided) carnivores which are terrestrial, and **pinniped** *(pinna,* pointed) ones which are aquatic. Fissipeds include seven rather diverse families: dog, raccoon, bear, mink, civet, hyena, and cat. The pinnipeds include three families: sea lions, seals, and walruses.

g. **Cetaceans** (Order **Cetaceiformes**). This order includes both the toothed whales, such as the sperm whales (like Moby Dick) and the porpoises, and also the whalebone or baleen whales, which lack teeth and possess great horny, brushlike sieves hanging around the edge of the upper jaw.

The large toothed whales often eat giant squid; the scars made by large squid suckers are often found on their skin and remains of giant (40-foot) squid are found in their stomachs. How whales manage to catch and devour such animals is not known. Porpoises eat mostly fishes. The toothed killer whales eat porpoises and anything else they can catch. Whalebone whales, like the gigantic blue whale, live on a diet of plankton, the minute life swarming in parts of the ocean, which they capture in the mouth with their whalebone sieves. These whales are the largest animals that have ever lived, exceeding even the largest dinosaurs by a factor of ten.

h. Artiodactyls (Order **Artiodactyliformes**) (*artios,* even, + *dactylos,* finger). This order includes the larger herbivorous mammals with an even number of toes. The long axis of the foot runs between the third and fourth digit. One suborder includes pigs, peccaries, and the hippopotamus; another the sheep, camels, cattle, deer, giraffes, and antelopes. Because many of these animals chew the cud, they are sometimes referred to as **ruminants** (*ruminare,* to chew the cud). The stomach is three- or four-chambered, the first being the rumen, a large pouch to hold hastily eaten food until it can be regurgitated and chewed in a safe place. Hoofed animals, both artiodactyls like sheep and perissodactyls like horses, are often called **ungulates** (*ungula,* hoof).

i. Perissodactyls (Order **Perissodactyliformes**) (*perissos,* odd, + *dactylos,* finger). The perissodactyls are the larger herbivorous mammals with an odd number of toes. The long axis of the foot runs through the third digit. There are only three living groups, each of family rank, the horse-ass-zebra group, the tapirs, and the rhinoceros.

j. Elephants (Order **Proboscidiformes**). The only two living species are the Indian and the African elephant. Before the dawn of history the long-haired, low-browed mastodons and the dome-headed mammoths both existed over all of North America and northern Eurasia and they are both recorded in many drawings of the cave men.

k. Conies (Order **Hyracoidiformes**). The strange little mammals belonging to this order constitute a long-standing zoological puzzle. *Hyrax,* the cony (a popular name it shares with a rodent, the pika), looks like a guinea pig (a rodent); its dentition, always an important feature in classification, resembles that of artiodactyls; its feet and reproductive system are like those of elephants in important respects. Serological tests with blood proteins have revealed that there is a closest relationship to the elephants.

l. Sea-cows (Order **Sireniformes**). The manatee and the dugong, or sea-cow, are large, gentle, herbivorous creatures with pectoral but no pelvic limbs. They inhabit coastal waters and frequently ascend rivers. The pectoral position of the breasts and the mother's habit of holding the young to them with her flippers is said to have given rise to the old sailors' tales of mermaids.

m. Armadillos, sloths, and anteaters. The orders **Xenarthriformes** (the armadillos, tree sloths, and South American anteaters), **Pholidotiformes** (the scaly anteater or pangolin), and **Tubulidentatiformes** (the aardvark or South African anteater) are all highly specialized or degenerate groups lacking teeth. At one time they were lumped together taxonomically as a single group as edentates.

ECOLOGY AND BEHAVIOR

The overriding characteristic which sets mammals apart from all other animal groups is their development of intelligence. It basically influences all their relationships with each other and with their environment, both living and nonliving. Their highly plastic behavior, subject to profound modification by experience, stands in marked contrast to the stereotyped sort of innate response characteristic of insects and even of reptiles and birds. The typical insect or reptile learns nothing whatever from its parents, and for a very good reason. Insects and reptiles lay their eggs and then either die or walk away. Even birds learn relatively little from their parents, so dominant in their lives are the innate or instinctive aspects of their behavior. With mammals plastic behavior is characteristic, though they too have innate patterns of response.

Correlated directly or indirectly with the development of intelligence is the development of three very important anatomical traits—a large complex brain, the mammary glands, and the placenta.

A keystone of mammalian development is the growth of the **brain,** and especially the cerebral cortex.

The development of the **mammary glands** and the resulting dependence of the young mammal on its mother's milk binds young and adult together. This has two results. First, it insures the young mammal of parental protection during the early crucial stages of learning the ways of the world in which it will live. The young insect or spider has little need for parental protection because it hatches into its world with a reasonably complete set of innate responses. These responses are adequate for most of the situations it will face, and they can be modified only to a slight degree in any case. Second, the obligatory association of the young and the adult mammals also provides an opportunity for the direct imitation of the adult by the young, a form of learning which is, of course, important in many species.

The third important mammalian anatomical characteristic is the **placenta,** the structure through which the unborn young receives food and oxygen from the mother and gives off carbon dioxide and other wastes. The placenta is the key structure which makes viviparity, or live birth, possible. Viviparity gives the developing embryo protection that the hardest egg shell can scarcely provide. It also means that of necessity the mother will be present when the young comes into the world, while in the ancestral reptile the female that laid the eggs is very seldom present when they hatch.

Parental nurture is not necessary when the young hatch with a fairly full set of innate responses, although it may still be an advantage when superimposed upon such equipment, as the birds and social insects demonstrate. But when the young are born without a repertory of prefabricated behavior patterns, parental nurture becomes essential. For launching into the world an animal that depends on intelligence, viviparity sets the stage, the mammary glands enforce the association of the immature and the experienced, while the cerebral cortex capitalizes on the opportunity.

Review and References

REVIEW TOPICS

1. Characterize the three major groups of mammals.

2. Discuss seven orders of mammals as illustrations of adaptive radiation.

3. What are the anatomical features of bats that are related to their ability to fly?

4. What three anatomical characters of mammals are correlated with the evolution of intelligence?

5. Characterize the three suborders of the primates.

6. Why place rabbits and rats in separate orders?

7. Compare and contrast Old World and New World primates.

8. What visible anatomical trait separates the two major groups of Cetaceans and how is it related to their diet?

9. Why not place the sea-cows with the Cetaceans?

10. What may arboreal life have contributed to the structural and physiological capabilities of primates?

11. Define: marsupium, allantois, brachiating, opposable thumb, prehensile, simplex uterus, ruminant, ungulate.

USEFUL REFERENCES

Anthony, H. E., *Field Book of North American Mammals,* New York, G. P. Putnam's Sons, 1928.

Buettner-Janusch, J., ed., *Evolution and Genetic Biology of Primates,* New York, Academic Press, 1965.

Burt, W. H., and R. P. Grossenheider, *A Field Guide to the Mammals,* Boston, Houghton Mifflin Company, 1952.

Greene, E. E., "Anatomy of the Rat," *Transactions of the American Philosophical Society,* vol. 27. Philadelphia, 1935.

Griffin, D. R., *Echoes of Bats and Men,* New York, Doubleday & Company, 1959.

Hartman, C. G., *Possums,* Austin, University of Texas Press, 1952.

Hartman, C. G., and W. L. Straus, *The Anatomy of the Rhesus Monkey,* Baltimore, The Williams & Wilkins Co., 1933.

Hooton, E., *Man's Poor Relations,* New York, Doubleday, Doran and Co., 1942.

Norris, K. S., *Whales, Dolphins, and Porpoises,* Berkeley, University of California Press. 1965.

Saunders, J. B. deC. M., and C. D. O'Malley, *Illustrations from the Works of Andreas Vesalius*, Cleveland, World Publishing Co., 1950.

Simpson, C. G., *The Principles of Classification, and the Classification of the Mammals,* New York, American Museum of Natural History, 1945.

Young, J. Z., *The Life of Mammals,* New York, Oxford University Press, 1957.

Part VI

Organ Systems, Mainly Mammalian

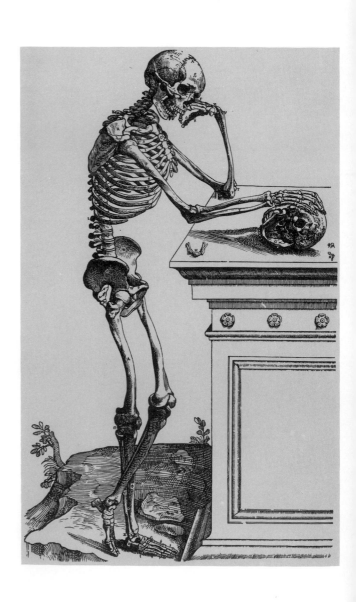

Any higher animal—honeybee, octopus, or man—is an affair of amazing complexity. To understand this complexity, the philosopher-scientists of classical antiquity devised a method that enjoys virtually universal use today. Instead of thinking about animals as indivisible wholes, they investigated them in terms of functional systems, such as the skeletal, digestive, reproductive, and nervous systems. This was the way human anatomy and physiology were taught in the famous medical school at Alexandria when Caesar and Cleopatra lived in that intercultural melting-pot of ancient learning.

The Alexandrian method, studying animals system by system, was the method of Vesalius in his great work on human anatomy, *De Humani Corporis Fabrica,* of 1543, which marks the beginning of modern biology. It is the approach that will be followed in the next seven chapters. Because earlier chapters have considered the organ systems of the invertebrates and the lower vertebrates, the emphasis in this study of organ systems will be mainly, but not exclusively, on mammals.

Chapter 25

Skeletal and Muscular Systems

Vesalius began his epoch-making study of human anatomy with the skeletal system and followed with a study of the muscles. Because the skeletal system forms the framework upon which the entire vertebrate organism is constructed, some knowledge of its parts, their relationships and functions, is essential for any clear understanding of how a vertebrate manages to live. After the skin, the muscles are the first organ system the anatomist meets when he begins to dissect. Muscles, along with nerves, are, of course, the key structures that distinguish animals from plants.

THE SKELETAL SYSTEM

Functions. The skeleton of a man or other mammal has four major functions. The first is to give **support** to the body. If something were suddenly to dissolve the skeleton of a man, he would immediately slump into a helpless blob. A specialized and essential aspect of the supportive function of the skeleton in mammals is the formation of the **rib cage.** Without this semi-rigid box, inhalation of air would be impossible.

A second function of the skeleton, and probably the first to appear in the evolution of the vertebrates, is to facilitate **locomotion.** The notochord in the primitive chordates and the backbone in the fishes are the keys to their superiority over the segmented worms in swimming ability. In the mammals the bones of the legs are highly specialized for locomotion in a variety of different ways. Compare, for example, the forelegs of a cat, a horse, a bat, a seal, and a man. (See Figs. 1–3 and 10–8.)

A third important function of the vertebrate skeleton is **protection.** This is also an extremely ancient skeletal function. Fossil armored fishes encased in their skeletons are known from early Paleozoic times. In mammals, the protection of the brain and the spinal cord is an essential function of the skull and the bony neural arches of the vertebrae.

Fourthly, **erythropoiesis,** the formation of red blood cells (and many white ones also), takes place both in the marrow of the long bones of the limbs and in the sternum between the tips of the ribs.

Components. As in all vertebrates from fish to man, the skeleton of the mammals has two main subdivisions. The **axial skeleton** is composed of the skull, the backbone, the ribs, the sternum, and the evolutionary remnants of the gill arches. The **appendicular skeleton** consists of the pectoral and pelvic girdles and their attached limbs. We shall consider in detail the components of each of these systems.

The **skull**—especially the human skull—has been an object of study for many centuries. Classical Greeks, medieval Arabians, the men of the Renaissance, the poet Goethe, and many others have contributed to our knowledge, but it was T. H. Huxley, Charles Darwin's champion, who established the modern view of the nature of the mammalian skull. The skulls of all mammals, including man, are built on the same plan, of the same bones, bone for bone homologous throughout. Only the relative sizes of the skull bones are different.

A comparison of the skull of a man and a cat (Fig. 25–2) will demonstrate this fact. In both, above the nostrils are the small **nasal** bones. Above these, over the forehead and above the eyes, are the **frontal** bones; behind them arching over the **temporal** bone of the ear region are the **parietals;** and at the back of the head are the fused **occipitals.** The cheek or **zygomatic** bone in each case is below the eye and extends back toward the angle of the jaw. The upper teeth are held in the **maxillary** and **premaxillary** bones. For many years it was supposed that lack of a premaxillary bone separated man from the apes. This error was corrected by none other than the German poet Goethe, who demonstrated the presence of a premaxillary in a wide variety of mammals and finally in the human skull. It can be best seen in the very young, for the premaxillary, which bears the incisor teeth, develops as a separate

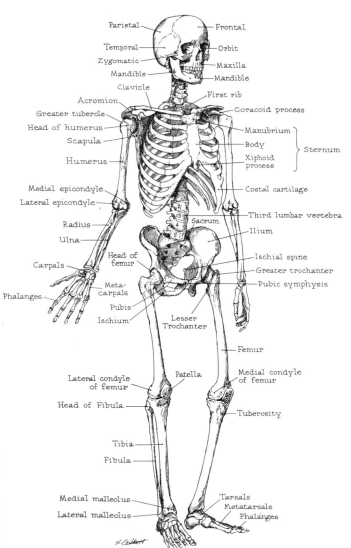

Fig. 25–1. The human skeleton. *(Reprinted by permission of Burgess Publishing Company from* Atlas of General Zoology, *1965, by S. G. Gilbert)*

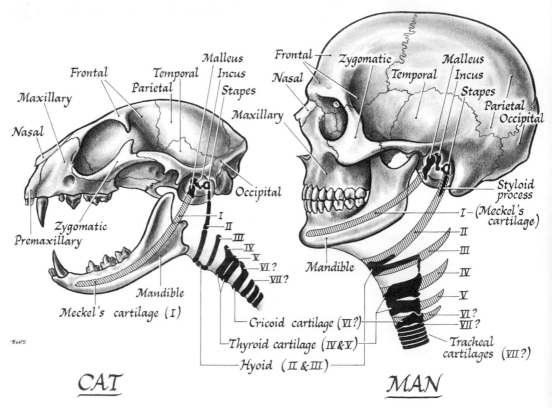

Labels on figure — CAT:

Maxillary, Frontal, Temporal Parietal, Malleus, Incus, Stapes, Nasal, Maxillary, Occipital, I, II, III, IV, V, VI?, VII?, Zygomatic, Premaxillary, Mandible, Meckel's cartilage (I), EWS

Labels on figure — MAN:

Frontal, Nasal, Zygomatic, Temporal, Malleus, Incus, Stapes, Parietal, Occipital, Styloid process, I – (Meckel's cartilage), II, III, IV, V, VI?, VII?, Mandible, Tracheal cartilages (VII?)

Shared lower labels:

Cricoid cartilage (VI?), Thyroid cartilage (IV & V), Hyoid (II & III)

CAT   MAN

Fig. 25 – 2. Skull and gill arches of the cat and of man. The Roman numerals refer to the gill arches represented by the skeletal structures shown.

ossification from the maxillary, which bears the canines and the more posterior teeth.

The ancient **gill arch skeleton** still plays an important role in mammals. Essentially it is the same as in the higher reptiles. As can be seen in Figure 25 – 2, the **mandible** is formed around **Meckel's cartilage** of the embryo, which represents the first gill arch in fishes. Of the chain of three tiny bones in the middle ear, the **malleus** and **incus** form from the upper end of the first gill arch, and the **stapes** is formed from the second gill arch. The **styloid process** on the skull and much of the **hyoid** bone at the base of the tongue are also formed from the second or hyoid arch. The third arch contributes to the hyoid bone. The fourth and fifth arches form the **thyroid cartilage** or Adam's apple. These facts, visible during embryonic development, correlated with facts from comparative anatomy and paleontology, support the conclusion that these structures do represent gill arches.

In mammals, the **backbone** is divided into five regions — cervical, thoracic, lumbar, sacral, and caudal. With the exception of only two or three species, there are precisely seven **cervical vertebrae** in the necks of all mammals — men, giraffes, whales, mice. The differences in length in these animals are due entirely to differences in lengths of the seven cervical vertebrae. Why this is so is unknown, and the more puzzling because birds with long necks, like swans and flamingos, possess many more cervical vertebrae than do birds with short necks, like owls. The **thoracic vertebrae** bear the **ribs,** one pair per vertebra. There are usually 12 to 14, depending on the species. There are 12 in *Homo sapiens* (of either sex). Except in porpoises and their aquatic relatives, the ribs are always well developed and meet ventrally (anteriorly in man), fusing more or less with the **sternum.** Thus is the semi-rigid chest cavity constructed. In the lumbar region are 5 to 7 lumbar **vertebrae,** again depending on the species. The ribs in this region are reduced in mammals to mere stubs fused to vertebrae. The sacrum consists of 5 to 7 fused **sacral vertebrae** with enlarged "rib" bases to which the pelvic girdle is rigidly attached. The **caudal vertebrae** vary from 4 in man to 25 or more in long-tailed mammals. Each vertebra throughout the backbone consists of a drum-shaped centrum, which develops around the embryonic notochord, and a neural arch extending up over the spinal cord.

The **appendicular skeleton,** consisting of limb girdles and limbs, has been highly modified in many of the mammals but the basic pattern is unchanged from the ancestral reptiles. Each limb is supported by a tripod of three bones. The bases of the tripods press against the axial skeleton, i.e., against the backbone. At the apex of the tripod, the three bones meet the first—i.e., the most proximal—bone of the leg. This is the humerus in the front leg, or arm, and the femur in the hind leg. The pair of tripods that support the front legs or the arms constitute the pectoral girdle; the pair that support the hind legs, the pelvic girdle.

A **pectoral tripod** consists of the **scapula** or shoulder blade, the **clavicle** or collar bone, and the **coracoid.** The scapula is a main support for muscles that move the arm; it is divided on its lateral surface by a prominent ridge ending in a prominent projection called the **acromion,** which forms the point of the shoulder. The coracoid, it will be recalled, is well developed in most reptiles and very large in birds (see Fig. 23–7). In mammals it becomes fused with the scapula during development and remains a small process which helps hold the humerus in place. The clavicle is vestigial or absent in carnivores and ungulates but prominent in bats and primates, where it holds the shoulders out and provides a strong support for flying and tree climbing. Where scapula, clavicle, and coracoid meet there is a smooth cavity, the **glenoid fossa,** against which the head of the humerus moves.

In the **pelvic girdle** each tripod consists of the **ilium,** which can be felt just below the beltline in a man, the **ischium** in the buttocks, and the **pubis** at the base of the abdomen. Where these three bones come together they make a deep cup, the **acetabulum,** into which the head of the femur fits like a ball into its socket. The units of the pelvic girdle are more or less rigidly fused together and to the sacrum. The whales and other cetaceans are, of course, exceptions. It is often asked why the pelvic girdle of mammals through which the young must be born should be fused in such a rigid manner. The

Fig. 25–3. Mammalian limb girdles. Above: pectoral girdle. Below: pelvic girdle. (Only one of the two tripods that make up each girdle is shown.) Glenoid cavity of shoulder corresponds to acetabulum of pelvic girdle, the place of attachment of the limb. The coracoid, so prominent in birds, is a mere extension of the scapula. In the cat and many mammals the clavicle is greatly reduced. The pelvic bones are closer to the reptilian type than are the pectoral.

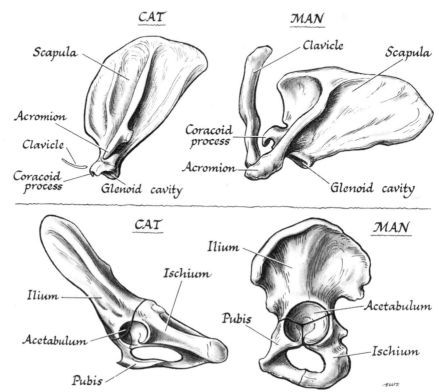

pectoral girdle, in marked contrast, is very loosely connected with the axial skeleton via several muscles and ligaments. It seems probable that the very different construction of the two limb girdles and their contrasting connection with the backbone is the result of adaptation for running and jumping. The rigid pelvis transmits the main push of the hind legs to the backbone and thus to the whole skeletal frame simultaneously. However, after making a leap, mammals from horses to rabbits land on their front legs. The flexible muscles of the pectoral girdle can help absorb the shock of landing.

The skeletons of front legs (or wings or arms) and hind legs are homologous bone for bone throughout the entire range of mammalian adaptations. In the forelimb are a single **humerus,** then an **ulna** and **radius** side by side, with the ulna making a hinge joint at the elbow, a set of **carpals** in the wrist, five **metacarpals,** at least in the embryo, and five **digits,** at least in the embryo. In the hind limb are a single **femur,** a **tibia** and slim **fibula** side by side in the shank, a set of **tarsals** in the ankle, and the five **metatarsals** and five **digits,** at least in the embryo. Compare the arm of a man, the flipper of a seal, the wing of a bat, and the column of an elephant (Fig. 1–3).

Units of the skeleton are held together by **ligaments,** bands of tough connective tissue composed of a protein, largely collagen. Similar bands that attach muscles to bones or to each other are called **tendons.**

Structure and Growth of Bones. On the level of tissues and cells, bones are formed of **Haversian systems.** Each "system" consists of a small canal, carrying blood vessels and nerves, surrounded by concentric layers of bone separated by bone-forming cells lying in microscopic cavities, **lacunae,** and interconnected by minute passageways, **canaliculi.**

The long bones of the limbs are composed of the shaft or **diaphysis,** at each end of which there is a disk of bone, the **epiphysis.** Between the shaft and the epiphysis is a growth disk or **epiphyseal line.** Two long bones move against each other in a joint at the distal surface of the epiphysis. Thus the function of the epiphysis is to protect the growing zone between it and the shaft where the bone grows in length. Sur-

Fig. 25–4. Cross section of bone, greatly magnified. The Haversian canals, centers of concentric rings of bone, are conduits for blood vessels and nerves. The bone-secreting cells lie between the concentric plates. (*After Kimber and Gray,* Anatomy and Physiology, *1942, The Macmillan Company*)

rounding the bone is a special membrane, the **periosteum.** The inner layer of the periosteum forms new bone, thus adding to the diameter of the shaft. At the same time within the marrow cavity are special cells which eat away the bone, thus enlarging the cavity.

The growth of bones is controlled by many factors going back ultimately to the genetic make-up. There is a regular order in which the epiphyses of the various human bones appear and then later fuse with the shaft. X-ray photographs of the bones of the hand and wrist give an excellent indication of physiological age, as contrasted with chronological age.

The formation of bone is profoundly influenced by vitamin D, by the pituitary, thyroid, and parathyroid glands, and by mechanical forces. Vitamin D, a sterol related structurally to the sex hormones and other biologically active substances, appears to facilitate the action of alkaline phosphatase. This enzyme is concerned with the absorption of calcium and phosphorus from the gut and their reabsorption in the kidney. It is also active in bone, where it breaks organic phosphorus compounds into the inorganic phosphates which help to form bone.

Circus giants and Tom Thumb dwarfs have been known for centuries, but not until about 1900 did anyone know what caused such skeletal anomalies. Since then an enormous amount of work has proved that excessive functioning of the anterior lobe of the pituitary,

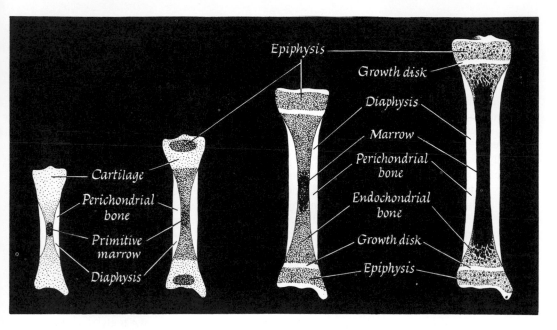

Fig. 25–5. Four stages in the growth of a long bone. Note the diaphysis or shaft and epiphysis or head, with growth disk or epiphyseal line between them.

if it occurs before the fusion of the epiphyses to the shafts of the long bones, results in **gigantism.** If it occurs after epiphyseal fusion, it results in **acromegaly,** a condition in which the bones of hands, feet, and face become greatly enlarged. Underfunction of the anterior pituitary results in **dwarfism.**

Surgical removal of the pituitary in dogs and rats produces dwarf animals. A purified extract of the anterior pituitary gland, containing a growth, i.e., **somatotropic,** hormone (STH), when injected into young rats will produce gigantism. Injected into older dogs it produces a form of acromegaly. This hormone is produced by the acidophil cells, those easily stained with acid dyes like eosin. Its mode of action is extremely uncertain.

Hypothyroidism produces an extremely feeble-minded type of dwarf, the **cretin,** with small and malformed bones. This condition can be greatly alleviated by feeding thyroid extract.

The parathyroid glands, small rounded structures lying against or even imbedded in the thyroid, control the calcium level in the blood and strongly influence bone formation. Many puzzles still exist about the action of these glands. It is certain, however, that both tumorous overgrowth of the parathyroids and injections of parathyroid extracts produce a high level of

Fig. 25–6. Age of appearance and of ultimate fusion of epiphyses to shafts of long bones. *f.m.,* fetal months; *B,* birth; *m,* months after birth; *y,* years.

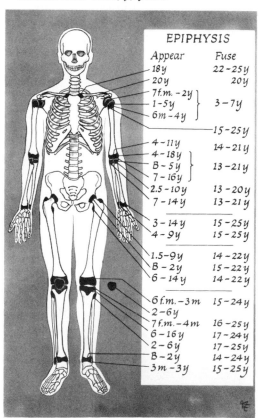

EPIPHYSIS	
Appear	Fuse
18y	22–25y
20y	20y
7f.m.–2y }	
1–5y	3–7y
6m–4y	
	15–25y
4–11y	14–21y
4–18y	
B–5y }	13–21y
7–16y	
2.5–10y	13–20y
7–14y	13–21y
3–14y	15–25y
4–9y	15–25y
1.5–9y	14–22y
B–2y	15–22y
6–14y	14–22y
6f.m.–3m	15–24y
2–6y	
7f.m.–4m	16–25y
6–16y	17–24y
2–6y	17–25y
B–2y	14–24y
3m–3y	15–25y

calcium and phosphorus in the blood and a progressive weakening and consequent bending and deformation of the bones. At the same time, when the bones are becoming decalcified, abnormal deposits of bony material form in kidneys, liver, heart, stomach wall, and other structures.

Equally puzzling and remarkable is the way bones respond to mechanical pressures. Within the ends of long bones, such as the femur, the place of the marrow cavity is taken by "spongy" bone. The major lines of this interior girder-work run along and parallel to the chief lines of mechanical stress. If such a bone is broken and then is improperly reset, the spongy bone is reoriented in accordance with the new line of stress.

THE MUSCULAR SYSTEM

Kinds of Muscles. The basic plan of the muscular system of mammals, like that of amphibians, reptiles, and birds, is merely a modification of the plan already seen in the shark (page 439). There are the same four major divisions: (1) the **axial** muscles, largely those of the body itself; (2) the **limb** muscles, which are derived from the axial muscles; (3) the **gill arch** muscles of face and throat; and (4) the **visceral** muscles,

chiefly those of the digestive tract, uterus, urinary bladder, and arteries.

It will be recalled that muscles are usually organized in **antagonistic pairs:** flexors which bend a leg, *vs.* extensors which straighten it; sphincters which encircle an opening such as the pupil of the eye and close it when they contract, *vs.* dilators which open it. Antagonistic muscle pairs occur from coelenterates to man. The explanation for antagonistic pairs is clear—muscles can pull but cannot push.

Muscles can often be divided into **extrinsic** muscles which move a leg, or other structure, with respect to the body as a whole, and **intrinsic** muscles which move parts of, say, a leg with respect to the leg itself. This distinction can be defined in terms of origin and insertion. The **origin** of a muscle is the point of attachment nearest the midline of the body; **insertion** is the attachment farthest from the midline. An extrinsic muscle of the eye, for example, is one with its origin on the skull and its insertion on the eyeball. These extrinsic ocular muscles move the eyeball as a whole. An intrinsic muscle of the arm is one which has both origin and insertion on the arm. The muscles of the forearm fall into this category.

In mammals the superficial muscles covering most of the chest, shoulders, and back are ex-

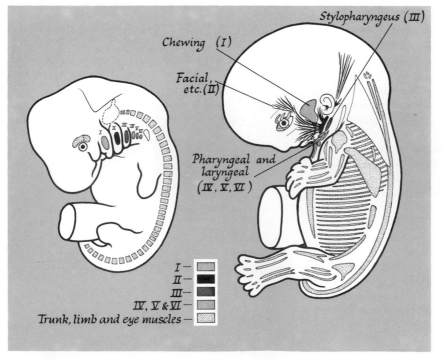

Fig. 25–7. Muscles of gill arches I-VI in man—their origin and fate as muscles of jaw, face, pharynx, and larynx—and the axial muscles of trunk, limbs, and eyes. (*After Hamilton, Boyd, and Mossman,* Human Embryology, *Williams & Wilkins,* © *W. Heffer & Sons, Ltd.*)

trinsic limb muscles which are enormously larger than in fishes. The intrinsic muscles of the legs have also undergone a vast increase in size during the course of evolution.

The deeper-lying axial muscles of the trunk form a set of antagonists. The epaxial muscles along the back straighten the spine and pull the neck and head dorsally, i.e., upwards, while the hypaxial muscles on abdomen and chest flex the body and pull the head ventrally.

In fishes the axial trunk muscles which power swimming are major; the muscles of the paired limbs (fins) are very minor. In terrestrial mammals, where the limbs are responsible for locomotion, the reverse holds true. The limb muscles, both extrinsic and intrinsic, have become as large or larger than all the trunk muscles taken together.

Histologically, i.e., as seen under a light microscope, muscles are of two types, striated and smooth. The striations of **striated muscle** are very fine and incredibly regular cross markings at right angles to the direction of contraction. They can be seen in living animals—in *Daphnia,* the crustacean water flea, for example—but even ground beef shows them. Until recently the meaning of the striations was completely unknown. Striated muscles are often called **skeletal muscles** because they are usually attached to bones, or **voluntary muscles** because for the most part they are under the control of the will. A light microscope photo of striated muscle is shown in the next column.

Smooth muscles lack fine cross striations. Smooth muscles are also called **visceral muscles** because they characterize the stomach, uterus, and other viscera, or **involuntary muscles** because they cannot be directly controlled by the will.

Heart or **cardiac muscle** is a special case. Though striated, cardiac muscle is involuntary and its fibers interbranch in a way not seen in other striated muscles.

The relationships of muscle types is shown in the following chart:

Voluntary	Skeletal		
		Striated	
	Cardiac		
Involuntary	{		
	Visceral	Smooth	

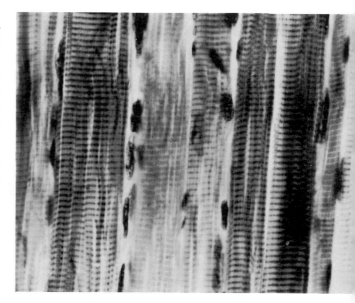

Fig. 25–8. Light microscope photo of striated muscle. *(Ward's Natural Science Establishment)*

Muscle Contraction. How does a muscle contract? Since the days of the ancient Greek philosopher-scientists men have thought about form and function but until very recently indeed there has been an impassable gulf between the anatomist who studied form and the physiologist who investigated function. The anatomist knew about the arrangement of extensors and flexors. The physiologist knew about such things as the speed of contraction and relaxation, the characteristics of fatigue, and even many of the chemical prerequisites and end products of muscle action. But no one knew what goes on inside the muscle itself. A muscle was what a physicist would call a "black box," impenetrable, perhaps unknowable. The electron microscope has given us a look inside that "black box," but to understand what can be seen it is necessary to know something about the "classical" knowledge of muscular contraction which is as valid as ever and will remain permanently true.

Modern knowledge about how muscles work began with Leonardo da Vinci (1452–1519), the Renaissance artist and inventor, and Andreas Vesalius (1514–1564), who revolutionized the science of anatomy by dissecting the

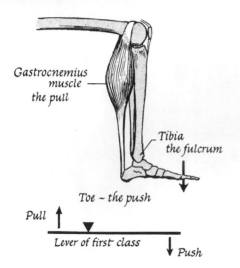

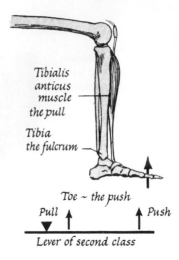

Gastrocnemius muscle the pull

Tibia the fulcrum

Toe ~ the push

Pull

Lever of first class

Push

Tibialis anticus muscle the pull

Tibia the fulcrum

Toe ~ the push

Pull

Push

Lever of second class

Fig. 25–9. Muscles in the leg of a frog (left) and a man (right) pull bones as levers.

human body. These men and their immediate successors worked on the level of gross anatomy and came to realize that muscles pull bones around like so many ropes and levers.

The most important early work after Vesalius was that of Luigi Galvani (1737–1798), professor of anatomy at Bologna and a contemporary of Benjamin Franklin, Priestley, Lavoisier, and George Washington. One day when Galvani and an assistant were experimenting with the then newly invented electric machines of the type now used in elementary courses in physics to demonstrate static electricity, they marveled to see the legs of a frog which they had dissected for another purpose contract violently when the spark was discharged. It seems a trivial observation and, as a matter of fact, had been noticed by several men before Galvani. But Galvani followed up this chance observation by a long series of dramatic if rather muddled experiments and theories. He soon found that not only the discharge of his electric machine would produce a contraction but also a mere touch on the frog's nerves or muscles with two different metals such as silver and copper, in such a way as to make an arc.

Galvani supposed that the metals released animal electricity that had been stored in the nerves and muscles. Volta, a physicist at Pavia, vigorously denied this. Both were right in part. Muscles do produce electrical potentials. This is easy to show by touching a muscle with copper wires connected to a galvanometer. The galvanometer must be sensitive, but no amplifier is necessary. A cut surface is negative by about 0.07 volt to an uninjured one.

With a pair of dry cell batteries, it can be shown that either a nerve or a muscle can be stimulated by an electric shock.

On the other hand, Volta was able to show that a super-sandwich made of an alternating series of zinc and copper plates, each separated by paper soaked in salt water, would produce a potent electric force. This was the first source of a continuous electric current, the first battery—born of a chance observation on frogs' legs in the closing years of the 18th century!

The physiologists of the 19th century gave us the **kymograph** (*kyma,* wave, + *graph,* to

Fig. 25–10. A modern kymograph: upper end of muscle is attached to a rigid rod, lower end to a lever which records contractions on a revolving drum. The lower lever is attached to a magnet (*M*) for timing the stimulus. *A* and *B* represent different positions of the stimulating electrode.

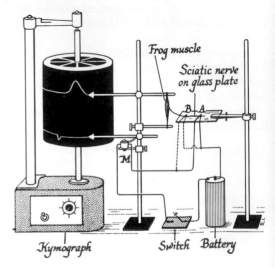

Frog muscle

Sciatic nerve on glass plate

B A

M

Kymograph   Switch   Battery

write), the instrument used to investigate the characteristics of contraction and relaxation. The muscle commonly studied, because of its convenience, is the gastrocnemius of a frog. This is the big muscle in the calf of the leg. One end of the muscle is fixed to a rigid rod, the other end (in the case of the gastrocnemius it is the tendon of Achilles just above the heel) is fastened to a lever which writes on the revolving drum of the kymograph. Whenever the muscle contracts the lever is raised and a corresponding wave is written on the drum. The nerve which innervates the muscle is carefully removed with the muscle so that its stimulation, as by an electric shock, will result in a muscle response.

Using kymographs and modern electronic timing gear it can be shown that for a single stimulus a muscle contraction consists of three parts, a latent period of about 0.5 millisecond (1 millisecond = 0.001 second), a period of contraction lasting from 10 to 100 milliseconds, and, thirdly, a period of relaxation lasting about twice as long. In normal contractions in an intact animal there is a whole volley of impulses from the nerve to the muscle so that contraction may be prolonged.

There is also an electrical change in the muscle known as the **action potential** which accompanies contraction. It is the changing action potentials of heart muscle which are recorded on the physician's electrocardiograph.

The Chemistry of Contraction. It has long been known that a muscle can contract in the absence of oxygen but that under such anaerobic conditions the **glycogen,** which represents stored energy in the muscle, disappears and **lactic acid** accumulates. After a relatively short time the muscle becomes fatigued, or at least will no longer respond to further stimulation. If **oxygen** is now supplied, the lactic acid disappears and the muscle regains its ability to contract. Under aerobic conditions lactic acid does not accumulate, though the glycogen is broken down into glucose and, as we now know, the glucose passes down the Embden-Meyerhof glycolytic pathway and is finally completely oxidized in the Krebs system of the mitochondria. It is hardly surprising that muscles are rich in mitochondria. They require energy in abundance.

When muscle contractions take place faster than the mitochondrial enzymes can provide energy as ATP packets, pyruvic acid accumulates at the end of the glycolytic pathway faster than the Krebs cycle can take it up. This excess pyruvic acid is promptly converted into lactic acid.

$$CH_3-\overset{\overset{\text{O}}{\|}}{C}-COOH \underset{\substack{\text{lactate} \\ \text{dehydrogenase}}}{\overset{DPNH_2 \rightarrow DPN}{\rightleftharpoons}} CH_3-\overset{\overset{\text{OH}}{|}}{\underset{H}{C}}-COOH$$

pyruvic acid   lactic acid

Fig. 25-11. Electron micrograph of heart muscle from a rat. Note the striations in the fibrils and the numerous mitochondria aligned in long rows. (*From Freeman,* Cellular Fine Structure, *Blakiston Div., McGraw-Hill Book Co., 1964)*

The lactic acid is later reconverted into pyruvic acid or other compounds in either the muscle itself or the liver, and oxidized in the mitochondrial Krebs cycle when oxygen becomes available. This is the chemical basis for being out of breath after violent exercise. One is "repaying" an **"oxygen debt"** as the Krebs cycle catches up with the material supplied to it by glycolysis.

That ATP and the numerous mitochondria play an important role in contraction is certain. But it has long been known that in addition to adenosine triphosphate there is another high-energy phosphate compound in muscles, **phosphocreatine** in the vertebrates and **phosphoarginine** in most invertebrates. These compounds are formed from creatine or arginine at the expense of ATP which is degraded to the less energy-rich ADP (adenosine diphosphate). It is possible that the energy-rich creatine is the compound directly involved with the mechanics of contraction. No one yet knows.

The first breakthrough into the "black box" of muscular contraction was achieved by the Hungarian-American Nobel prize winner, A. Szent-Györgyi. Two kinds of protein can be extracted from striated muscle, **actin** and **myosin.** When the two are combined and then squirted out of a fine pipette into very dilute KCl solution, the combined acto-myosin will contract when ATP is added as an energy source. Neither actin nor myosin alone will contract, no matter how much ATP is added; moreover, ATP is degraded to ADP in the process. These experiments strongly suggest that contraction is due to some kind of relationship between the two proteins.

The second breakthrough came from the electron microscope analysis of H. E. Huxley. Look again at the photo of the striated muscle. It will be seen that dark bands alternate with lighter ones and that each dark band is bisected by a narrow light one, and each lighter band by a very narrow dark line. Terminology has varied a bit but the wide dark bands are usually called **A bands,** A standing for anistropic, meaning that the molecules here are so completely oriented that they transmit polarized light only in a particular plane. The A bands can be shown by extraction techniques to be mostly myosin. The lighter stripe across the A band is called an **H band.** The large light bands

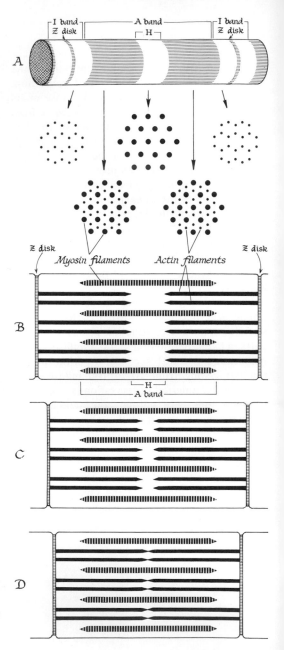

Fig. 25–12. Diagram of muscle structure and the sliding fiber theory of contraction. *A,* myofibril, and various cross sections. *B,* longitudinal section. *C* and *D,* contraction. Note that a section through the I band shows only thin actin fibers, a section near the center of the A band shows only thick myosin fibers, while a section intermediate shows both. During contraction the actin fibers move between the myosin fibers. *(After H. E. Huxley)*

are usually known as **I bands**, I for isotropic. The very dark narrow lines bisecting the I bands are terminal or **Z lines.** The I bands turn out to be mostly actin. A single unit from Z line to Z line is called a **sarcomere.**

With an electron microscope H. E. Huxley was able to show—and many others have since confirmed and extended his work—that the narrower actin fibers are attached to the Z lines at one end of each fiber and extend out to and in between the thicker myosin fibers. It is as though the bristles of two brushes were pushed in between each other. Cross sections viewed with an electron microscope show that when a muscle contracts, the actin fibers move in between the myosin fibers and thus shorten the sarcomere much as an extension ladder shortens when the two parts slide together. Cross sections through the I bands near the Z lines at the ends of sarcomeres show only thin actin filaments. Sections through the H stripe in the center of the A band show only heavier myosin filaments. Sections through the portion of the A bands adjacent to the I bands show both types of filaments. If this theory is correct, the A bands should not become narrower during contraction but the I bands should. They do.

What pulls the actin and myosin filaments along each other? No one can be certain but myosin filaments show regularly spaced, fingerlike protrusions which reach out and touch the actin filaments. Calcium ions and ATP are known to be required for contraction. Phosphocreatine can be presumed to play an essential role. The supply of ATP is provided in large part from the mitochondria which are found between the myofibrils. A fine tubular network or reticulum penetrates muscles in

Fig. 25–13. Electron microscope photo of a cross section through a flight muscle of an aphid—part of the evidence for the sliding fiber theory. Note that each heavy myosin fiber is surrounded by six thin actin fibers. Through which band of the muscle was this section cut? *(Kindness of David S. Smith)*

which energy-bearing compounds and waste products can be exchanged. Muscles contain small amounts of a third protein, **tropomyosin.** This may be in the Z bands at the ends of the sarcomeres or it may be in the fingerlike extensions of the myosin. But until much more is known about how the actin and myosin pull themselves together, the gap, as old as Aristotle, between form and function will not have been completely bridged.

Review and References

REVIEW TOPICS

1. Compare axial or appendicular skeleton in a shark and a mammal.

2. Discuss four functions of the mammalian skeletal system. Are there additional functions?

3. What is the role of each of the following in bone growth: periosteum, epiphyseal line, pituitary and parathyroid glands, mechanical stress, age?

4. Contrast the muscular system of a fish, a man, and a whale.

5. Distinguish smooth, cardiac, and striated muscle.

6. Define in regard to muscles: origin, insertion, tendon, sarcomere, Z line, A band, kymograph, action potential, Achilles tendon, extrinsic.

7. What structures in mammals are developed from gill arches?

8. What was the contribution to the knowledge of the skeletal and muscular systems of: Vesalius, da Vinci, Galvani, Volta, A. Szent-Györgyi, H. E. Huxley?

USEFUL REFERENCES

Ballard, W. W., *Comparative Anatomy and Embryology,* New York, The Ronald Press Company, 1964.

Bourne, G. H., ed. *Structure and Function of Muscle,* New York, Academic Press, 1960.

Davison, A., 5th ed. by F. A. Stromsten, *Mammalian Anatomy with Special Reference to the Cat,* Philadelphia, P. Blakiston's Son & Co., 1931.

Gray, H., *Anatomy of the Human Body,* 25th ed., Philadelphia, Lea & Febiger, 1959.

Miller, M. E., G. C. Christensen, and H. E. Evans, *Anatomy of the Dog,* Philadelphia, W. B. Saunders Co., 1964.

Chapter 26

Vascular System
and Oxygen Transport

An understanding of the vascular system is a prerequisite for a rational understanding of almost any other aspect of vertebrate physiology. Respiration, nutrition, excretion, even the hormones, cannot be understood without knowing how the bloodstream courses through the body. In addition, there are many practical uses of a knowledge of the vascular system— in medicine, space travel, deep-sea diving, agriculture, and other areas.

William Harvey and Circulation. The principle of circulation of the blood was first published in 1628 by William Harvey in his book, *Of the Motion of the Heart and Blood in Animals.* Until then it was standard to teach that the blood surges back and forth in the veins, and that the arteries contain air. Harvey's book is a major landmark in the history of the biological sciences because it made possible a rational physiology. Like Darwin, Harvey combined the discoveries and ideas of his predecessors with original observations of his own into a new synthesis.

There were three basic contributors to Harvey's synthesis. The first was Vesalius (1514–1564) who had published in 1543 the first accurate account of human anatomy and thereby showed that the arteries to any organ

and the veins from it were always of comparable magnitude. Second was Fabricius, one of Harvey's own teachers in the anatomical theatre in Padua, who demonstrated the presence of flaplike valves along the course of the larger veins that are so placed as to hinder the flow of blood away from the heart. Possibly the most crucial contribution of all was the argument of Michael Servetus that there is a pulmonary circulation in which blood passes from the heart to the lungs via the pulmonary arteries and returns to the heart via the pulmonary veins. Servetus had been burned at the stake in 1553 for his political and religious beliefs, and all his books consigned to the flames. But it is difficult to burn all the copies of a book. Matheus Columbus (a professor of anatomy and no relative of Christopher) stole the idea of Servetus word for word but, reprehensible as this was, it nevertheless made the concept of a pulmonary circulation available to Harvey.

Harvey marshalled his argument along three main lines. The first was anatomical. He noted the correspondence in size between the arteries and veins of any organ. That is not proof, but does constitute a necessary condition for a circulation. He clearly showed that the valves in the veins completely prevented blood from flowing in any direction except toward the

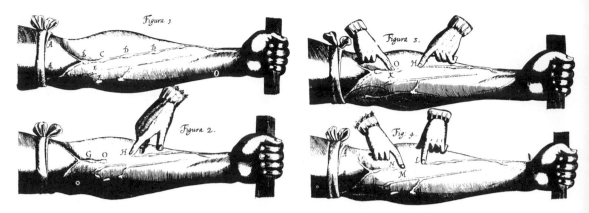

Fig. 26 – 1. William Harvey's classic experiment to demonstrate the action of the valves in the veins at *B, C, D, G, H,* and *O* in blocking the back-flow of blood from the elbow toward the hand.

heart. He also showed that the valves at the place where the arteries leave the heart permit blood to leave but not to enter the heart. As seen in Harvey's own figure (Fig. 26 – 1), if the veins in the forearm be made to stand out by applying a tourniquet above the elbow, it can be demonstrated by squeezing blood along the vein with a finger, that blood will flow in a direction toward the heart but not in the opposite direction.

Harvey's second line of reasoning was quantitative. He counted the number of times the heart of a dog beat per minute; then he sacrificed the animal and measured both the amount of blood the heart forces into the arteries with each beat (by measuring ventricular capacity) and the total volume of blood in the animal. By simple arithmetic he then showed that in a dog or a sheep the heart pumps out many times the total volume every hour. In man, the heart pumps out three to five liters per minute. In other words, the volume of blood passing through the heart every minute is as great as the total volume of blood in the body. Where can all this blood pumped by the heart come from or go to, if it does not travel in a sort of "circular motion"?

Lastly, Harvey backed up these arguments by a wide array of experiments on dogs, snakes, snails, even insects. If the veins entering the heart are tied off, the heart becomes empty of blood. If the arteries leaving it are tied, the heart remains permanently gorged.

ANATOMY

The Blood Vessels. In its embryology the vascular system of mammals reveals their fishy ancestry. Six pairs of aortic arches appear between more or less developed gill slits. The first two pairs of aortic arches degenerate. The third pair becomes the **internal carotid arteries.**

Fig. 26 – 2. Heart and aortic arches of a mammal. The dotted lines show the condition in the embryo. Animal is lying on its back. The heart and the external carotids are ventral to the intestine and pharynx. The dorsal aorta and internal carotids are dorsal to the intestine and to the pharynx with its gill slits.

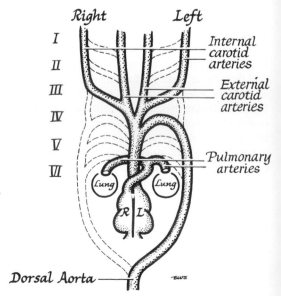

The ventral aorta is double in this region and becomes the **common carotids** leading up the neck from the fourth aortic arch. The fourth arch persists only on the left side and develops into the main or **dorsal aorta** carrying oxygenated blood down the back and thence to all parts of the body, except, of course, the head, neck, and lungs. The fifth pair of arches degenerate. From the sixth pair the **pulmonary arteries** to the lungs are developed.

To make blood vessels easier to dissect, anatomists have injected them with a wide variety of materials—mercury, paint, colored flour paste. The present technic, which has proved to be a very effective one, is injection with a colored, liquid latex which solidifies as rubber after injection.

It is important to remember that it is only in the thin-walled capillaries that the blood carries on its functions. There, oxygen and carbon dioxide are exchanged with the tissues, or, more precisely, with the lymph surrounding the tissues. It is in the capillaries that the exchanges of heat, food, wastes, water, hormones, and other substances occur.

In the adult mammal, deoxygenated blood from capillaries all over the body is returned through the veins to the right atrium (auricle) of the heart. It then passes into the right ventricle which pumps it into the lungs. As in all other vertebrates there is an hepatic portal vein which carries blood from the intestine to the liver. In the liver the digested and absorbed food is processed before being passed on through the hepatic vein to the inferior vena cava and so passed on to the heart for general distribution.

The Heart. The key structure in the vascular system is that muscular pump, the heart. Heart muscle is striated muscle with a difference. Anatomically the fibers form an interconnected network, instead of being straight as in ordinary striated muscle. Physiologically, cardiac muscle exhibits four important characteristics:

1. Cardiac muscle is inherently rhythmic. Isolated bits of heart muscle grown *in vitro* contract rhythmically. The heart itself continues to beat long after all nerves to it are severed.

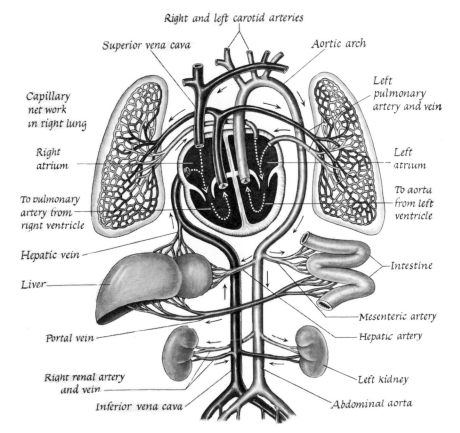

Fig. 26–3. Mammalian circulation. Note flap valves between the atria (auricles) and ventricles. The two flaps between the left atrium and left ventricle form the mitral valve, so called because it resembles a bishop's mitre. The three flaps between the right chambers of the heart (only two are shown) constitute the tricuspid valve. Note also the small semilunar valves at the openings from the ventricles into the great arteries.

Right and left carotid arteries

Superior vena cava

Aortic arch

Left pulmonary artery and vein

Capillary net work in right lung

Right atrium

Left atrium

To pulmonary artery from right ventricle

To aorta from left ventricle

Hepatic vein

Intestine

Liver

Mesenteric artery

Hepatic artery

Portal vein

Right renal artery and vein

Left kidney

Inferior vena cava

Abdominal aorta

2. After each contraction heart muscle has an extremely long refractory period during which it cannot be stimulated to contract. This insures that **diastole** (dilatation) and filling of the heart will occur. It is impossible to throw the heart into tetanus, or cramp, which happens easily to skeletal muscle.

3. The heart automatically adjusts the strength of its contraction to the amount of work it has to do. If it is filled with a large volume of blood, as in violent exercise, its walls are stretched and the contractions become correspondingly more powerful. This is Starling's "law of the heart."

4. To beat rhythmically heart muscle requires a proper salt balance. Sodium, potassium, and calcium must all be present in the fluid surrounding the organ. The ratio of these necessary ions is closely similar to that in sea water. The molecular mechanisms of the effects of salts are still unclear, but in general, high concentrations of calcium or sodium stop hearts in **systole** (contraction), high concentrations of potassium stop vertebrate hearts in

diastole. These discoveries were originally made on the frog heart by Sidney Ringer and led directly to all the physiological salt solutions now in use for intravenous administration and many other procedures.

The rate of the adult heart beat, however, is under nervous control. The characteristics of such control were first studied extensively by Carlson of Chicago on the heart of *Limulus,* the horseshoe "crab," in which the nerves of the heart can be very clearly dissected away from the heart itself. In mammals, the heart beat can be completely, though temporarily, inhibited by stimulation of the vagus nerves from the brain. This was first discovered by Lower in London who, back in 1669, stopped the heart beat by tying off the vagus nerves. He interpreted his results according to the theory then accepted that nerves induce contraction by transporting some kind of fluid to the muscles. Over a century and a half later Volkmann rediscovered vagus inhibition, and five years later, in 1845, the Weber brothers created "a tremendous sensation" at an international physiological con-

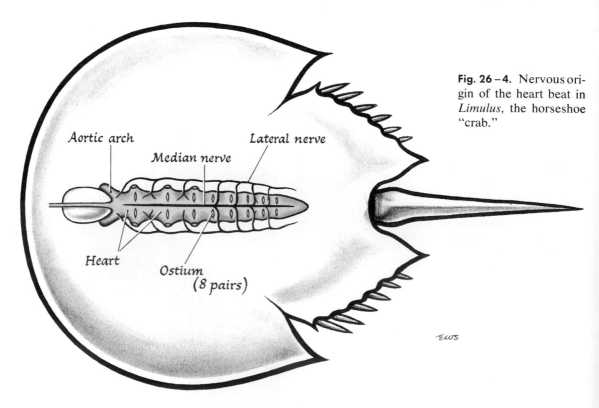

Fig. 26–4. Nervous origin of the heart beat in *Limulus,* the horseshoe "crab."

Aortic arch

Median nerve

Lateral nerve

Heart

Ostium (8 pairs)

gress in Naples with their demonstration of a
nerve, the vagus, which produced inhibition of
the heart when stimulated.

For decades no one knew how the vagus
caused inhibition. Then at 3 A.M. one spring
morning in 1921 Otto Loewi of the University
of Graz in Austria awoke with an idea, dressed,
and went to his laboratory at once. "At 5
o'clock," he writes, "the chemical transmission
[of the vagus impulse] was conclusively
proven." What Loewi did was to excise the
hearts from two frogs while leaving their nerves
intact. The first heart was washed with physiological salt solution which was allowed to pass
immediately into the second heart. When the
first heart was inhibited by vagal stimulation,
the second heart also stopped beating as soon
as the solution from the first heart reached it.
The inhibitory substance on analysis turned out
to be **acetylcholine,** a very important and widespread substance in the nervous system of
mammals as well as frogs.

The heart also receives accelerator nerves
from the sympathetic system. These nerves are
important in the Bainbridge reflex, which
speeds up the rate of beat when more blood
enters the heart. Stretch receptors in the walls
of the great veins just as they enter the heart
send impulses up to the medulla, whence impulses pass back down the spinal cord and ultimately out the accelerator nerves. This reflex
works with Starling's "law of the heart" to ad-
just it to greater demands. Note that this is a
self-adjusting, feedback system.

Within the heart itself there is a pacemaker,
the **sino-atrial** or **S.-A. node.** This is a small
mass of tissue that initiates the beat. It is located in the wall of the right atrium (auricle)
and develops from the embryonic sinus venosus. A second node, the **atrio-ventricular** or
A.V. node, is located between the walls of the
atria close to the ventricles. It is stimulated by
the contraction initiated by the S.A. node and
transmits an impulse throughout the walls of
the ventricles via the pseudomuscular tissue
called the **bundle of His.** (See Fig. 26–6.)

Like all muscles, the heart produces electrical changes on contraction. The voltages are
small, of the magnitude of only a few millivolts,
but strong enough to be picked up by electrodes
and magnified into a meaningful wave by an

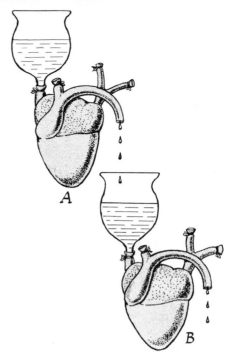

Fig. 26–5. Loewi's classic experiment to
prove the chemical mediation of vagus inhibition of the heart. When heart *A* was inhibited by vagus stimulation, heart *B* was then
also inhibited, though its only connection
with *A* is by saline which has passed through
A. *(Redrawn from Turner, General Endocrinology, W. B. Saunders, after R. W.
Gerard)*

oscillograph. Such a record is known as an
electrocardiogram. The waves are designated
PQRST. The P wave corresponds to the contraction of the atria or auricles; the QRS complex, to the contraction of the ventricles. The
T wave corresponds to the relaxation of the
ventricles. The interpretation of these waves in
various heart ailments is a science in itself.

The Lymphatics. The fluid directly bathing
the cells is not whole blood, which is confined
in capillaries, but **lymph.** The composition of
lymph is essentially that of the blood minus the
red and the white cells. The lymph vessels resemble capillaries and veins, possessing valves
which permit lymph to flow only toward the
heart. The flow is one way and empties into the
great veins to the right side of the heart in the
chest. Lymph is continually replenished by
seepage from the capillaries. In amphibians
feeble lymph hearts push lymph toward the

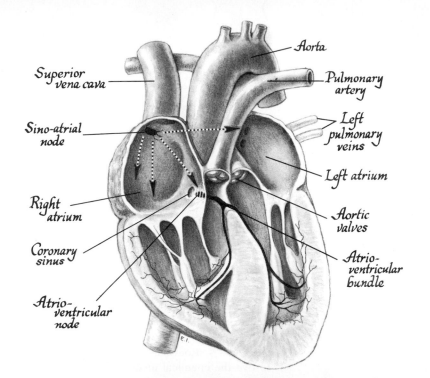

Superior
vena cava

Sino-atrial
node

Right
atrium

Coronary
sinus

Atrio-
ventricular
node

Aorta

Pulmonary
artery

Left
pulmonary
veins

Left atrium

Aortic
valves

Atrio-
ventricular
bundle

Fig. 26–6. Longisection through a mammalian heart showing the pacemaker or sino-atrial node on the wall of the right atrium, and the atrio-ventricular bundle which carries the impulse for contraction from the atrium out over the ventricles.

heart, but in mammals the motion of lymph is due entirely to other factors, chiefly the squeezing of the vessels in the normal course of the animal's motions plus valves which permit flow in one direction only.

Where the legs join the body, in the armpits and neck, and at several other sites, the lymph passes through glandular **lymph nodes** or glands. The lymph nodes are the site of production, during adult life, of **lymphocytes,** the white blood cells which produce antibodies against foreign proteins, invading bacteria, etc. Lymph nodes also "filter" foreign material out of the lymph. The lymphatic vessels coming from the intestine unite to form a major lymph vessel called the **thoracic duct** which empties into a vein just before it enters the heart. The thoracic duct carries digested lipids.

THE BLOOD AND ITS PROPERTIES

Composition. The blood consists of cells and a fluid, the plasma. Red cells, or **erythrocytes,** in mammals lack nuclei, except during their developmental stages which occur chiefly within the marrow of the long bones and sternum. The white cells are the **leucocytes.** About 75 per cent have a granular cytoplasm and a very irregular, or polymorphic, nucleus. These are the polymorphonuclear leucocytes, popularly called "polymorphs." About 70 per cent of all leucocytes are polymorph neutrophils, so-called because their cytoplasm stains in most types of dyes. Polymorph acidophils (or eosinophils), which stain with acid dyes, constitute about 4 per cent and the polymorph basophils about 1 per cent or less. The polymorphs ingest bacteria and cell debris. The remaining 25 or so per cent of the leucocytes are mostly either small lymphocytes or large monocytes. The lymphocytes manufacture antibodies. The absolute and relative abundance of various leucocytes is a useful diagnostic tool in medicine.

The first and primary function of the blood and lymph is to provide the cells of the body with a private ocean of at least approximately the same osmotic and acid-base properties as the prehistoric seas from which the ancestors of the vertebrates arose. Many additional functions exist: (2) to carry oxygen from lungs or gills to the body and carry carbon dioxide back; (3) to distribute digested food to all body cells and carry wastes to the kidneys and lungs; (4) to distribute heat properly; and (5) to carry hormones, antibodies, and various other substances.

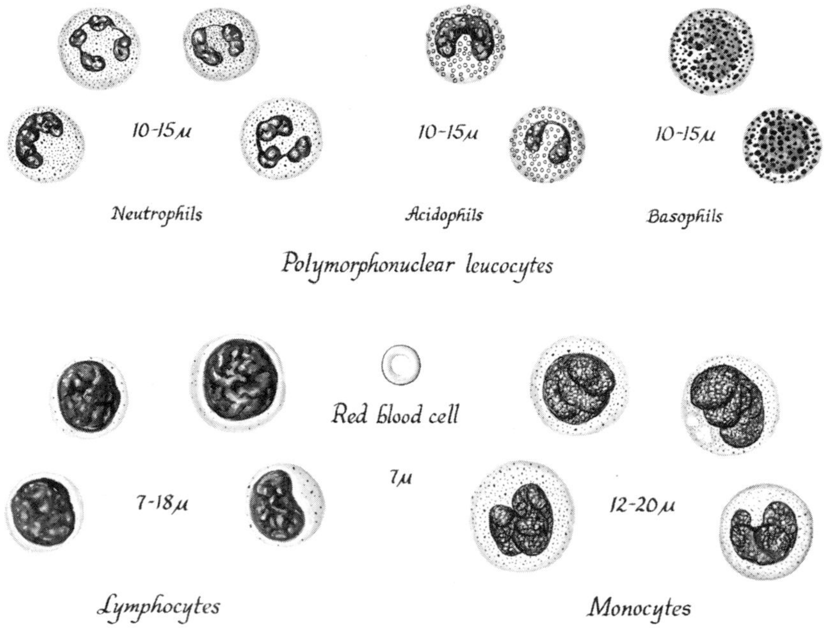

Fig. 26–7. Stained leucocytes or white blood cells of the three major types: polmorphonuclear leucocytes, lymphocytes, and monocytes. Note that there are three kinds of polymorphs — neutrophils, acidophils, and basophils. The red blood cell is included for scale.

10-15μ

Neutrophils

10-15μ

Acidophils

10-15μ

Basophils

Polymorphonuclear leucocytes

Red blood cell

7μ

7-18μ

12-20μ

Lymphocytes

Monocytes

The fluid part of whole blood is a straw-colored liquid called **plasma.** At least 90 per cent of the plasma is water, about 6 per cent protein and amino acids. The remainder is glucose and other carbohydrates, lipids, hormones, urea, salts (chiefly NaCl, KCl, and $CaCl_2$), bicarbonates, and other constituents. The three chief proteins are albumins, fibrinogen, which forms the clot, and globulins, which include antibodies against foreign proteins, toxins, etc. Plasma minus fibrinogen is unable to clot and is called **serum.** There are also very tiny bodies called **platelets** which are important in clotting.

Blood Pressures. Blood has two kinds of pressures which are quite distinct but which may nevertheless both affect the same process, such as kidney function. There are osmotic pressure and hydrostatic pressure.

Osmotic pressure is commonly defined as the force with which a solvent (in this case, water) moves through a selectively permeable membrane from a solution of lower solute (here glucose, salts, etc.) concentration to one of higher concentration. Not only kidney function but the integrity of all the cells depend on proper osmotic pressure for, if it becomes too high, fluid will be lost from the cells; if it becomes too low, the cells absorb water and ultimately swell up and burst. It is for this reason that

sterile distilled water cannot be used to supplement blood volume after hemorrhage. The actual osmotic pressure of human blood is that produced by a 0.9 per cent NaCl solution, i.e., over seven times atmospheric pressure!

The **hydrostatic pressure** of blood is the pressure given to it by the beating of the heart. The concept that there was such a thing as blood pressure was originated by an 18th century clergyman, Stephen Hales, who became interested in sap pressure in grapevines. He then investigated the problem in horses and discovered that by connecting a vertical tube to an artery in the neck, the pressure could be measured by recording the height to which water was forced in the tube. Nine feet six inches was what he found. Systolic pressure at contraction averages from 110 to 140 mm mercury in man and most mammals. Diastolic pressure ranges from about 75 to 90 mm mercury.

The regulation of blood pressure is a complex affair of great medical importance about which much is yet to be learned. It is known that blood pressure increases gradually with age. No one can be certain why this is so. Fairly rapid changes in blood pressure are known to be caused by the nervous system and are part of the essential homeostatic system of the animal. Increasing blood pressure in the aorta shortly after it leaves the heart sends nervous

539

impulses to the medulla of the brain. These impulses inhibit the sympathetic center which sends accelerator nerves to the heart and excite the vagal center which sends inhibitory impulses to the heart. The carotid arteries in the neck send similar impulses to the medulla. The result is a slower and less forceful heart beat and hence a decrease in blood pressure.

Chemoreceptors are located in both the curve of the aorta and the carotid bodies. Lack of oxygen in the blood stimulates these receptors to send impulses to the medulla which increases the heart beat and blood pressure. Generalized contraction or dilation of arterioles and capillaries also helps regulate blood pressure. Ischemia, i.e., lack of blood, in the brain or kidneys, leads to elevated blood pressure. Increased mechanical pressure due to a tumor or other agency in the brain causes increase of blood pressure. The kidneys play a dominant role in the control though it is impossible to determine whether they control blood pressure through nervous impulses to the medulla or by hormones or perhaps in both ways. Here again the self-regulatory homeostatic function is important. If blood pressure becomes too high the kidneys are damaged. If it falls below the osmotic pressure of the blood, the formation of urine stops.

Various chemicals affect blood pressure. Epinephrine (adrenalin), carbon dioxide, tobacco, vasopressin (a pituitary hormone), all increase blood pressure. Acetylcholine, histamine, and alcohol tend to decrease blood pressure by vasodilation.

Oxygen-Carbon Dioxide Transport. Water will carry some dissolved oxygen but not much. Exposed to ordinary air, which is roughly 21 per cent oxygen, water holds only about 0.5 ml oxygen per 100 ml water. The red hemoglobin of some annelids will make it possible for 100 ml of blood to hold about 10 ml oxygen, the hemoglobins of fishes about 15 ml, and of birds and mammals up to 20 ml, or even 30 ml of oxygen in the case of porpoises who are adapted for lengthy dives. The trick about hemoglobin is that it combines easily with oxygen when there is a high oxygen pressure, becoming scarlet oxyhemoglobin, and gives it up as readily when the oxygen pressure (concentration) falls as it does in the tissues of the body compared with gills, lungs, or moist skin. Hemoglobin is thus a very special kind of compound. It takes up a lot of oxygen, but also releases the oxygen readily.

Deep within the body the carbon dioxide (really carbonic acid)

$$CO_2 + H_2O \underset{\text{carbonic anhydrase}}{\overset{\text{carbonic anhydrase}}{\rightleftarrows}} H_2CO_3$$

results in acid conditions which facilitate the breakdown of oxyhemoglobin into oxygen and hemoglobin. The H_2CO_3, which is more acidic than hemoglobin, takes a potassium ion away from the hemoglobin and becomes potassium bicarbonate, $KHCO_3$. Once back in the lungs, the hemoglobin gains oxygen, becoming more acidic and, therefore, able to recapture the potassium. This means that potassium bicarbonate is reconverted to carbonic acid which, under the influence of the enzyme carbonic anhydrase in the red cells, breaks down into H_2O and CO_2 which is lost to the surrounding atmosphere or water.

Hemoglobin itself deserves a close look. It is a double molecule similar to chlorophyll, cytochrome, and vitamin B_{12} (cyanocobalamin). The heme part of the molecule is a typical porphyrin having an iron atom in the center where chlorophyll has a magnesium atom. The heme is united with a protein, the globin. This part of the hemoglobin differs from one species to another. Right down to and including the fishes, all vertebrate hemoglobins are basically the same, composed of four polypeptide chains each with a molecular weight of 17,000 and one heme group. In the lampreys there is only one peptide chain, but again a molecular weight of 17,000 and one heme group. Evidently vertebrates have had their hemoglobins with them from the start. Authentic though somewhat different hemoglobins are found among some protostomes, specifically the annelids, the arthropods, and the mollusks. Presumably this represents an independent evolutionary origin, which is a surprising fact when it is remembered that the peptide chain has 141 or 146 amino acids in an obligatory series. The porphyrin group, of course, is as widespread as the animal kingdom.

```
          CH₃        CH=CH₂
           |          |
           C=====C
          /          \
   HC—C              C=CH
      ‖      N        \
CH₃—C—C     ‖          C=C—CH₃
      |     N···Fe—N  /
COOH—(CH₂)₂—C—C        C=C—CH=CH₂
      \      ‖   N    /
   HC=C          C=CH
          \      /
           C====C
          /      \
        (CH₂)₂    CH₃
          |
         COOH
```

heme, the prosthetic group of hemoglobin

Immunity. The circulating blood plays a special role in immunity because the **leucocytes** have the power to ingest and destroy harmful bacteria and because the blood carries the **gamma globulins** which are antibodies. It will be recalled from the chapter on development, where the theories about antibody formation are discussed, that blood carries neutralizing agents called **antibodies.** They are formed against virtually any foreign protein, certain polysaccharides, and various other substances, possibly because these are associated with a protein in some way. Any material which elicits antibody is called an **antigen.**

Antibodies are themselves proteins. Some antibodies precipitate the foreign protein and are called **precipitins.** Others cause bacteria to clump together and are called **agglutinins.** Some neutralize poisons and are termed **antitoxins.** If an animal produces its own antibodies, it is said to have **active** immunity. If antibody produced by another organism, say a horse or sheep, is injected, the immunity is less lasting and is called **passive.**

Blood Groups. Mammals possess characteristic differences in blood proteins which separate the members of a single species into distinguishable classes. The A, B, O set of blood groups in man is a well-known example. The Rh groups, named after the rhesus monkey or macaque in which they were discovered, represent a class of blood groups that transcend even generic lines. These and other blood groups have been discussed in the chapter on genetics.

Coagulation. The coagulation of the blood appears simple, yet careful investigation has shown it to be one of the most complex of all known biological processes. At least 30 factors may play some role! From the point of view of the organism the problem seems to be that unless the blood clots reasonably promptly, death by hemorrhage might follow even a deep scratch. On the other hand, if the clot blocking a cut should extend into the arteries or veins and cause even a small fraction of the blood within the body to clot, death would also result.

From the welter of observations and theories the following facts stand out. The jellylike clot or **thrombus** is composed of a fibrous protein, **fibrin,** which is present in normal plasma in an unpolymerized form called **fibrinogen.** In order for fibrinogen to polymerize into fibrin, **calcium** ions must be present. This is why citric acid, which combines with calcium to form calcium citrate, can prevent clotting. What produces the conversion of fibrinogen to fibrin? This is done by another blood protein, the enzyme **thrombase** sometimes called simply **thrombin.** Apparently calcium is necessary for its action. Where does the thrombase come from? Apparently it is normally present as an inactive precursor **prothrombase** in the blood along with fibrinogen. Prothrombase is known to be formed in the liver. **Vitamin K,** an oil-soluble napthoquinone first isolated from alfalfa, is required for its synthesis.

So it seems that prothrombase is converted to thrombase which catalyzes the conversion of fibrinogen to the fibrin of the clot. What triggers the change in the prothrombase? This appears to be due to a **lipoprotein** which exists, again in an inactive precursor form, in some of the plasma globulins. It is activated by a group of substances given the noncommittal name **antihemophilic factors** that are released from injured tissues and from numerous tiny **blood platelets** when they come in contact with injured tissue.

It is worth noting that dicumerol, one of the most effective anticoagulants, is a competitive antagonist for the synthesis of vitamin K in the liver. Warfarin, a synthetic compound similar to dicumerol, is the most effective rat poison known. Hirudin, the anticoagulant from leeches, bedbugs, etc., and heparin both act immediately to prevent clotting, but their mode of action is unknown. They may interfere with prothrombase.

Review and References

REVIEW QUESTIONS

1. What lines of evidence did William Harvey marshal to support his theory about the circulation of the blood?

2. Trace the developmental fate of the six pairs of aortic arches in the six classes of vertebrates.

3. What are the major types of blood cells and their functions?

4. Trace the course of the blood from the left ventricle into the intestine and back to the left ventricle.

5. What is lymph?

6. What regulates the heart beat?

7. How are O_2 and CO_2 transported? Include anatomical, chemical, and physiological aspects.

8. What are the different ways in which hydrostatic blood pressure is regulated?

9. What is the role of the following: fibrinogen, thrombase, vitamin K, dicumarin, capillaries, hepatic portal vein, S.-A. node, plasma, antigen, carotid body?

10. Identify: William Harvey, Michael Servetus, Andreas Vesalius, Stephen Hales, Sidney Ringer, Otto Loewi.

USEFUL REFERENCES

Grollman, S., *The Human Body, Its Structure and Physiology,* New York, The Macmillan Company, 1964.

Ingram, V. M., *The Hemoglobins in Genetics and Evolution,* New York, Columbia University Press, 1963.

Krogh, A., *Comparative Physiology of Respiratory Mechanisms,* Philadelphia, University of Pennsylvania Press, 1959.

Tuttle, W. W., and B. A. Schottelius, *Textbook of Physiology,* St. Louis, C. V. Mosby, 1965.

Chapter 27

Nutrition and Respiration

No argument is necessary to justify the study of nutrition and its closely related processes of digestion, absorption, and respiration. Knowledge in these areas is important personally, nationally, and internationally. It does sometimes need to be emphasized that there is still much to be learned, and that many of the long-known facts will be reinterpreted in the light of new biochemical knowledge.

DIGESTION AND ABSORPTION

The Anatomy of Digestion. Matter and energy pathways begin for mammals, as for other animals, with the grasping and ingestion of food. These activities so condition the habits and structure of animals that **teeth** furnish the best clue to the nature of any mammal. In fact, a great comparative anatomist, Sir Richard Owen, paraphrased Archimedes' famous remark on discovering the principle of the lever, "Give me where to stand, and I will move the earth," by asserting, "Give me a tooth, and I will reconstruct the animal." It's an exaggeration, of course, but one that contains much truth.

Carnivores, like the cat and seal, have large canines and pointed molars. Herbivores, like the deer and horse, have reduced canines or none, and the molars have become grinders with flat, corrugated tops. Omnivores, like the primates, have generalized teeth.

The **pharynx** or throat follows immediately behind the **buccal** or mouth **cavity,** which contains that versatile organ, the **tongue.** The Eustachian tubes, remnants of the first gill slits, lead out to the eardrum from the posterior pharynx. In this region, the route of air from the dorsal portion of the pharynx to the trachea crosses the route of food and drink on its way to the esophagus, as in the amphibians.

The **esophagus** is merely a muscular tube conducting food from the pharynx past the heart and lungs into the stomach, which lies just below the diaphragm, a transverse muscular partition separating the coelom around the lungs from that surrounding the stomach, liver, and intestine. The structure of the wall of the esophagus is essentially the same as in the stomach or intestine. The cavity or lumen of all three is lined by an epithelium composed of squamous, i.e., thin flat cells, in the esophagus and tall columnar ones in the stomach and intestine. This epithelium is supported by a thin connective tissue sheet or lamina, and a thin muscular sheet. These consitute the **mucosa,** although this word is commonly used to refer solely to the epithelium. The submucosa encircling the mucosa consists of loose, fibrous connective tissue with numerous blood vessels

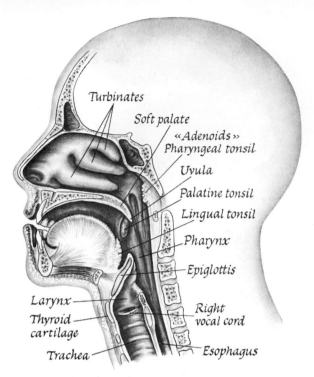

Fig. 27 – 1. Sagittal section through the head. As in the frog, the pathways of air and food cross in the pharynx in man.

Labels in figure:
Turbinates
Soft palate
«Adenoids»
Pharyngeal tonsil
Uvula
Palatine tonsil
Lingual tonsil
Pharynx
Epiglottis
Larynx
Thyroid cartilage
Right vocal cord
Trachea
Esophagus

and, in some parts of the digestive tract, glands. Outside of the submucosa is a layer of circular muscles, then a layer of longitudinal muscles, and finally, on the very outside, an epithelial covering. All these muscles are of the nonstriated type.

The **stomach** is an enlarged and specialized portion of the gut tube. The portion which the esophagus enters is known as the **cardiac region,** since it is nearer the heart. The opposite end is the **pyloric region.** The **pylorus** is the orifice between the stomach and the intestine. kept closed by a circular sphincter muscle.

In cattle, deer, camels, and the other even-toed ungulates which chew the cud—i.e., in all the artiodactyls except pigs and hippopotamuses—the stomach has four chambers. Food is hastily eaten without chewing and stored in a large pouch or **rumen** developed from the cardiac region of the stomach. Once the animal has retreated to a safe place, the food passes in small masses or cuds into the **reticulum** or honeycomb, where it is thoroughly coated with saliva and then regurgitated. After chewing, the

food is swallowed a second time, slips along a groove on one side of the reticulum, through the longitudinal folds of the **psalterium** and into the **abomasum,** the major digestive portion of the stomach. The four chambers of the stomach are shown in Figure 27 – 3.

Complex ciliates swarm in the stomach and in the large intestines of **ruminants,** as animals with these four-chambered stomachs are called. It is believed but not firmly proved that these commensals play an important part in the nutrition of their hosts. If so, cows may be as dependent on intestinal protozoa as are cockroaches and termites!

The first region of the **small intestine** into which the stomach empties is the **duodenum.** The common **bile duct,** carrying the secretions of both pancreas and liver, enters the duodenum not far from its origin at the pylorus. The remainder of the small intestine is much longer than the duodenum and leads into a shorter large intestine or **colon.** Where the small intestine enters the large, most mammals have one or two blind extensions or **diverticula.** They may be a foot or more in length, as in a rabbit, or merely finger-sized, like the human vermiform appendix. The colon ends in a short straight section, the **rectum,** which leads to the exterior via the **anus.**

Digestion. Mammals are equipped with an impressive battery of glands that secrete digestive enzymes. Some of the glands are unicellular; many, like the pancreas, are large and complex. The function of all these enzymes is hydrolysis, the splitting of large molecules, with the addition of water, into small molecules that can be absorbed through the wall of the digestive tract. It will be recalled (Chapter 3) that carbohydrates are ultimately broken down into glucose, lipids into glycerol and fatty acids, and proteins into amino acids.

The table on page 546 shows the main sources of mammalian digestive enzymes and their actions. Like other enzymes these are very sensitive to pH. Ptyalin, the amylase in saliva, works at a pH close to neutrality; the proteolytic gastric pepsin requires an acid pH; the pancreatic and intestinal enzymes require an alkaline environment for their activity.

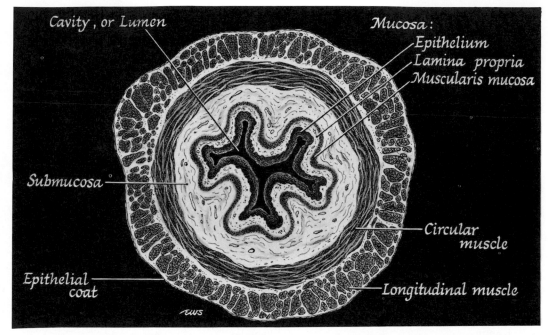

Fig. 27 – 2. A cross section of the esophagus shows the same layers of tissue as those in the stomach and intestine.

Ingested food is lubricated by **saliva** and more or less chewed before being swallowed — more in a rabbit, less in a fox. Mastication breaks up the food, facilitating swallowing and permitting digestive enzymes to come into contact with it. A small amount of chloride appears to be necessary for the enzyme **ptyalin** to hydrolyze starch. Boiling or baking starch ruptures the thin cellulose membranes enclosing starch grains and greatly aids its digestion.

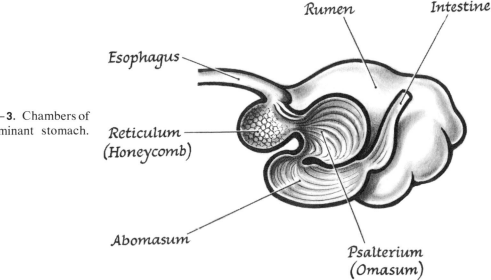

Fig. 27 – 3. Chambers of the ruminant stomach.

Principal Digestive Enzymes in Mammals

Substances in italics are absorbed through the walls of the intestinal villi

ENZYME	OCCURRENCE	SUBSTRATE	CHIEF PRODUCTS
Ptyalin	Saliva	Starch	Maltose
Pepsin	Gastric juice	Protein	Polypeptides
Amylases	Pancreatic juice	Starches	Maltose
Lipases		Lipids	*Glycerol and fatty acids*
Trypsin		Proteins	Peptides
Chymotrypsin		Polypeptides	Peptides
Peptidase		Peptides	*Amino acids*
Sucrase	Intestinal juice	Cane sugar	*Simple sugars*
Maltase		Maltose	*Simple sugars*
Lactase		Milk sugar	*Simple sugars*
Lipase		Lipids	*Glycerol and fatty acids*
Erepsin		Peptides	*Amino acids*
Peptidases		Peptides	*Amino acids*

After passing through the esophagus, the food enters the stomach. The action of the stomach is in part mechanical. Waves of muscular contraction, known as **peristaltic waves,** pass over the stomach, mixing the contents thoroughly with **gastric juice.** In the early days of X-rays W. B. Cannon at Harvard fed animals and men food mixed with radio-opaque metal salts and then watched the peristaltic churning of the stomach. By such methods it can be seen that strong emotions bring this rhythmic churning to a standstill and thus impede digestion of food.

The first successful explorations on the action of human gastric juice were made by a young army surgeon, William Beaumont, when he was stationed in Mackinac, then only a trading post at the head of Lake Michigan. His patient, Alexis St. Martin, had a severe gunshot wound in the abdomen which healed in such a way that a permanent opening remained from the exterior of the body into the stomach. Through this opening Beaumont was able to obtain relatively pure gastric juice so as to study its composition and its action on food-

stuffs. A similar but much improved method was later developed on dogs by the great Russian physiologist, Ivan Pavlov. He constructed a pouch surgically from part of the stomach by pinching it off with sutures so that no food entered the pouch. A permanent opening, or fistula, was then made into the pouch from the exterior of the dog's abdomen.

Gastric juice is a clear fluid containing about 0.4 per cent hydrochloric acid and two enzymes, **pepsin,** which splits proteins by hydrolysis into short chains of amino acids called peptides, and **rennin,** which clots milk. Why doesn't the stomach digest itself? Such cannibalism is physiologically possible. The lining of the stomach is normally protected against the pepsin by a coating of mucus. The enzyme-secreting cells do not make the enzyme in an active form, but as pepsinogen which becomes active pepsin only after it arrives in the acid gastric juice.

When the acid content of the stomach passes through the pylorus into the duodenum, the pancreas pours out **pancreatic juice.** The discovery of the way the intestine signals the pancreas to secrete is a landmark in the history of endocrinology. Bayliss and Starling, working in a dingy London laboratory, found that cutting the nerves either from the duodenum or to the pancreas did not prevent the pancreas from secreting at the proper time. Tying off the veins leaving the duodenum did (see Fig. 27–4). Hence it was clear that the duodenum signaled the pancreas to secrete by some message sent via the bloodstream. Specifically, the presence of acid material from the stomach in the normally alkaline duodenum stimulates it to secrete a material, called **secretin,** which is carried by the bloodstream to the pancreas. Secretin excites the pancreas to secrete its digestive juice. Bayliss and Starling (with some help from a professor of Greek) coined the word **hormone** (*hormon,* exciting) for such a substance.

Digestion in the intestine of mammals is due in part to the pancreatic juice which contains enzymes capable of hydrolytically splitting all three major classes of foodstuffs. The walls of the intestine also contain glands. In the submucosa of the duodenum, the first part of the intestine, multicellular glands with ducts empty into the lumen of the gut. It is extremely difficult to get a pure sample of their secretion. They certainly secrete mucus and perhaps that is all, though in the present state of our knowledge it is commonly believed that digestive enzymes are also present.

The lining of the intestine is not only covered with ridges or folds, but the surface, including the surface of the folds, is covered with **villi.** Each villus is a fingerlike protrusion covered with columnar epithelium and containing a core of fibrous connective tissue with capillaries and a lymph vessel. In between the villi are numerous "post-holes," called **crypts of Lieberkühn.** The mucosal epithelium not only covers the villi and the general lining of the gut but extends down into the crypts where cell division is frequently seen. Calculations based on the number of mitoses in animals where all mitosis is blocked in metaphase by colchicine indicate that the epithelial cells of the intestine are completely renewed every one and a half to two days!

The cells of the epithelium are of several types. There are mucus-secreting **goblet cells,**

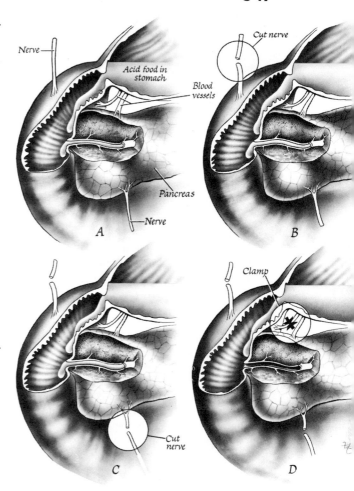

Fig. 27–4. Bayliss-Starling experiment to prove that the signal from the intestine to secrete pancreatic juice is transmitted not by nerves but by the bloodstream. *A* is the normal condition. *B* and *C* show that secretion occurs even after the sensory nerve from duodenum to pancreas and the efferent nerve to pancreas are cut. *D* shows lack of secretion after clamping off the vein from duodenum.

so called because the mucus forms a globular mass at the upper end of each cell. There are **absorptive cells** with striated borders at their free surfaces. Under the electron microscope these striated surfaces are revealed as composed of extremely fine microvilli. Probably their function is to increase the area of absorption. In the crypts are the mysterious **Paneth**

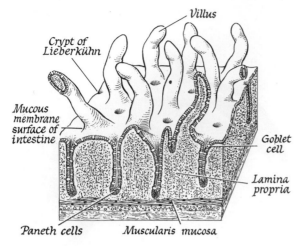

Mucous membrane surface of intestine — Paneth cells — Muscularis mucosa — Villus — Crypt of Lieberkühn — Goblet cell — Lamina propria

Fig. 27 – 5. Diagram of villi covering interior surface of the small intestine. Note the crypts of Lieberkühn extending down into the wall of the intestine. (*After Ham*, Histology, *5th ed., J. B. Lippincott*)

cells with their cytoplasm filled with acidophilic granules. Their function is unknown. Perhaps they secrete the various digestive enzymes of the small intestine. Some workers have thought they secreted anti-enzymes which prevent the self-digestion of the intestine. The only certainty is that, since the crypts are so numerous and the intestine so long, the number of Paneth cells must be enormous.

Absorption. Most of the digested food is absorbed in the intestine by the villi just described. The glucose and amino acids are passed as such into the capillaries whence they are carried to the liver in the hepatic portal vein. The absorption of fats is more complex and less understood. The glycerol is taken into the villi as such. The fatty acids unite with bile salts forming a water-soluble compound which enters the cells of the villi. Within the villi the fatty acids reunite with the glycerol forming lipids again. Most of this fat passes as a milky emulsion in the lymphatics of the mesentery up

to the thoracic duct and through it into the left subclavian vein to the heart and thus into the bloodstream.

Although the complete mechanism of absorption is not understood, it is clear that it is due to **active transport** rather than simple diffusion. This is evident from the fact that very low concentrations of glucose can be absorbed from the intestine into the bloodstream where the concentration of glucose is higher. To move molecules "uphill" against a concentration gradient requires the expenditure of energy. This thermodynamic consideration is confirmed by the fact that metabolic poisons quickly stop such absorption.

Roles of the Liver. The liver plays a key role in the fate of the digested food carried to it from the intestine by the hepatic portal vein. No organ, not even the brain, has been the object of such intense study by physicians and soothsayers from remote antiquity. Yet it was not until the latter years of the past century that Claude Bernard first learned something of its actual functions.

The glucose is converted in the liver into glycogen, we now know under the influence of insulin, and stored until the glucose in the blood falls to a threshold level, when the glycogen is reconverted into glucose.

A small percentage, perhaps less than 10 per cent, of the amino acids reaching the liver from the intestine pass through it into the general circulation. There they are taken up by the cells and utilized in forming the various proteins of the body.

The fate of amino acids in the liver raises important questions and highly controversial views about how much protein is necessary in the diet. In the liver, most amino acids have their amino groups taken from them and are thus broken into an hydroxy acid and ammonia, a process termed **deamination.**

$$R-\underset{\underset{H}{|}}{\overset{\overset{NH_2}{|}}{C}}-COOH + H_2O \xrightarrow{\text{deaminase}} R-\underset{\underset{H}{|}}{\overset{\overset{OH}{|}}{C}}-COOH + NH_3$$

amino acid   hydroxy acid   ammonia

$$R-\overset{\overset{\displaystyle NH_2}{|}}{\underset{\underset{\displaystyle H}{|}}{C}}-COOH + O_2 + H_2O \xrightarrow{\text{oxidase}} R-\overset{\overset{\displaystyle O}{\|}}{C}-COOH + NH_3 + H_2O_2$$

amino acid   keto acid   ammonia   hydrogen peroxide

Other amino acids may be oxidized with a similar result—ammonia, a keto acid, and hydrogen peroxide. The equation is illustrated above. The hydroxy or keto acids can readily be converted into glycogen or used almost directly by the Krebs aerobic cycle in any cell.

The NH_3, which is poisonous except in extremely low concentrations, is combined by the liver cells with another waste product, CO_2, to produce a colorless, odorless, and harmless compound, **urea,** which is carried by the bloodstream to the kidneys, where it is excreted. The over-all equation is simplicity itself.

$$2\ NH_3 + CO_2 \longrightarrow H_2N-\overset{\overset{\displaystyle O}{\|}}{C}-NH_2 + H_2O$$

urea

Modern investigation reveals that the actual synthesis of urea involves the use over and over again of ornithine, a long-chain amino acid with two $-NH_2$ groups:

$$H_2N-CH_2-CH_2-CH_2-\overset{\overset{\displaystyle NH_2}{|}}{\underset{\underset{\displaystyle H}{|}}{C}}-COOH$$

Hence, urea synthesis is called the **ornithine cycle.** The NH_3 and CO_2 are both united to ATP, forming carbamyl phosphate. This compound then unites with ornithine producing citrulline, which is merely ornithine with the

$H_2N-\overset{\overset{\displaystyle O}{\diagup\!\!\!}}{C}-$ from the ammonia and carbon dioxide attached to it. The citrulline is converted to arginino-succinic acid, and this in turn to arginine. Arginine is an amino acid with four nitrogen atoms! The arginine is then converted into ornithine and urea. At least five enzymes are involved. It seems a long process, but it has a long evolutionary history. The ornithine cycle may be diagrammed as follows:

carbamyl phosphate   → citrulline
ornithine

arginine ←   arginino-succinic acid

urea

How could anyone even suspect there is such a thing as the ornithine cycle? The discovery was made by the same Hans Krebs who later worked out the details of the aerobic citric acid cycle named after him. Krebs was studying the formation of urea by adding various amino acids to slices of liver fresh enough for the enzymes to be still active. He found that added ornithine or arginine greatly increased the production of urea, especially in the presence of added ammonia. This opened the door.

In addition to the synthesis of urea from amino acids and the storage of glucose as glycogen, the liver secretes bile, destroys "worn-out" red blood cells, makes prothrombase, stores vitamins, detoxifies miscellaneous harmful substances, and plays a role in lipid metabolism, as well as synthesizing its own proteins. Clever chemist, the liver!

Fig. 27–6. Amino acids in the liver. On demand, stored glycogen leaves the liver as sugar. (*After G. B. Moment,* General Biology, *2nd ed., Copyright 1950 by Appleton–Century–Crofts, Inc.*)

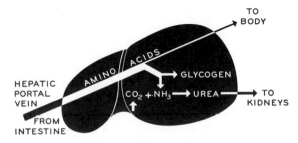

LIVER

NUTRITIONAL REQUIREMENTS

Mammals, like other heterotrophs, require outside sources of carbohydrates, lipids, proteins, and vitamins. Necessary water and various salts are usually inseparable from these principal foods.

Carbohydrates and Lipids. Carbohydrates are the primary fuel of life for man and many animals. In addition, they serve to protect the body proteins which will be utilized for fuel if the blood glucose falls too low. Lipids also can act in the same way. It will be recalled (page 58) that at the "lower" end of the glycolytic pathway acetyl-coenzyme A serves as a central metabolic crossroads. Pyruvic acid from the anaerobic breakdown of glucose is not the only substance fed into the Krebs aerobic cycle as acetyl-Co A; lipids and also amino acids from proteins are converted into the acetyl group, CH_3—$\overset{\displaystyle O}{\underset{}{C}}$—, which is linked to coenzyme A (a derivative of the vitamin pantothenic acid) and then fed into the Krebs cycle.

Lipids serve as essential constituents of cell membranes, as reservoirs of stored energy, as carriers of the fat-soluble vitamins, and possibly in other ways.

The **fuel or energy value** of any food is measured in heat units, called **calories.** One large calorie (kilocalorie), the unit usually employed, is defined as the amount of heat required to raise 1,000 grams of water through 1°Centigrade. The total caloric content of food can be determined by complete combustion in a heat-measuring device called a **bomb calorimeter.** The powdered food is ignited by an electric spark. The heat liberated is measured by the rise in temperature of the water in a jacket that surrounds the combustion chamber.

The metabolic rate of a man who is doing hard physical labor requires from 3,500 to 5,000 calories a day. A person doing sedentary or semi-sedentary work burns about 2,500 calories daily. To maintain a man's life, about 500 calories a day are necessary. Calories are obtained largely from carbohydrates and fats, but amino acids are commonly deprived of their ammonia groups by the liver and ultimately converted into carbohydrate. For a 150-pound man, about 10 ounces of protein a day is re-garded as satisfactory. Growing children need more in proportion to their weight, but even in an adult there is a continual renewal of tissue proteins. The half-life (time in which one-half of a substance is broken down) for proteins in the viscera of man is about ten days, for proteins in the muscles about two months.

Vitamins. Key dietary factors are the vitamins. They are essential for healthy everyday living as well as for extraordinary exertion. Many a voyage that began well has ended in catastrophe, and many a stout heart has sickened and died because of a lack of knowledge of vitamins. How our precious knowledge of vitamins was won should be part of the cultural heritage of every participant in our civilization. Consequently we will begin with a discussion of how vitamins were discovered, then define them in general, and end with a survey of important specific vitamins.

The discovery of vitamins grew out of the needs of explorers. For centuries **scurvy** had been the nightmare of sailors and explorers, as well as the curse of boarding schools and prisons. In his voyage around the Cape of Good Hope in 1498, Vasco da Gama lost almost two-thirds of his crew from scurvy. In the words of Dr. Logan Clendening, a noted medical historian:

> First a sailor's gums would begin to bleed. Then some of his teeth would fall out. The stench from his mouth would be horrible. Then great blotches would appear on the skin. The wrists and ankles would swell. A bloody diarrhea set in. Parts of the flesh would rot out. Finally, exhausted, delirious, loathsome, the poor wretch would pay his debt to nature.

The first recorded successful effort to control this scourge took place during an exploration of the St. Lawrence River in 1536 by Jacques Cartier. After he had lost 26 men, the rest were restored to health by a pine needle concoction prepared by the native Indians. In view of the dramatic nature of the need, it is difficult to understand why nothing came of this incident.

Eighty years later a surgeon named John Woodhall in the employ of the East India Company that regularly sent ships around the Cape of Good Hope, mentioned in print the value of lemon juice in preventing scurvy, and James Lind did the same 137 years later still. But such is the conservatism or stupidity or perhaps mere inertia of men, that it was not until 1768, over 230 years after Cartier's men were saved by pine needles, that the famous Captain Cook set out in *H.M.S. Endeavour* and proved the lemon juice theory on a long voyage in the South Pacific. Even today British sailors are called "limeys" from the lemons and limes that formed a part of their diet. In comparatively recent times the agent in citrus fruits which is responsible for preventing scurvy has been named vitamin C and has been identified as **ascorbic acid.**

The chemical identification of vitamins and a knowledge of their actual functions in cellular metabolism ultimately grew out of investigations into the cause of **beriberi,** a painful and once fatal disease of the nervous system. This knowledge came through the work of men in both the West and the Orient. Beriberi is an ancient curse in the Orient, and before 1880 was a serious problem in the Japanese navy. In that year a young physician, Dr. Takaki, returned from London convinced that the superior health of British sailors was due to their more varied diet. After meeting almost as much human inertia as Europeans had shown about lemons and scurvy, Takaki sent two ships on nine-month cruises. The crew of one ate the standard diet of polished rice; the crew of the other enjoyed a varied diet. Nearly a third of the crew living on polished rice developed beriberi, while there was only a handful of cases in the other ship. Within a decade the incidence of beriberi on Japanese ships fell from its previous level of 32 per cent to less than 0.1 per cent.

At about the same time the Dutch government sent a commission to Java to find out the cause of beriberi. It was the age of Pasteur and Koch, so it was not surprising that they decided beriberi is a germ disease and left a Doctor Eijkman to discover the germ. While of course he failed, he did notice that chickens living on table scraps of polished rice developed neuritis and paralysis much like beriberi. He also made the astute observation that chickens fed cheap unpolished rice failed to develop these symptoms. Next came a crucial experiment with

Fig. 27–7. Chicken with thiamine deficiency. The posture is typical of polyneuritis (beriberi) in birds. *(Kindness of the University of Wisconsin)*

human beings. A statistical and experimental study of over 10,000 prisoners in Java and nearby islands clearly showed that what was true of chickens was also true of men: a diet of polished rice results in beriberi; rice cuticle prevents it.

The actual chemical identification of vitamins came about in a very interesting way. In the 19th century a Russian investigator, Lunin, had found that when animals are fed on highly purified diets of carbohydrates, fats, and proteins, they sicken and die even though all three major food components are present. Many years later Hopkins, a pioneer biochemist at Cambridge, undertook to reinvestigate this old puzzle of Lunin and found in milk what he called an accessory food factor which was necessary in minute amounts for health. This announcement stimulated work in several laboratories and by 1912 Funk had isolated the first such substance from rice polishings. It was the anti-beriberi factor, which turned out to be **thiamine** (B_1). Funk coined a new word and called the factor a **vitamin.**

Modern Knowledge of Vitamins. Until rather recently nothing was known about the biochemical function of vitamins. Then almost simultaneously, physiologists discovered a "yellow enzyme" essential for the oxidation of foodstuffs within the cells, and nutritionists found a yellow vitamin, **riboflavin,** essential for normal growth in young birds and mammals and for the prevention of various eye and skin disorders in

Fig. 27–8. Crystals of thiamine hydrochloride (vitamin B$_1$). *(Kindness of Merck & Co.)*

The amount of vitamin in a preparation is assayed either by feeding a given amount to animals on diets known to lack the vitamin concerned, or by direct chemical tests. Up to the present, somewhat more than a dozen vitamins have been discovered. Many are water soluble, like vitamin C and the B vitamins. The rest are fat soluble. Some are heat stable, others are readily destroyed by heat. The table on page 553 gives the chemical name, the letter symbol (when one exists), dietary sources, and the function of most of the vitamins. Some of the more interesting ones are discussed further.

Ascorbic acid, or vitamin C, the anti-scurvy vitamin of lemons and limes, is not only essential for human life, but adequate amounts are needed for health, including healthy gums and resistance to infection. Ascorbic acid functions

adults. The "yellow enzyme" and riboflavin were found to be intimately associated, and from this fact came the knowledge that vitamins form part of enzyme systems.

Vitamins are coenzymes or the prosthetic groups of definite enzyme molecules. Most—perhaps all—enzymes consist of two parts, a larger protein portion and a smaller nonprotein portion. The protein part of the enzyme molecule is called the **apoenzyme,** the smaller nonprotein part, the **coenzyme.** The two together constitute the **holoenzyme.** If the coenzyme is very firmly bound to the apoenzyme, it is often called the **prosthetic group.** A coenzyme or prosthetic group is usually regarded as a vitamin for any particular animal only if the animal cannot manufacture it for itself.

The knowledge that vitamins form the nonprotein part of enzyme molecules is of much more than purely theoretical interest. It makes it possible to form medically useful drugs like sulfanilamide. Such substances are essentially fake vitamins, substances with which the protein part of the enzyme will unite but which will not make a functional enzyme. In such a way sulfanilamide blocks the enzymes of the bacteria. The same knowledge has made it possible to construct the most powerful poisons known—the infamous nerve poisons of warfare which act by blocking enzymes essential for nervous action.

Fig. 27–9. Child with rickets due to lack of calciferol, the fat-soluble vitamin D. *(Kindness of The Children's Hospital Medical Center, Boston)*

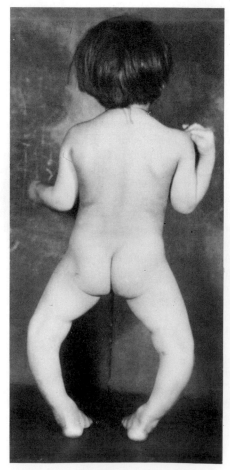

Important Vitamins

SOLUBILITY	CHEMICAL NAME	LETTER SYMBOL	FUNCTIONS	DIETARY SOURCES	HEAT STABILITY
Water soluble	Ascorbic acid	C	Anti-scurvy, Krebs cycle coenzyme	Citrus fruits, tomatoes, leafy vegetables	Labile
	Thiamine	B_1	Anti-beriberi, coenzyme in pyruvate metabolism	Milk, meats, leafy vegetables	Fairly stable in acid
	Cyano-cobal-amin	B_{12}	Anti-pernicious anemia, synthesis of purines	Milk, whey, soybeans, cotton seed	
	Niacin Nicotinic acid		Pellagra-preventive, NAD and NADP nucleotides	Peanuts, liver, chicken, fish, whole wheat	Stable
	Folic acid		Normal growth, blood formation	Meats, eggs, beans, yeast, leafy vegetables	Fairly labile
	Para-aminobenzoic acid		Normal growth	Many foods	
	Riboflavin	B_2	FAD respiratory coenzyme	Whey, most foods	Stable
	Pantothenic acid		Part of coenzyme A	Peanuts, lettuce, eggs	
	Pyridoxin	B_6	Anti-dermatitis, anti-acrodynia (rat)	Egg yolk, wheat germ, yeast	
	Inositol		Anti-alopecia (mouse), anti-fatty liver (rat)	Rootlets, sprouts, fruit, lean meat, yeast, milk	
	Biotin	H	Anti-eggwhite injury	Egg yolk, kidney, liver, tomatoes, yeast	
Fat soluble	β carotene	A	Healthy skin and mucous membrane, night vision	Milk, yellow and green vegetables	Stable
	Calciferol	D	Anti-rickets	Fish liver oils, butter, egg yolk	Stable
	"Menadione"	K	Normal blood clotting	Most foods	Stable
	Tocopherol	E	Anti-sterility, normal muscle development	Leafy vegetables, meat, yolks	Stable

as a coenzyme in the important Krebs metabolic cycle. It is one of the vitamins most easily lost in cooking. If vitamin C is retained, so are the others. The most certain source of this heat-labile substance is raw fruits and vegetables. The daily amount believed adequate for health is supplied by ¾ cup orange juice, or ¾ pound raw tomatoes, or ¼ pound raw cabbage. Lettuce is also a rich source. Cooking cabbage for half an hour destroys 80 per cent of its ascorbic acid. Cooking food for a minimum time in a minimum of water saves the maximum amount of this vitamin.

Nicotinic acid, or nicotinamide, the pellagra-preventive vitamin known as niacin, is, like the rest of the vitamins, essential for human life. The three D's of **pellagra:** dermatitis (a roughening and pigmentation of the skin), diarrhea, and dementia, should really be the four D's, for death is the end result. Niacin forms part of two coenzymes essential for the utilization of carbohydrate in muscles, yeast, and presumably

Fig. 27–10. Pellagra-afflicted hand before administration of niacin (above) and after (below). *(Kindness of the Southern Medical Association)*

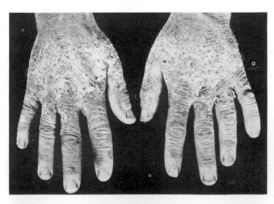

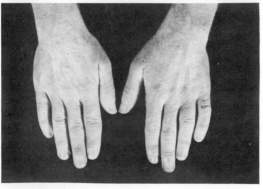

all cells. These are nicotinamide adenine dinucleotide (NAD) and nicotinamide adenine dinucleotide phosphate (NADP). In stability niacin is at the opposite pole from ascorbic acid. It is stable to heat, light, acids, alkalis, and oxidizing agents. Yeast, lean pork or beef, and liver are rich in niacin. Corn (maize) is very deficient in it, and most cases of pellagra occur in regions where corn is the chief article of diet.

Cyano-cobal-amin, or vitamin B_{12}, is the anti-pernicious anemia factor. **Pernicious anemia** was first described as a definite disease over a century ago by Thomas Addison, the same London physician who first described a disease of the adrenal cortex. Pernicious anemia remained almost invariably fatal until about 1925 when two young Boston physicians, George Minot and William Murphy, discovered that it could be successfully treated by feeding raw liver. By 1948 a crystalline preparation of high potency had been obtained from liver extracts. Recently two research teams clarified the chemical nature of this extremely complex vitamin. The size and international composition of these teams as well as their locations on opposite sides of the world typify the present-day organization of scientific investigation. The members of one team worked in Oxford, Princeton, and California; the other in Cambridge, and Middlesex, England, and with the Merck Company in New Jersey.

The interesting fact about the anti-pernicious anemia vitamin is that its molecule contains so many familiar components. There is a porphyrin square made up of the usual four pyrrole rings. But unlike the porphyrin which makes up the hemoglobin or cytochrome molecules and has an iron atom at its hub, or the porphyrin which makes chlorophyll and has a magnesium atom, the anti-anemia porphyrin has a cobalt atom at its center. Attached to this cobalt-containing porphyrin are a number of other familiar groups. One is a cyanide group. Another is part of a nucleotide with a phosphate group. Others are methyl groups and acetic acids carrying ammonia radicals.

The metabolic function of cyano-cobal-amin is very incompletely known. In addition to being essential for the formation of hemoglobin, it seems to be concerned with the synthesis of purines and pyrimidines, and hence with precursors of nucleic acids. It is an essential factor for the growth of rats, pigs, and chickens, and for certain bacteria. Cyano-cobal-amin is now obtained commercially as a by-product in the fermentations which yield aureomycin, terramycin, and other antibiotics.

Folic acid represents a group of water-soluble vitamins belonging to the B group. Pteroylglutamic acid is the most important. Without this factor birds and mammals fail to grow properly, become anemic (but with rather different symptoms from those of pernicious anemia) and generally ill. Although this vitamin is rather easily destroyed by heat, it is found in a wide variety of substances: yeast, eggs, most meats, leafy vegetables, liver, even dried beans.

Para-aminobenzoic acid is especially notable because it was the first vitamin known to be involved in antibiotic action, that of sulfanilamide. The close structural similarity between the two molecules is obvious even to the nonchemist. Apparently the protein apoenzyme cannot distinguish between *p*-aminobenzoic acid and the sulfanilamide, and consequently accepts the latter as its coenzyme or prosthetic group. This mistake renders the enzyme complex inactive. Fortunately many disease-producing bacteria are far more dependent on *p*-aminobenzoic acid than man is. Hence sulfanilamide injures the pathogenic bacteria sooner and more severely than it does the man. This vitamin is necessary for the continued growth and health of mammals. It belongs to the water-soluble B vitamins.

p-aminobenzoic acid   sulfanilamide

Beta carotene, or vitamin A, is essential for a healthy skin and for healthy mucous membranes lining the digestive, urinary, and reproductive tracts. It is also essential for vision in dim light, when the rods of the retina do most of the work. This is because the rods contain rhodopsin or visual purple, which is composed of vitamin A united with a protein. Light striking the rods initiates a nervous impulse by splitting the rhodopsin into its constituent protein and the carotene. Later the two substances recombine to form rhodopsin again. Thus it is easy to see why lack of this vitamin will cause night blindness.

Alpha-tocopherol, or vitamin E, is frequently called the anti-sterility factor, but it is not the only vitamin essential for reproduction. Vitamin E has various functions. The vitamin E content of birds' eggs is closely related to their ability to hatch. Severe muscular atrophy accompanies deprivation of vitamin E. Feeding adequate amounts also lessens the amount of vitamin A required in the diet. Like the other fat-soluble vitamins, A, D, and K, and unlike the water-soluble B's and C, vitamin E is extensively stored in the body.

The Protein Problem. Proteins are essential, or, more precisely, amino acids are essential. There is no doubt whatever about that. How much protein does a child or adult need for normal growth and health? The answer to this question is a fighting issue for some people and is often encrusted with ancient beliefs and modern prejudices. The fact that as much as 90 per cent of the ingested amino acids are quickly converted in the liver into glycogen and urea, which is merely excreted, has cast very serious doubt on the need for large amounts of protein. Not only do prejudices obstruct rational answers, so also does fundamental ignorance of many aspects of the scientific side of the problem. What are some of the important facts?

Severe protein deprivation leads to a severe disease, **kwashiorkor,** which means redboy, so called because of the characteristic dermatitis. It is so prevalent in parts of Africa, Central and South America, and Asia that special United Nations committees have been studying ways to eliminate the disease. The Institute of Nutrition of Central America and Panama in Guatemala has developed a mixture of cheap native vegetable proteins called INCAP #9 which is highly effective in the cure and prevention of kwashiorkor, but every locality presents special problems.

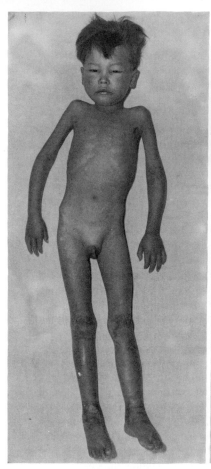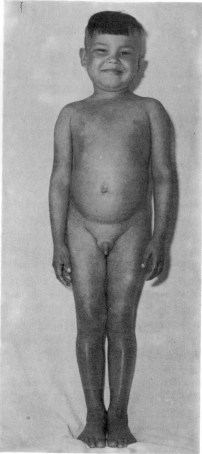

Fig. **27–11.** Boy with kwashiorkor is seen at left. Right: result of treatment with a mixture of plant proteins containing all the essential amino acids. (*Kindness of M. Behar*)

It is well known that amino acids are necessary to make up the proteins of the cytoplasm and nucleus of cells, as well as enzymes, muscles, and other specialized structures. Various amino acids form the starting points of particular compounds. Tyrosine, for example, is the origin of melanin, thyroxin, adrenalin, and other substances.

The amino acids which an animal must have in its diet for normal growth and health are called **essential amino acids** and a protein which has them all is known as **complete.** This does not mean that no additional amino acids are needed by the animal but only that from the "essential" ones any necessary additional acids can be made by the animal itself. In the body there are special enzymes, **transaminases,** which convert one amino acid into another. The so-called biological value of a particular protein depends on whether or not it has a good variety of amino acids.

Tryptophan (indol-phenyl-alanine) is essential in the diet for growth in rats and man.

Methionine is necessary for the liver to produce globulin. Arginine, phenylalanine, lysine, histidine, and several other amino acids are all essential in the diet.

In general, proteins from animal sources — meat, fish, eggs, cheese — are complete. Many plant proteins are not. This is the case with beans, peas, or grains after the germ has been removed. Fortunately many plant proteins supplement each other. For example, Indian corn, i.e., maize, is very poor in lysine but contains the other essential amino acids including methionine, which is deficient in beans. Beans, however, possess plenty of lysine. Obviously, if these two protein sources are mixed, their deficiencies cancel out. It has been found, however, that the two proteins must be eaten at the same meal to be effective in supplementing each other. Apparently there is no storage of amino acids in the body and in order to synthesize a protein, RNA must have available concurrently all the amino acids that are necessary.

A possibility of great importance for the future is the use of a corn mutant recently discovered at Purdue University in Indiana. The mutant forms protein rich in lysine. Because of the appearance of the kernels it has been named opaque-2. In tests on rats fed opaque-2, growth was about three times as fast as in control rats fed ordinary corn. Consequently, the probability seems high that this new corn will be of great usefulness in both agriculture and in promoting human health. Unfortunately the mutant gene is recessive so that growing and especially producing seed corn will have to be done with much care to prevent contamination with wind-blown wild-type pollen carrying the dominant gene.

Nitrogen Balance and Nitrogen Turnover. An individual is said to be in nitrogen balance when the amount of nitrogen excreted equals that ingested. Rapidly growing children and young animals, the pregnant, and individuals recovering from severe illness characteristically show a positive nitrogen balance, excreting less than they ingest. Most authorities claim that somewhere between 21 to 35 grams of "protein" per day is enough for an average man, 21 to 27 grams for a woman; in other words, from less than an ounce to about an ounce and a third at the maximum.

The factors which control the retention and utilization of amino acids, or protein if you will, are very poorly understood. The turnover of tissue protein is amazingly rapid. No seven years are required! Studies with radioactively labelled amino acids indicated that the half-life (when 50 per cent of the protein will have been renewed) is only about two weeks in most of the viscera, two months in skeletal muscle. Thus, in seven months much less than 10 per cent of the original protein is left. The old naturalists who compared life to a fountain were certainly not far wrong. The proteins in the cells are evidently in equilibrium with the amino acid "pool" in the cytoplasm and that with the amino acids in the blood.

In animals as unlike as earthworms and salamanders, and hence probably in all animals, regenerating tissues are able to take amino acids away from established tissues and build them into their own proteins. A starving salamander given no food will easily regenerate a new tail or leg, obviously at the expense of the rest of the body. The new structure can be amputated, and regeneration will take place a second or third time!

Pituitary growth hormone and testosterone each will increase protein synthesis to a certain though limited extent. Lack of insulin stops protein synthesis. It may be that pituitary growth hormones act at or near the level of RNA in a manner to be discussed in the chapter on hormones. They may increase cell permeability to amino acids. Some workers think that since growth hormone increases the utilization of fat for energy it thereby protects the proteins from being so used. When an animal is fed a mixture of amino acids, his requirements for one may be increased by increasing the amount of another amino acid in the diet. Why this should be no one knows.

RESPIRATION

Research into the problems of respiration in mammals has been strongly motivated from two sides. There has been an insistent philosophical interest because from time immemorial respiration, the "breath of life," has been regarded as synonymous with life itself. There have also been urgent practical problems involving respiration—in mining, in submarine and diving operations, in aviation, in the use of anesthetics, and in the diagnosis and treatment of metabolic diseases.

Knowledge of respiration has advanced in four major steps which correspond, in a very general way, to the four centuries during which research has pushed ahead. The facts and principles established at each step are permanently valid and will be presented in order, since they are essential to a firm understanding of this vital topic.

Early Research. The first step was achieved in the 17th century by Robert Boyle and his friends. Largely as a by-product of experiments with the newly invented air pumps, these young men, still in their early twenties, put to the test the old idea that life is like a flame. They obtained definite proof that a mouse cannot live long in air in which a candle has burned itself out, nor a candle burn in air in which a mouse has suffocated.

Classic Laws of Respiration. The establishment of the over-all laws of respiration was the achievement of the 18th century, largely by the work of Lavoisier, one of the discoverers of oxygen, and Simon Laplace, mathematician and astronomer.

These men placed animals in ingenious calorimeters (heat meters) designed to measure the amount of heat produced. They also made extensive chemical tests of air before and after it had been inhaled by men and animals. This and subsequent work proved that:

1. In respiration, animals obey the **law of conservation of energy.** Both a breathing guinea pig and burning charcoal give off the same amount of heat energy when the same amount of oxygen is used up.

2. In respiration, animals obey the **law of conservation of matter.** During respiration the amount of O_2 burned is equivalent to the amount of CO_2 produced. In a closed system there is no change in total weight.

The 19th century refined these fundamental observations and thereby added the third and fourth laws of respiration.

3. The **respiratory quotient,** that is, the volume of CO_2 given off divided by the O_2 consumed, is an indication of the type of food being burned. As can be seen from inspection of the equation:

$$C_6H_{12}O_6 \text{ (sugar)} + 6 \ O_2 \longrightarrow 6 \ H_2O + 6 \ CO_2$$

when sugar is burned the respiratory quotient is one. It will be recalled that according to Avogadro's law, equal numbers of gas molecules occupy equal volumes. Fat, however, has far less oxygen in proportion to carbon and hydrogen than sugar does; hence fat requires proportionally more oxygen to oxidize it completely into water and carbon dioxide. For example, the formula for beef fat is $C_{57}H_{110}O_6$. Simple arithmetic will show that 81.5 volumes of oxygen will be required for every 57 volumes of carbon dioxide produced. Hence the respiratory quotient, R.Q., will be less than one, in this case 0.7. The R.Q. of proteins is intermediate between that of fats and carbohydrates. The amount of protein being metabolized is usually determined, however, by measuring the amount of nitrogen-containing compounds in the urine.

4. In mammals the **basic metabolic rate** depends on size. The basal rate is the rate at which oxygen is used when the animal is at complete rest. The smaller the animal, the higher the B.M.R. The reason for this inverse relationship is clear. Mammals maintain a constant body temperature above their surroundings and hence lose heat to it. Any solid object can lose heat only from its surface. By the facts of solid geometry, the smaller an object is the more surface it has *in proportion* to its volume or mass. Therefore it follows that to maintain a given temperature a small animal must burn more glucose per pound of flesh than a large one.

Inspection of Figure 27–12, where the weight of several homoiotherms (warm-blooded animals) is plotted on semi-log paper against their respiratory rate, will reveal that as size goes down, metabolic rate skyrockets. Because of their high rate of oxidation, very small mammals, like shrews which weigh only 3 or 4 grams, must eat almost continuously and are rightly known for their voracious appetites. They eat approximately their own weight every 24 hours or starve to death. It is the equivalent of a 150-pound man eating three 50-pound meals a day! The graph also makes it clear that about 2.5 grams is the lower limit for size of a warm-blooded animal. Below that, food intake presents an impossible problem.

Max Rubner, who discovered this relation between size and metabolic rate, suggested that it was causally related to longevity. Whether this is true or not, respiratory metabolism, heart beat, and aging in mice all race at a very rapid pace compared with their slow march in elephants.

The achievement of the present century has been to discover the actual metabolic pathways and processes by which energy is derived from food within the cells. This topic has been discussed earlier, pages 56 to 64.

Mechanics of Breathing. There are three general schemes to get oxygen to the cells and to get carbon dioxide away. Feathery **gills,** where circulating blood is brought into close proximity to water, are found both in vertebrates and invertebrates. **Trachea** characterize insects and a few other invertebrates. They permeate the

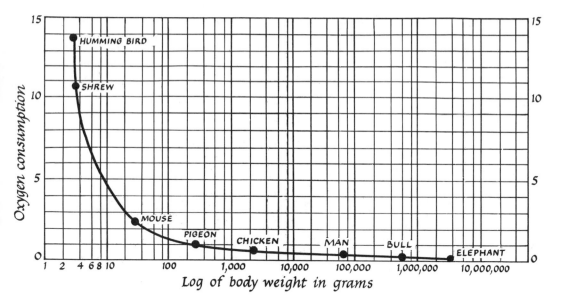

Fig. 27–12. Relation between oxygen consumption (in ml of O_2 per gram of wet body weight per hour) and actual weight of warm-blooded animals. Note that hummingbirds and shrews are close to the absolute minimum in size.

body with a treelike network of interconnected tubules penetrating the body almost completely. Like birds, mammals possess **lungs,** but unlike birds, the mechanics of lung action in mammals is simple.

At inspiration air is drawn into the lungs when a partial vacuum is created by the enlargement of the chest cavity. This is accomplished by the contraction of the muscles of ribs and diaphragm. The intercostal muscles between the ribs raise them and thereby enlarge the chest. The diaphragm is a dome-shaped sheet of muscle separating chest from abdominal cavity. When this muscle contracts it flattens the dome and thus likewise enlarges the cavity of the thorax and the volume of the lungs. During expiration the size of the chest cavity is decreased.

Air travels from the pharynx down the trachea and either the right or left bronchus into the corresponding lung. Each lung is attached only in the region of its bronchus. The rest of the lung hangs freely in its own pleural cavity. If a stab wound is made into a pleural cavity, air will be sucked in, the vacuum will be destroyed, and the lung collapses, making breathing impossible with that lung.

Regulation of Breathing. The new problems that the physiologists of the 19th century attacked were the physiological controls of breathing and the transport of O_2 and CO_2 by the blood. This last topic has been discussed in Chapter 26 on the circulation.

The control of breathing is under both chemical and nervous auspices and constitutes a beautiful self-regulating or **feedback mechanism.** Increasing concentrations of carbon dioxide in the blood stimulate a breathing center in the medulla, part of the myelencephalon. Impulses pass down the phrenic nerves from the brain to the diaphragm, cause it to contract, and thus produce inspiration. If the two phrenic nerves are cut, the diaphragm no longer contracts. Normally expansion of the lungs in turn stimulates sensory nerve endings, which send inhibitory impulses back to the brain via the two vagus nerves. Inhibition of the respiratory center in the medulla permits the diaphragm to relax, producing expiration. Impulses leading to exhalation also arise from the carotid body, a minor nerve center near the division of the external and internal carotid arteries, and from the aortic body, a similar nerve center on the aorta shortly after it leaves the heart. Movements of the joints of arms, hands, legs, and feet produce stimuli that accelerate the rate of breathing.

The role of carbon dioxide in stimulating breathing is of paramount importance to both anesthetists and high-altitude flyers. If a man breathes into a closed system in which his expired carbon dioxide is allowed to accumulate, his rate of breathing will increase markedly. If the expired carbon dioxide is absorbed, say by KOH, his breathing will increase only slightly. Note that in a closed system the decline in oxygen concentration will be the same in both cases.

The effects of lack of oxygen depend on the rapidity with which it occurs. If an aviator suddenly loses his oxygen supply or a miner walks into a pocket of methane or other gas, he is likely to "black out" very suddenly and completely. If the loss of oxygen is gradual, the results are quite different, but more or less the same whether the loss is due to carbon monoxide poisoning, alcoholism, or ascent into high altitudes. At first there is commonly a sense of well-being and competence. As the oxygen lack persists there comes a period of loss of judgment and unstable emotions, commonly accompanied by muscular incoordination, faulty vision, and poor memory. Fixed and irrelevant ideas are frequent. Finally, a feeling of sublime indifference and extreme weakness may end the series. In case of the continued deprivation of oxygen, these symptoms are followed by extreme nausea, convulsions, and finally death.

Too much oxygen is also dangerous. Various symptoms of toxicity begin to appear when the oxygen pressure (concentration) in the gas breathed by a mammal begins to exceed 0.8 atmospheres.

Review and References

REVIEW TOPICS

1. Identify by century and by scientific contribution: Hans Krebs, William Beaumont, W. B. Cannon, C. Bernard, Max Rubner, R. Boyle, A. L. Lavoisier, Bayliss and Starling, I. Pavlov.

2. In molecular terms, why does most food require digestion? What are the end-products of digestion from the three major classes of foods?

3. Why is absorption thought to be an active process?

4. What is the evidence that vitamins form part of enzyme molecules? (Recall Chapter 3.)

5. Give the chemical names and the functions of the water-soluble vitamins. Of the fat-soluble vitamins.

6. How could you prove that the stimulus from the duodenum to the pancreas to secrete is hormonal?

7. Discuss adaptations of the mammalian stomach. Of the mammalian intestine.

8. Discuss formation of urea.

9. What are the most important facts about protein requirements? What is the evidence that these "facts" are valid?

10. How is breathing regulated?

11. What are the "classical" laws of respiration?

12. What different roles does CO_2 play in the total process of respiration?

13. What is the adaptive advantage of having each lung in a separate pleural cavity?

USEFUL REFERENCES

Grollman, S., *The Human Body, Its Structure and Physiology,* New York, The Macmillan Company, 1964.

Krogh, A., *Comparative Physiology of Respiratory Mechanisms,* Philadelphia, University of Pennsylvania Press, 1959.

McHenry, E. W., and G. H. Beaton, *Basic Nutrition,* rev. ed., Philadelphia, J. B. Lippincott Co., 1963.

Chapter 28

Excretion

From amoeba to man excretory systems form an essential part of the homeostatic mechanisms which keep animals in physiological equilibrium. In an amoeba the primary – almost the sole – function of the contractile vacuole is to remove excess water. In other words, the contractile vacuole compensates for the fact that the animal lives in an environment that has a very low osmotic pressure. Control over the osmotic environment of the cells remains the primary function of the kidneys in mammals, but to this original function others have been added in the course of evolution. In man at least six important activities are centered in the kidneys and make them the most versatile organs of the body physiologically, with the possible exception of the liver. What the kidney does is not extremely difficult to discover though it has taken many decades and much hard thought and work. The way the kidney achieves all these results is only partially known even now. We will begin with the six chief functions.

WHAT THE KIDNEY DOES

The first function of the kidneys, both in evolution and in basic importance, is to hold constant the **osmotic pressure of the blood** so that it remains at a physiologically appropriate level. Were the blood to become too concentrated, the cells would shrivel; too dilute, and they would swell up and burst. Happily, you cannot dilute your blood no matter how much water you drink. With great precision, the kidneys will excrete exactly the correct amount of additional water. When water intake is restricted or water loss by evaporation increased (a man walking on a desert at 110°F loses a quart of water per hour from lungs and skin), then the kidneys excrete a smaller volume of more concentrated urine. The kidneys of camels are famous among physiologists for this ability. Various species of desert rats can do just as well.

A second important activity of the kidneys is to regulate the **pH of the blood plasma.** If the acidity of the plasma increases, i.e., if the pH falls, the kidneys excrete more hydrogen ions. If the blood becomes more alkaline, the kidneys excrete more bicarbonate. Since the concentration of sodium, calcium, and potassium bicarbonates in the plasma influences the osmotic pressure of the blood, it is obvious that the regulation of blood pH is closely related to the regulation of its osmotic pressure.

The elimination of **waste nitrogen** is a third major function of the kidneys. Most of the protein in the human diet is deaminated – has its nitrogen removed – as its constituent amino acids pass through the liver. This excess nitrogen is in the form of ammonia which is combined with CO_2 and converted into **urea** by the liver. Mammals also excrete nitrogen in the form of **creatinine** in small but virtually constant daily amounts. The actual amount is independent of the amount of protein ingested but depends on the total muscle mass of the individual. This is not too surprising since creatinine is a constituent of muscles.

Most mammals also secrete small amounts of nitrogen as **uric acid.** This compound may be built up from ammonia or other simple nitrogen compounds or it may be derived from the breakdown of the purines in nucleic acids. As can be seen below, uric acid is itself a purine not too different from adenine and guanine.

In man and most other mammals the uric acid is believed to come from the breakdown of DNA and RNA; in birds it is synthesized from waste nitrogen compounds for reasons to be discussed below. In most mammals uric acid is converted in the liver by the enzyme uricase into a simpler molecule, **allantoin,** which is then excreted. Man and the other primates, however, lack this enzyme and so secrete the uric acid as such. The amount of uric acid excreted is very small (0.008 – 0.2 grams per 24 hours) compared with the amount of urea eliminated (6 – 18 grams per 24 hours).

Uric acid is relatively harmless but when, for reasons which are very obscure but seem to have a genetic basis, its concentration in the human bloodstream becomes elevated, it is precipitated as more or less insoluble monosodium urate, especially in the joints. An extremely painful disease, gout, results. Mammals which have uricase in their livers are not supposed to be able to have gout. It is interesting to note that pigs and spiders lack the enzyme guanase so that the purine guanine is excreted as such, and guanine rather than urate gout has been observed in pigs.

Fourthly, the kidney excretes a very wide variety of substances, mostly **waste products** of liver metabolism or injurious substances processed by the liver. Included here is urochrome, a yellow pigment which gives urine its characteristic color. **Urochrome** is a degradation product of bile pigments ultimately derived from worn-out red blood cells. Among the virtually endless number of substances removed from the blood by the kidneys are glucose (if its concentration exceeds a threshold level), ketones and other products of deranged lipid and carbohydrate metabolism, breakdown products of the anti-nausea drug thalidomide, of coffee, and many other substances, vitamins, hormones, even a few amino acids.

A fifth and medically very important function of the mammalian kidney is the secretion of a substance which results in raising the hydrostatic pressure of the blood. The substance is **renin** (pronounced reenin). (Note that this is not rennin, spelled with two n's, an enzyme found in the stomach which coagulates the proteins of milk.) The kidney secretes renin whenever the blood pressure falls below a certain level. Because the kidney cannot form urine if the blood pressure is too low, it is adaptively important for it to have some automatic means of raising the pressure. Renin turns out to be an enzyme which acts on a protein in the blood to form a polypeptide called angiotensin. A second enzyme in the blood cuts off two amino acids from angiotensin, producing the active form which raises blood pressure by causing the arterioles to constrict.

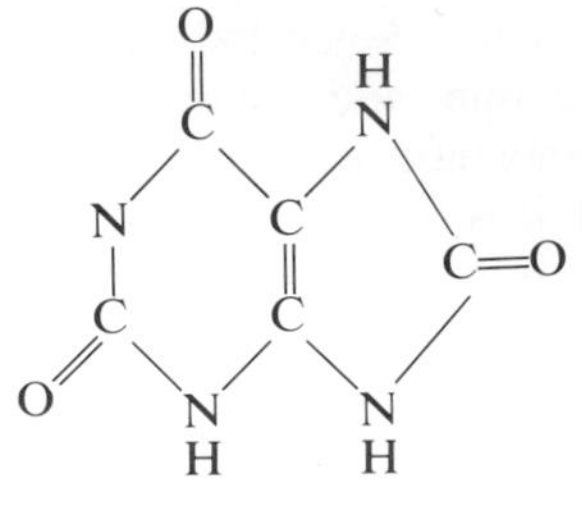

uric acid

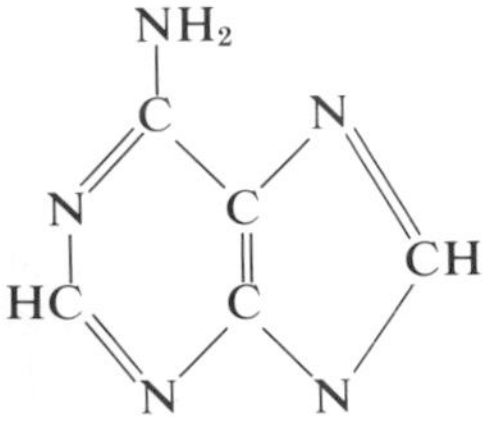

adenine

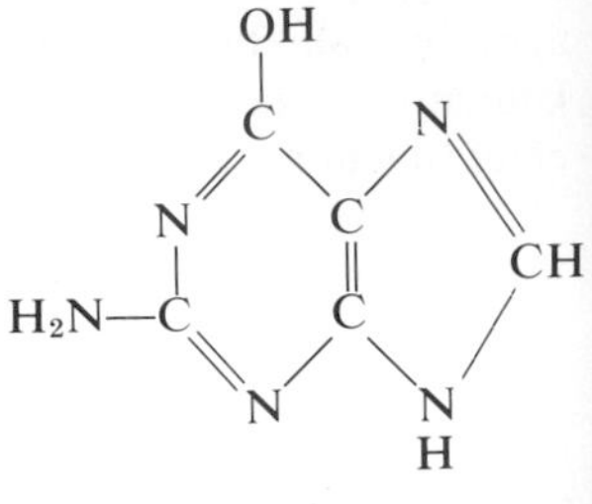

guanine

In addition to all this, there is a sixth important function located in the kidneys, the production of **erythropoietin,** a substance essential
for the formation of red blood cells. Normally
the formation of erythrocytes, a process called
erythropoiesis, exactly balances their aging and
destruction. In some indirect but effective
manner either hemorrhage or lack of oxygen, as
occurs in high altitudes, causes a marked increase in red cell production. Part of the evidence that the kidneys are involved is that if
they are removed, the increase in erythropoiesis is cut by about 90 per cent!

Thus the kidneys are the chief organs that
maintain the constancy of the "milieu inti-
rieure," the internal environment, as the pioneer
French physiologist, Claude Bernard, called the
blood and lymph.

THE ANATOMY OF EXCRETION

The gross anatomy of the mammalian excretory system is simple and essentially like that of
the reptiles. A pair of **kidneys** lie on either side
of the backbone a short distance posterior to
(below, in man) the diaphragm. They lie dorsal
to the coelom and are covered by the thin peritoneal epithelium which lines the coelomic cavity. Each kidney is served by a short **renal artery,** coming directly from the dorsal aorta, and
by a **renal vein.** From each kidney a **ureter**
carries urine to the **urinary bladder** in the pelvis. From the bladder the urine is conducted to
the exterior by the **urethra.**

The microscopic anatomy of the kidney was
first explored by Malpighi. He noticed small
round structures near the edges of the kidney.
They can be seen without dissection but with a
good hand lens close to the thin edges of a
frog's kidney. These little bodies are termed
Malphighian or **renal corpuscles.** Each renal
corpuscle is at the beginning of a long **tubule**
gether with which it forms the functional unit
of the kidney, the **nephron.** (See Fig. 20–21.)

Each renal corpuscle consists of a tuft of capillaries called the **glomerulus,** and its surrounding double-layered capsule called **Bowman's capsule.** The cavity between the capsule
layers opens into the beginning of the tubule.
This tubule is termed uriniferous, because it
produces urine. Immediately after its formation

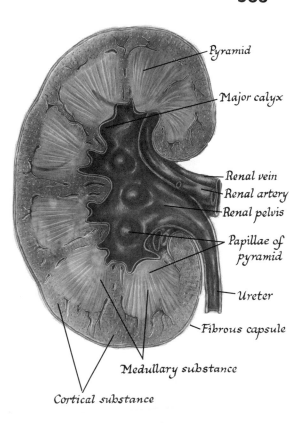

Pyramid

Major calyx

Renal vein
Renal artery
Renal pelvis

*Papillae of
pyramid*

Ureter

Fibrous capsule

Medullary substance

Cortical substance

Fig. 28–1. Mammalian kidney, longisection.
(After Grollman, The Human Body, Its
Structure and Physiology, *1964, The Mac-
millan Company)*

at Bowman's capsule the tubule becomes convoluted, then forms a long straight loop known
as **Henle's loop.** Each loop is about 3 cm long
and forms one of a cluster arranged in a so-
called pyramid pointing towards the central
region of the kidney. When a loop reaches
back to the renal corpuscle it forms a second or
distal convolution. The distal convolutions
empty into collecting tubes which in turn empty
into the pelvis of the kidney where the ureter
originates. It is important to note that the
blood vessels spread out over both proximal
and distal convolutions as well as Henle's loop.
Note also that there are a pair of vaso-constrictor nerves innervating the arteriole just before it
enters the glomerulus and again just as the
blood vessel leaves the glomerulus.

HOW THE KIDNEY WORKS

What does the kidney really do and how does it do it? This question is not only of evolutionary interest but also of the greatest medical importance. William Bowman discovered the capsule that bears his name a bit over a century ago and immediately proposed a theory of kidney action: **glomerular filtration** followed by **tubular secretion.** Carl Ludwig, the leader of the great Leipzig group of physiologists, immediately proposed a different theory, glomerular filtration followed by **reabsorption.** Thus arose a classic controversy which stimulated research the world over for decades and finally led to our present knowledge.

Filtration takes place from the glomerulus as long as the hydrostatic pressure of the blood exceeds the osmotic pressure. The hydrostatic pressure is imparted to the blood by the beating of the heart and tends to force the fluid constituents to pass through the thin membranes of the capillaries of the glomerulus and enter Bowman's capsule. On the other hand, blood proteins, urea, sugar, and other osmotically active blood components, all tend to pull liquid back into the blood. The hydrostatic pressure tending to force blood fluids out of the capillaries in the glomerulus is about 75 mm of mercury, an extremely high pressure due to the direct way the capillaries come off from the short, straight renal arteries which are themselves direct

Fig. 28–2. The Atlantic toadfish, *Opsanus tau,* which lacks renal corpuscles entirely. *(Kindness of William H. Amos)*

branches of the dorsal aorta. The osmotic pressure is about 30 mm of mercury.

This theory can be proved in three ways. If the hydrostatic pressure of the blood falls, due to a heart weakness or to experimental procedures, to a point where it is no greater than the osmotic pressure, the formation of urine will stop. If back pressure is applied up the ureter into the kidney, the formation of urine will stop when the applied pressure plus the osmotic pressure equal the hydrostatic pressure. Finally, direct proof can be obtained by collecting fluid from Bowman's capsule. The frog kidney was first used for such tests but other species have given confirming results. A small glass rod is pressed down to block the flow into the proximal tubule. As a result, Bowman's capsule swells up with fluid which can be collected in a fine glass micropipette. This fluid does, in fact, carry the same concentrations of salts, glucose, amino acids, urea, and other substances of small molecular size as does the blood plasma. It lacks the blood cells and the blood proteins. In other words, capsular fluid is merely a filtrate of the blood.

What about **reabsorption?** This is shown by the fact that if the glucose concentration in the blood does not exceed the threshold value of about 160 mg per ml none of it appears in the urine. Water too is reabsorbed, for the urine may be more concentrated than the fluid in Bowman's capsule. It has been shown that most of the sodium and chloride ions as well as bicarbonate are reabsorbed.

What about **secretion** of materials into the tubules? The first convincing evidence that tubular secretion as well as reabsorption is a fact came with the discovery that salt-water teleosts have either no glomeruli whatever or have reduced ones. The ugly little toadfish, *Opsanus tau,* of north Atlantic coastal waters must form its urine by secretion, because it lacks renal corpuscles entirely!

The first clear evidence for **active transport,** i.e., active secretion, in the mammalian kidney was gained by the use of an obvious method — obvious once you think of it. The dye phenol red is readily excreted in the urine after injection into the bloodstream. The dye could be in the urine entirely due to filtration and then concentration in the tubules by its failure to be reabsorbed with the watery part of the filtrate. The dye could be in the urine because of active secretion into the tubules. Or its presence might be the result of both processes. To test whether or not active secretion was taking place, the blood pressure in an experimental animal was lowered until filtration stopped. Phenol red was injected and later the tubules were observed to see if they were concentrating the dye. They were, especially in the proximal convolutions. In mammals, at least, there appears to be an active secretion of additional urea and other substances into the tubule.

Filtration into Bowman's capsule from the glomerulus is a passive process as far as the cells there are concerned. The necessary energy is provided by the heart beat. In contrast, reabsorption and secretion against a concentration gradient are both active processes which require energy at the site, i.e., in the tubule cells. Numerous mitochondria and abundant ATP would, therefore, be expected in tubular cells engaged in these activities. This expectation is fulfilled by electron microscope studies. Indeed the kidney has been found to require more energy per hour per gram of tissue than does an active muscle like the heart!

Cells specialized for absorption (in this case, reabsorption) would be expected to show the **brush border** familiar in the absorptive cells lining the intestine. Brush borders turn out to be characteristic of the cells in specific parts of the uriniferous tubules. Thus after more than a century and countless acrimonious publications as well as much hard and at times inspired work, it can confidently be said that both Bowman and Ludwig were right!

Regulation of Renal Action. The mammalian kidney is under both neural and hormonal control. A rich innervation reaches the kidney from both the sympathetic and parasympathetic nervous systems. By controlling the blood flow, these nerves indirectly regulate urine production.

The posterior lobe of the pituitary gland secretes an anti-diuretic hormone, **ADH,** which is essential for the normal reabsorption of water. If this hormone is lacking, the animal will secrete large quantities of urine, a condition called **diabetes insipidus,** in contrast to **diabetes**

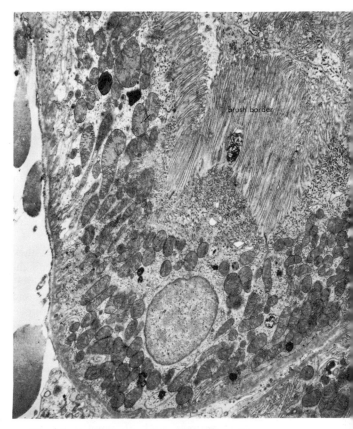

Fig. 28–3. Electron micrograph of brush border of typical absorption cell as seen in rat kidney. Note the large rounded nucleus in lower center and the numerous mitochondria. *(From Freeman,* Cellular Fine Structure. *Blakiston Div., McGraw-Hill Book Co., 1964)*

mellitus, of pancreatic origin, when the urine contains sugar.

The hormone **adrenalin** also affects urine flow by increasing blood pressure and possibly in other ways. If the adrenal cortex does not secrete properly there is marked retention of urea and other nitrogenous wastes, and a retention of potassium but a marked loss of sodium. These defects can be repaired by injection of deoxycorticosterone.

Finally the kidney itself produces the hormone-like substance, **renin,** which increases the blood pressure, and thus indirectly tends to increase urine flow. Renin is produced whenever the blood flow or oxygen supply to a kidney is reduced.

THE MODERN SYNTHESIS

Animals in general and the vertebrates specifically possess a bewildering variety of excretory structures and methods. Some fishes have kidneys with nephrons equipped with glomeruli essentially like those of a mammal while other fishes lack glomeruli completely. Some animals excrete urea, others retain much of it in their blood, still others do not produce appreciable amounts of urea. Modern knowledge of the fossil record, of the biochemistry of nitrogen wastes, and of the comparative anatomy and physiology of excretion enables us to make sense out of what had been a hodgepodge of apparently unrelated facts.

Some animals are **ammonotelic,** that is, they excrete most or all of their waste nitrogen simply as ammonia, NH_3. Most aquatic invertebrates, like the crustaceans, do this. Among vertebrates the ammonotelic groups comprise the teleosts and a few other fishes and larval amphibians like the tadpole. These animals all live in water which continuously bathes their gills. Ammonia is readily soluble in water and with a whole pond or lake to wash out the ammonia there is no problem. The kidneys play no important role.

Other animals, such as many fishes (other than teleosts), amphibians, turtles, and mammals, are **ureotelic,** that is, they excrete most of their waste nitrogen as urea produced by the ornithine cycle in the liver. Ornithine, an amino acid, takes up ammonia plus CO_2 and in a series of reactions releases urea plus ornithine again. Most ureotelic animals are terrestrial, with a good supply of available water but no gills. The clue is given by the frogs. When living as tadpoles in the water, waste ammonia is lost merely as ammonia. At metamorphosis into the more or less terrestrial frog which lacks gills, the liver gains new or increased amounts of enzymes so that the ornithine cycle becomes active and urea is produced. This harmless product can then be excreted dissolved in the urine.

Some fishes, notably sharks, produce considerable quantities of urea. The significance of these apparent exceptions will be discussed below.

The most completely terrestrial groups of animals, those living part of the time in the air or in deserts like the birds, lizards, insects, and land snails, are **uricotelic.** Almost all their waste nitrogen is built up into the relatively complex purine, uric acid. As any victim of gout knows, uric acid is relatively insoluble and forms even more insoluble salts, urates. This is precisely the adaptive point. Because uric acid precipitates out of solution so readily, most of the water can be reabsorbed, leaving, instead of any proper urine, the white or yellowish paste familiar in the droppings of birds and some reptiles. It is worth noting that aquatic larvae of some insects—mayflies, for example—excrete ammonia until they become adult, when they perform the same kind of switchover that the tadpole does.

In the light of these facts, the adaptive or **evolutionary explanation** of the various ways of handling excess nitrogen is becoming clear. So also is the presence or absence of a glomerulus. Fossil and other evidence has been accumulating in recent decades which indicates that although all the major groups of animals originated in the sea, the fishes originated in fresh water. Apparently, some primitive marine chordates took to swimming up into estuaries and rivers, taking advantage of the rich organic detritus that began washing down from the land after the land had finally been colonized by plants. This behavior is evidently what a notochord—and later a backbone—is all about. It enables the animals to swim upstream against the currents that would wash them out into the ocean.

But living in fresh water, with its very low osmotic pressure, presents a problem for any animal whose blood and tissues are isosmotic with sea water. No longer will it be sufficient to eliminate wastes merely by the possession of a ciliated tube leading from the coelom to the exterior. The high osmotic pressure of the blood will "pull in" water. Consequently, if the blood and lymph are not to become disastrously hypo-osmotic, i.e., have a lower osmotic pressure than the cells, some means must be developed to get rid of the excess water. Otherwise the cells would swell and be killed. Hence any mutation in the direction of a tuft of capillaries, that is, a glomerulus, which would filter off some of the fluid from the blood would be an advantage in natural selection. So also would any mutation that enabled the tube that carried

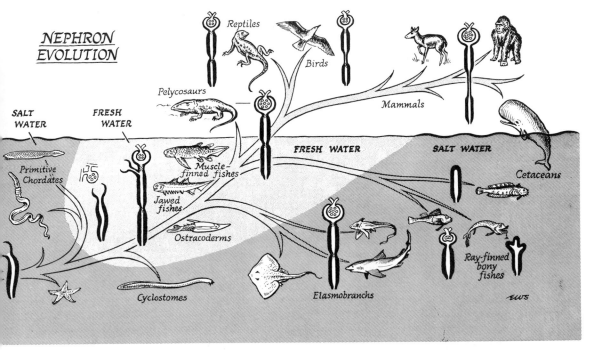

Fig. 28–4. Evolution of the vertebrate nephron. The nephrons, shown in black, are highly diagrammatic and are not all drawn to the same scale. Early salt-water animals (left) developed simple tubules. Most of their descendants, living in fresh water, evolved nephrons more efficient in water elimination. From these fresh-water forms arose land animals, some of which later returned to the sea. Both changes required ingenious modifications of nephron form and function. *(After "The Kidney" by H. W. Smith. Copyright © Jan. 1953 by Scientific American, Inc. All rights reserved)*

off the excess fluid to reabsorb glucose and other materials of value. In this path lies the evolution of the typical vertebrate kidney.

In the course of adaptive radiation at least three groups of vertebrates have returned from fresh water, or even land, to live again in the salty ocean. But by the time this happened, the sea had become saltier than it had been when those remote ancestral chordates started swimming up the rivers. Salts are continually being washed down from the continents into the ocean, and eon after eon of evaporation from the sea results in a great distillation which further concentrates the salts. The problem of adaptation has now been reversed. The animals returning to the sea found that their body fluids matched the ancient seas from which their ancestors had come and were definitely hypotonic to the "new" oceans. This more concentrated sea tended to pull water out of their bloodstream. The problem now was to conserve water. This problem has been met in several ways.

The **sharks** and other elasmobranchs were apparently the first to return to the sea. They met the osmotic problem by converting their waste nitrogen into urea, a relatively harmless compound, and retaining enough of it in their blood to raise the osmotic pressure to meet that of the surrounding sea water. As one physiologist has said, they are the only vertebrates to have achieved osmotic dominance over the oceans. There was virtually no structural change in the kidney.

The **bony fishes** returned to the sea somewhat later. Some species to a certain extent also converted waste nitrogen into urea and retained some of it in their blood. But many bony fishes which returned to the sea accumulated mutations in a new direction, the reduction of the glomerulus. This tended to eliminate the loss of much of the water at its source, namely, filtration in the renal corpuscle. In some species, such as the toadfish, *Opsanus tau,* the glomerulus has been completely abolished. However, it is not surprising that in an animal breathing by means of gills the abolition of the glomerulus was not enough. In some species retention of urea supplements the saving made by the lack of a glomerulus. In other, and sometimes the same, species salt is excreted from the blood by special glandular cells in the gills, thus keeping the osmotic pressure of the blood down.

The third group of vertebrates to return to live permanently in the sea are the **porpoises** and other cetaceans. The blood of marine mammals is more concentrated than that of terrestrial mammals but not enough more to hold water against the higher osmotic concentration of the sea. The resulting problem is at least alleviated by the fact that whales and porpoises are air breathing and so do not have gills constantly exposed to the sea water. Furthermore, marine mammals can secrete urine which is more concentrated than sea water. In other terms, their nephrons possess great powers of water reabsorption. Porpoises, dolphins, and some of the smaller whales live largely on bony fishes, which, as explained above, are hypo-osmotic to the sea water. Consequently, if they do not swallow appreciable amounts of sea water when they eat, a diet of teleosts will not add a disproportionate amount of salt. The large whales live on marine invertebrates whose blood and body fluids are more concentrated than that of any mammal. Physiological studies on whales are obviously extremely awkward but it has been calculated that if the kidneys could excrete somewhat more salt and urea and reabsorb more water than terrestrial mammals, all would be well. One might expect them to produce uric acid after the manner of birds but this does not seem to be the case.

It should be mentioned that marine birds which subsist on a diet of fishes and marine invertebrates not only conserve water by secreting uric acid paste instead of urine, but many of them also have salt-secreting glands within the nostrils.

Review and References

REVIEW TOPICS

1. Enumerate the functions of the mammalian kidney.

2. What is the evidence for tubular reabsorption? What are some of the substances reabsorbed?

3. What is the evidence for tubular secretion, i.e., active transport?

4. Define: ureter, urethra, Henle's loop, renal corpuscle, Bowman's capsule, renin, erythropoietin, diabetes insipidus, purine, isosmotic, elasmobranch.

5. How are ammonotelic, ureotelic, and uricotelic animals each adapted for their mode of life?

6. Would you expect a shark to have a higher blood pressure than a mammal? Why?

7. Under what circumstances is it an advantage to the kidney to secrete renin? Why?

8. What is the role of the anti-diuretic hormone?

9. Describe a single mammalian nephron.

10. What is noteworthy about excretion of creatinine, purines, phenol red, uric acid?

11. Why might the large whales be expected to excrete a uric acid paste instead of urine—in other words, to have an excretory physiology similar to that of birds?

USEFUL REFERENCES

Grollman, S., *The Human Body, Its Structure and Physiology,* New York, The Macmillan Company, 1964.

Prosser, C. L., and F. A. Brown, Jr., *Comparative Animal Physiology,* Philadelphia, W. B. Saunders Co., 1961.

Smith, H. W., *The Kidney: Structure and Function in Health and Disease,* New York, Oxford University Press, 1951.

Snively, W. D., *Sea Within Us: The Story of Our Body Fluids,* Philadelphia, J. B. Lippincott Co., 1960.

Tuttle, W. W., and B. A. Schottelius, *Textbook of Physiology,* 15th ed., St. Louis, The C. V. Mosby Co., 1965.

Chapter 29

Endocrine Systems

Hormones exert a general control over the intelligence, growth, reproduction, metabolism, and behavior of man and the other vertebrates. They also govern many aspects of the lives of invertebrates, notably the arthropods. Moreover, it is now becoming clear that most vertebrate hormone systems are under the control of the nervous system at some point.

The digestive glands and some of the other glands discussed in earlier chapters are known as **exocrine** glands because they possess ducts which carry the secretion — saliva, for example — from the gland of origin and empty it into some body cavity. The glands which produce hormones are called **endocrine** because they lack such ducts. Their products are taken up by the bloodstream and carried to one or more **"target organs,"** perhaps the comb and feathers of a rooster or the lining of the uterus of some mammal, and there have their effect.

Among vertebrates most endocrine glands secrete under the stimulus of specific hormones produced by the pituitary gland (itself an endocrine gland) on the under side of the brain. If the pituitary is removed, the thyroid, gonads, and other endocrine glands stop secreting and may even degenerate. On the other hand, these glands exert an inhibitory influence on the pituitary. In other words, the pituitary turns these glands on and they reach back, so to speak, and turn the pituitary off with their hormones. The result is a self-regulatory **feedback mechanism** which may result in a periodic rise and fall in hormone level. This is the explanation of the familiar female reproductive cycles in mammals. The same feedback mechanism may also lead to a steady-state equilibrium. Over these various cycles and responses the nervous system imposes a measure of control, sometimes slight, sometimes complete.

FOUNDATIONS OF ENDOCRINOLOGY

Historical Beginnings. Many observations are cited as the beginning of endocrinology. The effects of castration on the growth, bodily conformation, and behavior of domestic animals have been known for centuries. Eunuchs were commonplace in many of the civilizations of antiquity. In fact castrati were used as professional singers in Europe until about a century ago.

Scientific knowledge of hormones really dates from the 19th century. For example, about 1850, shortly after Johannes Müller and Jacob Henle, the most eminent physiologist and anatomist, respectively, of their time, had asserted that the ductless glands had little or no effect on animals, A. A. Berthold, a man otherwise unknown to history and located in a small

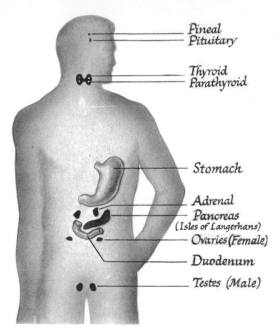

Fig. 29–1. Position of the endocrine glands in the human body.

provincial German university, showed by castration and by the transplantation of the testes that these glands of a rooster are essential for comb growth and normal rooster behavior. At the same time Thomas Addison, in London's famous Guy's Hospital, described a strange fatal disease in which the victim becomes a weird purple-gray and grows progressively weaker and more emaciated until death ensues. Autopsy always shows a diseased adrenal gland. This is the first accurate account of a disease associated with an endocrine disorder. It is only within the present decade that Addison's disease has been brought under even partial control through the use of ACTH (adrenocorticotrophic hormone) and synthetic adrenal steroids.

Certainly the discovery of J. F. von Mering and Oscar Minkowski in 1889 that dogs from whom the pancreas is removed develop diabetes is an important landmark in the history of endocrinology.

The first clear and convincing proof that a substance secreted by the cells of one organ could be carried by the bloodstream and produce a specific effect on a distant target organ was provided by the work of Bayliss and Starling in 1902. As described earlier (page 547),

when they discovered secretin and coined the word hormone the science of endocrinology was truly launched. It has been well said that it often requires a critical mass of data before a new concept wins general acceptance.

Methods of Study. A more or less standard procedure for the identification and study of endocrine glands has been developed through the years. The first step is usually examination of the suspected cells with an ordinary light microscope. The cells of endocrine glands — pituitary, gonad, adrenal, and the rest — suggest their secretory function by their structure. The cells tend to be cuboidal and filled with granules. The gland is well vascularized. With an electron microscope well-developed endoplasmic reticulum and Golgi complex are visible.

The orthodox test for actual endocrine activity is a double one. Remove the gland surgically, keeping a sharp lookout for accessory glands in unexpected places, and then observe the results. Implant the gland into another animal, or better yet, make an extract and inject. Both aqueous and fat-soluble extracts must be tried. Often the results have been spectacular. Sometimes, however, the effects of glands have been missed completely, because no one knew what effects to look for or else removed the glands at the wrong time in the life of the animal. This happened over and over again in the case of the adrenal, the thymus, and the pineal glands.

The third phase in the analysis of a hormone is chemical identification. To accumulate enough hormone sometimes requires almost superhuman efforts. To get enough of the insect growth hormone, for example, the glands of several barrels of insects had to be dissected out, homogenized, and the extract concentrated! Once the active material has been identified, the fourth step is the laboratory synthesis of the hormone molecule.

Chemical Nature of Hormones. Chemically, hormones fall into two major groups. Some are steroids; some are polypeptides or simply amino acids.

The sex hormones and the hormones of the adrenal cortex are **steroids.** This means they are fat-soluble compounds closely related to vitamin D, cholesterol, and bile salts. Other steroids include potent cancer-producing agents, embryonic inductors, and the very useful heart drug, digitalis.

All steroids are built around the same chemical nucleus consisting of four joined carbon rings. Three are six-carbon rings and one is a five-carbon ring. As shown in the formula, these rings are given conventional letters and their carbon atoms are given numbers for identification. A keto group, $-\overset{|}{C}=O$, in position 17, for example, makes a 17-ketosteroid. All the carbons in the basic steroid configuration, carbons 1 to 19, are derived from acetyl-Co A, mostly from acetic acid. Once again the pivotal position of acetyl-Co A becomes apparent. The various hormones are produced by adding keto, hydroxy, methyl, or other groups to one of the 19 carbons.

The hormones of the pituitary, thyroid, and pancreatic glands are proteins or, in the case of the thyroid, simply an amino acid. These hormones are water soluble. The hormone insulin from the pancreas, for example, consists of two chains, one of 21 and one of 30 amino acids. The pair of amino acid chains is held together at two fixed points on the polypeptide chains by disulfide bonds, i.e., $-S-S-$, between cystines. It will be recalled that cystine is an amino acid containing sulfur. The whole insulin molecule has a molecular weight of about 5,700. Glucagon, the other pancreatic hormone, which has an effect on blood sugar opposite to that of insulin, consists of a single chain of 29 amino acids and has a molecular weight of about 3,500. These are low molecular weights. Hemoglobin has a molecular weight of 68,000; the pituitary growth hormone, somatotropin, 25,000 to 48,000, depending on the species and probably on whether or not it is a double molecule.

How Do Hormones Work? There are three important theories of hormone action. The most recent and most convincing is that hormones work at the **gene level.** There is also good evidence that hormones work by changing the **permeability of cell membranes** and thus change metabolism by accelerating or blocking the entrance of certain substrates into the cell. A third theory holds that hormones act on **enzymes,** perhaps by acting as co-enzymes. The newest theory will be discussed first because the evidence for it is most convincing and because it may explain the data which support the other two.

The gene level theory originated in work in Germany on the insect hormone **ecdysone.** It will be recalled from the chapter on development that Beerman, Clever, and Karlson showed that ecdysone activated certain genetic loci on the chromosomes of the salivary glands of diptera and that this activation showed itself by puffing of specific regions. Other workers investigating bacteria demonstrated that the antibiotic actinomycin blocks the formation of new RNA. Other antibiotics were shown to block protein synthesis. Here then was the idea and the tools to test it.

In several laboratories here and abroad investigators working with different hormones on different animals have obtained convincing evidence for the following theory which is as simple as it is fundamental. Hormones initiate the transcription of specific parts of the genetic code, that is, initiate the formation of RNA presumably by combining with genetic repressors. New RNA, of course, means new enzymes. New enzymes mean changes in metabolism and a wide range of possible new products.

Clear evidence comes from studies of female sex hormone. If the ovaries of a rat are removed, the endometrium lining the uterus remains permanently in the reduced, anestrous condition. If estrogen is then injected into the rat, an increase in uterine RNA can be detected within half an hour. After three or four hours an increase in protein can be measured and the uterus begins to grow into the estrous condition. These facts in themselves support the theory. After hormone injection new RNA appears first, followed later by new protein.

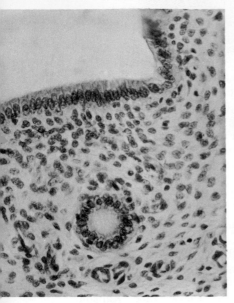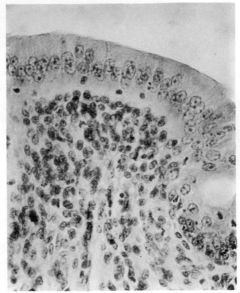

Fig. 29–2. Rat uterus. Left: after castration. Note the very thin, anestrous condition of the endometrial epithelium. Right: after castration and subsequent injection with estrogen. Note the striking enlargement of the endometrial cells while the mass of underlying mesodermal cells remain much the same. (*Kindness of Sheldon Segal*)

Confirming evidence has been obtained by the administration of actinomycin, which is known to inhibit formation of RNA, some time before injecting the female sex hormone. Under these conditions no new RNA appears, there is no subsequent increase in protein, and the uterus remains anestrous.

A second argument is the work on insulin. It has been known for over two centuries that patients with diabetes mellitus excrete sugar in their urine. More modern research has shown that the excretion of sugar is the result of a high level of glucose in the blood and that this is due to a lack of the hormone insulin normally secreted by the pancreas. However, the lack of insulin results in other defects such as the lack of the enzymes to synthesize fatty acids in the proper way and to make liver glycogen. Administration of insulin corrects both the blood glucose level and the lack of those enzymes.

What happens if actinomycin is given to a patient or to an experimental animal before the administration of insulin? If insulin acts by initiating the transcription of genetic information, i.e., if it results in the formation of new RNA, then any process which depends on new enzymes or other new proteins would not be corrected. The actinomycin would have blocked that. The results fit the gene level theory because the enzyme deficiencies are not corrected. However, the results in part fit the other theories about changes in cell permeability or effects on existing enzymes because the

level of sugar in the blood does fall to normal levels! Somehow more glucose gets into the cells but whether this is by some direct effect of insulin or due to some round-about result is extremely difficult to tell.

The more interesting of the two older theories holds that insulin lowers the concentration of blood glucose by facilitating glucose use. It will be recalled that all carbohydrates must be reduced to glucose before they can be metabolized, and that the first step in glucose utilization is its phosphorylation by ATP and the enzyme hexokinase.

$$\text{glucose} + \text{ATP} \xrightarrow[\text{kinase}]{\text{hexo-}} \text{glucose-6-phosphate} + \text{ADP}$$

Insulin by itself has no effect on the action of hexokinase but hexokinase is inhibited by some of the pituitary and adreno-cortical hormones. Insulin blocks this inhibition and thereby increases the utilization of glucose. It is very possible that the modes of action of steroid and protein hormones are different.

THE GLANDS AND THEIR HORMONES

The Thyroid. A mammal's thyroid gland forms two lobes pressed against either side of the trachea and connected with each other by a narrow band of thyroid tissue, so that the entire gland resembles a pair of saddle bags. Microscopic examination reveals that the gland is

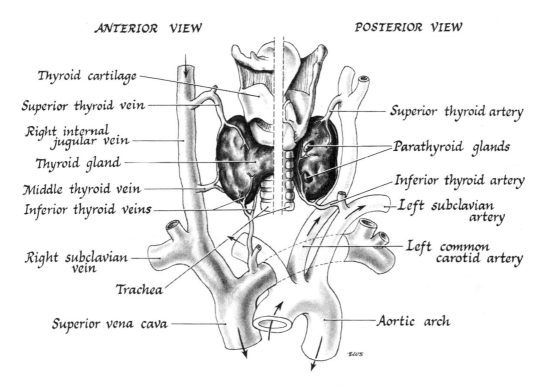

Thyroid cartilage

Superior thyroid vein

Right internal jugular vein

Thyroid gland

Middle thyroid vein

Inferior thyroid veins

Right subclavian vein

Trachea

Superior vena cava

Superior thyroid artery

Parathyroid glands

Inferior thyroid artery

Left subclavian artery

Left common carotid artery

Aortic arch

Fig. 29‑3. Thyroid, parathyroids, and adjacent structures in man; two views. *(After Turner,* General Endocrinology, *2nd ed., W. B. Saunders)*

composed of thousands of more or less spherical follicles made up of secretory cells enclosing a colloidal material. The gland is so highly vascularized that more blood flows through it, in proportion to its size, than through any other organ except perhaps the adrenal glands.

The thyroid gland has long thrust itself on human attention because of the drastic results of its malfunctioning. Marked underfunction, or **hypothyroidism,** in small children produces **cretins.** These pitiful individuals are greatly stunted, woefully feebleminded, and have characteristic bloated faces, and bodies with loose, wrinkled skin and coarse, sparse hair. Basal metabolism, body temperature, and heart rate all are abnormally low. If thyroid deficiency occurs in adult life the thyroid may enlarge greatly in an "attempt" at compensation, and form a swelling in the throat called a **goiter.** Sometimes goiter is accompanied by many symptoms of cretinism; in other cases it is not, perhaps depending on whether or not the enlarged gland supplies minimal needs.

Cretins and goiterous persons used to be commonly found in localities far from the sea,

Fig. 29‑4. Section through the thyroid gland of a normal dog, showing cross section of the rounded follicles containing a colloid rich in thyroxin and surrounded by the secretory thyroid cells. *(From Ham,* Histology, *4th ed., J. B. Lippincott)*

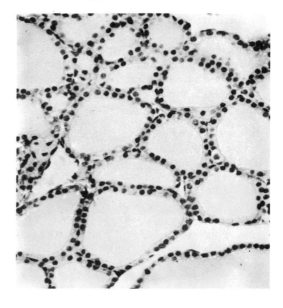

Fig. 29–5. Patient with exophthalmic goiter. Note the protruding eyeballs and swollen neck. *(Massachusetts General Hospital)*

such as isolated valleys in the Alps and Pyrenees and in the interior of continents, where there is a marked deficiency of iodine in the diet. Dramatic recoveries can be accomplished by feeding thyroid gland, iodine, or the synthetically made hormone thyroxin to hypothyroid patients. The blank face gains expression, the bloated body assumes a normal shape, and the mind brightens.

Hyperthyroidism, or oversecretion of the thyroid, sends the basal metabolism to abnormal heights and produces a hyperactive and unpleasantly irritable animal or man. Such patients commonly have protruding eyeballs (exophthalmia), a rapid heart beat, high metabolic

rate, and some thyroid enlargement, i.e., goiter.

The hormone of the thyroid gland is an amino acid, **thyroxin.** It is an iodine-carrying modification of another amino acid, tyrosine. Omitting some intermediate steps, the synthesis of thyroxin proceeds as shown at the bottom of the page. If two of the four atoms of iodine in thyroxin are exchanged for hydrogens, the potency is greatly reduced. If hydrogen is substituted for all four iodine atoms, the resulting compound is without thyroid activity in either mammal or tadpole.

That iodine is concentrated by the thyroid gland can be readily shown by injecting radioactive iodine into a mammal. Within an hour the iodine shows up in the cells constituting the walls of the thyroid follicles. Later the radioactive material appears within the follicles. The follicles become full of a colloidal thyroxin-globulin complex of high molecular weight, evidently a storage compound. Triiodothyronine (which is merely thyroxin with one fewer iodine atom) is found in blood and tissues and although in lower concentrations than thyroxin is, it is far more potent. Perhaps this is so merely because it does not bind with globulin like thyroxin itself does, and so penetrates into cells more easily.

The principal result of thyroxin on mammalian tissues is to increase cellular metabolism. Its role in the metamorphosis of amphibians has been discussed previously. The mechanism of its action there is unknown, but it probably indicates that the stimulating effect of thyroxin on the incorporation of amino acids into proteins by rat liver ribosomes has been localized at the step involving soluble RNA. Thyroxin has an effect on mitochondria like that of dinitrophenol, – it uncouples oxidative

tyrosine

diiodotyrosine

thyroxin

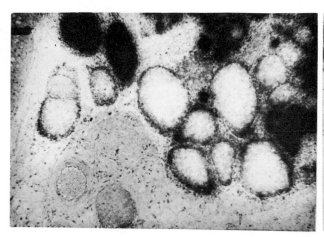 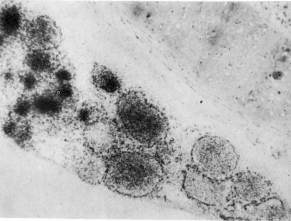

Fig. 29–6. Thyroid autographs of rats sacrificed after administration of radioactive iodine. Iodine is indicated by darkening of the photographic plate. Left: rat sacrificed after 1 hour. Iodine is concentrated just within the follicles shown in cross section. Right: rat sacrificed after 24 hours. Radioactive material is now distributed throughout the interior of the follicles. *(Kindness of C. P. Leblond and J. Gross)*

phosphorylation so that although sugar is oxidized and heat is liberated, no ATP is synthesized in the final flavo-protein-cytochrome pathway of oxidative respiration. It's a puzzle.

The activity of the thyroid gland is dependent on a thyrotropic hormone from the anterior lobe of the pituitary. Thyroxin itself inhibits the formation of thyrotropin either by acting directly on the anterior pituitary or through inhibiting cells in the hypothalamus, the action of which is required for the formation and release of thyrotropin by the pituitary. In amphibians the role of the hypothalamus seems well established. In any case, a feedback system between thyroid and anterior pituitary that maintains a very stable output of thyroxin is certain, modulated apparently by neural influences from the hypothalamus. It is worth noting that a synthetic pyrimidine, thiouracil, will block thyroxin formation. The fact that thiouracil is a pyrimidine suggests that this compound also might act at the gene level.

The Parathyroids. The parathyroids are four small glands either on or embedded in the thyroid, two on each side. In some way they control calcium and potassium metabolism. In dogs and carnivores generally, parathyroidectomy leads to a serious lowering of blood cal-

cium levels, muscular spasms increasing in severity into total tetany, and ultimate death. The symptoms are usually much less severe in omnivorous and herbivorous animals, although rabbits die promptly from severe and intractable tetany when deprived of their parathyroids. Rats can survive parathyroidectomy for long periods, but the bones become deossified in some regions while abnormal bony deposits occur at other sites. Cataract has been observed as a common concomitant of parathyroid deficiency in man.

The Adrenals. The adrenal glands of mammals are a pair of more or less rounded, highly vascularized structures situated either close to or against the kidneys—hence the name, *adrenal.* The central part of each gland is called the **medulla** and secretes two similar hormones which are modifications of the amino acid tyrosine and are often grouped together under the term **adrenalin.** The outer part of the gland, the **cortex,** secretes several steroids of which the best known is **cortisone.**

The hormones synthesized by the medulla are **epinephrine** and **norepinephrine.** They differ only in that epinephrine has a methyl group which norepinephrine lacks. The formulas for both compounds are given on the next page.

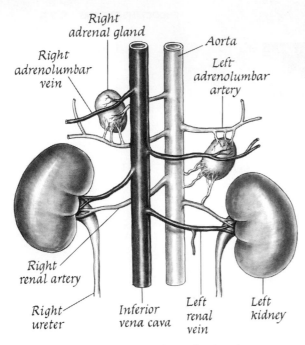

Fig. 29–7. Adrenals and related structures in the cat. Note excellent blood supply of the adrenals.

$$\text{HO}—\langle\text{ring}\rangle—\overset{|}{\text{CH}}—\text{CH}_2—\text{N}\overset{\text{H}}{\underset{\text{CH}_3}{}}$$
$$\overset{|}{\text{OH}}\quad\overset{|}{\text{OH}}$$

epinephrine

$$\text{HO}—\langle\text{ring}\rangle—\overset{|}{\text{CH}}—\text{CH}_2—\text{N}\overset{\text{H}}{\underset{\text{H}}{}}$$
$$\overset{|}{\text{OH}}\quad\overset{|}{\text{OH}}$$

norepinephrine

When injected into experimental animals the two hormones have similar but not identical effects. Epinephrine is the classic hormone which mobilizes the physiological resources of an animal "for fight or flight." Heart rate, blood pressure, and blood flow through muscles, liver, and brain are all increased. Blood sugar is also increased. Digestive and genital systems are inhibited. Norepinephrine inhibits everything that epinephrine does but it increases the heart rate only slightly and has little effect on blood flow through the various organs. Norepinephrine has only a very slight effect on blood glucose concentration, increasing it only about one-twentieth as much as epinephrine.

The relationship of these two very similar hormones is problematic. Norepinephrine is secreted in large amounts by carnivores like the cat and in very small amounts by herbivores such as the rabbit. It has been claimed that human subjects secrete more norepinephrine when angry and more epinephrine when merely passively afraid. However, it is important to remember that nervous impulses arriving via the sympathetic nervous system (see Fig. 31–9) are transmitted to their end organ, often a smooth muscle, by epinephrine. Also, there are reasons to believe that norepinephrine is merely the precursor of epinephrine and is converted into it by simple methylation.

The cortex of the adrenal glands is essential to life. About 30 different cortical steroids have been extracted but probably not more than half a dozen are normally active, and only three appear chiefly responsible for the multitudinous effects of these hormones. **Aldosterone** is essential for normal water and mineral metabolism although it influences many other bodily functions. **Cortisol** has some influence on water and mineral metabolism but a pronounced effect on carbohydrate, lipid, and protein metabolism and on inflammatory processes and response to various stresses such as cold, fever, great fatigue, pain, toxins, etc. The third major hormone is the familiar **cortisone** which has a very broad spectrum of effects including those produced by the other two.

aldosterone

cortisol

$$CH_2OH$$
$$C=O$$
$$OH$$

cortisone

The results of the gradual atrophy of the adrenal cortex, as in **Addison's disease,** has already been described. Extirpation of the glands brings death within a few days. Oversecretion or deranged secretion of the adrenal cortex is also a serious affliction. Some of the cortical hormones have a masculinizing effect. If oversecretion begins in childhood, the voice deepens and facial, axillary, and pubic hair develop in a typical or exaggerated masculine way even in genetic girls. Muscular development may produce an adultlike dwarf of herculean conformation. In genetic boys, although the penis may attain adult size, the testes remain infantile or even abnormally underdeveloped. Oversecretion in adults causes similar but less striking results. The bearded women of circuses are victims of adrenal disease.

In populations of mammals such as deer, woodchucks, and mice, a number of competent investigators have reported enlargement of the adrenal glands and decrease in reproductive competence under great crowding, i.e., stress. This response may be consistent and may act as a brake on population growth.

The secretion of the adrenal cortex is under the usual feedback control with the anterior pituitary which secretes a polypeptide ACTH, adreno-cortico-tropic hormone. Without it the cortex fails to secrete. Whether the cortical steroids regulate their own production by inhibiting the pituitary directly or by way of the hypothalamus is still uncertain, but the role for the hypothalamus seems highly probable.

The Pancreas. The pancreas is an elongate gland beside the intestine close to the stomach. It is sometimes sold, along with the thymus gland, as sweetbreads. It is a double gland. It secretes a digestive pancreatic juice via the pancreatic duct into the intestine, and two hor-

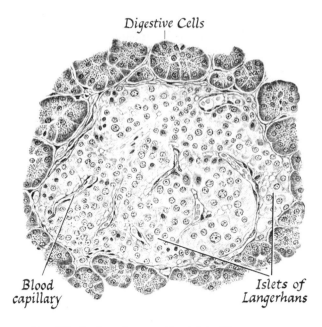

Fig. 29 – 8. Insulin-secreting islet of Langerhans surrounded by darkly staining acini or lobules which secrete pancreatic juice. *(From Smith and Copenhaver,* Bailey's Textbook of Histology, *Williams & Wilkins)*

mones, insulin and glucagon, elaborated in nests of cells called the **islets of Langerhans.** These islets lie scattered throughout the body of the gland except in some fishes where they form a separate lobe.

Lack of **insulin** causes diabetes mellitus, a disease described by the ancient Greeks as the ailment in which "the flesh melts away into urine." Nearly 2,000 years later a 17th century English anatomist and physician noticed that the urine of diabetics was sweet, so to the classic symptoms of excessive thirst, excessive urination, and great emaciation, a fourth was added, excretion of sugar.

About 200 years later still, in typical 19th century experiments, von Mering and Minkowski discovered something really new. Extirpation of the pancreas of a dog causes diabetes! It could not be from lack of the digestive juice, because if the pancreatic duct were brought to the surface of the body so all the pancreatic juice merely dropped to the ground, the dogs did not develop diabetes. In 1900 Eugene Opie, a member of the first class of the Johns

Hopkins Medical School, discovered that the islet cells in diabetic patients were atrophied.

Two kinds of cells, called arbitrarily alpha and beta cells, make up most of the islets of Langerhans. The **alpha cells** are somewhat larger than the beta cells, lie near the periphery of the islets, and have a granular cytoplasm which stains differently from the granules of the smaller, more centrally placed beta cells. It is the **beta cells** that atrophy in diabetes, and they are the ones that secrete insulin. Moreover, a synthetic pyrimidine called **alloxan** causes diabetes when administered to animals. The beta cells degenerate. The way alloxan knocks out the beta cells is unknown at this time, but it is interesting to note that pyrimidines form part of nucleic acids and to recall that thiouracil is also a pyrimidine.

The alpha cells secrete a hormone, **glucagon,** which has the opposite effect on blood glucose from insulin. Instead of decreasing the level of glucose, glucagon increases it. The existence of such a hormone came to light after it was found that patients from whom the entire pancreas had been removed (because of cancer) required less insulin to keep the blood sugar down to normal levels than patients with naturally occurring diabetes. This indicates that the pancreas produces something which tends to increase the concentration of glucose.

The dramatic story has often been told of how a young surgeon from a small Canadian city (where there were not enough patients to keep him busy) discovered how to extract insulin from the pancreas. The difficulty was that the potent digestive enzymes of the pancreas always tore the insulin molecules apart during the process of extraction. Frederick Banting solved that problem.

The Gonads. The actions and sources of the sex hormones will be discussed in Chapter 30 on reproduction. It seems highly probable that they all produce their effects on the growth and pigmentation of their various target organs by initiating the transcription of new RNA. This certainly seems to be the case with female sex hormone and the lining of the uterus. The effects which sex hormones have on the behavior of vertebrates appear to be due to direct action

of the hormone on specific cells in the brain, actually in the hypothalamus. This topic will be discussed more fully in the chapter on animal behavior.

It should be noted that although the primary **estrogen** (female sex hormone) produced by the Graafian follicles of the ovary is **estradiol,** this hormone is often found in a slightly modified form called **estrone** in many tissues including the ovary itself, the placenta, the adrenal cortex, and even the testis. Paradoxical as it seems, the testes and urine of stallions are among the richest sources of estrogen. Of course they carry even more male sex hormone, **androgen.** There has never been any satisfactory explanation for this fact. It may have some adaptive value. It may simply be due to some inefficient biochemical mechanism on the part of horses.

estradiol   estrone

Progesterone is secreted by the corpora lutea of the ovary after pregnancy has occurred; it is necessary for the continuance of the pregnancy. This hormone has a molecular structure similar to estradiol. So also do the androgens, **testosterone,** the form in which male sex hormone is secreted by the interstitial cells of Leydig in the testis, and **androsterone,** the slightly modified form in which it is excreted in the urine.

progesterone   testosterone

All these gonadal hormones are under the regulation of the anterior lobe of the pituitary which secretes gonadotropic hormones essential for the formation of sex hormones. They in turn inhibit the secretion of their respective gonadotropins.

The Pituitary. The pituitary gland, or hypophysis, is commonly called the "master gland," because it exerts a regulatory control over most of the other endocrine glands. It is beginning to appear, however, that the pituitary is not so much a master as an executive officer carrying out the instructions of the **hypothalamus** and perhaps also of the pineal body on top of the brain. In adults, the pituitary is located on the floor of the skull just behind the optic chiasma where the optic nerves cross as they enter the under side of the brain – a very awkward place to reach surgically!

Like many of the endocrines, the pituitary is a double gland. It develops from an upgrowth from the roof of the embryonic mouth which meets a downgrowth from the part of the brain which will become the hypothalamus. The portion of the gland that has grown up from the mouth forms the anterior lobe of the gland and the small intermediate lobe. The two together are often called the **adenohypophysis.** This usually makes up about 70 per cent of the mass of the pituitary. The portion which originates as a downgrowth from the future hypothalamus forms the posterior lobe and stem of the gland. This portion of the pituitary is often called the **neurohypophysis.**

All the hormones of the pituitary are polypeptides. Indeed some of them are large enough molecules to rank as proteins. The **anterior lobe** secretes somatotropin ("the" growth hormone), gonadotropins, thyrotropin, adrenocorticotropin (ACTH), a corpus luteum-stimulating hormone (LH), and a lactogenic hormone. The **posterior lobe** secretes an antidiuretic hormone (ADH) and oxytocin, a hormone which stimulates smooth muscles and is important in the release of milk on suckling and almost certainly in stimulating uterine contractions during parturition. The **intermediate lobe** produces a melanophore-dispersing hormone, intermedin, in lower vertebrates and probably in mammals as well.

The cells of the anterior lobe are of three major types according to staining and other characteristics. There are **acidophils,** so called because their cytoplasmic granules stain with acid dyes like eosin or orange G. These cells are often called eosinophils or alpha cells. There are **basophils,** in which the cytoplasm stains with basic dyes like methylene blue and aniline blue; they are often called beta cells. Thirdly, there are cells which resist staining and are therefore called **chromophobes.** They constitute roughly half the cells present.

Many attempts have been made to identify which cells secrete which hormone. There seems no substantial doubt that some, if not all, the acidophils secrete growth hormone. Several genetic strains of dwarf mice show a hereditary lack of alpha cells and no pituitary growth hormone. Human pituitary (Tom Thumb) dwarfs are deficient in alpha cells. Some of the beta cells or basophils evidently secrete a hormone related to the gonads. After castration by removal of either testes or ovaries, many of the basophils become enlarged as though engorged with secretion. Eventually the nucleus is pressed against the side of the cell, now called a "signet-ring" or castration cell. If the animal is treated with sex hormones these cells can no longer be found.

The importance of the anatomical relationships of the pituitary gland can scarcely be exaggerated. Not only does it lie closely adjacent to the under side of the hypothalamus but each lobe is functionally tied to the hypothalamus in a very special way. The posterior lobe is directly innervated by nerve fibers coming down the stalk of the gland from the hypothalamus. These are called **neurosecretory cells** because secretion granules can be observed to form in the cell bodies which lie in two groups (each called a "nucleus") in the brain. These granules then move down the axons into the posterior lobe of the pituitary.

The anterior lobe of the pituitary is connected also to its own set of neurosecretory cells in the hypothalamus, some of which are located in what is known as the median eminence. These nerve cells are innervated by other neurons further up in the brain and send their own axons down into the stalk of the pituitary where they end among the meshes of a small capillary network. The capillaries pick up the secretion

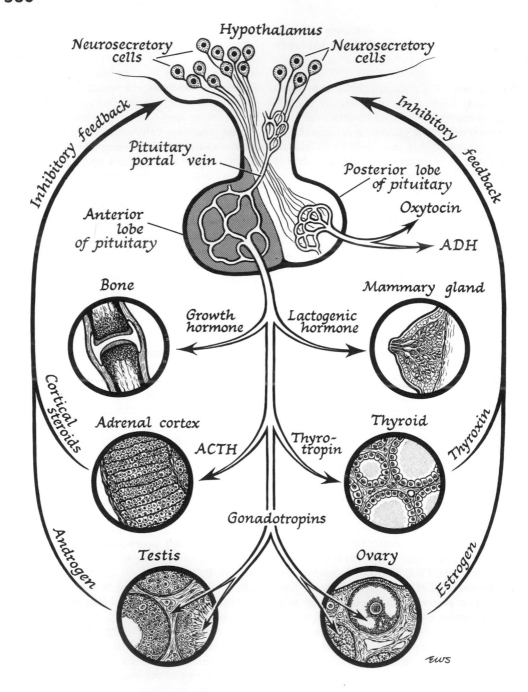

Fig. 29–9. The pituitary gland and its relation to its six major target organs and to the hypothalamus. Note that neurosecretory cells of the hypothalamus extend down and enter the posterior pituitary lobe, but not the anterior. Other neurosecretory cells end against capillaries whence blood passes into the anterior lobe via the pituitary portal vein.

from this group of neurosecretory cells and carry it in a **pituitary portal system** which almost immediately breaks up into a second set of capillaries within the anterior lobe. The blood supply of the posterior lobe is quite separate from this system of the anterior lobe.

The evidence for a regulatory **feedback control** between the pituitary and the hormones produced by ovaries, testes, thyroid, and adrenal cortex is unassailable. If the anterior pituitary is removed, the thyroid gland atrophies, the gonads fail to produce sex cells or sex hormones, reproductive cycles stop, the adrenal cortex fails. If one of these glands, the target organs for the pituitary, is removed, the level of the corresponding pituitary tropic hormone increases greatly. In the case of removal of either male or female gonads, characteristic castration cells appear in the anterior lobe. Injection of sex hormones or thyroxin, for example, depresses the amount of gonadotropin or thyrotropin secreted by the pituitary.

It is not yet completely settled whether the inhibitory effect of the various hormones is directly on the cells of the pituitary or on the neurosecretory cells in the hypothalamus, or on both. Here is some of the evidence. When part of the thyroid of a rat is removed, the pituitary increases its release of thyrotropin. The remaining piece of the thyroid gland then increases in size and ultimately the level of thyroxin in the blood is restored to normal levels. At the same time the level of thyrotropin returns to normal. So far no hint of a role for the hypothalamus and its neurosecretory cells. However, this sequence of events can be completely blocked by electrically destroying the cells in a very small and definitely localized place in the hypothalamus. If the thyroid is then removed, the pituitary behaves as though it knew nothing about it!

Using stereotactic instruments which make it possible to localize an electrode with great precision in the brain, similar experiments have been performed with success on a variety of mammals and with respect to gonadotropin and corticotropin as well as thyrotropin.

The idea that it is cells in the hypothalamus which sense the concentration of hormones in the bloodstream and then signal the pituitary to make the appropriate response is supported by recent discoveries in the field of behavioral studies. There is a pair of centers, well identified, in the hypothalamus which control eating in mammals. They respond to the level of glucose in the bloodstream and can be shown to concentrate labelled glucose. There is also a pair of centers in the hypothalamus which are sensitive to minute injections of estrogens and will cause estrous behavior in cats from which not only the ovaries but the whole reproductive tract has been removed.

The evolutionary explanation for the key role of the pituitary, whether as "master gland" or executive officer for the hypothalamus, in regulating most of the other endocrines remains unclear. Its connection with the hypothalamus where the centers for control of so many bodily functions—temperature regulation, water balance, appetite, sexual drives, blood pressure, and the like—are located would seem to be an important factor. It will be recalled (page 430) that the homolog of the vertebrate pituitary first appears as the **subneural gland** of certain marine chordates, the tunicates. There its basic function is to detect the presence of gametes from other tunicates in the water taken in for gill respiration and then to signal the animal's own gonads to shed its eggs and sperms. This insures synchronous spawning, highly important for a sedentary marine organism. It is noteworthy that extracts of the tunicate subneural gland will induce ovarian growth in adolescent mice and stimulate uterine contractions in adult mice.

Somatotropin and its dramatic effects on growth, especially of the skeleton, have already been discussed (page 525). Tumors or genes causing the acidophilic alpha cells of the anterior lobe either to over- or under-secrete result in circus giants and Tom Thumb dwarfs, or in cases where the hypersecretion begins after maturity, a disease called acromegaly. In fact a variety of abnormal conditions result from malfunction of some or all of the types of cells in the pituitary. Failure of sufficient thyrotropin, for example, produces a hypothyroidism and characteristic edema of the face and body generally. Somatotropin itself not only governs bone growth but also promotes the growth of muscles, and influences both lipid and carbohydrate metabolism.

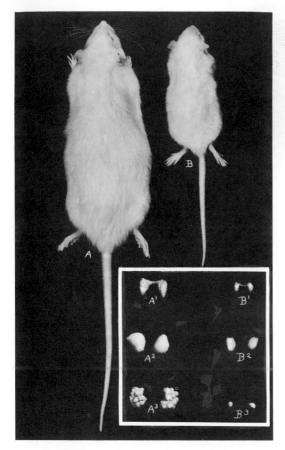

Fig. 29–10. Rat littermates, 144 days old. *A,* normal. *B,* hypophysectomized. A^1 and B^1 are the respective thyroids of the rats; A^2 and B^2, the adrenals; and A^3 and B^3, the ovaries. *(From Turner,* General Endocrinology, *2nd ed., W. B. Saunders)*

The Pineal Body. The pineal body is a small rounded structure on the dorsal side of the thalamic portion of the brain opposite the pituitary on the under side of the thalamus. In the adult frog the pineal body underlies the skull, but in mammals it is overgrown by the enormous cerebral hemispheres and the cerebellum. In many lizards the pineal body is a third eye; in frogs it contains **cone cells** closely similar under an electron microscope to the cones of the visual retina.

Over the years many investigators have attempted to discover what the pineal body, or gland as it is also called, was about. It has long been known that tumors of this structure in children are commonly associated with precocious sexual maturity or, paradoxically, sometimes with delayed sexual development! The answer was found only recently. Precocious sexual maturity is associated with tumors of the supporting tissue around the pineal which apparently choke the structure into inactivity. In addition, overgrowth of the pineal itself is associated with delayed puberty. These facts suggest that the pineal exerts an inhibitory effect on gonadal development. It has also been shown that the pineal gland is extensively innervated by fibers from the sympathetic nervous system.

A real breakthrough came with the discovery by Virginia Fiske that continuous illumination 24 hours a day results in a decrease in the weight of the rat pineal body and an increase in the size of the ovaries. Other investigators have shown that exposure of male hamsters to cycles of one hour of light and 23 hours of darkness will cause atrophy of the testes but that this effect can be prevented by removal of the pineal gland. It was then discovered that there is a circadian (roughly 24-hour) cycle of formation of an enzyme in the pineal which produces **melatonin.** Melatonin is a hormone derived from the amino acid tryptophan. This hormone slows down the estrous cycle and slows down ovarian development; it is produced only in the pineal body. Continuous illumination causes blocking of the formation of the melatonin-producing enzyme. Blinding a rat or severing the nerves to the pineal body blocks these effects that would result from continuous illumination. The site of action of melatonin is unknown. It could be the hypothalamus or directly on the gonads.

It certainly appears that the correlation between reproductive cycles in mammals and the season of the year or other time intervals is controlled by the pineal gland. It would be instructive to find out whether blinding blocks pineal rhythms in those lizards where the pineal body is a functional organ to the extent of having a rudimentary cornea over it. There is still much to be learned about the functioning of the pineal body.

The Thymus. The thymus has been the other enigmatic gland, often thought to play some role in retarding sexual development because it undergoes marked involution with the onset of sexual maturity. Many experimenters have removed the gland, which lies in the upper chest beneath the breastbone. Extracts have also been injected, but no significant results have followed either procedure. It has been found that if the thymus is removed promptly at birth, a mammal or bird will lack antibody-forming lymphocytes. Apparently the lymphocyte stemcells in the various lymph glands, which produce these blood cells in later life, come from cells which originate in the thymus. There is also some evidence that the thymus secretes some hormonelike material essential for proper lymphocyte development.

Review and References

REVIEW TOPICS

1. What is the evidence that the pituitary and the gonads are related as a feedback circuit? That the hypothalamus plays a key role in this cycle?

2. What is the evidence from endocrinology that a certain "critical mass" of data is necessary before a new idea is accepted?

3. What was the role of each of the following in the development of endocrinology: Thomas Addison, A. A. Berthold, Frederick Banting, Minkowski, Bayliss and Starling, Beerman?

4. What are the four stages in the orthodox study of hormones?

5. Which hormones are steroids and which polypeptides?

6. What is the evidence supporting the thesis that endocrines can act at the gene level?

7. What are the results of hypo- and hyper-function of the thyroid, of the adrenal cortex, of the anterior lobe of the pituitary, of the pineal?

8. What reasons are there for believing that all the effects of insulin may not take place at the gene level?

9. How are the two chief lobes of the pituitary gland linked to the hypothalamus?

10. Identify: epinephrine, progesterone, glucagon, actinomycin, oxytocin, somatotropin, acromegaly, subneural gland of a tunicate, cortisone.

11. Alloxan will inhibit the secretion of insulin by the pancreas; thiouracil will inhibit the secretion of thyroxin by the thyroid gland. What does the fact that both alloxan and thiouracil are pyrimidines suggest as to the mechanism of inhibition?

USEFUL REFERENCES

Barrington, E. J. W., *Hormones and Evolution,* Princeton, N. J., D. Van Nostrand Co., 1964.

Grollman, S., *The Human Body, Its Structure and Physiology,* New York, The Macmillan Co., 1964.

Harris, S., *Banting's Miracle: The Story of the Discoverer of Insulin,* Philadelphia, J. B. Lippincott Co., 1946.

Scharrer, E., and B. Scharrer, *Neuroendocrinology,* New York, Columbia University Press, 1963.

Turner, C. D., *General Endocrinology,* 3rd ed., Philadelphia, W. B. Saunders Co., 1961.

Chapter 30

Reproduction

Reproduction involves two conflicting requirements, if evolution is to take place. First is the basic requirement of self-duplication. Second is the production of novelty.

Without the first, obviously, life would not continue to exist. On the molecular level reproduction means replication of DNA. For cells it means mitosis. On the level of multicellular organisms reproduction means either some kind of asexual division in which fairly large replicates can be produced directly, or some kind of sexual reproduction in which the organism is reduced to the level of single cells. Why this second method?

The answer, of course, is the production of novelty, of variation. In a very real sense this is the opposite of reproduction. At the basic molecular level novelty is the result of two factors, errors in the replication of deoxyribose nucleic acid and the inherent properties of the DNA. The basic novelty produced on the molecular level is compounded on the level of cells by sexuality, that is, by the making of new combinations and permutations of chromosomes in the cycle of meiosis and fertilization. The variation produced by meiosis alone may be very great. With 23 pairs of chromosomes, each human may produce over 8,000,000 kinds of eggs or sperms. Fertilization multiplies these two possibilities by each other in the produc-

tion of the zygote. 8×10^6 multiplied by 8×10^6 equals 64×10^{12}, which is the number of possible kinds of zygotes from any marriage, and a very large number it is!

The reproductive systems of most animals are adapted to meet both requirements, duplication of the old and introduction of the new. Parthenogenesis, where there is meiosis but no fertilization, introduces variation which may be great but, lacking fertilization, there is no way for any mixing of the gene pool and evidently the result is very inferior from the evolutionary viewpoint. In any case, parthenogenesis is rare and found only in certain minor groups of crustaceans, aphids, rotifers, and a few other groups. Fertilization is possible in both **hermaphrodites,** where ovaries and testes are found in the same individual, and in **unisexual** (dioecious) species, where the two sexes occur in separate individuals. The second condition would seem to be more effective in producing new variations and combinations but both conditions are found in animals high and low on the scale of evolution. Among hermaphrodites are flatworms, ctenophores, earthworms and their close relatives, some marine and most fresh-water and terrestrial snails, and, among chordates, most of the tunicates. In contrast, jellyfish and other coelenterates are almost always unisexual. The fresh-water hydra is an exception in some species but not in all. Arthropods and vertebrates almost without exception have separate sexes. Both conditions are found among nematodes. This is also true of the mollusks, where the octopus and many of the marine snails have separate sexes. Many shellfish are **protandrous,** that is, male when small or poorly fed, female when fully grown.

In the earliest embryonic stages vertebrates have the structural rudiments to produce either sex. The direction of development is normally thrown one way or the other by the distribution of the sex chromosomes. Because some of the male and female reproductive structures develop from the same embryonic rudiments, normally functional hermaphrodites are theoretically not possible among vertebrates, and none are found. However, various sex mosaics, especially gynandromorphs, do occur and, at least in the most carefully studied cases, result from abnormal chromosomal distribution.

Among reptiles, birds, and mammals, adaptations for reproduction on land are superimposed on the more ancient adaptations for the production of novelty. This is, of course, the meaning of the amnion which gives these three classes of vertebrates their common name, the amniotes. It is the reason for internal fertilization, for eggs with impervious shells, and for the evolution of the mammalian uterus.

THE ANATOMY OF REPRODUCTION

The Male Reproductive System. The primary sex organs, the **gonads,** of male mammals are a pair of **testes** closely similar to those of reptiles and birds. Each testis is composed of a mass of **seminiferous tubules** in which meiosis and sperm development take place. The diploid **spermatogonia,** which multiply by mitosis, lie around the periphery of the tubule, the **primary and secondary spermatocytes** lie closer to the lumen of the tubule, and finally the haploid **spermatids** closest to the center. As in other animals, the spermatids develop into mature sperms while imbedded in the cytoplasm of nurse cells, usually called **Sertoli cells.** Still unknown is the physiological basis of developing sperms being lodged in Sertoli cells. A kind of differential phagocytosis by the Sertoli cells? A precocious type of fertilization by the spermatids?

Between the seminiferous tubules are masses of interstitial or **Leydig cells** which secrete **testosterone,** the male sex hormone.

Mature sperms pass through the lumens of the seminiferous tubules into the **epididymis,** a clump of coiled tubules lying against the testes, and finally into the **vas deferens.**

As indicated in Figure 30–2, the **accessory sex organs** in different mammals are much the same. Most species possess a **seminal vesicle,**

Fig. 30–1. Cross section of a human testis, typical of higher vertebrates. (*After Arey, Developmental Anatomy, W. B. Saunders*)

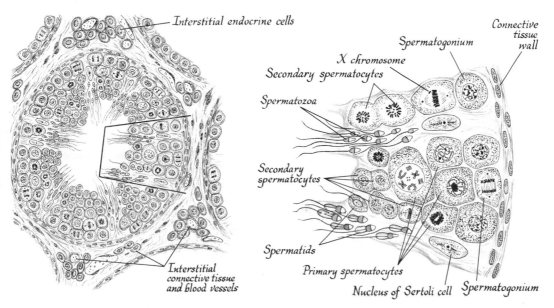

Interstitial endocrine cells

Connective tissue wall

Spermatogonium

X chromosome

Secondary spermatocytes

Spermatozoa

Secondary spermatocytes

Spermatids

Interstitial connective tissue and blood vessels

Primary spermatocytes

Nucleus of Sertoli cell   Spermatogonium

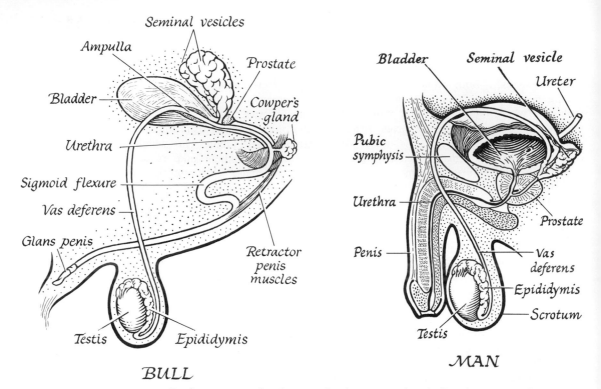

Labels on BULL diagram: Seminal vesicles, Ampulla, Prostate, Bladder, Cowper's gland, Urethra, Sigmoid flexure, Vas deferens, Glans penis, Retractor penis muscles, Testis, Epididymis

Labels on MAN diagram: Bladder, Seminal vesicle, Ureter, Pubic symphysis, Urethra, Penis, Prostate, Vas deferens, Epididymis, Scrotum, Testis

BULL   MAN

Fig. 30–2. Basic anatomy of male reproductive organs in a bull and a man. (*After Mavor, General Biology, 1941, The Macmillan Company*)

probably more accurately called a seminal gland because it is known to pour a secretion into the vas deferens, but whether it stores sperms is uncertain. Surrounding the junction of the vas deferens with the urethra from the urinary bladder is the **prostate gland.** Its secretion forms a major part of the **seminal fluid.** The position is unfortunate because in older males it has a tendency to enlarge and obstruct the flow of urine. A very small pair of glands, **Cowper's glands,** open into the urethra just below the prostate. Their secretion has a lubricating and acid-neutralizing function.

The seminal fluid is ejaculated into the vagina of the female by the **penis,** which is brought into a state of erection when specialized cavernous tissue within the penis becomes enlarged with blood. In some mammals, notably the carnivores, such as dogs and seals, the penis is further strengthened by a special bone.

The puzzling fact about the male reproductive system in mammals is the existence of the **scrotum.** This is essentially a muscular sac which acts as a thermo-regulator, keeping the temperature of the testes several degrees below body temperature. If the temperature of the scrotum of an experimental animal is kept at body temperature either by insulated wrapping or by surgically placing it within the abdomen, spermatogenesis ceases, and the seminiferous tubules show a degenerated appearance. This is probably why **cryptorchid** individuals, whose testes lie within the abdomen, are sterile. Yet the curious fact remains that in elephants, seals, and porpoises the testes are normally and continuously abdominal! They are, also, in birds where the body temperature averages about 40°–43°C (104°–108°F), a dangerous fever for a mammal! Furthermore, meiosis occurs in all females, and, of course, the ovaries are abdominal. A further complication is that male drosophilas become sterile in very hot weather.

The **secondary sexual characteristics** of male mammals differ greatly among the different orders. The lion with his mane and the moose with his antlers are familiar examples of sex differences. In porpoises and rodents secondary sexual characteristics are virtually nonexistent except in behavior. In some animals secondary sexual characteristics are under control

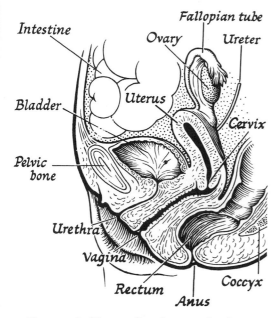

Fig. 30–3. Human female reproductive system. The cavity of the uterus is nearly at right angles to the vagina; the open ends of the Fallopian tubes clasp the ovaries. *(After Mavor,* General Biology, *1941, The Macmillan Company)*

of gonadal hormones, in some they are independent of sex hormones, and in some they are due to a combination of hormones and more local genetic action. In the common English house sparrow, for example, the color of the bill is a very sensitive indicator of the concentration of sex hormone in the blood. The marked difference in color pattern of feathers of males and females is independent of sex hormones and is seen in birds which have been castrated while still in their nestling down. The situation in mammals is still not clear but in some ways seems to resemble that in the sparrow.

The Female Reproductive System. Anatomically the female reproductive apparatus is even simpler than the male. A **vagina,** located between the openings of the urethra and the alimentary tract, is merely a tube lined with mucoid epithelium which leads into the **uterus** or womb. The evolution of the uterus and the placenta are the two new structures in mammalian reproduction.

At the opening of the uterus into the vagina is a thick muscular region, the **cervix.** In most groups of mammals the uterus is more or less double. Figure 30–4 shows varying conditions

Fig. 30–4. Comparative anatomy of four basic types of female reproductive tracts in mammals. The pair of ovaries and the oviducts or Fallopian tubes are shown at the upper end of each uterus. The thickened region represents the muscular cervix just above the vagina. *A,* duplex uterus of rat, mouse, and rabbit. *B,* bicornate uterus of pig and insectivores. *C,* bipartite uterus of cat, dog, cow, and ewe. *D,* simplex uterus of primates, including man.

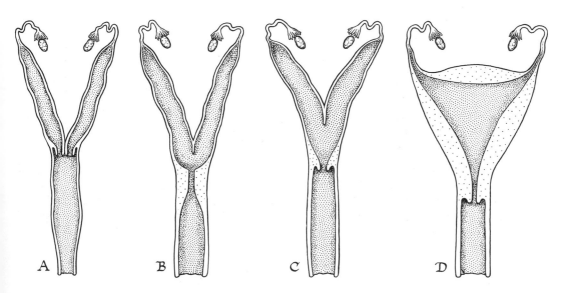

in a series of familiar animals. The inner end of each horn of the uterus is continued as the **oviduct,** known in human anatomy as the **Fallopian tube.** The oviduct on each side ends in a thin, funnel-shaped membrane that more or less encloses the ovary.

The mammalian **ovaries** are solid structures enclosed in a continuation of the peritoneal epithelium which lines the coelom. Over the ovaries this layer of cells is known as the **germinal epithelium.** From it groups of cells containing descendants of the primordial germ cells migrate into the interior of the ovary. Here the germ cells begin meiosis. Each egg cell grows enormously in size and is surrounded by layers of cells between which a cavity forms. This cavity enlarges and becomes filled with the **follicular fluid** rich in **estrogen,** the female sex hormone secreted by the cells surrounding the cavity. Outside these cells is a thin layer of smooth muscle fibers. The entire capsule is known as a **Graafian follicle.** The number of ova which mature at any one time depends on the species, normally one in women (the right and left ovaries are thought to alternate), three or four in vixen, seven or eight in mice. Some very delicate hormonal balance must control this number. Abnormally large numbers of eggs will mature after large injections of pituitary gonadotropin. Unless the dose administered is very carefully regulated, women have been found to produce multiple births, perhaps seven or eight stillborn fetuses, after treatment with this hormone.

Ovulation is the release of the mature egg, surrounded by a crowd of follicle cells, from the ovary. The ovum falls into the funnel-shaped opening of the oviduct or, very rarely, into the coelom. In many mammals, apparently in most species, ovulation occurs in response to an internal rhythm which involves a feedback system between ovaries and pituitary, and which is

Fig. 30–5. Diagrammatic mammalian ovary. The sequence of events in the maturing of a Graafian follicle and the formation of a corpus luteum is shown arbitrarily in a clockwise direction.

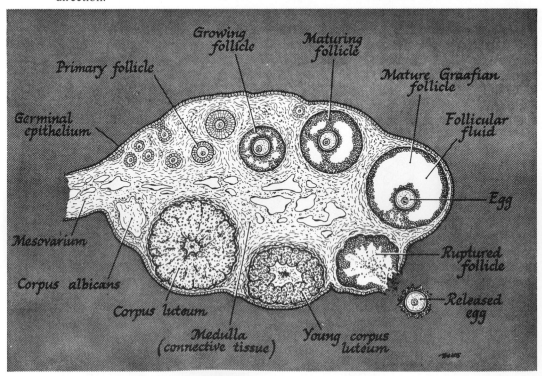

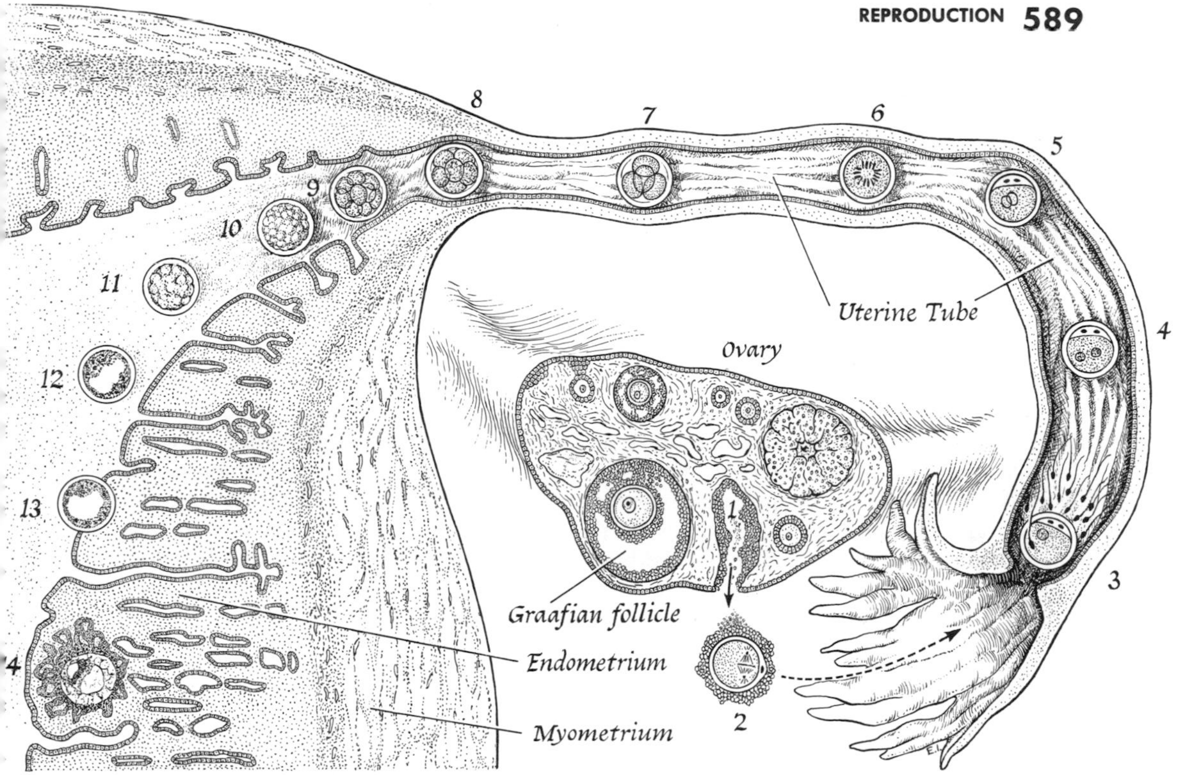

Fig. 30-6. Diagram of stages of the developing human ovum as it travels from the ovary to the uterus. *1,* follicle bursts. *2,* ovum with adhering granulosa cells; note the first polar body and the second maturation spindle. *3,* sperm enters egg; second maturation division occurs. *4,* male and female pronuclei present. *5,* pronuclei fuse. *6,* first cleavage division. *7, 8, 9,* early cleavage. *10,* morula. *11,* early gastrula. *12,* later gastrula. *13,* start of implantation. *14,* growing embryo fully implanted.

regulated also, at least in many mammals, by the hours of daylight and darkness. In a few species, such as rabbits and cats, ovulation occurs a definite time after the stimulus of mating.

Fertilization takes place at the upper end of the oviduct. The stimulus of mating induces the release of a hormone, **oxytocin,** which causes uterine and oviductal contractions that carry the sperms up the oviduct in remarkably quick time, in some species only two minutes to reach the upper end!

If pregnancy occurs, the developing egg and its surrounding cells signal the ovary by hormones. The result is that the cells of the ruptured follicles do not degenerate but instead proliferate and differentiate into a new structure, called from its yellowish color a **corpus luteum.** There are as many corpora lutea as there were ruptured follicles. They secrete

progesterone, a hormone essential to maintain pregnancy.

Cleavage of the ovum takes place as the zygote passes down the oviduct. This requires four or four and a half days. After this time the egg is in the late blastula stage (usually called the blastocyst). When it arrives in the uterus it becomes **implanted** in the uterus lining. If it seems strange that it takes almost exactly the same amount of time for the fertilized egg of a mouse to pass down the oviduct as it does the egg of an elephant, it should be remembered that the ova of these two species are nearly identical in size. The colossal difference in size of the adults is due to a difference in the number, not in the size of the cells. It is implantation which is, in some unknown way, prevented by the placement of a plastic ring or other such object within the uterus.

REPRODUCTIVE HORMONES

Both male and female sex hormones are **steroids** differing only (and rather slightly) in the chemical radicals attached to the basic sterol molecule of three benzene rings (the phenanthrene structure) and a five-carbon ring. Male sex hormones are termed **androgens,** female sex hormones **estrogens.**

Testosterone is secreted by the Leydig cells of the testes under the continuous stimulation of gonadotropin, a proteinaceous hormone from the pituitary gland at the base of the brain. Testosterone is responsible for the characteristic physical features of the male and is prerequisite for male behavior by its action on specific centers in the hypothalamus of the brain.

testosterone   estradiol

Estradiol is secreted by the cells of the Graafian follicles upon stimulation of gonadotropin from the pituitary, commonly called follicle-stimulating hormone, **FSH.** It is responsible for part of the development of the mammary glands and for female behavior. **Progesterone** is similar to estradiol in chemical structure. It is secreted by the corpora lutea and prepares the lining of the uterus for implantation and then maintains it. Progesterone also stimulates the growth of the actual milk-secreting cells.

Prolactin, a pituitary hormone, stimulates the secretion of milk. **Oxytocin,** another proteinaceous pituitary hormone, causes the flow of milk by producing contraction of smooth mammary muscles. Oxytocin also stimulates the contractions of the female reproductive tract which carry sperms up the uterus and oviducts.

CYCLES

Estrous Cycles. Ovulation in mammals occurs at more or less regular intervals, once a year for deer, every four to six months for dogs and cats, approximately every 28 days for women, every 21 days for mares and cows, every 4 or 5 days for rodents. The period of ovulation, or **estrus,** in many species, notably cats and cows, is accompanied by a period of restlessness and sexual receptivity known as "heat." In the higher primates the lining (**endometrium**) of the uterus undergoes growth, which prepares it for implantation of the blastocyst, culminating at about the time of ovulation. If no implantation and pregnancy take place, the hormones which have stimulated the growth of the endometrium recede, and the lining of the uterus is shed along with a certain amount of bleeding. This phenomenon is called **menstruation** from *mensis* meaning month. Menstruation will be discussed later in this chapter. A species with but one estrous period a year is termed monestrous; a species with several, polyestrous.

The timing of estrus is under complex control. As mentioned above, in a very few cases — the rabbit and cat, for example — although the estrus condition is due to other factors, the actual shedding of the eggs from the ovaries is due to the stimulus of copulation. Psychic or at least neural factors are important in the mouse. A group of female mice will show a great deal of asynchrony and variation in their estrous cycles which become regularized by the presence of a male even though he is separated from the females by a fine mesh cage. Since merely the used bedding from a male will produce this effect, it is clear that the actual stimulus is odor. The chachma baboon has an extremely regular sexual cycle of 32 days but this will be interrupted if the female is permitted to watch a fight between two other baboons. This would result in an automatic limitation on population growth when numbers became great enough to make fighting frequent.

Photoperiod, that is, the number of hours of daylight and of darkness, also has a profound influence on reproduction. It has been known since the epoch-making discoveries of W. Rowan in Saskatchewan that even in the coldest winter weather birds kept out of doors can be made to assume springtime sexual and migratory behavior by controlling the number of hours of light or, more accurately, the number of hours of uninterrupted darkness the birds experience. Similar control of reproductive phenomena has been found in many mammals.

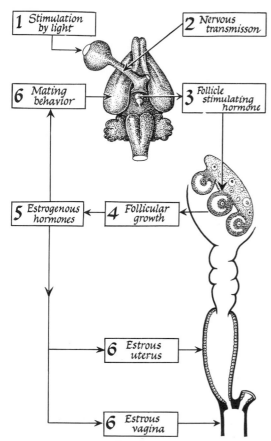

1 *Stimulation by light*

2 *Nervous transmisson*

6 *Mating behavior*

3 *Follicle stimulating hormone*

5 *Estrogenous hormones*

4 *Follicular growth*

6 *Estrous uterus*

6 *Estrous vagina*

Fig. 30-7. Endocrine control of reproduction in a female rabbit. Other mammals are similar, though in some, including the human, the number of hours of daylight may not have any effect.

In the rabbit the major events are as follows. Light stimulates the retinal cells and sends impulses back to the brain. Artificially increasing the hours of daylight will bring wild rabbits into estrus even in the dead of winter.

It has recently been shown that continuous 24-hour illumination results in an increase in the weight of the rat ovary and a decrease in the pineal gland, as discussed in the previous chapter.

The anterior lobe of the pituitary secretes gonadotropin, the FSH mentioned earlier, which stimulates the Graafian follicles to secrete estrone.

The **estrogen** produced by the ovary has five main effects. (1) It stimulates the growth of the lining of the vagina and uterus. (2) It stimulates the growth of the milk-secreting ducts of the mammary glands and stimulates the develop-

ment of female secondary sex characteristics in general. (3) It activates female reproductive behavior. (4) It stimulates the anterior pituitary to secrete a luteinizing hormone, LH, which triggers the release of eggs by the follicles and stimulates the growth of the corpora lutea. (5) It inhibits the secretion of the follicle-stimulating hormone in the pituitary. Thus it saws off the limb that supports it, for once the follicle-stimulating hormone of the pituitary is no longer present in the bloodstream, the follicles in the ovary regress, and the concentration of estrogen falls drastically. At this point the pituitary is again free to form FSH, the follicle-stimulating hormone, and so the cycle is repeated. There is no better example of a biological feedback or self-regulatory mechanism.

From these facts it might be concluded that the anterior pituitary and ovary constitute a self-sustaining oscillating system. Perhaps they do, and the role of the eyes and the pineal gland is to turn the oscillator on or off in such a way that it will be correlated either with the seasons or the time of day.

Uterine Cycles. In most mammals the **endometrium,** that is, the epithelial lining of the uterus, undergoes rhythmic cycles along with ovulatory and estrous cycles. The effect of estrogen on the endometrium of a castrated rat can be seen in Figure 29-2. In man and the higher primates the periodic sloughing of the lining of the uterus in the absence of pregnancy is known as **menstruation,** as mentioned earlier.

The story of the discovery of the scientific explanation of menstruation reads like a movie script. The scene opens with Gustav Born, pioneer experimental embryologist of Breslau lying on his deathbed. Born summons his best student and outlines a theory he knows he will never be able to test himself. He proposes that the corpora lutea, the solid yellowish masses of cells formed in the ovary from the follicle cells after they have discharged their eggs, are endocrine glands and that they are essential for the life of the embryo. The student spends the next ten years testing and finally proving this theory.

As now understood, the full sequence of events in the menstrual cycle runs as follows: Estrone, which stimulates the proliferation of the lining of the uterus, also stimulates the pituitary to secrete the luteinizing hormone, LH.

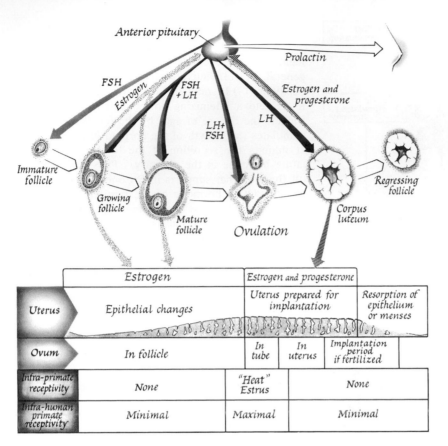

Fig. 30–8. Pituitary-ovary interaction and response of the uterus. The lower lines of the chart show the behavioral correlates in nonprimate mammals and in nonhuman primates.

	Estrogen	Estrogen and progesterone	
Uterus	Epithelial changes	Uterus prepared for implantation	Resorption of epithelium or menses
Ovum	In follicle	In tube / In uterus / Implantation period if fertilized	
Infra-primate receptivity	None	"Heat" Estrus	None
Infra-human primate receptivity	Minimal	Maximal	Minimal

The LH not only triggers ovulation, it also stimulates the growth of the corpus luteum, which as already described secretes progesterone which further stimulates the final stage of growth of the uterine lining, making it ready for implantation and nourishment of an embryo. If pregnancy does not take place, the corpus luteum degenerates, the concentration of progesterone consequently falls, the lining of the uterus loses its hormonal support and sloughs off in the characteristic bleeding. Menstruation can therefore be inhibited by suitable injections of progesterone. Ovulation usually occurs on or about the 14th day after the onset of menstrual bleeding, when the uterine lining is prepared to receive the early embryo, but again there is considerable variation.

If pregnancy occurs, the placenta itself acts as an endocrine gland, for it secretes both estrone and the luteinizing hormone. This additional supply of LH prevents the corpus luteum from degenerating. Consequently the supply of progesterone is maintained and the lining of the uterus is not sloughed off.

GESTATION AND BIRTH

Gestation. The period of growth of the embryo in the uterus is known as the period of gestation or pregnancy. Ever since the time of Aristotle zoologists have tried to find some firm correlations between the size of the animal, the number of young in a litter, and the length of the gestation period. In a general way, the larger the animal, the longer the period of gestation. (See table on next page.)

Parturition. The process of birth or parturition is brought about by the rhythmic involuntary contractions of the smooth muscles of the uterine wall. No event in the whole sweep of human life is more dramatic than the birth of a child. Yet about the precise events that end gestation and initiate labor, as the hard work of expelling the young is appropriately called, we are almost as ignorant as Aristotle, although we have many more facts and some more theories to build on. It is known from animal experimentation that neither pituitary nor ovary is

Gestation And Litter Data

ANIMAL	GESTATION PERIOD	LITTER SIZE	LIFE SPAN
Elephant	21 to 22 months	1	65 years
Whale	10 to 12 months	1	75 years
Horse	11 months	1 or 2	21 years
Cow	9 months	1 or 2	13 years
Human	9 months	1 to 5	70 years
Deer	8 months	1 or 2	12 years
Bear, black	7 months	1 to 3	22 years
Sheep	5 months	1 or 2	12 years
Pig	4 months	8 to 25	
Lion	108 days	2 to 4	20 years
Guinea pig	68 days		
Dog	63 days	3 to 12	20 years
Cat	56 days	3 to 12	20 years
Rabbit	32 days	4 to 7	8 years
Rat	20 to 21 days	4 to 10	3 years
Mouse	20 to 21 days	5 to 15	3 years
Opossum	13 days in utero, 50 in pouch, and 30 free nursling		

essential for normal birth, although a pituitary hormone will sometimes stimulate uterine contractions. Presumably the critical factors must reside in the uterus, placenta, and embryo. One possible clue—which like all clues may be misleading—is furnished by the cross between European and Hindi cattle. Gestation is longer in the Hindi cattle. In crosses, the length of gestation is determined by the fetus rather than the mother. Perhaps because we know so little, the subject is still beclouded with superstitions.

Parturition in any mammal in which the placenta is partly formed from the lining of the uterus, as is true in a woman, falls into three stages. During the first stage the muscular neck or cervix at the opening of the uterus into the vagina is dilated and the baby's head is somewhat molded until it can pass through the pelvic opening. This stage may last from a relatively few minutes to well over twelve hours, but two or three hours is usual. The second stage is brief and consists of the actual passage of the child through the pelvic outlet. The third stage follows after a brief interval and consists of the expulsion of the placenta and other membranes.

There has always been a great deal of concern about the amount of pain involved in this process. It varies greatly, depending on many factors both physical and psychological. The later stages of parturition are always times of potential danger, but many highly civilized people from Mme. Curie to an increasing number of present-day women have found no anesthetic necessary or desirable. Apparently in the final phases there is an hypnotic numbness. Like other branches of medicine, obstetrics is a blend of art and science requiring skilled judgment.

Circulatory Crisis. One of the most important of the adaptations of the newborn mammal has to do with the beginning of breathing and the sudden change in the circulation of the fetal blood. Before birth, most of the blood that enters the right side of the heart from the embryo's body does not go to the still-useless lungs. It passes instead either directly via an oval foramen (or window) into the left side of the heart, whence it is pumped into the dorsal aorta, or it passes out the pulmonary artery, but before it gets to the lungs it is shunted across a short ductus arteriosus (the duct of Botalli) to the dorsal aorta. From the dorsal aorta blood goes both to the embryo's body and also out the umbilical cord to the placenta.

After birth, when the placental circulation no longer can provide oxygen and get rid of carbon dioxide, the carbon dioxide increases in the blood, and this in turn stimulates the newborn

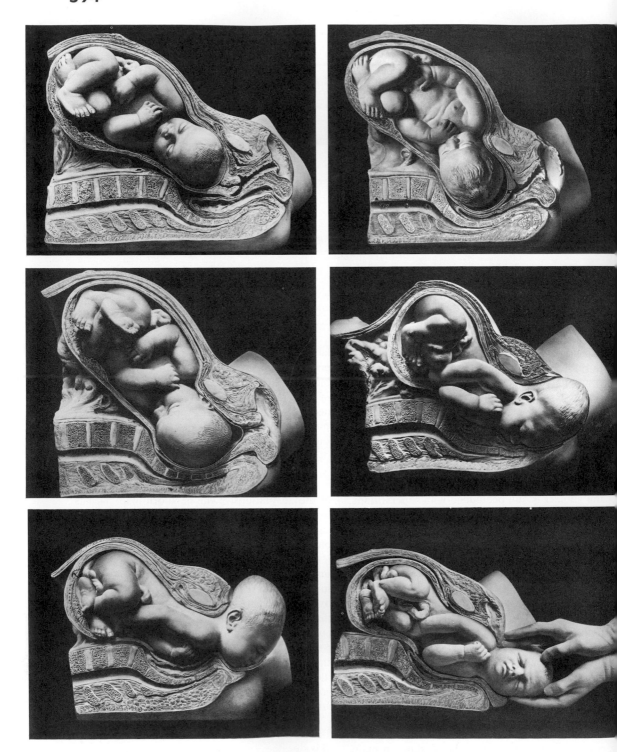

Fig. 30–9. Stages in human birth. *(Reproduced with permission from the* Birth Atlas, *published by Maternity Center Association, New York City)*

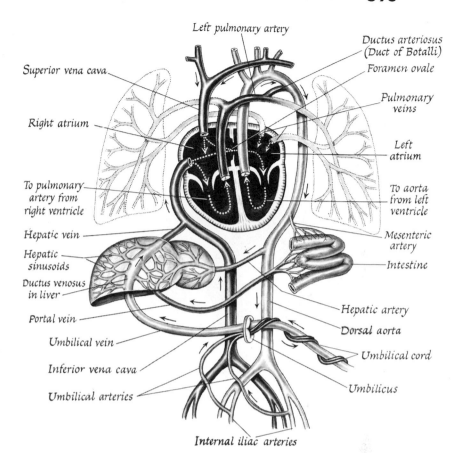

Left pulmonary artery

Ductus arteriosus (Duct of Botalli)

Foramen ovale

Superior vena cava

Pulmonary veins

Right atrium

Left atrium

To pulmonary artery from right ventricle

To aorta from left ventricle

Hepatic vein

Mesenteric artery

Hepatic sinusoids

Intestine

Ductus venosus in liver

Portal vein

Hepatic artery

Dorsal aorta

Umbilical vein

Umbilical cord

Inferior vena cava

Umbilicus

Umbilical arteries

Internal iliac arteries

Fig. 30–10. Fetal blood circulation. Note foramen ovale, duct of Botalli, ductus venosus, two umbilical arteries, and one umbilical vein.

to begin breathing. At the same time some stimulus, probably the CO_2, causes the circular muscles in the walls of the ductus arteriosus to contract, shutting off this route. These muscles never again relax, and in a few weeks the duct grows closed and is converted into a ligament. As a result, the blood from the right side of the heart is forced into the lungs. Consequently there is much more blood returning from the lungs to the left side of the heart. As a result, the pressure of blood on the two sides of the heart is equalized, blood no longer passes from the right to the left side through the oval foramen between the two sides of the heart, and this foramen grows closed. Thus the fetal circulation is abruptly changed to the adult circulation within a few minutes after birth.

Lactation. The process of lactation, or milk production and secretion, is under endocrine control. The rudiments of the mammary glands are laid down in embryos of both sexes. In females at puberty the estrone from the ovarian follicle cells stimulates the growth of the milk ducts and hence the general enlargement of the mammary glands. During maturity, and especially during pregnancy, progesterone from the corpus luteum stimulates the growth of alveoli, which are rounded glands of the tips of the branches of the milk ducts. After the birth, the maternal pituitary secretes a new hormone, **prolactin,** a lactogenic hormone. This hormone, first discovered in pigeons, causes the actual secretion of milk. The production of the lactogenic hormone seems to be due to the sudden fall in level of estrogen caused by the loss of the placenta, which has been secreting large quantities of both estrone and progesterone. Estrone has been used clinically to inhibit milk secretion. Mammals are not all alike in this respect, because small amounts of estrone increases milk production in cows and ewes.

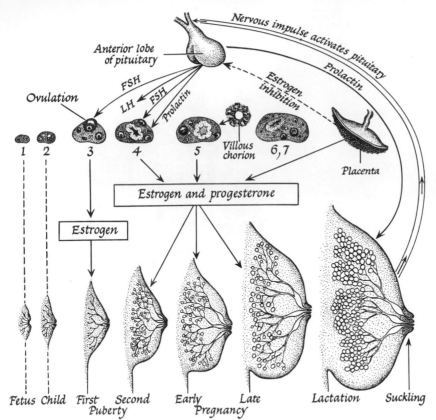

Nervous impulse activates pituitary

Anterior lobe of pituitary

FSH
LH
FSH
Prolactin

Ovulation

Estrogen inhibition

Prolactin

Villous chorion

Placenta

Estrogen and progesterone

Estrogen

1 2 3 4 5 6,7

Fetus Child First Puberty Second Early Pregnancy Late Lactation Suckling

Fig. 30–11. Hormone interactions between pituitary, ovary, placenta, and mammary glands. Progesterone stimulates growth of rounded alveoli at the ends of the milk ducts, but only prolactin causes secretion of milk. The numbers indicate ovarian development stages correlating with seven mammary gland stages shown.

Many "secondary" factors also govern lactation. Lack of the adrenal cortex or of thyroxin or insulin inhibits the mammary glands. Lastly, the mechanical stimulus of sucking stimulates the hypothalamic region of the brain, which in turn results in greater production of oxytocin by the pituitary. This hormone stimulates contraction of muscles within the mammary gland which squeeze milk to the outside. This fact can be effectively demonstrated by injecting oxytocin hormone into an anesthetized but lactating animal.

Review and References

REVIEW TOPICS

1. What is the evolutionary significance of sexuality? What is the evidence for the modern view?

2. Define: Sertoli cell, androgen, secondary spermatocyte, Leydig cells, urethra, uterine cervix, Graafian follicle, gonadotropin, corpus luteum, oxytocin.

3. Where do fertilization and cleavage of the ovum take place in the mammalian reproductive tract?

4. What factors control reproductive cycles in mammals and how do they do so?

5. What are the various effects of estrogens?

6. What is the circulatory crisis which occurs at the birth of a mammal? How is it met?

7. What are the various factors which control lactation? What are the possible adaptive advantages of having such diversified control?

USEFUL REFERENCES

Arey, L. B., *Developmental Anatomy,* 7th ed., Philadelphia, W. B. Saunders Co., 1965.

Corner, G. W., *Ourselves Unborn,* New Haven, Yale University Press, 1944.

Millen, J. W., *Nutritional Basis of Reproduction,* Springfield, Ill., Charles C Thomas, 1962.

Nalbandov, A. V., *Reproductive Physiology; Comparative Reproductive Physiology of Domestic Animals, Laboratory Animals, and Man,* San Francisco, W. H. Freeman, 1958.

Pincus, G., *The Control of Fertility,* New York, Academic Press, 1965.

Chapter 31

The Nervous System

Because the nervous system coordinates and directs the behavior of the whole organism and because it is the location of conscious purposes, its study involves some of the deepest of philosophical problems. In fact, those who seek to explore areas beyond the fringe of knowledge — "psychokinesis," for example, the direct action of mind on matter — should remember that whether or not thought can influence the way dice fall, conscious purposes and material actions are united within the central nervous system in some utterly unknown way. Here is a constellation of problems to challenge scientists and philosophers for centuries to come.

NERVOUS ORGANIZATION

Types of Nervous Systems. Four major types of nervous systems are found in the animals on this planet. The unit in every case is the same, the single nerve cell or neuron. **Neurons** occur in a great variety of forms but all are characterized by threadlike cytoplasmic extensions, often called **processes.** Some are elaborately branched, others are unbranched; some are microscopic, others are over a meter long.

The type of nervous organization characteristic of the **coelenterates** is the simplest. This consists of a rather diffuse **network** of nerve cells spreading over the entire body immediately underneath the ectoderm and ramifying into the mesogleal jelly and under the endoderm of the digestive coelenteron. Closely similar nerve nets are found in ctenophores, echinoderms, primitive chordates and, in fact, the nerve network in the wall of the human intestine. In addition to the nerve net, jellyfish possess a ring of **nerve fibers,** the processes of neurons, encircling the edge of the bell. In some species of jellyfish there are also **sense organs** — statocysts, chemosensory pits, and simple eyes.

A second type of neural organization is found in that vast and in many ways unique group, the **nematodes.** The importance of the nervous system in the life of these animals is evident from the fact that more than 50 per cent of all the cells in their bodies are nerve cells. Little is known about the functioning of this system. Anatomically it is very peculiar and in certain respects could hardly be more peculiar if it had been discovered on a planet in another solar system. For example, there are no big motor nerves extending out to the muscles as in other animals. Instead, the muscle cells send cytoplasmic filaments to the two main nerve cords! There is no single brain but rather a group of small nerve centers in the anterior end of the animal which are interconnected with each other in several ways including through a **ring** of nerve fibers encircling the pharynx. It is from this ring that the two main nerve cords extend back through the body wall.

597

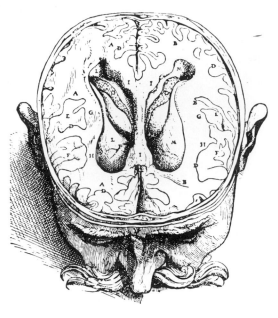

Fig. 31–1. Coronal section of the human brain showing the paired right and left ventricles. *(From Vesalius,* De Humani Corporis Fabrica, *1543)*

The third type of neural organization is the **annelid-arthropod** type. This is characteristic of the entire protostome branch of the animal kingdom (with the exception of the nematodes) and hence is found in the octopus and other mollusks as well as in earthworms, crustaceans, insects, spiders, and all their relatives. In its most primitive form, this type of organization consists of a double **chain of ganglia,** one ganglion per segment, extending along the ventral side of the body on the floor of the coelom. At the anterior end, a pair of connecting nerves encircle the pharynx or esophagus and meet dorsal to the gut, forming a suprapharyngeal ganglion or **brain.** The **circumpharyngeal connectives** may be very short and tightly pressed against the pharynx as in the earthworm, or long and free as in the lobster. The evolutionary explanation of this strange arrangement whereby the nerves encircle the pharynx has never been untangled.

The brain may be a ganglion little larger than any of the ganglia of the ventral chain or it may be very much larger. In the octopus, the brain consists of a fusion of dorsal and ventral ganglia forming a thick, doughnut-shaped ring around the esophagus. The organization of the octopus brain shows many similarities to the organiza-

tion of the vertebrate brain but also enough differences to offer an excellent point of triangulation in the investigation of brain function.

In the evolution of the crustaceans and the insects the thoracic ganglia show a marked tendency to coalesce and enlarge. In a sense, they come to form a thoracic brain to work the legs or the wings and legs.

The fourth major type of neural organization is the **vertebrate** pattern. In its embryonic development the nervous tissue first appears as a thickened strip of cells extending down the back on the surface of the body. This is a deuterostome trait. It will be recalled that the nerve cord along each arm of a starfish, also a deuterostome, is similar.

The vertebrate system consists of two main subsystems. The **central nervous system** (CNS) is made up of the **brain** and the **spinal cord.** The **peripheral nervous system** consists of the nerves which extend from the CNS to the various parts of the body. Although the central and peripheral nervous systems form one single, closely integrated system, it is convenient in analyzing structure and function to regard them separately and so this verbal and methodological distinction has come into use. The peripheral nervous system of vertebrates is itself separable into two divisions: the **somatic nervous system** which innervates the skeletal muscles, the skin, the major sense organs, etc., and is generally under the control of the will, and the **autonomic nervous system** which innervates the smooth muscles, especially of the viscera, the heart and blood vessels, etc., and is not under the direct control of the will. (If it be objected that the concept of the "will" is not a scientific concept, the author will not argue. One can avoid using the term, though at some cost in convenience and perhaps honesty.) The autonomic system in turn is composed of two divisions: the **sympathetic** and **parasympathetic.**

Neurons, the Basic Units. Despite their almost bewildering variety of form, nerve cells fall into three great classes. **Motor or efferent neurons** conduct impulses outward, away from the central nervous system to effector endorgans—muscles or glands. **Sensory or afferent neurons** conduct impulses toward the central nervous system from free sensory nerve ends or from nerve endings in complex sense organs.

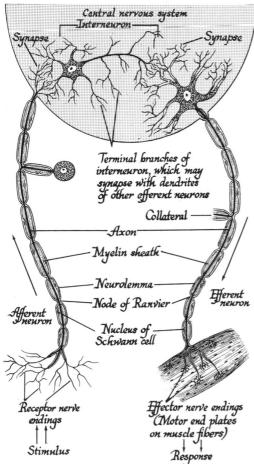

Fig. **31-2.** Afferent (sensory) neuron, association or interneuron, and efferent (motor) neuron. So connected they make simplest reflex arc.

Association or interneurons conduct impulses from one neuron to others within the central nervous system or some of its ganglia.

Each neuron consists of a cell body, the nucleus with its surrounding cytoplasm, and one to numerous filamentous extensions. Within the cytoplasm are numerous elongate granules called **Nissl bodies** which are now known to be RNA. The precise function of this RNA is uncertain. Do nerve cells, including big motor neurons sending impulses to the leg muscles, need a great deal of protein? The only function ever suggested for RNA beyond protein synthesis is some role in memory, but this is far from proved and would seem unlikely, though not impossible, in the case of motor neurons. Note that when poliomyelitis virus attacks the nervous system it characteristically causes disappearance of RNA in the large motor (ventral horn) cells of the spinal cord. It is the destruction of some or all of these cells which results in paralysis and muscular atrophy.

A nerve fiber carrying impulses toward the cell body of the neuron is a **dendrite;** a fiber conducting impulses away from the cell body is an **axon.** Each neuron usually has several short dendrites, often extensively branched, and one axon. In the case of nerves to the hands and feet, the axons of the motor neurons and the dendrites of the sensory neurons are very long. The cell bodies are located in or close to the spinal cord. The receptor or effector ends may be two meters away in an adult giraffe.

Fig. **31 – 3.** Diagram from an electron photomicrograph of an axon including a node of Ranvier. In the lower series, note how the Schwann cell wraps itself like a sheet around the axon, thus making the myelin sheath. *B* is a cross section at the dotted line in *A*.

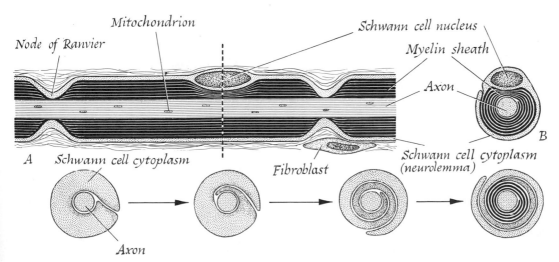

Most of the cranial and spinal nerves are myelinated. That is, they are covered with an insulating **myelin sheath** made of a series of **Schwann cells** that have wrapped themselves around the nerve fiber! The outermost membrane of the myelin sheath is conspicuous under a light microscope and is known as the **neurolemma.** The fact that Schwann cells encircle nerve fibers several times was discovered with the electron microscope. At intervals the myelin sheath is interrupted by exposed zones called **nodes of Ranvier.** They play an incompletely understood role in the transmission of the nervous impulse. Myelinated nerve fibers have been found to carry impulses faster than unmyelinated ones. Among the nerve cells both around and between cell bodies and the axons and dendrites are numerous supporting cells called **glia cells.**

The interneurons or association cells occur in many forms. Compare, for example, a pyramidal (*B* in Fig. 31–4) from the cerebral cortex with a Purkinje (*F*) from the cerebellum.

A **synapse** is the spot where the terminations of an axon transmit an impulse to another neuron. Synapses may be located at the tips of the dendrites of the receiving cell, or directly on the cell body as shown in Figure 31–5. The transmitting ends of the afferent fibers swell into tiny synaptic knobs or end-bulbs containing several small mitochondria and several dozen small synaptic vesicles. The functioning of the synapse, as far as it is understood, will be discussed later.

The visible nerves which appear as glistening white cords on dissection are composed, like telephone cables, of many fibers.

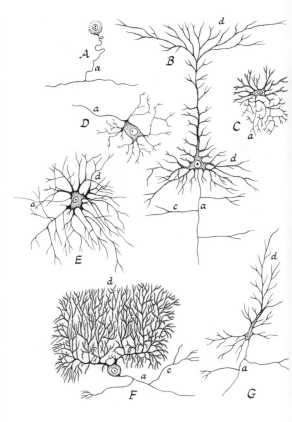

Fig. 31–4. Types of association or interneurons. *A*, bipolar from a spinal ganglion. *B*, pyramidal from the cerebral cortex. *C*, Golgi cell from the spinal cord. *D*, cerebellar neuron. *E*, anterior horn cell from the spinal cord. *F*, Purkinje cell from the mammalian cerebellum. *G*, fusiform cell from the cerebrum. *a*, axon; *c*, collateral branch; *d*, dendrite.

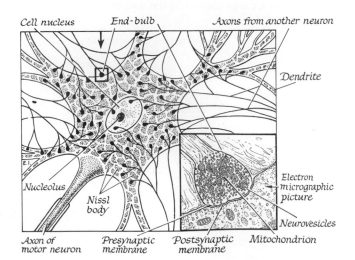

Cell nucleus *End-bulb* *Axons from another neuron*

Dendrite

Electron micrographic picture

Nucleolus

Nissl body

Neurovesicles

Axon of motor neuron *Presynaptic membrane* *Postsynaptic membrane* *Mitochondrion*

Fig. 31–5. Drawing of the cell body of a motor neuron to show its own dendrites and single axon and the numerous end-bulbs or synaptic knobs from other (afferent) nerve fibers pressing against the cell body.

The Vertebrate Central Nervous System. The most important fact about the **brain** and **spinal cord** is the way the neurons within them are *organized*. The important difference between the brain of a man and the brain of a fish does not lie on the level of biochemistry nor on the level of individual cells. The neurons of a man and a fish are very much the same individually. The way a nervous impulse passes along a nerve fiber is virtually identical in a man or a codfish or an octopus. What makes the difference is the cyto-architecture, the patterning of the cells in their interrelations with each other.

Within the brain and the spinal cord the regions occupied by cell bodies appear gray and are therefore called **gray matter.** Regions occupied by myelinated fibers appear white and are termed **white matter.** The white matter represents fiber tracts running either from one part of the brain to another, or up and down the spinal cord. In the brain most of the gray matter is located close to the surface making up the cerebral cortex. In the spinal cord, the gray matter is centrally located and forms an H or a butterfly in cross section A detailed discussion of brain structure will be postponed until after a consideration of the structure and function of the peripheral nerves which are much more open to successful investigation.

The Vertebrate Peripheral Nervous System. The peripheral nerves leave the central nervous system in pairs and thus show a segmental arrangement similar to that of annelids and arthropods. Nerves leaving the brain are known as cranial nerves, those leaving the spinal cord as spinal nerves.

In mammals there are 12 pairs of **cranial nerves.** They are numbered consecutively starting from the most anterior and continuing back to the beginning of the spinal cord. They also bear names sometimes indicative of their function and sometimes of their anatomical relationships. The cranial nerves are characterized as follows:

1. *Olfactory.* This pair of nerves innervates the sensory epithelium of the nose.

2. *Optic.* This pair of nerves carries the nerve fibers from the eyes into the brain on its under side, forming a chiasma where the nerve fibers cross just before entering.

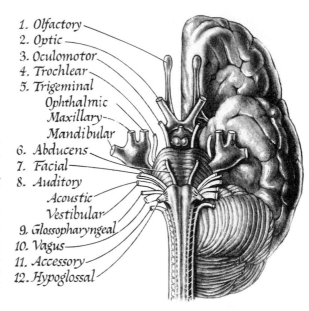

1. Olfactory
2. Optic
3. Oculomotor
4. Trochlear
5. Trigeminal
   Ophthalmic
   Maxillary
   Mandibular
6. Abducens
7. Facial
8. Auditory
   Acoustic
   Vestibular
9. Glossopharyngeal
10. Vagus
11. Accessory
12. Hypoglossal

Fig. 31–6. The 12 cranial nerves as they emerge from the under side of the human brain.

3. *Oculomotor.* As its name implies, this pair of nerves innervates (four of the six) muscles which move the eyeballs.

4. *Trochlear.* This pair also innervates muscles moving the eyeballs.

5. *Trigeminal.* This large pair of nerves is so named because each divides into three main branches. One branch extends over the face, one goes to the upper jaw and teeth, and one to the lower jaw and teeth. Dentists sometimes neatly anesthetize one half of the lower jaw by perfusing one of the lower (mandibular) branches of the trigeminal nerve.

6. *Abducens.* This is a pair of very small nerves innervating one of the muscles moving the eyeballs. It can be readily found in a shark because it leaves the brain closer to the dorsal surface than the others.

7. *Facial.* This pair of nerves innervates the face.

8. *Auditory.* This pair innervates the inner ear, both the cochlea, the organ of hearing, and the semicircular canals, the organs of equilibrium.

9. *Glossopharyngeal.* As its name suggests, this pair innervates the tongue and pharynx.

10. *Vagus.* Vagus means wandering and this pair of nerves extends down into the body cavity where it sends fibers into many organs, including the heart, the lungs, the stomach, and the intestine.

11 and 12. *Accessory and Hypoglossal.* These two pairs both innervate structures around the base of the throat and tongue.*

Some of the cranial nerves are purely sensory, carrying information into the brain. Some are purely motor, conducting impulses outward from the brain. Most are mixed and carry both afferent and efferent fibers.

The pairs of **spinal nerves** vary in number from 10 in a frog to several dozen in some fishes. In mammals they are commonly grouped as cervical, thoracic, lumbar, pelvic or sacral, and

*A famous mnemonic device in the ancient science of anatomy gives the order of the cranial nerves by the first letters of the words: On old Olympus' towering top, a Finn and German valse and hop.

Fig. 31–7. Dermatomes, i.e., areas of the body innervated by successive pairs of spinal nerves.

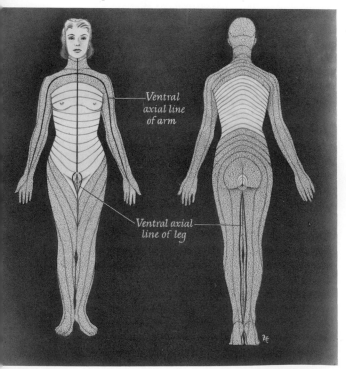

Ventral axial line of arm

Ventral axial line of leg

caudal spinal nerves. Each spinal nerve bifurcates into a dorsal, ganglionated sensory root and a ventral, unganglionated motor root just before it enters the spinal cord.

The Vertebrate Autonomic Nervous System. This system presides over organs and responses which are not under the direct control of the will—tear glands, heart, lungs, genitalia, gastrointestinal tract, blushing, sweating, and the like. It consists of two familiar divisions, sympathetic and parasympathetic. The two are antagonists and each end-organ is innervated by both. Where one excites, the other inhibits.

Both sympathetic and parasympathetic nerves consist of two sets of neurons, **pre-ganglionic** ones that have their cell bodies within the central nervous system and **post-ganglionic** ones that have their cell bodies outside the central nervous system.

The **sympathetic division** is composed of nerves having pre-ganglionic neurons with cell bodies within the gray matter of the thoracic and lumbar regions of the spinal cord and axons which pass out of the cord in the ventral motor roots of spinal nerves and then reach one of the chain of **sympathetic ganglia** by what is called the **white ramus** or branch. In a ganglion, the pre-ganglionic fiber may (1) synapse with a post-ganglionic fiber, (2) continue up or down the chain of sympathetic ganglia, or (3) continue out into the "solar plexus" or some other visceral ganglion and there synapse with a post-ganglionic fiber. The post-ganglionic fibers then extend for some distance, often considerable, to reach their end-organ.

Pre-ganglionic sympathetic fibers release acetylcholine at their ends. Post-ganglionic sympathetic fibers release epinephrine (adrenalin) and therefore are called **adrenergic.** Their stimulation also produces dilation of the pupil, acceleration of the heart beat, inhibition of gastrointestinal mobility, constriction of the pyloric, ileocolic, and anal sphincters, relaxation of the urinary bladder, secretion of sweat, and erection of hair.

The **parasympathetic division** consists of nerves having pre-ganglionic neurons with cell bodies located within the brain or the pelvic region of the spinal cord. The pre-ganglionic fibers travel all the way to the end-organ—

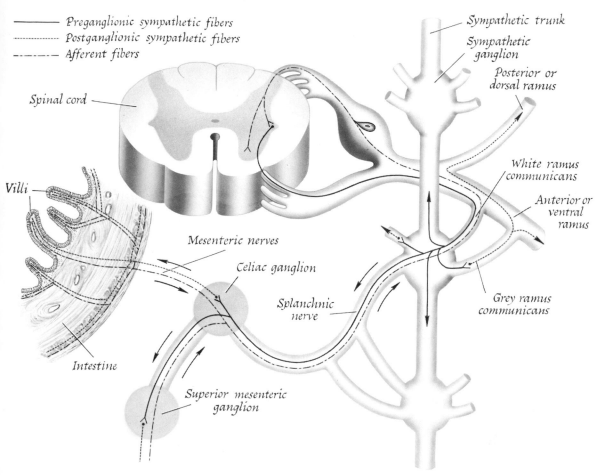

——————— *Preganglionic sympathetic fibers*
·············· *Postganglionic sympathetic fibers*
—·—·—·— *Afferent fibers*

Spinal cord

Villi

Mesenteric nerves

Celiac ganglion

Splanchnic nerve

Intestine

Superior mesenteric ganglion

Sympathetic trunk

Sympathetic ganglion

Posterior or dorsal ramus

White ramus communicans

Anterior or ventral ramus

Grey ramus communicans

Fig. 31 – 8. Relation of peripheral and autonomic nerves to the spinal cord.

heart, stomach, colon, etc. Within it they synapse with a very short post-ganglionic fiber which innervates the end-organ. The parasympathetic nerves to the eye and the salivary glands are exceptions because they do enter ganglia and there synapse with post-ganglionic fibers which travel some distance to their end-organs. All parasympathetic nerves, both pre- and post-ganglionic, release acetylcholine and are termed **cholinergic.** The effects of the parasympathetic nerves are opposite to those of the sympathetic nerves.

Ample evidence from many sources attests to the effectiveness of the relationship of the autonomic system and the highest centers in the brain. For example, the response of blushing can be induced by rather sophisticated causes of embarrassment.

NERVOUS ACTION

Reflex Action. Modern ideas about the action of the nervous system begin with the French mathematician and philosopher René Descartes in the 17th century. He proposed that the unit of action of the nervous system is the **nervous reflex.** By this he meant that a stimulus, such as light striking the eyes, would set off an impulse to the brain that would be reflected back from the brain through nerves to muscles in the arm, or some other location, and there produce a response.

One of the first men to find experimental confirmation for such a view was a versatile 18th century clergyman and amateur biologist, Stephen Hales, who also discovered blood pressure. Briefly, Hales found that you can

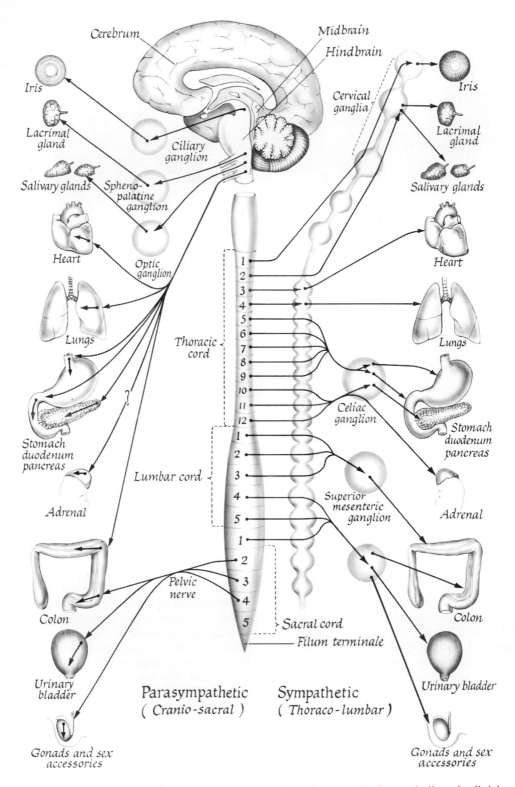

Fig. 31–9. Autonomic nervous system. The parasympathetic or cholinergic division is shown on the left, and the sympathetic or adrenergic on the right.

destroy a frog's brain, by decapitation if necessary, and still not destroy very precise responses to stimuli. A frog so treated is known as a **spinal animal.** If a small square of paper soaked in vinegar be placed on the back of such a frog, one of the hind legs will flick it off with great accuracy. Of course there is little flexibility in the reaction, for all "originality" is lost with the brain. If the spinal cord is destroyed by pushing a wire down inside the backbone, these spinal reflexes cease permanently. Here then is clear proof that such responses can be mediated solely by the spinal cord, without any assistance from the brain. A fact about these experiments which merits thought is that they involve nothing which would have prevented Aristotle from having performed them 2,000 years earlier.

"Spinal" men have occasionally been produced by war or other accidents. In the case of one army lieutenant, a piece of shrapnel completely severed his spinal cord between the fifth and sixth ribs. He retained control of his arms, but his legs were completely without sensation, nor was he able to move them at will. However, if a toe was pinched, his leg would bend at the knee and pull the foot back.

Since Hales' day much has been learned about reflexes. The actual course of the impulses in a spinal reflex were demonstrated in the 19th century by Bell and Magendie. Anatomists had long known that just before each spinal nerve enters the spinal cord it bifurcates into a dorsal (posterior in man) and a ventral (anterior in man) root and that the dorsal root includes a ganglion. These investigators showed that if the dorsal roots of the nerves to a leg are cut, the leg is without sensation but not paralyzed. If the ventral roots alone are cut, then the limb is paralyzed but not insensitive. Hence, the dorsal root is sensory and the ventral motor.

A number of reflexes concerned with breathing and with the heart beat have been discussed in previous chapters. An easily observed reflex is the papillary light reflex, although the neural pathways involved have turned out to be more complex than in a spinal reflex. Stand before a window and cover one eye completely for about two minutes. Then look in a mirror as you readmit light to the eye. You will observe that the pupil becomes smaller. This is due to a contraction of the sphincter muscle in the iris.

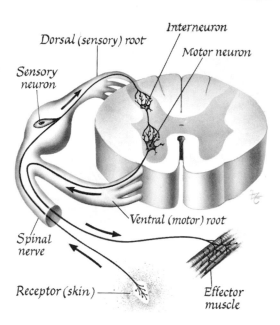

Fig. 31–10. Cross section of spinal cord to show a very simple reflex pathway.

Reflex action is simple to demonstrate in your pupil or in a spinal frog. But the neural mechanisms themselves are complex. Think for a moment of the intricate connections and interconnections necessary to place the toes of a frog's foot on a precise spot anywhere on its back! Moreover, in an intact frog the actions of the legs are under the overriding control of the brain, not just the cord. The subtle complexity of seemingly simple reflexes is shown by the fact of **reciprocal innervation** and its resultant **reciprocal inhibition.** These basic facts about the nervous system were discovered in the early years of the century by Sir Charles Sherrington and have been connected with his name ever since. If reciprocal inhibition did not exist, locomotion would be virtually impossible. It now appears possible that memory may be based on a modification of a mechanism very similar to reciprocal inhibition. (See page 648.)

What is reciprocal inhibition? It will be recalled that muscles are organized into antagonistic sets, flexors and extensors. For smooth motion of the arm or leg it is absolutely essential that the flexors should relax in proportion to the contraction of the extensors. Otherwise motion would be more absurdly jerky than in a primitive motion picture. Histologists

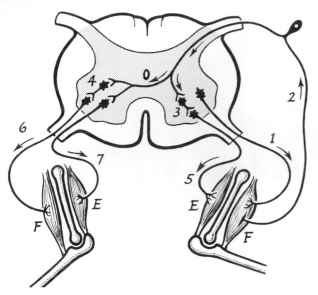

Fig. 31–11. Diagram to show neural pathways in reciprocal inhibition of frog legs. Motor neuron *1* stimulates *F*, a flexor muscle on the right, to contract. Sensory neuron *2* carries impulse from sensory "spindle" in the contracting muscle to very short interneurons (Renshaw neurons) *3* and *4*, within the spinal cord. These, in turn, stimulate inhibitory neurons *5*, to the extensor of the right leg, and *6*, to the flexor of the left leg, preventing them from contracting. Note that sensory neuron *2* may also stimulate motor neuron *7* to the extensor of the opposite leg. *(After H. C. Elliott)*

(students of tissues) have discovered sense organs, muscle spindles within muscles and Golgi organs in tendons, which detect the state of contraction or of stretch of the muscle. After a century of work much still remains to be discovered about the functions of these organs, but it has been established that each set acts as part of a feedback system so that when a given muscle is stimulated to contract, inhibitory impulses are sent to its antagonists.

Development of Reflex Behavior. The simple experiment with the spinal frog and a piece of paper soaked in vinegar raises some basic issues about animal and human behavior. In the course of its life, did the frog's spinal cord learn by trial and error, or in any other way, precisely what muscles to move and to what extent in order to flick off a piece of paper from any par-

ticular spot on the back? Or did the sensory, associative, and motor nerve fibers and synaptic connections grow in such a way that in the normal maturing of the nervous system a predetermined neuromotor pattern was established entirely without experience or learning? This is an old and still lively controversy. In the early 1930's many workers took the view that embryonic development leaves the vertebrate nervous system a completely plastic network, with no predetermined neuromotor pathways all set up and ready to go in specific directions. Behavior patterns were organized out of initially random motions. In other words, adult behavior patterns, all the way from flicking a scrap of paper off the back to complex nest-building, were believed to be essentially learned responses based on random trial and error.

At present the pendulum of opinion among zoologists is swinging in the other direction. No one denies the fact of learning or conditioning even among animals low in the scale of nervous complexity. Nevertheless an increasing mass of evidence indicates that it is not only the gross external form of the nervous system that is genetically determined. The internal organization of the nervous pathways and the synaptic connections within the brain and spinal cord are for the most part also organized by the genetic factors of growth and development, uninfluenced by factors outside the organism.

Some of the evidence for this newer emphasis comes from studies of the behavior of intact animals, especially insects, fishes, and birds. This aspect will be discussed in the chapter on animal behavior. Other evidence comes from analytic studies based on surgical modification of the nervous system. For these studies amphibians have again proved to be especially favorable material. They are easily obtained and extraordinarily hardy in the face of drastic procedures. Some of these experiments are so brilliantly conceived and so incisive and far-reaching in results that they are prerequisites to an up-to-date understanding of animal behavior.

In spinal reflexes, as shown by Hales in the 18th century, if the toe of a frog is pinched, the appropriate leg is bent at the knee to draw the toe away from the offending stimulus. What would happen if the sensory nerves coming from the right foot were switched over to the

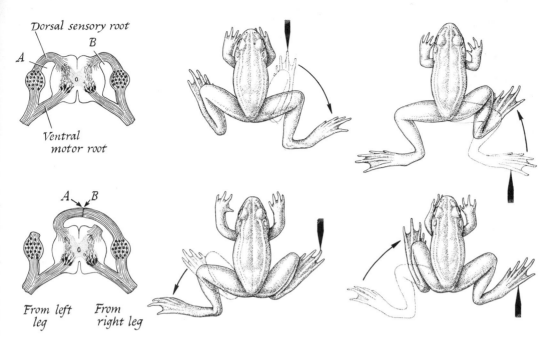

Fig. 31 – 12. Diagrammatic cross section of spinal cord and nerves in reflex arc, and frog's response to stimulus. Top: normal. Bottom: after dorsal sensory root of one side has been grafted onto sensory nerve of opposite side, stimulation of right leg causes response in left leg. *(After R. W. Sperry)*

left side of the spinal cord? This can be done in tadpoles, as shown in Figure 31 – 12. The sensory roots are cut along lines *A* and *B*, and then surfaces *A* and *B* are held together until healing has occurred. Nerve fibers from the right leg then grow, by the normal processes of regeneration, in toward the spinal cord. This they do by penetrating into the cut end of the dorsal root of the *left* side. After the central synaptic connections have been made, and the right foot develops, when the tadpole has become a frog, the right foot becomes sensitive to stimuli. However, *when the right foot is pinched, the left foot is pulled up.* Since these operations are performed on tadpoles before metamorphosis and the development of hind legs, it seems impossible to believe that learning by experience can play any part in these responses.

The Nervous Impulse. On the molecular level of physiology a question of great interest remains. What is a nervous impulse? Only a little over a century ago many people believed that the nature of the impulse which carries messages along a nerve could never be known. Whenever it is asserted that a particular prob-

lem can never be solved, the case of the nervous impulse is worth remembering. The most eminent physiologist of the first half of the 19th century, Johannes Müller, maintained that even the speed of a nervous impulse was unknowable. Yet the print was hardly more than decently dry on Müller's assertion when one of his own students, Hermann Helmholtz, showed that this could be done, and did it.

Helmholtz's method was simplicity itself. He used the frog which Müller had reintroduced into physiology – Bell and Magendie had used mammals – and exposed the great sciatic nerve which innervates the gastrocnemius muscle in the calf of the leg (see Fig. 21 – 3). He stimulated the nerve at two points, one fairly close to the muscle, the second at a carefully measured distance along the nerve from the first. He very accurately measured the time elapsing between application of the stimulus and contraction of the muscle, and discovered that the more of the nerve over which the impulse had to travel, the longer the time between the stimulus and the contraction. Simple arithmetic gives the speed of the nervous impulse. It varies somewhat from species to species and from nerve to

607

nerve. Nerves lacking the myelin sheath conduct impulses very slowly. In mammalian nerves at body temperature, the speed is about 325 feet per second, faster than a man can run but far slower than sound, which travels about 1,087 feet per second. Frog nerves conduct impulses at the rate of about 100 feet per second, or roughly 60 miles an hour.

New facts and new theories about the action of nerves have been accumulating ever since. These fall logically into three groups: what happens to a nerve cell at the time of stimulation; transmission of the nervous impulse; and how a nerve delivers its message either across a synapse or to an end-organ such as a muscle.

Irritability is a common and presumably universal attribute of protoplasm. In nerves this property has become specialized and heightened. The process by which the incident energy — whether the energy is light, heat, or something else — impinging on a sensory nerve ending is transduced, i.e., converted, into a nervous impulse is poorly understood but will be discussed in the section on sense organs.

A nervous impulse is a wave of **electronegativity** easily detected with a student-type galvanometer and a pair of electrodes. This wave of negativity is apparently not a mere accompaniment of the nervous impulse but is itself part of the driving mechanism much as a progressive wave of falling in a line of bricks is caused by each brick in falling hitting the next. With the wave of negativity goes a sudden and profound **change in permeability** of the cell membrane. As has just been pointed out, the speed is far too slow for these waves to be electric currents, which have a velocity virtually equal to the speed of light. Furthermore, a given nerve fiber does not carry impulses of different strengths or at different velocities. The only variable is the frequency with which impulses pass along a fiber. A nervous impulse is an **all-or-none** affair. Either it fires off or it doesn't. The only requirement is that the inciting stimulus — whether chemical, mechanical, or electrical — must attain a certain intensity, usually called the threshold. The wave of negativity neither increases nor decreases as it moves. The action at every point along the fiber is a local action.

The old analogy of the powder train is a good one here. In fact a spectacular demonstration can be made by pouring a very narrow path of smokeless gunpowder along the top of a laboratory table and then carefully igniting one end. The gunpowder train analogy thus illustrates the fact that the impulse is a function of local conditions and does not vary with the strength of the initial stimulus, provided only that the stimulus was sufficient to ignite the reaction. If one or more branches are made in the powder path, the analogy will illustrate a second basic principle which applies to the nervous system as a whole. The initial spark results in two, or four, or many burning powder trains. This is the **principle of amplification.** Because nerve action is local, total response depends on neural connections, not incident energy.

Modern ideas about the nature of this self-propagating event, the nervous impulse, are based on the theory of Julius Bernstein at the turn of the century. He pointed out that the wave of negativity could be explained on the following basis. The outside of the nerve cell and its fiber is positive and the inside negative. The cell membrane is semi-permeable, keeping more negatively charged ions inside and positively charged ones outside. A nervous impulse is a breakdown in the selective permeability permitting a relatively free passage of ions so that the membrane potential disappears. About 40 years later A. L. Hodgkin and A. F. Huxley at the Marine Laboratory in Plymouth, England, made the exciting discovery, using the giant nerve fibers of a squid, that one electrode can be inserted inside the nerve fiber, the other placed outside, and the actual potentials measured. The inside is indeed electronegative by about minus 60 millivolts (-0.06 volts) to the outside. Not only that, but as an impulse passes, the electric potential is not just neutralized, — the interior becomes electropositive to the outside by about $+ 50$ MV, markedly reversing the potential! (See Fig. 31–13.)

The explanation has not been easy, and all the answers are not in yet. In a resting cell there is about 20 times as high a concentration of potassium ions on the inside as on the outside. The concentrations of sodium and chloride ions are far higher outside than inside. The wave of negativity induces a transient change in permeability which permits positive sodium ions to enter. This further depresses the poten-

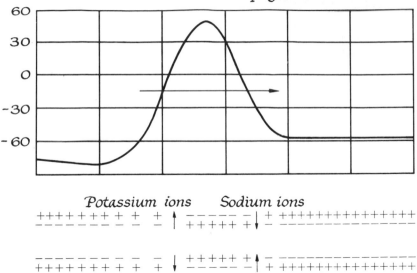

Fig. 31–13. A nervous impulse. Above: graph showing electrical charge. Below: diagram of a section through the nerve fiber showing the concomitant movements of sodium and potassium ions, and the resulting reversal of electrical charge between the inside and outside of the fiber.

tial so that the wave passes like fire along a fuse or a travelling electrical stimulus. Metabolic energy is required to restore the resting potential and the marked differences in ion concentration. This can be shown by the use of metabolic poisons. There is evidence that acetylcholine (to be discussed below) is important in this process. The mechanism which maintains the higher external concentration of sodium by the expenditure of metabolic energy is referred to as the **sodium pump.**

Synaptic Transmission. What happens when an impulse reaches a synapse at the end of its run? Axons terminate in one or a cluster of small **synaptic knobs** which press within about 20 millimicrons (the kind of gap only an electron microscope can see) of a dendrite or nerve cell body. Within the knob can be seen a few small mitochondria, indicating that some energy-using activity occurs there, and several dozen small vesicles. The vesicles evidently discharge a transmitter substance when an impulse arrives. This substance produces a lowering of the membrane potential of the receiving cell. If enough synaptic knobs discharge, the membrane is depolarized sufficiently to spark a nervous impulse. Thus it may be that stimuli must arrive from many sensory nerve fibers before a given interneuron or motor neuron will discharge.

The transmitter chemical is known to be **acetylcholine** for all motor nerves and for many of the nerves of the autonomic system. The dis-

covery of acetylcholine by Loewi as the substance liberated by the vagus nerve which inhibits the heart beat has already been told (page 537). Nerves which secrete acetylcholine are called **cholinergic.** After secretion at a synapse, acetylcholine is destroyed by a clean-up enzyme, **acetylcholinesterase.** Poisons which block the action of this enzyme are among the most powerful known. Despite the inherent danger, such nerve poisons are sometimes used against insects.

Other nerves secrete epinephrine or norepinephrine and are called **adrenergic.** They include the post-ganglionic nerves of the sympathetic nervous system. Several other substances are suspected of transmitting impulses across synaptic clefts in special cases. Acetylcholine is very widely distributed throughout the animal kingdom. So far epinephrine seems confined to vertebrates and earthworms!

The question of how transmitter substances produce their effects is still uncertain. A stimulating substance may decrease the external positivity of the receptor cell by causing pores in the receptor membrane to permit the ingress of positive sodium ions. Inhibition could be produced by opening pores which excluded sodium but permitted positive potassium ions to leak out. It can be shown experimentally that the threshold of stimulation can be increased by artificially making the interior of a nerve cell more negative than it normally is. Some investigators believe that different stimulator and inhibitor substances exist and are secreted by different nerves. Others believe that whether a transmitter substance stimulates or inhibits depends on the nature of the receiver cell membrane at the synaptic junction.

THE BRAIN

The human brain has been called many things—"that great ravelled knot," the "computer in the skull." And justifiably, because of all the structures known to man, the brain is the most complex, by several orders of magnitude. In fact, no computer remotely approaches the brain in complexity, much less in versatility. The number of neurons in the human brain has been calculated at about 12 billion. Vast numbers of them each receive branches from the axons of 10,000 other nerve cells. The number of possible combinations and permutations staggers the mind. Perhaps anyone familiar with Gödel's proof—that in mathematics there must always be an unproved axiom—may think it unfair to ask the brain to understand itself!

Complexity of interneuronal synaptic interconnections appears in the animal kingdom wherever complexity of behavior appears. A region of such tangled masses of interconnecting dendrites and branching axons is called a **neuropil.** Sometimes a neuropil looks like a thick brush pile in a total confusion; sometimes a pattern of organization, often a repeating pattern of confusion, is visible.

The brain of a higher insect contains a neuropil at its center with cell bodies around the periphery between the emerging nerves. Neuropils are found in the brain of the octopus and, of course, in the vertebrate brain. In a certain sense the gray matter of the human cerebral cortex is an extensive, seven-layered neuropil. It is from neuropils that the mysterious electrical brain waves originate. Some of these regions, like the big verticalis lobe of the octopus brain or the prefrontal lobes of the brain of mammals, can be removed in large part without having much, if any, measurable effect on subsequent behavior! Yet it is impossible to believe that such large, complex structures have been evolved in the course of natural selection without possessing some function. What goes on in a neuropil? Considerations of this sort have led a comparative neurophysiologist, T. H.

Bullock, to suggest that our present knowledge of the physiology of neurons, even when extrapolated, cannot wholly account for behavior. We must look for new and additional parameters in the physiology of complex systems of nerve cells.

Feedback. The first basic principle to remember in attempting to understand brain function is that the significant factor is the kind and degree of organizational complexity. As pointed out earlier, the important differences between the brain of a fish and the brain of a fisherman are not on the cellular level. It is a question of intercellular organization, of design.

One of the most vital aspects of the design of the brain is its neural feedback. This insight grew out of work during the last world war on self-regulating devices. Such so-called **servomechanisms** are designed to keep an airplane on a set course, to enable a radar-guided gun to seek out and follow a moving target, or to perform some other task requiring reactions to changing conditions. Servomechanisms are based on closed circuits or feedback, usually negative feedback.

Negative feedback is said to occur when some result of an action tends to counteract the action, and **positive feedback** when it tends to accentuate the action. For example, many furnaces are controlled by thermostats. When the temperature falls to a certain level the thermostat sends to the furnace motor a signal which turns it on. As soon as the temperature climbs to a predetermined value, the thermostat sends a signal which shuts off the motor. This is negative feedback. If the thermostat were set in such a way that the hotter the room, the faster it made the furnace motor run, then the feedback would be positive. The result of an action, in this case the heat, is referred to as the **output.** The productive action, in this case the fire, is referred to as the **input.** Feedback can now be defined as the process whereby information about the output of a process is circuited back to an early stage in the process so that the output is changed.

Servomechanisms of various kinds have been used since the 18th century, when James Watt invented the rotating flyball governor for steam engines and thereby made the age of steam a reality. In recent years electronic servomechanisms have generated a science of their own, **cybernetics.** Its devotees have drawn many interesting analogies between complex servomechanisms and the nervous system. They point to many self-adjusting reflexes such as those involved in breathing, locomotion, and posture. Many go further and profess to see purposive action as the result of negative feedback. An animal with a brain receiving impulses from an empty stomach will seek food until the presence of food in the stomach stops the impulses, just as an automatic missile will "seek" the target plane until its image is in the center of the guiding "eye" of the missile. If the missile begins to turn away from the target, the image of the target moving to one side of the "eye" results in negative feedback which compensates for the error of the missile and returns it to its course toward the plane. Consciousness, mental disease, and other difficult problems have been brought within the scope of cybernetics.

How far is this comparison between electronic servomechanisms and the nervous system just a verbal analogy, and how far, if at all, does it point toward reality? Before attempting to answer this question directly, we will survey the important anatomical and physiological features of the mammalian brain.

Brain Size. A great deal has been made of the relation of brain size to intelligence. In general, the larger the brain, the greater the potential intelligence. A large absolute size appears necessary to provide for complex associative activities, including feedback mechanisms of self-adjustment. However, absolute size must be corrected for total body size. An elephant or a whale has a larger brain than a man in absolute terms, but not in proportion to body weight. The great size of an elephant's brain is presumably due to the large number of neurons essential to the sending and receiving of signals to the enormous body mass, and does not represent an increase in the higher associative centers. At the other end of the size scale, the proportionality rule again breaks down. Insectivores like moles, with extremely modest intellectual abilities, possess brains larger than man's in proportion to total body size.

Actual brain size varies widely in the higher primates. In chimpanzees and gorillas the brain ranges from 325 to 650 cc in volume. In fossil man-apes it ranged from 450 to 700 cc, in fossil Java man 750 to 900, in Peking man 800 to 1,200, and in Neanderthal 1,100 to 1,550 cc. Although his brow was low and his features decidedly simian, brain size in Neanderthal man falls easily within the normal range of variation that is found in contemporary human populations.

Many attempts have been made to discover correlations between brain size or convolutions, on the one hand, and degree of intelligence and achievement in man, on the other. Except for obvious deformities such as those in microcephalic idiots, these efforts have not succeeded. Most men of outstanding intellectual ability have had brains in the upper half of the frequency distribution curve for size, but there have been a surprising number with brains well below average. It is not difficult to believe that along with size there may well be other factors—a slightly different twist of metabolism, for instance—that determine potential intelligence. And actual achievement is very clearly the resultant of many factors in addition to intelligence.

General Brain Structure. The mammalian brain, like that of all vertebrates, develops from five swellings at the anterior end of the embryonic neural tube. The most anterior forms a pair of swellings, right and left, together called the **telencephalon.** It is the dramatic growth of the roof or **pallium** of the telencephalon which constitutes the **cerebrum** and characterizes the mammals. The cavities within the cerebral hemispheres are known as **first and second ventricles** of the brain, or, more correctly, according to the new international code of nomenclature (the PNA), the **left and right lateral ventricles** of the brain. They are filled with cerebrospinal fluid and connected by way of the other brain ventricles to the neural canal extending down the spinal cord.

The second embryonic swelling of the neural tube forms the **diencephalon,** the walls of which are the **thalamus** and **hypothalamus.** Its cavity is the **third ventricle.** Dorsally placed on the diencephalon is the **pineal body,** ventrally is the

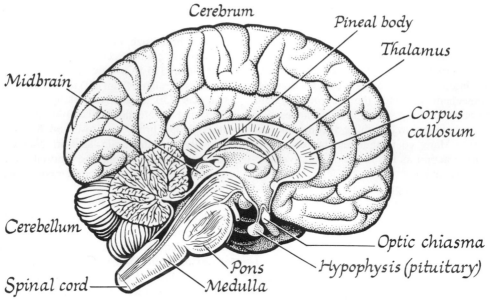

Cerebrum

Midbrain

Pineal body

Thalamus

Corpus callosum

Cerebellum

Optic chiasma

Spinal cord

Pons

Medulla

Hypophysis (pituitary)

Fig. 31 – 14. Left half of the human brain, median aspect. The corpus callosum (shown here in section) connects the two hemispheres. *(From Pauli,* The World of Life, *Houghton Mifflin)*

pituitary gland and the **optic chiasma** where the optic nerves enter the brain.

The third swelling is the **mesencephalon,** the dorsal portion of which forms the optic lobes, known collectively as the **optic tectum.** It is the destination of axons growing in from the optic nerves.

The fourth swelling or **metencephalon** develops into the **cerebellum** dorsally and the **pons** ventrally.

The fifth and last major division of the brain is the **myelencephalon,** commonly called the **medulla oblongata.** The **fourth ventricle** of the brain is the continuous cavity within the metencephalon and the myelencephalon.

The Cerebrum. The mammalian, and especially the human, cerebrum is the organ of thought and thereby clearly ranks as the supreme achievement of over 500 million years of

Fig. 31 – 15. Left hemisphere of the human brain, lateral view. Shaded areas are concerned with speech. Destruction of region *a* results in loss of ability to speak, of *b* to write words, of *c* to recognize spoken words, and of *d* to recognize written words. *(From Pauli,* The World of Life, *Houghton Mifflin)*

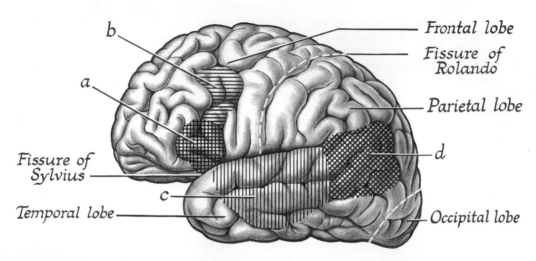

b

a

Frontal lobe

Fissure of Rolando

Parietal lobe

d

Fissure of Sylvius

c

Temporal lobe

Occipital lobe

evolution. It deserves a closer look. The cerebrum, as the two cerebral hemispheres are collectively called, is also called the **neopallium** or **neocortex** because it is a new development in vertebrate evolution, appearing first in the higher reptiles. The neopallium in mammals has pushed the old so-called archipallium, or paleocortex, which was chiefly concerned with smell, to one side so that about all that remains of it are the olfactory lobes on the ventral side of the brain.

In primitive mammals like the insectivores and rodents, the surface or **cortex** of the brain is smooth, but in many others, including the primates, the cortex is highly convoluted. In man a deep, more or less horizontal fissure, the **fissure of Sylvius,** separates the **temporal lobe** below from the **frontal** and **parietal lobes** above. The frontal lobe is separated from the parietal lobe by the vertical **fissure of Rolando,** which runs upward from the fissure of Sylvius to the top of the cerebrum. The region at the posterior and lower end of each hemisphere is known as the **occipital lobe.**

If the cerebral hemispheres are cut in half from left to right, it can be seen that the cortex, or superficial zone, is gray, whereas the inner portions are white with here and there rounded gray masses. The grayness of the gray matter is due to the presence of several billion cell bodies of neurons. The white of the white matter is due to the myelin sheaths of the axons of neurons. It is a mistake to regard intellectual ability as resident solely in the gray matter. The intercommunication systems represented by the white matter are equally essential. The rounded gray masses within the lower part of the brain are relay and shunting centers of neurons and are called **basal ganglia** or (to the confusion of students) **basal "nuclei."** (This, of course, is to use the word nucleus in its primary meaning of a kernel or central region.) The four largest of the basal ganglia make up the **corpus striatum,** which develops from the floor of the telencephalon and which constitutes the main bulk of the forebrain in birds. (See Chapter 23 on Birds.)

The paleocortex has four layers. The neocortex of a mammal possesses in contrast six definite, although not sharply delimited, horizontal layers. The relative thickness of the various layers differs in different parts of the cerebrum. By the use of silver stains and other methods, the cells and their rootlike processes may be revealed. (See Fig. 31–17.) Most of the cells are oriented with their long axes perpendicular to the surface of the cortex.

Our knowledge of the **cyto-architecture of the cortex** is still fragmentary. However, four facts seem well established:

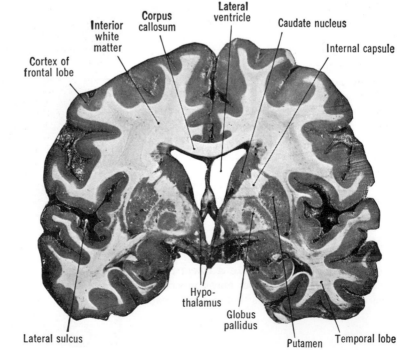

Fig. 31–16. Cross section of human brain. The gray matter is darkly stained. *(From Gardner, Fundamentals of Neurology, W. B. Saunders)*

Interior white matter
Corpus callosum
Lateral ventricle
Caudate nucleus
Internal capsule
Cortex of frontal lobe
Hypo-thalamus
Globus pallidus
Lateral sulcus
Putamen
Temporal lobe

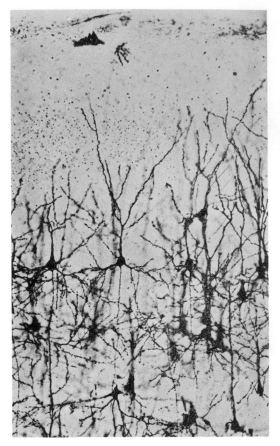

Fig. 31–17. Cells of the cerebral cortex of a cat, the central machinery of mental activity.

1. The fifth layer from the surface contains many large **pyramidal cells** each having one long dendrite extending well up into the second layer and many shorter dendrites branching either from the long dendrite or directly from the cell body. From the basal end of the cell body an axon extends down into the white matter and may end in one of the basal ganglia or continue down the spinal cord.

2. Most of the nerve fibers coming in from other parts of the nervous system end in the fourth layer, where they usually branch extensively and make various synaptic connections with motor or other efferent nerves. The afferent or sensory nerve may connect directly with a motor nerve to make a direct circuit, or an incoming sensory fiber may connect with one or more interneurons that in turn synapse with one or more motor cells to make a delayed circuit, delayed because time is always required for an impulse to cross a synapse.

3. It is now believed that a third type of connection constitutes the basic unit of the cortex and makes a simple feedback loop. This is indicated both by microscopic study of brain sections and by physiological experiments. An incoming afferent fiber makes a synaptic connection with the dendrites of a pyramidal motor cell which has a branching axon. The main branch of the axon extends down into the white matter of which it forms a part. The shorter branch loops back and stimulates one or more interneurons that in their turn restimulate the dendrite of the original motor cell. Thus a feedback or **reverberating circuit** is established. This is, of course, an oversimplification, as a glance at the photograph of a brain section will show. Many — perhaps a hundred or so — sensory nerve endings impinge synaptically on each motor cell. Whether any particular motor

Fig. 31–18. Basic unit of the neocortex of a higher mammal. Note sensory input fiber and pyramidal motor cell with its output fiber plus the lateral axon which swings back to stimulate several interneurons which restimulate the motor cell, thus constituting a self-sustaining feedback system.

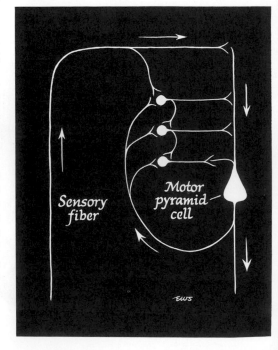

Sensory fiber

Motor pyramid cell

cell fires a nerve impulse down its axon to a muscle or other effector depends on whether or not it receives impulses from a sufficiently large number of sensory nerve endings.

4. The cells in the remaining four layers of the cortex are presumably interneurons concerned with association. Perhaps they are essentially complex systems of reverberating circuits. The total number of interneurons within and between the six layers of the cortex runs into billions.

The white matter immediately below the cortex contains innumerable fibers. Some, already mentioned, pass from the cortex down into the basal ganglia or directly into the spinal cord. Others connect the two cerebral hemispheres. It is these right-left communicating fibers which make up the corpus callosum. Still other bands of fibers run at right angles to the right-left fibers and connect anterior and posterior cortical areas.

The **corpus callosum** long stood as one of the outstanding puzzles of brain organization. It is easily the most massive fiber tract of the brain. Yet when it was completely cut in human patients in the course of surgery for tumors, no observable defects of any kind, subjective or objective, resulted! Cats or monkeys which have had the corpus callosum cut are virtually indistinguishable from intact animals in normal daily activities. But if the optic chiasma is cut as well as the corpus callosum, so that the right eye is connected only to the right side of the brain and the left eye only to the left side, the answer to the old puzzle can be found. If a cat or monkey so prepared is taught to make some discrimination using only its right eye — say, press a round not a square button to get food — it will be found when the right eye is covered and the left eye tested that the left side of the brain knows nothing about choosing the round button. If only the optic chiasma is cut while the callosum is left intact, then tricks learned with one eye are easily performed using the other. So it was learned that the function of the corpus callosum is to keep each side of the brain informed about what the other experiences. If something is learned in one hemisphere, the corpus callosum enables a duplicate "engram" or memory trace to be established in the other hemisphere.

By means of electrical stimulation, surgical removal, and the recording of small electrical changes on the brain surface that accompany

Fig. 31–19. Sensory and motor homunculi, showing the location on the cortex of the brain of the sensory and motor centers for various parts of the body. The sensory areas are just anterior to the central sulcus, or fissure of Rolando, and the motor areas just posterior. *(From G. B. Moment,* General Biology, *2nd ed. Copyright 1950 by Appleton–Century–Crofts, Inc. Reprinted by permission)*

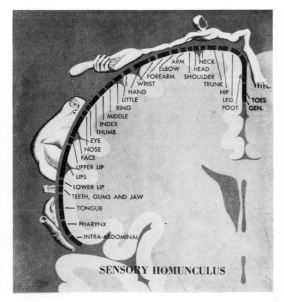

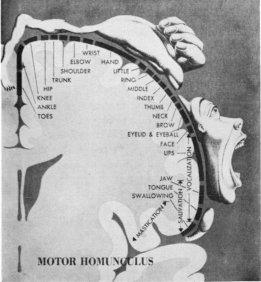

various activities, it has been possible to learn a fair amount about the general functions of different regions of the cerebrum. Injuries in the occipital lobe region result in impaired vision. There are important speech areas along the temporal lobe and on the lower part of the frontal lobe. Motor and sensory centers for the skeletal muscles are lined up along the fissure of Rolando, the motor centers on the anterior ridge or gyrus, the sensory centers along the posterior gyrus. Curiously enough, the body is represented upside down. If a point close to the top of the brain just anterior to the fissure of Rolando is stimulated electrically, the foot will twitch. If points lower down are stimulated, muscles in the legs, trunk, arms, neck, eyelids, and other parts of the head will move, in that order. Most of the frontal lobes represent a "silent" area of indefinite function, concerned with the higher associations.

Other Brain Areas. The structure of the **diencephalon** of a mammal is not greatly different from that in other vertebrates. Ventrally there is the optic chiasma where the optic nerves enter the brain. Just posterior to the chiasma is a slight swelling, the **infundibulum,** to which is attached the pituitary gland. The cavity within the diencephalon is the third ventricle. It is connected anteriorly with the first and second ventricles that lie respectively in the two cerebral hemispheres, and posteriorly to the fourth ventricle, which is mostly in the medulla oblongata. Dorsally there is a small pineal body, the function of which is only beginning to be known. The greatly thickened sides of the diencephalon are termed the thalami: the **epithalamus** above, the **thalamus** to the sides of the third ventricle, and the **hypothalamus** below. Most of the thalamus in mammals is in fact a neothalamus not present in reptiles. All the connections between thalamus and cortex—and they are legion—are reciprocal. We see here another feedback or reverberating system.

In the hypothalamus are centers for many of the emotional and subrational aspects of life. A center regulating sleep is here. Appropriate electrical stimulation of the hypothalamus in lightly anesthetized cats will provoke ferocious spasms of generalized rage, as though the cat were suddenly faced by a barking dog. Tumors of this region in man have produced long periods of inconsolable grief or continuous and equally inexplicable gaiety. A very narrowly delimited center in the hypothalamus of the rat controls appetite. With special modern instruments it is possible to make extremely localized lesions in the hypothalamus which result in voracious appetites. Such animals begin to eat ravenously before they are completely out from under the anesthetic. Interestingly enough, these rats are true gourmets; they not only eat several times as much as other rats, they are also far more particular about what they will and will not eat.

From the hypothalamus several fiber tracts run down into the posterior lobe of the pituitary gland. These neurons secrete a characteristic neurohormone which passes down the axons into the gland. It has been demonstrated that in this way the anterior pituitary may be brought into action by the nervous system.

The **mesencephalon** of mammals still retains, in its roof, paired lobes containing visual functions but it is not the dominant visual center.

The mammalian **metencephalon** has undergone a development second only to the telencephalon itself. Dorsally the **cerebellum** contains centers controlling the niceties of muscular action. The **pons,** ventrally located, contains many fibers connecting the right and left sides of the brain. The cerebellum forms part of an important feedback system governing voluntary motion. Impulses from the cerebral cortex sweep down through the pons and up into the cortex of the cerebellum. Thence they pass back to a basal ganglion (the dentate nucleus of the cerebellum) and then via the thalamus back to the cortex of the cerebrum. From the cerebral cortex the impulses may pass directly or indirectly into the spinal cord and thence to muscles, or again to the pons and cerebellum.

The fifth and last division of the vertebrate brain, the **myelencephalon,** forms the **medulla oblongata** in mammals, as in all other vertebrates. It consists mainly of fiber tracts passing to and from the rest of the brain and the spinal cord. Many of the fibers cross from one side of the brain stem to the other. Most of the spinal nerves (VI through XII) connect with the medulla. Reflexes concerned with breathing and the heart beat center here. Hence injury to the medulla can be quickly fatal.

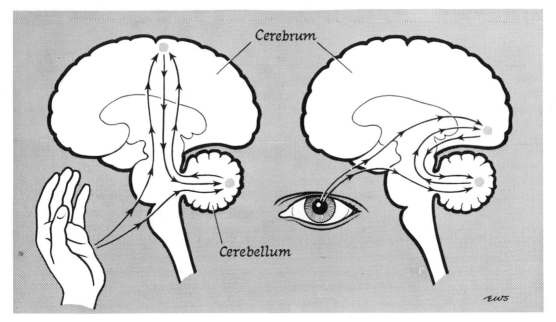

Cerebrum

Cerebellum

Fig. 31–20. Feedback circuits within the brain. Impulses originating in the periphery — the hands or eyes, for instance — pass to the cerebral cortex and from there to the cerebellum; they may then reverberate between the cerebrum and the cerebellum. Some impulses from sensory endings pass directly to the cerebellum. *(After "The Cerebellum" by Ray S. Snider. Copyright © 1958 by Scientific American, Inc. All rights reserved)*

THE SENSE ORGANS

Sense organs stand between us and the vibrating topless, bottomless world of interstellar and interatomic forces. Sense organs are transducers which translate various forms of energy — light, heat, sound, and certain molecular configurations — into the uniform language of the nervous system, that wave of negativity, the nervous impulse.

Smell. The ability to discriminate odors is the dominant sensory ability of most vertebrates and many other animals. If the olfactory antennae of an ant are severed, it can no longer recognize the members of its own colony and will attack friend and foe alike. Olfaction is a dominant sense in all but a few mammals and is correlated with the fact that most are color-blind creatures of the evening and predawn.

The sensitivity and discriminative ability of the human nose are indeed astounding from the chemical point of view. Hundreds of odors can be easily detected even though the concentration of odoriferous molecules is far below detection by ordinary chemical means. How is this achieved?

Many theories have been proposed; none is completely proved. There is much cogent evidence, however, for a theory which was suggested in primitive form by Lucretius in the 1st century B.C.! The sensation recognized as a particular odor is due to the size and shape of volatile molecules which allow or disallow them to fit into like-shaped receptor sites on the nerve endings of the olfactory epithelium. Studies on men and frogs indicate that there are about seven primary odors: camphoraceous, musky, floral, pepperminty, ethereal, pungent, and putrid. Seven primary odors would require seven differently shaped receptor sites, a by no means impossible demand. Elaborate investigations of the shapes of odorous molecules show that small roundish molecules, regardless of chemical constitution, give a camphorlike odor. All the molecules giving a floral odor are shaped like a key to a Yale lock, elongate with one large rounded end. Narrowly elongate molecules give the odor ethereal, very small molecules with positive charges like formic acid are pungent, and so on for all the primary odors. By mixing various combinations of the seven presumably primary odors, it has been possible to simulate a large variety of other odors.

Taste. The chemosensory ability called taste is far more restricted than is smell. In man there are only four recognized tastes: sweet, bitter, sour, and salty. Taste buds sensitive to each are restricted to special zones on the tongue—sweet and salty on the tip, sour along the sides, and bitter at the base. In fishes what appear to be taste buds are distributed widely over the body. In butterflies the taste cells are located in the front feet; if the feet are placed in a sweet solution, the coiled tongue will be extended.

From the zoological point of view one of the most interesting discoveries about taste is that animals far apart in the scale of life have closely similar tasting abilities, or perhaps "preferences." If a man and a blowfly are each asked to rank several sugars in order of sweetness, both will arrange them in the same order. Sucrose is sweeter than cellobiose, which is sweeter than lactose, which is sweeter than glucose. How do you ask a fly such a question? Dip its feet in a series of solutions of increasing concentrations of a sugar. When the fly reaches the first solution that tastes "sweet," it will lower its proboscis and suck up some of it. By comparing the minimal concentrations of different sugars that will elicit a response, information can be obtained about their relative "sweetness" to the fly.

Fig. 31–21. Blowfly in position for sweet-ness-tasting experiment. Wax block is attached to wing and used as "handle." Note the extended proboscis and taste-sensitive tarsus or "foot." *(After Vincent G. Dethier)*

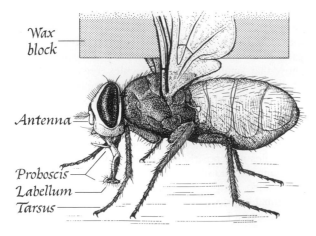

Wax block

Antenna

Proboscis
Labellum
Tarsus

Vision. Merely to summarize what is known about the organs and organelles of vision would require several large volumes. Some light-sensitive structures are as simple as the eyespot of a euglena. Others are as complex as the eyes of the higher insects or the vertebrates. Among the mollusks a beautiful and diversified series of photosensitive organs can be studied. Some mollusks possess true pinhole camera-type eyes which lack a lens but can produce a good image. Many snails possess eyes on their tentacles with cornea, lens, and retina. The eyes of *Pecten,* the scallop, are not only handsome objects around the edge of the mantle (Fig. 15–15), but are notable for having inverted retinas like those of vertebrates where the photosensitive nerve ends face away from the light source. The eyes of the squid and the octopus are closely similar to the vertebrate eye with cornea, lens, iris, anterior and posterior chamber and vitreous humor, and a retina backed up with a pigment layer. However, in these mollusks the retina is not inverted.

The evolutionary explanation for the various differences appears in the actual contingencies in the course of the history of the ancestors of the various groups of animals. The similarities, which are remarkable enough to have been discussed at length by professional philosophers such as Henri Bergson, apparently are due to adaptation to the facts of light waves and their behavior.

The eyes of all vertebrates are basically the same, from fish to man. Nocturnal vertebrates usually have larger eyes than do diurnal ones of comparable size. There are characteristic differences in pupillary size.

Mammals differ from all other vertebrates— from cyclostomes through birds—in regard to what happens to the optic nerve fibers at the optic chiasma. Everywhere except in mammals there is total decussation, that is, all the nerve fibers from the ganglion layer of the right eye cross over to the left side of the brain, and all the fibers from the left eye cross over to the right side. In mammals only those fibers from the nasal half of each retina decussate (Fig. 31–23). The result is that in man the fibers from the right half of each retina reach the tectum of the right optic lobe. Consequently, objects to the left of the field of vision stimulate

Fig. 31–22. Human eye, horizontal section. The posterior chamber is the small space between the iris and the attachment of the lens. *(From Pauli,* The World of Life, *Houghton Mifflin)*

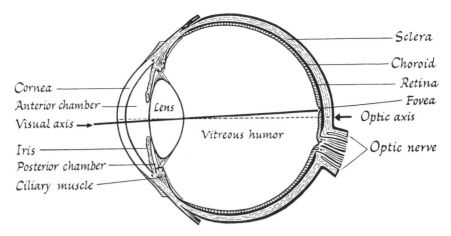

Cornea
Anterior chamber
Visual axis →
Iris
Posterior chamber
Ciliary muscle
Lens
Vitreous humor
Sclera
Choroid
Retina
Fovea
Optic axis
Optic nerve

Fig. 31–23. Neural pathways of the optic chiasma. Fibers from the right half of each retina reach the optic tectum (literally roof) of the right optic lobe. Likewise the fibers from the left half of each retina reach the tectum of the left optic lobe. *(After* Machinery of the Body *by Carlson and Johnson by permission of The University of Chicago Press. Copyright 1961 by The University of Chicago)*

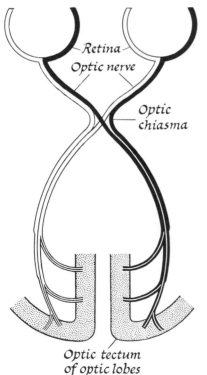

Retina
Optic nerve
Optic chiasma
Optic tectum of optic lobes

visual centers in the right optic lobe, and vice versa. The function of this partial decussation in mammals is very obscure. It seems to be related to binocular vision, because fewer and fewer fibers fail to decussate as the amount of binocular vision becomes less and less. Rabbits, for example, have only a small amount of overlap in the fields of vision of the two eyes and have a correspondingly small number of fibers that fail to cross over. However, it has been found that a number of vertebrates with complete or almost complete binocular vision, such as some fishes, owls, etc., have total decussation.

It will be recalled that the vertebrate eyeball is composed of three layers. The outermost is a white layer composed of tough connective tissue and called the **sclera** or sclerotic coat. As the sclerotic layer passes over the front of the eye it becomes the transparent **cornea.** Except in the region of the cornea, there is a heavily pigmented and vascular **choroid** layer immediately inside the sclerotic layer. Pressed against the choroid layer is the third of the layers of the eyeball, the retina.

The **retina** consists of three layers of cells. The layer bearing the photosensitive rods and cones lies next to the black choroid layer, and the rods and cones face into this away from the source of light. As we have seen, such "inverted" retinas are also found in flatworms and certain mollusks. Between the layer of rods and cones and the source of light are two additional cell layers. A middle retinal layer of bipolar interneurons conducts impulses from the

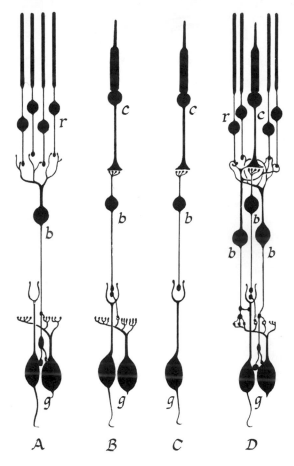

is no room for rods and cones where the ganglion cell fibers leave the eye, the beginning of the optic nerve is a blind spot.

Color vision is a property of the cones. Areas of the retina where rods predominate, as they do around the periphery, are highly sensitive in dim light but lack color vision. Areas with cones discriminate between colors.

Most mammals are color-blind. This is probably because most of them are either nocturnal or at least need their sharpest vision in the faint light of pre-dawn or dusk when the hunter and the hunted are abroad. Cats are completely color-blind, dogs and rats almost so. It is even unlikely that the bravest of bulls can see red. Color vision for man and the other primates appears to be a byproduct of arboreal life, where vision is of primary importance and danger from ground-living carnivores is minimal. Birds, many reptiles, and teleosts share with man the ability to distinguish color, that is, the wave length of light, in addition to its intensity.

What happens when light falls upon the retina that sends a pattern of nervous impulses racing up the optic nerves to the brain? If a frog or other vertebrate is killed in the dark and its retina exposed and then observed, it will be seen that the retina is purplish but rapidly bleaches to yellowish gray in the light. The original color is due to **rhodopsin** (*rhodon*, rose), also called visual purple, located in the **rods.** Rhodopsin itself is a compound molecule, a protein, **opsin,** plus a derivative of vitamin A, a carotenoid called **retinene.** It is for this reason that people whose diets are deficient in vitamin A have trouble seeing in dim light. That rhodopsin is in fact the pigment responsible for vision in dim light has been proven in a highly precise and elegant way. It is known from the laws of physics that to be effective, to produce some change, any radiation must be absorbed. Otherwise it merely passes through and nothing happens. It is also well known that different substances absorb light of different wave lengths. Rhodopsin best absorbs light of a wave length of 500 mμ. At either side of 500 mμ, absorbance falls off rapidly and in a characteristic curve. What is the curve of visual sensitivity in dim light of different wave lengths? Exactly the same as the absorption curve for rhodopsin!

Fig. 31–24. *A, B, C,* and *D* show different types of connections between cells of the retina. *g,* cells of ganglion cell layer; *b,* bipolar cells of middle cell layer; *r,* nuclei of rod-bearing cells; *c,* nuclei of cone-bearing cells. *(From Pauli,* The World of Life. *Houghton Mifflin)*

rod and cone cells to the ganglion cells, which lie on the inner surface of the retina adjacent to the glass-clear vitreous humor. The complexities of the retina, especially of the middle layer of bipolar cells with their many interconnections, enable the retina to take part in the organization of the picture before its representation in terms of nervous impulses is sent to the brain via the optic nerve. The big ganglion cells send their nerve fibers over the surface of the retina to converge at a point of exit which is the beginning of the optic nerve. Because there

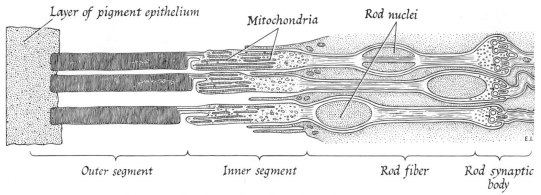

Layer of pigment epithelium   Mitochondria   Rod nuclei

Outer segment   Inner segment   Rod fiber   Rod synaptic body

Fig. 31–25. Diagram of retinal rods in the guinea pig eye.

The biochemistry has been worked out with great care. When quanta of light hit the rhodopsin in the rods the molecule is split into the protein, opsin, and the carotenoid, retinene. The results are the generation of a nervous impulse and the loss of the purple color. The reconstitution of rhodopsin requires a number of steps and may occur over more than one pathway. Both a photochemical reaction and an oxygen-dependent dark reaction can do the trick. Vitamin A from the bloodstream is converted into the immediate precursor of retinene by NAD, nicotinamide adenine dinucleotide.

What of **color vision?** In the early 1800's an English physicist, Thomas Young, proposed that ability to see color is due to three different pigments in the **cones.** By mixing red, green, and blue light, white light is experienced. Consequently special pigments sensitive to these three wave lengths would seem to offer a plausible basis for color vision. A pigment which absorbs in the red wave lengths and one absorbing in the green have been known for some time. It was not until 1964, over a century and a half after Young's suggestion, that the existence of a pigment which absorbs in the blue range was proved. This was achieved by using a microspectrophotometer capable of measuring the absorption of light passing through a single cone! Evidently there are three types of cones and our ability to distinguish colors depends on the proportions of different cones stimulated. Although there are about ten times as many rods as cones in the human retina, the rods don't interfere with color vision, perhaps because the rods do not function in bright light.

In color vision some of the philosophical problems of the nature and limitations of knowledge and communication can be seen in an acute form. How can you describe the redness of red to a totally color-blind person?

Until very recently nothing whatever was known about how the rods and cones transduced, i.e., translated, the incident energy of light quanta into a nervous impulse. A beginning has now been made with the electron microscope (Fig. 31–26). Rods are a long series of tightly packed membranes. These appear like a pile of microscopic dinner plates one on top of the other. In the cytoplasm of the cell bearing the rod, between the rod and the nucleus, are some mitochondria, but, far more interesting, the electron microscope reveals that the rod is connected into the cell body by what is unmistakably the basal structure of a cilium! Embryologists have long known that retinal cells have a tendency to produce cilia but no one knew the reason. Light-sensitive structures in many kinds of animals—jellyfish, starfish, scallops, *Amphioxus,* and primitive rhabdocoel flatworms, as well as vertebrates—have been found, under an electron microscope, to be composed of piles or more or less twisted masses of membranes. This is true also of the retinular cells in the rhabdomes of the compound eyes of arthropods. Presumably visual pigment is spread in or on these membranes. Since a nervous impulse is a change in EMF across the nerve cell membrane, it would not be surprising to find that when light splits rhodopsin into opsin and retinene a change in membrane potential is produced.

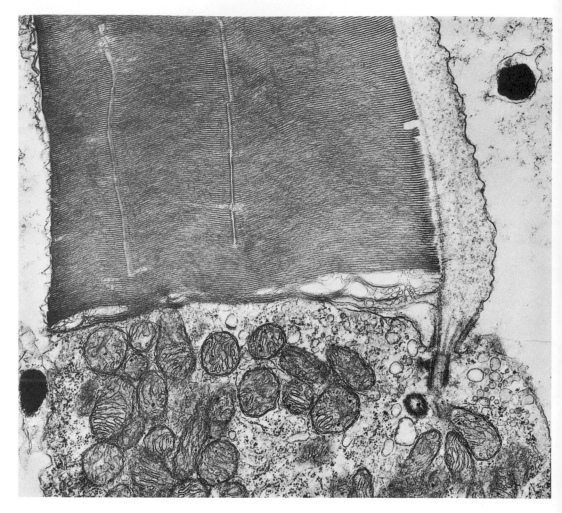

Fig. 31–26. A rod cell from a vertebrate retina (the Pacific treefrog, *Hyla regilla*), as seen under an electron microscope. The brushlike series of fine membranes is attached along the modified cilium visible on the right. The ciliary collar and several ciliary fibrils can be seen on the lower right where the connecting piece joins the series of membranes on the rod to the rest of the cell. About 25 mitochondria are visible in the cytoplasm. On the upper right is a pigment granule within a process from a retinal pigment cell. (*Kindness of R. M. Eakin*)

Hearing. The ears of mammals consist of three parts, the outer ear or **pinna,** the middle ear, and the inner ear. The **middle ear** develops from the first gill slit of the embryo and begins with the eardrum and extends down via the Eustachian tube into the pharynx. From the eardrum a chain of three tiny bones, the malleus, incus, and stapes, conducts the vibrations picked up by the eardrum and carries them across the upper end of the Eustachian tube to the inner ear. The evolutionary history of these three auditory ossicles has already been discussed in a previous section.

The **inner ear** consists of the three semicircular canals, the organs of equilibration, plus the cochlea, the organ of hearing. The cochlea resembles a snail shell made of a coiled tube which is itself divided along its length into three

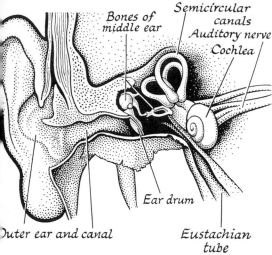

Fig. 31–27. The human ear. Semi-diagrammatic. *(From Pauli,* The World of Life, *Houghton Mifflin)*

parts. A ventral **scala tympani** and a dorsal **scala vestibuli** enclose between them a **cochlear canal,** roughly triangular in cross section. Extending the length of the cochlear canal and resting on its basement membrane is the **organ of Corti.** It consists essentially of several parallel rows of **sensory hair cells** overhung by a **tectorial membrane.** Different sounds are thought to cause the basement membrane to vibrate to different extents in different regions along its course. This stimulates the sensory hairs of the organ of Corti. The resulting nervous impulses pass along the eighth nerve into the brain where they are interpreted as sounds.

Other Senses. Lastly there is a great variety of small **sensory nerve endings** in the skin and throughout the body, especially in the muscles and tendons. There are special pain endings in the form of irregularly branching naked nerve fibers. There are Meissner's corpuscles for touch, Krause's end-bulbs for cold, Ruffini's corpuscles for heat. In fact, histologists have found more specialized nerve endings than psychologists can find sensations. Among the most important are the **proprioceptive endings** in muscles and tendons. The sensory nerves from these endings tell us about our own position, degree of muscle contraction, and motions, and thus constitute an important part of the feedback system that makes coordinated action possible. Several sensory nerve endings are shown on the next page.

Fig. 31–28. Cross section of human cochlea The organ of Corti contains sensory cells. *(After Fulton,* Physiology of the Nervous System, *Oxford University Press)*

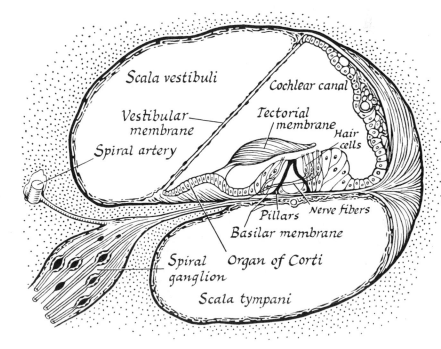

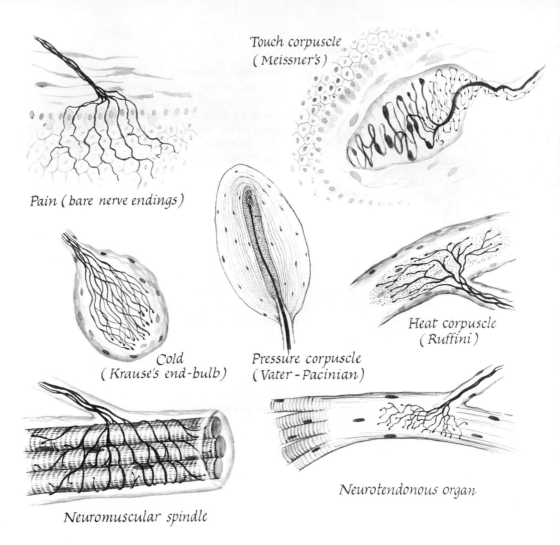

Touch corpuscle
(Meissner's)

Pain (bare nerve endings)

Cold
(Krause's end-bulb)

Pressure corpuscle
(Vater-Pacinian)

Heat corpuscle
(Ruffini)

Neurotendonous organ

Neuromuscular spindle

Fig. 31–29. Sensory nerve endings, including proprioceptors in muscles and tendons and touch, pain, pressure, cold, and heat endings in the skin.

Review and References

REVIEW TOPICS

1. Into what four major types can nervous systems be divided?

2. What are the major divisions of the vertebrate nervous system? Of the vertebrate brain?

3. What are the distinctions between the sympathetic and parasympathetic nervous systems? How are they related to the central nervous system?

4. What are the 12 cranial nerves and what do they do?

5. What factors complicate reflex actions? In what ways?

6. What is the evidence that not all reflexes are learned?

7. What is reciprocal inhibition? Why is it important in locomotion? A sea turtle swims using its right and left front flippers alternately. Trace the neural pathways involved.

8. How can it be definitely proved that a nervous impulse cannot be an electric current? What is a nervous impulse?

9. What and where are synapses? How do they function?

10. What may be the importance of neuropils? Where are they found?

11. What and where are the neocortex, optic tectum, hypothalamus, third ventricle of the brain, optic chiasma, sodium pump, nodes of Ranvier, dorsal sensory ganglia, organ of Corti?

12. How can a function for the corpus callosum be demonstrated?

13. Describe a specific neural feedback circuit.

14. What are the present theories of olfaction, "night" vision, color vision? How convincing are these theories? Why?

15. What was the contribution to an understanding of the nervous system made by: A. Vesalius, R. Descartes, Stephen Hales, Bell and Magendie, H. Helmholtz, Julius Bernstein, A. L. Hodgkin and A. F. Huxley, Otto Loewi?

16. What kinds of visual structures are found throughout the animal kingdom? Are their differences greatest on the level of gross anatomy, cell types, electron microscope-visible organization, biochemistry? Explain.

USEFUL REFERENCES

Ballard, W. W., *Comparative Anatomy and Embryology,* New York, The Ronald Press Company, 1964.

Bullock, T. H., and G. A. Horridge, *Structure and Function in the Nervous Systems of Invertebrates,* San Francisco, W. H. Freeman & Co., 1965.

Cannon, D. F., *Explorer of the Human Brain: Santiago Ramon y Cajal,* New York, H. Schuman, 1949.

Dethier, V. G., *How To Know A Fly,* San Francisco, Holden-Day, 1962.

Roeder, K. D., *Nerve Cells and Insect Behavior,* Cambridge, Mass., Harvard University Press, 1963.

Sherrington, C. S., *The Integrative Action of the Nervous System,* Cambridge, England, Cambridge University Press, 1947.

Wyburn, G. M., *The Nervous System: An Outline of the Structure and Function of the Human Nervous System and Sense Organs,* New York, Academic Press, 1960.

Young, J. Z., *A Model of the Brain,* Oxford, Clarendon Press, 1964.

Part VII

Animals and Their World

"All Things Flow Through All Things."

Attributed to Heraclitus, c. 500 B.C.

Chapter **32**

Animal Behavior

During the last decades zoological research has made its most notable advances on two very different levels of organization. One is the molecular level of biochemistry. Powerful new techniques have revealed facts about the utilization of energy within cells, and even about gene structure, which had once been thought unknowable. The other level of outstanding advance is the level of whole organisms. The study of the behavior of a host of animals— from alligators to bats and bees—is yielding a veritable flood of new facts and new theories. Old ideas are being re-examined and new concepts are in the making. Ultimately our ideas about human behavior and about the mysteries of mind and consciousness will see spectacular advances. But this is for the long future.

THE FISH vs. THE FISHERMAN: LEVELS OF ORGANIZATION

In our day new facts and new theories about animal behavior have become clear, making it possible to ask new and more searching questions. One of the most basic ideas that has emerged is that the essential difference between the behavior of animals high and low on the scale of life is not primarily a matter of biochemistry but rather of kind and degree of organization, specifically of cellular pattern. The brain of a man and the brain of a codfish are difficult indeed to distinguish biochemically. The neurons of both contain Nissl substance, the ribose nucleic acid characteristic of nerve cells. The motor fibers are coated with myelin in both cases and a nerve impulse is a wave of negativity of precisely the same kind in each case, although its speed is a bit slower in the cold-blooded animal. At the synapses where impulses pass from one nerve to another, the chemical compound acetylcholine functions alike in fish and man, in earthworm and jellyfish.

This does not mean that the functioning of the nervous system and thereby the behavior of an animal can be adequately understood without a knowledge of the biochemistry of its Nissl material or the physics and chemistry of a nerve impulse. On the contrary, this kind of information forms an essential component of such understanding. But in these respects neurons from a man, a codfish, or an earthworm are all but identical.

The difference in the behavior of the fisherman and the fish is grounded rather in the enormously greater complexity of cellular organization in the man. This applies first and foremost to the nervous system. The cerebral cortex of a fish is a thin sheet; that of a man is a thick, convoluted structure with six layers, each many cells in thickness. While the nervous system is specialized as the determinant of behavior, many other systems play important roles, some more, some less obvious. A fish cannot bait a hook, for it lacks hands; a man cannot obtain his oxygen from the water, for he lacks gills. Without adrenal glands a man cannot become angry in any full sense of the word. The most he can do is think about anger. All these considerations have given new life to the old science of anatomy. Especially is this true of the study of the gross structure and the cell architecture of the nervous system.

Thus it becomes evident once again that in passing from one level of organization to another, new properties emerge. A molecule of water is a vastly different thing from a gaseous mixture of atoms of hydrogen and oxygen, just as an atom of oxygen is something quite different from the electrons, protons, and other subatomic units of which it is composed. We have here a clear warning. The profound secrets of the nervous system are phenomena that characterize the higher levels of cellular organization. When the cells are separated and their contents analyzed valuable knowledge is obtained, but it throws only a remote and indirect light on the problems of brain function. A chemical analysis of the metal sides and leather head of a drum is inadequate by itself to explain the drum. The leather might as well be a shoe or an apron; the metal, nails or hammers. The ultimate problems of the nervous system which in some way make possible both artistic creation and conscious reason are sure to be even more subtle and baffling than we guess.

A second important consideration for both student and investigator to remember is the danger of easy generalization on the basis of either a few individual cases or a few kinds of animals. Psychologists have been criticized for talking about animal behavior in general when the only animal they really knew was the white rat. Some zoologists have appeared to believe that all animal behavior could be explained as simply as the turning of a plant toward a source of light, forgetting that the way auxin works to produce this result is itself far from completely understood. Any satisfactory view of animal behavior must include Jenning's parameciums clustered in a favorable spot due to "trial and error." It must include the sagacious elephant

and the apparently sagacious bees and wasps, of whom Fabre wrote: "Ils ne savent rien de rien"—they know nothing about anything. It must even include the jellyfish of our bays and estuaries that lacks any central nervous system and any but the simplest sense organs, and yet catches its food by swimming upward until it hits the surface of the water, when it turns over and slowly sinks to the bottom, then swims up to the surface again and repeats the performance endlessly, all day long.

THE ROLE OF HEREDITY IN BEHAVIOR

All behavior is ultimately an expression of the potentialities which lie hidden in the set of genes possessed by any plant, animal, or man. It is important to remember from the start that no behavior pattern, whether simple or complex, is inherited as such, any more than physical traits like brown eyes are inherited directly as brown eyes. The only things transmitted from one generation to the next are the nucleic acids and proteins which constitute the chromosomes, plus a coating of cytoplasm. Between the inherited genes and the end results to which they give rise stretches a long series of steps, as yet very incompletely understood. For the eye, cleavage and gastrulation of the egg are essential first steps. The induction of a neural plate by the underlying roof of the primitive gut must take place. The neural plate must form a brain. Optic lobes must grow out from this primitive brain and make contact with the sides of the head. A lens must be induced and the optic cup itself must undergo a complex series of developmental events.

The same principle applies to behavior. No inherited behavior pattern, like the particular kind of cocoon spun by a given species of caterpillar or the kind of nest constructed by a particular kind of bird, is inherited as a unitary entity. These complicated acts are written into the structure and function of the animal, its nervous system, its glands, its muscles, even its type of feet. No single gene is responsible, but rather the end result of the interactions of the products of many genes. True, the behavior could be blocked by any one of various single genes. A gene which prevented the development of silk glands, a gene which prevented the

Fig. 32–1. Winged reproductive ants, emerging from a colony for their first and only mating flight. *(Kindness of William H. Amos)*

secretion of the silk, or a gene which interfered with the development or proper functioning of the brain centers responsible for cocoon-making—any one of these would prevent the spinning of the cocoon.

In many cases heredity sets up a behavior reaction system all ready to go whenever the trigger is pulled. Winged ants emerging from their subterranean nurseries merely climb up a blade of grass, spread their wings, and fly up into the sky. There is no period of learning to fly that remotely resembles a child's learning to roller-skate or to swim. A considerable number of cases, especially among arthropods, are known in which one part of a complicated inherited behavior pattern is dependent for its appearance on previously performed acts. A caterpillar does not spin the tightly woven lining of its cocoon until after it has either constructed the various outer layers or else been tricked into spinning out an equivalent amount of silk. A somewhat similar situation has been observed in rats. A pregnant rat, before she gives birth to her young, constructs a crude nest by carrying wood shavings, crumpled paper, old rags, or other materials into a pile. This is an inherited instinctive act in the sense that it is characteristic of the species, is more or less stereotyped, and is not learned, any more than a caterpillar learns to spin the lining of its cocoon. Nevertheless, there are a number of prerequisites without which this inherited behavior will not appear. The rat must be in the last stages of pregnancy, the temperature of the room must not be too high, and the rat herself

must have had previous experience in carrying objects. If a rat is prevented from ever carrying anything—by raising it from soon after birth in empty cages—then this inherited behavior fails to appear. There is always a long series of interacting steps between the genes and the end results. Overt behavior may or may not be a part of this series.

Types of Hereditary Behavior. In the course of evolution, three major hereditary types of behavior have evolved. They may be exemplified by coelenterates, arthropods, and vertebrates, particularly the mammals.

The set of genes that causes an egg to develop into a **coelenterate** produces a particular type of neuromuscular system. This kind of neuromuscular system permits only very simple types of reaction. The monotonous behavior of a coastal jellyfish already described is typical. The jellyfish swims up to the surface, turns over, and drifts down until it hits bottom, then swims up to the surface again, over and over, day after day.

The **arthropods** inherit genes which permit a highly varied repertory of acts. The genetic factors which induce an egg to develop into an ant or a wasp produce a particular type of sense organs, central nervous system, muscles, wings, and other effectors. These in their turn permit a diversified and complex behavior. This behavior is for the most part rigidly stereotyped; learning plays a role but a minor one, and even a glimmer of intelligence is questionable. A newly hatched male mosquito does not have to learn what the "song" of a female mosquito is like. Without previous sexual experience he will fly to a tuning fork emitting the correct tone.

The **vertebrates** inherit genes which produce a type of nervous system permitting highly plastic behavior. What the animal does is profoundly modified by experience. Innate, unlearned behavior is still important, especially among the lower vertebrates. No one has to teach a young male alligator to regard a roar about two octaves below middle C as a challenge, or a female to find it an invitation. But in all vertebrates, even fishes, learning plays an important role, and in the case of mammals, the predominant role. The ability to learn is a property of the vertebrate nervous system and therefore no less and no more a product of heredity than is the possession of a repertory of prefabricated instinctive responses.

So far we have considered primarily the larger inherited types of behavior that are common to an entire species or even an entire phylum. What about particular differences in behavior which exist between members of the same species and which might be expected to follow simple Mendelian laws? Certain well-known examples in drosophila come to mind. There is a single gene which behaves as a simple Mendelian recessive in producing vestigial wings. Individuals homozygous for this gene lead fairly normal lives but can never fly. In the wasp *Habrobracon,* sex mosaics have been studied in which the head is of one sex

and the rest of the body is of the other sex. Behavior always follows the sex of the head.

More interesting would be some gene-produced change in the nervous system which was accompanied by a definite behavioral change. The search for such traits has little more than begun, but a number of informative cases have been discovered. Some breeds of dogs, such as bloodhounds, beagles, foxhounds, and springer spaniels, are known as "open trailers." When following the fresh scent of a rabbit or other game, they "give tongue," a characteristic loud baying and yelling sound. Other breeds, like the airedale, collie, English setter, and fox terrier, are "mute trailers," and will follow and even overtake their prey without saying anything about it. Eight different crosses have been made between these breeds, always with the same result regardless of which breed was represented by the mother. The first generation always barked when following a "hot" trail, but the bark was always the yapping of the mute trailer rather than the rolling bay of the hound. The collie-hound cross was followed into the second generation. Random segregation of the factors for hair length and type of bark produced all four possible combinations: short hair and baying, short hair and yapping, long hair and yapping, and finally the double recessive, long hair and baying.

Certain strains of mice, when subjected to a loud noise, suffer severe muscular cramps which pass quickly into hideous and usually

Fig. 32–2. Mice of sensitive strain in audiogenic convulsions on hearing a loud doorbell. Note that the black nonsensitives are alert but are not in convulsions. *(Photo by Kirkland, courtesy Life Magazine, Time, Inc., from project of Ginsburg and Miller, University of Chicago)*

fatal convulsions. This happens when they are placed in a washtub with a doorbell attached. Otherwise the mice appear normal. This case is instructive because it illustrates the influence of environment on a hereditary trait. As long as these mice keep away from doorbells and firecrackers they are quite normal.

But much remains to be learned. Different breeds of sheep have markedly different and characteristic behavioral traits. Many of the traits are known to appear in individuals raised from young lambhood in isolation from adult sheep so that "flock tradition" or imitation of their elders is largely or entirely eliminated as a cause. Merinos and Dorsets, for example, get up at different times in the morning (the Merinos like to stay in bed). The urge to flock tightly together is far stronger in Merinos. A Merino which suddenly discovers that he has become separated from his flock, which may merely have moved over the brow of a small hill, is thrown into a panic. Under similar circumstances a Dorset of the same sex and age and of very similar size is displeased, but acts with composure. No wild racing off first in one direction and then in another! The list of differences is long, but with sheep as with most other animals no accurately controlled studies or appropriate crosses have been made.

The same state of ignorance holds for ourselves. There is some evidence that musical ability may have analyzable hereditary components, but as already discussed in Chapter 8, these are among the most difficult problems, and no easy or early solution is to be expected.

THE WAY OF INSTINCT

The word instinct has acquired a very bad reputation among psychologists and other critical people, for several reasons. It has been widely used in a very loose sense as a synonym for any habitual or unconscious act. An American driving a car in England meets an emergency and suddenly steers over to the right-hand side of the road by "instinct." Worse yet, instinct has been used by journalists, literary writers, and others to lend a spurious air of scientific authenticity to ideas which may or may not contain some truth, but for which there is no solid scientific basis. The "work instinct," the "death instinct," the "leadership instinct," are all examples of this kind of pseudo-scientific nonsense. And to some schools of psychology, instinct is a type of behavior which by definition is unanalyzable.

In zoology, on the other hand, the word instinct has always carried a very useful meaning. First let us be clear what it means. Konrad Lorenz, one of the leaders in the modern study of instinctive modes of behavior from a zoological point of view, defines instincts as "unlearned, species-specific motor patterns." An American physiological psychologist, M. A. Wenger, has defined an instinct in essentially the same way, as "a pattern of activity that is common to a given species and that occurs without opportunity for learning."

It is the part of wisdom to recall that Charles Darwin in his great book *Origin of Species* began his chapter on instincts by saying, "I will not attempt any definition of instinct." He boldly claims that everyone understands what is meant and then proceeds to give the example of the cuckoo. This bird lays its eggs in other birds' nests. When the young cuckoo hatches it ejects the rightful eggs in a particular manner which is really a gymnastic feat, because the rightful eggs are almost as big as the young cuckoo. The North American cowbird also lays its eggs in other birds' nests and, as Lorenz has pointed out, mates when adult, not with the species by which it was raised, but with other cowbirds.

However, because even the existence of instincts has been recently challenged by certain animal psychologists, it is important to get clear what zoologists mean. Instincts are types of behavior which fulfill the following conditions:

1. Instincts are species-specific, i.e., characteristic of a given species.

2. Instincts can be performed without an opportunity for learning although they may change with repetition. A particular species of caterpillar spins a particular type of cocoon in a particular series of acts only once in its life and without ever having seen it done.

3. Instincts are more or less stereotyped motor patterns. The more complex ones usually consist of a series of rigid steps which must be followed in a certain unchangeable sequence.

4. Instinctive acts are immediately adaptive, in contrast to the random trial-and-error type of behavior associated with learning.

It should be added that although instincts are characteristic of given species, and some are unique to a single species, many are common to several species or even to a whole family, just as anatomical traits are. This is true among animals as widely separated as pigeons (in their manner of drinking) and butterflies (in their manner of making a landing).

The word instinct suggests a fairly complex behavior like nest-building. Taxes, or tropisms, also fit our definition of instinct. A **taxis** is an orientation of an animal toward or away from a stimulus. The brown-tailed moth caterpillar climbing up when hungry is exhibiting a taxis, a negative geotaxis. In climbing toward the source of gravity it shows positive geotaxis.

Importance of Instinct to Zoology. There are several reasons why instincts are of especial importance to the zoologist. First, they form a very conspicuous part of animal life, vertebrate as well as invertebrate. The web-weaving of spiders, the mating reactions of hens, the migrations of fishes, the language of bees, the construction of mud nests by wasps and of hanging nests by Baltimore orioles, the courtship of salamanders, all these and a thousand and one other species-specific, unlearned, stereotyped motor activities abound in nature.

A second reason for the zoologist's interest is that because instincts are species-constant they are an aid in solving the twin problems of classification and evolution. A particular kind of spider can be identified as surely and far more easily by observing the structure of the web it spins than by determining the way the chelicerae join the head or the relative positions of anal tubercle and spinnerets. Many species of spiders spin webs of each of the four types

Fig. 32–3. Four types of orb web characteristic of different species of spiders. Top to bottom: in *Araneus*, the spider's "hide-out" is connected to the orb by "telegraph" lines. In *Zygiella*, the lair is in the framework of the orb and connected to the center by a strong signal line between two radii without spiral threads. In *Argiope*, the black and yellow garden spider, the white stabilimentum is directly above and below the orb center. *Metepeira* weaves an irregular hub and a labyrinthine snare above the orb.

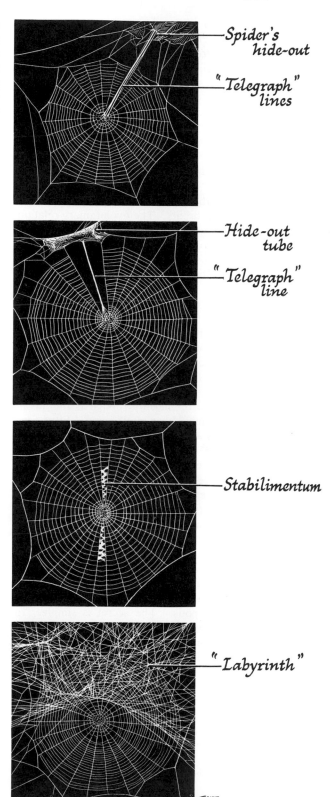

Spider's hide-out
"Telegraph" lines

Hide-out tube
"Telegraph" line

Stabilimentum

"Labyrinth"

shown in Figure 32 – 3, yet each species has its own characteristic signature. Illustrators of detective stories are often rather careless about this, but the spiders, never.

Bird songs are commonly used by people the world over to identify species. In more serious scientific work, it has been shown that the only diagnostic trait shared by all the birds in the pigeon group is not any structure, but a type of behavior. Pigeons put their heads down into water and drink like horses. With few exceptions, other birds take a bill full of water and then raise their heads to allow the water to run down their throats. The evolutionary relations of various ducks and crickets have been clarified by a comparative study of their behavior.

Thirdly, it is only reasonable to suppose that any inborn behavior pattern is the expression of an inherited pattern in the central nervous system. This conviction immediately lends new impetus to the study of neurology. In some truly beautiful experiments to be described later, the location in the brain of the "directions," so to speak, for several instinctive acts has already been found.

Instinct vs. Intelligence. What is the advantage of instincts over intelligence? Fifty years ago it was the belief of biologists, and some psychologists, that instinct was a kind of evolutionary precursor of intelligence. This idea has now been almost completely abandoned in favor of the view that the animal kingdom has evolved in two major directions. In one, the arthropod line, instinctive actions predominate; in the other, especially the warm-blooded vertebrates, learning and intelligence predominate, or at least play an important role.

The efficiency of instinct is proved by the staggering biological success of insects and other arthropods. The secret is simple. Instincts furnish an animal whose life is short with prefabricated answers to his problems. No time need be lost in the inevitably wasteful trial and error of learning. Imagine a spider trying to spin a web by pure trial and error! It took mankind centuries to develop fish nets, which do not equal spider webs for complexity.

Birds are a more familiar case. The type of nest a species builds is determined by instinctive acts. Weaverbirds, for example, hand-raised without nests for four generations, will build typical weaverbird nests when given a chance. Try to imagine a pair of robins learning by pure trial and error without any previous experience how to incubate their eggs. Should they construct a nest of fine twigs and plant fibers like a mockingbird, or a bulky nest of grass and rootlets like a hermit thrush? Or why not a hanging cup suspended from a forked branch like a vireo, or a deep sock like an oriole? Or any one of hundreds of other possible designs? The absurdity of these questions emphasizes the overwhelming importance of instinctive behavior in the lives of birds.

The only known alternative for instinct would be imprinting, a kind of infantile memory which will be discussed more fully later. This may play some role in the selection of the nesting site and of the material, though there is no evidence that it does. But as anyone who has tried to put a watch together will testify, knowing what materials to use is a very different thing from knowing how to put them together. In a robin's nest the beautiful bowl of dried mud that lines the rough outer layer is invisible in any case, since it is covered by the inner lining of fine grasses.

Without instincts the lives of most animals would collapse in utter chaos. The spider would not know how to spin a web or court a mate. The bird would never incubate the eggs at all, much less construct a nest and feed its young. The alternative way of life, where learning and intelligence play the dominant role, requires (1) the proper type of nervous system and other anatomical prerequisites, and (2) either parental teaching and social tradition or plenty of time for trial and error and other time-consuming and possibly dangerous types of learning.

In brief, instincts are adaptations in the same way that structures are adaptations. Primarily they are reflections of the structure of the nervous system, though of course the proper effectors — wings, silk glands, antlers, etc. — must also be present. What is the evolutionary origin of these innate actions? Mutation producing variation in many different directions, followed by natural selection. A male mosquito which inherits a gene making him insensitive to the singing of the female would simply not leave any descendants. The rabbit with genes producing a "quick-freeze" when the shadow of a hawk passes by has a better chance to transmit these genes than the rabbit whose genes permit him to keep moving. Note also that the evolution of innate behavior patterns must proceed in reasonably close coordination with the evolution of gross anatomical traits. A bird having a duck's bill and the reactions of a hawk is a biologically unworkable animal, like a hawk with the webbed feet of a duck. As Charles Darwin put it in his *Origin of Species,* the gradual process of evolution "is applicable to instincts as well as to corporeal structure."

Some Instincts Among Invertebrates. *Daphnia,* the common water flea, is indifferent to light as long as the water is close to neutral in its acid-alkaline balance. If the water becomes acid, as by an increase in carbon dioxide dissolved in it, these little animals become strongly and positively phototaxic—they rush toward the light, and can even be guided around an aquarium with a flashlight. Note that this positive phototaxis fulfills the four criteria given for an instinctive action. It is characteristic of the species, it is more or less stereotyped, and it takes place without learning.

Also, it is adaptive. In a pond, the water usually becomes acid only when the oxygen is exhausted and carbon dioxide has accumulated. Swimming toward the light would normally bring the daphnias up to the surface where a supply of oxygen would be found. Of course, in a glass-bottomed aquarium, daphnias will swim to the bottom if a light is held there.

Note that there are two parts to this reaction. The water must be acid and there must be a light. The acidity is an **essential precondition,** the light is the **directing stimulus.** In higher animals, especially in birds and mammals, the essential preconditions are commonly nutritional or hormonal. A hen with a high level of sex hormone in her blood, or a female dog in like circumstances, responds to many stimuli very differently from similar individuals without such hormones.

Insects and spiders have long stood as the best examples of animals dominated by instincts. We shall give three well-studied examples. When the caterpillar of the *Platysamia* (*Hyalophora*) *cecropia* moth grows to full size, some internal change, presumably chiefly hormonal because metamorphosis is known to be

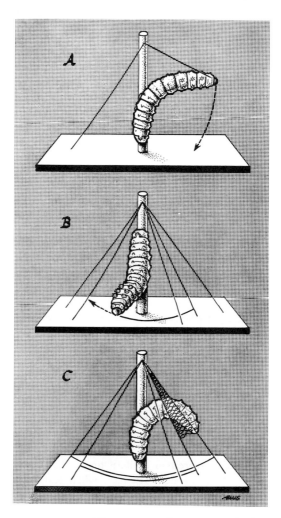

Fig. 32-4. Three stages in cocoon-spinning by caterpillar of cecropia moth, an excellent example of an innate or self-differentiating behavior pattern, performed in the same way by all members of the species and but once in a lifetime. (*After "Brains and Cocoons" by W. G. Van der Kloot. Copyright © Apr. 1956 by Scientific American, Inc. All rights reserved*)

under hormonal control, induces the caterpillar to begin wandering. A corner of some kind where two large twigs meet furnishes the stimulus that precipitates the next stage of behavior. Here the caterpillar stops and spins its cocoon in a series of definite steps. First with head upward it makes the tentlike supports; then head downward it makes the floor; then head up again, it fills in the sides with figure 8's of silk. Lastly come the interior layers. The cecropia caterpillar makes an especially beautiful case because it performs this stereotyped series of acts only once in its life, and does so without any possibility of learning.

Moreover, this caterpillar illustrates an additional trait common to most of the more complex innate types of behavior. Once begun, the behavior tends to be continued mechanically step after step regardless of whether the first step was successful or not; nor can the series be started in the middle. Apparently each step serves as the stimulus for the following step. The cecropia caterpillar begins the interior layers after it has spun out 60 per cent of its silk, whether the caterpillar is inside a normal outer envelope or has been tricked into allowing the first 60 per cent of its silk to be wound up on a reel.

The rigid correlation between the species of spider and the type of web it spins, or whether it spins a web at all, has been described. (See page 356.) Once a spider has begun an orb web it cannot go back to repair damages. If an experimenter breaks some of the spokes after the main spiral is begun, the spider does not repair the spokes, and the resulting web is a truly deplorable mess.

The most sensational case of instinctive behavior discovered in modern times is the language of honeybees. In fact, when Karl von Frisch first announced his discovery he was widely greeted by scepticism, but his observations have now been confirmed by all who have taken the trouble to look. A bee returning to the hive after a successful flight with her crop full of nectar does a little dance, a tail-wagging dance. This dance "tells" other bees both how far away the food is and its direction in relation to the position of the sun.

In performing the dance the bee makes a short run about twice its own length while vigorously wagging its abdomen. At the end of the run the bee turns in a half circle, right or left, to its starting point and then repeats the tail-wagging run. The number of turns per 15 seconds depends on the distance of the food source from the hive. The closer to home the food, the more dances per unit of time. Strong headwinds make the bees overestimate the distance. Perhaps the number of turns in the dance depends on fatigue, perhaps on some inner time sense, perhaps on other factors.

The surface of the honeycomb on which the bee dances is a vertical wall. If the tail-wagging run is directly upward, this indicates that the food is directly toward the sun. If the tail-wagging run is directly downward, it indicates the food is directly away from the sun. If the wagging run is at an angle of 60° left of straight up, the food is to be found in a direction at 60° to the left of the sun. (See Fig. 32–6.)

When a bee returns to the hive and "dances" in a certain direction, depending on the direction of the sun in relation to the flight course of the bee to the food, its behavior has clearly been modified by experience. Why is this not

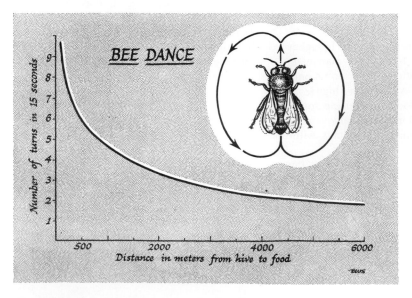

Fig. 32–5. Inverse relation between the rapidity of the bee's dance and the distance of food from the hive. (*After von Frisch*)

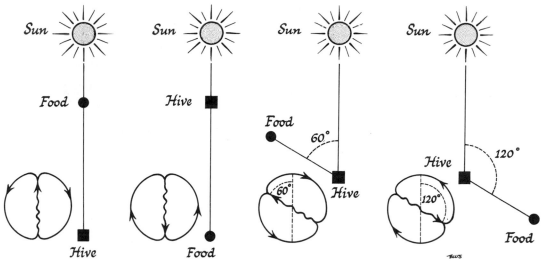

Fig. 32-6. The relation of the angle between the direction of the sun and the location of the food, and the angle of the bee's "waggle" dance with the vertical. The wiggled line in the circle represents the waggle dance. *(After von Frisch)*

learning? When a second bee observes the dance and then flies off in a direction which depends on the direction of the dance, why not call this learning? You can, but note that you would be using "learning" in a very peculiar sense. Both the character of the dance of the first bee and the direction of the flight of the second are unlearned responses. Honeybees do not teach each other how to respond in a dance to the direction of the sun, nor how to respond to a dance by the direction of outgoing flight. There is no period of trial and error and conditioning. The individual responds to different stimuli in a rigid and stereotyped manner.

The evolutionary origin and perfection of such a "language" may have taken millions of years of mutation and natural selection; but the fossil record of insects extends back to the Permian, over 200 million years ago. Moreover, it has recently been discovered that other insects such as blowflies, which have no known "language" or social organization, nevertheless execute a little irregular sort of dance after eating. From such precursors the "language" of the bees probably evolved.

Instincts Among Vertebrates. Instinctive behavior permeates the lives of vertebrates, too. Among fishes, the most famous instance is Aristotle's catfish. Over 2,000 years ago the great philosopher described how the male catfish in the rivers of Greece guards the eggs in its shallow nest on the bottom. In modern times this account was regarded as a fairy tale until Louis Agassiz discovered that North American catfish behave in the same way. In our own day the most fruitful studies on instinctive behavior in fishes have been on migrating salmon and on the stickleback. It has been shown that salmon find their way up streams by smells in the water. A male sticklefish builds a nest of woven weeds and defends a territory surrounding it. Defense of a well-defined territory by animals during the breeding season is a discovery of the 20th century and is now known to be common among fishes, lizards, birds, and some mammals.

For patterns of instinctive behavior in amphibians and reptiles we can recall the elaborate courtship rituals of salamanders (page 471 and Fig. 21-19), and mention the remarkable response of the male alligator to the sound of a French horn playing B flat two octaves below middle C, or the way adult sea turtles come up on the beach, untaught, to lay their eggs, and how the newly hatched turtles immediately scramble toward the ocean provided they can see the sky.

The essential role of instinctive behavior in birds has just been discussed in connection with nest-building. Modern knowledge about the meaning of bird song as a warning to other males to keep out of the singer's territory and an invitation to females to enter it, has also been discussed (page 505). It is surely a remarkable fact that in spite of the attention given to bird song by poets and by mankind in general over the centuries, the meaning of the song for the bird was discovered only in the lifetime of persons now living. In some species the song is completely predetermined in the nervous system and appears in typical form among males raised in isolation. In other species the inherited nervous system permits song modification by environmental influences. Mockingbirds and parrots are extreme example of the latter group.

Another recently discovered innate aspect of bird behavior, which has widespread applicability perhaps even among mammals, is the importance of **"sign stimuli."** This is merely a convenient name for some special feature of a general stimulus situation which triggers the responses. Usually the sign stimulus is part of a pattern, but the key part. The pattern, the relationship, is what is called in German *Gestalt,* a configuration.

For example, a male English robin will attack a little bundle of red feathers more readily than a complete stuffed male with the red breast feathers painted gray or brown. It is the redness of the feathers that provides the sign stimulus which precipitates and directs the attack. But note that the red feathers must be part of a general situation. They must be within the territory of the male. In addition, the male must have a territory he is motivated to defend. The high level of sex hormones in the male's blood constitutes a predisposing stimulus.

Another well-studied case is the red spot near the end of the yellow bill of the common harbor gull, *Larus.* Zoologists had not known the significance of this red spot, or indeed that it had any special significance, until students of animal behavior discovered that it is the directive sign stimulus at which gull chicks peck when begging for food. If the spot is painted out, or painted on another part of the head, the chicks appear greatly puzzled. Note again that this red spot is a red spot on a bill and the bill is on a gull's head, and the chick itself must be hungry. The red breast is relevant to sexual rivalry in males; the red spot on the bill, to juvenile feeding behavior.

A third example concerns escape from enemies and reveals with great clarity the complex,

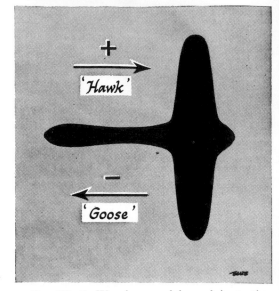

Fig. 32-7. Wooden model used in testing escape reactions of fowl.

gestalt, or pattern character of animal responses. If a model shaped as shown in Figure 32-7 is pulled along a wire over the heads of ducks or geese, they pay little attention if it is pulled so that the long "neck" goes ahead. Apparently it then resembles a goose. But if the same model is pulled in the opposite direction, the long "neck" now appears to be a tail and the short "tail" as a head—and the whole object looks like a hawk. Ducks and geese scurry for cover. Similar responses to moving overhead objects can be seen in domestic chickens raised in incubators and completely innocent of any experience with hawks. Domestic chickens exhibit many stereotyped innate responses. Some will be discussed below in relation to endocrine factors.

Are there instincts in mammals, even in man himself? Clearly mammals lack elaborate prefabricated patterns of behavior comparable to the nest-building of birds or the web construction of spiders. But there do seem to be innate responses to various stimuli, certain sounds, tastes, odors, or sights. It has even been suggested that there are sign stimuli to which human beings respond. Without training, small children like the taste of sugar. Moreover, the relative sweetness of different kinds of sugar—sucrose, glucose, mannose, lactose, and the like—appears to be the same to a man as to a fly. But for most of the simplest questions in this area we have no answers. Some people like onions, some do not. To what extent is such a preference due to innate factors and to what extent to learning, perhaps early unconscious conditioning? No one really knows. It is common and certain knowledge that male dogs are highly stimulated by odors, imperceptible to human beings, which are given off by female dogs in the estrous state. No learning on the part of the male is necessary for the arousal of a state of excitement when whiffing such an odor.

There are clearly a number of stereotyped, inherited, motor responses in mammals. Blindfolded cats dropped upside down have an unlearned righting reaction that enables them to land feet first. Female dogs often experience false or pseudo-pregnancies. This condition may follow the period of estrus in the absence of mating. The breasts become enlarged and may leak milk, but the most striking changes are behavioral. A beagle bitch which has never seen a puppy except when she was a puppy herself will, in a false pregnancy, steal children's dolls and guard and mother them most determinedly. At other times the bitch pays no more attention to dolls than to books on a shelf.

MIXED BEHAVIOR

In many cases, especially among higher vertebrates, behavior shows a mixture of instinctive and learned factors. For example, the male English chaffinch has a distinctive **song** by which the species can be easily recognized in the field even though some variation is common between one male and another, much as is the case with canaries. If males are artificially incubated and hand-raised without any opportunity of hearing adults sing, they will nonetheless sing a year later when they become sexually mature. Their songs are readily identified as chaffinch but are somewhat peculiar even to human ears. If nestling male chaffinches listen to tape recordings of adult males singing, they will sing after the manner of the recordings the next spring when they begin to sing. Normally, of course, male chaffinches sing like their own fathers. By the use of tapes it has been shown that males will learn new songs, actually slight variations on the basic chaffinch theme, for the

first three years of life. After that, learning appears to be impossible. Thus the song of any individual male is in part innate and in part learned and it must be learned during the first three years.

Virtually all learning is dependent on what is known technically as **reinforcements**, i.e., rewards and punishments. What is the reinforcement for the learning of the song by a male chaffinch while still in his nest? It is indeed difficult to see!

An illustration of mixed behavior of a very different kind, at least one in which learning plays the larger rather than the minor role, is seen in what has been called **behavioral "drift"** or **"contaminants."** This occurs when an animal is trained, i.e., learns to perform certain actions, but after a time shows traces of some innate action pattern. For example, pigs can be trained to pick up wooden "coins," carry them a short distance, and then deposit them in a large "piggy bank." It was found, however, that after several days, the pigs, instead of picking up the coin, running to the bank, and making a deposit, would stop halfway there, toss the coin in the air, and go through rooting motions with their snouts as though they were rooting for food in the earth. Raccoons trained to do the same routine would stop after a while and act as though washing the coin even though no water was present. The full meaning of these facts is not clear, but they suggest caution in making sweeping generalizations about the behavior of higher animals.

THE WAY OF LEARNING

Learning, which is not quite the same thing as intelligence, may be defined as a more or less permanent change in behavior due to past experience recorded in the nervous system. To specify that it is recorded in the nervous system excludes a change in behavior due to a mutilating accident—loss of a wing, for example. To specify that it is more or less permanent excludes changes which occur after an animal has experienced a full meal or any similar temporary physiological change. A hungry animal and a satiated one usually act very differently, but the hunger will return, and with it the old behavior.

Whether a response is learned, or is not learned but innate, can be determined only after careful study; this is a place where it is dangerous to jump to conclusions. Chickens illustrate the distinction very clearly. Hens can be trained to come to be fed when someone bangs on a dishpan. Chickens that are not accustomed to being fed after this noise pay little or no attention to it. There is nothing innate in the response beyond the fact that hens can be so trained. In marked contrast, the mating crouch of a hen is an innate or instinctive response. It is species-specific, i.e., characteristic of the species, and is a very rigidly stereotyped act performed in exactly the same way with head, wings, feet, and tail held in a particular way. Most important of all, it occurs without any opportunity for learning. Hens hatched in incubators, completely isolated from all male chicks at the age of 24 hours, and raised in complete isolation from all older chickens nevertheless show this striking response to the approach of any large object as soon as they attain sexual maturity. This response, then, is dependent on the presence of sex hormones. It is an impressive illustration of the power of an innate response to see a young hen start to run from a man, only to be caught by this innate reaction and frozen to the spot. Since most domestic animals are not raised in complete isolation from older members of their kind, it is usually difficult to be sure to what extent any particular behavior is innate and to what extent it is learned.

Most animals can learn. Only among the protozoans and the sponges has it been impossible to demonstrate learning.

Learning occurs readily among that vast majority of animals whose lives are governed primarily by instinct. It is possible to train honeybees to come to a glass dish filled with sugar water placed over a blue card rather than a yellow one. It is worth noting that it is the color the bee sees just before she sucks the sugar water that she records in her brain. This must be so, because if the blue card is slipped out and a yellow one substituted after she has begun to feed, she will still return to the blue card. This time sequence is similar to those to be noted below in relation to conditioned responses.

Fig. 32-8. Power of abstract generalization? The canary has learned to look for the food pellet under the one *different* object in a series. *(Kindness of Nicholas Pastore)*

Birds obviously learn many things—where to find food and water, how to find their way back to their nests, even the appearance of traps. The most remarkable instance of learning in birds is found among canaries. These little birds can form an abstract generalization. For example, a canary can learn to find a food pellet under the unique object in a series, irrespective of the actual object itself. Thus, in a series of aspirin tablets and one screw, the canary looks correctly under the screw. In a series of screws and one chessman, the bird looks under the chessman. Birds evidently possess a remarkable combination of innate responses and learning ability.

It is in mammals, of course, that learning ability reaches its height and is accompanied by true problem-solving intelligence which is so different from the learning found among insects.

But before we consider these matters we shall first describe briefly the main types of learning and the way they are studied, because this will be important to know in the following section giving a synoptic view of animal behavior. We shall also summarize the zoological prerequisites for the development of behavior based primarily on intelligence.

Five Major Types of Learning. The first type of learning studied with physiological precision is called **classical conditioning.** Its investigation was developed by Ivan Pavlov in Russia. and by others elsewhere. In this type of study the dog, pig, goat, or other mammal remains standing in a large box and responds to a stimulus by salivating, raising a foot, or in some other way. The primary or **unconditioned stimulus** is commonly food or a mild electric shock. If just before meat is given, the dog sees a red light or hears a bell, he will salivate on seeing a red light or hearing a bell after a few trials, even though no meat is given. The light or the bell is then known as the **conditioned stimulus.** Observe that the response is a relatively simple reflex type of action—salivation, raising a foot, or increased heart rate.

The second type of learning is called **instrumental learning.** The animal is called upon to perform some act, perhaps a rather complicated act, instead of merely exhibiting a relatively simple reflex. The animal must do something, operate. Hence this is sometimes called **operant conditioning.** Secondly, the animal is motivated, usually by hunger. The methods are simple. The animal is kept without food or

Fig. 32–9. Animal in a set-up for a Pavlovian study of conditioned responses.

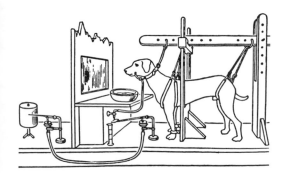

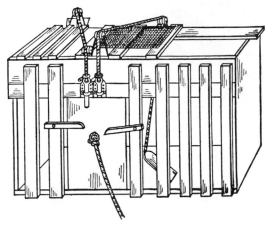

Fig. 32–10. Thorndike's puzzle box for cats. The animal must learn by trial and error how to open the door and get out of the box to reach food. *(From Thorndike, Human Learning, Century, 1931)*

without water to provide the motivation and then placed in a maze, a Thorndike puzzle box, or a Skinner serve-yourself box. In the old puzzle boxes the animal had to discover a way to escape. The rat, cat, monkey, or other animal had to push, pull, turn, lift, and otherwise manipulate the various parts of the box, perhaps in a particular order, until he happened on the correct act which opened the door to freedom and food. In the Skinner box the animal learns that by pressing a lever, a simple type of slot machine will serve him a pellet of food or a drink. The advantage of this device is that the number of times the lever is pressed can be automatically recorded and thus the rate of learning, the intensity of response, and other factors can be measured objectively. Note that both the Thorndike puzzle box and the Skinner serve-yourself box depend on an initial period of exploratory trial-and-error behavior.

The third type of learning is called **perceptual learning** or, sometimes, **insight learning.** Usage of these terms varies and is a reflection of our basic lack of understanding of the process of learning. The animal, like the canary choosing the unique object in a series, learns to make more or less abstract discriminations. Insight learning is said to occur when an animal does not go through a period of trial and error, but surveys the problem and then acts correctly on

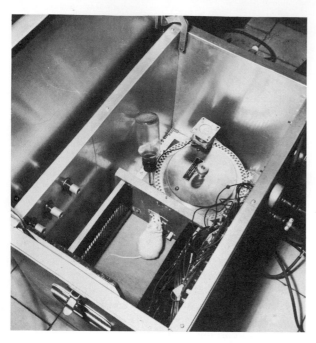

Fig. 32-11. Mouse in a Skinner "do-it yourself" box. The animal must press a lever to receive food. The number and timing of the mouse's actions are recorded. *(W. Fleischer, Harvard University New Office)*

the first try. Insight learning is regarded as a fourth type by some people, but by others as a variety of trial-and-error learning with the trials and errors made mentally on the basis of previous experience.

A type of learning of great interest is **exposure learning.** In this type there are no rewards or punishments, i.e., no reinforcements—at least there are none in any usual meaning of the words. The case already described of the nestling male chaffinch, who learns the song he hears his father singing even though he himself will not sing until a year later, is an excellent example. Rats will learn about a maze merely by walking around in it without reward. The animal learns by what appears to be simple exposure to the stimulus. This type of learning may be related to the way some people appear to be able to learn languages by hearing tape recordings during their "sleep." If this is true, and if present experimental hints that drugs which promote RNA and protein synthesis may enhance memory, we may indeed be on the threshhold of an explosive revolution in human education!

A fifth and very special type of learning has been discovered in recent years in birds; it has been named **imprinting.** Typical imprinting takes place only during a brief critical period occurring several hours after hatching, it is very persistent, and like exposure learning there is no obvious reward except in terms of some kind of self-reward. It now appears that very early experience in dogs and monkeys and other animals has a profound and lasting effect on long-subsequent behavior. Whether such influences should be called imprinting is an open question.

In ducks, geese, and wild-type chickens, the newly hatched bird becomes imprinted by the first large moving object that it sees within the first hours after hatching. Thereafter it will follow that object to the exclusion of all others. Normally this first large moving object is the mother duck, goose, or chicken. However, if the eggs are hatched in an incubator and the first large moving object is a man, a male duck, or a mechanical floor polisher, then the duckling is imprinted by this inappropriate object and will follow it with great and enduring persistence. A remarkable fact about imprinting, at least in ducklings, is that if the duckling has to work—for example, is forced to scramble over little obstacles—to follow the box or

Fig. 32-12. Gosling, imprinted on a box, remains with the box despite the presence of other geese in the vicinity. *(Kindness of A. Ogden Ramsey)*

whatever is being used for the imprinting, then the imprinting becomes more firmly established in less time than were the little duck merely walking over a smooth floor. This fact suggests a relationship between imprinting and operant conditioning. Since there is no reward except the act itself, there seems also to be a relation between imprinting and exposure learning.

In puppies it has been found that there is a critical period centering around the 6th and 7th weeks of life when they become most readily and permanently tamed. If puppies have no contact whatever with human beings until after they are 14 weeks old, it is virtually impossible ever to make them into friendly pets.

The most surprising results have been attained with rhesus monkeys. Harry Harlow and Robert Zimmerman at the University of Wisconsin undertook to develop a completely healthy colony of monkeys free of the infections of various kinds which are passed on from parents to offspring in most colonies. The obvious method was to rear monkeys from birth in isolation from their mothers. Such monkeys were healthy but the surprise was that they were highly abnormal in their behavior. They acted frightened and withdrawn. When they became sexually mature, which they did at the normal time, they showed no interest whatever in mating and only a few of the females could be bred even by placing them with patient and experienced males.

How widespread imprinting in either a narrow or a broad sense may be in the animal kingdom is not yet known. The indications are that it is very widespread among vertebrates. In addition to occurring in birds and mammals, it very probably takes place among certain fishes. The ability of migrating salmon to return to the small tributary in which they were hatched, even though it is but one of many streams in a river system, may be due to imprinting with the characteristic smell of the water.

Zoological Preconditions of Intelligence. What are the zoological preconditions for the development of intelligence and learning? If an animal is not born, or hatched, with a set of ready-made behavior patterns to meet all the usual situations of life, but is to depend on learning and live by his wits, he clearly must

Fig. 32-13. Emotionally disturbed young adult monkeys raised in isolation without any parent. *(Photo by Sponholz for the University of Wisconsin Primate Laboratory)*

have a protected period when he can learn and make errors. The essence of learning is precisely that one does not know instinctively the best way of doing something the first time he tries. This means that in addition to a highly developed brain some degree of parental care is essential if a high level of intelligence is to be attained. It will be recalled from Chapter 24 that two key anatomical structures assure parental care in mammals: the placenta which makes viviparity possible, and the mammary glands which both nurture the offspring and make obligatory a prolonged association between mother and offspring, a period during which learning is possible.

The fact that man and the monkeys had tree-living ancestors is now believed to be a primary reason why intelligence could develop. It will be recalled from our discussion of the primates that an arboreal existence places a high premium on a skillful grasping hand and good eyesight, with binocular vision able to judge distance—since a miscalculated jump may be one's last. Life in the trees also provides a safe environment away from ground predators. Hence the primates almost alone among mammals are not nocturnal and are blessed with color vision. Under these circumstances natural selection could favor the more intelligent brain which permitted a more advantageous use of hands and eyes. On the ground everything must be sacrificed to quick reactions. If the cat takes too much time to think, the mouse has escaped. If the mouse hesitates to weigh the advantages and disadvantages of alternative courses of action, he gets eaten. But in the trees there is time to think. Natural selection in historical fact did favor the evolution of intelligence.

A SYNOPTIC VIEW

In the course of evolution, animals have developed two very different modes of meeting the challenges of life. One emphasizes instinct, the other learning and intelligence. The question arises — what underlying mechanisms do the two have in common? Both are grounded in the nervous system and both are products of natural selection. Is there anything else?

In recent years it has become increasingly clear that a great deal of behavior can be divided into two general categories. The first is **appetitive behavior,** due to drive, motivation, or so-called need. This type of behavior is often a general restlessness, as though the animal were seeking something, which in a sense he is, although he may not be conscious of it. The second general category is **consummatory behavior,** which consists of the specific acts that consummate or fulfil the appetite or drive. These tend to be much more stereotyped and are directed toward very specific goals. A hungry hawk flies almost ceaselessly back and forth and round about. This is appetitive behavior. The hawk's sudden strike for the rabbit and the subsequent killing and eating constitute the consummatory acts.

Other examples abound. A caterpillar ready to spin a cocoon is filled with a compelling wanderlust. A certain type of branch in a stick, or some other angle, constitutes the stimulus that precipitates the consummatory act, which is the spinning of the cocoon. Hungry rats, placed in a new cage, explore their environment in more or less random, trial and error fashion until they stumble upon the lever to press that

will open the door or deliver food. A sexually mature male spider, with the ends of his pedipalps swollen with sperms and looking like boxing gloves, leaves his web and succumbs to a wanderlust, i.e., to appetitive behavior. The wandering appears undirected and random. A web inhabited by a female of his species brings his wandering to an end and initiates a series of more and more stereotyped acts which lead to the transfer of sperms. Both the instinct-dominated caterpillar on a twig and the smart rat in a Skinner box begin with appetitive behavior. Subjectively, the animal begins with some kind of motive, drive, or "need," perhaps hunger, thirst, or curiosity.

The main difference between the ways of instinct and of intelligence lies in the character of the consummatory acts. In animals dominated by instinctive behavior, the consummatory act is one or another of its repertory of ready-made behavior patterns. In animals where learning and intelligence are important, the consummatory act depends on previous experience, i.e., on learning. The behavior of a hungry spider is to construct a web of a highly stereotyped kind. Who can predict the behavior of a hungry man?

There is often a specific sign stimulus which elicits the consummatory act, especially if innate. Hungry seagull chicks peck at a red spot on the parent's beak. The parent obliges with some food. Incubator gull chicks will peck vigorously at a large red disk for the first day or so after hatching. But if it never rewards them with food, they stop pecking it.

NEURAL BASIS OF BEHAVIOR

Ever since the days of the ancient Greeks, men have wondered how the nervous system coordinates behavior. Where in the brain are the directions for all the complicated instinctive acts animals perform without learning? In what kind of code are the directions written? How are memories encoded in the brain? How can hormones in the bloodstream radically alter an animal's behavior? What, even, is the relationship of the nervous system to consciousness? No questions as difficult as these challenge us in the entire scope of the biological sciences, and it is altogether likely that they will continue to be a challenge for many centuries to come. Nevertheless, real progress toward obtaining answers has been made.

Methods of Investigation. There are four major methods of investigating the neurological basis of behavior. The first method is to investigate the microanatomy of the nervous system. The brain and spinal cord can be carefully preserved, cut into paper-thin sections, and stained for microscopic examination. This method reveals the tracts of the nerve fibers which conduct impulses from one part of the nervous system to another. It also reveals the incredibly complex patterns of hundreds of millions of nerve cells which compose the cerebral cortex.

A second method is surgical. A definite area of the brain or nerve cord can be removed surgically or destroyed by an electric cautery. It is well known that removal of certain regions in the mammalian brain regularly produces deficiencies in vision; removal of other regions, deficiencies in hearing or some other function. Very often a considerable amount of recovery is possible, especially if the area removed is not too large. Sometimes the results are extremely puzzling. There is a region in the human brain, for example, which if removed will lead not to blindness, for the patient can see as well as ever, but to a lack of ability to recognize objects by sight. A bell seems an utterly strange thing until the patient hears it ring, when he recognizes it instantly—"of course, a bell."

The third method is localized stimulation of various regions of the brain with small electric shocks. Such shocks regularly produce contractions of certain muscles when certain brain areas are stimulated. The map of the motor areas of the human brain shown in Figure 31–19 was made in this way. Stimulation of the hypothalamus has given dramatic effects, to be described below.

A fourth method of determining the function of parts of the brain is to "listen" electrically to the passage of nervous impulses. The electrical changes can be picked up on delicate electrodes, led off on wires, and then amplified electronically. In this way the parts of the nervous system that are transmitting signals under any particular circumstances can be located.

An enormous scientific literature has grown up presenting the results obtained by these methods. We shall consider three typical and important cases.

Some Typical Cases. In the cecropia caterpillar, whose stepwise cocoon-spinning has already been described, it has been found that destruction or removal of a particular region of the brain will completely prevent the construction of the cocoon. This is the **corpus pedunculatum,** or peduncled body, a rounded eminence on top of the caterpillar's brain. It consists of a complex network of nerve cells and sends two peduncles, or stemlike columns of nerve fibers, into the rest of the brain. The "directions" for spinning the cocoon apparently are located within the corpus. No one knows in what form these "instructions" are encoded. Perhaps impulses entering the corpus pendunculatum pass through a network of synapses so patterned that the nervous impulses which emerge direct the muscles of the caterpillar to go through the series of spinning motions.

One important feature of the neural mechanism for cocoon spinning is a feedback system. Most of the impulses coming from the corpus pedunculatum go out to the muscles, but some are fed back into the corpus pedunculatum again so that the activity is self-sustaining. Why doesn't a caterpillar continue to spin forever? A good question, one with no clear and certain answer. Several plausible guesses are possible. Perhaps using up the silk is a factor; perhaps changes in the molting hormones that cause the caterpillar to pupate inactivate the corpus pedunculatum. Perhaps the continued activity of spinning finally sets off inhibitory processes.

In mammals a remarkable series of experiments has revealed the presence of narrowly localized areas within the **hypothalamus** (the part of the brain associated with the pituitary gland) which govern appetite, thirst, sleep, sex drives, anger, and even a generalized pleasure.

In rats, and probably in all mammals including man, a pair of nuclei in the hypothalamus controls satiety and another pair controls eating. (Remember that neurologists mean by a nucleus a group of nerve cells, not the sac containing the chromosomes within a single cell.)

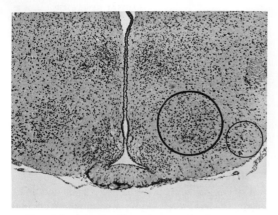

Fig. 32–14. Section of a rat brain, showing the satiety center (the area of the larger circle) and the eating or appetite center, lateral and a bit ventral. Each center is double, one on each side of the hypothalamus. *(Kindness of Jean Mayer)*

The ventro-medial nucleus, enclosed within the bigger circle in Figure 32–14, contains cells that tell an animal that it has had enough to eat and should stop. If this **satiety center** or nucleus on both sides of the hypothalamus is carefully destroyed by an electric needle point inserted into the brain, the rat becomes a ravenous eater and as a result becomes enormously obese. Such animals pass through three phases. As soon as they recover from the operation—in fact, while they still may be groggy from it—they attack food and eat voraciously. After about a day, they settle down to a steady program of eating until they have more than doubled their weight. It is as though a 150-pound man came to weigh 300 or even 350 pounds. The third phase is a static one in which the animal maintains its abnormal weight but cuts down on its eating. However, it can be induced to gorge itself again merely by starving for a day or two.

The question now arises as to how the satiety center "knows" when the animal has had enough to eat. It is common knowledge that the level of glucose in the blood rises after eating and falls during starvation. There is now good evidence that it is the action of glucose directly on the satiety centers in the ventro-medial region of the hypothalamus that gives the stop signal. If animals are fed glucose to which a toxic atom of gold has been added by a sulfur link (i.e., gold thioglucose), the cells in the satiety center are selectively killed. Evidently these cells have a special affinity for glucose which is far greater than that of any other cells of the body. They take in the glucose and along with it the poisonous gold. As a result of their destruction the satiety center is put out of order and the rat becomes obese.

Lateral and a bit ventral to each satiety center is a smaller group of nerve cells. These make up an **eating center.** If both these ventro-lateral nuclei are destroyed, a rat will stop eating more or less permanently.

Most remarkable of all is the discovery of a localized **pleasure center** in the hypothalamus. Like so many important scientific discoveries, from X-rays to penicillin, this one was made accidentally by an astute observer. In rats it is possible to insert a fine metal electrode into a specific part of the brain and hold it there permanently by a plastic holder screwed to the

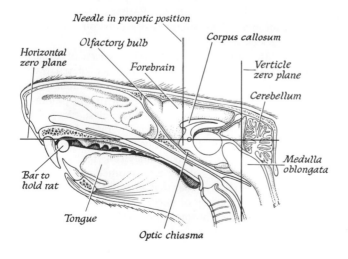

Needle in preoptic position
Olfactory bulb
Corpus callosum
Horizontal zero plane
Forebrain
Verticle zero plane
Cerebellum
Bar to hold rat
Medulla oblongata
Tongue
Optic chiasma

Fig. 32–15. Longitudinal section through the head of a rat illustrating the method of placing a needle in a precise location within the brain.

skull. Such holders heal in place and apparently are unnoticed by the rat. The experimenter attempted to place the permanent electrode in the sleep center, but missed. The rat concerned was given a small electric shock via the electrodes whenever it approached a certain corner of its cage. Instead of going to sleep, the rat kept running over to the corner where it received the minute electric shock in its hypothalamus. The next step was to place the animal in a Skinner box where it could administer a shock to its own brain by pressing a lever. The rat quickly learned to press the lever to obtain a shock of 0.0004 or fewer amperes lasting less than a second. Such rats pressed the lever anywhere from 500 to 5,000 times an hour! Control rats with the electrode in other parts of their brain pressed the bar only a dozen or so times an hour during random exploratory movements like those of any normal rat.

Indwelling micro-electrodes in the correct parts of the hypothalamus of goats, monkeys, and other mammals have confirmed the early discoveries on rats and mice. In monkeys, for example, it is possible to connect the indwelling micro-electrodes to small transistor radios strapped to the animal. If one set of electrodes is positioned in the center for angry aggression and another in the center for friendly indifference, then the behavior of the monkey can be dramatically controlled from a distance by radio signals.

Equally spectacular results have been attained in birds. If micro-electrodes are inserted into the correct region of the brain of a hen turkey, she will immediately perform typical male courting behavior, spreading and "rotating" her tail feathers, strutting, etc., when shown a model of a female turkey's head, *provided* a 0.1 milliampere current is applied in one of the electrodes.

Thus it now seems certain that the centers for appetitive behavior, drives, and general motivation lie in the hypothalamus, its associated region of the brain, and the temporal lobes. The cerebral cortex controls the consummatory acts, that is, the specific manner in which the motivations are expressed. The incredibly complex six-layered organization of the mammalian cortex, with its intricate feedback and other interconnections, has already been discussed in Chapter 31.

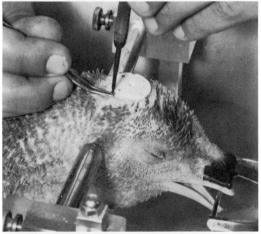

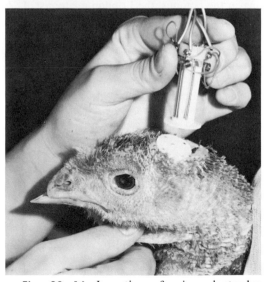

Fig. 32–16. Insertion of micro-electrodes into the brain of an anesthetized hen turkey. *(R. S. Beese, Penna. Agr. Exper. Station)*

Biochemical Basis of Memory. For many decades men have sought the memory trace or "engram" in the brain, but completely without success. Now at last very promising clues are at hand as to the form in which learning is recorded and, in some animals, even where. In both flatworms and rats several investigators seem to have transferred learning by transferring RNA from trained animals to untrained. Some of the experiments on flatworms could not be repeated by other workers in other laboratories, but some have been so confirmed. There are those who challenge the results on rats. However, there are enough confirmations to give many people the feeling—it is no more than that—that there is some real connection between RNA and learning. Furthermore, it has been shown that antimetabolites like azoguanine, which interferes with RNA synthesis, and puromycin, which is known to block protein synthesis, also block memory in goldfish and some other animals. Substances which enhance RNA synthesis are said to enhance memory also.

If RNA and/or proteins are the agents of recorded experience, it does not necessarily mean that there is an RNA code "word" saying, for example, "When you see a red light, turn left in the maze to get the food." On the basis of his long series of experiments on learning in the octopus, the London anatomist, J. Z. Young, formulates the role of RNA in terms of the familiar circuitry of the nervous system. An octopus can be trained to come forward on seeing a crab and grab it, or to retreat when it sees an equally delicious-looking crab accompanied by a white square. In both cases the visual image will pass up the same optic nerves to the visual center within the brain. But somewhere within the central nervous system there must be a fork. If the impulses take one branch, the muscles that make the animal advance will be activated. If the impulses take the other path, the muscles causing the animal to retreat will be activated.

Here it is necessary to recall an often-overlooked fact about the central nervous system, namely, the presence of numerous relatively short cells impinging on the longer circuits but having no recognized function. If the neural

impulses that resulted from the presentation of crab-plus-white-square and that stimulated the muscles of retreat also stimulated some of those smaller cells to throw up some kind of an RNA-protein roadblock on the way to the nerves to the muscles of advance and attack, then the basis for a permanent neural record would exist. The record would be in the permanence of that roadblock. If every time the white square was shown, the retreat muscles were stimulated and the RNA roadblock formed, it would be reasonable to suppose that an habitual or conditioned response had become established. This concept receives very strong support indeed from the well-known and long-established phenomenon of reciprocal innervation and reciprocal inhibition as seen, for example, in the motions of the arms and legs. This topic was discussed in the chapter on the nervous system (page 605).

How would such a theory explain the transfer of learning from one animal to another by cross-feeding RNA? It would be necessary to assume that the RNA and the proteins of every neural tract and fiber were uniquely different. This is not a difficult assumption. There is evidence from the development of the nervous system in the embryology of vertebrates that each nerve fiber is in fact somehow different from every other and for this reason will travel to a particular site in the developing brain. Many questions—some trivial, some profound—remain to be answered, but a beginning has been made.

HORMONES AND BEHAVIOR

Behavior is profoundly influenced by hormones. The hormonal control of the migrations of birds, of the mating crouch of a hen, and of the female dog in false pregnancy which steals dolls to mother, have all been described earlier. Other examples are frequent, especially among birds and mammals. The male mockingbird or cardinal which has been fighting off the female in his territory all winter acts very differently toward her with the approach of spring. First he permits her to eat with him at the feeding station and presently he begins to feed her himself. Even normally songless female canaries can be made to sing like typical males by the implantation of a pellet of testosterone under the skin. They will continue to sing for several weeks until the pellet of hormone is completely absorbed.

What do hormones in the bloodstream do to the nervous system that so profoundly affects behavior? Very convincing evidence shows that at least sex hormones induce sexual behavior by direct action on centers in the central nervous system. A female cat which has not only been spayed, i.e., ovariectomized, but has also had other reproductive organs, uterus and vagina, removed, can be caused to behave like a normal female in estrus, i.e., to welcome a male rather than to treat him with angry rejection, by the implantation of minute pellets of diethyl stilbesterol in precisely the right part of the hypothalamus. If female sex hormone is radioactively labelled with carbon-14 and injected into the bloodstream, it will be found that the hormone is selectively localized by special cells in the hypothalamus. Thus the situation is closely similar to that already described in the case of gold thioglucose which, when fed to a rat, becomes selectively localized in the satiety centers in the hypothalamus.

CIRCADIAN RHYTHMS AND BIOLOGICAL CLOCKS

Many animals show one or more rhythms that have a period of approximately 24 hours, hence the name circa-dian (approximately a day) rhythms. The common fiddler crab becomes very dark during the day, pale at night. Many rodents are active at night and quiescent during the day. Circadian rhythms have been well demonstrated in *Drosophila*, in *Euglena*, and even in the respiration of potatoes. The existence of such rhythms is not surprising but what does dumbfound many people is that many of the rhythms will persist for many weeks in a constant environment. In the pioneer investigations of Frank A. Brown and his collaborators, fiddler crabs were kept in continual complete darkness in rooms with constant temperature and humidity and no disturbances of any known kind. Yet the rhythm continued. Persistence of the rhythm under conditions as constant as they can be made has been abundantly confirmed by many workers on many species.

The real problem is, how do the animals measure time? Some people think that animals carry an internal metabolic clock of some kind. None has ever been identified. Others think that in some way animals tell time by sensing daily changes in some pervasive factor—most likely changes in the earth's magnetic field—which does exhibit circadian rhythms. But no one has been able to prove this either. It has been demonstrated that both birds (see Fig. 23–13 and page 501) and honeybees have an accurate time sense which enables them to compensate for the different positions of the sun in the sky at different times of day. But as little is known about the mechanism here as with fiddler crabs or fruit flies.

ANIMAL SOCIETIES

What is social behavior? **Social behavior** will be defined here, more or less arbitrarily, as the behavior of three or more animals reacting directly to each other. This definition excludes the mating of a single pair of animals, which in most of the animal kingdom is an isolated event that does not lead to anything that could be called social behavior unless the term is extended to include all population studies. At the same time this definition includes most parent-offspring relationships, since these are at the base of the highly developed societies of insects and mammals.

To be truly social, in the sense used here, the animals must respond to each other. This is a different thing from responding to some result of the presence of each other. For example, a crowd of daphnias in a small aquarium will use up the oxygen. This will affect their common behavior. They will all collect close to the surface of the water, but each daphnia acts independently of every other. It would have made no difference had the oxygen been used up in some entirely different manner. Likewise, a group of parameciums crowded around a clump of bacteria is not social behavior, since each arrived where it is independently. An aggregation is not necessarily a society.

In marked contrast is the behavior of a newly hatched group of fishes or squids. Both exhibit a very strong schooling instinct. If a stick is placed in the water and moved through the school, the little squids or fishes can be made to separate into two groups as they swim past the stick. But the divided school snaps back into a single group as though drawn together by powerful magnetic forces just as soon as the leading individuals are a few inches beyond the stick. Many birds are gregarious, and migrate and nest in flocks. The precise integration of all the members of a flock of pigeons as they maneuver in the air is a striking sight.

Many mammals live in social groups. In carnivores these are commonly families. Wolf packs, for instance, usually consist of an old male, one or perhaps two adult females, plus several young though full-grown individuals. Herbivorous animals—elephants, bison, sheep, and the like—commonly make herds of many individuals. The innate differences in herding tendencies between different breeds of sheep have already been described.

Many birds and mammals, if forced to live in a confined space, soon develop **"pecking orders"** or social hierarchies. Among a group of hens one will soon become dominant, able to peck any other hen in the henhouse and drive her from food. Hen number two feels free to peck any hen except hen number one. The third hen in the hierarchy can peck any hen except numbers one and two. And so the series continues. Similar series have been found in cows, mice, and other animals.

A number of facts should be noted about pecking orders. The first is that they can arise only among animals that can recognize each other as individuals and have an ability to learn. Nothing like a pecking order has been found among worms or among ants or bees, where life is governed by innate reactions, and even the queen bee does not dominate the colony in the sense of giving directions.

The position of an animal in a pecking order depends on many variables, including his own past experience. Initially it is the largest, most aggressive, and strongest individual which heads the pecking order. Animals low on the list can be raised to a higher status by several methods.

Simple isolation from the group for a time may have this result. Perhaps isolation gives animals close to the bottom of the ladder a chance to get enough food and so build up their strength. Mice can be advanced in a pecking order by isolating them from the group and then arranging a series of encounters with other mice in which they will be victors. Apparently this increases their self-confidence. Doses of sex hormone will cause chickens to rise in the pecking order.

Knowledge of pecking orders has some practical value. If a cow who is number one in her herd is transferred to another herd where her position is unknown and where the other cows "presume" she is very low on the scale, she will become "morose" and fail to eat properly, and her milk production will fall. Chickens and other animals very low on these scales may not get enough to eat to develop properly.

On the other hand, for the species as a whole, a pecking order may possess definite advantages because it almost eliminates the waste motion of continually fighting over food, drink, and space. Pecking orders cannot develop if the population is too large. Probably there are simply too many animals for any one individual to remember who stands where. The rigidity of the pecking orders differs greatly among different species. There is much more give and take among canaries and pigeons than among hens.

It is easy to draw comparisons between certain human situations and these pecking orders. Finding moral lessons and the justification of one's own prejudices in animal behavior is as old as Aesop and as contemporary as Disney, but it is not science. If you search far enough in the animal kingdom, it is possible to find almost any specified type of behavior. In certain parrot societies not only do both parents incubate the eggs, but the males secrete a true milk from glands in the throat and with it nourish the young. Male pigeons also secrete a true milk. But man is neither a pigeon nor a chicken, neither a wolf nor an ape, but a creature who must seek his own destiny.

Social Organization. Social organization that is both complex and more or less enduring has been achieved only among insects and mammals. The form and basis of the organization in these two groups is so different that comparison is difficult. They belong to different phyla widely separated by hundreds of millions of years of independent evolution. Insect life is dominated by stereotyped innate responses. In the smooth-running insect societies of the ants, bees, wasps, or termites, there is no teaching, no giving of orders, no councils of war or peace. Every member is born with information coded into his nervous system telling him or her exactly what to do in the life of the colony.

In mammalian societies, whether of elephants or primates, the young have much to learn. No one is born with specific instructions about what to do, or when. There are, of course, certain innate tendencies which underlie mammalian societies. Cats, from tigers to ocelots, do not form societies. It has been well said, "One tiger to a hill." Porpoises, sheep, wolves, and monkeys have a strong social tendency but not the repertory of specific acts that insects possess. The leader of an elephant herd or of a pack of baboons is not a creature radically different from all others and clearly distinguishable as the leader at birth, in the way a queen bee is distinguishable. On the contrary, all the young are much alike at birth. In brief, the basic differences between these two types of societies arise primarily out of the differences between instinctive and learned behavior.

There are some resemblances between the two societies. In the course of evolution both appear to have developed out of families rather than aggregations of adults. Even today there are many species of ants and wasps in which a colony consists solely of a fertilized female and a single brood of her offspring. Natural selection has favored queens whose first eggs developed into workers that did not mature sexually but built up a large nest from which there could emerge great numbers of sexually mature individuals developed from the queen's later eggs. In this way sterile castes came to be evolved. Primate societies are either families or groups of families. In the great apes, such as the gorilla, the group is usually composed of a single dominant pair with their children of various ages. Among the rhesus monkeys, or macaques, there is usually a single dominant male

and from one or two to over a dozen females, with their offspring. The bachelor males are forced to maneuver about the fringes of the group.

The ties which bind these societies together are but poorly understood. Bees continually exchange food. It has been shown more than once that a poison or, more recently, a radioactive material fed to a few bees is soon found in many others. In one test, six workers were fed radioactive phosphorus. Within 27 hours approximately 50 per cent of the bees in a hive containing 24,000 bees contained detectable amounts of the radioactive material. A queen termite and her eggs exude some substance which worker termites eagerly lap up and pass on to other members of the colony—the so-called "social hormones." In mammals the ties are mostly psychological. The panic of the lost sheep (especially if it is a Merino) is proverbial.

There are wide divergences among different insect and different mammal societies. Termites, it will be recalled from the chapter on insects, have a more complex organization than ants or bees. There are more castes, and both males and females are workers. As one wit put it, the termites are the only one of the thirty-odd groups of social insects which has succeeded in getting any work out of the males. Primate societies also differ. The Old World or catarrhine monkeys tend to a more rigid social organization dominated by a single male. The New World or platyrrhine monkeys, with their prehensile tails, have a looser social organization, and although the bands stay close together and both recognize and defend a particular territory, they are not dominated by any individual male. They are far more arboreal than their Old World cousins, and the greater amount of tree life may be reflected in their different social structure.

The scientific study of animal behavior and its biological basis is still in its infancy. Consequently it is well to end this chapter with the words used by Karl von Frisch to conclude his book on the senses and the language of the bees: "Thus we see, after travelling a long way, that we have not reached the end of the road, but stand instead at the threshold of new problems."

Review and References

REVIEW TOPICS

1. Define instinctive behavior. By what steps is it related to the genes? Why is it of special interest to the zoologist?

2. What are the five main types of learning? How are they studied? What is imprinting? How is learning related to genes?

3. Using specific examples, compare and contrast appetitive and consummatory behavior in animals in which instinct is predominant and in those in which learning is predominant.

4. Behavior often involves a so-called predisposing stimulus or condition and a sign stimulus. Describe three examples, including one in a vertebrate.

5. A honeybee returns to her hive with her crop full of nectar and performs many dances in rapid succession with the "wagging" run at an angle of 45° to the vertical. Is the source of honey far or near? In what direction? What is a possible evolutionary origin and history for this bee "language"?

6. Define and give an example of: taxis, gestalt phenomenon, learning, imprinting, sign stimulus, conditioned response, appetitive behavior, trial and error, neurological feedback.

7. What are four major methods of investigating the neurological basis of behavior? What results have been attained regarding motor centers? Centers controlling appetite? Satiety? Pleasure?

8. What is the evidence that RNA may be involved with recording experience in the central nervous system?

9. What is reciprocal inhibition? How may it be similar to part of the memory mechanism?

10. What is the evidence that at least some hormones influence behavior by acting directly on brain centers rather than by influencing peripheral structures which in turn send neural impulses to the brain and thus influence behavior?

11. What possible mechanisms might be responsible for the time sense of animals?

12. What are pecking orders? How may they be modified? What may be their adaptive meaning?

13. In what ways are the origin and character of social organizations the same in insects and mammals? In what ways different?

USEFUL REFERENCES

Bonner, J. T., *Cells and Societies,* Princeton, N.J., Princeton University Press, 1955.

Davis, D. E., *Integral Animal Behavior,* New York, The Macmillan Company, 1966.

Dethier, V. G., and E. Stellar, *Animal Behavior, Its Evolutionary and Neurological Basis,* Englewood Cliffs, N.J., Prentice-Hall, 1961.

Fabre, J. H. C., *Insect World* (1914), E. W. Teale, ed., New York, Dodd, Mead & Co., 1949.

Lincoln, F. C., *Migration of Birds,* New York, Doubleday & Company, 1952.

Lorenz, K. Z., *King Solomon's Ring,* London, Methuen, 1952.

Southwick, C. H., ed., *Primate Social Behavior,* Princeton, N.J., D. Van Nostrand Co., 1963.

Stone, C. P., ed., *Comparative Psychology,* Englewood Cliffs, N. J., Prentice-Hall, 1951.

Thorpe, W. H., *Learning and Instinct in Animals,* Cambridge, Mass., Harvard University Press, 1956.

Tinbergen, N., *The Herring Gull's World,* London, Collins, 1953.

Tinbergen, N., *The Study of Instinct,* Oxford, Clarendon Press, 1951.

von Frisch, K., *Bees: Their Vision, Chemical Senses, and Language,* Ithaca, N.Y., Cornell University Press, 1950.

Wells, M. J., *Brain and Behaviour in Cephalopods,* Stanford, Calif., Stanford University Press, 1962.

Chapter 33

Ecology

Ecology is the science concerned with how living things relate to each other and to the non-living environment in which history has placed them. The term is derived from the Greek *oikos,* meaning a house or a household, and indicates the study of the total economy of living organisms in the broadest possible sense of the word. Ecology deals with different kinds of environments from tropical forests and treeless plains to the open ocean and even the life on the under side of a lily pad. Ecology encompasses food chains and how energy is captured and utilized by plants and animal communities. Above all, ecology deals with the diverse aspects of populations and the dynamics of populations — their ranges, their fluctuations, their interactions, their evolution.

The ecologist seeks to learn why an animal behaves as it does, not in terms of neural and endocrinological mechanisms — though he is interested in these also — but to discover how the behavior fits the animal for the kind of life it lives. Laboratory experiments for an ecologist serve primarily to establish models or generalizations with which the world of nature can be compared. In this manner the ecologist endeavors to make sense out of what the American philosopher William James used to call the "big blooming confusion" of the world we live in.

Direct Human Interest. Ecology appeals to the interest of large numbers of people because the problems it tackles impinge on men and women everywhere. Furthermore, in the words of Gilbert White, the 18th century naturalist of Selborne, "The economy of nature is full of wonders great and wonders small." The modern ecologist asks many questions which Gilbert White and his contemporaries never dreamed of. Most of our questions fall into one of three areas. The first group of questions asks: What determines the distribution of a particular species? What is the real reason that there are no snakes in Ireland? Why have starlings successfully colonized most areas of the United States, while skylarks, which have been introduced several times, have not?

A second series of questions involves the food and energy chains in nature. Ecologists like to point out that the adage, "All flesh is grass," is true in a literal as well as a figurative sense. Of the oceans it can be said, "All fishes are diatoms." Questions of this sort range from the dramatic "Who eats whom?" to the quiet but no less important ones of where animals get the necessary trace elements in their diets and how the flow of energy for living activities is directed and utilized and what cycles various elements undergo.

653

Fig. 33–1. European rabbits, introduced into Australia where no natural enemies existed, multiplied to such an extent that they ate most of the grass and herbs over thousands of acres. This area was lost for grazing of cattle and sheep, and the bare soil was in danger of serious erosion by rain. *(Dunston — Black Star)*

The third type of question, which really includes all the others, concerns populations. How many deer may be shot per year in a given region without depleting the population? How may a population of rats or of disease germs be minimized or even exterminated? Why are there about 30 different species of birds in a typical temperate forest while there are often over 300 species in a tropical forest? Why are the fishes in one lake all small, while those in another lake are large? Do human populations have anything to learn from the study of populations of lower animals?

Practical Value. The practical value of ecology is great. It is the science which makes possible the wise management of forests and of game and fish. It underlies the most profitable use of soils. It is the essential basis of any intelligent conservation program.

Marine ecology has yielded information of major importance for the fisheries industry. Enthusiasts believe that in the future mankind may be able to farm the oceans as he now farms the land. Because nearly 75 per cent of the earth's surface is ocean, this is indeed an exciting possibility. Careful studies have been made of the yield of diatoms and other minute green plants which constitute the basic food in the sea. The annual crop in terms of pounds of dry weight per acre per year varies, according to the part of the ocean, from an amount equal to that of a forest to that of grass on a semi-arid plain.

Ecology, furthermore, has considerable medical importance because the occurrence and spread of disease, whether transmitted by mosquitos, rat fleas, or sneezes, is a problem in the rise and fall of populations: populations of bacteria, of sick fleas, and sick men. Ecology is a young science, full of unknowns and challenging problems.

ENVIRONMENTS

One of the first tasks of ecology is to bring some logical order out of the diverse kinds of environments in which animals live and to discover how animals fit into their environments. The **range** of a species is the entire geographical area over which the animal may be found. As we have seen, the range of *Rana pipiens,* the meadow frog, is from northern Canada to Panama, and from the Atlantic coast almost to the Pacific. The **habitat** of an animal is the particular kind of environment in which it lives. The habitat of *R. pipiens* is damp meadows and along the edges of small streams and ponds.

The ecological **niche** occupied by an animal is usually defined as its ecological role in its particular place in its environment. It is also said that the niche that an animal species occupies reflects the requirements for living of that animal. The ecological niche of *R. pipiens* is that of a small carnivore in moist locations. Thus niche is an abstract, functional term, as commonly used in ecology.

Terrestrial environments change in a regular and similar way in passing from north to south and from mountaintops to valleys. These changes are not always imperceptible transitions whereby one group of plants and animals slowly replaces another. On the contrary, the change may occur in a series of fairly abrupt steps separating well-defined life zones. Each zone supports a characteristic living community called a **biome.** Thus there is a deciduous forest biome, a prairie biome, and so on. The line of contact between two biomes, large or small, is termed an **ecotone.** Theoretically, this is a zone of tension between the communities. Ecotones are often characterized by special animals and plants which thrive only in such transitional regions. The quail (bobwhite) is such a species, which seems to require for successful breeding to nest close to the edge of a wood, preferably where forest, meadow, and shrub meet. Probably the most well-known of the ecotones are the tree lines often observed on mountainsides and in the far north, and the tide line where the sea meets the land.

The Seven Major Land Biomes. From the north polar regions to the equator there are seven major biomes. The polar regions, together with snow-capped peaks, constitute **arctic zones,** similar in many ways though not identical. Except in a more or less sporadic form this arctic zone is without life.

South or below the arctic zone is the **tundra.** This is a vast treeless region extending across northern Canada and northern Siberia. The **alpine zone,** above the tree line on mountains, corresponds to the tundra. The characteristic plants are sphagnum and other mosses, reindeer "moss" and other lichens, and a few small shrubby bushes. The flowering herbaceous plants of the tundra are noted for their showy blossoms. Muskoxen, reindeer, snow hares, caribou, arctic foxes, and wolves are characteristic mammals. In the brief summer, insects—especially flies and mosquitos—and nesting migratory birds abound. In New Hampshire, the tundra or Alpine zone begins on Mount Washington at less than 5,000 feet, while in the Rockies the tree line is up at the 11,000 to 12,000 foot level. On Mount Popocatepetl in Mexico the tree line is higher still, at some 15,000 feet or more. Not all the factors that determine the position of the tree line are understood. Temperature is of course paramount, but its action is subject to considerable modification. In some places isolated areas of trees grow far north of the tree line. In some places the line is sharp; in other regions there is a transition zone of stunted trees.

Fig. 33–2. Transition zone of bushes and stunted trees characteristic of some alpine regions. Cove Mountain, Utah. (*U.S. Forest Service*)

South of the tundra is a belt of conifers, spruce, firs, and pines called the **taiga.** Birch and aspens occur here and there through the taiga and are usually the first trees to grow up after a fire. The moose is the characteristic large mammal, rodents and mink are abundant small ones. Intermediate and also abundant are lynxes, black bears, wolves, and martens.

South of the taiga is the familiar **deciduous forest** of hardwoods. In the northern part of the zone, beeches and maples tend to predominate; in the southern, oaks and hickory. The Virginia deer, the black bear, and the opossum are characteristic, although the yellow-spotted black salamander, *Ambystoma maculatum,* of the woodlands is used as an "index animal" for this zone in the eastern United States.

In many parts of the world **grasslands,** variously termed prairies, steppes, veldts, or pampas, occur, commonly south of the deciduous zone. It is in this kind of environment that the evolution of horses, antelopes, and kangaroos took place. In some regions the prairie extends northward virtually to the coniferous taiga, without any intervening deciduous zone. In other places the deciduous zone is replaced by a southern coniferous region when soil and moisture conditions are right.

The **tropical rain forest** makes a sixth major life zone. Such regions are found in Central America, northern South America, equatorial Africa, and southern Asia and the East Indies. The pattern of trees is radically different from that in other types of forest. Few northern forests are composed of more than a dozen species, and great stands can be found composed of but one or two species. In tropical rain forests, however, several hundred kinds of trees are commonly found intermixed. Moreover, the vegetation is stratified. Great ironwood, banak, and other trees tower to a height of 125 feet or more. Below them, in partial shade, there is a second layer of trees, and beneath these in turn is a mass of small trees, bushes, and plants of many kinds. In this environment it is little wonder that many of the animals are treedwellers. In British Guiana 31 out of 59 species of mammals are arboreal.

A seventh zone is **desert,** which may occur at almost any latitude. In the Americas the typical plant is the cactus. Thorny bushes with waxy leaves characterize deserts everywhere. Animal life is sparse and mostly nocturnal.

Various minor biomes, more or less related to the major ones, occur in various parts of the world. Chapparal biomes of dwarf evergreen

Fig. 33–3. The major biomes from the pole towards the equator and from mountaintop to sea level.

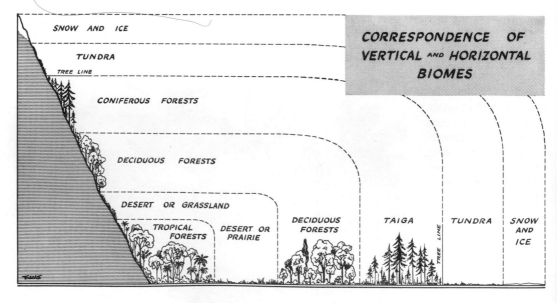

SNOW AND ICE

TUNDRA

TREE LINE

CONIFEROUS FORESTS

DECIDUOUS FORESTS

DESERT OR GRASSLAND

TROPICAL FORESTS

DESERT OR PRAIRIE

CORRESPONDENCE OF VERTICAL AND HORIZONTAL BIOMES

DECIDUOUS FORESTS

TAIGA

TREE LINE

TUNDRA

SNOW AND ICE

oaks and other shrubby trees are found in temperate and subtropical regions with a rainy winter and a hot, dry summer. Some six million acres of California are covered with chaparral. The shores of the Mediterranean are also covered with chaparral in many places. Special climatic and soil conditions have produced special biomes in other parts of the world. The northwest coast of the United States wears a nontropical rain forest. Much of Florida possesses a broad-leafed evergreen biome characterized by magnolias, live oaks, hollies, figs, gums, and palms.

The character of a biome is determined by climate, which includes temperature, rainfall, and amount of sunlight, and by the character of the soil. The relative importance of climate and soil in controlling the living community varies from one region to another. No tropical rain forest can arise in the Great Plains area or in the Ohio Valley of the United States, no matter what the soil conditions. In other regions, as in some parts of southeastern United States, soil seems to be the determining factor, within, of course, the limits set by climate.

Microclimates. The climate that matters for any animal is obviously the climate in which it actually lives. This may be very different from the general climate of the geographical region constituting the range of the species. An insect living in the treetops lives in a veritable desert, compared with the insect living on the forest floor where evaporation is only about 7 per cent of that near the tops of the trees. Conditions under stones, on the north side of boulders, or a few inches under the sand of a beach are almost always quite different from those of the general surroundings. This means that temperature and moisture readings recorded on the very best and most modern equipment within a standard weather bureau louvered box set on a post a meter above ground level cannot be directly related to the animals in the vicinity. Those animals may and often do enjoy a very different set of conditions.

Consider the Arizona desert. As the table reveals, desert animals which enter burrows during the day experience a vastly different temperature from that prevailing on the surface of the sand.

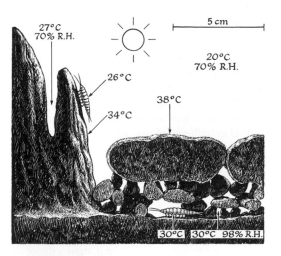

Fig. 33–4. Diagram of microhabitats and microclimates inhabited by common semi-terrestrial beach crustaceans. Note the difference between conditions of temperature and relative humidity on the surface of the pebbles and under them. (*After E. B. Edney*)

Temperatures in the Arizona Desert
(*data from G. L. Clarke*)

Air	42.5°C	108°F
Surface	71.5°	160°
10 cm below surface	41.1°	104°
30 cm below surface	29.0°	82°

The semi-terrestrial crustaceans, common on the ocean shores, are subject to much less drastic changes in temperature and humidity than those of their general environment because they actually inhabit a microhabitat with its own microclimate.

Atmosphere. All of the physical factors of the environment in which plants and animals live have been modified in greater or lesser degree by the presence of living organisms. We live at the bottom of an ocean of air which surrounds our planet. Approximately 80 per cent of the air is nitrogen which has come down to us from the ages before life appeared on earth, but the story of oxygen is very different.

It is now well established that the oxygen in the atmosphere was not always there but is the product of photosynthesis, and hence has accumulated since the appearance of aquatic green plants. Few physical factors are of greater importance. Without oxygen, active animal life as we know it would be impossible. Without oxygen in the atmosphere the amount of radiation reaching the earth's surface would be so great that life on land would be virtually impossible.

The amount of moisture and CO_2 in the air are also influenced by plant and animal life. The composition of the ocean is continually being modified by the swarming myriads of organisms within it. Think of the millions of tons of lime that have been removed from the sea by the protozoans whose shells formed the chalk deposits. Even the amount of light and the temperature are modified, though to a slight degree, by the presence of plants and their effects on the amount of moisture, carbon dioxide, and oxygen in the atmosphere.

The Study of Soils. The soil is a very special case among the physical factors of the environment, partly because it has not merely been modified by living organisms but has actually been made by them. Without a covering of

plants, the surface of the earth would be bare rock, washed by wind and rain. Because soil is of such crucial importance in agriculture, and because it can be improved or so easily damaged beyond repair, a special soil science has grown up, called **pedology**. The Russians and Scandinavians have been leaders in this field, and consequently a number of the terms are derived from their languages.

As can be seen in any freshly cut bank, soil consists of a series of layers, so-called **horizons**. The uppermost horizons are commonly known as **topsoil**, technically the **A horizons**. The uppermost surface of soil is a surface layer (A_{00}) of undecomposed debris consisting of leaves, twigs, animal remains, and the like, called **litter**. Beneath this is a layer (A_0) of matted and more or less decomposed organic matter, called **leaf mold**. True soil begins with a dark horizon (A_1) of **humus**. This layer is composed of a high content of organic matter, thoroughly mixed with miscellaneous rock particles. Like the two

Fig. 33–5. Section through three major types of soil, showing the layers or so-called horizons. (Semi-diagrammatic)

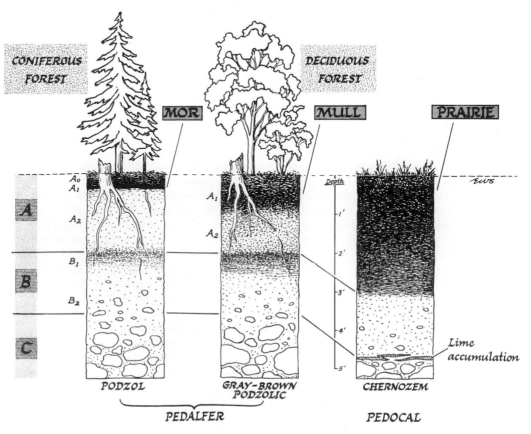

layers above it, it is rich in microscopic and semi-microscopic animals Below the humus is a lighter colored layer, the A_2 horizon, from which most of the soluble materials have been leached, that is, washed out, by sinking rain water. In prairie soils, which are the deep black chernozems, the leached A_2 layer is said to be missing or, if listed as present, is virtually unleached.

The **subsoil,** or **B horizons,** lacks appreciable amounts of organic matter and contains few soil organisms, either animals, fungi, or bacteria. It is said to be mineralized. The upper layer of the subsoil, termed the B_1 horizon, is dark with the minerals leached from the topsoil. The deeper B_2 horizon is a tightly packed mineral soil, which may show a bottom layer of lime or other mineral deposits just above the C_1 **horizon** of weathered bed rock.

In different climates, especially different temperatures and rainfalls, the relative thickness of the soil horizons, as well as other soil characteristics, differ greatly. Under the coniferous forest of the taiga, the humus or A_1 horizon is very shallow and very sharply demarcated from the leached A_2 layer. Such a soil is called **mor.** The humus is very low in calcium, lacking in nitrates, and definitely acid, its pH ranging from 3.0 to 6.5. Fungi play a prominent role in its decomposition. Earthworms, which are important soil formers, are rare in it and limited to acid-tolerant species, mainly surface dwellers such as *Bimastus eiseni* and *Dendrobaena octaedra,* which seldom burrow down deeper than a few inches.

Under the temperate deciduous forest, the A_1 horizon is much thicker and the A_2 less thoroughly leached and richer in organic matter. This type of soil is called **mull.** It is much richer in calcium than is mor, nitrates are present, and the pH ranges from acid to slightly alkaline (4.5 to 8.0). Bacteria play a prominent part in its decomposition. Earthworms are relatively abundant, and deep-burrowing species such as the familiar *Lumbricus terrestris* and *Helodrilus caliginosus* are present.

Prairie soil, or **chernozem,** contrasts markedly with both mor and mull. Physically the A horizon of humus is extremely thick and fairly uniform. Leaching is minimal. The main causal factor seems to be the small rainfall.

Most of the water is absorbed by the humus and the grass roots in the A horizon. Capillarity during surface drying, and ascent of sap in roots return dissolved minerals to the upper layers. As someone has said, the water in this type of soil is "hung from the top, like Monday's wash."

Soils are classified as the **chernozems,** with little leaching, and the **podzols,** whether mors or mulls, with much leaching. Podzols are commonly much richer in aluminum and iron and deficient in calcium, and hence are reddish or brown in color. For this reason they are often termed **pedalfers** (*pedon,* ground, + *aluminium,* + *ferum,* iron). Such soils are characteristic of the eastern half of the United States. Chernozems are characteristic of the dryer great plains and western regions and are rich in calcium. Consequently they are termed **pedocals** (*pedon,* ground, + *calcium*).

Ecological Succession and Soil Development. In most parts of the world today the community of plants and animals in a region remains constant decade after decade, presumably for many centuries. Such a stable fauna and flora constitute an ecological **climax** or a climax community. Each of the major biomes, deciduous forest, tundra, etc., represents such a climax which remains stable unless marked climatic changes take place. Whenever a climax community is upset or destroyed, as by fire, which may be caused by lightning, or by cutting the trees and cultivating the soil, or whenever new areas of rock, or sand, or even a new fresh-water pond appears, then the climax is restored through a regular series of stages known as a **sere.** Each stage of a sere is characterized by its own typical plants and animals.

In the deciduous forest zone of the temperate regions of the northern hemisphere, annual herbaceous plants appear first after a severe fire as they did in the rubble areas of bombed cities after World War II. These are followed in a year or two by various kinds of grasses, then shrubs, and following them pines and birches or perhaps scrub oaks. These are at last superseded by the beech-oak-hickory climax.

Various other seres have been studied, notably the one observed when vegetation begins to grow over a sand dune or to fill up a fresh-water

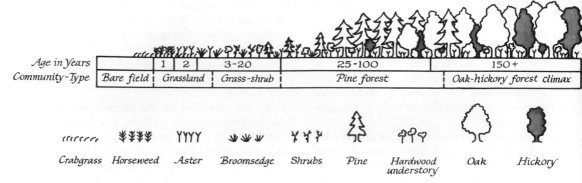

Fig. 33-6. The stages of a sere leading from a bare field abandoned after "overfarming" up to the deciduous forest climax. Note that the entire process required at least 150 years. *(After Odum, Fundamentals of Ecology, 2nd ed., W. B. Saunders)*

pond. The Great Succession in the northern hemisphere is the reforestation of the land following the last glaciation of the Pleistocene. This process is only now beginning to draw to a close. The retreating glaciers left tundra conditions. Even in southern United States, remains of musk-ox, mastodons, and other far northern animals have been found. In time the tundra became coniferous taiga and this in turn gave way to the deciduous forest which is today's climax community in most of eastern and central North America and Europe.

The causes of ecological successions are complex and are different in different cases. The situation following the destruction of a forest by a fire is not the same as after its destruction by a glacier. Climatic factors are important in all cases but after a fire the climate commonly remains the same. The change from grassland to bushes to trees of various sorts depends largely on the effects on the environment of the plants, and to some extent of the animals. One community so changes things that some other group of plants and animals are able to replace them. The shade on the forest floor may finally become so deep that the seedlings of the trees casting the shade cannot develop, although seedlings of a different kind of tree can.

Changes in the character of the soil play a key role in the movement of the stages of the sere in time. Some ecologists believe that deep-burrowing earthworms are the chief agents in converting the mor soils of the taiga

with their thin, sharply limited layer of humus into the mull soils of the deciduous forests with their thick and much less sharply delimited humus or topsoil. Charles Darwin published an extended account of the way earthworms cultivate the soil. He showed that all the humus of the soil of England has passed many times through the bodies of earthworms. Recent measurements have substantiated his findings. As already noted, earthworms burrow into both the topsoil and the subsoil, pass it through their bodies, and leave it in castings on the surface of the ground. In light dry soil, this commonly amounts to two to three tons per acre per year. In moist pastures it may be ten tons, while in certain tropical localities values up to 100 tons per acre per year have been measured.

There can be no question that earthworms play a very important role in soil dynamics, once they have become abundant. They continually deepen the topsoil, both by bringing subsoil to the surface and by dragging leaves into their burrows. Their burrows open the way for water and air to penetrate the soil. Soil becomes finer, and its colloidal properties become modified in passing through earthworms. It is easy to believe that earthworms are primarily responsible for the difference between the shallow humus of mor and the deep humus of mull soils. The unanswered question is whether earthworms are the key factor in the conversion of one type of soil to the other. It is quite possible that deep-burrowing species of earthworms cannot enter the mor under the taiga until some other factors have changed the acidity of the humus.

Earthworms are by no means the only animals of the soil, although they are probably the most important. The fauna of the soil is at least as abundant and often more abundant than the fauna of fresh-water lakes or most parts of the ocean. The A_0 horizons of litter and leaf mold abound with invertebrates. Ingenious new methods for extracting the microfauna of the soil are being developed and have already yielded significant results. In addition to a vast horde of insects and insect larvae, the soil is the normal environment for teeming populations of nematodes, many of great destructiveness to crops, plus enormous numbers of minute arachnids, mites, tardigrades, collembola, crustaceans, microannelids, rotifers, and even protozoans, especially amoebas and flagellates. Potatoes cannot be successfully grown unless the nematode egg count is lower than 40 per gram of soil.

The Study of Lakes. The scientific study of lakes is known as **limnology.** Lakes are classified into three types on the basis of the amount of nutrition they provide for fishes and other inhabitants. **Eutrophic** lakes are relatively shallow and contain a good supply of nutrients for algae and pond weeds, and therefore for crustaceans, and therefore for little fishes, and therefore for larger fishes. Lake Mendota in Wisconsin and many of the lakes in Scandinavia are well-studied examples of eutrophic lakes. **Oligotrophic** lakes are deep, relatively poor in nutrients and animals, and rich in oxygen. The Great Lakes and the Finger Lakes of New York are typically oligotrophic. **Dystrophic** lakes are usually parts of bogs; the nutrients are present but various organic acids and other substances inhibit the growth of plants and animals.

In recent years the United States government has developed a farm pond program through the Soil Conservation Service. Over 350,000 ponds have been made by damming small streams. They are routinely stocked with bluegill sunfish and with bass of the same size at the rate of 1,500 bluegills per acre of pond surface and 100 bass if the pond is to be fertilized with either manure or chemicals, and about half as

many if not. At the end of a year, the sunfish on which the bass feed average about 4 ounces each and the bass about 1 pound.

Unfertilized ponds yield from 40 to 150 pounds of fish an acre, while fertilized ponds yield from 200 to 400 pounds an acre. Both represent eutrophic conditions. The fishes feed on each other and on plankton. In these ponds the fertilizer feeds the algae which constitute the phyto- or plant plankton. This serves as food for daphnia, cyclops, and other crustaceans which are the most important members of the zooplankton. The crustaceans in turn are eaten by the smaller fishes which are then eaten by the larger fishes.

The amount of fertilizer must be enough to produce a luxuriant growth, a so-called "bloom," of algae early in the summer. However, there must not be such a thick soup of algae that when they die off in the winter the processes of decay will use up all the oxygen and kill the fishes. The number of fishes initially introduced into the pond is also a very important factor. When bluegills are added at the rate of 1,500 per acre, they attain a weight of about 4 ounces in 12 months, but if 180,000 per acre are added, they average only 0.02 ounces. At the rate of 1,500 per acre without fertilization, the average weight is 1.1 ounce.

Most lakes in the temperate zone undergo a very important complete turnover of the water every spring and fall. Because this thoroughly mixes the dissolved oxygen and mineral nutrients in the lake, it stimulates plant and animal growth. The peculiar behavior of the water can be understood only by remembering that water is densest, i.e., heaviest, at 4°C, about 39°F. Thereafter as water becomes still colder, it expands and becomes lighter. In the fall, as the surface water cools, it becomes heavier and sinks. Warmer water rises, becomes cold, and in turn sinks. This process continues until the entire lake is at 4°C.

In the winter, as the water cools to below 4°C, it no longer sinks but remains on the surface and ultimately forms a layer of ice. Except for a very thin layer immediately under the ice, lake water never falls below 4°C. This is a doubly fortunate circumstance for living things. It means that in the water they are protected from freezing temperatures. It also means that

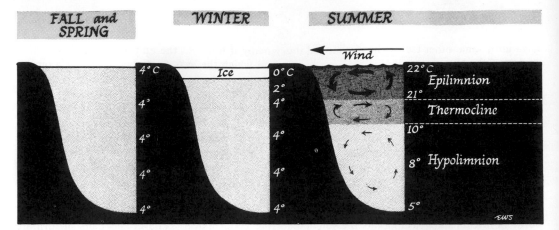

Fig. 33–7. Seasonal turnover of water in lakes. The curious fact that water is densest and therefore heaviest at 4°C, and becomes lighter as it cools below 4°, is a key factor. Wind and gravity assist.

the lakes are available as favorable environments, for if water continued to contract as it became colder and colder, ice would begin forming on the bottom of lakes and gradually fill up the pond with ice. Under these circumstances ice would never leave the bottoms of lakes except in the southern edge of the temperate region.

In spring, after the ice melts, the thin layer of water at the surface and below 4°C in temperature warms, becomes heavier, and sinks until all the lake again becomes 4°. As the surface water, heated by the sun, becomes warmer than 4°, it does not sink but forms a warm surface layer. This is pushed by the prevailing wind against one shore of the lake. Water at that shore sinks (rather than piling up), while at the same time at the opposite shore, cooler water rises to replace that blown away. As a result, a counter-current is set up in slightly deeper water. Since all this water is warmer, i.e., lighter, than the remainder in the lake, it forms a superficial layer of warm water called the **epilimnion.** Immediately below the epilimnion is a thin layer of water where the temperature falls very suddenly, the **thermocline.** The depth at which the thermocline occurs depends on season, winds, and other factors. In some lakes the thermocline begins within 6 feet of the surface, while in Lake Cayuga, one of the deep narrow Finger Lakes of New York, it may be 30 feet below the surface. Below the thermocline is the **hypolimnion.** This is a zone of relatively uniform and cold temperature extending to the bottom. Just as the current along the

under surface of the epilimnion produces a current in the thermocline, so the current in the thermocline produces a slight current in the hypolimnion. The result is a very gradual and slight warming of the hypolimnion.

In deep oligotrophic lakes, the hypolimnion has a supply of oxygen and is hence inhabited by cold-water species such as *Mysis,* a kind of shrimp, and by lake trout. In eutrophic lakes there is virtually no oxygen in the hypolimnion, partly because the algae in the epilimnion prevent the sunlight necessary for oxygen-producing photosynthesis to occur in the hypolimnion, and partly because the continual "rain" of dead organisms from above uses any available oxygen. The fauna on the bottom of such lakes consists of insect larvae, some of which are red with hemoglobin, and other organisms adapted for low oxygen concentrations. Fishes are scarce. In the autumn, as the water cools at the surface, it sinks; warm water rises, and becomes cool to sink in its turn. Thus there is a complete fall turnover of the water until it is all at 4°C.

Streams and Rivers. Streams and rivers present special problems and opportunities for animals. In the rapids, animals are adapted for holding firm to rocks and often possess flattened, streamlined bodies. Unless the waters are polluted with sewage, oxygen is abundant. Stream salamanders commonly lack lungs and breathe merely through skin capillaries. **Estuaries** are tidal zones where fresh water enters the sea. In a sense, such regions are ecotones where tension exists between the fresh-water and marine biomes. For a variety of reasons such environments are extremely favorable for animal life. Crabs, oysters, clams, teleosts, jellyfish, ctenophores, and many planktonic species abound.

Oceans and Currents. The large-scale scientific study of the oceans began with the world survey cruise of the *Challenger* from 1872 to 1876. The 50 enormous volumes which resulted from that voyage form the basis of our knowledge of marine ecology.

Key factors in the life of the sea are the **ocean currents.** These are primarily wind-driven. North of the equator the tradewinds blow continually from the northeast toward the southwest. South of the equator the tradewinds blow continually from the southeast toward the northwest. The result produces great equatorial currents flowing westward on either side of the equator, in both the Atlantic and the Pacific Oceans. When these westward currents strike the continents they are deflected north and south. This is the source of the Gulf Stream, flowing north along the east coast of North America, and of the Kuroshio (Japan) current, flowing northward from the Philippines along the coasts of China and Japan. The westerly winds in the temperate zones of both the northern and southern hemispheres help propel the Gulf Stream and the Kuroshio current to the west coasts of Europe and of North America. The final result is a circular motion. In the southern hemisphere the Peru or Humboldt current, flowing northward along the west coast of South America, and the Benguela current, flowing northward along the west coast of Africa, are due to similar forces. It is the Peru current that enables penguins to live close to the equator off the coast of South America.

There is another very different kind of current known as the arctic creep. In the seas around both north and south poles, the frigid waters sink and flow slowly along the bottom toward the equator. Here the water gradually rises to replace that which is lost by evaporation under the tropical sun.

The oceans are divided into several general regions depending on the depth of the bottom. Most continents are surrounded by a **continental shelf,** a more or less flat plain under about 200 meters (roughly 600 feet) of water but in some places much less. (A football field is 360 feet between goal posts.) Off the east coast of Florida the continental shelf is only a few miles wide and hardly exists at all directly opposite the Bahamas, but off the west coast of Florida and off New England the shelf extends out approximately 200 miles. The shelf itself and the waters over the shelf constitute the **neritic zone.** The part of the neritic zone near shore with water up to about 50 meters and usually strong wave action and enough light for plant growth, is termed **littoral.**

Beyond the neritic zone is the **oceanic zone.** This is the part of the ocean which the navies of the world call "blue water." The bottom slopes rapidly from the continental shelf down to depths of 3,000 meters and lower. The regions of these great depths are the **abyssal regions.** No light ever penetrates this far. The temperature is virtually constant at 37.4°F (about 3°C). Part of the ocean bottom in this abyssal region is a flat plain but there are great mountain ranges, mile-deep trenches exceeding the Grand Canyon of the Colorado River in dimensions, and extensive regions of hills and what appear like river valleys.

The animals in each of these regions are characteristically different. The animals that live near shore are called littoral; those which live at sea, especially far out in the open ocean, are called **pelagic.** Those myriads of floating or feebly swimming organisms that live near the surface of the ocean, either in the neritic or oceanic zone, are called **plankton** — zooplankton if animals, phytoplankton if plants. Strongly swimming animals are called **nekton.** Those which live on the bottom, especially at great depths, are called **benthos.**

The most important members of the plankton are the diatoms, which constitute the basic plant food of the sea, and the copepods, which feed on the diatoms. Every phylum is represented in the marine plankton in the form of floating eggs, larvae, or adults, or as all three. Very often members of the plankton are transparent and have special adaptations for floating. Animals living at great depths in eternal cold and darkness are bizarre by any standards.

A very interesting and economically important difference between the marine populations near the poles and those near the equator is that

Fig. 33–8. Representatives of marine plankton. Note the amazing variety of species and body forms. Virtually every phylum is represented in the plankton either as floating eggs, larvae, or adults.

in the polar seas there are enormous numbers of individuals but relatively few species. In ecological terms the **biomass** is very great. In tropical waters the situation is reversed. There are relatively few individuals, but a great variety of different species. The biomass is small. The explanation for this contrast is obscure, but it will be recalled that a similar contrast, in so far as number of species is concerned, exists between northern and tropical forests.

Although oceans cover nearly 75 per cent of the earth's surface, almost all the fishing done by man takes place over the continental shelves. Thus only a tiny fraction of the vast ocean is used for the production of human food. The only significant exception is the whaling industry and many of the whales are captured near shore. It is worth noting that the baleen group of whales live exclusively on plankton, especially swarms of small oceanic crustaceans, while the toothed whales feed on giant squid and other members of the nekton.

Instrumentation of Oceanography. The classic tools of the oceanographer, or oceanologist, are a set of nets and trawls which can be towed through the water at fixed depths or along the bottom, a number of Nansen bottles, and a good pair of sea legs. A Nansen bottle is fixed at a certain point on a wire which is weighted and let down into the water to the desired depth. Since the bottle is open at both ends, water merely passes through it as it descends. Thus the bottle at all times contains a sample of the water at the depth at which it happens to be. Alongside the bottle is a special type of mercury thermometer. When the bottle and thermometer have reached the designated depth, a metal weight with a hole bored in it is sent down the wire. When this "messenger" hits the catch which holds the upper end of the bottle to the wire, the catch opens, permitting the bottle to fall over so that it hangs down from the lower catch. This action causes valves at each end of the bottle to close, trapping the water sample. At the same time the jerk of the releasing of the catch and the falling over of the bottle causes the mercury column in the thermometer to break in a special twist in the glass tube. Thus part of the mercury column is trapped in such a way that the temperature at the specified depth can be determined after the thermometer has been raised to the surface. (See Fig. 33–9.)

664

In preparation for the coming modern age of ocean exploration and use, a wide variety of new instruments are being developed. Buoys adjusted to float at particular levels and equipped with powerful radio signalling devices make it possible to track currents and also their temperatures as never before. Whales and fishes can be equipped with indwelling transistor radios for tracking over long periods of time. Sonar and radar devices make it possible to map bottom depths and contours and to locate schools of fishes and swarms of crustaceans and other animals. Stable floating work "platforms" have been constructed which resemble elongated tubular boats, one end of which can be filled with water to up-end the contraption. The upper end with the work rooms is then supported by a deep probe extending many feet down into the water so as to be free of wave action. Probably most important of all are the newly equipped ocean-going research ships and the large laboratories for analyzing their findings which have recently been built here and abroad.

Fig. 33–9. Nansen water-sampling bottle and reversing thermometer. *(After A. Vine, International Science and Technology, Dec., 1965)*

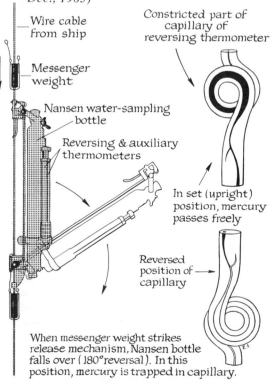

Wire cable from ship

Messenger weight

Nansen water-sampling bottle

Reversing & auxiliary thermometers

Constricted part of capillary of reversing thermometer

In set (upright) position, mercury passes freely

Reversed position of capillary

When messenger weight strikes release mechanism, Nansen bottle falls over (180° reversal). In this position, mercury is trapped in capillary.

MATTER AND ENERGY PATHWAYS

The major matter and energy pathways for animals begin in plants – with photosynthesis in the green plants, with the fixation of nitrogen by microorganisms, and with the absorption of various minerals from the soil and the sea, again by plants. In photosynthesis the energy of the sun is trapped and locked up in sugar molecules at the same time that carbon dioxide from the atmosphere is united with the hydrogen of water, and free molecular oxygen is released as a waste product. The familiar overall equation:

$$6 \, CO_2 \; + \; 6 \, H_2O \longrightarrow C_6H_{12}O_6 \; + \; 6 \, O_2$$

gives the facts of primary importance to the ecologist. He is concerned with the sources of the raw materials and the energy, their amounts, and what happens to them after they have been processed by plants, rather than with the biochemical machinery which enables chlorophyll to trap energy. He is interested in the effects that the withdrawal of all this CO_2 may have on the entire living community, and what effects the release of oxygen may have. He needs to know how much energy and matter a given community requires, how productive a given geographical region is, and how productive it might become. He wants to know where all the matter and energy comes from, where it goes, and how it gets there.

A basic difference is at once apparent between the pathways for matter and for energy. The elements of which protoplasm is built, both the "big five" – carbon, oxygen, hydrogen, nitrogen, and phosphorus – and the various elements like iron, sulfur, sodium, calcium, potassium, iodine, and others required in small or even trace amounts, are used by different living things over and over again. Their pathways are cyclical. In marked contrast, energy moves on a one-way street. It comes from the sun, is trapped by chlorophyll, and is utilized by living things in the three well-recognized ways, i.e., to construct complex molecules, to do the work of moving substances across membranes in working against osmotic pressures and in secretion, and to bring about muscular and other types of protoplasmic motion. Ultimately the complex large molecules are broken down, by one agent or another, and the energy is dissipated as heat, often in the random Brownian motion of molecules. In terms of thermodynamics, entropy is increased, and animals therefore require a continual source of negative entropy if they are to maintain their improbable structures and the activities that are part of them. Life on this planet is thus dependent on an outside source, the sun, for its energy, while it can reuse its supply of matter over and over again.

The three most carefully studied cycles of matter in the living world are the carbon, nitrogen, and phosphorus cycles. It should be remembered that all the elements that enter into living things are neither destroyed nor increased but they are passed on again to the environment.

The Carbon Cycle. The carbon cycle can be said to begin with the formation of a carbohydrate in photosynthesis as just explained. The carbohydrate may be built into the body of a plant directly, or part of the carbohydrate, including carbon, may be utilized in the formation of lipids and proteins and other more complex substances, such as nucleic acids or hormones. If the plant is eaten by an animal, the carbon becomes incorporated—in the most literal possible sense of that word—into the substance of the animal. The carbon is returned to the atmosphere as CO_2 in the respiration of plants and animals. Any carbon caught in the corpse of a plant or animal is utilized by the microorganisms of decay, and they in their respiration return the carbon to the air as CO_2. The cycles of oxygen and of hydrogen are obviously closely linked to the carbon cycle.

The Nitrogen Cycle. The primary source of nitrogen is the atmosphere. Although the air is roughly 80 per cent nitrogen, animals cannot utilize the gaseous form of this essential element, because it is extremely inert. Lightning "fixes" nitrogen, that is, forces it into chemical combination with other elements. This fixed nitrogen is washed out of the air by rain and reaches the earth as ammonia, NH_3, or nitrate, HNO_3. Most nitrogen fixation is carried on by special nitrogen-fixing bacteria in the sea or the soil. The nodules on the roots of peas, beans, and other legumes are specialized structures

inhabited by nitrogen-fixing bacteria and are the most effective agents known for this purpose. Between 1 and 6 pounds of atmospheric nitrogen are fixed per acre per year, depending on the type of soil and the presence of legumes.

The nitrates, either from bacterial or other sources, are absorbed by plants and converted into amino acids and proteins. Plant proteins are the only ultimate source of all animal proteins. The nitrogen is returned to the soil or the seawater by way of the bacteria of decay, which convert animal and plant proteins and urea to ammonia, or by animals which excrete ammonia instead of urea or uric acid. The ammonia is utilized by nitrite bacteria both in the soil and in the sea; they convert it to nitrites (NO_2). These in turn are converted into nitrates by nitrate bacteria, after which nitrogen is again available for plants. These are the main features of the nitrogen cycle. There is also some nitrogen fixed by blue-green algae and perhaps by other organisms. Certain denitrifying bacteria utilize fixed nitrogen as a source of energy and release free nitrogen as waste. Many plants are able to absorb and utilize nitrites even better than nitrates. Animals are not an essential part of the nitrogen cycle.

The Phosphorus Cycle. Phosphorus is a rare element compared with nitrogen, but because it is concerned with energy-transfer mechanisms within cells, it is equally important. The dissolved phosphates in soil and in the sea are derived from erosion of phosphate-containing rocks. The phosphate is absorbed by plants and built into plant and animal compounds. The phosphorus is returned to the soil and the ocean by phosphatizing decay bacteria. It seems unlikely that the phosphate content of agricultural soil is being maintained. Soils in the Mississippi valley that have been under cultivation for 50 years show a 36 per cent reduction of their P_2O_5, compared with virgin soil of the same type.

Food and Energy Chains. When food chains are actually studied, they turn out to be pyramids leading from the basic plant source to herbivores and then up through a series of carnivores of increasing size but decreasing numbers. The principle is illustrated by a more or less hypothetical Eskimo who eats nothing but polar bears, which eat seals, which eat large fishes, which eat small fishes, which eat crustaceans and other plankton animals, which eat diatoms. The total mass of protoplasm, the so-called biomass, becomes less and less as the pyramid is ascended. This is because animals live within the laws of conservation of matter and energy. Regardless of how efficient any animal is, catching its food and all the other activities of living require expenditures. Actually the amount of energy represented at any one trophic level of such a pyramid is only about one-tenth that represented at the adjacent lower level. Not only is there a pyramid of biomass and of energy but there is also a pyramid of individuals. All three factors narrow sharply as one trophic level is placed on top of another.

A good example of a **pyramid of numbers** of individuals is an acre of Kentucky blue grass which represents about 6 million plants, about 700,000 herbivorous invertebrates, about 350,000 carnivorous invertebrates such as spiders, ants, and predatory beetles, and about 3 carnivorous vertebrates such as birds and moles. A square mile of Arizona range which was studied supported 1 coyote, 2 hawks and 2 owls, 45 jackrabbits, 8,000 wood and kangaroo rats, and 18,000 mice. This case illustrates another aspect of nutritional relationship between animals. When two species occupy the same nutritional level in a food-population pyramid, the species with the smaller body size will generally have the larger number of individuals but it will not necessarily have the larger biomass.

A certain Wisconsin lake can serve as a more or less typical example of a **pyramid of biomass.** There were, one summer, about 1,000 kilograms of plants, the primary producers, per hectare (1 hectare = 2.47 acres); there were about 114 kilograms of animals on the second trophic level, i.e., 114 kilos of herbivores, per hectare; and about 38 kilograms of animals on the third major trophic level, i.e., 38 kilos of carnivores.

A bog lake in Minnesota can illustrate a **pyramid of energy** represented in the three major trophic levels. The level of primary producers, actually primary receivers of energy, yielded a

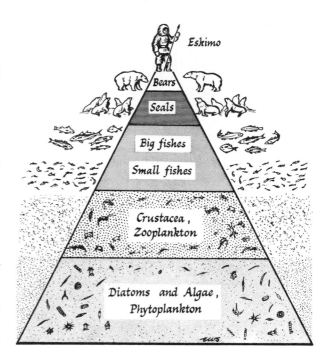

Fig. 33–10. The closer a species of animals stands to the ultimate food source in green plants, the larger its population, or, more accurately, its biomass. (Not to scale)

total of 70 calories from the plants per unit of volume of bog; the second major trophic level, that of the herbivores, yielded 7.0 calories for the same volume; and the third major level, that of the carnivores, yielded only 1.3 calories per unit of volume.

The amount of energy stored in a sample of coal or of animals can be measured in a **bomb calorimeter.** The animals are homogenized and then completely dried; the resulting powder is weighed and placed within a metal container that can be immersed in water. The "bomb" is filled with oxygen, then immersed in a carefully measured amount of water at an accurately known temperature. The oxygen is ignited by an electric spark. The heat liberated by the resulting explosive total combustion of the dried animals is absorbed by the water surrounding the metal container and as a result the temperature of the water is raised. Thus the number of calories present in a given weight of dried animals can be calculated, once the weight of the water is known and the number of degrees through which its temperature is raised is determined.

Productivity. The ecological question of paramount importance for mankind is how to determine the potential productivity of any particular type of environment, terrestrial, fresh-water, or marine, and then to discover how the maximum productive potential can be attained. It is obvious from a consideration of the facts about ecological pyramids of numbers, biomass, and energy that the closer to the primary producers at the bottom of the pyramid any species lives, the greater its supply of matter and energy will be in any environment.

The actual productivity of a piece of land or water in terms of the biomass of plants or animals it can or does produce turns out to be difficult and rather tricky to measure, except under rather special conditions. Four methods are in common use.

The **harvest method** is the most obvious and works well enough in certain simple situations. In a field where only one crop of the plant you happen to be interested in can be grown per year, you can harvest 100 per cent of the crop and measure its amount. The situation in a lake or forest or swamp, not to mention the ocean, is far different. To obtain a 100 per cent harvest is often extremely difficult. Fishes in a lake may be killed with a chemical such as rotenone and those which float to the surface counted and weighed. Skin divers can attempt to make a census of the far larger numbers, perhaps the vast majority, which sink to the bottom. The activities involved in making such a census may profoundly disturb the water of the lake, the bodies of the dead fishes will add nutrients, the oxygen and carbon dioxide content will be changed, so that any accurate control census a year later may be taken under such different historical circumstances that it is no real control on the first census.

An even greater difficulty lies in the fact that the mass of animals existing at any one time is only a very rough indication of actual productivity and even less an indication of potential productivity. Two lakes or two parts of the ocean may contain the same biomass, but in one the standing population may have been reached only after a relatively long period of time and if much were removed, would require a long time to regain its original size. In the other lake the turnover of population may be very rapid, or could and would become so if any significant number of animals were removed. Hence if the same number were harvested from each lake, it would require a far longer period of time for the population in the less productive lake to regain its original size than in the more productive one. How is one to know how often to harvest to get a true measure of productivity? How often to harvest raises the question, to be discussed in the following section on population dynamics, of the drastically different results of "harvesting" animals such as fishes or deer at different points on their population curves.

It has even been thought by some ecologists that differences in rate of turnover rather than differences in actual productivity can explain the ecological paradox that the biomass present in polar seas is so much greater than in the sunny tropical oceans where you would expect the greatest productivity.

A second method of measuring productivity is to determine the **oxygen production** as a measure of the amount of photosynthesis. This is more difficult than it sounds. Plants themselves as well as microorganisms and the animals in the lake use oxygen. Some ingenious workers have measured the rate at which oxygen is depleted from the hypolimnion during the summer. It will be recalled that during the summer there is no appreciable exchange between the water above the thermocline of a lake where oxygen from the air and from green plants is available and the deep water below the thermocline where there are no green plants and no access to atmospheric oxygen. The more productive the lake, the more organic debris will fall down into the hypolimnion, be metabolized by organisms there, and lead to exhaustion of the oxygen supply. This undoubtedly is true but only in certain special lakes.

The **disappearance of minerals** from a body of water has also been used as a measure of rate of productivity. It has to be remembered that, in any closed body of water, the fauna and flora will reuse the minerals already present and that new supplies are being washed in by rivers and streams at various rates. The chief place where this method has been useful, and it is an important place, is in certain parts of the ocean. There are places where nitrogen and phosphorus accumulate in the water during the winter and are utilized by phytoplankton in the spring. The rate of use, or at least disappearance from the water, can be determined.

Radioactive tracers, specifically phosphorus-32 which has a half life of about two weeks and hence is fairly safe to use, have been introduced into ponds and the rate of incorporation into phytoplankton determined. This method seems to hold real promise for lake studies and possibly marine studies as well.

In summary, productivity depends on many very different kinds of factors. The amount of sunlight is, of course, basic. So also are temperature, moisture, sources of mineral nutrients, and the position of the animals on the population curve when harvesting is done. Easily the most important of all is the genetic constitution of the members of the population. This has been dramatically demonstrated in the case of such crops as hybrid corn and new varieties of wheat, but it is most certainly true of animals as well. It is here that those who would cultivate the oceans must look, as well as at currents and temperatures.

THE DYNAMICS OF POPULATIONS

The study of populations has been a major concern of zoologists ever since Charles Darwin enunciated his theory of evolution based on natural selection. The tremendous reproductive potential of plants and animals is one of the most powerful of evolutionary forces. The study of populations is central to all the problems of ecology; and no part of ecology has more important practical aspects than a knowledge of the causes and characteristics of the rise and fall of populations. From the practical point of view, the problem is how to minimize undesirable populations and maximize desirable ones.

The major factors controlling population size can be more or less arbitrarily divided into three categories—habitat, predation, and competition within species. Some ecologists emphasize the role of population density on population growth and speak of density-dependent and density-independent factors. Others deny the existence of truly density-independent factors.

Effect of Habitat. The habitat includes both living and nonliving features. Tree squirrels do not live on treeless plains. Often a whole ecological community of animals depends on a plant community. When the plant biome disappears, the animal community must disappear also. This happened along the Atlantic coast of the United States when the fields of eelgrass on tidal flats were all killed by an eelgrass disease. The populations of scallops, certain polychaetes, aurelia jellyfish, and many other animals shrank almost to the vanishing point. A similar thing happens to forest populations whenever fields are cleared. If the plants which provide food or shelter for a given species of animal are rare, the animal will also become rare.

The nonliving factors include climate, amount of sunshine, soil, and topographical features. Marine animals cannot survive in fresh water with its extremely low osmotic pressure. Tropical fishes cannot live in the cold waters of the north.

Effect of Predation. The second factor influencing population size is predation, both by obvious carnivores and by bacteria and other parasitic organisms. It is difficult to determine accurately how important predation by carnivores or even by disease organisms really is. It is entirely possible that there are cases in nature, perhaps many cases, where the number of individuals eaten is so small in proportion to the total population of the prey that predation makes no measurable difference. This seems highly probable when the predator population is limited by some factor other than the supply of prey. For example, ospreys live by catching fishes out of the ocean. The supply of possible prey is therefore enormous, if not absolutely unlimited. But ospreys are held in check by the limited number of suitable nesting sites, which must be isolated from the birds' own enemies and fairly close to the water. In some populations, such as those of fishes in lakes, it has been shown that removing small fishes will permit those left to grow faster to a larger size than would have been possible under the initial crowded conditions. Recent studies of several lakes in Oklahoma show that it is practically impossible to deplete a healthy population of fishes by predation with a hook and line. Of course if the lake is fished with a seine, the entire population can be caught.

There are other well-established cases where predation has drastically reduced and virtually exterminated the prey. This can be rather easily demonstrated in the laboratory. If a ciliate called *Didinium,* which attacks and eats parameciums, is placed in a culture of its prey, the population of didiniums will increase and, after a time, the population of parameciums will decrease until final extinction. At this point, of course, the predators are faced with an irremediable famine and become extinct also. If the finger-bowl world of parameciums and didiniums is complicated by the introduction of obstacles which will partially hide prey from predator, then irregular fluctuations of population abundance and scarcity will be observed. The more complex the environment, the longer will the cycles continue. Clearly, the more complex situation more closely resembles the condition of nature.

Predators have been used successfully in nature on various occasions. The African "cannibal" snail, *Gonaxis,* has been used effectively to reduce the population of Japanese edible snails that were damaging crops on Pacific islands and also to control a snail which fed on citrus leaves in California. On islands where the mongoose was introduced, it is credited with exterminating certain birds by eating their eggs.

The likelihood, however, is that in the vast majority of prey-predator relationships, a relatively stable equilibrium has been attained in the course of evolution. Were this not so, either the prey or the predator, or both, would have become extinct ages ago. This is why the introduction of new predators produces such spectacular results. It is also why the elimination of the restraints imposed by predators may produce disastrous results for the prey.

One of the best-authenticated cases occurred among the deer on the Kaibab plateau, an area of about 700,000 acres in Arizona. When the plateau was first surveyed, there were approximately 4,000 deer, plus numerous wolves and pumas. Strenuous human efforts then removed all or most of the predators. The deer population rose to over 100,000. The result was a famine among the deer. Leaves were pulled off trees as far up as a deer could reach by standing on its hind legs. In the two following winters 40 per cent of the herd died of starvation and the population dwindled to 10,000. The all-too-familiar signs of overgrazing—damaged trees, sparse grass and shrubs, and actual soil erosion—will continue to be evident for years to come. The reproductive potential of the deer had been adjusted by natural selection to compensate for loss from predation. When the restraint of the predators was removed, the population increased, to its own detriment.

Public attention is often focused on populations which fluctuate at more or less regular intervals. The classic case is that of the snowshoe hare and the Canada lynx. Records kept from about 1800 by the Hudson's Bay Company reveal oscillations with about a 10-year wave length. In general, when hares are abundant so are the lynxes; and, as would be expected, the population peaks for the lynxes tend to come slightly later than those for the hares. A number of such prey-predator cycles are known: among others, lions and zebras, snowy owls and lemmings.

It was long supposed that there was a causal relationship between the numbers of the prey and their food. Volterra and Lotka described these prey-predator cycles in mathematical terms; so they are commonly referred to as Volterra-Lotka cycles. The oscillations certainly exist, but there is now good reason to believe that in some cases at least, the number of the predators merely rides up and down with the fluctuations in the numbers of the prey. For example, on Anticosti, a large island about 100 miles long situated in the Gulf of St. Lawrence, the population of snowshoe hares rises and falls as it does on the mainland of Canada, despite the fact that there are no lynxes at all on Anticosti. The fluctuations in the hares are perhaps due to several cooperating factors—competition for food plants, increased incidence of disease with crowding, or the effects of fighting among themselves.

Competition Within Species. In addition to the general habitat and predation, a third important factor in controlling population size is competition within species. Students of evolution commonly believe that this type of competition is the most severe of all. Sparrows do not compete with ducks, much less with turtles or sunfish. The more different any two organisms, the less the competition. All seed-eating birds, for example, compete to some extent with other seed-eaters. But as anyone who has raised various kinds of finches knows, these birds have very strong food preferences, often based on bill size. Only two individuals of the same species will choose exactly the same seeds.

Owing to recent studies, intraspecific competition in house mice is better understood than in any other species. The method is to place two or three breeding pairs in rooms with nesting boxes and food. As long as there is plenty of food and enough nesting sites, the population increases with virtually no emigration from the room. When the population reaches a level where all the food is eaten up every day, then enough mice emigrate to keep the population stationary at this high level. The birth rate remains as before. It is a curious fact that the mice which emigrate represent a typical cross section of the colony, not just the young or the old or the most vigorous, but some of both sexes and all ages except nestlings.

If there is no escape from the room when the population catches up with the food supply, the picture is very different. First, the nurslings die. Then the birth of new litters stops. The older mice gradually die off, presumably of old age. As this happens, the total number of mice in the colony falls, but the average weight of the individuals gradually increases so that the total weight of the colony remains constant. The amount of food given per day is adequate for a certain biomass of mice, irrespective of whether it is divided among a larger number of thin mice or a smaller number of fatter ones.

What mechanism brings reproduction to a standstill in such a mouse colony? Apparently a very important factor is the **emotional effect** of the continual fighting which the food crisis causes. The adrenal glands become noticeably enlarged, and the reproductive endocrines are in some way thrown off balance. Thus there is in these mice a kind of **negative feedback** mechanism which sets limits to the population when it begins to press against the food supply. In marked contrast, the Kaibab deer lack an effective built-in control mechanism, although signs of adrenal damage have been found in other crowded deer populations as well as in woodchucks and other species.

Negative feedback is the kind usually found among living organisms. Many actions produce some counteraction which checks the results of the first and restores the organism to equilibrium. **Positive,** or "runaway," **feedbacks** have also been reported in animals. It is as though a thermostat, once the temperature had risen to a given point, instead of turning the heat down, turned on more heat, and then when the temperature climbed still higher, turned on the heat still more. Positive feedbacks soon lead to disaster. One such has already been mentioned as a possible factor in the extinction of the passenger pigeon. In any case, several sea birds are known — gulls and guillemots — among which the smaller the nesting colony, the fewer eggs hatch and the fewer young are raised. This leads to a vicious downward spiral. It is as though every time the temperature fell, the thermostat turned the heat down even more.

Population Growth Curves. The free growth of a population in an open environment can be regarded as a positive feedback situation. The more individuals, the faster the population grows; and the faster the population grows, the more individuals; and so on, the faster, the faster. As Malthus pointed out in 1798, populations tend to grow logarithmically, like money at compound interest. At first, in a new environment, a population increases faster and faster, and then in a finite environment (and all environments, whether test tubes or continents, are finite) growth begins to slow down more and more. The result is an **S-shaped** or **logistic curve.**

This curve of population growth has the widest possible application, for the very simple but basic reason that all animals reproduce in a geometrical rather than an arithmetical series. In other words, in a unit of time a population does not add a fixed number of new individuals regardless of its own size, but the new individuals become part of the reproductive capital and add their own share of new individuals. The curves illustrated here are taken from studies of yeast cells and fruit flies, but they hold similarly for mice and deer and men. More precisely, the increase in population is proportional to N, the total number of individuals in the population. The actual rate of increase depends on the reproductive ability, r, of the individuals. This factor is very large for

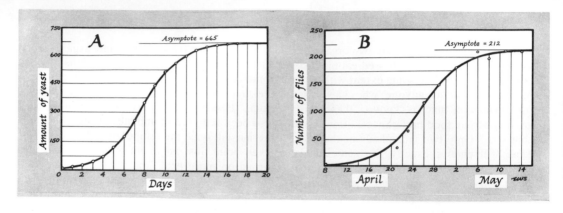

Fig. 33–11. The universal logistic curve of population growth in a finite environment. *A,* curve derived from the growth of a population of yeast cells. *B,* curve derived from a population of fruit flies.

oysters, moderate for mice, and smaller for elephants. The rate of increase is not only determined by $r \times N$, but is correlated with how close N is to the upper possible limit in any finite environment — test tube, milk bottle, or Kaibab plateau. This factor is $\dfrac{(K - N)}{K}$, where K is the maximum possible population. In the beginning, when N is very small, this factor is approximately equal to one. As N increases, this factor becomes smaller and smaller until $N = K$, when $\dfrac{(K - N)}{K} = 0$, and increase in size ceases. In terms of calculus, the growth rate at any point $\dfrac{dN}{dt} = \dfrac{rN(K - N)}{K}$.

Some Practical Applications. One important practical application of the facts expressed by this formula concerns the best time to harvest from a population of fishes or deer or other organisms. Removing a certain number of individuals when a population is close to the lower end of its curve will produce a marked depressing effect. Removing the same number at the upper end of the curve will either have no appreciable effect or will allow those left to attain a somewhat greater size. This is the principle back of the fact that emigration from overpopulated countries furnishes no permanent cure for the overcrowding.

Not only can much larger harvests be reaped when the harvesting is done close to the top of the population curve, but a harvest of any given size can be taken with far less effort. This has been demonstrated in the case of the codfish. If one population is about three times as large as another, it will require only about one-third the fishing effort (time towing nets, etc.) to harvest the same amount of fishes from the large as from the small population.

From the human point of view the objective is often harvests in reverse, the diminution or elimination of an undesirable population. Here the strategy must be to press hard with the control measures when the population curve is at its lowest, if permanent results are to be achieved. The older chemical methods with DDT and various neurological and enzymatic poisons can be very effective in controlling insects, rodents, and sometimes even nematodes. But they have very serious and undesirable side effects. Most of these poisons are very long-lasting, if not indestructible. They get into food chains and are transmitted from plants to herbivores and then up the chain of carnivores. The bald eagle has picked up enough of these poisons so that its eggs often fail to hatch even though the adults are not killed. Moreover, these poisons, when used over a forest or a swamp, kill indiscriminately many if not all wild life species.

Consequently there has been a determined hunt for biological means of control. These methods are generally far safer and some are entirely safe, such as the use of sterilized males. Others, however, carry their own potential dangers as when a parasite against an unwanted animal is imported from another country.

Three types of methods of population control deserve special mention.

672

Fig. 33–12. An illustration of the principle of maximal yield with minimal effort. The upper rectangles represent the number of one-, two-, three-, and four-year-old fishes in the stock populations. The lower represent the fishes caught. The same number of pounds of fish are harvested in both cases, but three times as many hours towing nets is required with the smaller population and more of the fish are small in size. (*After T. Park in Allee, Emerson et al.,* Animal Ecology, *W. B. Saunders*)

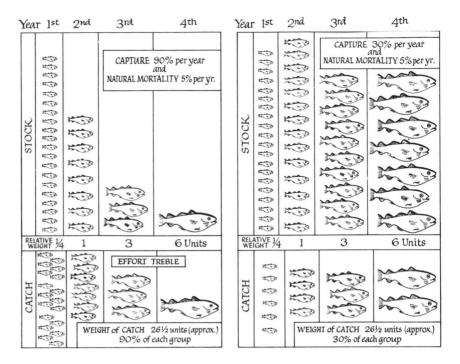

Perhaps the most ingenious is the use of **sterilized males.** Unfortunately, although this method has been a spectacular success, it is expensive and can be used only against species where the females mate only once. The U.S. Department of Agriculture has, for example, used this method against the highly destructive screwworm fly which produces maggots that attack the flesh of cattle. In one campaign they raised and sterilized by X-rays 100 million male flies per week. These were set loose from planes flying over the infested country. Within two years the screwworm fly was completely eliminated over wide areas. Over $200 million worth of damage to cattle is reliably estimated to have been averted within a three-year period.

A second method is a very neat combination of chemical and biological techniques. **Sex attractants** are identified in female insects, the secretion is analyzed chemically, and its molecular structure determined. Then it is possible to manufacture the material commercially and use it to lure males into traps or to poisoned bait, a far safer method than spraying poisons on whole plants or whole forests. This technique holds great promise for the future. The sex attractant of the female gypsy moth, a species highly destructive to coniferous and deciduous forests and to fruit trees, has been identi-

fied and is sold under the name of Gyplure (see page 396). Its success will be of great interest. The gypsy moth was introduced into Massachusetts about 1868 by an entomologist said to be an amateur. In any case, he "didn't know it was loaded." Millions of dollars of destruction has been the result, and more millions have been spent spraying orchards with lead arsenate, introducing a small beetle which eats the gypsy moth larvae, and spraying forests by plane with DDT. Perhaps sex attractants will be the answer. A similar attractant has been identified from cockroaches by drawing air over thousands of females and washing out its odors.

A third method is the introduction of **bacterial or viral diseases** in order to devastate an unwanted population. This carries obvious dangers. One must be certain that the disease will not attack other, desirable species. This method has been very successful against the great rabbit plagues of Australia where all other known methods had failed. The pathogen used was the myxomatosis virus which is transmitted from one rabbit to another by a mosquito. Two bacterial diseases have been very successful in controlling and all but eradicating the Japanese beetle in the United States after the various insects which parasitize this beetle in Japan had been introduced to no avail.

Competition Between Species. Many different species of animals inhabit the same habitat—a spruce forest, a grassy meadow, a pond, or whatnot. Do any two species occupy the same ecological niche within their habitat? Charles Darwin suggested long ago that this was highly unlikely because either one or the other species would, in all probability, be at least slightly better adapted and hence, over a long period of time, able to outbreed the less well adapted and finally eliminate it. In more recent years J. Grinnell, on the basis of a long study of California birds, came to the conclusion that no two species did in fact occupy the same ecological niche. Within the following decade the same idea was supported by V. Volterra in Italy and G. F. Gause in the U.S.S.R. and came to be called the **principle of competitive exclusion.** The application of this principle makes it possible to see some rationale in the pattern of sympatric species. The case of the five common species of frogs in eastern North America has already been presented.

It is commonplace to find two or many species living together and apparently competing, i.e., occupying the same niche. Careful scrutiny in every case so far has shown that the different species actually occupy different though sometimes slightly overlapping niches. A well-known case investigated by R. H. MacArthur is that of the five species of warblers which live during the nesting season in the spruce forests of the north. He found that each species had a different zone of the tree where it specialized in hunting for food, although there was a certain amount of overlap. One species hunted for insects almost exclusively among the fresh growth at the tips of the branches near the top of the tree. Another species specialized in the foliage over a year old beneath the new spring growth, another specialized in hunting on the leafless branches close to the trunk and in the upper part of the tree, another chose a similar zone but close to the ground. Not only was the location of food-hunting different, but there certainly would also be a difference, though not an absolute one, between the insects and spiders available in these various localities.

Another instructive case is that of the over 50 species of nematodes which have been identified inhabiting cow dung in meadows. Careful study again reveals that there is, at the very least, far from universal competition among all these species. Some live only on the surface, others only in the interior. Some flourish only when the dung is relatively fresh, others when it is somewhat aged, and still others when it is all but dried and washed away. The bacteria and other microorganisms on which nematodes feed are of many kinds so there is a rich opportunity for a group of species living together at the same time to eat quite different things—any one of a dozen kinds of wild yeasts, fungi, and of course many kinds of bacteria. Differences in the wild yeasts eaten by the larvae of different kinds of drosophila have been well established.

At present ecologists are attempting to apply **mathematical models** to biological situations to see how close fits they can make and if a mathematical approach will help answer some old problems and open up new ones. There seems to be a relation, for example, between total population size, the number of related species, and the various sizes of the populations of the different species. But exactly what this relationship is remains unclear. In many cases pairs of sympatric species are closely similar save that one is roughly twice the weight of the other. Why not roughly thrice or four times the weight of the smaller species? Such pairs are seen in the downy and hairy woodpeckers, and in weasels, flycatchers, terns, frogs, and cats. When there is a group of similar species, such as the wild mice, which are all closely of the same size, then they have been found to live in different habitats.

A Synoptic View of Population Dynamics. Most of the factors influencing population growth so far discussed are clearly dependent on the density of the population. This is surely true of the psychic factors due to crowding which inhibit reproductive success in various species, such as mice crowded into a small room. It is true also of the birds which do not nest well in rookeries with less than a certain minimum number of nesting pairs. There is no doubt that the general curve describing the growth of populations of animals or bacteria is

Fig. 33–13. *H.M.S. Challenger.* The 69,000-mile voyage of this laboratory ship (1872-1876) opened a new era in the scientific knowledge of the life of the seas. The vast collections obtained resulted in 50 thick folio volumes of the *Challenger Report,* describing something of the physics and chemistry of the ocean and its life.

governed by the density-dependent fraction, $\frac{K-N}{K}$, where K is the maximum possible population in any specified environment and N is the number of individuals present at any specified time.

But other factors profoundly influence population growth, such as temperature, the amount of sunlight, and the size of the universe an animal inhabits. Such factors are often called density-independent factors. However, some ecologists argue that in nature there are no true density-independent factors, since the effects of even temperature or rainfall may indeed become density-dependent when members of a large population find them either more difficult or easier to meet than the members of a small population.

Another possibility is to divide the factors influencing a population into the physical and the biotic, or living, factors. This is a valid distinction as long as it is remembered that the physical, or nonliving, environment has been profoundly modified by the living world. As shown earlier in this chapter, the air itself would be without oxygen were it not for photosynthetic plants. The truth is clearly that the growth curve of a population is governed by a considerable number of different forces, just as the trajectory of a missile is determined partly by its own propulsive force, partly by gravity, partly by its direction in respect to the rotation of the earth, and partly by wind. Zoology would be simple if animal behavior could be reduced to so few factors.

The unexplored possibilities in ecology, both terrestrial and marine, are fully as great today as in the 1870's when Her Majesty's Ship *Challenger* set sail to explore the seven seas and all that in them lies.

Review and References

1. What are the seven principal land biomes from the north polar region to the equator? What organisms characterize each?

2. What is the difference between podzol and chernozem soils? Mors and mulls? Pedalfers and pedocals? What is the role of earthworms in soil building?

3. Define: biome, biomass, habitat, ecological niche, ecotone, thermocline, plankton, benthos, oligotrophic, pelagic.

4. How may a knowledge of a microclimate help support the principle of competitive exclusion?

5. Explain the spring and fall water turnover in lakes. What is the biological importance?

6. What are the various possible routes in the carbon, nitrogen, and phosphorus cycles?

7. What factors change one stage of a sere into the succeeding stage?

8. What are some typical food chains in the sea, in lakes, and on the land? What is the relationship of the size of individual animals in a population to their numbers? To their distance from the base of a food pyramid? Why?

9. If oceanic whale-farming became a reality, which type of whale would be more efficient as a meat and oil producer, the Moby Dick type of toothed whale which eats large animals or the baleen type which feeds on plankton? Why? In a limited area what would be the order of magnitude of the difference between the total weight of whales of the two types that could be supported?

10. Why is productivity such a tricky thing to measure? What is the role of genetic factors?

11. Discuss three major factors influencing population size.

12. What has been learned of population dynamics by studies of yeast and drosophila? Of deer? Of house mice?

13. What are Volterra-Lotka cycles? What reasons are there for believing they are caused by prey-predator interactions? What reasons for thinking fluctuations in the prey are primarily responsible?

14. Explain what is meant by the growth index, $\dfrac{K - N}{K}$

15. Using populations of sunfish and deer, and the characteristic animals of the tundra and the deciduous forests as examples, discuss the relative importance of density-dependent and density-independent factors in population size and character. To what extent are density-independent factors to be equated with the nonliving factors of the environment?

USEFUL REFERENCES

Bates, M., *The Nature of Natural History,* New York, Charles Scribner's Sons, 1950.

Bennett, G. W., *Management of Artificial Lakes and Ponds,* New York, Reinhold Publishing Corp., 1962.

Clarke, G. L., *Elements of Ecology,* New York, John Wiley & Sons, 1954.

Fraser, J., *Nature Adrift, the Story of Marine Plankton,* Philadelphia, Dufour Editions, 1962.

Kendeigh, S. C., *Animal Ecology,* Englewood Cliffs, N.J., Prentice-Hall, 1961.

Kevan, D. K. McE., ed., *Soil Zoology,* New York, Academic Press, 1955.

Klopfer, P. H., *Behavioral Aspects of Ecology,* Englewood Cliffs, N.J., Prentice-Hall, 1962.

Krutch, J. W., *The Voice of the Desert,* New York, William Sloane Associates, 1957.

Lack, D., *The Natural Regulation of Animal Numbers,* Oxford, Clarendon Press, 1954.

Morgan, A. H., *Field Book of Animals in Winter*, New York, G. P. Putnam's Sons, 1939.

Odum, E. P., *Fundamentals of Ecology,* Philadelphia, W. B. Saunders Co., 1953.

Sverdrup, H. U., M. W. Johnson, and R. H. Fleming, *The Oceans,* Englewood Cliffs, N.J., Prentice-Hall, 1942.

White, G., *The Natural History of Selborne,* New York, E. P. Dutton & Co., 1949.

Classification of the Animal Kingdom

The following table presents the phyla and classes of the animal kingdom. In some groups, the subclasses, orders, or other taxons are included. Fossil groups are usually excluded. No radical departures from commonly accepted practice will be found, but the student should remember that while there is little disagreement among zoologists about the major divisions, there are sometimes many different opinions about smaller groups. This table is based on the work of R. W. Pennak but differs from it in several respects.

Phylum Protozoa

Class Flagellata (Mastigophora)

Subclass Phytomastigina

Order Chrysomonadiniformes
Order Chloromonadiniformes
Order Cryptomonadiniformes
Order Dinoflagellatiformes
Order Euglenoidiniformes
Order Phytomonadiniformes

Subclass Zoomastigina

Order Hypermastiginiformes
Order Polymastiginiformes
Order Protomonadiniformes
Order Rhizomastiginiformes

Class Sarcodina

Order Amoebiniformes
Order Foraminiferiformes
Order Heliozoiformes
Order Mycetozoiformes
Order Proteomyxiformes
Order Radiolariformes
Order Testaceiformes

Class Sporozoa

Subclass Cnidosporidia

Order Actinomyxidiformes
Order Helicosporidiformes
Order Microsporidiformes
Order Myxosporidiformes

Subclass Haplosporidia
Subclass Sarcosporidia
Subclass Telosporidia

Order Coccidiformes
Order Gregarinidiformes
Order Hemosporidiformes

Class Ciliata

Order Chonotrichiformes
Order Holotrichiformes
Order Peritrichiformes

Order Spirotrichiformes
   Suborder Ctenostomata
   Suborder Heterotricha
   Suborder Hypotricha
   Suborder Oligotricha
Class Suctoria
Phylum Porifera
Class Calcarea
Order Homocoeliformes
Order Heterocoeliformes
Class Hexactinellida
Order Hexasterophoriformes
Order Amphidiscophoriformes
Class Demospongiae
 Subclass Tetractinellida
 Subclass Monaxonida
 Subclass Keratosa
Phylum Coelenterata
Class Hydrozoa
Order Hydroidiformes
   Suborder Anthomedusae
   Suborder Leptomedusae
   Suborder Limnomedusae
Order Hydrocoralliniformes
   Suborder Milleporina
   Suborder Stylasterina
Order Trachyliniformes
   Suborder Trachymedusae
   Suborder Narcomedusae
   Suborder Pteromedusae
Order Siphonophoriformes

Class Scyphozoa
Order Stauromedusiformes
Order Cubomedusiformes
Order Coronatiformes
Order Discomedusiformes
Class Anthozoa
 Subclass Alcyonaria
Order Alcyonaceiformes
Order Coenothecaliformes
Order Gorgonaceiformes
Order Pennatulaceiformes
Order Stoloniferiformes
Order Telestaceiformes
 Subclass Zoantharia
Order Actiniariformes
Order Madreporariformes
Order Zonanthideiformes
Order Antipathariformes
Order Cerianthariformes

Phylum Ctenophora
      Class Tentaculata
                Order Cestidiformes
                Order Cydippidiformes
                Order Lobatiformes
                Order Platycteneiformes
      Class Nuda

Protostoma

Phylum Platyhelminthes
      Class Turbellaria (turbellarians)
                Order Acoeliformes
                Order Rhabdocoeliformes
                Order Alloeocoeliformes
                Order Tricladidiformes
                Order Polycladidiformes
      Class Trematoda (flukes)
                Order Monogeneiformes
                Order Digeneiformes
                Order Aspidocotyleiformes
      Class Cestoidea (tapeworms)
        Subclass Cestodaria
        Subclass Cestoda
                Order Aporideiformes
                Order Cyclophyllideiformes
                Order Diphyllideiformes
                Order Lecanicephaloideiformes
                Order Nippotaenideiformes
                Order Proteocephaloideiformes
                Order Tetraphyllideiformes
                Order Trypanorhynchiformes
                Order Pseudophyllideiformes

Phylum Mesozoa
      Class Dicyema
      Class Orthonectida
Phylum Nemertinea
      Class Anopla
                Order Palaeonemertineiformes
                Order Heteronemertineiformes
      Class Enopla
                Order Hoplonemertineiformes
                Order Bdellonemertineiformes

Phylum Aschelminthes
     Subphylum Nematoda (nematodes)
      Class Aphasmidea
                Order Chromadoridiformes
                Order Enoplidiformes
      Class Phasmidea
                Order Tylenchidiformes
                Order Rhabditidiformes
                Order Spiruridiformes

Subphylum Nematomorpha (horsehair worms, etc.)
    Class Gordioidea
    Class Nectonematoidea
Subphylum Trochelminthes (rotifers)
    Class Digononta
            Order Seisonideiformes
            Order Bdelloideiformes
    Class Monogononta
            Order Flosculariaceiformes
            Order Collothecaceiformes
            Order Ploimiformes
Subphylum Gastrotricha
Subphylum Kinorhyncha
Subphylum Priapulida

Phylum Entoprocta

Phylum Acanthocephala

Phylum Bryozoa
    Class Phylactolaemata
    Class Gymnolaemata
    Class Stenolaemata

Phylum Brachiopoda
    Class Inarticulata
    Class Articulata (lampshells)

Phylum Phoronidea

Phylum Tardigrada

Phylum Annelida
    Class Archiannelida
    Class Polychaeta (polychaetes)
            Order Errantiformes (clamworms)
            Order Sedentariformes (fanworms)
    Class Oligochaeta (oligochaetes)
            Order Plesioporiformes (naids, *Tubifex*)
            Order Opisthoporiformes (earthworms)
            Order Prosoporiformes (branchiobdellids)
    Class Hirudinea (leeches)
            Order Acanthobdelliformes
            Order Rhynchobdelliformes
            Order Arhynchobdelliformes
    Class Myzostoma

Phylum Onychophora

Phylum Sipunculoidea

Phylum Echiuroidea

Phylum Mollusca
   Class Amphineura (chitons)
   Class Monoplacophora (shield shells)
   Class Scaphopoda (elephant tusk shells)
   Class Gastropoda (snails)
          Order Prosobranchiformes
          Order Opisthobranchiformes
          Order Pulmonatiformes
   Class Pelecypoda (clams, oysters)
          Order Protobranchiformes
          Order Filibranchiformes
          Order Eulamellibranchiformes
          Order Septibranchiformes
   Class Cephalopoda (cephalopods)
          Order Tetrabranchiformes (nautilus)
          Order Dibranchiformes (squids, octopuses)

Phylum Arthropoda
   Class Merostomata
          Order Xiphosuriformes (horseshoe crabs)
   Class Pycnogonida (sea-spiders)
   Class Arachnida
          Order Scorpioidiformes (scorpions)
          Order Amblypygiformes (tarantulas)
          Order Schizomidiformes (whip-scorpions, pedipalps)
          Order Palpigradiformes (palpigrads)
          Order Araneiformes (spiders)
          Order Solpugidiformes (solpugids)
          Order Pseudoscorpioidiformes (pseudoscorpions)
          Order Phalngidiformes
          Order Ricinuleiformes (ricinules)
          Order Acariniformes (ticks, mites)
             Suborder Trombidoidea
             Suborder Hydrachnoidea
             Suborder Ixodoidea
             Suborder Parasitoidea
             Suborder Oribatoidea
             Suborder Acaroidea
             Suborder Demodicoidea
          Order Opilioniformes (harvestmen, daddy longlegs)
          Order Solifugiformes (wind scorpions)
   Class Crustacea
    Subclass Branchiopoda (branchiopods)
      Division Eubranchiopoda
          Order Anostraciformes (*Artemia,* brine shrimps)
          Order Notostraciformes (tadpole shrimps)
          Order Conchostraciformes (clam shrimps)
      Division Oligobranchiopoda
          Order Cladoceriformes (water fleas)

Subclass Copepoda (copepods)
    Order Eucopepodiformes
        Suborder Calanoida
        Suborder Harpacticoida
        Suborder Cyclopoida
        Suborder Notodelphyoida
        Suborder Monstrilloida
        Suborder Caligoida
        Suborder Lernaeopodoida
    Order Branchiuriformes
Subclass Mystacocarida
Subclass Cephalocarida
Subclass Ostracoda (ostracods)
    Order Podocopiformes
    Order Myodocopiformes
    Order Cladocopiformes
    Order Platycopiformes
Subclass Cirripedia (barnacles)
    Order Thoraciciformes
    Order Acrothoraciciformes
    Order Apodiformes
    Order Rhizocephaliformes
    Order Ascothoraciciformes
Subclass Malacostraca
  Division Leptostraca
    Order Nebaliaceiformes
  Division Eumalacostraca
   Subdivision Syncarida
    Order Anaspidaceiformes
    Order Bathynellaceiformes
   Subdivision Peracarida
    Order Mysidaceiformes (mysid shrimps)
    Order Thermosbaenaceiformes
    Order Spelaeogriphaceiformes
    Order Cumaceiformes
    Order Tanaidaceiformes
    Order Isopodiformes (pill-bugs, beach lice)
    Order Amphipodiformes (beach fleas)
   Subdivision Hoplocarida
    Order Stomatopodiformes
   Subdivision Eucarida
    Order Euphausiaceiformes (krill)
    Order Decapodiformes
      Section Natantia
        Suborder Penaeidea (shrimps, prawns)
        Suborder Caridea (shrimps, prawns)
        Suborder Stenopodidea (banded shrimps)
      Section Reptantia
        Suborder Macrura (lobsters, crayfish)
        Suborder Anomura (hermit, sand crabs)
        Suborder Brachyura (crabs)

Class Diplopoda (millipedes)

> *Order* Pselapognathiformes
> *Order* Limacomorphiformes
> *Order* Oniscomorphiformes
> *Order* Polydesmoideiformes
> *Order* Nematomorphoideiformes
> *Order* Juliformiformes
> *Order* Colobognathiformes

Class Chilopoda (centipedes)

> *Order* Scutigeromorphiformes
> *Order* Lithobiomorphiformes
> *Order* Scolopendromorphiformes
> *Order* Geophilomorphiformes

Class Pauropoda
Class Symphyla
Class Insecta

> *Subclass* Apterygota

> > *Order* Proturiformes (proturans)
> > *Order* Thysanuriformes (silverfish, bristletails)
> > *Order* Collemboliformes (springtails)
> > *Order* Apteriformes (apterans)

> *Subclass* Pterygota

> > *Order* Orthopteriformes (grasshoppers, crickets, cockroaches)
> > *Order* Grylloblattodeiformes (grylloblattids)
> > *Order* Phasmidiformes (walking sticks)
> > *Order* Mantodeiformes (praying mantis)
> > *Order* Dermapteriformes (earwigs)
> > *Order* Plecopteriformes (stone flies)
> > *Order* Isopteriformes (termites)
> > *Order* Zorapteriformes (zorapterans)
> > *Order* Embiopteriformes (embiids)
> > *Order* Corrodentiformes (book lice)
> > *Order* Mallophagiformes (chewing and bird lice)
> > *Order* Anopluriformes (sucking lice)
> > *Order* Ephemeriformes (mayflies)
> > *Order* Odonatiformes (dragonflies, damselflies)
> > *Order* Thysanopteriformes (thrips)
> > *Order* Hemipteriformes (bugs)
> > > *Suborder* Cryptocerata (mostly aquatic)
> > > *Suborder* Gymnocerata (mostly terrestrial)
> > *Order* Homopteriformes (aphids, cicadas)
> > *Order* Mecopteriformes (scorpion flies)
> > *Order* Megalopteriformes (dobson flies)
> > *Order* Neuropteriformes (lacewings, ant lions)
> > *Order* Trichopteriformes (caddis flies)
> > *Order* Raphidiodeiformes (snake flies)
> > *Order* Lepidopteriformes
> > > *Suborder* Frenatae (moths)
> > > *Suborder* Rhopalocera (butterflies)
> > *Order* Dipteriformes (flies, mosquitos, gnats)
> > > *Suborder* Orthorrhapha
> > > *Suborder* Cyclorrhapha

Order Siphonapteriformes (fleas)
Order Coleopteriformes (beetles)
    Suborder Adephaga
    Suborder Polyphaga
Order Strepsipteriformes (*Stylops*)
Order Hymenopteriformes (ants, bees)

Phylum Linguatulida

Deuterostoma

Phylum Echinodermata (living groups only)
    Subphylum Pelmatozoa
        Class Crinoidea (sea lilies)
    Subphylum Eleutherozoa
        Class Holothuroidea (sea cucumbers, trepang)
        Class Echinoidea (sea urchins, sand dollars)
        Class Asteroidea (starfish)
        Class Ophiuroidea (brittle stars)

Phylum Chaetognatha

Phylum Pogonophora

Phylum Chordata
    Subphylum Hemichordata (Enteropneusta) (acorn worms)
    Subphylum Pterobranchiata
        Class Rhabdopleuridea
        Class Cephalodiscidea
    Subphylum Tunicata (tunicates)
        Class Ascidiacea
        Class Thaliacea
        Class Larvacea
    Subphylum Cephalochordata (*Amphioxus*)
    Subphylum Vertebrata
        Class Agnatha (jawless fishes)
           Subclass Ostracodermi
           Subclass Cyclostomata (lampreys)
        Class Ichthyognatha (jawed fishes)
           Subclass Placodermi
           Subclass Chondrichthyes (elasmobranchs)
               Order Selachiformes
                  Suborder Squali (sharks)
                  Suborder Batoidea (skates, sawfish)
               Order Holocephaliformes (ratfish)
           Subclass Actinopterygii (ray-finned fishes)
              Superorder Chondrostei
                 Order Cladistiformes (*Polypterus*)
                 Order Chondrosteiformes (sturgeons, paddlefish)
              Superorder Holostei
                 Order Protospondyliformes (*Amia*, fresh-water dogfish)
                 Order Ginglymodiformes (gar pikes)

Superorder Teleostei
    Order Isospondyliformes (herring, salmon)
    Order Haplomiformes (pikes)
    Order Bathyclupeiformes (deep-sea herring)
    Order Iniomiformes (lantern fish)
    Order Ateleopiformes
    Order Giganturoideiformes (giganturans)
    Order Lyomeriformes (gulpers)
    Order Mormyriformes (African electric eels)
    Order Ostariophysiformes (catfish, electric eels, carp)
    Order Apodiformes (eels)
    Order Colocephaliformes (moray eels)
    Order Heteromiformes (spiny eels)
    Order Synentognathiformes
    Order Cyprinodontiformes (killifish)
    Order Salmoperciformes (troutperches)
    Order Solenichthyiformes (sea horses, pipe fish)
    Order Anacanthiniformes (cods, hakes, pollacks)
    Order Allotriognathiformes (ribbon fish, oar fish)
    Order Berycomorphiformes (squirrel fish)
    Order Zeomorphiformes (John dorries)
    Order Percomorphiformes (perch, bass, tuna)
    Order Scleropareiformes (sticklebacks)
    Order Hypostomidiformes (dragon fish)
    Order Heterosomatiformes (halibuts, flounders)
    Order Discocephaliformes (ramoras)
    Order Plectognathiformes (puffer fish)
    Order Malacichthyiformes (ragfish)
    Order Chaudhureiformes (Burmese eels)
    Order Xenopterygiformes (cling fish)
    Order Haplodociformes (toadfish, midshipman)
    Order Pediculatiformes (angler fish, sea devils)
    Order Opisthomiformes (snout eels)
    Order Symbranchiformes (tropical swamp eels)
Subclass Sarcopterygii (muscle-finned fishes)
    Superorder Crossopterygii
    Order Coelacanthiniformes (*Latimeria chalumnae*)
    Superorder Dipnoi (lungfishes)
    Order Sirenoideiformes

Class Amphibia

    Order Stegocephaliformes
    Order Gymnophioniformes (Apodiformes) (caecilians)
    Order Caudatiformes (Urodeliformes) (salamanders)
    Order Salientiformes (Anuriformes) (frogs, toads)

Class Reptilia
  Subclass Anapsida

    Order Cheloniformes (turtles, tortoises)
  Subclass Lepidosauria

    Order Rhynchocephaliformes (*Sphenodon,* tuatara)

Order Squamatiformes
    Suborder Lacertilia (Sauria) (lizards)
    Suborder Serpentes (Ophidia) (snakes)
Order Crocodiliformes (Loricatiformes) (alligators)
Order Saurischiformes (large dinosaurs)
Order Ornithischiformes (birdlike dinosaurs)
Order Pterosauriformes (extinct flying reptiles)

Subclass Synapsida
    Order Therapsidiformes (mammal-like dinosaurs)

Class Aves
  Subclass Archeornithes (*Archaeopteryx*)
  Subclass Neornithes
    Superorder Palaeognathae
      Order Apterygiformes (kiwis)
      Order Casuariformes (cassowaries, emus)
      Order Rheiformes (rheas)
      Order Struthioniformes (ostriches)
      Order Tinamiformes (tinamous)
    Superorder Neognathae
      Order Sphenisciformes (penguins)
      Order Gaviformes (loons)
      Order Podicipitiformes (grebes)
      Order Procellariformes (albatrosses, petrels)
      Order Pelecaniformes (pelicans, gannets)
      Order Ciconiformes (storks, flamingos)
      Order Anseriformes (ducks, geese, swans)
      Order Falconiformes (vultures, eagles)
      Order Galliformes (grouse, chickens)
      Order Gruiformes (cranes, coots, rails)
      Order Charadriformes (gulls, killdeers)
      Order Columbiformes (pigeons, doves)
      Order Cuculiformes (cuckoos, roadrunners)
      Order Psittaciformes (parrots)
      Order Strigiformes (owls)
      Order Caprimuligiformes (whip-poor-wills)
      Order Micropodiformes (swifts)
      Order Coliformes (mouse-birds)
      Order Trogoniformes (trogons)
      Order Coraciformes (kingfishers)
      Order Piciformes (woodpeckers, toucans)
      Order Passeriformes (perching birds)

Class Mammalia
  Subclass Prototheria (monotremes)
    Order Monotrematiformes (duckbilled platypus)
  Subclass Metatheria (marsupials)
    Order Polyprotodontiformes (opossums)
    Order Coenolestoiformes
    Order Diprotodontiformes (kangaroos, kaolas)

Subclass Eutheria (placentals)

    Order Insectivoriformes (moles, hedgehogs)

    Order Dermopteriformes (flying lemurs)

    Order Chiropteriformes (bats)

    Order Primatiformes

        Suborder Tupaioidea (tree shrews)

        Suborder Lemuroidea (lemurs)

            Family Indridae

            Family Lemuridae

        Suborder Daubentonioidea (aye-aye)

        Suborder Lorisoidea (loris, pottos)

            Family Galagidae

            Family Lorisidae

        Suborder Tarsoidea (*Tarsius*)

        Suborder Anthropoidea

            Superfamily Ceboidea (Platyrrhini) (New World monkeys)

                Family Callithricidae (marmosets)

                Family Cebidae (spider, howler, capuchin monkeys)

            Superfamily Cercopithecoidea (Catarrhini) (Old World monkeys)

                Family Cercopithecidae (baboons, macaques, langurs)

                Family Colobidae (sakis, titis)

            Superfamily Hominoidea

                Family Hominidae (man)

                Family Simiidae (anthropoid apes)

    Order Edentatiformes (armadillos, sloths)

    Order Pholidotiformes (pangolins)

    Order Lagomorphiformes (rabbits, pikas)

    Order Rodentiformes (rats, beavers, squirrels)

    Order Cetaceiformes

        Suborder Odontoceti (toothed whales, porpoises)

        Suborder Mysticeti (whalebone whales)

    Order Carnivoriformes

        Suborder Fissipedia (dogs, cats, bears)

        Suborder Pinnipedia (seals, walruses)

    Order Tubulidentatiformes (aardvarks)

    Order Proboscidiformes (elephants)

    Order Hyracoidiformes (conies)

    Order Sireniformes (sea-cows, manatees)

    Order Perissodactyliformes (horses, rhinos)

    Order Artiodactyliformes (cattle, sheep, pigs, giraffes, hippos)

Glossary of Biological Terms

aboral   away from or opposite the mouth

acid   a substance which gives off hydrogen ions (H⁺) and turns litmus pink

acidophil   cell or particle staining with acid dyes; eosinophil

acoelous   without a cavity; pertaining to a taxon of flatworms lacking both gut and coelom

acontium   one of the threadlike filaments growing from the edge of a mesentery in a sea anemone or other anthozoan and containing nematocysts

ACTH   adrenocorticotrophic hormone of the pituitary

actinula   an eight-armed, actively crawling larva of certain hydrozoan coelenterates

adrenalin (epinephrine)   the hormone of the adrenal medulla and most sympathetic nerves, a derivative of the amino acid tyrosine; the hormone of fear, anger, and excitement

adrenergic   liberating adrenalin or a similar substance; nerves of the sympathetic system

aerobic   in the presence of molecular oxygen

afferent   conducting toward a given structure. Sensory nerves are afferent.

allantois   vascular embryonic membrane growing out of the hind gut and coming to lie under the shell or against the lining of the uterus, and functioning as lung and kidney

allele   one of two or more genes occupying the same relative position on homologous chromosomes, and therefore pairing at meiosis, but producing different developmental effects

allopatric   occupying different territories

ambulacral   of a covered alley; one of the radial axes of an echinoderm

amino acid   one of the units into which proteins break down; an amino acid consists of a central carbon atom to which is attached a H atom, a carboxyl radical, an ammonia radical, plus a fourth group

amnion   embryonic membrane enclosing an embryo

amphid   one of a pair of chemoreceptor sense organs on a nematode

anabolism   constructive metabolism, building up complex chemical structures and requiring energy

anadromous   migrating upstream

anaerobic   without molecular oxygen

analogy   similarity of function without basic similarity of structure

anaphase   the stage of mitosis or meiosis during which the sets of chromosomes move to opposite ends of the spindle

anastomosis   interconnection, as of blood vessels or nerves

androgen   a male sex hormone, especially testosterone

anion   a negatively charged ion

antibody   a protein (globulin) that counteracts a foreign protein or other substance in an animal

antigen   any substance, usually a protein, that elicits the formation of antibodies

apoenzyme   the protein part of an enzyme

appetitive behavior   restless, more or less random behavior, especially wandering; drive

archenteron   gut of an early embryo

artifact   structure or appearance due to human interference, such as the treatment of a cell with chemicals

ascon   like a sack; a simple type of sponge

atoll   a more or less circular coral reef enclosing a lagoon without a central island

atom   the smallest particle of an element that can exist

ATP   adenosine triphosphate, the chief energy-carrying molecule within cells

atrium   a chamber or cavity, such as one of the chambers receiving blood in the heart, or the cavity containing the pharynx of a tunicate

auricle ear or earlike structure, such as the protruding portion of one of the atria of the heart

autogamy meiosis followed by self-fertilization of such a kind that the individual is rendered homozygous; found in ciliates

autonomic nervous system the "involuntary" nervous system made up of sympathetic and parasympathetic divisions

autosome any chromosome except the sex chromosomes, X and Y or W and V

autotroph an organism, such as a green plant, that can manufacture its own food from simple inorganic compounds such as water and CO_2

axenic a culture containing only a single species of organism

axon the long fiber from a neuron, usually the fiber carrying impulses away from the cell body

base a substance that gives off hydroxyl ions (OH^-) and turns litmus blue; an alkali

basophil cell or particle staining with basic dyes

biomass total amount (weight) of living material in any area or volume

biome a major life zone, such as the tundra or a tropical forest, including the stages of its development; a living community

bipinnaria bilateral larva of a starfish

blastema bud of embryonic cells at a cut surface in an early stage of regeneration or development

blastocoel cavity of the blastula

blastomere one of the relatively large cells into which an egg divides

blastopore the opening into the archenteron formed during gastrulation

blastula a hollow ball of cells formed in early stages of embryonic development

brachial of the arms

brachiation use of the arms, especially in swinging from branch to branch

branchial of the gills

brei a "soup" usually prepared by homogenizing cells

browsing eating leaves off branches, in contradistinction to grazing of grass from the ground

Calorie (large) kilocalorie; the amount of heat energy required to raise 1,000 grams of water 1°C. This unit is commonly used in dietetics.

calorie (small) the amount of heat energy required to raise 1 gram of water 1°C. This unit is commonly used in cellular biochemistry.

calyptoblastic pertaining to a hydranth protected by a cup-shaped sheath

carbohydrate a sugar or starchlike compound, general formula $C_x(H_2O)_y$

cardiac of the heart

carinate keel-like; having a prominent ridge or keel on the breastbone, as in most birds

catadromous migrating downstream, usually into the sea to breed

cation a positively charged ion

caudal of the tail

centriole a basal granule or kinetosome at each pole of a mitotic figure or at the base of a cilium

centromere *see* kinetochore

centrosome a granule in the cytoplasm close to the nucleus; it forms the center of the mitotic aster

cephalic of the head

cercaria tadpole-shaped larval trematode formed from a redia and infective for the definitive vertebrate host

cervical of the neck

cervix a neck, especially of the uterus

chernozem prairie soil with a thick uniform topsoil and little leaching

chiasma a crossing, especially of the optic nerves as they enter the brain, or of chromosomes in meiosis

chitin a proteinaceous material used as skeleton by coelenterates, arthropods, and other animals, and some molds

chlorophyll the green magnesium porphyrin compound that is essential for photosynthesis

cholinergic liberating acetylcholine; the nerves of the voluntary and parasympathetic systems

chromatid one of the two strands of a recently duplicated chromosome while still held to its sister duplicate by the kinetochore

chromatophore color bearer; in squids a multicellular structure

chromosome one of the deeply staining, rod-shaped structures in the nucleus, composed of protein and nucleic acid; these are the physical basis of heredity

chrysalis pupa of a moth or butterfly

cilium   short, hairlike, living process from the surface of a cell, capable of active movement and consisting of two central fibrils surrounded by a circle of nine and enclosed in a membranous sheath; usually many on one cell

circadian   of approximately 24 hours

clitoris   the homolog in the female of the penis

cloaca   the common terminal passageway for the digestive, excretory, and reproductive systems; also its opening to the exterior

cnidocil   sensitive cilialike structure on a nematoblast cell which triggers the discharge of the nematocyst

coacervate   a colloidal globule sharply demarcated from its surrounding medium

coelenteron   combined gut and body cavity of coelenterates; gastrovascular cavity

coelom   body cavity of higher phyla, formed between layers of mesoderm and lined with an epithelium of mesodermal origin

coenosarc   living portion of a hydroid branch, usually surrounded by a nonliving proteinaceous perisarc

coenzyme   the smaller, nonprotein part of an enzyme, usually a vitamin

consummatory behavior   the specific acts that fulfill an appetite or drive

coronary   encircling or crownlike, as certain blood vessels of the heart

corpus striatum   brain centers in the floor of the telencephalon

cortex   literally the bark; any superficial layer, especially of brain or gland

cutaneous   of the skin

cytoplasm   all the protoplasm of a cell except that of the nucleus

dendrite   a nerve fiber, usually branching, that carries impulses toward the cell body of a neuron

deoxyribose (desoxyribose)   a five-carbon sugar having less oxygen than the formula $C_x(H_2O)_y$ suggests

dermis   inner of the two primary layers of vertebrate skin, derived from mesoderm and containing blood vessels and nerves

desmosome   one of a pair of electron-dense disks of adjacent cell membranes; believed to have an adhesive function

diaphragm   a relatively thin membrane covering an opening or separating two cavities; especially the muscle sheet between chest and abdominal cavities

diastole   relaxation phase of the heart beat

dictyosome   *see* mitochondrion

diploblastic   having only two germ layers, ectoderm and endoderm

diploid   possessing two sets of chromosomes

distal   farther from the base or center

diurnal   associated with daylight

diverticulum   a blind sac

dorsal   pertaining to the back; in vertebrates, the side having the backbone

DPN   *see* NAD

duodenum   first portion of the small intestine in vertebrates

ecdysis   molt

ecotone   line of contact between two ecological communities, as where forest and prairie meet

ectoderm   outer embryonic layer of cells which forms the outer layers of skin and the nervous system in the adult

efferent   conducting away from a given structure. Motor nerves are efferent.

endoderm   innermost embryonic layer of cells which forms the alimentary canal and its derivatives such as liver, lungs, and pancreas

endoplastic reticulum   ergastoplasm, the irregular mass of double membranes within the cytoplasm of cells along which ribosomes are commonly seen

endopod   inner (medial) branch of a crustacean appendage

endostyle   hypobranchial (below the gills) groove in tunicates and *Amphioxus,* homologous with the thyroid

enteron   gut

enzyme   an organic catalyst consisting of a protein and a nonprotein part

epidermal   above the dermis; the superficial layers of vertebrate skin of ectodermal origin

epinephrine   *see* adrenalin

epiphysis   end portion of a long bone which ossifies separately; the pineal gland

epithelium   any sheet of cells forming a pavementlike covering or cavity lining

erythrocyte   red blood cell

esophagus   gullet; passage between throat (pharynx) and stomach

estradiol   a very potent form of estrone

estrogen   a female sex hormone, especially estrone

estrone   a female sex hormone that promotes growth of female reproductive structures and female behavior

estrus   heat; a condition of sexual receptivity or desire

eukaryote   a cell or organism able to undergo mitosis, contrasted with bacteria and certain fungi which are protokaryotes

exopod   outer (lateral) branch of a crustacean appendage

extrinsic muscle   one moving an organ in relation to the rest of the body

facilitation   effect of the summation of a series of impulses reaching a neuron

FAD   flavin adenine dinucleotide, a hydrogen acceptor in series between the phosphopyridine nucleotides and the cytochromes

flagellum   hairlike living process, usually longer than the cell from which it grows, capable of active movement and consisting of two central fibrils surrounded by a circle of nine and enclosed in a membranous sheath; usually not more than two or three from one cell

flame cell   an excretory cell enclosing a flamelike tuft of long cilia

folic acid   a B vitamin, pteroylglutamic acid, essential for growth, red blood cell formation, etc.

foramen (pl. **foramina**)   opening; *foramen magnum,* opening at base of skull for exit of spinal cord

FSH   follicle-stimulating hormone of the anterior pituitary

gamete   either an egg or a sperm

gametogenesis   formation of gametes

gamont   a uninucleate protozoan which at maturity divides repeatedly, forming gametes

gastric   of the stomach

gastrulation   inpushing of the lower part of a blastula which forms the archenteron and the germ layers

gene   an hereditary factor following Mendel's laws

genetic drift   change in the average genetic composition of population due to nonrepresentative sampling when the population becomes very small

genotype   the genetical type; the complement of genes in a given animal

genus   a group of related species

germ cell   a reproductive cell, especially a gamete—egg or sperm

germ layer   one of the three primary embryonic layers of cells, ectoderm, mesoderm, and endoderm

germplasm   reproductive cells and their precursors; genetic inheritance of a species

glochidium   larval fresh-water clam living parasitically on gills and fins of fishes

glomerulus   a tuft of capillaries within the Bowman's capsule of the kidney

glutathione   a tripeptide containing sulfhydryl (—SH) found in the tissues and body fluids of worms and all higher animals

glycogen   "animal starch"; it is converted into glucose by hydrolysis

glycolysis   anaerobic breakdown of foodstuffs; fermentation; the Embden-Meyerhof series of reactions

gnotobiotic   a culture with a known mixture of species

Golgi material (or apparatus)   membranes usually near the nucleus and functioning in secretion

gonad   sex gland producing either sperms, eggs, or both

gonophore   egg- or sperm-bearing structure

gymnoblastic   pertaining to a hydranth without a protecting cuplike sheath

habitat   the type of environment in which an animal lives, such as a swamp or a wooded hillside

haploid   possessing a single set of chromosomes

hepatic   of the liver

heterosis   hybrid vigor, the "evident superiority of the hybrid over the better parent in any measurable character"

heterotroph   an organism dependent on others for complex organic nutrients

heterozygous   having different maternal and paternal genes at any specific locus; not pure bred for a given trait

hexokinase an enzyme responsible for the initial phosphorylation of glucose in metabolism

histology the science of tissues

holoenzyme the protein apoenzyme plus the coenzyme (or prosthetic group)

homoiothermal with constant, self-regulated body temperature; "warm blooded"

homology similarity of structure based on common ancestry, regardless of function

homozygous having both maternal and paternal genes alike at a certain locus, pure bred at a certain locus

hydranth vase-shaped or cylindrical portion of a hydroid polyp bearing tentacles and, normally, a mouth and hypostome

hydroid a polyp; a hydralike or sea anemonelike form

hydrolysis splitting of one molecule into two with the addition of water

hypertonic having a concentration high enough to gain water across a membrane from another solution

hypostome region immediately below the mouth, especially in coelenterates

hypotonic having a concentration low enough to lose water across a membrane to another solution

hypotrich a flattened ciliate that "crawls" on tufts of cilia

imago the adult instar

implantation process by which the mammalian embryo (as a blastocyst) becomes imbedded in the lining of the uterus

incisors cutting teeth located across the anterior part of upper or lower jaws

insertion (of a muscle) point of attachment furthest from the midline of the body; the distal attachment

instar a stage between molts, as in insects, crustaceans, nematodes, etc.

intermedin a hormone of the intermediate lobe of the pituitary causing dispersion of melanophore granules and hence darkening of the skin in fishes, etc.

interstitial in the interstices; between other cells or structures

intrinsic muscle one moving a part of an organ in relation to other parts of the same organ

ion a charged particle into which a molecule

may dissociate in solution; *see also* anion, cation

isomer a compound having the same composition as another compound but different properties because of different configuration of the constituent atoms

isotonic having the same osmotic concentration

isotope an atom possessing the same chemical but different physical properties as another due to differing atomic mass or radioactivity

jugular of the neck

karyotype the general appearance of the somatic chromosomes for a species, with regard to number, size, and shape

katabolism destructive metabolism, breaking down molecules and releasing energy

Keimbahn the "germtrack"; the germ or reproductive cells collectively in contrast to the somatic or body cells

kinetochore the spindle-attachment point of a chromosome; the centromere

kinetosome self-reproducing basal granule of a cilium or flagellum; also a centriole

kymograph an instrument that records heart or muscle contractions, etc., as a waving line on a revolving drum

labial of the lips

lagena a fingerlike extension from the sacculus, containing the sensory epithelium of hearing in reptiles, etc.

larynx structure containing the vocal cords

leucocyte white blood cell

leucon with many rounded flagellated chambers; a complex type of sponge

LH luteinizing hormone; the pituitary hormone that stimulates development of the corpora lutea

ligament a cord or band of inelastic connective tissue connecting one bone with another

limnology the study of lakes

lingual of the tongue

lipid a fatlike substance

littoral of or pertaining to a shore

locus position, often of a gene on a chromosome

luciferin the light-emitting substance of animals, an aldehyde associated with a flavin nucleotide

lumen cavity of a duct or sac

macronucleus the large nucleus of most ciliates; does not participate in sexual reproduction

madreporite the "eye" of a starfish; a sievelike structure serving as intake for the water vascular system

manubrium upper part of sternum (breastbone) in a vertebrate; structure bearing the mouth in a jellyfish

medusa a jellyfish

meiosis the process, always requiring two cell divisions, whereby the diploid number of chromosomes is reduced to the haploid number, i.e., to one set

melanophore cell bearing melanin; pigment cell

mesenchyme more or less diffuse connective tissue pervading and supporting most organs

mesentery thin supporting membrane within the body cavity of many kinds of animals; in vertebrates a double layer of peritoneal membrane connecting the alimentary canal to the dorsal side of the coelom

mesoderm middle layer of embryonic cells which forms the lining of the coelom, the muscles, bones, connective tissue, and vascular system

mesoglea jellylike substance between ecto- and endoderm in certain coelenterates

metabolism the sum of all the chemical processes occuring within a living unit; the chemical aspects of respiration

metaphase stage of mitosis or meiosis during which the kinetochores of the chromosomes are aligned on the equator of the spindle

metazoan many-celled animal

micronucleus small nucleus of ciliates which functions in sexual reproduction

miracidium minute ciliated larva of a trematode

mitochondrion (pl. **mitochondria**) a cytoplasmic rod or particle associated with enzymes of oxidative respiration

mitosis the process of cell division whereby the chromosomes are duplicated and separated equally into the two daughter cells

ml milliliter, one thousandth of a liter, closely approximating 1 cc

molar solution one containing 1 gram molecular weight per 1 liter of water

molecule smallest possible unit of a compound substance, consisting of two or more atoms

monopodial type of growth characteristic of gymnoblastic hydroids in which the main stem and branches are tipped by a permanent hydranth

mor very shallow topsoil characteristic of coniferous forests

mull thick topsoil characteristic of deciduous forests

mutation sudden and relatively permanent change in a gene; genetic change due to chromosomal alteration

myelin fatty insulating sheath around a nerve fiber

NAD nictoinamide adenine dinucleotide (formerly called DPN), a niacin-containing hydrogen acceptor on the pathway to cytochrome

NADP nicotinamide adenine dinucleotide phosphate (formerly termed TPN)

nematoblast a cell that produces nematocysts

nematocyst cyst containing a poison and an explosive thread; characteristic of coelenterates

neoteny attainment of sexual maturity in a larval or juvenile condition

neuron a nerve cell

niche particular role an animal plays in the economy of its habitat; also the particular location it prefers

nidamental of a nest; secreting a protective gel around eggs

Nissl body elongate particle of ribose nucleic acid in a neuron

notochord stiff but flexible rod of cells extending the length of a chordate just ventral to the nerve cord; the backbone forms around it

nucleolus small rounded body within a nucleus, composed of RNA, and attached to a particular chromosome

nucleotide a unit of which nucleic acids are built, containing a nitrogen base, a deoxyribose sugar, and a phosphoric acid

nymph a larval instar of an insect with gradual metamorphosis, such as a grasshopper

ommatidium a unit of a compound eye

operculum   any covering, especially of the gills in fishes or the opening of a tube in polychaetes

ophthalmic   pertaining to the eyes

oral   pertaining to the mouth

organ   a multicellular structure adapted for a specific use or uses

organelle   a specialized structure with a particular function within a cell or a one-celled animal

organic   containing carbon; having to do with living organisms

origin (of a muscle)   point of attachment nearest to the midline of the body; the proximal attachment

osmosis   passage of water through a semipermeable membrane

otocyst   cyst containing sand grains or other concretions; an organ of equilibration

ovary   egg-forming structure

ovulation   discharge of the egg from the ovary

ovum   egg cell with nucleus and cytoplasm

oxytocin   pitocin, a posterior pituitary hormone stimulating uterine contraction and milk release

pallium   roof of the telencephalon, very thin in fishes, thick in man where it is the cerebral cortex; mantle of a mollusk or brachiopod

pangenesis   the erroneous theory that hereditary factors come from all parts of the parents' bodies

parapodium   fleshy leglike appendage of an annelid

pathogen   disease-producer

pecten   comb or comblike structure, especially the black vascular structure within the vitreous chamber of a bird's eye

pedalfer   roughly equivalent to podzol; a soil rich in aluminum and iron

pedicellaria   minute pincerlike organ on the surface of an echinoderm

pedocal   roughly equivalent to chernozem; a soil rich in calcium

pedogenesis   reproduction by young or larval animals especially if parthenogenetic; *see also* neoteny

pedology   scientific study of the soil

pelagic   living in the sea far from shore

pentadactyl   five-toed

peptide   two or more amino acids linked together

perisarc   nonliving proteinaceous tubular sheath surrounding the living portion of the hydroid stem

peristalsis   wavelike muscular contractions in the intestine

peritoneum   mesodermal membrane lining the coelom

pharynx   throat

phasmid   one of a pair of minute glands located in the tail of certain nematodes

phenocopy   a phenotype characteristic of one genotype produced in another genotype by environmental influences

phenotype   the visible or realized type

phosphorylation   the process of combination with phosphate, often with the production of a high energy bond

pitocin   *see* oxytocin

pitressin   vasopressin, a posterior pituitary hormone that maintains the contractile tone of the renal blood vessels, so preventing diabetes insipidus

plankton   the floating or feebly swimming life on or near the surface of a body of water

planula   minute, elongate, ciliated larva of a coelenterate

pleural   of the sides, especially the cavity containing the lungs

pluteus   minute, triangular or tent-shaped larva of a sea urchin

podzol   soil that has undergone some leaching whether mor or mull, contrasted with chernozem

poikilothermal   pertaining to an animal whose temperature remains close to that of the environment; "cold-blooded"

polyp   a hydroid; resembling a hydra

polypeptide   one of the decomposition products of proteins, composed of a chain of amino acids

porphyrin   a compound found in hemoglobin, chlorophyll, cytochrome, and vitamin B_{12}; it consists of four pyrrole rings, C_4H_5N

process (in anatomy)   more or less slender projection as of a bone

progesterone   hormone of the corpus luteum, necessary to maintain pregnancy

proglottid   one of the "segments" of a tapeworm

prolactin a pituitary hormone inducing milk secretion in mammals and pigeons

prophase the stage of mitosis or meiosis during which the nuclear membrane disappears and the chromosomes become shorter and thicker

prosopyle cell with cytoplasm enclosing a pore through which water enters a flagellated chamber of a sponge

prosthetic group the smaller, nonprotein coenzyme portion of an enzyme that is firmly bound to the protein apoenzyme

protandry condition of being male when young, female when fully grown

protopod basal (proximal) portion of a crustacean's appendage

proximal nearer the base or center

pseudocoel body cavity of a nematode and certain other groups which is not completely lined with a mesodermal epithelium

pulmonary of the lungs

pupa quiescent instar that molts into the adult or imago

pylorus opening from stomach to duodenum

radula flexible ribbonlike band of minute teeth in several parallel rows, characteristic of mollusks

ramus branch

range geographical area within which an animal may be found

ratite having a flat breastbone, as in several groups of primitive birds

redia wormlike intermediate stage in the life cycle of a trematode; forms cercarias

reduction the opposite of oxidation; addition of an electron or a hydrogen atom to a molecule

reflex unit of action of the nervous system involving a sensory neuron, an association neuron or neurons, and one or more motor neurons

renal of the kidney

resolving power ability of a lens to distinguish two lines as separate

respiratory quotient the amount of CO_2 produced in respiration divided by the amount of O_2 consumed

rhabdite small rod-shaped capsule in the ectoderm of a flatworm

rhabdoid any of several types of minute rod-shaped structures, including rhabdites

and chondrocysts, in the epidermis of flatworms

rhabdome central crystalline rod of an ommatidium

rhodopsin visual purple; a compound of carotene (vitamin A) plus a protein

rhopalium complex marginal sense organ of a scyphozoan jellyfish

ribosome chunky, oval, cytoplasmic particle commonly found on endoplasmic membranes; it is composed of RNA and protein and is the site of translation of mRNA in the synthesis of proteins

RNA ribose nucleic acid

rostellum crown of hooks on the scolex of a tapeworm

sacculus small sac, especially the lower of the two in the inner ear and connected to the semicircular canals

schizont multinucleate protozoan which breaks up asexually into many small cells

scolex the "head" of a tapeworm

scrotum sac containing testes

scyphistoma small hydroid stage of a scyphozoan which undergoes strobilization

septum partition

sere series of plant and animal communities that follow each other in a gradual but definite sequence ending in a climax typical of a particular climate and part of the world

siphonoglyph ciliated groove extending along the pharynx of a sea anemone or other anthozoan

solute a substance, such as salt, that is dissolved in another substance, the solvent, such as water

solvent a fluid in which something is dissolved

soma all the body except the germ cells

species a group of interbreeding or potentially interbreeding organisms; a population sharing the same gene pool

sphincter circular muscle closing an orifice

spiracle opening concerned with breathing

squamous flattened or scaly

statoblast a mass of embryonic cells covered by a protective coat, characteristic of bryozoans

statocyst a cyst containing sand or other weight and acting as an organ of equilibration

sternum   a midventral bone or other structure, especially in the chest

steroid   a compound based on three benzene rings plus a five-carbon ring all joined together; sex and adrenal cortex hormones are steroids

stolon   a rootlike or branchlike outgrowth, usually budding new individuals

subchelate   pertaining to a prehensile claw formed by bending the terminal segment back over the next-to-terminal segment

substrate   the material on which an enzyme acts; the foundation to which an animal adheres

sycon   with flagellated chambers radiating from a central cavity; a moderately complex sponge

symbiosis   the intimate living together of two species, often with mutual benefit

sympatric   occupying the same territory

sympodial   type of growth characteristic of calyptoblastic hydroids in which the main stem and branches are tipped with the youngest hydranth

synapse   zone of transmission of a nervous impulse from one neuron to another either between two dendrites or between a terminal "button" and a nerve cell body

syngamy   fusion of gametes; union of egg and sperm

systole   contraction phase of the heart beat

taiga   biome characterized by conifers, lying between tundra and deciduous forests

taxis   the orientation of an animal with respect to a source of stimulus

taxon   a taxonomic unit, such as a species, genus, or phylum

taxonomy   the science of classification

telophase   the final stage of mitosis or meiosis during which the nuclear membrane is reformed and the chromosomes become diffuse

telson   broad median posterior extension of terminal body segment of many crustaceans

tendon   cord or sheet of connective tissue connecting a muscle to a bone or another muscle

tergum   skeletal plate covering the back or dorsal side

test   a rigid shell, especially of an echinoderm

testis (pl. **testes**)   the structure in which sperms are formed

testosterone   male sex hormone

theca   covering or case

thorax   the chest

tornaria   larval hemichordate resembling an echinoderm larva

TPN   *see* NADP

translocation   interchange of a chromosomal piece between nonhomologous chromosomes

tritiated   containing tritium, i.e., containing hydrogen of mass number 3, hence radioactive

trichite   minute stiff rod or a pair of rods

trichocyst   elongate vesicle just under the pellicle of a ciliate and capable of extruding a long thread

triploblastic   having three germ layers, ecto-, meso-, and endoderm

tropism   orientation of an animal in a field of force; often restricted to the turning of part of a sessile animal

tundra   the alpine zone, a treeless zone north or at a greater elevation than the taiga or zone of conifers

ureter   duct carrying urine from the kidneys to the urinary bladder in mammals; loosely, any duct carrying urine toward the exterior

urethra   duct carrying urine from the urinary bladder to the exterior

uroid   taillike, or a taillike structure

uterus   the structure within a female in which early development of the young takes place; the womb

utriculus   a small sac, especially the upper of the two in the inner ear

vagina   passage from exterior to uterus

vas deferens   duct carrying sperms and seminal fluid from testis toward the exterior

velum   a thin membranous structure; the flat muscle band around the edge of a hydrozoan jellyfish; the knifelike part of a bee's antenna-cleaner

ventral   under side; in vertebrates the side opposite to the backbone

viscera   internal organs

vitamin   a dietary constituent essential in very small amounts; the nonprotein or coenzyme component of an enzyme

vitelline   pertaining to yolk

womb   uterus

zygote   cell formed by the fusion of two gametes; a fertilized egg

Index

The location of figures is indicated by the letter f after the page number.

Illustrations not credited elsewhere: page 264, M. Woodbridge Williams; page 402, The Oceanic Institute, Oahu, Hawaii; page 518, from Andreas Vesalius, *De Humani Corporis Fabrica,* 1543; page 626, F. B. Grunzweig, Photo Researchers Inc.

Animal Groups

and their possible interrelationships

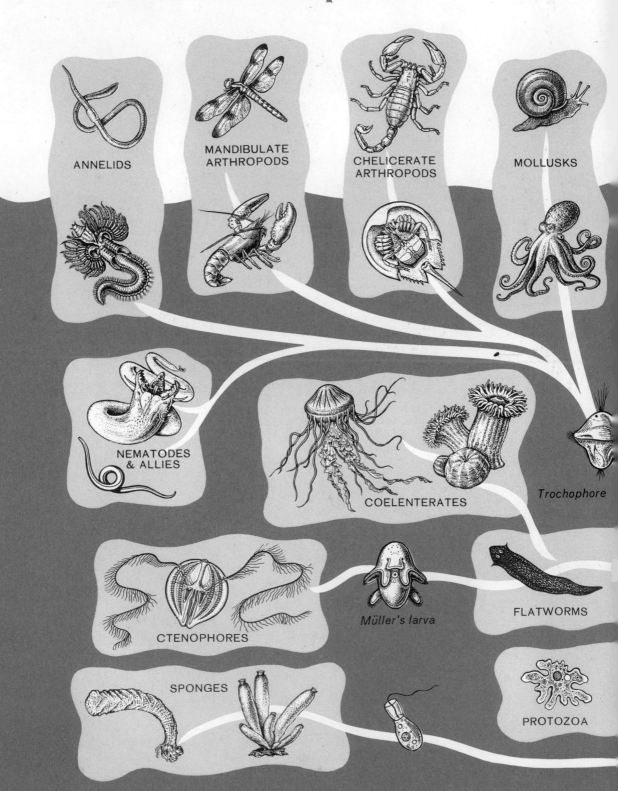

ANNELIDS

MANDIBULATE ARTHROPODS

CHELICERATE ARTHROPODS

MOLLUSKS

NEMATODES & ALLIES

COELENTERATES

Trochophore

CTENOPHORES

Müller's larva

FLATWORMS

SPONGES

PROTOZOA